ANNUAL REVIEW OF PHYSIOLOGY

EDITORIAL COMMITTEE (1995)

Responsible for the organization of Volume 57
(Editorial Committee, 1993)

Production Editor   SANDRA H. COOPERMAN
Subject Indexer   STEVEN M. SORENSEN

ANNUAL REVIEW OF PHYSIOLOGY

VOLUME 57, 1995

JOSEPH F. HOFFMAN, *Editor*

Yale University School of Medicine

PAUL De WEER, *Associate Editor*

University of Pennsylvania School of Medicine

ANNUAL REVIEW INC. 4139 EL CAMINO WAY, P.O. BOX 10139 PALO ALTO, CALIFORNIA 94303-0139

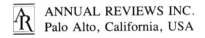

ANNUAL REVIEWS INC.
Palo Alto, California, USA

International Standard Serial Number: 0066–4278
International Standard Book Number: 0–8243–0357–1
Library of Congress Catalog Card Number: 39-15404

Annual Review and publication titles are registered trademarks of Annual Reviews Inc.

⊗ The paper used in this publication meets the minimum requirements of American National Standard for Information Sciences—Permanence of Paper for Printed Library Materials, ANSI Z39.48-1984.

Annual Reviews Inc. and the Editors of its publications assume no responsibility for the statements expressed by the contributors to this *Review.*

Typesetting by Kachina Typesetting Inc., Tempe, Arizona; John Olson, President; Marty Mullins, Typesetting Coordinator; and by the Annual Reviews Inc. Editorial Staff

PRINTED AND BOUND IN THE UNITED STATES OF AMERICA

PREFACE

This preface deals first with the accessibility of the literature that comprises the corpus of our field, and second with the articles and format presented in this volume.

Each volume of the *Annual Review of Physiology* is dedicated to review articles on selected topics and/or areas of our field. The concern here is not ony with a current and comprehensive survey of the specialized literature but also with the navigational ease with which pertinent articles can be identified.

Most authors are aware of the remarkable advances that have occurred with end-user search systems dealing with bibliographical databases. The availability of these systems, as exemplified by MEDLINE and Internet gophers, has altered forever the way we access information, especially in the biomedical sciences. Even so, these systems may limit a reviewer's or researcher's access to findings and ideas. MEDLINE, for example, covers journal literature published since 1966, whereas the coverage of books is much less extensive (back to the 1970s), despite recent updates. One concern is the extent to which "old" literature represents "lost" literature, although lost literature is not a new problem exacerbated by the emergence of the current databases. Another concern is whether the citation of relevant articles prior to 1966 is becoming more difficult if not less frequent. The responsibility for critical review of the literature is (and always has been) in the hands of the writer/investigator. This is so whether the new or old (i.e. *Index Medicus*) databases are taken as the sink or the source. It is hoped that the articles that appear in the ARP will help to offset these limitations and to provide useful insights and access to publications in our field.

This volume of ARP, as others before, presents articles surveying recent developments in the various fields of physiology. The articles in each section attempt to be thematic. This year our Special Topic section focuses on nitric oxide. Various aspects of nitric oxide physiology are also discussed in other sections, thus underlining the interdisciplinary theme of this subject.

As always, the Editorial Committee invites comments and criticisms as well as suggestions for future themes, subjects, and authors.

JOSEPH F. HOFFMAN
EDITOR

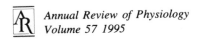

Annual Review of Physiology
Volume 57 1995

CONTENTS

viii   Contents   *(continued)*

OTHER REVIEWS OF INTEREST TO PHYSIOLOGISTS

From the *Annual Review of Biochemistry*, Volume 64 (1995):

Human Carbonic Anhydrase and Carbonic Anhydrase Deficiencies, W. Sly and
P. Y. Hu

Structure and Function of Voltage-Gated Ion Channels, W. Catterall

From the *Annual Review of Medicine*, Volume 46 (1995):

The Nuclear Hormone Receptor Gene Superfamily, R. C. J. Ribeiro, P. J. Kushner,
and J. D. Baxter

Molecular Biology of Diabetes Insipidus, T. M. Fujiwara, K. Morgan,
and D. G. Bichet

*Voltage-Gated Channelopathies: Inherited Disorders Caused By Abnormal Sodium,
Chloride, and Calcium Regulation in Skeletal Muscle*, E. P. Hoffman

From the *Annual Review of Neuroscience*, Volume 18 (1995):

Creating a Unified Representation of Visual and Auditory Space in the Brain,
E. I. Knudsen and M. S. Brainard

Dynamic Regulation of Receptive Fields and Maps in the Adult Sensory Cortex,
N. W. Weinberger

Signal Transduction in Drosophila *Photoreceptors*, R. Ranganathan,
D. M. Malicki, and C. S. Zuker

Long-Term Synaptic Depression, D. J. Linden and J. A. Connor

Learning and Memory in the Vestibulo-Ocular Reflex, S. du Lac, J. L. Raymond,
T. J. Sejnowski, and S. G. Lisberger

The Role of Agrin in Synapse Formation, M. A. Bowe and J. R. Fallon

From the *Annual Review of Nutrition*, Volume 14 (1994):

Nitric Oxide Synthases: Why So Complex? B. S. S. Masters

From the *Annual Review of Pharmacology & Toxicology*, Volume 35 (1995):

A Research Trail Over Half a Century, R. F. Furchgott

Adenosine Receptor Subtypes: Characterization and Therapeutic Regulation,
M. E. Olah and G. L. Stiles

*Inhibition of Constitutive and Inducible Nitric Oxide Synthase: Potential Selective
Inhibition*, J. M. Fukuto and G. Chaudhuri

Nitric Oxide in the Nervous System, J. Zhang and S. H. Snyder

Molecular Strategies for Therapy of Cystic Fibrosis, J. A. Wagner, A. C. Chao,
and P. Gardner

The Pharmacology of the Gastric Acid Pump: The H^+,K^+ ATPase, G. Sachs

ANNUAL REVIEWS INC. is a nonprofit scientific publisher established to promote the advancement of the sciences. Beginning in 1932 with the *Annual Review of Biochemistry*, the Company has pursued as its principal function the publication of high-quality, reasonably priced *Annual Review* volumes. The volumes are organized by Editors and Editorial Committees who invite qualified authors to contribute critical articles reviewing significant developments within each major discipline. The Editor-in-Chief invites those interested in serving as future Editorial Committee members to communicate directly with him. Annual Reviews Inc. is administered by a Board of Directors, whose members serve without compensation.

For the convenience of readers, a detachable order form/envelope is bound into the back of this volume.

H. J. Schützmann

Annu. Rev. Physiol. 1995. 57:1–18

AMARCORD[1]

Hans J. Schatzmann

Department of Veterinary Pharmacology, University of Bern, Switzerland

> Unfortunately, one has to choose between describing science, and doing it.
> John Maynard Smith

YEARS OF LEARNING

I was born 1924 in Bern. My father was a physician who had obtained his training before the First World War. He believed in the power of rational thinking and in his spare time entertained my younger brother and myself with various scientific tricks. He showed us, by letting rise to the ceiling the ashes of burning tissue paper, that air becomes lighter upon heating; we learned about catalysis by setting aflame a lump of sugar endued with papa's cigar ashes; imperceptible rotation of the ambient world was demonstrated with a makeshift Foucault pendulum of watch and chain fastened to the luggage rack in a railway carriage proceeding through one of the coiled tunnels in the Alps. We learned to avoid splashing by pouring liquid down a glass rod and to fold a paper filter zig-zag without any zig-zags. When my tonsils were removed, the loss of pleasure in swallowing food was compensated by the gift of the book *Du und die Natur* (You and Nature) (61), which presents modern physics in a humorous yet fairly accurate way for the layman. As it still stands on my bookshelf, I find that it carries a motto by A. S. Eddington (which I do not dare to retranslate into English) saying that what we find on the distant shores of Nature are our own footprints. So much for epistemology. But what about application of science? When, in 1936, I was comfortably reading in my hospital bed, smashing atoms seemed an amusing pastime, as one could take Lord Rutherford's word for it that, "anybody who was seeking for a source of power in atomic disintegration was talking moonshine," and yet uranium fission came true three years hence, and Hiroshima was only nine years off. The generation of my parents, mistaken as its perception of science may have

---

[1]Amarcord is the title of a film by Federico Fellini and means *io mi ricordo*.

1

0066–4278/95/0315–0001$05.00

been, saw its hopes for a world amenable to perpetual improvement through science-based technology shattered by the experience of the 1914–18 war, which was an outburst of destructive irrationalism, staged with the help of a seemingly rational advance in weaponry. Our disenchantment came when we realized that scientific thinking in no way improved human attitude and witnessed that many scientists (and representatives of other academic branches) were obsequious to fascism and that science was wholly unable to stop mankind from stumbling into the next abyss of despair. As if this were not enough, science handed over to technocrats exploits of unprecedented ambiguity by tampering with the two nuclei in nature [Erwin Chargaff (19)]. We know the misuses of nuclear physics; we hope never to see those possible with the cell nucleus.

School was mostly tedious and at times truly painful, but at least free of charge. Memorizing the shape of letters and learning by rote the multiplication table was not all that bad, but—again—the application revealed the stupidity of the system: in writing compositions we were not allowed to delete anything, with the result that we did not learn to express in writing our genuine thoughts; whenever an error was on the paper, we had to twist the planned sentence so as to use up the mistaken signs. Another nonsense was standing in the benches while the master murmured a chain of arithmetic operations; he who succeeded in shouting the correct result first was allowed to sit down. The teachers probably were aware of the ravage done by the official plans for forming the mind and tried to make good for the weekly ordeal by reading to us on Saturdays from 11 to 12 a.m., edifying pieces of literature like *The Canterville Ghost* (111) or *Pallieter* (103). In the Gymnasium we were exposed during six years to six hours a week of Latin without acquiring the ability to read simple texts in classical Latin fluently. Things improved when, in the last three years, we caught glimpse of the spiritual life of the past by reading worthwhile texts from Molière to Shaw (to mention the more amusing ones) and obtained a first initiation to calculus.

When we felt like exploring the real world, we made more or less risky excursions to the mountains. Traveling abroad was impossible because the abominable war was going on in Europe.

STUDYING MEDICINE IN BERN

In the autumn of 1944, the Gymnasium ended with an examination consisting of confused discussions with experts from the University, giving a raw deal to the intentions of Cromwell in 1647 and to the significance of *La chèvre de M. Seguin,* and I became a medical student for the simple reason that law or divinity were out of the question and that with science I was afraid to be soon out of my depth. In the physics course, I readily discovered that my lack of understanding was not due to the poor teaching we had had in school but to my naive attitude: I was not prepared to accept that physics and the rest of science are not trying to understand the world, that is to find meaning, but to explain events. Explaining (as a meeting's witty chairman once said) amounts to "reducing a new unaccountable mystery to one already known." And yet, serious scientists hope for the moment when the ardent struggle for explanation will, by accident, push open the door to reality.

Teaching in biology was excellent. W. Schopfer, amidst the greenery in the botanical garden, told us about plant physiology, sparing us the drudgery of systematic botany. Fritz Baltzer taught us sound animal genetics and was particularly fascinating when talking about developmental physiology and its mechanisms revealed by the *Organisatorexperimente* of Spemann. Reading recently the delightful book *The Triumph of the Embryo* (114) was like a direct continuation of what I had learned fifty years ago. Baltzer was an irascible man and could get very angry about our stupidity in the laboratory; one day we had to observe a little planarian that came in a watchglass full of water. The creature stuck to the glass, and for some forgotten reason it would have been desirable to look at its belly. Baltzer was very indignant that nobody had the brains and the guts to pour off the water and put the dish upside down under the microscope.

Human anatomy was taught by H. Bluntschli: to those who have read *Arms and the Man* by Shaw, the name is familiar as the very embodiment of Swiss mentality. He had left Germany in 1933 after nineteen years of teaching in Frankfurt and was the incarnation of the professorial idea.

Physiology was in a curious state. Some topics looked fairly settled such as energy balance, overall muscle metabolism, or oxygen transport by hemoglobin. The period certainly was over when physiologists did experiments that revealed the properties of levers rather than those of muscle, and the subtle experiments by A. V. Hill on muscle heat (50, 51) aroused much interest. However, today it is difficult to imagine what neurophysiology looked like without the Hodgkin-Huxley-Katz ionic theory of resting and action potential, or muscle physiology without the notion of sliding filaments of the Huxleys. In such fields we were offered precarious theories that we intuitively refused to believe without a chance of disproving them, which made us uneasy. A. von Muralt tried to convince us of the value of optical methods such as the study of birefringence in muscle. His teaching included experiments done by the students on themselves: We ran around with Haldane bags, pushed needles into each other's arms, and tubes down each other's esophagi, and on Jungfraujoch (3500 m above sea level) ascertained the appearance of Cheyne-Stokes respiration in healthy subjects during sleep. In the clinical sciences, two radically different personalities impressed me: H. Goldmann, the ophthalmologist, did it by his universal interests, and E. Glanzmann, the pediatrician, by a mixture of secret empathy with his little patients and keen scientific observation (which led e.g. to the discovery of thrombasthenia).

DISCOVERING THE LONG BREATH OF SCIENCE

After graduating from medical school in 1951, I asked Professor Wilbrandt whether he could use me as an assistant in the pharmacology department. It was located in a drab building within the hospital area, whereto Wilbrandt had moved from physiology in 1945. His research interest pivoted around trans-membrane transport in red cells, yet all sorts of other experiments were going on in the laboratory. One of these was the 1948 study by Wilbrandt & Koller (109) on calcium-sodium antagonism in frog heart contraction in which they closely missed the point of Na/Ca exchange, twenty years before its successful unraveling by Harald Reuter (80), who later succeeded Wilbrandt in the Institute. Transport meant any kind of penetration of matter across the membrane. A peculiar aspect was that most everything was done by measurement of cell swelling and shrinking by light absorption changes upon hemolysis (108). In a paper of 1960 (110), the optical method was compared to flame photometric measurements of induced K leak, which demonstrated that the former was reliable. The K leak was elicited by a depolarizing low chloride, sucrose medium. The phenomenon had lingered since 1900 (5, 22, 23, 26, 58, 63, 67, 68, 107). When Wilbrandt presented the paper, he suggested that the human red cell is endowed with a cation channel that resembles the one in excitable cells in being activated at low and inactivating at high depolarization. The method of replacing NaCl by sucrose, however, is ambiguous because depolarization might not be the (only) cause for the channel opening, as it drastically lowers ionic strength and raises the external proton concentration on account of the internal one. This was duly pointed out by H. Passow (110). In addition, the inactivation was probably an artefact due to agglutination of the cells at very low salt concentration. The problem still interests investigators (8, 60); the effect does not vanish if the ionic strength is maintained by using salts of nonpenetrating anions instead of sucrose (46) and quite recently it was even obtained under electric depolarization in patch-clamped red cells (21). However, the channel thus demonstrated in erythrocytes is quite different from the one instrumental in the generation of the action potential in nerve and muscle.

CHANCE

Measuring things forces us to grapple with probabilities. By the middle of this century, the need for statistical analysis of biological experiments was generally acknowledged. My doctoral thesis, written at the medical clinic while I still was a student, starts with a quotation from Gravesande (1688–

1742) stating that "regularities are often missed when only a few events are examined and are detected when many are considered." Statistical mathematics is, of course, a vast field and an old concern of scientists and gamblers (9, 34, 47, 56, 64). Amazingly, since Geronimo Cardano's *De Ludo Aleae Liber,* it took four centuries to develop until it could elegantly handle probabilistic problems in biology (35). However, conceptual subtleties (6, 7, 13, 31, 54, 62, 73) escaped me initially; I failed to appreciate the difference between the question of how probable it is that an event occurs and how likely it is that my reasoning about it is well-founded (30). Such distinctions imperceptibly lead to fundamental questions about man's ways of inferring from what he experiences. Our interaction with objects in the scientific context is tainted with doubtful hesitation: (*a*) Is the general uncertainty we live with a consequence of the impossibility of knowing the complete set of initial conditions (the complete history) of a system (e.g. the position and velocity of each of the 2.7×10^{22} molecules in a liter of gas); or (*b*) is chance (*der Zufall, le hasard*) rather than natural laws the gist of reality (82)? The chaotic behavior of deterministic systems displaying nonlinear characteristics owing to internal feedbacks (14, 18, 32, 81) is a form of unpredictability similar to the first instance, being also due to limits of our ratiocination. For biological systems that are always a good deal more complicated than a liter of gas, unpredictability is certainly caused by the imperfection of our thinking. However, at the dimension of elementary particles (electrons, photons), randomness indeed seems to reside in the object (82). But this conviction does not mean victory for the second assumption because things like electrons, being mental constructs arising beyond the pathway of perception, do not have the innocence of what we ordinarily call an object. It seems doubtful whether Heisenberg's indeterminacy principle (49) is hiding the essence of the particle from us for "objective" or for mental reasons. Whatever the answer may be, doubt is not our fault, but our fate since the Cartesian cut, which separates the world into *res extensa* and *res cogitans,* does not resolve the problem as much as it begs the question asked.

Could it be that randomness in the subatomic realm accounts for otherwise inexplicable properties of living things, of which the most unaccountable one is, of course, the entity called awareness, consciousness, or apperception? The last biological question seems to be whether our mind differs from computers in a built-in random element of the nontrivial sort encountered in physics and if, therefore, it is the matter side of mind (the brain) that is responsible for our irreducible subjectivity, our ability to say I, to experience beauty, joy, hope, disgust, hatred, and despair, rather than the program part of it that could be run on any suitable mechanical, hydrodynamic, or electric machine. We are different from the contrivances we build, and R. Penrose must certainly be thanked for his consummate demonstration that a computer cannot answer the question how it feels to be a computer and for asserting that this is no laughing matter at all (74).

FIRST ENCOUNTER WITH A PUMP

It is reported that O. Warburg, when a scientist's merits were extolled, used to ask, *Was hat er denn gefunden?* ("what has he found, after all?"). Discoveries are held in higher esteem than work that merely systematizes knowledge or elaborates on the obvious. Regrettably, I have found only two things apparently worth the while of my colleagues: (*a*) It occurred to me that cardiac glycosides (CGs) inhibit the Na-K pump in human red cells (84); (*b*) I happened to demonstrate the existence of an outwardly directed calcium pump in the plasma membrane of the same cells (89, 91, 94, 95).

The CG story is a nice example of success by serendipity. In my first year in pharmacology, W. Wilbrandt proposed that mineralocorticoids (MCs) might stimulate Na transport in the kidney tubule because they chelate the ion and function as a mobile Na carrier or as the Na-binding site in a pump protein. This idea is, of course, utterly wrong, since we have learned later that steroidal hormones activate gene expression via intracellular receptors. However, it is always risky to be dismissive; there is a vivid discussion today again about direct actions of aldosterone on the cellular membrane (69, 104).

Since I had learned to operate the newly acquired emission flame photometer, Wilbrandt asked me to go ahead an prove his theory. First I had to convince myself of the existence of something that might correspond to the word Na pump. As early as 1902, E. Overton in Würzburg (better known for his theory of general anesthesia) postulated the necessity of an uphill ejection of Na from cardiac muscle because he had evidence that Na enters the cells during the action potential (70). The name pump was attached to the hypothetical mechanism by R. Dean in 1941 (24). In 1954, G. Gardos showed that K is accumulated by resealed red cells if ATP is present inside (37). Ian Glynn (41) quotes three papers (27, 77, 98) appearing around 1960 that dispelled any doubt about the nature of the red cell Na-K pump, to which Post adds another one (39). When I addressed the question, nothing was clear: The coupling of the Na and K movement within the pump and the ATPase function had not been demonstrated. I cooled human red cells to 4°C for several days, which had been shown by French authors in the 1930s to cause them to lose K and gain Na. Upon warming, they recovered their normal cation content. Later I loaded the cells with Na and ATP by reversal of hemolysis and saw (90) what Gardos had shown (37). The loading by reversal of hemolysis was a Hungarian invention (102), which looked unbelievable before one saw it work in one's own lab.

As for the MC stimulation of pumping, I was denied any success. Not only was the failure frustrating, but it made me seem obstructive to progress. In my exasperation, I decided to try some other steroid, namely the one contained in the molecule of k-strophanthoside. I was not aware that the stereochemistry of cardenolides differ from that of cholestane-type steroid hormones. Vaguely, I expected them to do what MCs failed to achieve by the following train of reasoning: (a) MCs stimulate renal Na transport, (b) CGs increase the force of the heart beat, (c) removing some Na from the medium is also positively inotropic, (d) therefore, CGs might stimulate Na extrusion from the cardiac myocyte, (e) in this they are specific for the heart, as MCs are specific for the kidney, (f) red cells may have cardiac specificity. However, I was not long in deciding that instead of stimulation, there was clearcut inhibition of the Na-K pumping. Since glycolysis seemed unaffected, I concluded that the action was directed towards the pump. This is quite correct, although others (105) later showed that, by an interesting feedback, there is a 10% decline of glycolysis if the pump is inhibited by whatever means. My gas volumetric measurements had missed these 10%.

The observation found some interest for several reasons: (a) When the Na/Ca exchange was discovered (2, 80), the inhibition of the Na pump afforded a plausible explanation for the cardiotonic effect of CGs (see below). (b) It is a genuine drug action of a vegetable substance and yet is of extreme specificity, which gives some occasion for philosophical musing. (c) It is useful in recognizing abnormal modes of the pump (40), which are all blocked by CGs. (d) It settles the question whether water flow across a membrane is driven by Na movement (96). (e) It helps deciding whether any uphill transport is secondary, i.e. driven by a Na gradient. (f) It was used to show that the pump is indeed an ATP-consuming enzyme. In 1957, Jens Christian Skou discovered in nerve microsomes (from *Carcinus maenas*) an ATPase that required both Na and K (98) in the medium for high activity. Skou was at the time not a transport physiologist, yet surmised that his enzyme might be involved in Na-K transport; he happened, during a meeting in Vienna in 1958, to talk about it to Robert Post, who at once saw that this enzyme was the Na-K pump and, therefore, asked Skou whether it could be inhibited by ouabain, which provoked in Skou the counterquestion "what is ouabain?" According to the accounts (75, 99) given by the two protagonists of the scene, his next move was to telephone to Aarhus to have his people test this Somali stuff (which is g-strophanthin).[2]

Post's narrative (76) reports that Wilbrandt interpreted the inhibition of the pump by CGs as competition with MCs (101) which, firstly, was not found

---

[2] The word for an arrow poison in the Somali language was attached by botanists to the scientific name of the tree yielding the poison (*Acocanthera ouabaio*). From this plant, Arnaud isolated something called ouabain, which he later also found in the seeds of strophanthus species.

by Glynn (40) and was eventually revoked (57) and, secondly, if it existed, e.g. in rat tissue (85), would not prove the original theory.

Joe Hoffman clearly showed in red cells that CGs act externally, that medium K antagonizes them noncompetitively in binding to a site other than that for CG attachment, and that what is antagonized is CG binding (52). A comprehensive study (10, 11, 12) led to the conclusion that CG binding requires ATP (and Mg^{2+}) and that its rate is inversely proportional to the turnover rate of the pump when it exchanges Na-K or K-K, but not when running in the Na-Na mode, which is compatible with the idea that CGs bind to the phosphorylated E_2 form of the pump and is in accord with the observed fact that K_o inhibits and Na_o enhances their action (88).

DEAD ENDS

After two years in pharmacology, I worked for two years in a hospital as an intern. After this digression, I had another one: I went west, first to San Francisco and then to Boston where I entered the Biophysical Laboratory of Harvard Medical School, directed by A. K. Solomon. He had decided to have transport phenomena looked into by several groups. One project was to find out, by micropuncture studies, what was driving water movement in the proximal tubule of the *Necturus* kidney. Shortly before I arrived in Boston, Erich Windhager (who later succeeded R. F. Pitts at Cornell University) had started putting these endeavors on a sound footing. He invented a table with a trough for aerating the gills of the anesthetized animal in water and replaced mercury for occluding the examined length of tubule by mineral oil stained with Sudan Black B (the pioneers of the group of A. N. Richards used either mercury or oil). As we were not successful in perfusing the tubule, always having fluid leaks at the delivering or the collecting pipette, we adopted a technique that was given the dainty name of stopped-flow perfusion, which effectively hides what is meant (97). In essence, we filled the tubule with the test fluid between two oil droplets and after 20 min retrieved as much as possible for the measurement of e.g. ^{14}C-inulin concentration. The true tubular volume and surface were measured on latex casts of the lumen after the experiment. We were soon joined by Guillermo Whittembury from Peru (who later worked at the IVIC in Caracas). The three of us formed a sort of team, and we had a lot of fun. I remember our exhilaration when Guillermo, reading a text Erich and I had written, exclaimed with conviction "it is almost Spanish." We found the following explanation for the unexpected observation: our English was biased by our German, which in turn was corrupted by our dubious schooling in Latin, which brought us full cycle to an idiom smacking of a modern Latin language.

According to Erich (112) "by 1958, evidence for the passive reabsorption of water and the active nature of sodium transport in the proximal tubule of the amphibian kidney had been established unequivocally," apparently by the efforts of these days (96, 106, 113) (although the outcome was not very doubtful to start with).

BRUSHING BY SMOOTH MUSCLE

After my return to Bern late in 1958, I incurred the risk of becoming a smooth muscle physiologist. Not inappropriately for a pharmacologist, I was fascinated by the electrophysiology of the guinea pig taenia coli, which had been made respectable by Edith Bülbring in Oxford. After having done some length-tension studies, some sucrose gap recording of action potentials, and calcium flux measurements in this preparation (87), I dared to visit Edith. I think that all who knew her felt a deep admiration for her; any awe her erudition and her energy inspired was alleviated by the infectious joy with which she went about scientific endeavor. I remember the atmosphere of bustling life in her laboratory, with people dissecting, recording, running to the dark room with exposed films, and in the middle of all the animated activity, Edith asking blandly "and what am I to do?" as if she were in need for guidance by the young people around her.

However, I finally came to the conclusion that poking microelectrodes into so small a cell as that of smooth muscle was too difficult for me (although Dr. Osa from Fukuoka showed me how it is done) and that without it, no progress was possible.

ANOTHER ENCOUNTER WITH A PUMP

This work, however, stimulated my interest in calcium afresh, and we came back to smooth muscle Ca problems several times afterwards (16, 53). Calcium was already central in understanding the action of CGs; early in the century, Otto Loewi had demonstrated that CGs enable the contracting heart to make better use of a reduced Ca^{2+} concentration, but that even large concentrations of the drug do not elicit tension without Ca^{2+} (65). When, in 1968/69, the Na/Ca exchange was discovered (2, 80), the puzzle was solved why slowing of the Na-K pump increases the force of the heart: with more internal Na, there is much more internal Ca^{2+} to be pumped by and released from the sarcoplasmic reticulum (SR). But quite some time before the advent of the Na/Ca exchange, I worried about the obvious non-equilibrium distribution of Ca^{2+} across cell membranes and returned to the red cell in the hope of achieving something.

By 1964 it had become clear that even in erythrocytes the intracellular Ca^{2+} concentration is far below the external one, although nobody conjectured how extremely low it is. In 1961/62 it was recognized that there is an ATP driven active Ca uptake into vesicles derived from skeletal muscle SR (28, 29, 48), and that the enigmatic relaxing factor of Marsh found in muscle extract is not simply a protein, but is identical with these vesicles. I wondered whether a similar Ca-pump in the surface membrane of red cells might account for Ca extrusion to the exterior. The first obstacle I encountered was that cold storage did not raise red cell Ca measurably in reasonable time. So I resorted again to reversal of hemolysis in metabolically starved cells. However, I was not aware that orthodoxy had it that erythrocytes do not reseal in Ca-containing media. My friend Virgilio Lew later remarked in this context, with a mischievous twinkle in his eyes, that ignorance is an ingredient of scientific success (we know as a matter of course that red cells with high internal Ca^{2+} concentration are leaky to K owing to the Ca^{2+}-sensitive K-channel discovered by G. Gardos (38); but this is a quite different story). In my very first experiment, Ca did not emerge from the cells, but further entered them. I guessed (and it is still a guess 28 years later) that the NaATP, added in millimolar concentration, complexed so much of the internal Ca^{2+} that there was an inwardly directed large Ca^{2+} gradient that swamped the pump. Therefore, in the next experiment, I added an excess of Mg to saturate any binding sites for divalent cations and now there was Ca movement in the outward direction and, for that matter, in an uphill fashion (89). We later learned that Mg^{2+} is an absolute requirement for the Ca pump. So this was again a streak of luck. Without ATP from the bottle, there was much less Ca transport and for a shorter time. It took me the better part of ten years to convince myself that this was another primary cation transport system, while others were quicker in taking it for granted. Meanwhile, Ca pumps have been found in the surface membrane of many cells; notably, Peter Baker's uncoupled Ca efflux from the squid axon (4) turned out to be one of them. Interestingly, they are not an invention of animal life, but seem to be older achievements since they appear in green plants and even in pro-karyotes.

In 1972/73 matters grew complicated by the demonstration in red cells of an activator protein (12a) dissolved in the cytosol, whose efficacy seemed, somehow, to depend on Ca^{2+} (82a,b,c). The riddle was resolved when in 1977, it was discovered that, in contrast to the SR mechanism, the surface membrane pump is stimulated by Ca-calmodulin (42, 59). One of the scientists involved was Frank Vincenzi, who had been in Bern when the pump first saw the light and had contributed to its description (95). Further, the red cell type differs from the SR type in some functional details that can probably be tracked down to different position of some equilibria of reaction steps beyond phosphoryla-tion (1, 92).

It was probably my interest in lipase attack on the Na pump (86) that gave me, years later, the privilege of having Ben Roelofsen from Utrecht working with us, which led to his brilliant description of the lipid requirement of the

Ca pump (79). This is about the only paper on which my name appears, although I contributed neither to the experiments nor to the writing.

Workers who have enormously furthered the insight into the behavior of the Ca pump have summarized current knowledge. Rega & Garrahan presented a comprehensive monograph (78), and Carafoli & Chiesi (17) have recently described the more molecular aspects.

It is a question worth being asked, why do excitable cells have two mechanisms for extruding Ca, namely the ATP-driven pump and the Na/Ca exchanger? It has been said that the exchanger (which in the squid axon is ten times faster than the pump) copes with heavy loads of Ca, e.g. after a train of action potentials, while the pump (having a higher Ca_i^{2+}-affinity than the exchanger) mops up the last traces of Ca to achieve Ca_i^{2+} concentrations of $< 10^{-7}M$. This is, I am afraid, a fallacious argument: the exchanger will impose its own equilibrium value for Ca_i^{2+} concentration, which can be approached from below as well as from above. The pump probably is a safety device, still able to keep Ca_i^{2+} low should Na_i for some reason escape the control by the Na-K pump. Thanks to the exchanger the Ca pump is even capable of lowering Na_i indirectly. Dog red cells present an experiment of nature to demonstrate this possibility. They lack a Na-K pump and prevent unlimited Na entry, which leads to swelling and eventual rupture, by extruding Na in exchange for Ca, i.e. at the expense of energy expenditure by the Ca pump, and thus they are able to keep Na_i fixed, albeit high (71, 72).

BECOMING A VET

While the calcium work was in progress, I was offered the position of pharmacologist at the Veterinary Faculty. This made me more independent, the moderate teaching load seemed favorable to much laboratory work, and the frugal allowance guaranteed for my never becoming an administrator. Silvio Weidmann henceforth referred to me as *collega bestialis*. The lab was tucked away in three rooms, which were ample for myself, an assistant, and two technicians. The institute later grew somewhat and since everybody found dishwashing delectable and was able to weigh out 58.44 g of sodium chloride, one of the technicians' salaries was used to pay graduate students a small remuneration.

Teaching pharmacology to medical or veterinary students is a mixed pleasure. In the first clinical year, most of them want to see pus and be charitable, and theoretical topics bore them. This, however, was quite different with those twenty nine students who, over the years, volunteered to work in the lab for their theses. Nearly all of them not only did reliable work, but even caught the miasma of scientific enthusiasm (which is so different from the self-assertiveness seen in many established members of the profession). I am opposed to the notion that "those people" simply mess up the lab and that the title of doctor of medicine should be meted out after only some years of routine diagnostic work in microbiology, pathology, or the like. I thought it important in the 1970s and think it more so today, with all the automatization in research and diagnostics, that professionals who flatter themselves for having been at the University should have experienced once in their lives how much labor and painful doubt are invested in obtaining the merest detail of human knowledge. To my mind it is one of the odious defects of our educational system that, while you are young enough to truly learn, you are constantly told how things are and seldom how they came about.

MISCELLANEA

In the 1980s it was reported that magnesium is extruded from avian (44), human (33), and rat (45) red cells in exchange for Na, provided that there is ATP present in the cells, a mechanism that resembles what has been described for the squid axon (3, 25). We tinkered with this system (36, 66, 93) and it appears to me that it differs markedly from the analogous exchanger for Na/Ca in excitable cells; it stops below 100 µM internal Mg^{2+} concentrations (which is, of course, most appropriate), and it is not easily reversed when the cation gradients are inverted.

In 1983, Felix Graf, working for his thesis, discovered a novel calcium phenomenon in skeletal muscle (43) (which is also reflected by the action of calcium entry blockers; 55): Exposure to Ca^{2+}-free KCl solution for several seconds causes a transient contracture, much as Ca^{2+}-containing KCl solution does, yet after repolarization, the muscle stays paralyzed to a new voltage challenge, even if Ca^{2+} is again admitted, and although caffeine still normally contracts the muscle. A nominal explanation for the finding proposes that the voltage sensor (the dihydropyridine receptor) does not return from one of the inactivated states unless external Ca^{2+} is present (15)—at the right moment, one must add. A strong hyperpolarization seems to overcome the paralysis, yet the Ca_o^{2+}-dependence of the excitation-contraction coupling is still shrouded in mystery.

Being implanted in a veterinary school, I felt obliged to do, or let others do, something practical (which veterinarians cherish immensely). We did—at a time when this was not yet commonplace—pharmacokinetics in farm animals and horses. Another beastly occupation was measuring fermentation rates in ruminal fluid. The reticulo-rumen is an extraordinary site in the midst of our oxygen-replete world, where bacteria re-enact, with the connivance of the animal, a version of the life in the primordial soup with ingredients like carbon dioxide, hydrogen, methane, formate, and ammonia, and offer the host nicely reduced foodstuffs (acetate, propionate, butyrate) for respiratory energy production, and amino acids made from scratch, namely ammonia. At times the lab looked like a alchemist's shop with all the apparatus for steam distillation of volatile fatty acids.

We also looked at cattle red cells' handling of cations which, in fetal cells at birth, is normal (i.e. similar to that in human cells), yet later on deviates, in that the cells in a majority of individuals become high Na, low K erythrocytes owing to a type of Na-K pump that has a comparatively high affinity for internal K (20, 100). A decline of activity with age is also seen in the Ca-pump of cattle red cells (115).

A few times we had an opportunity to study red cells from human subjects suffering from hereditary hemolytic anemias with a disturbed cation traffic, which led to increased Na_i concentration. In all cases this was not a matter of a defective Na-pump, but of an increased leak flow. Except for one case, the abnormal cation handling did not account for the cells' propensity to lyse in the circulation.

APOLOGIA

I whiled away 38 years studying (at the taxpayers' expense) the behavior of inorganic ions inside living matter. It probably turned out this way by chance, but the question may be asked if this can be justified. To which my answer is that the ways in which cells handle water and salt are at least as marvelous as reproduction, self-organization, speciation, photosynthesis, chemical respiration, intercellular communication, sensory perception, purposeful motility, social behavior, and what-not among the characteristics of life. In evolution, macromolecules arose in a surrounding in which salt was unavoidable in the pervasive water, but instead of just putting up with ionized Na, K, Ca, Mg, Cl, SO_4, HCO_3 (not to speak of Fe, Cu, Zn, Co, Se) cells have learned to use them for the most vital purpose of excitability and control of coordinate action in multicellular organisms for which active transports (pumps) are a prerequisite. We are made of more material from the universe than just C, H, N, and S, which once more underpins the conviction that organisms, including humans, are an outgrowth (Thomas Mann called it a disease) from the totality of things existing and not a creation apart, or as Professor G. A. Tammann, the Basel astronomer, says in a pleasant movie by M. von Gunten, "We are children of the stars."

With all the sequencing and cloning and site-directed-mutagenerating, we are still ignorant of the knack of biomembranes in converting chemical energy of ATP hydrolysis into thermodynamically uphill movements of sodium and calcium. The story is far from complete, perhaps because all research is "like peeling an infinite onion" as Aser Rothstein says. At any rate, everyone of us must be content with having removed but a thin layer from a rather superficial region of the bulb and with having thereby contributed a trifle to reduce the state of mind in which everything has the same likelihood (31).

Literature Cited

1. Adamo HP, Rega AF, Garrahan PJ. 1988. Pre-steady state phosphorylation of human red cell Ca^{2+}- ATPase. *J. Biol. Chem.* 263:17548–54
2. Baker PF, Blaustein MP, Hodgkin AL, Steinhardt RA. 1967. The effect of sodium concentration on calcium movements in giant axons of *Loligo forbesi. J. Physiol.* 192:43P
3. Baker PF, Crawford AC. 1972. Mobility and transport of magnesium in squid axons. *J. Physiol.* 227:855–74
4. Baker PF, McNaughton PA. 1978. The influence of extracellular calcium binding on the calcium efflux from squid axons. *J. Physiol.* 276:127–50
5. Bang I. 1909. Physico-chemische Verhältnisse der Blutkörperchen. *Biochem. Zeitschr.* 16:255–76
6. Barnard GA. 1958. Thomas Bayes—A Biographical Note. *Biometrika* 45:293–95
7. Bayes Th. 1763. An essay towards solving a problem in the doctrine of chances. *Philos. Trans. R. Soc.* 53:370–418
8. Bernhardt I, Hall AC, Ellory JC. 1991. Effect of low ionic strength media on passive human red cell monovalent cation transport. *J. Physiol.* 434:489–506
9. Bernoulli J. 1899. *Wahrscheinlichkeitsrechnung (Ars conjectandi), 1713.* Trans. R Haussner, W Engelmann. Leipzig
10. Bodemann HH, Hoffman JF. 1976. Side-dependent effects of internal versus external Na and K on ouabain binding to reconstituted human red blood cell ghosts. *J. Gen. Physiol.* 67:497–525
11. Bodemann HH, Hoffman JF. 1976. Comparison of the side-dependent effects of Na and K on orthophosphate, UTP and ATP-promoted ouabain binding to reconstituted human red blood cell ghosts. *J. Gen. Physiol.* 67:527–45
12. Bodemann HH, Hoffman JF. 1976. Effects of Mg and Ca on the side-dependencies of Na and K on ouabain binding to red blood cell ghosts and the control of Na transport by internal Mg. *J. Gen. Physiol.* 67:547–61
12a. Bond GH, Clough DL. 1973. A soluble protein activator of $(Mg^{2+}+ Ca^{2+})$-dependent ATPase in human red cell membranes. *Biochim. Biophys. Acta* 323:592–99
13. Boole G. 1953. *Studies in Logic and Probability.* London: Watts. 500 pp.
14. Briggs J, Peat FD. 1989. *Turbulent Mirror.* New York: Harper & Row. 222 pp.
15. Brum G, Fitts R, Pizarro S, Rios E. 1988. Voltage sensors of the frog skeletal muscle membrane require calcium to function in excitation-contraction coupling. *J. Physiol.* 398:475–505
16. Bürgin H. 1979. The role of calcium in the mechanical performance of cattle ruminant muscle. *J. Vet. Pharmacol. Therap.* 2:305–11
17. Carafoli E, Chiesi M. 1992. Calcium pumps in the plasma and intracellular membranes. *Curr. Topics Cell. Regul.* 32:209–41
18. Casti JL. 1990. *Searching for Certainty.* New York: Morrow . 496 pp.
19. Chargaff E. 1980. *Das Feuer des Heraklit.* Stuttgart: Klett-Cotta. 290 pp. 2te. Aufl.
20. Christinaz P, Schatzmann HJ. 1972. High potassium and low potassium erythrocytes in cattle. *J. Physiol.* 224:391–406
21. Christophersen P, Bennekou P. 1991. Evidence for a voltage-gated, non-selective cation channel in the human red cell membrane. *Biochim. Biophys. Acta* 1147:103–6
22. Cotterell D, Whittam R. 1971. The influence of the chloride gradient across red cell membranes on sodium and potassium movements. *J. Physiol.* 214:509–36
23. Davson H. 1939. Studies on the permeability of erythrocytes. VI. The effect of reducing the salt content of the medium surrounding the cell. *Biochem. J.* 33:389–401

24. Dean RB. 1941. Theories of electrolyte equilibrium in muscle. *Biol. Symp.* 3: 331–48

25. DiPolo R, Beaugé L. 1988. An ATP-dependent Na^+/Mg^{2+} counter-transport is the only mechanism for Mg extrusion in squid axons. *Biochim. Biophys. Acta* 946:424–28

26. Donlon JA, Rothstein A. 1969. The cation permeability of erythrocytes in low ionic strength media of various tonicity. *J. Membr. Biol.* 1:37–52

27. Dunham ET, Glynn IM. 1961. Adenosine triphosphatase activity and the active movement of alkali metal ions. *J. Physiol.* 156:274–93

28. Ebashi S. 1961. Calcium binding activity of vesicular relaxing factor. *J. Biochem.* 50:236–44

29. Ebashi S, Lipmann F. 1962. Adenosine triphosphate linked concentration of calcium ions in a particulate fraction of rabbit muscle. *J. Cell. Biol.* 14:389–400

30. Edwards AWF. 1972. *Likelyhood.* Cambridge/London/New York: Cambridge Univ. Press. 235 pp.

31. Edwards AWF. 1991. Bayesian reasoning in science. *Nature* 352:386–87

32. Ekeland I. 1991. *Au Hasard.* ed. Seuil, 6e Paris. 199 pp.

33. Féray JC, Garay R. 1986. A Na^+-stimulated Mg^{2+}-transport system in human red blood cells. *Biochim. Biophys. Acta* 856:76–84

34. Fermat P de. 1679. *Varia opera mathematica D. Petri Fermat Senatoris Tolsani.* Tolosae: Apud Ioannem Pech Typographum

35. Fisher RA. 1990. *Statistical Methods, Experimental Design and Scientific Inference.* ed. JH Bennett, pp. 362, 248, 180. Oxford: Oxford Univ. Press

36. Frenkel EJ, Graziani M, Schatzmann HJ. 1989. ATP requirement of the sodium-dependent magnesium extrusion from human red blood cells. *J. Physiol.* 414:385–97

37. Gardos G. 1954. Akkumulation der Kaliumionen durch menschliche Blutkörperchen. *Acta Physiol. Hung.* 6: 191–99

38. Gardos G. 1958. The function of calcium in the potassium permeability of human erythrocytes. *Biochim. Biophys. Acta* 30: 653–54

39. Glynn IM. 1956. Sodium and potassium movements in human red cells. *J. Physiol.* 134:278–310

40. Glynn IM. 1957. The action of cardiac glycosides on sodium and potassium movements in human red cells. *J. Physiol.* 136:148–73

41. Glynn IM. 1993. All hands to the sodium pump. *J. Physiol.* 462:1–30

42. Gopinath RM, Vincenzi FF. 1977. Phosphodiesterase protein activator mimics red blood cell cytoplasmic activator of $(Ca^{2+}+Mg^{2+})$-ATPase. *Biochem. Biophys. Res. Comm.* 77:1203–9

43. Graf F, Schatzmann HJ. 1984. Some effects of removal of external calcium on pig striated muscle. *J. Physiol.* 349:1–13

44. Günther T, Vormann J, Förster R. 1984. Regulation of intracellular magnesium by Mg^{2+} efflux. *Biochem. Biophys. Res. Comm.* 119:124–31

45. Günther T, Vormann J, Höllriegl V. 1990. Characterization of Na-dependent Mg^{2+}- efflux from Mg^{2+}- loaded rat erythrocytes. *Biochim. Biophys. Acta* 1023:455–61

46. Halperin JA, Brugnara C, Tosteson MT, Van Ha T, Tosteson DC. 1989. Voltage-activated cation transport in human erythrocytes. *Am. J. Physiol.* 256:C986–96

47. Hara K. 1981. *L'oeuvre mathématique de Pascal.* Osaka Univ. Mem. Fac. Lett. 21:52–61

48. Hasselbach W, Makinose M. 1961. Die Calcium-pumpe der Erschlaffungsgrana des Muskels und ihre Abhängigkeit von der ATP Spaltung. *Biochem. Zeitschr.* 333:518–28

49. Heitler W. 1962. *Der Mensch und die naturwisenschaftliche Erkenntnis.* Braunschweig: Vieweg & Sohn. 75 pp. 2te. Aufl.

50. Hill AV. 1938. The heat of shortening and the dynamic constants of muscle. *Proc. R. Soc. London Ser. B* 126:136–95

51. Hill AV, Howarth JV. 1959. The reversal of chemical reactions in contracting muscle during an an applied stretch. *Proc. R. Soc. London Ser. B* 151:169–93

52. Hoffman JF. 1966. The red cell membrane and the transport of sodium and potassium. *Am. J. Med.* 41:666–78

53. Hotz R. 1988. *Bedeutung rezeptorgesteuerter und potential- abhängiger Calciumkanäle für die Kontraktion der Arteria mesenterica cranialis vom Schwein.* Vet. MD thesis. Univ. Bern. 77 pp.

54. Howson C, Urbach P. 1991. Bayesian reasoning in science. *Nature* 350:371–74

55. Hui CS, Milton RL, Eisenberg RS. 1984. Charge movement in skeletal muscle fibers paralyzed by the calcium-entry blocker D-600. *Proc. Natl. Acad. Sci. USA* 81:2582–85

56. Huygens Ch. 1920. Oeuvres complètes publiées par la Société Hollandaise des sciences. XIV Calcul de probabilités

(van rekeningh in spelen van geluck) 1656.

57. Iff HW, Schindler R, Wilbrandt W. 1962. Zur Frage einer antagonistischen Wirkung von Herzglycosiden und Nebennierensteroiden am Kationentransport der Erythrozytenmembran. *Experientia* 18:314–15

58. Jacobs MH, Parpart AK. 1933. Osmotic properties of the erythrocyte. VI. The influence of the escape of salts on hemolysis by hypotonic solutions. *Biol. Bull. Marine Biol. Lab. Woods Hole* 65:512–28

59. Jarrett HW, Penniston JT. 1977. Partial purification of the $Ca^{2+}+Mg^{2+}$ ATPase activator from human erythrocytes. Its similarity to the activator of 3′:5′-cyclic nucleotide phosphodiesterase. *Biochem. Biophys. Res. Commun.* 77:1210–16

60. Jones GS, Knauf PA. 1985. Mechanism of the increase in cation permeability of human erythrocytes in low-chloride media. Involvement of the anion transport protein capnophorin. *J. Gen. Physiol.* 86:721–38

61. Karlson P. 1934. *Du und die Natur.* Berlin: Deutscher Verlag. 369 pp.

62. Keynes JM. 1926. *Ueber Wahrscheinlichkeit.* Transl. FM Urban, JA Barth. Leipzig. 369 pp.

63. La Celle PL, Rothstein A. 1966. The passive permeability of the red blood cell to cations. *J Gen. Physiol.* 50:171–88

64. Laplace P Simon Marquis de. 1816. *Essai philosophique sur les probabilités.* 3e ed. 8e Paris

65. Loewi O. 1917. Ueber den Zusammenhang zwischen Digitalis-und Kalziumwirkung. *Arch. exp. Path. Pharmakol.* 82:131–58

66. Lüdi H, Schatzmann HJ. 1987. Some properties of a system for sodium-dependent outward movement of magnesium from metabolizing human red blood cells. *J. Physiol.* 390:367–82

67. Maizels M. 1935. The permeation of erythrocytes by cations. *Biochem. J.* 29:1970–82

68. Mond R. 1927. Umkehr der Anionenpermeabilität der roten Blutkörperchen in eine elektive Durchlässigkeit für Kationen. *Pflügers Arch.* 217:618–30

69. Moura AM, Worcel M. 1984. Direct action of aldosterone on transmembrane ^{22}Na efflux from arterial smooth muscle. *Hypertension* 6:425–30

70. Overton E. 1902. Beiträge zur allgemeinen Muskel-und Nerven- physiologie. II. Ueber die Unentbehrlichkeit von Natrium (oder Lithium) Ionen für die Kontraktion des Muskels. *Pflügers Arch.* 92:346–86

71. Parker JC. 1978. Sodium and calcium movements in dog red blood cells. *J. Gen. Physiol.* 71:1–17

72. Parker JC. 1979. Active and passive calcium movements in dog red blood cells and resealed ghosts. *Am. J. Physiol.* 237:C10–16

73. Peirce CS. 1932. 6. The doctrine of chances; 7. The probability of induction; 8. A theory of probable inference. In *Collected Papers,* ed. C Hartshorne, P Weiss, 2:389–477. Cambridge: Harvard Univ. Press

74. Penrose R. 1989. *The Emperor's New Mind.* Oxford/New York/Melbourne: Oxford Univ. Press. 466 pp.

75. Post RL. 1974. A reminiscence about sodium potassium ATPase. *Ann. NY Acad. Sci.* 242:6–11

76. Post RL. 1989. Seeds of sodium-potassium ATPase. *Annu. Rev. Physiol.* 51:1–15

77. Post RL, Merritt CR, Kinsolving CR, Albright CD. 1960. Membrane adenosine triphosphatase as a participant in the active transport of sodium and potassium in the human erythrocyte. *J. Biol. Chem.* 235:1796–1802

78. Rega AF, Garrahan PJ. 1986. *The Calcium Pump of Plasma Membranes.* Boca Raton, Fla: CRC Press. 173 pp.

79. Roelofsen B, Schatzmann HJ. 1977. The lipid requirement of the $(Ca^{2+}+Mg^{2+})$-ATPase in the human erythrocyte membrane, as studied by various highly purified phospholipases. *Biochim. Biophys. Acta.* 464:17–36

80. Reuter H, Seitz N. 1968. The dependence of calcium efflux from cardiac muscle on temperature and external ion composition. *J. Physiol.* 195:451–70

81. Ruelle D. 1991. *Chance and Chaos.* Princeton: Princeton Univ. Press. 195 pp.

82. Ruhla C. 1989. *La physique du hasard.* Paris: Hachette. 269 pp. Transl. G Barton. 1992. *The Physics of Chance.* New York: Oxford Univ. Press (From French)

82a. Scharff O. 1972. The influence of calcium ions on the preparation of the (Ca^{2+}, Mg^{2+})-activated membrane ATPase in human red cells. *Scand. J. Clin. Lab. Invest.* 39:313–20

82b. Scharff O. 1976. Ca^{2+} activation of membrane-bound (Ca^{2+}, Mg^{2+})-dependent ATPase from human erythrocytes prepared in the presence or absence of Ca. *Biochim. Biophys. Acta* 443:206–18

82c. Scharff O, Foder B. 1977. Low Ca^{2+} concentrations controlling two kinetic states of Ca^{2+}-ATPase from human erythrocytes. *Biochim. Biophys. Acta* 483:416–24

83. Schatzmann HJ. 1953. *Ueber die Unabhängigkeit der renalen Wasserausscheidung vom Blutdruck bei pathologischen Hochdruckuzständen.* MD thesis. Univ. Bern. 16 pp.

84. Schatzmann HJ. 1953. Herzglykoside als Hemmstoffe für den aktiven Kalium- und Natriumtransport durch die Erythrozytenmembran. *Helv. Physiol. Pharmacol. Acta* 11:346–54

85. Schatzmann HJ. 1959. Kompetitiver Antagonismus zwischen g-Strophanthin und Corticosteron an isolierten Streifen von Rattenaorten. *Experientia* 15:73–74

86. Schatzmann HJ. 1962. Lipoprotein nature of red cell adenosine triphosphatase. *Nature* 196:677

87. Schatzmann HJ. 1964. Erregung und Kontraktion glatter Vertebratenmuskeln. *Erg. Physiol. Biol. Chem. exp. Pharmakol.* 55:29–130

88. Schatzmann HJ. 1965. The role of Na^+ and K^+ in the ouabain-inhibition of the $Na^+ + K^+$-activated membrane adenosine triphosphatase. *Biochim. Biophys. Acta* 94:89–96

89. Schatzmann HJ. 1966. ATP-dependent Ca^{2+}-extrusion from human red cells. *Experientia* 22:364–68

90. Schatzmann HJ. 1967. Effect of cardiac glycosides on active Na-K-transport. *Protoplasma* 63:136–42

91. Schatzmann HJ. 1973. Dependence on calcium concentration and stoichiometry of the calcium pump in human red cells. *J. Physiol.* 235:551–69

92. Schatzmann HJ. 1989. The calcium pump of the surface membrane and of the sarcoplasmic reticulum. *Annu. Rev. Physiol.* 51:473–85

93. Schatzmann HJ. 1993. Asymmetry of the magnesium sodium exchange across the human red cell membrane. *Biochim. Biophys. Acta* 1148:15–18

94. Schatzmann HJ, Rossi GL. 1971. $(Ca^{2+} + Mg^{2+})$-activated membrane ATPases in human red cells and their possible relations to cation transport. *Biochim. Biophys. Acta* 241:379–92

95. Schatzmann HJ, Vincenzi FF. 1969. Calcium movements across the membrane of human red cells. *J. Physiol.* 201:369–95

96. Schatzmann HJ, Windhager EE, Solomon AK. 1958. Single proximal tubules of the *Necturus* kidney. II Effect of 2,4-dinitrophenol and ouabain on water reabsorption. *Am. J. Physiol.* 195:570–74

97. Shipp JC, Hanenson IB, Windhager EE, Schatzmann HJ, Whittembury G, et al.

1958. Single proximal tubules of the *Necturus* kidney. Methods for micropuncture and microperfusion. *Am. J. Physiol.* 195:563–69

98. Skou JCh. 1957. The influence of some cations on an adenosine triphosphatase from peripheral nerves. *Biochim. Biophys. Acta* 23:394–401

99. Skou JCh. 1989. The identification of the sodium pump as the membrane bound Na/K-ATPase. A commentary. *Biochim. Biophys. Acta* 1000:435–38

100. Stucki P, Schatzmann HJ. 1983. The response to potassium of the Na-K pump ATPase in low-K red blood cells from cattle at birth and in later life. *Experientia* 39:535–36

101. Sulser F, Wilbrandt W. 1957. Die Wirkung von Corticosteroiden und Herzglycosiden auf Ionentransporte am Erythrozyten. *Helv. Physiol. Pharmacol. Acta* 15:C37

102. Szekely M, Manyai S, Straub FB. 1952. Ueber den Mechanismus der osmotischen Haemolyse. *Acta Physiol. Hung.* 3:571–84

103. Timmermans F. 1992. *Pallieter.* Transl. A Valeton-Hoos. Frankfurt a. Main/ Leipzig: Insel Taschenbuch

104. Wehling M, Christ M, Gerzer R. 1993. Aldosterone-specific membrane receptors and related rapid, non-genomic effects. *Trends Pharmacol. Sci.* 14:1–3

105. Whittam R, Ager ME, Wiley JS. 1964. Control of lactate production by membrane adenosine triphosphatase activity in human erythrocytes. *Nature* 202:1111–12

106. Whittembury G, Oken DE, Windhager EE, Solomon AK. 1959. Single proximal tubules, of the *Necturus* kidney. VI Dependence of H_2O-movement on osmotic gradients. *Am. J. Physiol.* 197:1121–27

107. Wilbrandt W. 1940. Die Ionenpermeabilität der Erythrozyten in Nichtleiterlösungen. *Pflügers Arch.* 243:537–56

108. Wilbrandt W. 1955. Osmotische Erscheinungen und osmotische Methoden an Erythrozyten. In *Hoppe-Seyler/ Thierfelder, Handbuch der physiol.-pathophysiol.-chem. Analyse. 10. Aufl. Bd.II,* 49–71

109. Wilbrandt W, Koller H. 1948. Die Calciumwirkung am Froschherzen als Funktion des Ionengleichgewichts zwischen Zellmembran und Umgebung. *Helv. Physiol. Pharmacol. Acta* 6:208–21

110. Wilbrandt W, Schatzmann HJ. 1960. Changes in the passive cation permeability of erythrocytes in low-electrolyte

media. In *Ciba Foundation Study Group 5; Regulation of the Inorganic Ion Content of Cells,* ed. GEW Wolstenholme CM O'Connor, pp. 34–52. London: Churchill

111. Wilde O. 1979. The Canterville ghost. In *Complete Shorter Fiction,* ed. I Murray, pp. 59–87. New York: Oxford Univ. Press

112. Windhager EE. 1987. Micropuncture and microperfusion. In *Renal Physiology: People and Ideas,* pp. 101–29. Bethesda, MD: Am. Physiol. Soc.

113. Windhager EE, Whittembury G, Oken DE, Schatzmann HJ, Solomon AK. 1959. Single proximal tubules of the *Necturus* kidney. III Dependence of H_2O-movement on NaCl concentration. *Am. J. Physiol.* 197:313–18

114. Wolpert L. 1991. *The Triumph of the Embryo.* New York: Oxford Univ. Press. 211 pp.

115. Zimmermann A, Schatzmann HJ. 1985. Calcium transport by red blood cell membranes from young and adult cattle. *Experientia* 41:743–45

Annu. Rev. Physiol. 1995. 57:19–42

THERMAL ADAPTATION IN BIOLOGICAL MEMBRANES: Is Homeoviscous Adaptation the Explanation?

Jeffrey R. Hazel

Department of Zoology, Arizona State University, Tempe, Arizona 85287–1501

KEY WORDS: homeoviscous adaptation, lipid, membrane, membrane fluidity, phase behavior, phospholipid, temperature

INTRODUCTION

The phase behavior and physical properties of lipids in biological membranes are exquisitely sensitive to changes in temperature (50). Because membranes (*a*) act as physical barriers to solute diffusion, (*b*) mediate the transmembrane movement of specific solutes, (*c*) regulate the utilization of energy stored in transmembrane ion gradients, (*d*) provide an organizing matrix for the assembly of multicomponent metabolic and signal transduction pathways, and (*e*) supply precursors for the generation of lipid-derived second messengers, temperature-induced perturbations in membrane organization pose a serious challenge to the maintenance of physiological function in poikilotherms. However, poikilotherms exploit the diversity of lipid structure to fashion membranes with physical properties appropriate to their thermal circumstance and, in this way, restore membrane function following thermal challenge. Based on the finding that membrane lipids of *Escherichia coli* grown at 43 and 15°C displayed similar physical properties when compared at their respective growth temperatures, Sinensky concluded that membrane fluidity was defended as growth temperature changes and referred to this cellular homeostatic response as homeoviscous adaptation (HVA) (94). Since the original exposition of this hypothesis, HVA has emerged as the most commonly employed paradigm to assess the efficacy of thermal adaptation in biological membranes and to explain patterns of temperature-induced change in membrane lipid composi-

19

tion (23). The goals of this review are to assess critically the role of HVA in the thermal adaptation of biological membranes and to explore alternative explanations for patterns of thermotropic lipid restructuring.

MEMBRANE CONSTRAINTS TO GROWTH AND FUNCTION AT DIFFERENT TEMPERATURES

Thermal Perturbation of Membrane Structure and Function

One consequence of poikilothermy is perturbation of membrane organization when cell or body temperature changes. Effects of temperature are most evident as altered properties of the acyl chain domain in the bilayer interior. At physiological temperatures, gauche rotamers (rotations about carbon-carbon single bonds) freely propagate up and down the length of the fatty acyl chains, which results in a relatively fluid, disordered liquid-crystalline phase (Figure 1) (72). However, acyl chain motion is moderately constrained for 8–10 carbon atoms extending from the membrane surface primarily by the covalent attachment and parallel alignment of the hydrocarbon chains (11). When temperature drops below the physiological range, acyl chains, at some defined point (the gel/fluid or chain-melting transition temperature, T_m), adopt the all-*trans* conformation and pack efficiently to form a highly ordered gel phase (Figure 1). However, in biological membranes, a region of phase separation (consisting of coexisting domains of fluid and gel phase lipids) may extend over a temperature range of 10–15°C due to the diversity of lipid species present (59). Conversely, when temperature exceeds the physiological range, some lipids [most notably phosphatidylethanolamine (PE)] assume the inverted hexagonal (H_{II}) phase (Figure 1), which results in a loss of bilayer integrity (67, 91). The transition to the H_{II} phase (occurring at T_h) is driven, in part, by a temperature-induced change in phospholipid molecular geometry from a cylindrical to a conical shape (refer to Figure 1). Although conical lipids can accommodate increased disorder in the acyl domain, they cannot alone form a lamellar or bilayer phase. Finally, even in the absence of lipid phase transitions, rising temperature increases the rate and extent of acyl chain motion (111).

Thermal perturbation of lipid phase state has a profound impact on membrane structure and function. For example, transition from the fluid to gel phase (*a*) induces the clustering of integral membrane proteins, which are largely excluded from domains of gel phase lipids (54); (*b*) reduces the activity of many membrane-associated enzymes (52, 108); (*c*) slows the rate of lateral protein diffusion within the plane of the bilayer, thereby reducing the efficiency of diffusion-coupled processes (45); and (*d*) markedly increases the permeability to cations and water, presumably because of packing defects that form at boundaries between microdomains of gel and fluid phase lipids (10, 95).

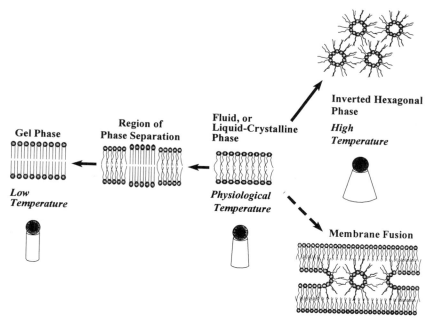

Figure 1   Solid arrows indicate the effects of either a rise or drop in temperature on the phase behavior and molecular geometry of membrane phospholipids. The physiological temperature refers to the temperature at which an organism is either adapted or acclimated. The dashed arrow illustrates the presumed involvement of the inverted hexagonal phase in membrane fusion.

Furthermore, temperature effects too slight to induce phase transitions can also significantly affect membrane function. Activities as diverse as Na$^+$/K$^+$-ATPase in lamb kidney (47), chloride transport in secretory granules of rat pancreas (40), the binding, uptake, and degradation of LDL by rat hepatocytes (61), collision coupling between components of the β-adrenergic signal transduction pathway (46), the rotational mobility of sarcoplasmic reticular Ca^{2+}-ATPase (99), and the passive permeability of fluid phase membranes (26) are all positively correlated with membrane fluidity, which is, in turn, determined by temperature.

Membrane Constraints to Growth and Function

Considerable evidence indicates that the phase state and/or physical properties of membrane lipids contribute to the definition of the thermal limits for growth and function. For example, in *Acholeplasma laidlawii* enriched in relatively high melting point fatty acids, growth is inhibited at low temperatures when more than 50% of the membrane lipid is present in the gel phase and ceases entirely when the proportion of gel phase lipids reaches 90%, which indicates a growth requirement for fluid phase lipids (70). Similarly, loss of photosynthetic activity at cold temperature in the cyanobacterium *Anacystis nidulans* coincides with the onset of phase separation in the plasma membrane (77). In addition, butylated hydroxytoluene, a perturber of lipid bilayers, improves the survival of mammalian cells at temperatures below the fluid/gel transition of their membrane lipids, which further supports a functional requirement for fluid phase lipids (60).

Whether membranes also constrain growth and function at elevated temperatures is less clear. The leakage of K^+ from muscle fibers at elevated temperatures has been implicated as a cause of heat death in crayfish (42), and in *Acholeplasma,* the maximum growth temperature is decreased in cells grown on low melting point fatty acids (70). Furthermore, *E. coli* regulate the phospholipid composition of their membranes so that the H_{II} phase transition occurs approximately 10°C above the growth temperature (85). Thus either increases in membrane permeability or formation of nonlamellar phases, with the consequent loss of bilayer integrity, may constrain growth and function at high temperatures, just as formation of the gel phase does at low temperatures.

Membrane properties may also influence physiological performance in the interval between T_m and T_h. For example, in *Acholeplasma* grown on various fatty acid mixtures containing perdeuterated palmitate (a nonperturbing ^{2}H-NMR probe of membrane order), maximal growth rates were restricted to a range of average molecular order parameters (S_{mol}—a measure of the time-averaged orientation of the ^{2}H-C bond vector relative to the bilayer normal) between 0.140 and 0.177 (74).

MEMBRANE REMODELING: The Basis of Thermal Adaptation

The inherent sensitivity of the phase behavior and physical properties of membrane lipids to changes in temperature restricts the thermal range over which a designated set of membrane constituents can function effectively. Consequently, to function over a broad range of environmental temperatures, poikilothermic organisms must restructure their membranes so that lipids of appropriate physical properties are matched to the prevailing thermal conditions. Accordingly, the most commonly observed cellular response to altered temperature is a remodeling of biological membranes. Growth at low temperature invariably leads to one or a combination of the following adjustments to membrane lipid composition: (*a*) increased proportions of *cis* unsaturated fatty acids (UFA), particularly long-chain polyunsaturated fatty acids (PUFA) in the most cold-tolerant animals (49), or branched-chain fatty acids in some microorganisms (103); (*b*) elevated proportions of PE relative to PC in animal cell membranes (82) or, in higher plants, monoglucosyldiglyceride (MGDG) to diglucosyldiglyceride (DGDG) (105) so that the ratio of bilayer-stabilizing to bilayer-destabilizing lipids increases with growth temperature; and (*c*) reduced proportions of plasmalogens (i.e. alk-1-enyl ether) compared to diacyl phospholipids, particularly in nervous tissue (68). The interested reader is referred to Reference 50 for a more thorough discussion of these compensatory responses.

ADAPTIVE EXPLANATIONS FOR MEMBRANE REMODELING

Homeoviscous Adaptation

The paradigm most widely invoked to explain the temperature-induced remodeling of membrane lipid composition is homeoviscous adaptation. According to this hypothesis, optimal membrane function is restricted to a limited range of membrane fluidities. As temperature is raised acutely, fluidity is increased beyond the optimal range and the membrane becomes "hyperfluid." Conversely, as temperature drops, fluidity falls below the optimal range and membrane activities are constrained. Consequently, persistent exposure to temperatures either above or below those required to maintain optimal fluidity initiates acclimatory (within the lifetime of an individual) or adaptational (over evolutionary time) alterations in lipid composition that largely offset the direct effects of temperature on membrane lipid fluidity.

In assessing the extent of HVA, it is important to recognize that, due in part to the range of motions displayed by lipid molecules (from rotamer formation within an acyl chain to the lateral diffusion of a phospholipid within the plane of the bilayer), membrane fluidity cannot be defined with rigor. No single technique for estimating fluidity is sensitive to the entire range of motions available to membrane lipids and, as a result, estimates of fluidity are biased by the type(s) of motions sensed. The steady-state fluorescence anisotropy of 1,6-diphenyl-1,3,5-hexatriene (DPH) has been most widely used in the comparative literature to assess membrane fluidity. However, because DPH is an asymmetrical molecule and does not undergo isotropic rotation within a membrane, the average extent of acyl chain motion, or membrane order, contributes more to the observed anisotropy than do acyl chain dynamics (65). Thus for the purposes of this review, fluidity measurements derived from the steady-state anisotropy of DPH are described in terms of membrane order, and HVA implies the conservation of lipid order (a static description of the time-averaged disposition in space of membrane constituents) rather than rates of molecular motion.

THE EVIDENCE FOR HOMEOVISCOUS ADAPTATION   The most compelling evidence in support of HVA is derived from interspecific comparisons by Cossins and colleagues of membrane order in synaptosomal preparations of various vertebrates (14, 21). Recently these original studies were expanded to include a broader range of species comparisons, a better-characterized membrane fraction, and the application of time-resolved anisotropy measurements, which permit the unambiguous separation of rate and order effects (4). As illustrated in Figure 2 (*solid symbols*), membrane order, i.e. the anisotropy value, when measured at a common temperature (20°C), is lowest in synaptosomes of Antarctic fish (of the genus *Notothenia*) and highest for homeothermic vertebrates (rat and pigeon), with values for temperate fish being intermediate between these extremes. Consequently, the rank sequence of membrane order [Antarctic fish (−1°C) < perch (15°C) < convict cichlid (28°C) < rat (37°C) < pigeon (42°C)] correlates directly with body or habitat temperature, which indicates that evolutionary adaptation to cold environments produces membranes of significantly lower order. Conversely, when compared at the respective cell or body temperatures *(open symbols)*, membrane order is roughly equivalent in all species, which illustrates the phenomenon of HVA. Similar trends in lipid order have been reported for comparisons between Arctic and tropical copepods (34), sarcoplasmic reticular membranes of rabbit and winter flounder (111), and mitochondrial membranes of warm- and cold-water abalones (25). Regression of the temperature required to produce a specified anisotropy on body temperature (slope = 1.0 for perfect compensation) for the data reported in Figure 2 indicates that interspecific differences in lipid anisotropy compensate for only 70% of the direct effects of temperature on membrane order. However, use of *trans*-parinaric acid, a probe more closely resembling the acyl chains of membrane phospholipids than DPH, indicates nearly perfect compensation of membrane order. In addition, time-resolved anisotropy measurements indicate that it is those features of membrane structure that influence the amplitude of probe motion, i.e. membrane order, rather than its reorientational rate that are under adaptive regulatory control (4). Efficacies of interspecific HVA generally fall between 0.7 and 1.0 (20).

HVA is also a common outcome of temperature acclimation in eurythermal poikilotherms, as illustrated in Figure 3 (*left*) for basolateral membranes of rainbow trout enterocytes. Although an excursion by 20°C-acclimated trout into 5°C water orders the membrane to the extent indicated by a rise in polarization from point A to B, subsequent acclimation to 5°C disorders the membrane by an amount equivalent to the drop in polarization between points B and C. Because lipid order is similar in 20°C- and 5°C-acclimated trout when compared at the respective acclimation temperatures, membrane order is conserved. Recent application of Fourier transform infrared (FT-IR) spectroscopy to living cells of *Acholeplasma laidlawii* B (75) and time-resolved fluorescence polarization techniques to isolated membranes of *Bacillus subtilis* (51) confirm that conformational order rather than the rate of lipid motion is the feature of membrane organization subject to regulation when temperature changes. Furthermore, in *Acholeplasma,* the point of regulation corresponds to the occurrence of 1.5 gauche rotamers per acyl chain regardless of growth temperature (75). Although reports of perfect compensation are not unusual [other examples include the plasma membranes of fish lymphocytes (1, 6) and thylakoid membranes of oleander (83)], more commonly the efficacies of intraspecific HVA range between 20 and 50% (reviewed in 20, 23), depending on membrane type. For example, mitochondria commonly exhibit higher efficacies of HVA (0.5–0.75) than do other membranes (18, 22).

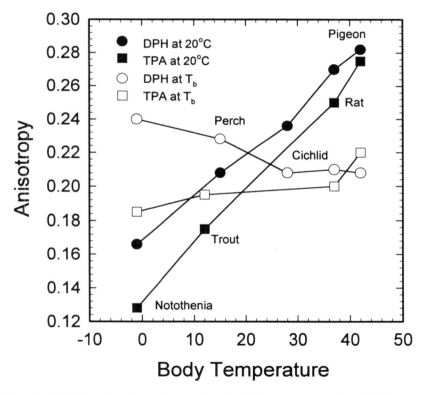

Figure 2   Anisotropy values for the fluorescent probes DPH and *trans*-parinaric acid (TPA) as a function of body temperature for several vertebrates, when measured either at a constant temperature of 20°C (*solid symbols*) or at the body temperature of the respective species (*open symbols*). The species illustrated include the Antarctic fish *Notothenia neglecta*; the rainbow trout *Oncorhynchus mykiss*; the perch *Perca fluviatilis*; the convict cichlid *Cichlasoma nigrofaciatum*; the rat *Rattus rattus*; and the feral pigeon *Columbia livia* (data are from 4).

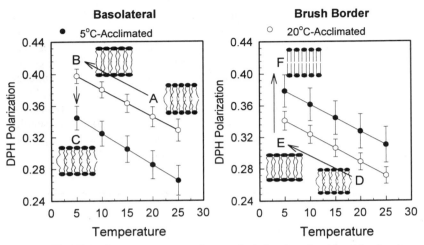

Figure 3 The effect of temperature on membrane order in basolateral and brush border plasma membrane domains of enterocytes isolated from 5°C- and 20°C-acclimated rainbow trout (data are from 24).

Interestingly, the capacity for acclimatory HVA appears to be a basic cellular response displayed not only by microorganisms (56, 75, 88), but also by cells of vertebrate poikilotherms. For example, in vitro acclimation experiments employing either cell lines established in tissue culture (7, 106), or cells [either red blood cells (29) or hepatocytes (114)] freshly isolated from temperate fish document efficacies of HVA varying from 34 to 100%.

ADAPTIVE SIGNIFICANCE OF HVA   The conservation of membrane order over a wide range of vertebrate species differing in body temperature provides strong circumstantial evidence for the adaptive significance of HVA, yet there is remarkably little direct evidence to support this view. Robust correlations between membrane order and the activity of Na^+/K^+-ATPase (47) indicate that the lipid environment of the enzyme can constrain protein motions required for catalysis. Thermal compensation of membrane order could therefore conceivably stabilize and/or optimize the active conformations of integral membrane proteins. Adaptational and acclimatory shifts in the sensitivity to thermal denaturation by membrane-associated enzymes provide the strongest evidence in support of this view. For example, the LT_{50} (the temperature required to reduce enzyme activity by 50% in a 15 min period) of Na^+/K^+-ATPase is nearly 3°C lower (44.9 vs 47.7°C) in the less-ordered synaptosomes of 6°C- than 28°C-acclimated goldfish, and perturbation of membrane order by the addition of *n*-hexanol also reduces thermostability (15). Furthermore, for a variety of both inter- and intraspecific comparisons, differences in LT_{50} for synaptosomal Na^+/K^+-ATPase co-vary closely with differences in the extent of HVA, which suggests a causal relationship between membrane order and the susceptibility of the enzyme to thermal denaturation (19). Similarly, thermal denaturation of chlorophyll in thylakoid membranes of oleander (83) and vertebrate rhodopsin in comparisons among fish, amphibians, and mammals (107) commences at equivalent values of membrane order regardless of thermal history, although denaturation occurs at higher temperatures in warm- than cold-acclimated or adapted organisms. Acclimatory shifts in membrane order and the temperature at which cytochrome c oxidase is inactivated in mitochondrial membranes of abalone (25), coupled with the demonstration that reductions in membrane order induced either by low temperature acclimation or the application of *n*-hexanol reduce the heat resistance of ciliary activity in *Anodonta* gill (62), further support a role for HVA in modulating protein thermostability.

Although the above data implicate HVA in the resistance adaptation of membrane function, there is little direct evidence to support a role for HVA in the capacity adaptations (i.e. modulation of the rates of enzyme activity) of poikilothermic organisms. In a few instances, reductions in membrane order following cold acclimation have been correlated with higher rates of Na^+/K^+-ATPase activity (84, 90), but in no case has a causal relationship between catalytic rate and membrane order been independently established. More commonly, reductions in membrane order, although not actually measured, have been invoked to explain increased activities of membrane-associated enzymes in cases where enzyme titres were not increased by cold acclimation (9, 48, 115). Nevertheless, in cold-acclimating goldfish, compensatory adjustments in the cold-block temperature of spinal reflexes are strongly correlated with temporal changes in the order of synaptosomal membranes (17), which suggests a role for HVA in the acclimation of neural function. Furthermore, isothermal catalytic hydrogenation of plasma membrane lipids in the cyanobacterium *Synechocystis* PCC6803 stimulates the expression of a Δ^{12} desaturase, just as does a drop in temperature, which suggests that hydrocarbon order is the membrane attribute subject to adaptive regulation (110).

Limitations of HVA as an Adaptive Paradigm

There is little doubt that in many poikilotherms temperature-induced restructuring of membrane lipid composition results in some degree of HVA. This, coupled with the intuitive appeal of such a straightforward mechanism of cellular homeostasis, has frequently resulted in HVA being the only paradigm considered when interpreting the pattern of temperature-induced changes in membrane lipid composition and the extent of thermal compensation in biological membranes. Yet there are numerous examples of membrane responses to altered growth temperature that are either inconsistent with or difficult to explain in terms of HVA, which suggests that mechanisms other than the defense of lipid order may also contribute to the thermal compensation of membrane function. The limitations of HVA as a general paradigm for membrane adaptation are further explored within the context of specific observations that are difficult to reconcile with the hypothesis.

VARIABILITY IN THE EXTENT AND OCCURRENCE OF HVA   As noted above, the efficacy of HVA varies widely, ranging from 20 to 100% for acclimatory HVA, and averaging ~ 70% for evolutionary HVA. However, comparisons between several species of cold (5–10°C, from the North Atlantic/Pacific and Baltic Sea)- and warm (20-27°C, South China Sea)-adapted teleost fish indicate only a 7–10% compensation of lipid order in hepatic phospholipids (28). In addition, a total lack of HVA has been reported for both sarcoplasmic reticular membranes and the apical plasma membrane domains of enterocytes in teleost fish (16, 108). Furthermore, as illustrated in Figure 3 (*right*), apical membrane domains isolated from trout enterocytes display a highly significant inverse compensation in lipid order. Not only does an acute drop in temperature from 20 to 5°C order the membrane by an amount equivalent to the interval between D and E, but acclimation to 5°C further orders the membrane to an extent indicated by the interval from E to F; consequently, the apical membrane domain is significantly more ordered in 5°C- than in 20°C-acclimated trout. Collectively, these data indicate that there is no consistent relationship between either the direction or magnitude of HVA and the thermal stress. Thus, although it is possible that moderate degrees of HVA could result in perfect compensation of function in some membranes, or that variable degrees of HVA could compensate function to different extents in different membranes, the tendency of cold exposure to disorder some membranes, while not influencing or ordering others, argues against the regulation of membrane order as a generally applicable paradigm of membrane adaptation.

THERMAL COMPENSATION OF MEMBRANE FUNCTION WITHOUT HVA   Thermal compensation of membrane function and the capacity for HVA are not tightly linked. For example, although rates of calcium uptake are consistently higher in sarcoplasmic reticular membranes of cold- compared with warm-acclimated fish (108), these membranes consistently reveal no (16) or only limited capacity (108) for HVA. In addition, although increased rates of sodium pump activity in red blood cells of 3°C- compared with 20°C-acclimated trout coincided with reduced lipid order at certain times of the year, at other times no compensation in pump activity could be demonstrated in spite of HVA (efficacy ~ 30–40%) (84). Furthermore, in Arctic charr, *Salvelinus alpinus,* neither the activity nor thermal stability of Na^+/K^+-ATPase in basolateral membranes of kidney was altered by cold acclimation in spite of substantial HVA (efficacy ~ 78%); instead a reduction in passive ion fluxes (which were 60% lower in 5°C- than 20°C-acclimated fish) appears to be the major acclimatory adjustment responsible for the maintenance of cation gradients at low temperature (90). In contrast, in the roach *Rutilus rutilus,* which coexists with Arctic charr in subalpine lakes of central Europe, the density of sodium pump sites was increased fourfold by cold acclimation, whereas the efficacy of HVA was relatively modest (~ 20%). Thus, although *R. rutilus* and *S. alpinus* maintain ion gradients at low temperature by fundamentally different mechanisms (an acclimatory increase in transport capacity for *R. rutilus* as opposed to diminished passive dissipation of ion gradients in *S. alpinus*) in neither species does HVA play an essential role in the acclimatory response. Finally, the low temperature suppression of immune function in poikilothermic vertebrates, which in channel catfish is due primarily to an inhibitory effect on the activity of helper T cells (5), cannot be attributed to a lack of HVA, because compensation of membrane order is nearly perfect in the plasma membranes of both B and T cells (6). Interestingly, oleic acid (18:1*n*9), but not linoleic acid (18:2*n*6), can rescue ~ 60% of the con A-induced T cell proliferation normally inhibited at low temperatures (5). However, since 18:2 is no less effective than 18:1 in fluidizing membranes, it is difficult to explain the fatty acid specificity of these immune rescue experiments in terms of modulation of lipid order. These few examples clearly illustrate that thermal compensation of membrane function can occur in the absence of HVA and vice versa, thus calling into question a consistent causal relationship between modulation of lipid order and the conservation of membrane function.

MEMBRANE REMODELING NOT CONSISTENT WITH HVA   Two aspects of temperature-induced membrane restructuring are particularly difficult to explain in terms of HVA. One is a preference for the accumulation of long-chain PUFA at low temperature, and the other is a positive correlation between growth temperature and the ratio of bilayer-stabilizing to bilayer-destabilizing lipids.

The low-temperature accumulation of PUFA   Increased unsaturation of membrane lipids promotes survival at cold temperatures. For example, desaturase mutants of the cyanobacterium *Synechocystis* PCC6803 are more sensitive than wild-type to low-temperature inhibition of photosynthesis (44), and strains of *Arabidopsis* deficient in fatty acid desaturation fail to grow and eventually die at 6°C, whereas wild-type plants grow and develop normally at this temperature (73). Furthermore, the transfer of a desaturase gene from chilling-resistant *Synechocystis* into chilling-sensitive *Anacystis nidulans* lowers the T_m of plasma membrane lipids in the transformed cells by 4–8°C and increases the tolerance of the latter to low temperatures (112). Conversely, reduced levels of lipid unsaturation promote survival at warm temperatures because hydrogenation of thylakoid membranes in pea seedlings increases their resistance to heat stress (109); however, the complete loss of PUFA in desaturase mutants of *Synechocystis* actually reduces heat tolerance (43). Because *cis* double bonds introduce a kink into the acyl chain, UFAs pack less compactly and thus offset, to a significant degree, the increase in membrane lipid order caused by a drop in temperature. However, from the standpoint of modulating lipid order, it is unclear why most winter-active poikilotherms accumulate PUFA rather than monoenes in their membrane lipids when grown at low temperature (113) because it is well established that not all double bonds in a fatty acid have an equivalent impact on membrane physical properties. For example, substituting oleic acid ($18:1n9$) for palmitic acid ($16:0$) at the *sn*-2 position of dipalmitoyl-PC (to form $16:0/18:1$-PC) reduces the melting point by 50°C, whereas the incorporation of a second double bond to form $16:0/18:2$-PC lowers the melting point by an additional 22°C. However, introduction of a third double bond, resulting in the formation of $16:0/18:3$-PC, actually increases the melting point slightly (by 3°C) (12). Furthermore, T_m values for $16:0/16:1$- and $16:0/22:6$-PC do not differ significantly (-12 vs -10°C, respectively) (101). Thus from the standpoint of altering membrane physical properties, monoenoic fatty acids are superior to PUFAs with respect to the magnitude (expressed on a per double bond basis) of the changes they produce and the lower metabolic cost of their production. Consequently, if lipid order is the membrane parameter subject to regulation, monoenes are expected to play a more prominent role than they do in the restructuring process. The fact that they do not implies that other aspect(s) of membrane architecture must be conserved during the acclimation process.

The balance between bilayer-stabilizing and bilayer-destabilizing lipids   A second compositional adjustment difficult to reconcile with HVA is the increased abundance of bilayer-destabilizing lipids such as PE in membranes of cold-adapted poikilotherms because elevated proportions of PE (relative to PC) commonly order rather than fluidize a membrane. For example, gel/fluid transition temperatures for PE are generally about 20°C higher than those for PCs of similar acyl chain composition due, in part, to the reduced hydration and stearic bulk of the ethanolamine compared to the choline headgroup and the capacity for hydrogen bonding between the headgroups of PE but not PC (92). In addition, because bilayer-destabilizing lipids are conically shaped (53), they increase the lateral pressure within the plane of the bilayer and the tendency of the bilayer to curve, thus displacing the phase behavior of the membrane to a point in closer proximity to the H_{II} phase transition (91). Thermal modulation of headgroup composition (reflected in altered PE/PC and

MGDG/DGDG ratios) may thus have a greater adaptive impact on membrane phase behavior than on hydrocarbon order.

THE LACK OF CORRELATION BETWEEN MEMBRANE FUNCTION AND ACYL CHAIN ORDER   In spite of many correlative data supporting a causal link between lipid order and membrane function (see above), there is an equally compelling body of evidence indicating that many aspects of membrane organization can influence function to a greater extent than changes in lipid order (64). For example, although activity of the reconstituted glucose transporter of human erythrocytes increases markedly at the gel/fluid transition in bilayers of PC (a zwitterionic phospholipid), activity was unaffected as the membrane passed through this same transition in bilayers of phosphatidic acid, phosphatidyl-glycerol, or phosphatidylserine (all acidic phospholipids), which suggests that membrane surface charge can stabilize the transporter against the most extreme changes in membrane order (104). Furthermore, activity of the transporter in gel phase bilayers of distearoyl (di-$C_{18:0}$) PC (at 10°C) was similar to that in fluid phase bilayers of dimyristoyl (di-$C_{14:0}$) PC (at 60°) and greater than the activity supported by dioleoyl (di-$C_{18:1}$) PC, even though the latter has a much lower melting point (i.e. is significantly less ordered) (10). Similarly, the activity of rat brain protein kinase C, although insensitive to lipid order, is dependent on the packing arrangement of phospholipid headgroups in the interfacial region of the bilayer (98). Activity of the sarcoplasmic reticular Ca^{2+}-ATPase also varies little with degree of acyl chain unsaturation (64), but does depend on the chain length of the reconstituting phospholipid (with optimal activity being supported by C_{16-20} acyl chains) (100), which indicates that an appropriate bilayer thickness is required to prevent a mismatch between the hydrophobic thickness of the bilayer and the transmembrane span of the protein (13, 100). Furthermore, the nicotinic acetylcholine receptor displays an obligate requirement for cholesterol (36) and a lipid compositional depen-dence of ion channel activity (102) that cannot be explained by modulation of lipid order (35). Finally, the activities and regulatory properties of several membrane-associated enzymes are more sensitive to the balance between conically and cylindrically shaped phospholipids than to lipid order per se (55, 78, 98). These few examples illustrate the diversity of variables that influence membrane function and suggest that an adaptive focus confined to effects of lipid order is too restrictive to be of general use.

A Dynamic Phase Behavior Model of Membrane Adaptation

The concept of HVA is an adaptational extension of the fluid mosaic membrane model, which emphasizes the lack of long-range order in membranes and the functional importance of maintaining an appropriate lipid fluidity (97). Although this model has been extremely useful in guiding membrane research (96), the failure of HVA to explain apparently fundamental patterns of lipid remodeling in poikilotherms, the lack of a consistent relationship between altered growth temperature and either the extent or direction of adjustments in lipid order, and the failure of membrane function and compensations of membrane function to be consistently correlated with changes in acyl chain order suggest that features of membrane organization other than lipid order are subject to regulation when environmental conditions change.

One feature of membrane organization, only recently appreciated, is the existence of discrete membrane domains. Not only do the apical and basolateral domains of epithelial cell plasma membranes differ significantly with respect to lipid composition, morphology, protein content, and function (93), but microdomains of protein and lipid have been directly demonstrated in plasma membranes of cells lacking epithelial polarity by fluorescence recovery after photobleaching (30) and fluorescence digital imaging microscopy techniques (86, 87). Microdomains of cholesterol (32, 58) and phospholipids (39, 81) have also been inferred from less direct measurements. Furthermore, the activation of lipases by signal transduction pathways may create specific microdomains of regulatory significance to the activity of colocalized membrane-associated processes because of local accumulation of reaction products (76). The extent to which microdomain heterogeneity is perturbed by temperature or conserved by the processes of thermal acclimation remains to be determined. In this context, the adaptive significance of temperature-induced alterations in membrane lipid composition may relate to the conservation of dynamic membrane properties, including the maintenance of an appropriate balance between membrane microdomains and the ability to regulate intracellular membrane traffic, i.e. the dynamic phase behavior of a membrane, rather than to the fine tuning of lipid order.

McElhaney (69, 70) is a leading proponent of the significance of regulating lipid phase state rather than membrane physical properties at altered growth temperatures because structural rearrangements are most extensive and functional perturbations most severe when the phase state of a membrane changes. Since many microorganisms can grow and function normally with membranes of widely different fluidities (37), whereas growth is impaired when a critical proportion (in *E. coli,* 50%) of the membrane lipid is present in the gel phase, McElhaney has proposed the term homeophasic adaptation (HPA) to describe this pattern of thermal adaptation in microorganisms. HPA thus extends the effective range of growth temperatures by preventing transition to the gel phase. There are numerous examples among microorganisms of adaptive alterations in the phase behavior of membrane lipids following a period of growth at altered temperature. For example, in plasma membranes of *Anacystis nidulans,* the onset of phase separation occurs at 5 and 16°C in cells grown at

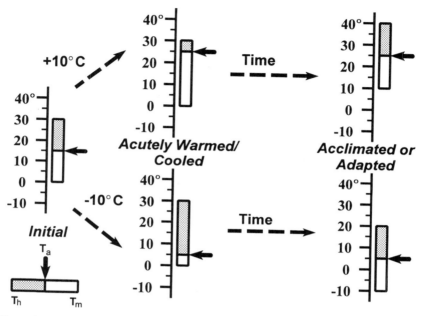

Figure 4 A dynamic phase behavior model of thermal adaptation in biological membranes. An acute rise or drop in temperature (*diagonal arrows*) alters the relationship between the ambient or body temperature (T_a, i.e. the temperature at which the membrane is functioning) and the transitions to the gel (T_m) and H_{II} (T_h) phases (a rise in temperature decreases the interval between T_a and T_h, while increasing the interval between T_m and T_a, whereas a drop in temperature has the opposite effects). Acclimation or adaptation to an altered temperature (*horizontal arrows*) restores the proximity of T_a to T_h and T_m.

28 and 38°C, respectively (38); similar results have been widely reported among other microorganisms and plants (see 50).

A dynamic phase behavior model of membrane adaptation has been developed by broadening the concept of HPA to encompass the full range of membrane phase behavior and to emphasize the dynamic (i.e. the propensity to form nonbilayer phases) rather than the static phase behavior (i.e. the lipid phase actually present) of a membrane. According to this model, it is the relationship between the ambient temperature (T_a) and the temperatures of the gel/fluid and H_{II} phase transitions that is conserved when growth temperature changes. As illustrated in Figure 4, a rise in temperature decreases the interval (*shaded bar*) between T_a and the temperature of the H_{II} phase transition (T_h), while simultaneously moving the membrane farther away from the gel/fluid transition (T_m); a drop in temperature has the opposite effects. Accordingly, temperature acclimation or adaptation, by altering the chemical composition of the membrane, modifies both T_m and T_h so that the operational temperature (T_a) remains at a suitable interval above T_m, yet below T_h.

The proximity of a membrane to the H_{II} phase transition may be a particularly important functional attribute because the H_{II} phase has been postulated to be an intermediate in membrane fusion (33), and regulation of fusion events is central to the control of intracellular membrane traffic (via exo- and endocytosis). Although membrane fusion is a protein mediated and regulated process, it is clearly influenced by lipids intrinsic and extrinsic to the bilayer (79, 116). The concept of dynamic phase behavior predicts that at physiological temperatures a membrane must be positioned close enough to the H_{II} transition, i.e. be sufficiently unstable, to permit the fusion events associated with normal membrane traffic, yet be stable enough to prevent these processes from occurring in an unregulated fashion (66). Alternatively, cell function will be compromised at low temperature because the interval between T_a and T_h is increased, and membrane traffic is thereby inhibited. A rise in temperature, on the other hand, destabilizes the lamellar phase by decreasing the interval between T_a and T_h, thereby increasing the probability of unregulated fusion events and the loss of bilayer integrity. The marked temperature sensitivity of membrane traffic supports the dynamic phase behavior concept. For example, the transport of cholesterol from its site of synthesis in the endoplasmic reticulum to its primary cellular location in the plasma membrane ceases at temperatures below 15°C in a variety of mammalian cell lines (27, 57, 63). Furthermore, in the yeast *Saccharomyces cerevisiae,* the maintenance of Golgi secretory activity requires a high ratio of bilayer-destabilizing (PI) to bilayer-stabilizing (PC) lipids, which is maintained, in part, by the activity of a PI/PC transfer protein (71). Conversely, membranes that do not engage in vesicular commerce with the plasma membrane possess relatively large amounts of bilayer-stabilizing lipids such as PC (2).

Interspecific conservation of dynamic phase behavior is suggested by the observation that rates of endocytosis by the absorptive epithelium of poikilothermic goodeid fish embryos are maintained down to 5°C but, in mammalian cells, are blocked by moderate cold exposure (~ 15°C) (89). Similarly, the critical temperature, T^*, at which membrane lipid extracts from bacteria, squid axon, and red blood cell and brain membranes of mammals assemble spontaneously into unilamellar structures corresponds to the physiological temperature of the cells from which the lipids were extracted (41).

The dynamic phase behavior model also explains some aspects of membrane restructuring not consistent with HVA. In particular, the positive correlation between growth temperature and the PC/PE ratio in animal cell membranes can be viewed as a homeostatic mechanism to restore (by increasing the proportions of bilayer-stabilizing phospholipids, i.e. PC) the appropriate interval between T_a and T_h, which is otherwise reduced as temperature rises. Indeed, the balance between bilayer-stabilizing and destabilizing lipids may be the principle means of regulating dynamic phase behavior. For example, in mutant strains of *E. coli* lacking the ability to synthesize PE (a bilayer-destabilizing phospholipid), which normally accounts for 70–80% of membrane phospholipids in wild-type strains, PE is replaced by cardiolipin (CL) and phosphatidylglycerol (PG) (85). Both CL and PG can form the H_{II} phase, but only in the presence of divalent cations. Interestingly, mutant strains, unlike the wild-type, display an obligate requirement for high concentrations of divalent cations. Furthermore, although the relative proportions of PG and CL varied widely in membrane lipids depending on the type (Ca^{2+}, Mg^{2+}, or Sr^{2+}) and concentration of divalent cation, all cultures experienced a transition to a nonbilayer phase at approximately 10°C above the growth temperature. As illustrated in Figure 5, despite substantial differences in membrane lipid composition (see figure inset), cells grown with either $MgCl_2$ or $CaCl_2$ display remarkably similar phase behavior, characterized by an H_{II} transition midpoint at 55°C when measured in the presence of the divalent cation present during cell growth (*solid symbols*). However, phase behaviors diverge when tested in

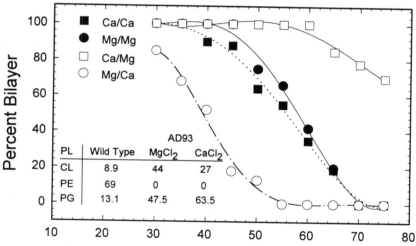

Figure 5 The temperature dependence of the bilayer to hexagonal (H_{II}) phase transition in phospholipids of mutant strains of *E. coli* unable to synthesize PE and grown in the presence of either 50 mM $MgCl_2$ or $CaCl_2$. Phase behavior of the isolated lipids was determined in the presence of either 50 mM $MgCl_2$ or $CaCl_2$. The designation Mg/Mg indicates phase behavior tested in the presence of $MgCl_2$ for phospholipids isolated from cells grown in $MgCl_2$; conversely, the designation Mg/Ca indicates phase behavior of phospholipid extracts from cells grown in $MgCl_2$, but tested in the presence of $CaCl_2$. The inset shows the phospholipid composition (in mol%) of wild-type and mutant strains (redrawn from 85).

the presence of the alternate cation (Figure 5, *open symbols*), which indicates that the differences in lipid composition do indeed influence lipid phase behavior. These data imply that the propensity to form a nonbilayer phase is regulated by variations in membrane lipid composition so that the dynamic phase behavior of the membrane remains independent of growth conditions. Although a monolayer containing high levels of conically-shaped lipids will spontaneously curve to minimize the headgroup packing energy, and in an extreme case collapse to form the hexagonal phase, a monolayer prevented from curving by the presence of other phospholipids that prefer a lamellar phase will be internally stressed (or frustrated) and possess an associated potential energy expressed as the propensity to form the hexagonal phase (91). The available evidence suggests that it is the balance between these opposing forces within a membrane, i.e. the dynamic phase behavior, rather than the actual phase state of a membrane, that is subject to regulation when growth conditions change.

Finally, differences in the dynamic properties of PUFA and monoenes derived from molecular simulations of the ^{2}H-NMR spectra of isolinoleic acid (18:2) (6, 9) provide a mechanistic explanation for the preferential accumulation of PUFA at low temperatures that is more consistent with the concept of dynamic phase behavior than modulation of lipid order (3). Although monoenes markedly reduce membrane order, they cannot pack regularly to form a tightly sealed bilayer that restricts cation permeability. In contrast, the multiple double bonds of PUFA, because they increase the extent of acyl chain motion and yet order the membrane in their immediate vicinity (8), simultaneously maintain an appropriate dynamic state of bilayer and permeability characteristics compatible with biological function.

CONCLUSIONS

The available evidence indicates that the HVA hypothesis does not adequately reflect the specificity of lipid-protein interactions, the microdomain heterogeneity of biological membranes, or the diversity of membrane attributes that can influence function, and cannot explain several consistently observed patterns of temperature-dependent changes in membrane lipid composition. Furthermore, even though effects of temperature on the physical properties and phase behavior of membrane lipids pervade all aspects of membrane function, modification of membrane lipid composition should be acknowledged as but one component of a broader repertoire of adaptive responses to altered temperatures. For example, proliferation of mitochondrial and sarcoplasmic reticular membranes is an important acclimatory response of many poikilotherms to cold temperatures (31, 80). Alternatively, altered expression of membrane proteins appears to contribute to the thermal adaptation of membrane function in some cases. Thus the diversity of membrane adaptations to temperature is unlikely to be captured by lipid-based adjustments alone. Nevertheless, the widespread and generally similar effects of growth temperature on the membrane lipid composition of microorganisms, fungi, plants, and animals provide compelling evidence that some attribute(s) of membrane lipid organization other than, or in addition to, lipid order are subject to physiological regulation. An adaptational perspective emphasizing the dynamics of lipid phase behavior as developed in this review may provide insights into those properties that must be conserved in order for membrane function to be maintained at extremes of environmental temperature.

ACKNOWLEDGMENT

This work was supported by National Science Foundation grant IBN 9205234.

Literature Cited

1. Abruzzini AF, Ingram LO, Clem LW. 1982. Temperature-mediated processes in teleost immunity: homeoviscous adaptation in teleost lymphocytes (41300). *Proc. Soc. Exp. Biol. Med.* 169:12–18

2. Allan D, Kallen K. 1993. Transport of lipids to the plasma membrane in animal cells. *Prog. Lipid Res.* 32(2):195–219

3. Baenziger JE, Jarrell HC, Smith ICP. 1992. Molecular motions and dynamics of a diunsaturated acyl chain in a lipid bilayer: Implications for the role of polyunsaturation in biological membranes. *Biochemistry* 31(13):3377–385

4. Behan-Martin MK, Jones GR, Bowler K, Cossins AR. 1993. A near perfect temperature adaptation of bilayer order in vertebrate brain membranes. *Biochim. Biophys. Acta* 1151:216–22

5. Bly JE, Buttke TM, Clem LW. 1990. Differential effects of temperature and exogenous fatty acids on mitogen-induced proliferation in channel catfish T and B lymphocytes. *Comp. Biochem. Physiol.* 95A(3):417–24

6. Bly JE, Clem LW. 1988. Temperature-mediated processes in teleost immunity: homeoviscous adaptation by channel catfish peripheral blood cells. *Comp. Biochem. Physiol.* 91A(3):481–85

7. Bols NC, Mosser DD, Steels GB. 1992. Temperature studies and recent advances with fish cells in vitro. *Comp. Biochem. Physiol. A* 103(1):1–14

8. Brenner RR. 1984. Effect of unsaturated acids on membrane structure and enzyme kinetics. *Prog. Lipid Res.* 23:69–96

9. Caldwell RS. 1969. Thermal compensation of respiratory enzymes in tissues of the goldfish (*Carassius auratus* L.). *Comp. Biochem. Physiol.* 31:79–90

10. Carruthers A, Melchior DL. 1984. Human erythrocyte hexose transporter activity is governed by bilayer lipid composition in reconstituted vesicles. *Biochemistry* 23(26):6901–11

11. Collins JM, Dominey RN, Grogan WM. 1990. Shape of the fluidity gradient in the plasma membrane of living HeLa cells. *J. Lipid Res.* 31:261–70

12. Coolbear KP, Berde CB, Keough KMW. 1983. Gel to liquid-crystalline phase transitions of aqueous dispersions of polyunsaturated mixed-acid phosphatidylcholines. *Biochemistry* 22(6):1466–73

13. Cornea RL, Thomas DD. 1994. Effects of membrane thickness on the molecular dynamics and enzymatic activity of reconstituted Ca-ATPase. *Biochemistry* 33(10):2912–20

14. Cossins AR, Behan MK, Jones G, Bowler K. 1987. Lipid-protein interactions in the adaptive regulation of mem-

brane function. *Biochem. Soc. Trans.* 15(1):77–81

15. Cossins AR, Bowler K, Prosser CL. 1981. Homeoviscous adaptation and its effects upon membrane-bound proteins. *J. Thermal. Biol.* 6:183–87

16. Cossins AR, Christiansen JA, Prosser CL. 1978. Adaptation of biological membranes to temperature—the lack of homeoviscous adaptation in the sarcoplasmic reticulum. *Biochim. Biophys. Acta* 511:442–54

17. Cossins AR, Friedlander MJ, Prosser CL. 1977. Correlations between behavioral temperature adaptations of goldfish and the viscosity and fatty acid composition of their synaptic membranes. *J. Comp. Physiol.* 120:109–21

18. Cossins AR, Kent J, Prosser CL. 1980. A steady state and differential polarised phase fluorometric study of the liver microsomal and mitochondrial membranes of thermally acclimated green sunfish (*Lepomis cyanellus*). *Biochim. Biophys. Acta* 599:341–58

19. Cossins AR, Lee JAC, Lewis RNAH, Bowler K. 1986. The adaptation to cold of membrane order and ($Na^+ + K^+$)-ATPase properties. In *Living in the Cold,* ed. HC Heller, pp. 13–18. Amsterdam: Elsevier

20. Cossins AR, MacDonald AG. 1989. The adaptation of biological membranes to temperature and pressure: fish from the deep and cold. *J. Bioenerg. Biomembr.* 21(1):115–35

21. Cossins AR, Prosser CL. 1978. Evolutionary adaptation of membranes to temperature. *Proc. Natl. Acad. Sci. USA* 75(4):2040–43

22. Cossins AR, Prosser CL. 1982. Variable homeoviscous responses of different brain membranes of thermally acclimated goldfish. *Biochim. Biophys. Acta* 687:303–9

23. Cossins AR, Sinensky M. 1986. Adaptation of membranes to temperature, pressure, and exogenous lipids. In *Physiology of Membrane Fluidity,* ed. M Shinitzky, pp. 1–20. Boca Raton, Fla: CRC Press

24. Crockett EL, Hazel JR. 1994. Basolateral and apical plasma membrane domains of trout enterocytes display distinct responses to temperature acclimation. *J. Exp. Biol.* Submitted

25. Dahlhoff E, Somero GN. 1993. Effects of temperature on mitochondria from abalone (genus *Haliotis*): adaptive plasticity and its limits. *J. Exp. Biol.* 185: 151–68

26. DeGrella RF, Simoni RD. 1982. Intracellular transport of cholesterol to the plasma membrane. *J. Biol. Chem.* 257 (23):14256–62

27. de Kruijff B, De Greef WJ, van Eyk RVW, Demel RA, van Deenen LLM. 1973. The effect of different fatty acid and sterol composition on the erythritol flux through the cell membrane of *Acholeplasma laidlawii*. *Biochim. Biophys. Acta* 298:479–99

28. Dey I, Buda C, Wiik T, Halver JE, Farkas T. 1993. Molecular and structural composition of phospholipid membranes in livers of marine and freshwater fish in relation to temperature. *Proc. Natl. Acad. Sci. USA* 90:7498–502

29. Dey I, Farkas T. 1992. Temperature shifts induce adaptive changes in the physical state of carp (*Cyprinus carpio* L.) erythrocyte plasma membranes in vitro. *Fish Physiol. Biochem.* 10(4):347–55

30. Edidin M. 1993. Patches and fences—probing for plasma membrane domains. *J. Cell Sci.* (Suppl. 17):165–69

31. Eggington S, Sidell BD. 1989. Thermal acclimation induces adaptive changes in subcellular structure of fish skeletal muscle. *Am. J. Physiol.* 256(25):R1–9

32. El Yandouzi E, Zlatkine P, Moll G, Le Grimellec C. 1994. Cholesterol distribution in renal epithelial cells LLC-Pk1 as determined by cholesterol oxidase: evidence that glutaraldehyde fixation masks plasma membrane cholesterol pools. *Biochemistry* 33(8):2329–34

33. Ellens H, Siegal DP, Alford D, Yeagle PL, Boni L, et al. 1989. Membrane fusion and inverted phases. *Biochemistry* 28(9):3692–703

34. Farkas T, Storebakken T, Bhosie NB. 1988. Composition and physical state of phospholipids in Calanoid copepods from India and Norway. *Lipids* 23:619–22

35. Fernandez-Ballester G, Castresana J, Fernandez AM, Arrondo JR, Ferragut JA, Gonzalez-Ros JM. 1994. A role for cholesterol as a structural effector of the nicotinic acetylcholine receptor. *Biochemistry* 33(13):4065–71

36. Fong TM, McNamee MG. 1986. Correlation between acetylcholine receptor function and structural properties of membranes. *Biochemistry* 25(4):830–40

37. Fukunaga N, Russel NJ. 1990. Membrane lipid composition and glucose uptake in two psychrotolerant bacteria from Antarctica. *J. Gen. Microbiol.* 136: 1669–73

38. Furtado D, Williams WP, Brain APR, Quinn PJ. 1979. Phase separations in membranes of *Anacystis nidulans* grown

at different temperatures. *Biochim. Biophys. Acta* 555:352–57

39. Gascard P, Sauvage M, Sulpice J, Giraud F. 1993. Characterization of structural and functional phosphoinositide domains in human erythrocyte membranes. *Biochemistry* 32(23):5941–48

40. Gasser KW, Goldsmith A, Hopfer U. 1990. Regulation of chloride transport in parotid secretory granules by membrane fluidity. *Biochemistry* 29(31): 7282–88

41. Gershfeld NL, Mudd CP, Tajima K, Berger RL. 1993. Critical temperature for unilamellar vesicle formation in dimyristoylphosphatidylcholine dispersions from specific heat measurements. *Biophys. J.* 65:1174–79

42. Gladwell RT, Bowler K, Duncan CJ. 1975. Heat death in the crayfish *Austropotamobius pallipes*—ion movements and their effects on excitable tissues during heat death. *J. Thermal Biol.* 1:79–94

43. Gombos Z, Wada H, Hideg E, Murata N. 1994. The unsaturation of membrane lipids stabilizes photosynthesis against heat stress. *Plant Physiol.* 104:563–67

44. Gombos Z, Wada H, Murata N. 1992. Unsaturation of fatty acids in membrane lipids enhances tolerance of the *Cyanobacterium synechocystis* PCC6803 to low-temperature photoinhibition. *Proc. Natl. Acad. Sci. USA* 89:9959–63

45. Goversriemslag JWP, Janssen MP, Zwaal RFA, Rosing J. 1992. Effect of membrane fluidity and fatty acid composition on the prothrombin-converting activity of phospholipid vesicles. *Biochemistry* 31(41):10000–8

46. Hanski E, Rimon G, Levitzki A. 1979. Adenylate cyclase activation by the beta-adrenergic receptors as a diffuson-controlled process. *Biochemistry* 18(5): 846–53

47. Harris WE. 1985. Modulation of (Na+, K+)-ATPase activity by the lipid bilayer examined with dansylated phosphatidylserine. *Biochemistry* 24(12): 2873–83

48. Hazel JR. 1972. The effect of thermal acclimation upon succinic dehydrogenase activity from the epaxial muscle of the common goldfish (*Carassius auratus*)—II. Lipid reactivation of the soluble enzyme. *Comp. Biochem. Physiol.* 43B:863–82

49. Hazel JR. 1988. Homeoviscous adaptation in animal cell membranes. In *Advances in Membrane Fluidity— Physiological Regulation of Membrane Fluidity*, ed. RC Aloia, CC Curtain, LM Gordon, 6:149–88. New York: Liss

50. Hazel JR, Williams EE. 1990. The role of alterations in membrane lipid composition in enabling physiological adaptation of organisms to their physical environment. *Prog. Lipid Res.* 29(3): 167–227

51. Herman P, Konopásek I, Plásek J, Svobodová J. 1994. Time-resolved polarized fluorescence studies of the temperature adaptation in Bacillus subtilus using DPH and TMA-DPH fluorescent probes. *Biochim. Biophys. Acta* 1190:1–8

52. Houslay MD, Gordon LM. 1982. The activity of adenylate cyclase is regulated by the nature of its lipid environment. *Curr. Top. Membr. Transp.* 18:179–231

53. Israelachvili JN, Marcelja S, Horn RG. 1980. Physical principles of membrane organization. *Q. Rev. Biophys.* 13(2): 121–200

54. James R, Branton D. 1973. Lipid- and temperature-dependent structural changes in *Acholplasma laidlawii* cell membranes. *Biochim. Biophys. Acta* 323: 378–90

55. Jamil H, Hatch GM, Vance DE. 1993. Evidence that binding of CTP:phosphocholine cytidylyltransferase to membranes in rat hepatocytes is modulated by the ratio of bilayer- to non-bilayer-forming lipids. *Biochem. J.* 291:419–27

56. Jurado AS, Pinheiro TJT, Madeira VMC. 1991. Physical studies on membrane lipids of *Bacillus stearothermophilus* temperature and calcium effects. *Arch. Biochem. Biophys.* 289(1): 167–79

57. Kaplan MR, Simoni RD. 1985. Transport of cholesterol from the endoplasmic reticulum to the plasma membrane. *J. Cell Biol.* 101:446–53

58. Kavecansky J, Joiner CH, Schroeder F. 1994. Erythrocyte membrane lateral sterol domains: a dehydroergosterol fluorescence polarization study. *Biochemistry* 33(10):2880–90

59. Killian JA, Fabrie CHJP, Baart W, Morein S, Dekruijff B. 1992. Effects of temperature variation and phenethyl alcohol addition on acyl chain order and lipid organization in *Escherichia coli* derived membrane systems. A H^2-NMR and P^{31}-NMR study. *Biochim. Biophys. Acta* 1105:253–62

60. Kruuv J, Glofcheski D, Cheng K-H, Campbell SD, Al-Qysi HMA, et al. 1983. Factors influencing survival and growth of mammalian cells exposed to hypothermia. I. Effects of temperature and membrane lipid perturbers. *J. Cell. Physiol.* 115:179–85

61. Kuo P, Weinfeld M, Loscalzo J. 1990.

Effect of membrane fatty acyl composition on LDL metabolism in Hep G2 hepatocytes. *Biochemistry* 29(28):6626–32

62. Lagerspetz KYH. 1985. Membrane order and ATPase activity as correlates of thermal resistance acclimation of ciliary activity in the gills of *Anodonta*. *J. Therm. Biol.* 10(1):21–28

63. Lange Y, Muraski MF. 1988. Topographic heterogeneity in cholesterol biosynthesis. *J. Biol. Chem.* 263(19): 9366–73

64. Lee AG. 1991. Lipids and their effects on membrane proteins: evidence against a role for fluidity. *Prog. Lipid Res.* 30(4):323–48

65. Lentz BR. 1989. Membrane "fluidity" as detected by diphenylhexatriene probes. *Chem. Phys. Lipids* 50:171–90

66. Lindblom G, Rilfors L. 1989. Cubic phases and isotropic structures formed by membrane lipids—possible biological relevance. *Biochim. Biophys. Acta* 988:221–56

67. Mariani P, Rivas E, Luzzati V, Delacroix H. 1990. Polymorphism of a lipid extract from *Pseudomonas fluorescens:* structure analysis of a hexagonal phase and of a novel cubic phase of extinction symbol Fd—. *Biochemistry* 29(29): 6799–810

68. Matheson DF, Oei R, Roots BI. 1980. Changes in the fatty acyl composition of phospholipids in the optic tectum and optic nerve of temperature-acclimated goldfish. *Physiol. Zool.* 53(1): 57–69

69. McElhaney RN. 1984. The structure and function of the *Acholeplasma laidlawii* plasma membrane. *Biochim. Biophys. Acta* 779:1–42

70. McElhaney RN. 1984. The relationship between membrane lipid fluidity and phase state and the ability of bacteria and mycoplasmas to grow and survive at various temperatures. *Biomembranes* 12:249–76

71. Mcgee TP, Skinner HB, Whitters EA, Henry SA, Bankaitis VA. 1994. A phosphatidylinositol transfer protein controls the phosphatidylcholine content of yeast Golgi membranes. *J. Cell Biol.* 124(3): 273–87

72. Mendelsohn R, Davies MA, Brauner JW, Schuster HF, Dluhy RA. 1989. Quantitative determination of conformational disorder in the acyl chains of phospholipid bilayers by infrared spectroscsopy. *Biochemistry* 28(22):8934–39

73. Miquel M, James D, Dooner H, Browse J. 1993. Arabidopsis requires polyunsaturated lipids for low-temperature survival. *Proc. Natl. Acad. Sci. USA* 90: 6208–12

74. Monck MA, Bloom M, Lafleur M, Lewis RNAH, McElhaney RN, Cullis PR. 1992. Influence of lipid composition on the orientational order in *Acholeplasma laidlawii* strain-B membranes: A deuterium NMR study. *Biochemistry* 31(41):10037–43

75. Moore DJ, Mendelsohn R. 1994. Adaptation to altered growth temperatures in *Acholeplasma laidlawii* B: Fourier transform infrared studies of acyl chain conformational order in live cells. *Biochemistry* 33(13):4080–85

76. Muderhwa JM, Brockman HL. 1992. Lateral lipid distribution is a major regulator of lipase activity—Implications for lipid-mediated signal transduction. *J. Biol. Chem.* 267(34):24184–92

77. Murata N. 1989. Low temperature effects on cyanobacterial membranes. *J. Bioenerg. Biomembr.* 21(1):61–75

78. Navarro J, Toivio-Kinnucan M, Racker E. 1984. Effect of lipid composition on the calcium/adenosine 5′-triphosphate coupling ratio of the Ca^{2+}-ATPase of sarcoplasmic reticulum. *Biochemistry* 23(1):130–35

79. Paiement J, Lavoie C, Gavino GR, Gavino VC. 1994. Modulation of GTP-dependent fusion by linoleic and arachidonic acid in derivatives of rough endoplasmic reticulum from rat liver. *Biochim. Biophys. Acta* 1190:199–212

80. Penney RK, Goldspink G. 1980. Temperature adaptation of sarcoplasmic reticulum of fish muscle. *J. Therm. Biol.* 5:63–68

81. Prenner E, Sommer A, Kungl A, Stütz H, Friedl H, Hermetter A. 1993. Inequivalence of fluorescent choline and ethanolamine phospholipids in the erythrocyte membrane—fluorescence lifetime determination in the frequency and time domain. *Arch. Biochem. Biophys.* 305(2):473–76

82. Pruitt NL. 1988. Membrane lipid composition and overwintering strategy in thermally acclimated crayfish. *Am. J. Physiol.* 254(23):R870–76

83. Raison JK, Roberts JKM, Berry JA. 1982. Correlations between the thermal stability of chloroplast (thylakoid) membranes and the composition of their polar lipids upon acclimation of the higher plant, *Nerium oleander,* to growth temperature. *Biochim. Biophys. Acta* 688: 218–28

84. Raynard RS, Cossins AR. 1991. Homeoviscous adaptation and thermal compensation of sodium pump of trout

erythrocytes. *Am. J. Physiol.* 260(29): R916–24

85. Rietveld AG, Killian JA, Dowhan W, de Kruijff B. 1993. Polymorphic regulation of membrane phospholipid composition in *Escherichia coli. J. Biol. Chem.* 268(17):12427–33

86. Rodgers W, Glaser M. 1991. Characterization of lipid domains in erythrocyte membranes. *Proc. Natl. Acad. Sci. USA* 88:1364–68

87. Rodgers W, Glaser M. 1993. Distributions of proteins and lipids in the erythrocyte membrane. *Biochemistry* 32(47): 12591–98

88. Russell NJ, Fukunaga N. 1990. A comparison of thermal adaptation of membrane lipids in psychrophilic and thermophilic bacteria. *FEMS Micro. Rev.* 75:171–82

89. Schindler JF, de Vries U. 1988. Endocytosis at 0°C, 5°C, and 10°C 5n the trophotaenial absorptive cells of goodeid embryos (Teleostei). *Cell Tissue Res.* 254:399–402

90. Schwarzbaum PJ, Wieser W, Cossins AR. 1992. Species-specific responses of membranes and the $Na^+ + K^+$ pump to temperature change in the kidney of two species of freshwater fish, roach (*Rutilus rutilus*) and arctic char (*Salvelinus alpinus*). *Physiol. Zool.* 65(1):17–34

91. Seddon JM. 1990. Structure of the inverted hexagonal (HII) phase, and nonlamellar phase transitions of lipids. *Biochim. Biophys. Acta* 1031:1–69

92. Silvius JR, Brown PM, O'Leary TJ. 1986. Role of head group structure in the phase behavior of aminophospholipids. 1. Hydrated and dehydrated lamellar phases of saturated phosphatidylethanolamine analogues. *Biochemistry* 25(25):4249–58

93. Simons K, van Meer G. 1988. Lipid sorting in epithelial cells. *Biochemistry* 27(17):6197–202

94. Sinensky M. 1974. Homeoviscous adaptation—a homeostatic process that regulates viscosity of membrane lipids in *Escherichia coli. Proc. Natl. Acad. Sci. USA* 71:522–25

95. Singer M. 1981. Permeability of phosphatidylcholine and phosphatidylethanolamine bilayers. *Chem. Phys. Lipids.* 28:253–67

96. Singer SJ. 1992. The structure and function of membranes—A personal memoir. *J. Membr. Biol.* 129:3–12

97. Singer SJ, Nicholson GL. 1972. The fluid mosaic model of the structure of cell membranes. *Science* 175:720–31

98. Slater SJ, Kelly MB, Taddeo FJ, Ho CJ, Rubin E, Stubbs CD. 1994. The modulation of protein kinase C activity by membrane lipid bilayer structure. *J. Biol. Chem.* 269(7):4866–71

99. Squier TC, Bigelow DJ, Thomas DD. 1988. Lipid fluidity directly modulates the overall protein rotational mobility of the Ca-ATPase in sarcoplasmic reticulum. *J. Biol. Chem.* 263(19):9178–86

100. Starling AP, East JM, Lee AG. 1993. Effects of phosphatidylcholine fatty acyl chain length on calcium binding and other functions of the $(Ca^{2+}-Mg^{2+})$-ATPase. *Biochemistry* 32(6):1593–600

101. Stubbs CD, Smith AD. 1984. The modification of mammalian membrane polyunsaturated fatty acid composition in relation to membrane fluidity and function. *Biochim. Biophys. Acta* 779:89–137

102. Sunshine C, McNamee MG. 1994. Lipid modulation of nicotinic acetylcholine receptor function: the role of membrane lipid composition and fluidity. *Biochim. Biophys Acta* 1191:59–64

103. Suutari M, Laakso S. 1992. Changes in fatty acid branching and unsaturation of *Streptomyces griseus* and *Brevibacterium fermentans* as a response to growth temperature. *Appl. Environ. Microbiol.* 58(7):2338–40

104. Tefft RE, Carruthers A, Melchior DL. 1986. Reconstituted human erythrocyte sugar transporter activity is determined by bilayer lipid head groups. *Biochemistry* 25(12):3709–18

105. Thompson GA. 1989. Membrane acclimation by unicellular organisms in response to temperature change. *J. Bioenerg. Biomembr.* 21(1):43–59

106. Tsugawa K, Lagerspetz KYH. 1990. Direct adaptation of cells to temperature: membrane fluidity of goldfish cells cultured in vitro at different temperatures. *Comp. Biochem. Physiol.* 96A(1):57–60

107. Tyurin VA, Kagan VE, Shukolyukov SA, Klaan NK, Novikov KN, Azizova OA. 1979. Thermal stability of rhodopsin and protein-lipid interactions in the photoreceptor membranes of homeothermic and poikilothermic animals. *J. Thermal Biol.* 4:203–8

108. Ushio H, Watabe S. 1993. Effects of temperature acclimation on Ca^{2+}-ATPase of the carp sarcoplasmic reticulum. *J. Exp. Zool.* 265:9–17

109. Vigh L, Gombos Z, Horvath I, Joo F. 1989. Saturation of membrane lipids by hydrogenation induces thermal stability in chloroplast inhibiting the heat-dependent stimulation of photosystem I-mediated electron transport. *Biochim. Biophys. Acta* 979:361–64

110. Vigh L, Los DA, Horváth I, Murata N.

1993. The primary signal in the biological perception of temperature: Pd-catalyzed hydrogenation of membrane lipids stimulated the expression of the *desA* gene in *Synechocystis* PCC6803. *Proc. Natl. Acad. Sci. USA* 90:9090–94

111. Vrbjar N, Kean KT, Szabo A, Senak L, Mendelsohn R, Keough KMW. 1992. Sarcoplasmic reticulum from rabbit and winter flounder: temperature-dependence of protein conformation and lipid motion. *Biochim. Biophys. Acta* 1107:1–11

112. Wada H, Gombos Z, Murata N. 1990. Enhancement of chilling tolerance of a cyanobacterium by genetic manipulation of fatty acid desaturation. *Nature* 347: 200–3

113. Williams EE, Hazel JR. 1993. The role of docosahexaenoic acid-containing molecular species of phospholipid in the thermal adaptation of biological membranes. In *Essential Fatty Acids and Eicosanoids,* ed. A Sinclair, R Gibson, pp. 128–33. Champaign, Ill: Am. Oil Chemist's Soc.

114. Williams EE, Hazel JR. 1994. Membrane fluidity and hemilayer temperature sensitivity in trout hepatocytes during brief in vitro cold exposure. *Am. J. Physiol.* 266(35):R773–80

115. Wodtke E. 1981. Temperature adaptation of biological membranes—Compensation of the molar activity of cytochrome c oxidase in the mitochondrial energy-transducing membrane during thermal acclimation of the carp. *Biochim. Biophys. Acta* 640:710–20

116. Yeagle PL, Smith FT, Young JE, Flanagan TD. 1994. Inhibition of membrane fusion by lysophosphatidylcholine. *Biochemistry* 33(7):1820–27

Annu. Rev. Physiol. 1995. 57:43–68

PROTEINS AND TEMPERATURE

George N. Somero

Department of Zoology, Oregon State University, Corvallis, Oregon 97331–2914

KEY WORDS: acclimation, adaptation, denaturation, heat shock, thermophile

---

INTRODUCTION: New Interests and Insights in Temperature-Protein Interactions

Temperature relationships of organisms historically have been one of the most active areas of study in comparative and environmental physiology (21, 52, 110). Experimentation has evolved from descriptions of effects at the whole organism level to characterization of biochemical and molecular mechanisms that help to establish the thermal sensitivities, optima, and tolerance limits of differently adapted species and differently acclimated or acclimatized populations of a single species. These mechanistic studies have examined several types of structures and processes including membranes and their temperature–dependent lipid compositions (48), antifreeze and ice–nucleating molecules involved in freeze avoidance or freeze tolerance (31, 37, 150), temperature–dependent pH regulatory patterns (113, 114), and evolutionary and acclimatory changes in enzymatic and structural proteins, the latter of which are the focus of this review.

Most early studies of temperature-protein interactions were concerned with temperature effects on catalytic rates, acclimation of enzymatic activities to compensate for temperature changes, and interspecific differences in protein thermal stability (7, 21, 47, 52). Recent work has elaborated on these themes and has concentrated increasingly on two phenomena: (*a*) adaptive variations in structural and kinetic properties among homologues of proteins, differences that may be pivotal in establishing organisms' thermal optima and distribution patterns, and (*b*) temperature effects on protein expression. Fortuitously for comparative physiologists studying temperature effects, recent work in cellular, molecular, and structural biology has led to major advances in the understanding of basic features of temperature effects on protein structure and

43

function and gene regulation. Although most of these new discoveries have been made in experimental contexts that bear little resemblance to the real world thermal conditions experienced by organisms, they nonetheless have several important implications for comparative physiology, which serve as subjects for this review.

Several factors underlie the increased interests of cellular, molecular, and structural biologists in temperature-protein interactions. One is the desire to understand more fully the basic thermodynamic principles governing protein folding and assembly. Recent advances in theory (35, 65, 66, 109) have been paired with innovative molecular biological approaches that have allowed the predicted effects of specific amino acid substitutions on thermal stability to be tested with genetically engineered proteins (64, 83, 86, 88–90). These studies have greatly increased our understanding of the fundamental thermodynamics of protein folding and have revealed many of the ways in which even very minor alterations in primary structure can lead to changes in heat stability or kinetic properties (2, 18, 144).

A second major impetus for study of protein-temperature relationships came from the recent discovery and characterization of hyperthermophilic bacteria capable of growing at temperatures as high as 113°C (58, 118, 132, 152). The demonstration that many proteins of these unique members of the archaebacteria and eubacteria have significant half-lives in vitro at temperatures near 90–100°C has heightened interest in discovering the mechanisms by which, and the extent to which, proteins based on the 20 commonly found amino acids can be adapted to work at near–boiling temperatures (66, 118, 152). Discovery of hyperthermophilic bacteria has given rise to controversies over the upper temperature limits of life (11, 14, 98, 135, 143) and the physical conditions under which life arose (98). Study of hyperthermophiles also has emphasized the importance of both heat shock proteins (hsps) (136, 137) and low molecular weight protein stabilizers (49, 152) in conferring resistance of proteins to high temperatures in vivo.

Thirdly, an extremely important basis for heightened interest in temperature-protein interactions has come from study of the heat shock response (78, 79, 100, 142). Heat shock proteins, an evolutionarily conserved set of proteins belonging to several molecular weight classes, whose synthesis is triggered by elevated temperatures and other stresses (e.g. heavy metals, alcohol, and ischemia), are likely to be critical elements in the thermal relationships of all taxa. Study of hsps has led to further interest in the mechanisms that govern protein folding and in ways in which thermal stress on proteins is transduced into changes in gene expression (23, 111).

Lastly, concerns about possible effects of global warming have caused many comparative and environmental physiologists to take a renewed look at thermal relationships and the role played by temperature in establishing species' distribution patterns and performance capacities (29, 41, 53, 59–61). The role of temperature in establishing biogeographical patterning has long been recognized, but the physiological and molecular mechanisms responsible for establishing and maintaining these patterns are not well resolved. Furthermore, past studies in thermal biology generally have not examined effects of relatively small changes in temperature of the order predicted by many climate change models (29, 41). We thus are unable to estimate the minimal amounts of change in habitat temperature that could be sufficient to alter species' distribution patterns.

To relate recent discoveries about temperature-protein interactions made in these different disciplines to concerns of comparative, environmental, and evolutionary physiologists, this review focuses on the following questions: (*a*) What are the underlying determinants of protein thermal sensitivity? (*b*) What traits of proteins are most affected by changes in temperature, and why? (*c*) How much (or how little) change in temperature is adequate to perturb these traits sufficiently to favor selection for new protein variants? (*d*) How is conservation of these critical traits achieved? How much change in amino acid sequence is required to adapt a protein to new temperatures, and where in the sequence are these amino acid substitutions localized? (*e*) What factors influence the range of temperatures over which a protein maintains satisfactory structure and function? How do homologous proteins of stenotherms and eurytherms differ? (*f*) How are changes in cell temperature transduced into altered gene expression? (*g*) How do the protective effects of heat shock proteins and other extrinsic stabilizers, e.g. low molecular weight organic solutes, serve to counteract thermal perturbation of protein structure? (*h*) What aspects of protein structure constrain life to temperatures no higher than approximately 110°C? (*i*) Lastly, as an overriding theme, we ask what these diverse features of temperature-protein interactions suggest about the roles of proteins in establishing environmental optima, tolerance limits, and biogeographical patterning.

WHY ARE PROTEINS SO SENSITIVE TO TEMPERATURE?

This fundamental question is really two distinct questions. One question concerns proximate cause and asks how the thermal stabilities of proteins can be explained by the thermodynamics of protein folding and assembly. The second question concerns what Mayr (91) would term an ultimate evolutionary cause and asks why selection has favored the particular level of structural stability characteristic of extant proteins. One might rephrase this second question by asking why naturally occurring proteins are not more thermally stable?

The central fact that underlies answers to the how and why questions raised above is the following: Despite occurrence of hundreds of noncovalent bonds (hydrogen bonds, electrostatic interactions, and hydrophobic interactions) between amino acid residues within a protein, and between protein and solvent, net stabilization free energies of most proteins are of the order of only a few noncovalent bonds. Estimated ranges are given as 8–17 kcal/mol (30–65 kJ/mol) (66) and 5–20 kcal/mole (35). The marginal stabilities of proteins reflect offsetting effects of structure–stabilizing influences, chiefly burial of hydrophobic residues within the protein interior (hydrophobic effect), and destabilizing influences, primarily reduction in configurational entropy during folding (35, 65, 66, 109). This fine balance between stability and lability, which is found in virtually all proteins, in all taxa, is a strikingly consistent feature of protein evolution (7, 66).

TEMPERATURE ADAPTATION AND PROTEIN STRUCTURAL STABILITY

The stability–lability balance seems even more remarkable when considered in conjunction with two further observations. First, thermal stabilities of orthologous homologues (interspecific or interpopulational variants of a protein encoded by a common gene; 94) almost invariably are positively correlated with adaptation temperature. This relationship has been seen for structural proteins including lens crystallins (Figure 1; 92), actin (133), and numerous enzymes (7, 29, 36, 42, 52, 82, 128). Thus the balance between stabilizing and destabilizing forces is adjusted precisely and regularly during evolution at different temperatures, such that at physiological temperatures, homologous proteins of differently adapted species retain similar structural stabilities (7, 66). Second, recent studies using genetic engineering techniques have shown that protein thermal stability can be increased by introducing extremely minor changes in amino acid sequence (64, 88, 89). Sequencing studies of orthologous homologues differing in thermal stability have reached the same conclusion (55, 66, 108). Nishiyama et al (96) showed that for malate dehydrogenase of the bacterium *Thermus flavus* a single base change causing a single amino acid substitution resulted in alterations in thermal stability, Michaelis-Menten constants for substrate and cofactor, and catalytic rate constant. Malcolm et al (83), using site–directed mutagenesis methods to alter enzyme thermal stability, studied possible pathways of lysozyme evolution. They were able to increase thermal stability by making minor changes in sequence that led to altered packing of hydrophobic side chains. Despite the ease with which thermostability could be modified in the laboratory, selection has not favored sequences yielding the most stable lysozyme structures. These studies show that, were it to be adaptive to organisms, their proteins could evolve to become

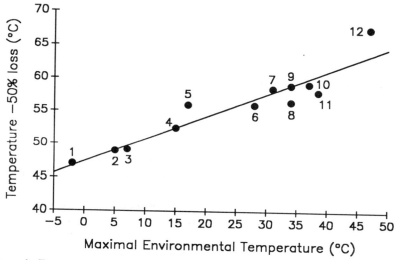

Figure 1 Temperature of 50% loss of structure for eye lens crystallins of differently adapted species: (1) *Pagothenia borchgrevinki* (Antarctic fish); (2) *Coryphaenoides armatus* (deep-sea fish); (3) *Coryphaenoides rupestris* (deep-sea fish); (4) *Oncorhynchus mykiss* (rainbow trout); (5) *Cebidichthys violaceus* (tidepool fish); (6) *Rana muscosa* (frog); (7) *Alticus kirkii* (Red Sea fish); (8) *Rana erythraea* (frog); (9) *Gekko gecko* (lizard); (10) *Rattus norwegicus* (rat); (11) *Tropidurus hispidus* (reptile); (12) *Dipsosaurus dorsalis* (desert iguana) (figure modified after McFall-Ngai & Horwitz, 92).

much more thermally stable than they are. What constrains natural selection for enhanced protein thermal stability?

To resolve what may appear to be an evolutionary paradox, it is essential to recognize that protein function almost always involves rapid, reversible changes in protein conformation (27). Proteins must have enough structural stability at physiological temperatures to allow retention of specific three-dimensional conformations required for function, e.g. for recognizing and binding ligands, yet this stability must not be so great as to prevent rapid and precise alterations in structure during binding, catalysis, metabolic regulation, and control of gene expression. To allow these structural changes to occur rapidly and with high sensitivity to regulatory signals, proteins can be neither too rigid nor too flexible. Thus selection for protein stability appears to favor a balance between lability and stability of structure rather than maximal stability.

Selection for protein stability also may reflect requirements for protein turnover in the cell. A protein that is too labile may have a short half-life, and especially if this protein is needed at high concentrations, its continued synthesis at high levels may exact large energy costs. Conversely, a protein that is too rigid may have an abnormally long half-life and may be difficult to remove from the cell when its activity is no longer required. Thus the delicate balance found in proteins between stability and lability may benefit protein turnover as well as protein function.

TEMPERATURE ADAPTATION AND PROTEIN FUNCTION

Conservation of K_m Values in Orthologous Homologues of Enzymes

Ligand binding is an especially temperature–sensitive trait because it depends on three events easily disrupted by temperature: (a) maintenance of a precise binding site geometry by the protein, (b) establishment of noncovalent bonds between binding site and ligand, and (c) for many enzymes, a change in protein conformation as part of the binding event. The sensitivities of ligand binding to changes in temperature have been characterized for orthologous homologues of several classes of enzymes (9, 19, 29, 43, 82, 93, 103, 104, 121–123, 147, 148). Figure 2 presents data for pyruvate binding by homologues of muscle-type lactate dehydrogenase (A_4-LDH). For A_4-LDH, as for most enzymes so examined, increases in measurement temperature reduce ligand binding ability, as manifested by increases in apparent Michaelis-Menten constants (K_m). For orthologous homologues of differently thermally adapted species, K_m vs temperature responses differ in ways that reflect the absolute body temperatures and the ranges of body temperatures that the species normally encounter. In reflection of absolute body temperature, set points of K_m differ among species: K_m values for enzymes from warm–adapted species are lower at any common temperature of measurement than K_ms of homologues from cold–adapted species (Figure 2). As a result of these compensatory differences in set point, temperature–dependent K_m values for orthologous homologues are similar in differently adapted species at their normal body temperatures.

Comparisons of orthologous homologues from different taxa show that thermal responses of enzymes are due to the species' evolutionary thermal history, not to phylogeny per se. For example, the A_4-LDH of a heat–adapted goby fish (*Gillichthys seta*), which lives in shallow tide pools at the edge of the Baja California desert, has kinetic properties similar to the A_4-LDH homologue of a thermophilic desert reptile (*Dipsosaurus dorsalis*), whose body temperature is similar to that of the desert shore fish.

Adaptation in k_{cat} Values

Another functional property of enzymes that varies with evolutionary adaptation temperature is the catalytic rate constant (k_{cat}), which specifies the rate at

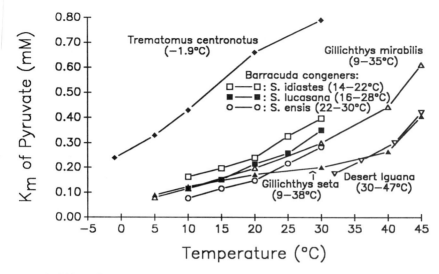

Figure 2   Effects of temperature on the Michaelis-Menten constant (K_m) of pyruvate for A4-lactate dehydrogenases of animals adapted to different temperatures (physiological temperature ranges given in parentheses). Sources of data: barracuda A4-LDHs (44); desert iguana (36); *Gillichthys mirabilis* and *Gillichthys seta* (E Winter & G Somero, unpublished); and *Trematomus centronotus* (J Podrabsky & G Somero, unpublished).

which a single active site can catalyze conversion of substrate to product. Enzymes from cold–adapted species have, at a common temperature of measurement, higher k_{cat} values than the orthologous homologues from warm–adapted species (15, 44, 52, 68, 81, 103). Thus these differences in k_{cat} are temperature compensatory in that they act to offset the effects of differences in adaptation temperature on catalytic rate. As found in comparisons of K_m values, there is substantial conservation of k_{cat} at the normal body temperatures of different species (44). Conservation of the k_{cat}/K_m ratio, which provides an estimate of activity at physiological substrate concentrations, may be even more pronounced because values for these two kinetic parameters often increase in tandem (40, 103; see below).

Because k_{cat} is highly modifiable during evolution, as well as through genetic engineering methods (18, 106), the question arises as to why selection has not favored the highest possible k_{cat} values. The general answer to this question is that the evolution of a single trait of an enzyme does not occur in a vacuum, independently of other aspects of enzyme function and structure. One restriction on reduction in k_{cat} values may be selection on thermal stability. For some enzymes, k_{cat}s are determined by the energy costs of conformational changes that accompany rate–limiting steps in catalysis. For example, the rate–determining step in the LDH reaction is a conformational change that opens the binding site and allows dissociation of products (1, 18, 54). Thus, to a first approximation, the more flexible the enzyme, the more rapidly can substrate turnover take place. However, the importance of maintaining the appropriate balance between stability and flexibility of the enzyme structure discussed above may limit selection for higher k_{cat} values if one consequence of increasing k_{cat} is too great a reduction in enzyme stability.

The lower k_{cat} values of enzymes of warm–adapted species also may relate to thermodynamics of ligand binding. The lower set points for K_m found for enzymes of warm–adapted species indicate that the enzyme-substrate complex has a low free energy relative to the complex of a cold–adapted species. The additional stabilization energy invested in binding raises the activation free energy barrier to catalysis, i.e. decreases k_{cat} (40, 52). The cold–adapted enzyme has a higher free energy in the ground state complex than the warm–adapted enzyme, i.e. K_m is higher at a common temperature but gains a lower free energy of activation as a result. Thus selection for appropriate K_m values may determine the size of k_{cat}. The observation that high K_ms are associated with high k_{cat}s for many enzymes suggests a linkage between binding and activation energies (40).

Adjustments in Enzyme Concentration

Achieving adequate levels of catalytic activity at different temperatures may involve adjustments in enzyme concentration, especially during acclimation or acclimatization. Enzymes of ectotherms often exhibit increased activities during acclimation to low temperatures, although patterns differ among enzymes and species (21, 47). The system in which the mechanistic basis for enhanced levels of enzymes in cold–adapted organisms is best understood is the LDH-B allozyme system in the eurythermal teleost *Fundulus heteroclitus* (25, 26). Northern (Maine) populations of this species have significantly higher levels of LDH-B activity in heart compared to southern (Georgia) populations. The higher LDH-B levels are correlated with higher levels of the mRNA for this protein. The higher mRNA levels, in turn, appear to be a consequence of a higher level of *ldh-b* gene transcription in the northern populations. Enhanced transcription was not noted for all genes: Neither total mRNA synthesis nor synthesis of actin and tubulin messages differed between populations. The different steady–state concentrations of LDH-B in heart of the northern and southern populations of *Fundulus* contribute more to temperature compensation of LDH activity than do the kinetic differences that distinguish the two allozymes characteristic of the two populations (26, 108; see below).

WHAT AMOUNT OF CHANGE IN TEMPERATURE IS SUFFICIENT TO ELICIT ADAPTATION OF PROTEINS?

Comparative studies of homologous proteins of differently adapted species have shown that differences in average or maximal body temperature among species of only a few degrees C are correlated with temperature–adaptive changes in K_m, k_{cat}, and thermal stability (29, 43, 44). A_4-LDHs of temperate, subtropical, and tropical barracuda congeners (genus *Sphyraena*), whose mid-range body temperatures differ by only 3–8°C, exhibit on a narrow temperature scale the same pattern of K_m conservation found in taxonomically broad comparisons of fishes, reptiles, and mammals adapted to temperatures ranging from $-1.86°C$ to 40–47°C (Figure 2; 44). The barracuda A_4-LDHs also differ in k_{cat} (44). Adaptive differences in activation energy, thermal stability, and K_m of NADH were found for cytosolic malate dehydrogenases (cMDHs) of five species of molluscs belonging to the genus *Haliotis* (abalones) that occur at different latitudes and tidal heights (29). Adaptive differences between cMDH homologues were observed for species whose maximal habitat temperatures differed by only 4°C. Although data of this type do not allow one to specify the smallest change in temperature that is adequate to favor selection on thermal responses of proteins, they do indicate that changes in temperature of only a few degrees C may have measurable consequences on biogeographical patterning (29, 41, 127).

THERMAL BREADTH OF PROTEIN FUNCTION: Mechanisms of Enzymatic Eurythermality

Orthologous Homologues from Stenothermal and Eurythermal Species

Despite the high sensitivities proteins show to changes in temperature, many eurythermal ectotherms are able to sustain satisfactory protein function over temperature ranges as large as 20–30°C. What distinguishes the proteins of extreme eurytherms from the homologues of extreme stenotherms? Thermal sensitivity of K_m differs between homologous proteins of stenothermal and eurythermal species, as shown in Figure 2: Compare A_4-LDH of a stenothermal Antarctic fish (*Trematomus centronotus*), whose upper lethal temperature is near 8°C (129), with A_4-LDH of a highly eurythermal goby *Gillichthys seta*, whose seasonal temperature range is approximately 9 to 38°C (33). Proteins from extremely eurythermal species like *G. seta* exhibit the ability to retain stable values for K_m over the wide temperature ranges characteristic of their habitats. These may be "Jack-of-all-temperature" proteins (61) that could contribute importantly to establishing wide breadths of thermal performance (59,

60). In contrast, rapid increases in K_m with temperature are seen for proteins of cold–adapted stenotherms like Antarctic fishes (9, 128, 148). Heat–induced loss of ligand–binding ability may be instrumental in establishing upper thermal tolerance limits. Large increases in K_m frequently are observed at temperatures near those causing heat death (5, 6, 9, 128).

The structural basis of interspecific differences in temperature effects on K_m is not known. It seems probable that heat–induced changes in enzyme conformation, rather than interspecific differences in active site sequence, are responsible for these effects. The amino acid residues involved in substrate binding tend to be fully conserved among orthologous homologues of enzymes (for LDH, see 24). Distortion by temperature of the steric configuration of these common residues thus seems likely to underlie reductions in binding with rising temperature. Changes in K_m induced by temperature may be a highly sensitive bioassay for subtle, yet functionally important, changes in enzyme conformation that are difficult to detect by conventional physical methods (36, 128).

Enzyme Polymorphism: Allelic Orthologous Variants (Allozymes)

Species that occur over wide ranges of temperature, e.g. along latitudinal or altitudinal thermal gradients, possess multiple allelic variants of enzymes (allozymes) that exhibit differences in thermal stabilities and kinetic properties (5, 50, 53, 72, 93, 103, 104, 107, 122, 123, 139–141, 151). Differences between cold- and warm–adapted populations of a species in frequencies of the genes encoding the differently adapted allozymes may ensure that the appropriate allozyme variant is dominant in a population. Powers and colleagues (107, 108) have studied latitudinally separated populations of the eurythermal fish *Fundulus heteroclitus*. For many enzymes of *Fundulus*, allozyme variants were not detected, but several enzymes showed clines in allozyme frequency. To date, six of these enzymes have been found to differ in kinetics or thermal stability in ways that seem to be temperature adaptive (108). For LDH-B (B_4-LDH), the allozyme prevalent in northern populations appears better adapted for function at low temperatures than the allozyme from southern populations, based on temperature effects on K_m, maximal velocity, and k_{cat}/K_m ratio (103, 104). Differences in LDH-B allozymes among populations were correlated with differences in swimming performance, erythrocyte ATP concentrations, hatching time, and developmental rate (108).

Only about 15% of the 28 loci screened in largemouth bass (*Micropterus salmoides*) populations along a north to south gradient exhibited allelic variants whose clines reflected differences in temperature regime (101). The number of these loci encoding allozymes with different thermal optima is not known. Estimating the fraction of enzyme–encoding loci that encode temperature–

adaptive allozymes is extremely difficult. First, as shown for the *Fundulus* system (108) and for species pairs separated by the Isthmus of Panama (43), allelic variants that differ in functional properties and thermal stability may exhibit identical electrophoretic migration on native gels. Conversely, allozymes that differ in charge (electrophoretic mobility) may not exhibit functional differences (43, 108). Second, it is not a simple matter to determine whether allozymes are, in fact, adaptively different. Subtle changes in functional properties and stability may be difficult to determine experimentally, and of course, it is logically impossible to prove that no differences exist between allozymes. Comparisons of allozymes would need to include measurements of diverse traits, including K_m value, k_{cat} value, inhibition constants, stabilities, turnover rates in the cell and, for some proteins, their potential for cellular compartmentalization, for thorough characterization (108). Relating variations in allozyme structural and kinetic properties to physiological performance and reproductive success represents a further challenge. Few studies to date have attempted this depth and breadth of analysis. Thus it is premature to draw general conclusions about the importance of allozyme variants in enhancing the eurythermality of species found over wide thermal ranges. Although this mechanism for broadening thermal tolerance or performance ranges may be important at the populational level, there are obvious genetic constraints at the individual level. If an individual must be heterozygous at numerous loci to gain the advantage of allozyme–based eurythermality of protein function, the larger the number of loci that encode allozymes with different thermal optima, the more unlikely it is that this mechanism of eurythermality works for the individual. Therefore, for the individual, occurrence of a single form of a protein that has kinetic properties that are stable over a wide temperature range appears to be a more suitable mechanism for enhancing eurythermality.

Paralogous Homologues and Temperature Adaptation

The occurrence in a species of two or more variants of a given type of enzyme that are encoded by multiple gene loci (paralogous isozymes) and that differ in thermal optima can provide another mechanism for broadening the temperature range of protein function (52, 67). Differential expression as a function of exposure temperature could facilitate adaptation in such cases by favoring synthesis of only the isozyme that is appropriate for the current thermal regime.

Several examples of this type of protein polymorphism have been discovered. In muscle of differently acclimated goldfish, expression of isoforms of Ca^{2+}-adenosine triphosphatase with different thermal stabilities was found to vary with acclimation temperature (63). Isoforms of a myosin light chain protein were shown to vary with acclimation temperature in another eurythermal fish, the carp (*Cyprinus carpio*) (28). Temperature acclimation of rainbow trout induced different isoforms of acetylcholinesterases in brain; the effects of temperature on the K_m of acetylcholine differed between the two isoforms in an adaptive manner (10).

The cytosolic form of malate dehydrogenase (cMDH) in teleost fishes is encoded by two gene loci (119, 120). One paralogous homologue is more thermally stable than the other and has a lower set point for the K_m of NADH (76, 77). In the eurythermal goby fish *Gillichthys mirabilis*, the ratio of expression of heat stable and heat labile cMDH isoforms varied seasonally in naturally acclimatized fishes and as a function of laboratory acclimation temperature (77). The change in isozyme ratio effects a conservation of K_m of NADH over the wide temperature range experienced by this species. Differences in ratio of expression of cMDH isozymes also exist among differently adapted species. In barracuda, the heat–labile, high K_m isoform of cMDH could not be detected in a tropical species *Sphyraena ensis*, although it was present in two temperate and one subtropical species (76). Absence of the thermolabile cMDH in *S. ensis* could reflect loss of the gene or a failure to express it under conditions of continuously high ambient temperatures.

These examples illustrate that paralogous homologues whose expression is correlated with, and perhaps regulated by, ambient temperature can play roles in temperature adaptation. However, for most enzymes thus far studied, multiple paralogous isozyme forms with different thermal sensitivities have not been detected (124). For many paralogous isozymes generated either through tandem gene duplication or polyploidy, adaptive variation appears linked to tissue–specific functional requirements rather than adaptation to temperature (130, 138).

AT WHAT SITES, AND BY HOW MUCH, ARE PROTEIN SEQUENCES MODIFIED TO ALTER STABILITY AND FUNCTION?

Active site sequences are highly conserved among homologous proteins (24, 66), a reflection of constraints placed on active site structure by the catalytic mechanism and the geometries and charge proteins of ligands. For example, A-type LDHs of all species examined, including birds, mammals, an elasmobranch, and several teleost fishes, have identical amino acid sequences in the active site and catalytic loop region (24; M McFall-Ngai et al, unpublished observations). The latter region is the section of the enzyme that collapses over the bound cofactor and substrate to form the functional ternary complex (1, 54). Despite this sequence conservation, A_4-LDHs differ substantially in K_m of pyruvate (19, 128, 148; Figure 2), K_m of NADH (147), k_{cat} (44, 81), and thermal stability (36, 128). For some A_4-LDH and B_4-LDHs, adaptive changes in structure lie at subunit-subunit contact points, distant from the active site

(108; M McFall-Ngai et al, unpublished obsevations). Alterations in the strengths of subunit-subunit interactions may affect thermal stability and the energy changes associated with conformational changes that accompany binding and catalysis, e.g. the changes in loop movement that occur following ligand binding. Thus a change in primary structure that occurs distantly from the active site, but which influences the energy costs of conformational changes near and around the active site, could contribute to the energetics of enzymatic function. For A_4- and B_4-LDHs, only minor amounts of change in sequence at subunit contact sites are sufficient to change protein stability and kinetics. For two closely related barracuda species, *Sphyraena idiastes* and *S. lucasana,* whose A_4-LDHs differ in temperature-K_m relationships (Figure 2), only a single difference in sequence was detected (M McFall-Ngai et al, unpublished observations), replacement of an aspartate in *S. lucasana* by asparagine in *S. idiastes* at position 9 in the sequence, which lies at a subunit contact site (1, 54). The net change in structure involves only the replacement of a negatively charged oxygen (aspartate) with a neutral amino group (asparagine). A similar observation was made by Powers et al (108), who showed that differences in thermal stability between allozymes of B_4-LDH could be accounted for by a single amino acid substitution at a subunit contact site (position 185). When a serine residue at position 185 was replaced with an alanine, a significant reduction in thermal stability occurred. The net change in structure was only an addition (serine) or deletion (alanine) of a single hydroxyl group.

Genetic engineering studies also have shown that thermal stability and kinetic properties can be modified with only minor changes in sequence. Wilkinson et al (144) reduced K_m of ATP for tyrosyl-tRNA synthetase by 100-fold through a single amino acid substitution. Matthews and colleagues (88–90) and others (64) have shown that replacing glycyl residues with alanyl residues is an especially effective mechanism for enhancing thermal stability. The bases of this enhancement of stability appear to be twofold. First, by substituting an alanyl residue for a glycyl residue, the configurational entropy of the unfolded protein is reduced. By reducing the magnitude of the entropy increase that accompanies unfolding, the native conformation of the protein is stabilized. Second, alanyl residues will be more effective than glycyl residues in hydrophobic stabilization of proteins. Genetic engineering studies have shown that changes in hydrophobicity can effect regular shifts in protein thermal stability (83, 86). In comparisons of proteins from mesophilic and thermophilic (including hyperthermophilic) bacteria, a trend towards increased hydrophobicity has been reported (66, 118, 152).

These new discoveries about the amounts and locations of adaptive changes in sequence raise important questions about protein evolution. First, in view of the minor amount of change in primary structure needed to effect adaptive differences in enzyme function and structure, how rapid are rates of adaptive protein change? Recent studies of evolutionary temperature adaptation by bacteria (12, 13, 74) and *Drosophila* (62) in the laboratory show that rates of adaptation are rapid. It will be interesting to learn if these adaptations can be linked to minor changes in protein sequence of the sort discovered in naturally evolving populations.

A further question based on recent structure-function studies relates to the neutralist-selectionist controversy (94, 108). In view of the important effects of extremely minor changes in structure located outside the active site, it is clear that extreme caution is required in drawing conclusions about the putative neutrality of amino acid substitutions.

PROTECTION OF PROTEINS BY ORGANIC SOLUTES AND INORGANIC IONS

Because of the low net stabilization free energies of proteins and the fact that the protein-water-solute system of the cell is a single thermodynamic unit, modifications in the milieu in which proteins occur can play a major role in establishing thermal stability of structure and function (131, 134). The role of small solutes in effecting protein stability and function in the face of temperature change has been especially well characterized for one of the smallest entities in the cell, the proton (113, 114, 125, 126). Temperature–dependent changes in intracellular pH (pH_i) such as occur in vivo (51, 113) lead to stabilization of K_m values (145, 148), catalytic velocities (46), subunit assembly (45), and protein compartmentalization (116).

Organic solutes used in osmotic balance may play an important role in stabilizing proteins in the face of thermal stress. In the thermophilic archaebacterium *Methanothermus fervidus,* the major intracellular anion is 2–3-diphosphoglycerate (2,3-DPG)(49). High concentrations of 2,3-DPG appear to afford protection against thermal denaturation to the proteins of the species, which unlike proteins of most thermophiles, do not have an inherently high thermal stability. Elevated concentrations of structure–stabilizing inorganic ions also contribute to protein stabilization in hyperthermophiles (152). In yeast (*Saccharomyces cerevisiae*), heat stress may lead to accumulation of high intracellular concentrations of trehalose, a strong stabilizer of proteins and membranes (56, 57). Glycerol, another protein–stabilizing solute, is found at high concentrations in cells of osmotically concentrated organisms found at high temperatures, e.g. thermotolerant eukaryotic algae like *Duneliella* spp. (146). High concentrations of glycerol also have been found in animals facing low temperatures, e.g. in certain Arctic marine fishes that are almost isosmotic with seawater (112) and in freeze-tolerant terrestrial invertebrates (37, 150). Taurine and strombine are proposed to be cryoprotectants in the intertidal mollusc *Mytilus edulis* (80). Protection of proteins from cold denaturation

(109), as well as from heat denaturation, may be afforded by stabilizing organic solutes.

The classes of organic osmolytes accumulated in different species may depend on adaptation temperature (95, 131). Some organic osmolytes can stabilize proteins only at low temperatures because they have hydrophobic regions that can bind to and denature proteins at high temperature (8, 95). These osmolytes appear to be absent in heat-tolerant species, where stabilizers like glycerol and other polyhydric alcohols (polyols) that lack a strong hydrophobic moment are accumulated (131).

For membrane–associated proteins, the specific composition of the lipid bilayer may influence thermal sensitivity (20, 138). For example, thermal stability of a membrane ATPase was increased as a result of the lipid changes occurring during warm acclimation (20).

THE HEAT SHOCK RESPONSE: Rescue Systems for Perturbed Proteins

Study of hsps is one of the currently most active areas of research in cellular and molecular biology (79, 100). Although only a small fraction of the seven to eight hundred papers published per year on hsps deals with heat stress in natural environments, many of the basic findings of laboratory studies on hsp function and expression have important implications for questions about the determinants of organisms' thermal tolerance ranges and mechanisms for transducing temperature effects on proteins into alterations in gene expression.

Induced Thermal Tolerance and Expression of Hsps

Many organisms exhibit increased heat tolerance following brief exposures to high temperatures. This induced thermal tolerance or heat hardening allows survival at temperatures that would otherwise prove lethal (100). Evidence for the importance of hsps in enhancing thermal tolerance includes: (*a*) Hsps are induced rapidly following thermal stress in most species and cell types (100). The extent of enhanced hsp expression may be large [up to ~ 1000–fold in *Drosophila* (70)]. (*b*). With enhanced expression of hsps, there typically is a rapid, parallel increase in heat tolerance (75, 100). (*c*) Introduction and expression of an additional heat shock gene can increase cells' thermal tolerance (73). (*d*) Reduction or elimination of capacity for heat hardening occurs with silencing or removal of one or more of the genes encoding hsps (117). (*e*) Introduction of an antibody to a hsp into the cell can lower thermal tolerance (115). (*f*) Differences in thermal tolerance among closely related species are correlated with occurrence of heat shock genes (16). (*g*) Developmental stages that lack the ability to express hsps are typically sensitive to thermal stress

(17). (*h*) Thermally denatured proteins can be reactivated in vitro by the activities of hsps (99).

As this final observation suggests, many of the hsps belong to the broad family of proteins termed chaperones. The chaperone proteins assist in the correct folding, oligomerization, and compartmentalization of other proteins (38). Unfolded proteins form complexes with chaperones through hydrophobic contacts, and the chaperone facilitates correct (re)folding of the bound protein (38, 85). The requirements for elevated levels of chaperone proteins at high body temperatures can be understood in part in the context of protein "breathing." Because proteins have low net stabilization free energies, they continually partially unfold and refold, i.e. breathe. During the breathing process, hydrophobic regions normally buried within the folded protein may be exposed to solvent. If these newly exposed patches contact other hydrophobic sites, e.g. on nascent polypeptides or other unfolded proteins, nonspecific protein aggregates of denatured proteins can form. If heat increases the rates or extents of protein breathing, the danger of forming such aggregates will rise with body temperature. Nascent polypeptides present the same danger to the cell: Hydrophobic regions not yet buried within the protein interior can form nonspecific aggregates with other hydrophobic entities. Heat stress is likely to be especially severe for organisms synthesizing proteins at a high rate because of the increased levels of nascent polypeptides in the cell. Both constitutively expressed and heat–inducible chaperones, i.e. hsps, act to prevent formation of nonspecific aggregates. Despite this similarity of function, there is evidence that the benefits of some hsps, e.g. hsp70, may be restricted to periods of thermal stress; hsps at high concentrations may be disadvantageous to cells under nonstressful conditions (39).

One unknown aspect of hsp function is their possible role in conserving thermally sensitive enzyme kinetic properties. For example, it is not known if hsps can protect enzymes from heat-induced loss of binding ability. If rapid increases in K_m with rising temperature are due to only very subtle and rapid shifts in configuration of residues involved in ligand binding and do not entail exposure of hydrophobic patches that can be recognized by hsps, then protection of this aspect of enzyme function by hsps may not be possible, even though hsps may assist in correct refolding of enzymes suffering more extensive structural unfoldings than those responsible for K_m perturbation.

Although most attention has been given to heat-induced synthesis of chaperones, cold shock also can induce synthesis of a set of stress proteins. In insects, cold shock–induced proteins of the 70- and 90-kDa classes (30, 69, 149), and hsp70 was induced by subphysiological temperatures in mammalian neutrophils (22). Low temperatures tend to destabilize hydrophobic interactions, and some proteins exhibit cold denaturation (109). Thus cold stress, like heat stress, appears to require enhanced function of chaperone proteins.

Evolutionary and Acclimatory Changes in the Heat Shock Response

Although the heat shock response is ubiquitous, it varies among species and populations in several ways including (a) the temperature at which hsp synthesis is induced, (b) the levels of hsps that are accumulated in the cells, and (c) the specific types of hsps that are synthesized. Comparisons of the heat shock response in species evolutionarily adapted to different temperatures have shown that threshold induction temperatures needed to trigger (increase) expression of hsps are positively correlated with normal body temperature. Threshold induction temperatures typically lie several degrees C above normal body temperature (100), and range from slightly above 0°C for Antarctic fishes (84) to 95–102°C for hyperthermophilic bacteria (102, 137).

Threshold induction temperatures are not genetically "hard–wired" for a species. Differently acclimatized or acclimated individuals of a species may show differences in threshold induction temperature of several degrees C. In the eurythermal goby fish *Gillichthys mirabilis,* the threshold induction temperatures for synthesis of hsp90 in brain were 36–38°C for 30°C-acclimated fish, 28°C for 20°C-acclimated fish, and 24°C for 10°C-acclimated fish (32). Similar differences in induction temperature were found in *Gillichthys* collected in the field at different seasons (33). Acclimation of medaka fish (*Oryzias latipes*) led to shifts in heat shock induction temperatures (97), but catfish hepatocytes cultured at different temperatures failed to show any shift in induction temperature (71). The latter observation suggests that caution should be used in extrapolating from laboratory studies of hsp synthesis in isolated cells to effects occurring in whole organisms in their natural thermal regimes.

Changes in induction temperature with thermal acclimation or acclimatization may seem surprising in view of the likelihood that the intrinsic thermal stabilities of cellular proteins are not likely to vary with acclimation or acclimatization, except in cases like cMDH in eurythermal teleosts (see above). A clue to the resolution of this paradox is provided by the finding that concentrations of hsps rise with acclimation temperature (33), a change that may alter the set point of the "cellular thermometer," which regulates expression of hsps (see below).

The role of "standing stock" hsp concentrations in determining heat tolerance and in setting induction temperatures in different species is not known. Current information is inadequate to determine whether species evolutionarily adapted to different temperatures differ with respect to concentrations of heat shock proteins. A priori one might expect that warm–adapted species would not require higher standing stock concentrations of hsps than cold–adapted species. Because protein thermal stability is higher for proteins from warm–adapted species (Figure 1), proteins of warm–adapted species at their physiological temperatures may not experience any higher extents of unfolding than the homologous, less thermally stable proteins of cold–adapted species at their lower body temperatures. It is not known whether hsp homologues themselves differ in thermal stability among differently thermally adapted species.

Resolving questions about interspecific variations in classes of hsps used and in standing stock hsp concentrations will require precise measurements using quantitative antibody methods. These questions will be difficult to resolve for several reasons: (a) Different species exploit different classes of hsps to gain heat tolerance (34, 100). (b) Different organs of a given species may rely on different classes of hsps (34). (c) Different classes of hsps may be recruited to cope with moderate and extreme thermal stresses (100). (d) Although hsps are evolutionarily conserved, antibodies may not be available for an epitope common to all homologues.

Cellular Thermometers Based on Temperature-Induced Changes in Protein Structure

The sensitivity of protein conformation and aggregation state to temperature may underlie mechanisms that regulate heat shock gene expression and provide a basis for cellular thermometers that can detect the extent of heat stress encountered by a cell (23). In one model for regulation of heat shock genes in eukaryotes, a prototype that applies to many but not all species, a protein termed the heat shock factor (HSF) binds reversibly, in a temperature-dependent manner, to the heat shock element (HSE), a *cis* regulatory factor upstream of the genes encoding hsps (23). The basis of the temperature sensitivity of HSF binding to the HSE has been conjectured to involve a temperature-dependent trimerization of HSF, the multimeric state of HSF required for binding to HSE. Two mechanisms for temperature–dependent trimerization have been hypothesized. One predicts that a temperature–dependent change in HSF conformation permits trimerization and, then, binding to HSE (111). The second hypothesis proposes that binding of a hsp, e.g. hsp70, to HSF prevents trimerization and gene activation (23). When heat stress occurs, increased levels of partially unfolded proteins shift the distribution of hsp70 away from complexes with HSF towards binding to heat–damaged proteins. When released from complexes with hsp70, HSF can trimerize and then bind to HSE. This second model predicts that high concentrations of a hsp could raise the threshold induction temperature of hsp gene expression (33). It remains unclear to what extent these two models for control of hsp–encoding genes are correct. The models have heuristic value, however, by providing a conceptual framework for explaining how temperature–induced changes in protein conformation can act as a cellular thermometer and provide a means for regulating expression of heat shock genes. These models for regulation of hsp expression through temperature–dependent effects on equilibria involving protein conformational change and protein-protein interactions would seem to have broad applicability for control of other temperature–regulated genes.

WHAT ESTABLISHES THE UPPER THERMAL LIMITS OF PROTEINS—AND THE UPPER TEMPERATURE LIMITS OF LIFE?

In view of the several mechanisms available for enhancing protein thermal stability, including changes in primary structure, regulation of stabilizing solutes and pH values, and expression of hsps, the upper temperature limits for protein stability are of interest. The finding that, despite intense efforts, no microbe has been cultured that can withstand temperatures above approximately 113°C suggests that the upper temperature limit to life lies near this temperature (132). There are strong grounds for attributing this thermal limit to proteins, specifically to high temperature effects on the principal types of bonds that stabilize protein structure. Hydrophobic interactions, which play a dominant role in stabilizing the folded states of proteins, may cease to be effective above approximately 100°C (66). The basis of hydrophobic stabilization lies in induced changes in water structure by exposed hydrophobic groups (66, 109). Within the biological temperature range, exposure of hydrophobic groups to water leads to a reduction in system entropy because of an increase in solvent order around these exposed groups. This decrease in entropy favors burial of hydrophobic groups. As temperature approaches 100°C and above, increased thermal motion of water minimizes its ability to organize around hydrophobic groups. The loss of entropy due to interactions between water and hydrophobic groups is reduced and, therefore, so is the contribution of hydrophobic stabilization. Covalent bonds in proteins and other biomolecules also face thermal damage at high temperatures (2–4, 14, 143). For example, temperatures above 100°C lead to hydrolysis of peptide bonds at aspartyl residues and deamidation of asparagine residues (2–4).

Attempts to enhance thermal stabilities of proteins through introduction of disulfide bridges have met with mixed success. Disulfide bridges are rare in intracellular proteins (66), and when they are introduced as a mechanism for enhancing thermal stability, they may distort the protein and reduce both stability and function. Introduction of multiple disulfide bridges into a disulfide–free protein, T4 lysozyme, increased thermal stability above that of the wild–type enzyme, which denatures in vitro near 42°C (87). However, the highest denaturation temperature that could be obtained even with triple disulfide mutants was only ~ 65°C. It would seem that no amount of protein engineering involving the 20 commonly occurring amino acids can generate proteins with stabilities at temperatures much above 100°C.

Neither hsps nor other extrinsic stabilizers are likely to increase significantly the upper limit for protein stability. Hsps, like other proteins, face damage from hydrolysis and loss of hydrophobic stabilization at high temperatures. Loss of the hydrophobic effect would also hamper chaperone binding to unfolded proteins. There is no evidence that hsps prevent hydrolysis of covalent bonds at high temperatures, although reburial through chaperone activity of exposed hydrolysis–sensitive sites might reduce rates of irreversible denaturation. Organic and inorganic stabilizers of proteins generally exert their influences through water structure effects (134). Because water structure is strongly reduced at high temperatures, it is unlikely that stabilizing solutes would be effective in stabilizing proteins under these conditions.

The role of solvent in establishing protein stability is such that damage to covalent bonds due to hydrolysis could be reduced only if water activity were greatly lowered. However, such a change in cellular hydration state might preclude normal metabolic activity. It is noteworthy that resistant spore stages of many species often exhibit extremely low water activities and maintain high concentrations of hsps and protein-stabilizing solutes (56, 57, 105). The absolute limits to protein stability, then, may depend on cessation of physiological activity and entry into an anhydrobiotic state in which resistance of proteins to high and low extremes of temperature is pronounced.

ACKNOWLEDGMENTS

I thank Drs. Elizabeth Dahlhoff, Gretchen Hofmann, and John Ruben for stimulating discussions of ideas presented in this review. Portions of the work discussed were supported by National Science Foundation grant IBN 9206660.

Literature Cited

1. Abad-Zapatero C, Griffith J, Sussman J, Rossman M. 1987. Refined crystal structure of dogfish M_4 apo–lactate dehydrogenase. *J. Mol. Biol.* 198:445–67
2. Ahern TJ, Casal JI, Petsko GA, Klibanov AM. 1987. Control of oligomeric enzyme thermostability by protein engineering. *Proc. Natl. Acad. Sci. USA* 84: 675–79
3. Ahern TJ, Klibanov AM. 1985. The mechanism of irreversible enzyme inactivation at 100°C. *Science* 228:1280–84
4. Ahern TJ, Klibanov AM. 1988. Analysis of processes causing thermal inactivation of enzymes. *Methods Biochem. Anal.* 33:91–127

5. Alahiotis SN. 1982. Adaptation of *Drosophila* enzymes to temperature. IV. Natural selection at the alcohol dehydrogenase locus. *Genetics* 59:81–87
6. Alahiotis S, Berger E. 1978. Adaptation of *Drosophila* enzymes to temperature: I. Acetylcholinesterase and NADP–dependent isocitrate dehydrogenase. *Comp. Biochem. Physiol.* 61B:199–202
7. Alexandrov VYa. 1969. Conformational flexibility of proteins, their resistance to proteinases and temperature conditions of life. *Curr. Mod. Biol.* 3:9–19
8. Arakawa T, Carpenter JF, Kita YA, Crowe JH. 1990. The basis for toxicity

of certain cryoprotectants: a hypothesis. *Cryobiology* 27:401–15

9. Baldwin J. 1971. Adaptation of enzymes to temperature: acetylcholinesterases in the central nervous system of fishes. *Comp. Biochem. Physiol.* 40:181–87

10. Baldwin J, Hochachka PW. 1970. Functional significance of isoenzymes in thermal acclimatization: acetylcholinesterases from trout brain. *Biochem. J.* 116:883–87

11. Baross JA, Deming JW. 1983. Growth of "black smoker" bacteria at temperatures of at least 250°C. *Nature* 303:423–26

12. Bennett AF, Dao KM, Lenski RE. 1990. Rapid evolution in response to high temperature selection. *Nature* 346:79–81

13. Bennett AF, Lenski RE. 1993. Evolutionary adaptation to temperature. II. Thermal niches of experimental lines of *Escherichia coli. Evolution* 47:1–12

14. Bernhardt G, Ludemann HD, Jaenicke R, Konig H, Stetter KO. 1984. Biomolecules are unstable under "Black Smoker" conditions. *Naturwissenschaften* 71:583–86

15. Borgmann U, Moon TW. 1975. A comparison of lactate dehydrogenases from an ectothermic and an endothermic animal. *Can. J. Biochem.* 53:998–1004

16. Bosch TCG, Krylow SM, Bode HR, Steele RE. 1988. Thermotolerance and synthesis of heat shock proteins: These responses are present in *Hydra attenuata* but absent in *Hydra oligactis. Proc. Natl. Acad. Sci. USA* 85:7927–31

17. Browder LW, Pollock RM, Neckells RW, Heikkila JJ, Winning RS. 1988. Developmental regulation of the heat shock response. In *Genomic Adaptability in Cell Specialization,* ed. MA Bernardino, L Etrin, pp. 97–147. New York: Plenum

18. Clarke AR, Atkinson T, Holbrook JJ. 1989. From analysis to synthesis: new ligand binding sites on the lactate dehydrogenase framework. Part I. *Trends Biochem. Sci.* 14:101–5

19. Coppes JL, Somero GN. 1990. Temperature-adaptive differences between the M_4-lactate dehydrogenases of stenothermal and eurythermal Sciaenid fishes. *J. Exp. Zool.* 254:127–31

20. Cossins AR. 1983. Homeoviscous adaptation of membranes. In *Cellular Acclimatization to Environmental Change,* ed. AR Cossins, P Sheterline. pp. 3–32. London: Cambridge Univ. Press

21. Cossins AR, Bowler K. 1987. *Temperature Biology of Animals.* London: Chapman & Hall, 339 pp.

22. Cox G, Moseley P, Hunninghake GW.

1993. Induction of heat shock protein 70 in neutrophils during exposure to subphysiologic temperatures. *J. Infect. Diseases* 167:769–71

23. Craig EA, Gross CA. 1991. Is hsp70 the cellular thermometer? *Trends Biochem. Sci.* 16:135–40

24. Crawford DL, Constantino HR, Powers DA. 1989. Lactate dehydrogenase-B cDNA from the teleost *Fundulus heteroclitus:* Evolutionary implications. *Mol. Biol. Evol.* 6:369–83

25. Crawford DL, Powers DA. 1989. Molecular basis of evolutionary adaptation at the lactate dehydrogenase-B locus in the fish *Fundulus heteroclitus. Proc. Natl. Acad. Sci. USA* 86:9365–69

26. Crawford DL, Powers DA. 1992. Evolutionary adaptation to different thermal environments via transcriptional regulation. *Mol. Biol. Evol.* 9:806–13

27. Creighton TE. 1984. *Proteins: Structures and Molecular Properties.* New York: Freeman. 507 pp.

28. Crockford T, Johnston IA. 1990. Temperature acclimation and the expression of contractile protein isoforms in the skeletal muscles of the common carp (*Cyprinus carpio* L.). *J. Comp. Physiol. B.* 160:23–30

29. Dahlhoff EP, Somero GN. 1993. Kinetic and structural adaptations of cytosolic malate dehydrogenases of eastern Pacific abalones (genus *Haliotis*) from different thermal habitats: biochemical correlates of biogeographical patterning. *J. Exp. Biol.* 185:137–50

30. Denlinger DL, Lee RE, Yocum GD, Kukal O. 1992. Role of chilling in the acquisition of cold tolerance and the capacitation to express stress proteins in diapausing pharate larvae of the gypsy moth, *Lymantria dispar. Arch. Insect Biochem. Physiol.* 21:271–80

31. DeVries AL, Cheng C-HC. 1992. The role of antifreeze glycopeptides and peptides in the survival of cold-water fishes. In *Water and Life,* ed. GN Somero, CB Osmond, CL Bolis. pp. 301–15. Berlin: Springer-Verlag

32. Dietz TJ. 1994. Acclimation of the threshold induction temperatures for 70-kDa and 90-kDa heat shock proteins in the fish *Gillichthys mirabilis. J. Exp. Biol.* 188:333–38

33. Dietz TJ, Somero GN. 1992. The threshold induction temperature of the 90-kDa heat shock protein is subject to acclimatization in eurythermal goby fishes (genus *Gillichthys). Proc. Natl. Acad. Sci. USA.* 89:3389–93

34. Dietz TJ, Somero GN. 1993. Interspecific and intertissue differences in heat

shock protein concentration and threshold induction temperatures. *Physiol. Zool.* 66:863–80

35. Dill KA. 1990. Dominant forces in protein folding. *Biochemistry* 29:7133–55

36. Donahue EV. 1982. *Lactate dehydrogenase: structural aspects of environmental adaptation.* PhD thesis. Univ. Calif., San Diego. 176 pp.

37. Duman JG, Wu SW, Xu L, Tursman D, Olsen TM. 1991. Adaptations of insects to subzero temperatures. *Q. Rev. Biol.* 66:387–410

38. Ellis RJ, Van der Vies SM. 1991. Molecular chaperones. *Annu. Rev. Biochem.* 60:321–47

39. Feder JH, Rossi JM, Solomon J, Somomon N, Lindquist S. 1992. The consequences of expressing hsp70 in *Drosophila* cells at normal temperatures. *Genes Dev.* 6:1402–13

40. Fersht AR. 1985. *Enzyme Structure and Mechanism,* pp. 312–19. New York: Freeman. 475 pp.

41. Fields P, Graham JB, Rosenblatt RH, Somero GN. Effects of expected global climate change on marine faunas. *Trends Ecol. Evol.* 8:361–66

42. Genicot S, Feller G, Gerday C. 1988. Trypsin from Antarctic fish (*Paranotothenia magellanica* Forster) as compared with trout (*Salmo gairdneri*) trypsin. *Comp. Biochem. Physiol.* 90B:601–9

43. Graves JE, Rosenblatt RH, Somero GN. 1984. Kinetic and electrophoretic differentiation of lactate dehydrogenases of teleost species-pairs from the Atlantic and Pacific coasts of Panama. *Evolution* 37:30–37

44. Graves JE, Somero GN. 1982. Electrophoretic and functional enzymic evolution in four species of eastern Pacific barracudas from different thermal environments. *Evolution* 36:91–106

45. Hand SC, Somero GN. 1983. Phosphofructokinase of the hibernator *Citellus beecheyi:* temperature and pH regulation of activity via influences on the tetramer-dimer equilibrium. *Physiol. Zool.* 56:380–88

46. Hazel JR, McKinley SJ, Sellner PA. 1978. The effect of assay temperature upon the pH optima of enzymes from poikilotherms: a test of the imidazole alphastat hypothesis. *J. Comp. Physiol. B* 123:97–104

47. Hazel JR, Prosser CL. 1974. Molecular mechanisms of temperature compensation in poikilotherms. *Physiol. Rev.* 54:620–77

48. Hazel JR, Williams EE. 1990. The role of alterations in membrane lipid composition in enabling physiological adaptations to organisms to their physical environment. *Prog. Lipid Res.* 29:167–227

49. Hensel R, Konig H. 1988. Thermoadaptation of methanogenic bacteria by intracellular ion concentration. *FEMS Microbiol. Lett.* 49:75–79

50. Hines SS, Philipp DP, Childers WF, Whitt GS. 1983. Thermal kinetic differences between allelic isozymes of malate dehydrogenase (Mdh-B locus) of largemouth bass, *Micropterus salmoides. Biochem. Genet.* 21:1143–51

51. Hitzig BM, Wann-Cherng P, Burt T, Okunieff P, Johnson DC. 1994. ^{1}H-NMR measurement of fractional dissociation of imidazole in intact animals. *Am. J. Physiol.* 266:R1008–15

52. Hochachka PW, Somero GN. 1984. Temperature adaptation. In *Biochemical Adaptation,* pp. 355–449. Princeton: Princeton Univ. Press. 537 pp.

53. Hoffmann AA, Parsons PA. 1991. *Evolutionary Genetics and Environmental Stress.* Oxford: Oxford Univ. Press. 284 pp.

54. Holbrook JJ, Liljas A, Steindel SJ, Rossmann MG. 1975. Lactate dehydrogenase. In *The Enzymes,* ed. PD Boyer, 2:191–292. New York: Academic

55. Deleted in proof

56. Hottiger T, Boller T, Wiemken A. 1987. Rapid changes of heat and desiccation tolerance correlated with changes of trehalose content in *Saccharomyces cerevisiae* cells subjected to temperature shifts. *FEBS Lett.* 220:113–15

57. Hottiger T, Boller T, Wiemken A. 1989. Correlation of trehalose content and heat resistance in yeast mutants altered in the RAS/adenylate cyclase pathway: is trehalose a thermoprotectant? *FEBS Lett.* 255:432–34

58. Huber R, Kurr M. Jannasch HW, Stetter KO. 1989. A novel group of abyssal methogenic archaebacteria (*Methanopyrus*) growing at 100°C. *Nature* 342:833–34

59. Huey RB, Bennett AF. 1990. Physiological adjustments to fluctuating thermal environments: an ecological and evolutionary perspective. In *Stress Proteins in Biology and Medicine,* ed. R Morimoto, A Tissieres, C Georgopoulos, pp. 37–59. New York: Cold Spring Harbor Press

60. Huey RB, Kingsolver JG. 1989. Evolution of thermal sensitivity of ectotherm performance. *Trends Ecol. Evol.* 4:131–35

61. Huey RB, Kingsolver JG. 1993. Evolu-

tion of resistance to high temperature in ectotherms. *Am. Nat.* 142:S21–46

62. Huey RB, Partridge L, Fowler K. 1991. Thermal sensitivity of *Drosophila melanogaster* responds rapidly to laboratory natural selection. *Evolution* 45: 751–56

63. Hwang GC, Watabe S, Hashimoto K. 1990. Changes in carp myosin ATPase induced by temperature acclimation. *J. Comp. Physiol. B* 160:233–39

64. Imanaka T, Shibazaki M, Takagi M. 1986. A new way of enhancing the thermostability of proteases. *Nature* 324: 695–97

65. Jaenicke R. 1991. Protein folding: local structures, domains, subunits, and assemblies. *Biochemistry* 30:3147–61

66. Jaenicke R. 1991. Protein stability and molecular adaptation to extreme conditions. *Eur. J. Biochem.* 202:715–28

67. Johnston IA. 1983. Cellular responses to altered body temperature: the role of alterations in the expression of protein isoforms. See Ref. 20, pp. 121–43

68. Johnston IA, Walesby NJ. 1978. Molecular mechanisms of temperature adaptation in fish myofibrillar adenosine triphosphatases. *J. Comp. Physiol.* 119: 195–206

69. Joplin KH, Yocum GD, Denlinger DL. 1990. Cold shock elicits expression of heat shock proteins in the flesh fly, *Sarcophaga crassipalis. J. Insect Physiol.* 36:825–34

70. Klemenz R, Hultmark D, Gehring WJ. 1985. Selective translation of heat shock mRNA in *Drosophila melanogaster* depends on sequence information in the leader. *EMBO J.* 4:2053–60

71. Koban M, Graham G, Prosser CL. 1987. Induction of heat shock protein synthesis in teleost hepatocytes: effects of acclimation temperature. *Physiol. Zool.* 60: 645–50

72. Koehn RK. 1969. Esterase heterogeneity: Dynamics of a population. *Science* 163:943–44

73. Lavoie JN, Gingras-Breton G, Ranguay RM, Landry J. 1993. Induction of Chinese hamster *HSP27* gene expression in mouse cells confers resistance to heat shock. *J. Biol. Chem.* 268:3420–29

74. Lenski RE, Bennett AF. 1993. Evolutionary response of *Escherichia coli* to thermal stress. *Am. Nat.* 142:47–64 (Suppl.)

75. Li GC, Petersen NS, Mitchell HK. 1982. Induced thermal tolerance and heat shock protein synthesis in Chinese hamster ovary cells. *Br. J. Cancer* 45:132–36

76. Lin JJ, Somero GN. 1994. Thermal adaptation of cytoplasmic malate dehydro-

genases of eastern Pacific barracudas (genus *Sphyraena*): the role of differential isozyme expression. *J. Exp. Biol.* In press

77. Lin JJ, Somero GN. 1994. Temperature-dependent changes in expression of thermostable and thermolabile isozymes of cytoplasmic malate dehydrogenase (cMDH) in the eurythermal goby fish *Gillichthys mirabilis. Physiol. Zool.* In press

78. Lindquist S. 1986. The heat shock response. *Annu. Rev. Biochem.* 55:1151–91

79. Lindquist S, Craig EA. 1988. The heat-shock proteins. *Annu. Rev. Genet.* 22: 631–77

80. Loomis S, Carpenter JF, Crowe JH. 1988. Identification of strombine and taurine as cryoprotectants in the intertidal bivalve *Mytilus edulis. Biochim. Biophys. Acta* 943:113–18

81. Low PS, Bada JL, Somero GN. 1973. Temperature adaptation of enzymes: roles of the free energy, the enthalpy, and the entropy of activation. *Proc. Natl. Acad. Sci. USA* 70:430–32

82. Low PS, Somero GN. 1976. Adaptation of muscle pyruvate kinases to environmental temperature and pressure. *J. Exp. Zool.* 198:1–12

83. Malcolm BA, Wilson KP, Matthews BW, Kirsch JF, Wilson AC. 1990. Ancestral lysozymes reconstructed, neutrality tested, and thermostability linked to hydrocarbon packing. *Nature* 345:86–89

84. Maresca B, Patriarca E, Goldenberg C, Sacco M. 1988. Heat shock and cold adaptation in Antarctic fishes: a molecular approach. *Comp. Biochem. Physiol.* 90B:623–29

85. Martin J, Langer T, Boteva R, Schramel A, Horwich AL, et al. 1991. Chaperonin-mediated protein folding at the surface of groEL through a 'molten globule'–like intermediate. *Nature* 352:36–42

86. Matsumura M, Becktel WJ, Matthews BW. 1988. Hydrophobic stabilization in T4 lysozyme determined directly by multiple substitutions of Ile 3. *Nature* 334:406–10

87. Matsumura M, Signor G, Matthews BW. 1989. Substantial increase of protein stability by multiple disulphide bonds. *Nature* 342:291–93

88. Matthews BW. 1987. Genetic and structural analysis of the protein stability problem. *Biochemistry* 26:6885–88

89. Matthews BW. 1993. Structural and genetic analysis of protein stability. *Annu. Rev. Biochem.* 62:139–60

90. Matthews BW, Nicholson H, Becktel WJ. 1987. Enhanced protein thermosta-

bility from site–directed mutations that decrease entropy of unfolding. *Proc. Natl. Acad. Sci. USA* 84:6663–67

91. Mayr E. 1982. *The Growth of Biological Thought*, p. 67. Cambridge: Harvard Univ. Press. 974 pp.

92. McFall-Ngai M, Horwitz J. 1990. A comparative study of the thermal stability of the vertebrate eye lens: Antarctic fish to the desert iguana. *Exp. Eye Res.* 50:703–09

93. Merritt RB. 1972. Geographic distribution and enzymatic properties of lactate dehydrogenase allozymes in the fathead minnow, *Pimephales promelas*. *Am. Nat.* 106:174–84

94. Nei M. 1987. *Molecular Evolutionary Genetics*. New York: Columbia Univ. Press. 512 pp.

95. Nishiguchi MK, Somero GN. 1992. Temperature– and concentration–dependence of compatibility of the organic osmolyte β-dimethylsulfoniopropionate. *Cryobiology* 29:118–24

96. Nishiyama M, Matsubara N, Yamamoto K, Iijima S, Uozumi T, Beppu T. 1986. Nucleotide sequence of the malate dehydrogenase gene of *Thermus flavus* and its mutation directing an increase in enzyme activity. *J. Biol. Chem.* 261: 14178–83

97. Oda S, Matani H, Naruse K, Shima A. 1991. Synthesis of heat shock proteins in the isolated fin of the medaka, *Oryzias latipes*, acclimated to various temperatures. *Comp. Biochem. Physiol.* 98B: 587–91

98. Pace NR. 1991. Origin of life—facing up to the physical setting. *Cell* 65:531–33

99. Palleros DR, Welch WJ, Fink AL. 1991. Interaction of hsp70 with unfolded proteins: Effects of temperature and nucleotides on the kinetics of binding. *Proc. Natl. Acad. Sci. USA* 88:5719–23

100. Parsell, DA, Lindquist S. 1994. The function of heat-shock proteins in stress tolerance: degradation and reactivation of damaged proteins. *Annu. Rev. Genet.* 27:437–96

101. Phillip DP, Childers WF, Whitt GS. 1985. Correlations of allele frequencies with physical and environmental variables for populations of largemouth bass, *Micropterus salmoides* (Lacepede). *J. Fish Biol.* 27:347–65

102. Phipps BM, Typke D, Heger R, Volker S, Hoffmann A, et al. 1993. Structure of a molecular chaperone from a thermophilic archaebacterium. *Nature* 361: 475–77

103. Place AR, Powers DA. 1979. Genetic variation and relative catalytic efficiencies: Lactate dehydrogenase B allozymes of *Fundulus heteroclitus*. *Proc. Natl. Acad. Sci. USA* 76:2354–56

104. Place AR, Powers DA. 1984. Purification and characterization of the lactate dehydrogenase (LDH-B_4) allozymes of *Fundulus heteroclitus*. *J. Biol. Chem.* 259:1309–18

105. Plesset J, Ludwig JR, Cox BS, McLaughlin CS. 1987. Effect of cell cycle position on thermotolerance in *Saccharomyces cerevisiae*. *J. Bact.* 169: 779–84

106. Poteete AR, Sun D-P, Nicholson H, Matthews BW. 1991. Second-site revertants of an inactive T4 lysozyme mutant restore activity by restructuring the active site cleft. *Biochemistry* 30:1425–32

107. Powers DA, Ropson I, Brown DC, Van Beneden R, Cashon R, et al. 1986. Genetic variation in *Fundulus heteroclitus*: geographic distribution. *Am. Zool.* 26: 131–44

108. Powers DA, Smith M, Gonzalez-Villasenor I, DiMichelle L, Crawford D, et al. 1993. A multidisciplinary approach to the selectionist/neutralist controversy using the model teleost, *Fundulus heteroclitus*. In *Oxford Surveys in Evolutionary Biology*, ed. D Futuyma, J Antonovics, 9:43–107. Oxford: Oxford Univ. Press

109. Privalov PL, Gill SJ. 1989. The hydrophobic effect: a reappraisal. *Pure Appl. Chem.* 61:1097–104

110. Prosser CL, Heath JE. 1990. Temperature. In *Comparative Animal Physiology, Fourth Ed.: Environmental and Metabolic Animal Physiology*, pp. 109–65. New York: Wiley-Liss. 578 pp.

111. Rabindran SK, Haroun RI, Clos J, Wisniewshi J, Wu C. 1993. Regulation of heat shock factor trimer formation: Role of a conserved leucine zipper. *Science* 259:230–34

112. Raymond JA. 1992. Glycerol is a colligative antifreeze in some northern fishes. *J. Exp. Zool.* 262:347–52

113. Reeves RB. 1977. The interaction of body temperature and acid-base balance in ectothermic vertebrates. *Annu. Rev. Physiol.* 39:559–86

114. Reeves RB. 1985. Alphastat regulation of intracellular acid-base state? In *Circulation, Respiration, and Metabolism*, ed R Gilles, pp. 414–23. Berlin: Springer-Verlag

115. Riabowol KT, Mizzen LA, Welch WJ. 1988. Heat shock is lethal to fibroblasts microinjected with antibodies against HSP70. *Science* 242:433–36

116. Roberts SJ, Lowery MS, Somero GN. 1988. Regulation of binding of phos-

phofructokinase to myofibrils in the red and white muscle of the barred sand bass, *Paralabrax nebulifer* (Serranidae). *J. Exp. Biol.* 137:13–27

117. Sanchez Y, Lindquist SL. 1990. HSP104 required for induced thermotolerance. *Science* 248:1112–15

118. Schultes V, Deutzmann R, Jaenicke R. 1990. Complete amino acid sequence of glyceraldehyde-3-phosphate dehydrogenase from the hyperthermophilic eubacterium *Thermotoga maritima. Eur. J. Biochem.* 192:25–31

119. Schwantes MLB, Schwantes AR. 1982. Adaptive features of ectothermic enzymes. I. Temperature effects on the malate dehydrogenase from a temperate fish *Leiostomus xanthurus. Comp. Biochem. Physiol.* 72B:49–58

120. Schwantes MLB, Schwantes AR. 1982. Adaptive features of ectothermic enzymes. II. The effects of acclimation temperature on malate dehydrogenase of the spot, *Leiostomus xanthurus. Comp. Biochem. Physiol.* 72B:59–64

121. Siebenaller JF, Murray TF. 1994. The effects of hydrostatic pressure on the low-K_m GTPase in brain membranes from two congeneric marine fishes. *J. Comp. Physiol. B* 163:626–32

122. Simon J-P, Potuin C, Blanchard M-H. 1983. Thermal adaptation and acclimation of higher plants at the enzyme level: kinetic properties of NAD malate dehydrogenase and glutamate oxaloacetate transaminase in two genotypes of *Arabidopsis thaliana* (Brassicaceae). *Oecologia* 60:143–48

123. Simon J-P, Charest C, Peloquin M-J. 1986. Adaptation and acclimation of higher plants at the enzyme level: kinetic properties of NAD malate dehydrogenase in three species of *Viola. J. Ecol.* 74:19–32

124. Somero GN. 1975. The role of isozymes in adaptation to varying temperatures. In *Isozymes II: Physiological Function,* ed. CL Markert, pp. 221–34. New York: Academic

125. Somero GN. 1981. pH-temperature interactions on proteins: principles of optimal pH and buffer system design. *Marine Biol. Lett.* 2:163–78

126. Somero GN. 1986. Protons, osmolytes, and fitness of the internal milieu for protein function. *Am. J. Physiol.* 251: R197–213

127. Somero GN. 1986. Protein adaptation and biogeography: Threshold effects on molecular evolution. *Trends Ecol. Evol.* 1:124–27

128. Somero GN. 1991. Biochemical mechanisms of cold adaptation and steno-

thermality in Antactic fish. In *Biology of Antarctic Fish,* ed. G di Prisco, B Maresca, B Tota, pp. 232–47. Berlin: Springer-Verlag

129. Somero GN, DeVries AL. 1967. Temperature tolerance of some Antarctic fishes. *Science* 156:257–58

130. Somero GN, Lowery MS, Roberts SJ. 1991. Compartmentation of animal enzymes: physiological and evolutionary significance. *Am. Zool.* 31:493–503

131. Somero GN, Yancey PH. 1994. Organic osmolytes. In *Handbook of Physiology: Cell Physiology,* ed. J Hoffman, J Jamieson. Oxford: Oxford Univ. Press. In press

132. Stetter KO, Fiala G, Huber G, Huber R, Segerer A. 1990. Hyperthermophilic microorganisms. *FEMS Microbiol. Rev.* 75:117–24

133. Swezey RR, Somero GN. 1982. Polymerization thermodynamics and structural stabilities of skeletal muscle actins from vertebrates adapted to different temperatures and pressures. *Biochemistry* 21:4496–503

134. Timasheff SN. 1992. A physicochemical basis for the selection of osmolytes by Nature. In *Water and Life,* ed. GN Somero, CB Osmond, CL Bolis, pp. 70–84. Berlin: Springer-Verlag

135. Trent JD, Chastain RA, Yayanos AA. 1984. Possible artefactual basis for apparent bacterial growth at 250°C. *Nature* 307:737–40

136. Trent JD, Nimmesgern E, Wall JS, Hartl RU, Horwich AL. 1991. A molecular chaperone from a thermophilic archaebacterium is related to the eukaryotic protein t-complex polypeptide-1. *Nature* 354:490–93

137. Trent JD, Osipiuk J, Pinkau T. 1990. Acquired thermotolerance and heat shock in the extremely thermophilic archaebacterium *Sulfolobus* sp. Strain B12. *J. Bact.* 172:1478–84

138. Tyurin VA, Kagan VE, Shukolyukov SA, Klaan NK, Nivikov NK, Azizova OA. 1979. Thermal stability of rhodopsin and protein-lipid interactions in the photoreceptor membranes of homeothermic and poikilothermic animals. *J. Therm. Biol.* 4:203–8

138. Ureta T. 1978. The role of isozymes in metabolism: A model of metabolic pathways as the basis for the biological role of isozymes. *Curr. Top. Cell. Reg.* 13: 233–58

139. Watt WB. 1977. Adaptation at specific loci. I. Natural selection on phosphoglucose isomerase of *Colias* butterflies: Biochemical and population aspects. *Genetics* 87:177–94

140. Watt WB, Boggs CL. 1987. Allelic isozymes as probes of the evolution of metabolic organization. *Isozymes: Curr. Top. Biol. Med. Res.* 15:27–47

141. Watt WB, Cassin RC, Swan MS. 1983. Adaptation at specific loci. III. Field behavior and survivorship differences among *Colias* PGI genotypes are predictable from in vitro biochemistry. *Genetics* 103:725–39

142. Welch WJ. 1992. Mammalian stress response: Cell physiology, structure/function of stress proteins, and implications for medicine and disease. *Physiol. Rev.* 72:1063–81

143. White RH. 1984. Hydrolytic stability of biomolecules at high temperatures and its implication for life at 250°C. *Nature* 310:430–33

144. Wilkinson AJ, Fersht AR, Blow DM, Carter P, Winter G. 1984. A large increase in enzyme-substrate affinity by protein engineering. *Nature* 307:187–88

145. Wilson TL. 1977. Interrelations between pH and temperature for the catalytic rate of the M_4 isozyme of lactate dehydrogenase (EC 1.1.1.27) from goldfish (*Carassius auratus* L.). *Arch. Biochem. Biophys.* 179:378–90

146. Yancey PH, Clark ME, Hand SC, Bowlus RD, Somero GN. 1983. Living with water stress: Evolution of osmolyte systems. *Science* 217:1214–22

147. Yancey PH, Siebenaller JF. 1987. Coenzyme binding ability of homologs of M_4-lactate dehydrogenase in temperature adaptation. *Biochim. Biophys. Acta* 924:483–91

148. Yancey PH, Somero GN. 1978. Temperature dependence of intracellular pH: its role in the conservation of pyruvate K_m values of vertebrate lactate dehydrogenase. *J. Comp. Physiol. B* 125:129–34

149. Yocum GD, Joplin KH, Denlinger DL. 1991. Expression of heat shock proteins in response to high and low temperature extremes in diapausing pharate larvae of the gypsy moth. *Arch. Insect Biochem. Physiol.* 18:239–49

150. Zachariassen KE. 1985. Physiology of cold tolerance in insects. *Physiol. Rev.* 65:799–832

151. Zamer WE, Hoffmann RJ. 1989. Allozymes of glucose-6-phosphate isomerase differentially modulate pentose shunt metabolism in the sea anemone *Metridium senile. Proc. Natl. Acad. Sci. USA* 86:2737–41

152. Zwickl P, Fabry S, Bogedain C, Haas A, Hensel R. 1990. Glyceraldehyde-3-phosphate dehydrogenase from the hyperthermophilic archaebacterium *Pyrococcus woesei:* Characterization of the enzyme, cloning and sequencing of the gene, and expression in *Escherichia coli. J. Bact.* 172:4329–38

Annu. Rev. Physiol. 1995. 57:69–95

THE EVOLUTION OF ENDOTHERMY IN MAMMALS AND BIRDS: From Physiology to Fossils

John Ruben

Zoology Department, Oregon State University, Corvallis, Oregon 97331–2914

KEY WORDS: avian endothermy, mammalian endothermy, dinosaur endothermy

INTRODUCTION

Continuous, metabolically based maintenance of high and relatively stable body temperature in the face of greatly fluctuating ambient temperature is among the most remarkable attributes of mammals and birds. Such warm-bloodedness or, more correctly, endothermic homeothermy, generally results from a combination of high resting, aerobically supported heat production rates (about five- to tenfold that of reptiles) in virtually all soft tissues, and insulation sufficient to retard excessive heat loss. As a consequence, many temperature-sensitive physiological processes in birds and mammals proceed at relatively stable rates over a wide range of ambient temperatures.

In contrast, most organisms cannot thermoregulate in this way because endogenous heat production is insufficient to alter body temperature, and internal heat is necessarily derived primarily from the environment (ectothermic poikilothermy). These organisms tend to be thermoconformers whose body temperature frequently corresponds passively with environmental temperature. Usually such thermoconformity in thermally homogeneous environments (e.g. many marine or freshwater ecosystems) does not result in severe physiological disruption: genetic adaptation and/or phenotypic acclimation of numerous biochemical traits to ecologically relevant temperatures often ameliorate effects of temperature (e.g. enzyme function; G Somero, this volume) and membrane structure (J Hazel, this volume; see also 63).

69

Air has minimal thermal conductivity, and many, but not all, ectothermic terrestrial species are surprisingly adept at diurnal behavioral thermoregulation via basking (for solar radiation) and microhabitat selection (69). Although they are essentially nocturnal thermoconformers, a number of lizards seasonally maintain relatively constant diurnal body temperature, often significantly higher than ambient temperatures, and similar to that of many birds and mammals (3). Some particularly large tropical lizards (e.g. *Varanus komodoensis*) even achieve near–homeothermy by virtue of their relatively small surface area:volume ratio and correspondingly low rate of nocturnal heat loss (inertial homeothermy) (89). It is quite possible that many of the earliest (Paleozoic) reptiles maintained diurnal temperatures similar to those of their living descendants including birds and mammals (see below).

Birds and mammals maintain constant deep body temperatures largely by (*a*) minimizing thermal conductance with fur or feathers and, in some cases, by storing significant amount of fat subcutaneously (reptiles maintain fat stores internally), and (*b*) sustaining metabolic heat production equivalent to the rate at which body heat is lost to the environment. To compensate for particularly accelerated rates of heat loss, oxygen consumption increases at cold ambient temperatures. There is also a range of ambient temperatures over which heat production rates are minimal (basal metabolic rate or BMR) and constant.

In response to ambient cold, enhanced heat production in birds is achieved primarily by shivering thermogenesis (114), especially via isometric contraction of antagonistic groups of flight muscles (83). Most mammals also shiver in response to acute cold exposure (62). In response to long–term cold exposure, many placental mammals also rely on nonshivering thermogenesis (NST) for accelerated rates of metabolic heat production (66). NST results from hormonally mediated elevation of metabolic rate and is occasionally two to four times greater than basal rates (49). Brown adipose tissue (brown fat), a specialized thermogenic tissue, is closely associated with NST in some placental mammals, especially hibernating and/or cold-adapted mammals, as well as in the newborn of many species (61, 108).

A few snakes (e.g. *Python*) and some large-size fish (including some billfish, tunas, and lamnid sharks) are able to maintain somewhat greater than ambient core or deep body temperatures (17, 110). This is accomplished in brooding female pythons by enhanced heat production via powerful, spasmodic axial muscle contractions. Fish combine high activity levels with well–developed vascular countercurrent heat exchange (*rete mirable*) systems; some taxa utilize highly specialized heater cells that help to elevate central nervous system temperatures.

However, endothermy in those taxa is not truly comparable to that of birds and mammals: In the absence of constant heat-generating skeletal muscle contractions, it is unlikely that sufficient heat is generated to maintain elevated whole–body temperatures. In any case, body temperature in these taxa is not known to exceed ambient temperature by more than about 10–25°C. Thus the source and magnitude of caloric expenditure as well as the stability and marked elevation of body temperature associated with avian and mammalian endothermy are truly unique among the Metazoa.

Although endothermy is thought to have evolved independently in birds and mammals (76), the specific factor(s) responsible for the origin of avian and, especially, mammalian endothermy has historically been the subject of considerable speculation and debate. A broad range of selective factors resulting in the evolution of avian and mammalian endothermy has been proposed including (but not limited to) selection for (a) increased brain size (70), (b) improved postural attributes (24), (c) enhanced thermoregulatory capacity (17, 34, 85), and (d) increased aerobic capacity during exercise (15, 102). Hypotheses c and d are the most generally accepted. In the most traditional, thermoregulatory hypothesis, the evolution of high resting metabolic rate in mammals has been attributed primarily to selection for endothermically based thermoregulation in early (Mesozoic) mammals and their ancestors, the cynodont therapsid reptiles. Selection for high and stable body temperature is hypothesized to have optimized thermally dependent rate processes and, thereby, to have facilitated niche expansion, e.g. extended periods of diel trophic activity and/or ability to survive generally cooler environments.

On the basis of a relatively constant ratio of maximal:minimal oxygen consumption rates in a variety of active ecto- and endothermic tetrapods, the aerobic capacity model suggests that the initial factor responsible for the evolution of high avian and mammalian resting metabolic rates was, instead, selection for increased powers of sustainable, aerobically supported physical activity. According to this scenario, elevated avian and mammalian metabolic rates were initially advantageous for generation of higher levels of sustainable activity. Therefore, the original selective advantages of elevated aerobic metabolic rates had little or nothing to do with selection for increased resting metabolic rates or thermoregulatory powers. However, chronic selection for expansion of aerobically supported activity levels, combined with the described linkage of resting and active metabolic rates, led simultaneously to elevated rates of resting oxygen consumption. Eventually, resting oxygen consumption rates in birds and mammals were sufficiently elevated to achieve endothermic homeothermy.

A variety of illuminating data relating to the biology and paleontology of endothermy have appeared within the past decade. The robustness of any theory on the origin of endothermy hinges on its consistency with this new data base. In the following pages, I review our current understanding of pertinent aspects of the physiology of avian and mammalian endothermy with a view toward synthesis of the most likely scenario for the origin of endothermy in these taxa. I also review the metabolic status of the therapsid reptiles and dinosaurs, long–extinct ancestors, respectively, of mammals and birds.

THE EVOLUTIONARY PHYSIOLOGY OF AVIAN AND MAMMALIAN ENDOTHERMY

Thermal Conductance in Birds and Mammals

Very early [200 million years (My) ago] mammals have occasionally been modeled as small (50 gm) "metabolic reptiles" with fur coats (34). However, merely placing an insulatory layer on a reptile does not, by itself, result in significant homeothermy, as Cowles clearly demonstrated by dressing lizards in custom–cut mink coats (33). Nevertheless, in order to maintain constant body temperature over often widely varied ambient temperatures, most birds and mammals require insulative covering sufficient to block excessive heat loss. Compared to extant reptiles, the presence of feathers or fur and, often, subcutaneously stored fat, considerably reduces rates of conductive heat loss to the environment in small to medium-size birds and mammals. To masses of ~10 kg, thermal conductance (Joules $g^{-1}/h^{-1}/°C^{-1}$) in endotherms scales at least an order of magnitude less than for reptiles of equivalent size. However, because of small surface area:volume ratios, large reptiles (>20–30 kg) probably have thermal conductance values that approach those of large mammals (89).

These data suggest that hypothetical endothermic homeothermy in small dinosaurs and mammal–like reptiles without feathers or fur was unlikely to have been achieved in a manner similar to that of modern endotherms (109).

Temperature Set Point and Resting Metabolic Rate

High body temperature (i.e. 37–42°C) is typical of many, but not all, birds and mammals. Body temperatures of egg–laying mammals, the monotremes [echidnas (*Bradypus*) and the platypus (*Ornithorhynchus*)], are maintained normally at 30–32°C (107), considerably below those of most placental mammals (~36–39°C) (90), marsupial mammals (35°C), and birds (37–42°C) (39). This discrepancy has been widely viewed as symptomatic of the physiologically primitive position of monotremes, somewhere below the intermediate marsupials and higher eutherian mammals. However, there is no compelling reason to regard lower body temperature as physiologically inferior or primitive. Monotreme temperatures are similar to those reported for several placental mammals including some edentates and insectivores (37, 41). Echidnas and platypus are good thermoregulators during acute cold exposure, regulating temperature and increasing heat production down to or below freezing ambient temperatures (107).

Metabolic rates in mammals may vary with nutritional status (75) and dietary habits (88), but basal rates in monotremes are low compared to those of most other mammals and birds (20, 39, 55, 80, 87). However, temperature–corrected metabolic rates (i.e. accounting for Q_{10} effects) in echidnas are within 5% of the mean for all mammals and nonpasserine birds (106). In contrast, temperature–corrected resting metabolic values for all reptiles are only about 10–20% of the mean for endotherms (14). Previously reported intermediate oxygen consumption data for some large turtles (93) are no longer considered valid (see below). Similarly, some insectivore placental mammals [e.g. hedgehogs (*Erinacea*), and tenrecs (*Tenrec, Setifer*)] are reported to have reptilian–type energetics (34), but basal rates of these taxa are also about fivefold those of equivalent-size reptiles (86). A significant increment above reptilian resting metabolic rates has occurred in all mammalian and avian orders, which suggests the presence of fully developed endothermy in Mesozoic Era members of these groups (see below).

Low resting metabolic rates of extant reptiles are not necessarily associated with minimal body temperature or unsophisticated temperature control mechanisms. As in endotherms, the reptilian hypothalamus is the primary thermostatic control center (5), and many lizards thermoregulate behaviorally during extended periods of diurnal activity at body temperatures that overlap those of endotherms (3). Mammals, birds, and a number of extant reptiles also exhibit an adaptive, endotherm–like fever response in which the thermoregulatory set point is elevated significantly (e.g. from 37.4 to 39.6°C in the lizard *Dipsosaurus*) by the action of endogenous and exogenous pyrogens on the hypothalamus (50, 77). Accordingly, attainment of avian or mammalian metabolic status need not have involved radical modification of ancestral thermostatic sensors or temperature regimes maintained behaviorally by the reptilian progenitors of these groups.

Whatever the primitive mammalian thermostatic set point might have been, it remains unclear if endothermic, or near–endothermic, metabolic status in Early Mesozoic "proto-mammals" was accompanied by simultaneous development of the typical mammalian pattern of homeothermy. Monotremes are not homeothermic when inactive in chronic cold (e.g. 10°C ambient), and body temperature of a number of primitive therian taxa appears variable, especially during activity (2, 34, 38).

Avian and mammalian hibernation, torpor, and estivation (when body temperature is allowed to fall well below normothermic levels) represent tightly controlled, adaptive responses to seasonal cold or aridity; they are not a regression to a more primitive, ectothermic pattern of metabolism and body temperature control (113).

Activity Metabolism in Reptiles, Birds, and Mammals

Most animals use aerobically based metabolism to fuel low to moderate levels of activity. As activity level (e.g. running speed) increases, oxygen consumption rises to meet increased demand for ATP production. Activity requiring power output in excess of that supported by oxygen consumption is fueled by anaerobic metabolism, via lactic acid production. In comparison to the aerobic capacities of endotherms, maximal oxygen consumption and aerobic scope in ectotherms are proportionately as low as resting metabolic rate (11). During maximal activity, oxygen consumption in active reptiles can be increased by about tenfold at any particular body temperature. Thus at body temperatures characteristic of endotherms, oxygen consumption levels in a number of max-imally active ectotherms are approximately equal to resting metabolic rates in many mammals and birds (6). Most mammals and birds are also capable of increasing oxygen consumption by an average of tenfold or more (62). Levels of aerobic metabolism achieved by endotherms are therefore considerably in excess of those attained by reptiles. For example, resting and active rates of oxygen consumption in a 1–kg snake (*Masticophis*) at 35°C are about 1.7 and 16 cc $O_2 \cdot min^{-1}$, respectively; comparable values for a 1–kg mammal, the potaroo (*Potorous*), are 10 and 130 cc $O_2 \cdot min^{-1}$ (62, 101). Although ratios of resting:maximal rates of oxygen consumption are similar, the capacity of endotherms for supporting activity aerobically exceeds that of ectotherms by an order of magnitude (15).

Routine patterns of activity in reptiles, mammals, and birds reflect these variations in activity metabolism. In comparison to aerobic potential, net cost of locomotion in terrestrial vertebrates is high, and even modest levels of activity quickly outpace the aerobic scopes of ectothermic vertebrates. The metabolic power that can be obtained anaerobically dwarfs the meager aerobic capacities of most ectothermic vertebrates, and moderate levels of activity in these taxa appear attainable only with the support of anaerobiosis. This pattern of activity physiology is capable of supporting moderate to high rates of exercise for only about 2 to 5 min. Consequently, terrestrial ectotherms lack stamina for moderate activity and exhaust relatively quickly. Recovery is often slow and hours are sometimes required for complete restoration to the preactive resting condition (15).

The ectothermic pattern of activity physiology was profoundly altered dur-ing the parallel evolution of birds and mammals. Expansion of aerobic scope has resulted in substantially increased routine activity levels, stamina, and endurance. Accordingly, compared to most reptiles, the incidence of lower power, but higher-endurance, oxidative–type skeletal muscle fibers is greatly increased in birds and mammals (23, 96). Maximal sustainable speeds of mammals are six- to sevenfold those of lizards of equal size, and long distance, sustained flapping flight is clearly beyond the metabolic capacities of modern reptiles (15).

The evolution of endothermy has not, apparently, resulted in elevation of maximal total metabolic rate (aerobic + anaerobic contribution) during burst levels of activity (103), and maximal, nonsustainable running speeds of mammals and lizards are not significantly different (51). This is because in all animals anaerobic metabolism provides the additional energy required at speeds in excess of those at which oxygen consumption becomes maximal. In ectotherms, lactate production provides absolutely and proportionately more energy for burst activity than does anaerobiosis in endotherms. Accordingly, maximal running speeds in mammals are generally only about twice sustainable levels, in comparison with 10- to 30-fold increments in lizards (15).

Clearly, capacities for, and consequences of, anaerobiosis play a greater role in influencing behavior in the lower vertebrates than in mammals and birds. The ectothermic ancestors of endotherms would similarly have been subject to these behavioral constraints of low stamina.

Oxygen Delivery Systems in Birds and Mammals

Aerobic metabolic rates consistent with routine avian and mammalian activity levels markedly exceed capacities of reptilian oxygen delivery systems. Endothermy was probably associated with the evolution of appropriately expanded pulmonary and cardiovascular systems. Accordingly, compared to extant reptiles, birds and mammals exhibit increased lung vascularization and ventilation rates, expanded cardiovascular function, and blood oxygen carrying capacities, as well as elevated tissue vascularization, myoglobin levels, and oxygen extraction rates (115).

There are, however, marked avian vs mammalian differences in these attributes that emphasize independent origin of endothermy in birds and mammals. For example, (a) the avian lung extracts oxygen from inhaled air at about twice the efficiency as the mammalian lung (ca 40 vs 20%), and resting birds usually breathe at about 30–50% the frequency of equivalent-size mammals (79). Typically, birds maintain greater tidal volumes (air volume/breath), yet have relatively smaller vascularized portions of their lungs (79). During the respiratory cycle, the avian lung maintains a constant volume through the bellows–like action of its nonvascularized air sacs, which generate a one-way flow of air through the parabronchi and a cross-current pattern of air-capillary gas exchange (105). The mammalian lung is ventilated largely by a muscular diaphragm that functions to alter lung volume and to generate a bidirectional flow of air across gas exchange surfaces (alveoli) (115); (b) birds, unlike mammals, possess an atrio-ventricular ring of Purkinje fibers on the right side of the heart that runs up and around the right atrio-ventricular valve (36), and avian cardiac stroke volume, output, and arterial pressure generally exceed those parameters in mammals (95); (c) avian red blood cells are nucleated and larger than the enucleated red blood cells of mammals; and (d) mammals retain the left aortic arch, while birds retain the right arch.

Enhanced oxygen delivery systems in mammals seem to have evolved in association with the requisites of activity physiology, rather than for support of elevated resting metabolic rates per se. For example, the mammalian diaphragm, a respiration-ventilation support structure that probably appeared about the time of origin of endothermy, seems essential to facilitate rates of aerobiosis required during exercise. It is, however, superfluous for maintenance of resting metabolism and endothermic homeothermy (104). Additionally, aerobic metabolic rates in a number of active lizards (e.g. *Varanus*) overlap resting oxygen consumption rates of many endotherms (6, 9). Thus it is possible, but unlikely, that Mesozoic Era ancestors of birds or mammals might have achieved endothermic rates of resting metabolism utilizing preexisting reptilian oxygen delivery systems.

Endothermy at the Organ and Tissue Level

It has long been recognized that about 70% of heat production at rest in humans is generated by the internal organs (i.e. liver, kidneys, brain, heart, intestines), even though they comprise only about 8% of total body mass (1). There is increasing evidence that two related factors largely account for the increment in mammalian vs reptilian resting oxygen consumption rates: (a) In mammals, the internal organs are more massive than those structures in reptiles, and (b) mass–specific metabolic rates of mammalian internal organs are markedly greater than in reptiles.

The major internal organs (including liver, kidney, heart, and brain) of the bearded dragon lizard (*Amphibolurus*) comprise 5.3% of total body mass compared to 10% in the laboratory mouse (*Mus*). Mammalian internal organ mass scales according to the equation $0.18 \ M^{0.83}$, while similar structures in reptiles scale at $0.14 \ M^{0.75}$ (M = grams body mass). Consequently, not only are internal organ mass elevations, or a constants, greater in mammals, but doubling of reptilian body mass results in an average increment of 54% in internal organ size, while doubling body mass in mammals is accompanied by a 68% increase in internal organ mass. These values correspond well with mass doubling–related increments in total resting metabolic rate in these taxa (i.e. 54 and 71% for reptiles and mammals, respectively) (43, 71). In birds, relative heart mass, kidney mass, and resting metabolism also scale equivalently to increasing body mass (35).

Variation in ectotherm-endotherm resting metabolic rate is also mirrored by in vitro oxygen consumption rates of tissues from the internal organs. When incubated at similar temperatures (37°C), slices of liver, kidney, and brain from the laboratory rat (*Rattus*) had mass–specific oxygen consumption rates approximately 4.3, 3.8, and 1.6 times as great as oxygen consumption rates of similar tissue slices from the lizard *Amphibolurus* (19, 44).

Unlike the minor contribution of striated musculature to resting metabolism, energy production (both aerobic and anaerobic) during exercise is primarily a product of the skeletal muscles, which comprise about 45% of total body mass in mammals. At the organ and tissue level, factors underlying high metabolic capacity of the striated musculature in endotherms are similar to those associated with high resting metabolic rate of the viscera: In mammals each unit mass of skeletal muscle has a relatively high capacity for active metabolic rate, and there is proportionately more total mass of skeletal muscle in most endotherms than is present in ectotherms. Mammalian skeletal muscle mass (in grams) scales at $0.42M^{1.01}$, compared to $0.19M^{1.09}$ in reptiles (42), and potential maximal oxygen consumption rates (as indexed by cytochrome oxidase activity•mg wet tissue^{-1}min^{-1}) rates in skeletal muscle of the lab rat and the lizards *Sauromalas* and *Varanus* approximate variation in maximal rates of aerobiosis in these taxa (8).

The Cellular Physiology of Endothermy

The primary function of animal substrate metabolism is to sustain mitochondrial synthesis of ATP, the biologically widespread and readily usable form of energy, for varied kinds of work. Metabolically generated heat is usually a by-product of biochemical inefficiencies associated with the synthesis and utilization of ATP. There is a consistent difference between the mitochondrial membrane surface area of a variety of tissues from endotherms and ectotherms that indicates cellular and even subcellular bases for the increased metabolic rate of endotherms.

Mitochondrial membrane surfaces house the enzymes largely responsible for aerobic metabolism (e.g. cytochrome oxidase, the terminal respiratory enzyme that is also responsible for oxygen consumption), and expanded mitochondrial surface can reasonably be expected to correlate with greater tissue enzyme levels and higher overall metabolic rates. Electron microscopy indicates that in liver, kidney, heart, and brain tissue of the rat, total mitochondrial membrane surface area averages about fourfold greater than in similar organs from lizards (43). Approximately half of this difference stems from the relatively larger mass of these metabolically active tissues in endotherms (see above), and the other half from greater mitochondrial density in these tissues. Accordingly, mass–specific tissue cytochrome oxidase enzyme activity from visceral tissues (expressed as nmol O_2•mg wet tissue^{-1}min^{-1}) in endotherms also averages about twice the enzymatic activity of ectotherms (71). Thus tissues from organs largely responsible for resting metabolic rate show increases in total mitochondrial membrane surface area and oxidative enzyme activity levels that approximate the variation in resting metabolism between ectotherms and endotherms.

These findings help clarify cellular-subcellular energy sources associated with increased resting metabolic rates in endotherms. They also provide evidence for an incremental transition from ectotherm to endotherm resting metabolic rates. In endotherms, visceral tissue mitochondrial membrane density and mass–specific aerobic enzymatic activity are each twice those of the same tissues in ectotherms. Consequently, individual mitochondria of ecto- and endotherms are essentially similar, at least relative to their mitochondrial-specific metabolic rates. Perhaps mammalian and, by extension avian, resting metabolic rates evolved by simple, incremental addition of relatively unmodified visceral mitochondria in Paleozoic and/or Mesozoic Era proto-mammals and birds. The ontogeny of endothermy in mammals seems to recapitulate the evolutionary scenario described above: In the tamar wallaby (*Macropus*), a postnatal increment in resting metabolic rate (from ectothermic to endothermic levels) closely tracks a proportionate, incremental expansion of visceral tissue mitochondrial-membrane surface area (73).

Active or maximal metabolic rates are determined largely by skeletal and cardiac muscles. Compared to their weight in reptiles, skeletal and cardiac muscles in small to medium–size mammals are about 30 and 65% more massive, respectively. Total skeletal and cardiac mitochondrial-membrane surface area in mammals is about 220 and 290% that of reptiles (43). This membrane surface-area differential is not as great as the fourfold difference for the internal organs, but mitochondrial membranes isolated from mammalian skeletal muscle have about twice the enzymatic activity (mg^{-1} mitochondrial protein) of those isolated from reptilian muscle (71). Consequently, unlike visceral mitochondria, which are associated with maintenance of resting metabolism, those supporting skeletal muscular activity in endotherms seem to have undergone qualitative, as well as quantitative changes, compared to muscle mitochondria of reptiles (i.e. compared with ectotherm-endotherm alterations in visceral mitochondria, there is relatively less elevation of total mitochondrial-membrane density in muscle tissue of endotherms, but each unit of mitochondrial-membrane surface area is capable of generating about twice the metabolic power of most visceral mitochondrial membranes).

Differences in the power output capacity of mitochondrial membranes from muscle vs visceral tissue of endotherms invite speculation regarding why such variation might have evolved. The histology of ecto- and endotherm striated muscle fibers is relatively conservative in both the range of muscle fiber diameter, as well as with respect to myofibrillar architecture (53, 57). Presumably, this conservatism is related to intracellular limitations on optimal gas and nutrient diffusion distances (especially in red, high-endurance fibers), as well as to functional constraints associated with the intracellular packing of contractile proteins (64). Additionally, electron microscopy suggests that in skeletal muscle, maximal mitochondrial fat oxidation rate is tightly linked to the magnitude of surface area contact between individual mitochondria and cytoplasmic lipid droplet stores (30). Together these factors might well have imposed restrictions on the quantity of mitochondrial-membrane surface area that could have been added to striated or cardiac muscle fibers during the course of avian and mammalian evolution. Perhaps the solution to this problem was simply to add relatively fewer but higher–power mitochondria to these muscle fibers. Liver, kidney, and brain cells seem to have enhanced their capacity for mitochondrial power output by simply increasing quantities of relatively unmodified ectothermal–type mitochondria.

An increase in individual mitochondrial power output and/or net mitochondrial membrane density helps to identify expanded sources of energy required to sustain endothermic metabolic rates. These data do not, however, account for physiological attributes of birds and mammals that necessitate the generation of elevated quantities of metabolic energy. A partial explanation might involve the nature of mammalian and avian plasma membranes and maintenance of their sodium potassium ion gradients. These gradients, which are generated by Na^+-K^+-ATPase pumps (sodium pumps), are necessary for support of a variety of functions including action potential generation and the active cellular uptake of organic molecules (e.g. amino acids, sugars, etc) for cellular nutrition and protein synthesis (31). The plasma membranes of pigeon (*Columba*) liver cells and lab rat liver and kidney cells, when compared to those of lizards, seem particularly leaky to Na^+ and K^+ ions (72). These leaky plasma membranes apparently require generation of significantly increased levels of metabolic energy in order to maintain normal solute concentration gradients at the plasma membrane (i.e. relatively high $[K^+]$ at the inner surface and relatively high $[Na^+]$ at the outer surface) (44).

This increased leakiness in mammalian plasma membranes is correlated with marked elevation (~50–60%) of tissue protein and phospholipid concentrations. Compared to reptiles, there is also a qualitative alteration in plasma membrane phospholipid composition, at least in the mammalian liver and kidney. Plasma membranes from each of these organs in mammals have significantly reduced total unsaturated fatty acids, but a 35% greater concentration of polyunsaturated fatty acids (greater unsaturation index). In addition, certain long-chain polyunsaturated fatty acids, specifically arachidonic and docosahexanoic acids, 20– and 22–carbon phospholipids, respectively, are relatively more plentiful. Another polyunsaturated long-chain fatty acid, linoleic acid (18–carbon), occurs with less frequency in mammals than in reptiles (71).

These changes in membrane protein and phospholipid composition may well be causally linked to increased leakiness and, ultimately, to the increased metabolic cost of plasma membrane ion-gradient maintenance in the cells of endotherms. Compared to reptiles, mammals exhibit increased metabolic sensitivity to thyroxin. In incubated mammalian liver slices, metabolic rate, mitochondrial-membrane surface area, membrane polyunsaturated fatty acid composition, and liver transmembrane Na^+-K^+ flux are all enhanced by increased thyroxin levels (19, 74). Additionally, there is an inverse relationship between increasing body weight vs mass–specific metabolic rate and cardiac tissue concentrations of docosahexanoic acid, one of the phospholipids that occurs in especially high concentrations in mammalian liver and kidney cells (56).

The evolution of these leaky, supposedly inefficient, plasma membranes in endotherms was proposed to be a necessary link for increased thermogenesis, rather than to fulfill expanded demands for plasma membrane work per se (72). A similar thermogenesis–dedicated explanation has been offered for enhanced heat production associated with increased rates of futile proton (H^+) cycling at the apparently leaky inner mitochondrial membranes of birds and mammals (19). As with mass-specific metabolism, mass–specific rates of mitochondrial proton leakage seem to decrease with increasing body size in mammals. Accordingly, variation in thermogenic proton leakiness has been proposed to account for mass–related differences in mammalian resting metabolic rates (i.e. the "mouse-elephant" metabolism curve) (94). However, this explanation fails to account for virtually identical mass–related changes in metabolic rates of almost all ectotherms (58), taxa in which it is hardly likely that any aspect of cellular metabolism is dedicated expressly to heat production.

If the ultimate function of increased plasma- and/or mitochondrial-membrane leakiness were simply to facilitate endogenous heat production in endotherms, then compared to reptiles, a greater proportion of total cellular metabolism in mammals and birds should be associated with these processes. Vertebrate tissues clearly specialized for thermogenesis dedicate high fractions of total cellular metabolism to membrane ion gradient maintenance, e.g. mammalian brown adipose tissue (61, 66) and billfish brain heater organs (17). However, in vitro incubation of ectotherm and endotherm liver and kidney slices demonstrates that similar fractions of total tissue oxygen consumption (~25–35%) are devoted to maintenance of plasma- and mitochondrial-ion homeostasis (19, 72). There is no compelling reason to assume that either the mitochondrial or plasma leaky membrane fractions of general resting metabolism have more to do with a necessity for heat production in endotherms than they do in ectotherms. Certainly, there is a large increment in absolute rates of metabolism devoted to maintenance of leaky membranes in endotherms; however, metabolic rates devoted to all cellular functions in endotherms have increased by about the same magnitude.

These observations suggest that the evolution of endothermy may have initially involved more substantive quantitative, rather than qualitative, changes in many aspects of cellular physiology. Symmetry of membrane– and nonmembrane–devoted expenditures of resting metabolic energy in endotherms parallels the previously described equality of ATP–generating capacity in many mitochondria of ecto- and endotherms. Perhaps the evolution of endothermy at the cellular and subcellular level was associated largely with the need to accommodate intensified rates of cellular functions, many of which were qualitatively similar to those of the ectothermic ancestors of birds and mammals. Concomitant requirements for increased production of ATP might have been fueled, at least initially, by incremental additions of relatively unmodified mitochondria.

Rather than focusing on energy consumption rate of any one particular aspect of cellular metabolism, perhaps it is more appropriate to ask why total oxygen consumption rate in endotherms is so high. Physiological patterns described above indicate that elevation of metabolic rate primarily for endothermic thermoregulation seems unlikely. Additionally, incipient endothermy in proto-mammals (Late Permian, 250 My; theriodont therapsids) appeared first in wolf–like inhabitants of equable subtropical regions (see below). These animals were probably inertial homeotherms, and the benefit of elevated endogenous heat production rates for thermoregulatory purposes was unlikely to have been worth the increased metabolic cost (85).

Endothermic metabolic rates could be driven by high rates of molecular turnover and synthesis. In mammals, protein turnover rates and metabolism scale equivalently with increased body mass (91), and compared to reptiles, the 50% higher protein and phospholipid contents of mammalian tissues (see above) might signal increased levels of turnover and resynthesis of these compounds, necessitating higher rates of aerobic metabolism and ATP production. The leaky plasma membranes of endotherms also correlate with this scenario: Increased sodium pump activity is associated with enhanced plasma membrane active cotransport of a variety of molecules including nutrients and amino acids essential for metabolism and molecular synthesis (31).

What aspects of mammalian and avian physiology might necessitate higher rates of molecular turnover and synthesis? In lab rats, trout (*Oncorhynchus*), and carp (*Cyprinus*), high endurance, frequently used oxidative–type skeletal muscle fibers analogous to those that predominate in most mammals and birds are associated with markedly higher rates of protein turnover than are their high speed, but less often used, white–type muscle fibers, similar to those that predominate in many reptiles (23, 52, 54, 67, 81, 96). Increased frequency of exercise per se is also associated with accelerated protein turnover rates (68). Perhaps the origin of avian and mammalian endothermy involved selection for increased levels of routine, sustainable activity supported by high concentrations of metabolically expensive, high endurance, oxidative-type skeletal muscle fibers. Elevation of ancestral resting metabolic rate might, therefore, have been driven by enhanced requirements for ATP production, linked tightly to an increased demand for a variety of support and resupply functions provided by the viscera. These enhanced visceral (resting) functions probably included synthesis of amino acids and proteins, urea production and elimination, digestion and storage of nutrients, processing of lactic acid, etc.

Finally, several authors have suggested that various extinct taxa may have been endothermic early in life then somehow switched to ectothermy at maturity (65); others have suggested seasonal alteration of ectothermy and near–endothermy (47). Similarly, during the course of their 200–million year history, crocodilians are proposed to have been ancestrally ectothermic, then endothermic, and then subsequently reverted to unmodified ectothermy (24). Such notions should be regarded with caution—although endothermy may well have evolved incrementally, endothermic metabolic physiology is ultimately associated with profound restructuring at the molecular, cellular, and organ system levels of organization (e.g. increased levels of membrane polyunsaturated phospholipids, high power muscle mitochondria, elevated tissue protein and phospholipid content, pulmonary and cardiovascular specialization, etc). No living endotherm exhibits anything resembling mid–life shifts from endo- to tru ectothermy, and it is difficult to imagine how such a complex transformation could be accomplished effectively. It is equally difficult to envision any lineage of endotherms successfully reacquiring traditional ectothermy subsequent to achieving true endothermic homeothermy.

THE FOSSIL EVIDENCE FOR ENDOTHERMY IN MAMMALS, BIRDS, AND THEIR ANCESTORS

Endothermy in the Fossil Record

Physiology obviously provides fundamental information regarding mechanisms of endothermy in extant animals. However, physiology provides no historical perspective into ancient environments or long–extinct taxa associated with the origin of tetrapod endothermy. Both parameters are likely to yield essential insight into selective factors associated with the origin and subsequent evolution of avian and mammalian metabolic rates. Thus paleontological data are fundamental to construction of a comprehensive scenario for the origin and evolution of endothermy. Potential signals of endothermy such as elevated blood-oxygen carrying capacity, complex lungs, mitochondrial density, etc are not preserved in fossils. Virtually all previous interpretations of the metabolic status of extinct taxa have centered on speculative and/or circumstantial evidence, including predator-prey ratios, fossilized trackways, fossil bone oxygen isotope ratios, and paleoclimatological inferences, or on correlations with mammalian or avian morphology, such as posture, relative brain size, and bone histology. These arguments are equivocal, at best (16, 27, 47, 78). Furthermore, the majority of the morphological arguments used previously, including especially bone histology data, are based predominantly on apparent similarities to the mammalian or avian condition, without a clear functional correlation to distinctly endothermic processes (16).

Until recently, no empirical studies were available that described a preservable structure with an unambiguous and exclusive functional relationship to endothermy. This situation has changed with the discovery that the nasal respiratory turbinate bones in mammals, and possibly birds, are tightly and causally linked to high ventilation rates and endothermy in these taxa (59). Evidence for the presence or absence of these structures is often preserved in fossils of long–extinct species, and promises exciting new insight into the chronology and selective factors associated with evolution of endothermy.

The Evolution of Endothermy in Mammals and Mammal–like Reptiles

Extant mammals, which include prototherians (egg–laying mammals) and therians (marsupial and placental mammals), probably last shared a common ancestor about 160 My (100). At any particular mass, all extant mammals maintain generally similar temperature–corrected metabolic rates and are alike in a wide range of other endothermy-related physiological processes and anatomical structures (e.g. hair, nonnucleated red blood cells, lung structure, blood oxygen carrying capacity, diaphragm, sweat glands, etc). Consequently, it is most parsimonious to assume the group's common Mesozoic Era ancestor had achieved a similar, endothermic grade of respiratory physiology (16).

Interpretation of more ancient mammalian or premammalian physiological status rests with linkage of fossilized morphology to metabolic rate. Mammalia probably evolved from cynodont therapsids, or mammal–like reptiles, by sometime late in the Triassic Period (~200 My) (100), and it has long been suggested that at least near–endothermy had been achieved in late therapsids (21). In the "breathing-runner" scenario, the semi–upright posture of many Triassic Period cynodont therapsids is taken to signal the presence of at least near–mammalian metabolic status in that group [as well as in basal (Paleozoic Era) archosaurs, early crocodiles, rhynchosaurs (Triassic relatives of the living tuatara), pterosaurs, and dinosaurs] (24). Sprawling, lizard–like, lateral undulatory locomotion is hypothesized as having reduced or precluded the ability to simultaneously breathe and run, while the upright, parasagittal stride of running mammals and, presumably, late cynodont therapsids, supposedly facilitated lung ventilation, an active lifestyle, and endothermy. However, this supposition is inconsistent with responses to graded activity in running lizards insofar as (a) oxygen consumption increases with increased locomotory speed and remains maximal to at least 300% of highest sustainable speeds, and (b) blood oxygen concentration and extraction remain at or near optimal over a similar range of running speeds. These data are clearly inconsistent with apnea in running lizards. While this scenario may have limited merit, its underlying assumption is probably an oversimplification and appears to be a poor test of endothermy (13).

There is a far stronger causal association with endothermy for the respiratory turbinates, the maxilloturbinate bones, of virtually all extant mammals. These thin but highly complex structures in the anterior nasal passages counteract the desiccating effects associated with high ventilation rates by facilitating a countercurrent exchange of respiratory heat and water between respired air and the moist lining of the turbinals. As cool external air is inhaled, it absorbs heat and moisture from the turbinal linings. This prevents desiccation of the lungs, but it also cools the turbinal epithelia and creates a thermal gradient along the turbinates. During exhalation, this process is reversed: Warm air from the lungs, now fully saturated with water vapor, is cooled as it once again passes over the turbinates. The exhaled air becomes supersaturated as a result of this cooling, and excess water vapor condenses on the turbinal surfaces where it can be reclaimed and recycled, rather than lost to the environment. Over time, a substantial amount of water can thus be saved (59).

This respiratory water-recovery mechanism is documented in a series of extant mammalian species from xeric to mesic environments; when use of the maxilloturbinates was experimentally precluded, respiratory water loss was significantly above normal in all cases. Furthermore, complex respiratory turbinates occur in birds (4), but are completely absent in all extant reptiles including species of arid habitats (60). These structures appear to have a fundamental association with high pulmonary ventilation rates and thus with endothermy. In birds and mammals, endothermy is supported by elevated lung ventilation rates: Even at rest, ventilation rates of birds and mammals are at least 3.5–5 times greater than those of similar–sized reptiles (10). Ratios of these differences in the field must be markedly higher. Respiratory water loss is of much greater potential significance to endotherms and the need for its reduction more immediate.

Mammalian maxilloturbinals have no homologues among extant ectotherms (116). In extant reptiles, one to three simple nasal conchae may be present, but these are exclusively olfactory in function. Like the mammalian naso- and ethmoturbinals, they are typically located in the posterodorsal olfactory portion of the nasal cavity. There are no structures in the reptilian nasal cavity specifically designed for recovery of respiratory water vapor. It is, therefore, likely that maxilloturbinates evolved to compensate for the increased water loss associated with high ventilation rates of mammalian endothermy (59).

In fossil mammals and mammal–like reptiles, the presence of nasal turbinates are most readily revealed via bony ridges by which these structures attach to the walls of the nasal cavity. Attachment ridges for olfactory turbinals are located posterodorsally, away from the main flow of respiratory air, whereas those of the respiratory maxilloturbinals are situated in the anterolateral portion, directly in the path of respired air. Ridges for olfactory (naso- and ethmo-) turbinals are found throughout the mammal–like reptiles including earlier, ancestral forms such as pelycosaurs. However, rudimentary anterolateral rostral ridges for support of respiratory- (maxillo-) turbinate bones first appear in some late Paleozoic Era theriodont therapsids, e.g. *Glanosuchus,* a wolf–like pristerognathid therocephalian. Accordingly, initial phases in the evolution of mammalian oxygen consumption rates may have begun as early as the Late Permian Period (250 My), some 40 to 50 million years prior to the origin of the Mammalia. Lower-Middle Triassic cynodont therapsids (e.g. the galesaurid *Thrinaxodon* and the traversodontid *Massetognathus*), as well as the earliest mammals (e.g. *Morganucodon*), appear to have had maxilloturbinate development comparable to that of extant mammals, presumably with a similar capacity for respiratory water recovery. This represents the first compelling evidence that ventilation rates, and by extension, metabolic rates of the earliest mammals, and at least some late mammal–like reptiles, may have approached or been equal to those of extant mammals (60).

It is difficult to overstate the almost Rosetta Stone–like significance of incipient maxilloturbinates in therocephalians. Thermoregulatory-based models for the origin of mammalian endothermy are largely falsified if the earliest, incremental steps toward mammalian metabolic rate occurred in large, Late Permian therapsids. Many therocephalians were dog–, bear–, or lion–like, medium to large (20–100 kg) carnivores that inhabited regions with subtropical to tropical climates. They were sufficiently large that, whether hairy or scaly, their thermal conductance was likely similar to that of large mammals (89). Accordingly, they were probably inertial homeotherms, and thermoregulatory-related expenditure of metabolic energy was unlikely to have been necessary (85).

The Metabolic Status of Birds and Dinosaurs

Birds are accomplished endotherms and many (especially the songbirds) maintain the highest body temperatures and metabolic rates of any tetrapods. The fossil record indicates that modern bird orders were fairly well–defined by about 60 My (25), therefore avian endothermy is likely to have been fully developed by about Late Cretaceous-Early Tertiary Periods.

Because the birds are a monophyletic group, no extant endothermic sister taxon exists from which pre–Cenozoic Era inheritance of endothermy can be logically inferred. The earliest known bird is the famous *Archaeopteryx lithographica,* a fully feathered, late Jurassic (145 My) archaeornithine with striking skeletal similarity to some carnivorous dinosaurs (92). Recently described circumstantial evidence hints that *Archaeopteryx* might well have been an ectotherm (27, 102). Nevertheless, *Archaeopteryx* is conventionally assumed to have been endothermic because its well-developed plumage is thought to have been reflective of ambient radiation, sufficient to preclude effective ectothermic thermoregulation (18). However, the presence of a fully developed set of flight feathers in Mesozoic Era avian ancestors of extant birds does not necessarily signal the presence of endothermy, or even an approach to it. Like modern reptiles, some living birds utilize behavioral thermoregulation to absorb ambient heat across feathered skin. During nocturnal periods of low ambient temperatures, body temperature in the roadrunner (*Geococcyx californianus*) declines by about 4°C. After sunrise, the roadrunner basks in solar radiation and warms ectothermically to normal body temperature. Additionally, a number of other fully feathered extant birds can readily absorb and use incident solar energy. An ectothermic *Archaeopteryx,* which is thought to have lived in a warm, sunny climate, might easily have had similar behavioral thermoregulatory capacity. A fully feathered *Archaeopteryx* could have been either ectothermic or endothermic, and the appearance of well-developed plumage so early in avian history might strictly have indicated the evolution of powered flight, rather than any particular thermoregulatory pattern (102).

Anatomical similarity between some theropod dinosaurs and *Archaeopteryx* is marked. The evidence strongly indicates a close phyletic relationship between the theropod dromaeosaurids (e.g. *Velociraptor, Deinonychus*) and primitive birds, and it is reasonable to hypothesize that an as yet unknown Early or Mid-Jurassic Period dromaeosaurid was ancestral to archaeopterygians and later birds (92). If dromaeosaurids were endothermic, then endothermic metabolic status in this lineage would likely have predated the origin of Aves. The presence or absence of endothermy in dinosaurs has been a topic of considerable discussion and sometimes acrimonious debate over the past twenty years. In the past, proponents have advanced a variety of elaborate scenarios for dinosaur endothermy based, for example, on dinosaur posture, predator-prey ratios, brain size, trackways, and fossil:bone oxygen isotope ratios. Certainly, many large dinosaurs were inertial homeotherms, but few, if any, of these arguments provide unambiguous evidence for endothermy in dinosaurs (16, 27, 47, 78).

Current hypotheses regarding possible dinosaur endothermy center on the assumed relationship of bone histology to growth rates in ecto- and endotherms. Two histological types of compact bone (lamellar-zonal and fibro-lamellar) have been recognized in extant vertebrates that differ qualitatively in their fibril organization and degree of vascularization. The primary bone of extant amphibians and reptiles is termed lamellar-zonal. Here, compact bone is deposited by relatively few primary osteons, principally by periosteal deposition. Histologically, lamellar-zonal bone has a layered appearance, within which incremental growth lines are occasionally recognized. It is also poorly vascularized. In the fibro-lamellar bone of many birds, mammals, and dinosaurs, most of the bony matrix is deposited by abundant primary osteons, which produces a fibrous, woven appearance (97). Fibro-lamellar bone is well vascularized (27).

Lamellar-zonal bone has been associated with ectothermy and fibro-lamellar with endothermy. Fibro-lamellar bone is often correlated with high growth rate, which requires rapid deposition of calcium salts. Such rapid growth is supposedly possible only in systems with high metabolic rates associated with endothermy. Thus the primary correlation is, supposedly, between growth rate and bone structure (98, 40). Accordingly, it has been widely accepted that growth rates of extant endotherms are about an order of magnitude greater than in ectotherms (82). Given the widespread occurrence of fibro-lamellar bone in dinosaurs, their growth is often assumed to have been rapid, as in birds and mammals, and according to this scenario, they must have been endothermic, or nearly so, similar to mammals and birds, (48).

Much of this scenario is inconsistent with a variety of paleontological and biological data. For example, fibro-lamellar bone is absent in many small, rapidly growing endotherms, and its presence in a labyrinthodont amphibian and in some clearly ectothermic cotylosaurs, pelycosaurs, and dicynodont therapsids is particularly puzzling (29, 45, 46). Moreover, long bones in numerous dinosaurian genera have regions of both fibro-lamellar and lamellar-zonal histology (98). A number of workers have suggested that fibro-lamellar bone in dinosaurs might be more indicative of high, stable body temperature, such as might have been found in many inertially homeothermic, but possibly ectothermic, dinosaurs (85), rather than a reflection of high metabolic rate. Significantly, fibro-lamellar bone has been reported in young, rapidly growing farm–raised crocodiles (22) as well as in wild alligators (99).

Bone histology notwithstanding, there is also reason to question the presumed variation in growth rates between endotherms and reptiles, especially crocodilians, the closest living relatives of birds and dinosaurs. In the most frequently cited comparative study, regressions for maximal sustained growth rates (g/day) for all amniotes scaled positively (slope ~0.7) with increasing adult body mass, but reptile y-intercept elevations (a constants) were reportedly only about 10% those of ectotherms (26). However, criteria for calculating these regressions were not equivalent: Endotherm adult weight approximated mass at sexual maturity, and mass at a similar stage in the ectotherm life cycle would seem appropriate for developing truly comparable regressions for both groups. Nevertheless, American alligator (*Alligator mississippiensis*) adult weight was plotted at 160 kg, a value far in excess of the species' actual 30 kg mass at sexual maturity (7). In addition, growth rate for the alligator was listed at 28 g/day, rather than the more accurate 42 g/day (T Case, personal

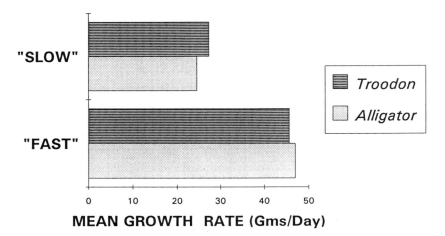

Figure 1 Growth rates for the bipedal theropod dinosaur *Troodon* and the American alligator. For *Troodon,* "Fast" and "Slow" rates are based on estimates that adult body size (50 kg) was attained from 3 to 5 yr of age (111). For the alligator, "Slow" growth rates are based on mean daily mass increment in wild population hatchlings to a weight of 50 kg [mass was converted from original length data in McIlhenny (84); mass-length conversion formula from Coulson et al (32)]. Alligator "Fast" rates are taken from farm–grown individuals (R Coulson, unpublished data; 32).

communication). If the corrected daily growth increment, as well as the more appropriate 30 kg adult mass, is assumed for the American alligator, growth rate for this ectotherm is actually about fourfold that of marsupials and approximates growth rates in many placental mammals. Additionally, alligator growth rates are virtually indistinguishable from estimated growth rates for the bipedal theropod dinosaur *Troodon* (Figure 1).

Bone oxygen isotope (^{18}O) data purporting to demonstrate relatively little in vivo variation between extremity and deep body (= core) temperatures in the large theropod *Tyrannosaurus rex* have also been suggested as indicative of endothermy in this genus (4a). This interpretation is based on the assumption that, unlike ectotherms, endotherms maintain relatively uniform extremity vs core temperatures. However, the stability of bone oxygen isotopes during fossilization is uncertain (89a). Moreover, there are voluminous data indicating that extremity vs core body temperatures in extant birds and mammals are often as variable as those of ectotherms including *Alligator* (1a, 48, 82; for *Alligator,* S Turpin & J Spotila, unpublished information).

Numerous authors have suggested that some dinosaurs may have had intermediate metabolic rates, somewhere between those of typical ectotherms and endotherms (109). Justification for this scenario is occasionally founded on the supposed existence of a modern analogue: giant sea turtles (the 400+ kg leatherback *Dermochelys*) with resting metabolic rates reportedly intermediate to those predicted by allometric relationships for reptiles and mammals (93). However, recent reassessment indicates that resting oxygen consumption rate for the leatherbacks is actually equivalent to predicted rates for reptiles of their mass (F Paladino, unpublished information). Significantly, leatherback turtle muscle citrate synthase enzyme activity also falls within the normal range for reptiles (F Paladino, unpublished information).

To date, none of the characteristics proposed in support of dinosaur endothermy is uniformly absent in modern reptiles or has a clear functional association with high metabolic rates. The contention of endothermy in dinosaurs and/or early birds remains unproven.

OVERVIEW AND IMPLICATIONS OF THE CURRENT DATA

Given the antiquity of the earliest birds and mammals, many factors that influenced their origins will forever remain unknown. Nevertheless, as described above, recent physiological and paleontological discoveries have facilitated new insights into the chronology and biology of the evolution of endothermy in these groups, especially mammals. Fossilized evidence indicates that in the therapsid-mammal lineage, elevated lung ventilation rates and accelerated routine metabolic rates in large (>40 kg), Late Permian Period therocephalians from warm climates preceded the evolution of mammals by some 40 million years. Subsequently, mammalian or near–mammalian metabolic rates may well have been attained in late cynodont (Triassic Period) therapsids. At least initially, elevation of resting metabolic rate was probably associated with increased demand for cellular work and aerobically based ATP synthesis, rather than for thermogenesis. Elevated tissue demand for oxygen was presumably facilitated by expansion of pulmonary-cardiovascular capacities and primarily by quantitative, rather than qualitative, alterations at cellular and tissue levels (e.g. increments in oxidative enzyme activity, increased numbers of mitochondria, etc). It is possible, but unproven, that attainment of endothermic metabolic status in late therapsids and/or early mammals was accompanied by simultaneous development of homeothermic thermoregulatory patterns typical of most extant mammals. The existence of an extensive pelage (as yet unknown) in late therapsids and/or very early mammals would be consistent with at least near capacity for fully developed endothermic homeothermy.

The chronological development of endothermy in the dinosaurian-avian lineage remains poorly understood. There is little, if any, compelling evidence for elevated metabolic rates in any dinosaurs or early (Late Jurassic-Early

Cretaceous Period) birds. Some intriguing indirect evidence hints at ecto-thermy in dinosaurs and early birds (e.g. ectotherm–like annular growth rings in long bones of these taxa; 28), but more definitive evidence will probably emerge with physiological and paleontological investigation of avian nasal respiratory turbinates. Although independently derived, these structures in birds strongly resemble mammalian maxilloturbinates, and avian turbinates may prove to have a similar association with high rates of lung ventilation and metabolism. The presence, or absence, of early avian, or possibly dinosaurian, respiratory turbinates may provide the first reliable, causally linked evidence of metabolic rate in these taxa.

Incipient endothermy in large, Late Permian therapsids of warm climates, as well as recent physiological data, indicate that, at least initially, selection for increased thermoregulatory powers had little to do with the evolution of mammalian endothermy. Alternatively, the aerobic capacity model for the origin of mammalian endothermy would seem to be reinforced by these new data: Selection for increased aerobic capacity in Permian theriodont therapsids, many of which appear to have been active predators, would have yielded immediate benefits in terms of expanded capacity for prey pursuit, predator avoidance, courtship, and for maintenance of increased territory size (15). Significantly, increased capacities for aerobic metabolism seemed mediated by genetic factors insofar as they have been shown to be heritable, persistent through time, and variable among individuals (12).

In all classes of vertebrates, maximum rates of aerobiosis exceed resting rates by an average ratio of about ten to fifteen, being less in sedentary species and greater in more active taxa. Presumably, expansion of maximal capacity for aerobiosis was similarly linked with increased resting metabolic rates in Permian therapsids. Continued selection for expanded aerobic capacity in Permian and Triassic therapsids eventually resulted in resting thermogenesis, perhaps sufficient for endogenously based thermoregulation in late cynodonts and/or early mammals.

Although the aerobic capacity scenario seems most consistent with current physiological and paleontological data, certain aspects of the model await further resolution. For example, the mechanism of linkage between resting and maximal rates of oxygen consumption remains problematic, particularly be-cause primary sources of endogenous heat at rest (visceral tissue) are distinct from those during activity (myogenic). However, as discussed above, high levels of routine activity in birds and mammals may well necessitate significant expansion of metabolically demanding visceral support functions including digestion, amino acid synthesis, lactic acid and urea processing, etc.

Additionally, it is presently unknown if comparisons of phenotypic aspects of resting:maximal metabolic ratios are equally as consistent at inter- and intraspecific levels as they are at the ordinal and class level. However, it is noteworthy that the only phylogenetically based intraspecific analysis using independent contrast algorithms indicates that resting and maximal rates of metabolism are positively correlated in anuran amphibians (112).

ACKNOWLEDGMENTS

The following individuals provided contributions of data, opinions, etc that have been of invaluable assistance in preparation of this review: Dave Weishampel, Roland Coulson, Frank Paladino, Ted Case, James Waters, David Varricchio, Jaap Hillenius, Richard Tracy, Tim Rowe, Peter Dodson, Albert F. Bennett, Jim Spotila, and members of George Somero's laboratory. I am particularly indebted to James Farlow, Paul Licht, and George Somero for their insightful criticisms and careful reviews of early versions of the manuscript.

Literature Cited

1. Aschoff J, Gunther B, Kramer K. 1971. *Energiehaushalt und Temperaturregulation.* Munich: Urban und Schwarzenberg

1a. Aschoff J, Wever R. 1958. Kern und Schale im Warmehaushalt des Menschen. *Naturwissenschaften* 45:477–85

2. Augee ML. 1978. Monotremes and the evolution of homeothermy. *Austral. Zool.* 20:111–19

3. Avery RA. 1982. Field studies of body temperatures and thermoregulation. In *Biology of the Reptilia*, ed. C Gans, FH Pough, 12:93–166. London: Academic. 536 pp.

4. Bang BG. 1971. Functional anatomy of the olfactory system in 23 orders of birds. *Acta Anat.* 79:1–76 (Suppl. 58)

4a. Barrick RE, Showers WJ. 1994. Thermophysiology of *Tyrannosaurus rex:* evidence from oxygen isotopes. *Science* 265:222–24

5. Bartholemew GA. 1982. Physiological control of body temperature. See Ref. 3, pp. 167–211

6. Bartholemew GA, Tucker VA. 1964. Oxygen consumption in relation to temperature and size in varanid lizards. *Physiol. Zool.* 37:341–54

7. Bellairs A. 1970. *The Life of Reptiles.* New York: Universe. 590 pp.

8. Bennett AF. 1972. A comparison of activities of metabolic enzymes in lizards and rats. *Comp. Biochem. Physiol.* 42:637–47

9. Bennett AF. 1972. The effects of activity on oxygen consumption, oxygen debt, and heart rate in the lizards *Varanus gouldii* and *Sauromalas hispidis. J. Comp. Physiol.* 81:289–99

10. Bennett AF. 1973. Ventilation in two species of lizards during rest and activity. *Comp. Biochem. Physiol.* 46A:653–71

11. Bennett AF. 1982. The energetics of reptilian activity. See Ref. 3, 13:155–99

12. Bennett AF. 1991. The evolution of activity capacity. *J. Exp. Biol.* 160:1–23

13. Bennett AF. 1994. Exercise performance in reptiles. *Adv. Veter. Sci. Comp. Med.* 38: In press

14. Bennett AF, Dawson WR. 1976. Metabolism. In *Biology of the Reptilia*, ed. C Gans, WR Dawson, 5:127–223. London: Academic

15. Bennett AF, Ruben JA. 1979. Endothermy and activity in vertebrates. *Science* 206:649–54

16. Bennett AF, Ruben JA. 1986. The metabolic and thermoregulatory status of therapsids. In *The Ecology and Biology of Mammal–like Reptiles*, ed. N Hotton, PD MacLean, JJ Roth, EC Roth, pp. 207–18. Washington DC: Smithsonian Inst. Press. 326 pp.

17. Block BA. 1991. Endothermy in fish: thermogenesis, ecology and evolution. In *Biochemistry and Molecular Biology of Fishes*, ed. PW Hochachka, T

Mommsen, 1:269–311. Amsterdam: Elsevier

18. Bock, WJ. 1985. The arboreal theory for the origin of birds. In *The Beginnings of Birds*, ed. MK Hecht, JH Ostrom, G Viohl, P Wellenhofer, pp 199–207. Eichstatt: Freunde des Jura-Museums

19. Brand DB, Couture P, Else PL, Withers KW, Hulbert AJ. 1991. Evolution of energy metabolism. *Biochem. J.* 275:81–6

20. Brody S. 1945. *Bioenergetics and Growth: With Special Reference to the Efficiency Complex in Domestic Animals.* New York: Reinhold. 1023 pp. (reprinted 1964)

21. Brink AS. 1956. Speculations on some advanced mammalian characteristics in the higher mammal–like reptiles. *Paleontol. Afr.* 4:77–95

22. Buffrenil V. 1980. Mise en evidence de l'incidence des conditions de mileu sur la croissance de *Crocodylus siamensis* (Schneider, 1801) et valeur des marques de croissance squélettiques pour l'evaluation de l'age individuel. *Arch. Zool. Exp. Gen.* 121:63–76

23. Butler PJ. 1991. Exercise in birds. *J. Exp. Biol.* 160:233–62

24. Carrier DR. 1987. The evolution of locomotor stamina in tetrapods: circumventing a mechanical constraint. *Paleobiology* 13:326–41

25. Carroll RL. 1988. *Vertebrate Paleontology and Evolution.* New York: Freeman. 698 pp.

26. Case TJ. 1978. On the evolution and adaptative significance of postnatal growth rates in the terrestrial vertebrates. *Q. Rev. Biol.* 53:243–82

27. Chinsamy A. 1994. Dinosaur bone histology: Implications and inferences. In *The Dino Fest Souvenir Volume*, ed. GD Rosenberg, JF Pachut, D Wolberg. Knoxville, Tenn.: Paleontol. Soc. In press

28. Chinsamy A, Chiappe LM, Dodson P. 1994. Growth rings in Mesozoic birds. *Nature* 368:196–97

29. Chinsamy A, Rubidge BS. 1993. Dicynodont (Therapsida) bone histology: phylogenetic and physiological implications. *Paleontol. Afr.* 30:97–102

30. Classen H, Hoppeler H, Tuscher L, Wu XY, Saucedo C, Weber JM. 1993. Oxidative substrate pathways and symmorphosis: IV. Relating substrate oxidation to muscle cell structure. *Proc. XXXII Congress IUPS, Glasgow, Scot.* 319.6/0

31. Clausen T, van Hardeveld C, Everts MS. 1991. Significance of cation transport in control of energy metabolism and thermogenesis. *Physiol. Rev.* 71:733–74

32. Coulson RA, Herbert JD, Coulson TD. 1989. Biochemistry and physiology of alligator metabolism in vivo. *Am. Zool.* 29:921–34

33. Cowles RB. 1958. Possible origin of dermal temperature regulation. *Evolution* 12:347–57

34. Crompton AW, Taylor CR, Jagger JA. 1978. Evolution of homeothermy in mammals. *Nature* 272:333–36

35. Daan S, Dirkjan M, Groenewold A. 1990. Avian basal metabolic rates: their association with body composition and energy expenditure in nature. *Am. J. Physiol.* 259:R333–40

36. Davies F. 1930. The conducting system of the bird's heart. *J. Anat.* 64:9–34

37. Dawson TJ. 1973. "Primitive" mammals. In *Comparative Physiology of Thermoregulation*, ed. GC Whittow, 12:1–46. New York: Academic

38. Dawson TJ, Grant TR. 1980. Metabolic capabilities of monotremes and the evolution of homeothermy. In *Comparative Physiology: Primitive Mammals*, ed. K Schmidt-Nielsen, CR Taylor, L Bolis, pp. 140–47. Cambridge: Cambridge Univ. Press

39. Dawson TJ, Hulbert AJ. 1970. Standard metabolism, body temperature, and surface areas of Australian marsupials. *Am. J. Physiol.* 218:1233–38

40. de Ricqles A. 1980. Tissue structure of dinosaur bone: functional significance and possible relation to dinosaur physiology. In *A Cold Look at the Warm–Blooded Dinosaurs*, ed. RDK Thomas, EC Olson, pp. 103–9. Boulder, Colo.: Westview

41. Eisenberg JF. 1980. Biological strategies in living conservative mammals. See Ref. 38, pp. 13–30

42. Else PL, Hulbert AJ. 1981. Comparison of the "mammal machine" and the "reptile machine": energy production. *Am. J. Physiol.* 240:R3–9

43. Else PL, Hulbert AJ. 1985. An allometric comparison of the mitochondria of mammalian and reptilian tissues: the implications for the evolution of endothermy. *J. Comp. Physiol.* 156:3–11

44. Else PL, Hulbert AJ. 1987. Evolution of mammalian endothermic metabolism: "leaky" membranes as a source of heat. *Am. J. Physiol.* 253:R1–7

45. Enlow DH. 1969. The bone of reptiles. In *Biology of the Reptilia*, ed. C Gans, A Bellairs, TS Parsons, 1:45–80. New York: Academic

46. Enlow DH, Brown SO. 1957. A comparative histological study of fossil and

recent bone tissue. Part 2. *Texas J. Sci.* 9:186–214

47. Farlow JO. 1990. Dinosaur energetics and thermal biology. In *The Dinosauria,* ed. DB Weishampel, P Dodson, O Halszka, pp 43–55. Berkeley: Univ. Calif. Press. 733 pp.

48. Farlow JO. 1993. On the rareness of big, fierce animals: speculations about the body sizes, population densities, and geographic ranges of predatory mammals and large carnivorous dinosaurs. *Am. J. Sci.* 293:167–99

49. Feist DD, White RG. 1989. Terrestrial mammals in cold. In *Advances in Comparative Environmental Physiology,* ed. LCH Wang, pp. 327–60. Berlin: Springer-Verlag

50. Firth BT, Turner JS. 1982. Sensoral, neural and hormonal aspects of thermoregulation. See Ref. 3, pp. 214–74

51. Garland T Jr. 1982. Scaling maximal running speed and maximal aerobic speed to body mass in mammals and lizards. *Physiologist* 25:338

52. Garlick PJ, Maltin CA, Bailee AGS, Delday MI, Grubb DA. 1989. Fiber-type composition of nine rat muscles. II. Relationship to protein turnover. *Am. J. Physiol.* 257:E828–32

53. Goldspink G. 1972. Postembryonic growth and differentiation of striated muscle. In *Structure and Function of Muscle,* ed. GH Bourne, 1:179–236. New York: Academic

54. Goldspink G, Marshall PA, Watt PW. 1984. Protein synthesis in red and white skeletal muscle of carp (*Cyprinus carpio*) measured in vivo and the effect of temperature. *J. Physiol.* 361:42

55. Grant TR, Dawson TJ. 1978. Temperature in the platypus, *Ornithorhynchus anatinus:* production and loss of metabolic heat in air and water. *Physiol. Zool.* 51:315–32

56. Gudbarjarnason SB, Doell SB, Oskarsdottir G, Hallgrimsson J. 1978. Modification of phospholipids and catecholamine stress tolerance. In *Tocopherol, Oxygen and Biomembranes,* ed. C de Duve, O Hayaishi, pp. 297–310. Amsterdam: Elsevier

57. Guthe KF. 1981. Reptilian muscle: Fine structure and physical parameters. In *Biology of the Reptilia,* ed. C Gans, H Pough, 11:265–354. London: Academic

58. Hemmingsen AM. 1960. Energy metabolism as related to body size and respiratory surfaces, and its evolution. *Rep. Steno. Hosp.* 9:1–110

59. Hillenius WJ. 1992. The evolution of nasal turbinates and mammalian endothermy. *Paleobiology* 18:17–29

60. Hillenius WJ. 1994. Turbinates in therapsids: evidence for Late Permian origins of mammalian endothermy. *Evolution.* In press

61. Himms-Hagen J. 1990. Brown adipose tissue thermogenesis: interdisciplinary studies. *FASEB J.* 4:2890–98

62. Hinds DS, Baudinette RV, MacMillen RE, Halpern EA. 1993. Maximum metabolism and the aerobic factorial scope of endotherms. *J. Exp. Biol.* 182:41–56

63. Hochachka PW, Somero GN. 1984. *Biochemical Adaptation.* Princeton: Princeton Univ. Press. 537 pp.

64. Hoppeler H, Billeter R. 1991. Conditions for oxygen and substrate transport in muscles in exercising mammals. *J. Exp. Biol.* 160:263–83

65. Horner JR, Lessem D. 1993. *T. Rex.* New York: Simon-Schuster. 239 pp.

66. Horwitz, BA. 1989. Biochemical mechanisms and control of cold-induced cellular thermogenesis in placental mammals. See Ref. 49, pp. 84–116

67. Houlihan DF. 1991. Protein turnover in ectotherms and its relationships to energetics. In *Advances in Comparative and Environmental Physiology,* ed. R Gilles, pp. 1–43. Berlin: Springer-Verlag

68. Houlihan DF, Laurent P. 1987. Effects of exercise training on performance, growth, and protein turnover of rainbow trout (*Salmo gairdneri*). *Can. J. Fish Aquatic Sci.* 44:1614–21

69. Huey RB. 1982. Temperature, physiology, and the ecology of reptiles. See Ref. 3, pp. 26–90

70. Hulbert AJ. 1980. The evolution of energy metabolism in mammals. See Ref. 41, pp. 129–39

71. Hulbert AJ, Else PL. 1989. Evolution of mammalian endothermic metabolism: mitochondrial activity and cell composition. *Am. J. Physiol.* 256:R63–69

72. Hulbert AJ, Else PL. 1990. The cellular basis of endothermic metabolism: A role for "leaky" membranes? *News Physiol. Sci.* 5:25–28

73. Hulbert AJ, Mantaj, W, Janssens H. 1991. Development of mammalian endothermic metabolism: quantitative changes in tissue mitochondria. *Am. J. Physiol.* 261:R561–68

74. Ismail-Beigi F. 1988. Thyroid thermogenesis: regulation of (Na$^+$+K$^+$)-adenosine triphosphate and active Na, K transport. *Am. Zool.* 28:363–71

75. Izraely HI, Choshniak CE, Stevens CE, Shkolnik A. 1989. Energy digestion and nitrogen economy of the domesticated donkey (*Equus asinus*) in relation to food quality. *J. Arid Environ.* 17:97–101

76. Kemp TS. 1988. Haemothermia or Archosauria?: the interrelationships of mammals, birds, and crocodiles. *Biol. J. Linn. Soc. London* 92:67–104

77. Kluger MJ, Ringler DH, Anver MR. 1975. Fever and survival. *Science* 188: 166–68

78. Kolodny Y, Luz B. 1993. Dinosaur thermal physiology from ^{18}O in bone phosphate; is it possible? In *Second Oxford Workshop on Bone Diagenesis Abstracts.* Oxford: Oxford Univ. Press. p. 217

79. Lasiewski RC, Calder WA. 1971. A preliminary allometric analysis of respiratory variables in resting birds. *Respir. Physiol.* 11:152–66

80. Lasiewski RC, Dawson WR. 1967. Reexamination of the relation between standard metabolic rate and weight in birds. *Condor* 69:13–23

81. Lewis EM, Kelly FJ, Goldspink DF. 1984. Pre– and post–natal growth and protein turnover in smooth muscle heart and slow– and fast–twitch skeletal muscles of the rat. *Biochem. J.* 217:517–26

82. Lucas SG, 1994. *Dinosaurs.* Dubuque, IA: Brown. 290 pp.

83. Marsh RL, Dawson WR. 1989. Avian adjustments to cold. See Ref. 49, pp. 205–53

84. McIlhenny EA. 1934. Notes on incubation and growth of alligators. *Copeia* 1934:80–8

85. McNab BK. 1978. The evolution of homeothermy in the phylogeny of mammals. *Am. Nat.* 112:1–21

86. McNab BK. 1980. Energetics and the limits to a temperate distribution in armadillos. *J. Mammal.* 61:606–27

87. McNab BK. 1984. Physiological convergence amongst ant–eating and termite–eating mammals. *J. Zool. London* 203:485–510

88. McNab BK. 1988. Complication inherent in scaling the basal rate of metabolism in mammals. *Q. Rev. Biol.* 63: 25–54

89. McNab BK, Auffenberg WA. 1976. The effect of large body size on the temperature regulation of the Komodo dragon, *Varanus komodoensis. Comp. Biochem. Physiol.* 55A:345–50

89a. Morell V. 1994. Warm–blooded dino debate blows hot and cold. *Science* 265: 188

90. Morrison PR, Ryser FA. 1952. Weight and body temperatures in mammals. *Science* 116:231–32

91. Munro HN, Downie ED. 1964. Relationship of liver composition to intensity of protein metabolism in different mammals. *Nature* 203:603–4

92. Ostrom JH. 1976. Archaeopteryx and the origin of birds. *Biol. J. Linn. Soc. London* 8:81–182

93. Paladino FA. 1990. Metabolism of leatherback turtles, gigantothermy, and thermoregulation of dinosaurs. *Nature* 344: 858–60

94. Porter RK, Brand DB. 1993. Body mass dependence of H^+ leak in mitochondria and its relevance to metabolic rate. *Nature* 362:628–29

95. Prosser CL. 1973. *Comparative Animal Physiology.* Philadelphia: Saunders. 966 pp.

96. Putnam RW, Gleeson TT, Bennett AF. 1980. Histological determination of the fiber composition of locomotory muscles in a lizard, *Dipsosaurus dorsalis. J. Exp. Zool* 214:303–9

97. Reid REH. 1987. Bone and dinosaur "endothermy." *Mod. Geol.* 11:133–54

98. Reid REH. 1990. Zonal growth rings in dinosaurs. *Mod. Geol.* 14:19–48

99. Reid REH. 1993. Cyclical growth in the long bones of a sauropod dinosaur. *Acta Paleontol. Polonica* 28:225

100. Rowe T. 1992. Phylogenetic systematics and the early history of mammals. In *Mammalian Phylogeny,* ed. FS Szalay, MC McKenna, pp. 129–45. Berlin: Springer-Verlag. 249 pp.

101. Ruben JA. 1976. Aerobic and anaerobic metabolism during activity in snakes. *J. Comp. Physiol.* 109:147–57

102. Ruben JA. 1991. Reptilian physiology and flight capacity of *Archaeopteryx. Evolution* 45:1–17

103. Ruben JA, Battalia DE. 1979. Aerobic and anaerobic metabolism during activity in small rodents. *J. Exp. Biol.* 208: 73–6

104. Ruben JA, Bennett AF, Hisaw FL. 1987. Selective factors in the origin of the mammalian diaphragm. *Paleobiology* 13:54–9

105. Scheid P, Piiper J. 1989. Respiratory mechanics and air flow in birds. In *Form and Function in Birds,* ed. AS King, J McLelland, 4:369–91. New York: Academic

106. Schmidt-Nielsen K. 1984. *Scaling: Why is Animal Size So Important?* Cambridge: Cambridge Univ. Press. 241 pp.

107. Schmidt-Nielsen K, Dawson TJ, Crawford EC Jr. 1966. Temperature regulation in the echidna (*Tachyglossus aculeatus*). *J. Cell. Physiol.* 67:63–72

108. Smith RE, Horwitz BA. 1969. Brown fat and thermogenesis. *Physiol. Rev.* 49:330–425

109. Spotila JR, O'Connor MP, Dodson P, Paladino FV. 1991. Hot and cold run-

ning dinosaurs: size, metabolism and migration. *Mod. Geol.* 16:203–27

110. van Mierop LHS, Barnard, SM. 1978. Further observations on thermoregulation in the brooding female python *Python molurus bivattatus* (Serpentes: Boidae). *Copeia* 1978:615–21

111. Varricchio DJ. 1993. Bone microstructure of the Upper Cretaceous theropod dinosaur *Troodon formosus. J. Vert. Paleontol.* 13:99–104

112. Walton BM. 1993. Physiology and phylogeny: the evolution of locomotor energetics in hylid frogs. *Am. Nat.* 141:26–50

113. Wang LCH. 1989. Ecological, physiological, and biochemical aspects of torpor in mammals and birds. See Ref. 65, pp. 361–401

114. West GC. 1965. Shivering and heat production in wild birds. *Physiol. Zool.* 38:110–20

115. Withers PC. 1992. *Comparative Animal Physiology.* Fort Worth, Tex.: Saunders Coll. Press. 949 pp.

116. Wittmer LM. 1992. *Ontogeny, phylogeny and airsacs: the importance of soft-tissue inference in the interpretation of facial evolution in Archosauria.* PhD thesis. Johns Hopkins Univ., Baltimore. 461 pp.

Annu. Rev. Physiol. 1995. 57:97–114

LEUKOCYTE TRAFFIC IN THE LUNG

James C. Hogg

University of British Columbia, Pulmonary Research Laboratory, St. Paul's Hospital, 1081 Burrard Street, Vancouver, British Columbia, V6Z 1Y6 Canada

Claire M. Doerschuk

Riley Hospital for Children, Room 2750, 702 Barnhill Drive, Indianapolis, Indiana 46202-5225

KEY WORDS: bronchial circulation, pulmonary vasculature, adhesion molecules, polymorphonuclear leukocytes

INTRODUCTION

An adult human with a cardiac output of 5 liters/min pumps approximately 7200 liters of blood through the pulmonary circulation in 24 h. An additional 1% of the cardiac output (72 liters over 24 h) flows through the bronchial circulation to supply the conducting airways and blood vessels, lymphatic collections, and portions of the pleural surface (22). The bronchial and pulmonary venous outflow becomes confluent in the peripheral lung and drains into the left heart. However, the bronchial venous drainage from the central bronchovascular structures and lymphatics empty into the azygous and hemiazygos system and then into the right heart. As each liter of circulating blood contains approximately 10^9 leukocytes, their traffic through the bronchial and pulmonary microvessels is enormous. The purpose of this brief review is to discuss the similarities and differences between these two lung vascular beds.

LEUKOCYTE TRAFFIC IN THE PULMONARY CIRCULATION

Quantitative histological studies have established that the human pulmonary vasculature contains 2.8×10^{11} individual capillary segments spread out over

97

0066–4278/95/0315–0097$05.00

an estimated 10^8 alveoli (73). This means that each alveolus contains approximately 1000 capillary segments distributed over the many walls that make up its polyhedral structure. Staub & Schultz (67) have estimated that erythrocytes pass through an average of 15 alveolar wall networks spread over seven different alveoli as they journey from the arteriole to the venule. The interconnecting network of capillary segments in each alveolar wall (Figure 1) provides a huge number of parallel routes for cell traffic.

The erythrocyte (RBC) has a discoid shape with a similar maximum diameter to the spherical white blood cell (WBC) (24). However, the RBCs are less restricted by the capillary bed than WBCs because they can rapidly reduce their maximum diameter by folding when they encounter a narrow capillary. Physiological studies from several laboratories have established that RBCs require about a second to transit through the pulmonary capillary bed (35, 39), whereas direct observations by Lien and associates (41) and indirect studies from our own laboratory (26) have shown that polymorphonuclear leukocytes (PMNs) may take 60–100 times longer to make the same journey. The lung capillary bed can accommodate circulating cells traveling at these different speeds because the interconnecting network of short segments (Figure 1) allows the faster-moving RBCs to stream around segments that are temporarily filled with slower-moving PMNs. This concentrates the WBCs with respect to RBCs in the pulmonary capillary bed as compared to the peripheral blood, and accounts for the majority of the so-called marginated pool of WBCs in the lung (24).

Recent studies of both animal and human lungs (13) have shown that fully dilated capillary segments have an average diameter of 7.5 ± 2.3 μm and an average length of 14.4 ± 5.8 μm, which are in good agreement with previous autopsy findings (73). Glazier et al (19) found that in dogs these dimensions vary with lung height because the gravitational effect on vascular transmural pressure dilates capillaries toward the bottom of the lung. Because spherical PMNs have an average diameter of 6.8 ± 0.8 μm, all those with a diameter greater than one standard deviation above the mean (i.e. > 7.6 μm) will be restricted by capillary segments with a diameter smaller than their mean (i.e. < 7.5 μm) (10). The PMN must deform to pass through these restrictions, and the differences in capillary restriction imposed by the effect of gravity on the microvessels accounts for the difference in retention of labeled PMN in the upper compared to the lower regions of the lung (24, 43, 49).

Any reduction in capillary size enhances the difference between PMN and RBC transit times in lung microvessels. Markos et al (48) trained patients to perform forced expiratory maneuvers against an obstruction during elective cardiac catherization. The rise in alveolar pressure in relation to vascular pressure produced by this maneuver compressed the capillary bed and resulted in an immediate arteriovenous (AV) difference for WBCs across the lungs.

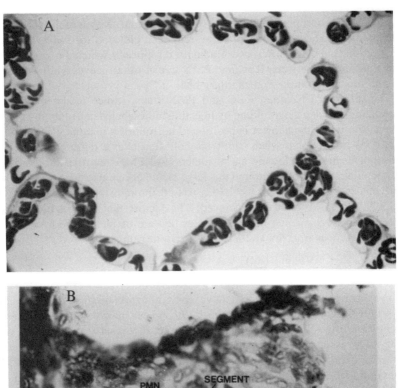

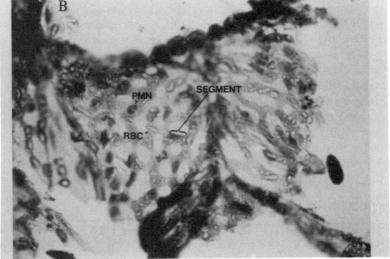

Figure 1 The histology of the alveolar capillary network is shown in cross-section (*A*) and en face (*B*). Comparison of the two figures shows that the alveolar capillaries consist of a network of short, interconnecting segments.

This AV difference reversed rapidly when the capillary compression was removed by returning alveolar pressure to normal. Subsequent studies in animals (47), where alveolar pressure remained elevated for longer periods, showed that this AV difference gradually disappears, which suggests that a new equilibrium between RBC and PMN transit times is eventually achieved in a chronically compressed capillary bed.

The difference between RBC and PMN transit times in the pulmonary circulation has also been studied by injecting radiolabeled cells into the central circulation while the subject is positioned in front of a gamma camera. Muir et al (55) showed that when data were collected over a region of interest in the right ventricle following an IV injection of PMNs and RBCs, these two cell populations traveled through this large chamber in unison. However, when the cells reached the lung, the RBCs passed through the pulmonary region quickly, but the PMNs were delayed. The factors that control blood flow, volume, and transit time in any vascular bed are of interest with respect to these differences in PMN and RBC traffic in the lung.

$$\text{Time (sec)} = \frac{\text{Volume (ml)}}{\text{Flow (ml/s)}} \qquad 1.$$

shows that transit times shorten with vascular dilatation because flow increases in proportion to vessel radius to the fourth power, and volume increases in proportion to vessel radius squared. Therefore, the observed increase in capillary size associated with the gravitationally induced increase in vascular transmural pressure (19) predicts the shorter transit times and lower PMN retention that have been observed in dependent lung regions (24, 43, 49).

These studies show that the pulmonary circulation concentrates WBCs with respect to RBCs and allows WBCs to come into close contact with the pulmonary capillary endothelium for prolonged periods under normal conditions. Although the small vessels entering and exiting the capillary bed also concentrate leukocytes with respect to RBCs, this accounts for a much smaller proportion of the total concentration of WBCs with respect to RBCs in the lung (29).

LEUKOCYTE TRAFFIC IN THE BRONCHIAL CIRCULATION

Miller's classic study of the bronchial vascular system (53) established that two to three branches of the bronchial artery accompany each of the major branches of the bronchial tree. These vessels interconnect to form an arterial plexus around the airway that sends small penetrating branches through the muscle into the submucosa. The arteriolar branches of these vessels supply a submucosal capillary network that drains into a venous plexus on the inner

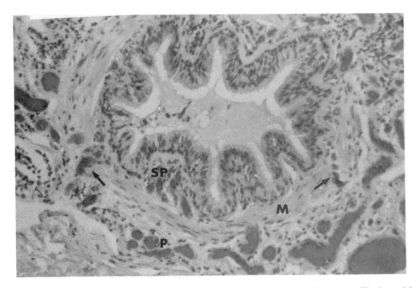

Figure 2   The bronchial vessels of an airway from a patient who died with asthma. The bronchial microvessels have two separate capillary plexi. The submucosal plexus (SP) is connected to a plexus of slightly larger vessels (P) found outside the airway smooth muscle (M) by interconnecting vessels (*arrow*) that run through the muscle layer.

surface of the muscle. This venous plexus sends short connectors back through the muscular layer where they divide and form a second plexus of slightly larger capillaries in the adventitia of the airway wall (Figure 2). Relatively little is known about the factors that distribute flow between the submucosal capillaries and those outside the muscle layer. Although these two sets of microvessels appear to be arranged in series, it is possible that they are perfused in parallel under some circumstances.

In addition to the tissue in the airway and vessel walls, the bronchial artery supplies the bronchial lymphatic tissue. The arterial supply of a lymph node enters at the hilum and travels in the trabecula to the cortex of the node where it forms a capillary bed (74). The postcapillary venules lie in the diffuse cortex of the node and are lined by a cuboidal endothelium, which gave rise to the term high endothelial venule (HEV). Classic studies performed by Gowans et al (20) established that these HEVs serve as the major site of migration of lymphocytes between blood and lymph. The nature of leukocyte traffic in the bronchial circulation has not been studied to the same degree as it has been in other systemic vessels or in the pulmonary capillary bed. However, if the bronchial vessels are the same as other systemic vascular beds, the sites of both margination and migration of leukocytes will be different from that observed in the pulmonary vessels.

Leukocyte Migration

The movement of leukocytes from the vascular space into the tissue is a normal process that provides the lung tissue with the monocytes/macrophages required to clear foreign material and the lymphocytes needed to maintain immune surveillance. The polymorphonuclear leukocytes are unique in that they remain within the vascular space unless they are required to migrate into an inflammatory site. The current concepts of leukocyte endothelial interaction have been dominated by studies of systemic microvessels showing that leukocytes are first tethered to the endothelium of the postcapillary venules by transient adhesion that is mediated by members of the selectin family of adhesion molecules (1, 2, 5, 7, 21, 40, 51). This induces the WBCs to leave the flowing stream of circulating cells and roll along the endothelial surface. Stronger adhesion to the endothelial surface is mediated by leukocyte integrins that bind poorly to their ligands unless they are activated by chemokines (33, 64). The fact that leukocytes are normally in prolonged contact with the capillary endothelium in the pulmonary microvessels (26, 27, 41) suggests that the cascade that has been worked out for systemic vessels may not be relevant to events in pulmonary capillaries.

Leukocyte Margination in Pulmonary and Systemic Microvessels

The concentration of leukocytes on the endothelial surface is increased by either capillary sequestration or leukocyte rolling in postcapillary venules. Although these events probably occur in both the pulmonary and systemic vessels, capillary sequestration appears to dominate the process in the pulmonary circulation and rolling in postcapillary venules in the systemic vascular bed. The important difference is that the WBCs are already in close contact with the endothelium in the pulmonary capillaries, whereas they must leave a flowing stream of cells to come in contact with the endothelium of the postcapillary venules. Both mechanisms increase the contact between WBC and endothelium, but the changes required to produce this effect are different.

Leukocyte Adhesion to Endothelial Cells

The pro–adhesive state that initiates leukocyte emigration is controlled by a network of mediators derived from many sources (11, 44, 46, 50, 63). Tumor necrosis factor-α (TNF-α), interferon-γ (IFN), and interleukin-1 (IL-1) overlap with respect to their ability to create a pro–adhesive state on the surface of the endothelium (11, 29, 57, 62). IL-1 and TNF-α also induce increased production of the chemotactic cytokines (68). The chemokines comprise a superfamily of small proteins secreted by several cell types (2, 33, 64). They have a conserved structure containing two cysteine pairs and are divided into α or β subfamilies based on whether the first cysteine pair is separated by an intervening amino acid (CXC = α chemokines) or not (CC = β chemokines). TNF and IL-1 induce the transcription of the α chemokine IL-8, which primarily attracts neutrophils (33, 64, 68). The β chemokines preferentially induce the migration of macrophages, and members of both α and β families probably act cooperatively to induce selective migration of leukocyte subsets in different inflammatory settings (2). A major function of chemokines such as IL-8 may be to provide the trigger that activates the integrins to bind firmly to the endothelium. Other mediators including IL-4, IL-6, IL-10, and transforming growth factor β (TGF-β) appear to function primarily to down-regulate the acute inflammatory response (3, 38, 54, 57).

Three families of molecules mediate leukocyte-endothelial cell adhesion (2, 5, 8, 18, 21, 25, 34, 55, 58, 60, 66, 69), the integrin family (CD11/CD18), the immunoglobulin superfamily (ICAM-1, PECAM-1), and the selectin family (L-selectin, E-selectin and P-selectin) (Figure 3). Neutrophils express the ad-

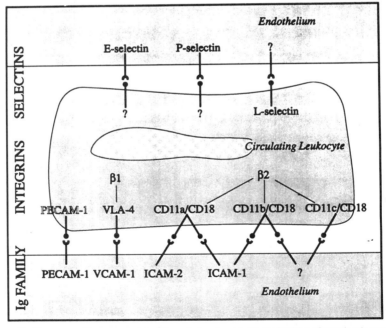

Figure 3   Summary of the current state of knowledge about the three families of proteins that control the migration of leukocytes out of the vascular space. The selectin family is found on the endothelium (E- and P-selectin) and on the circulating leukocyte (L-selectin). The integrins are divided into β1 and β2 subfamilies that are located on the circulating leukocytes and interact with their ligands on the IgG family of adhesion proteins found on the endothelium. PECAM-1 is a special case of an IgG family protein because it interacts with itself and with the circulating leukocytes (see the text for further explanation).

hesion molecule receptor, CD11/CD18, on their surface as three heterodimers, CD11a/CD18, CD11b/CD18, and CD11c/CD18, in a quiescent state. A large pool of CD11b/CD18 is contained within the membranes of the specific granules. Upon activation by a chemotactic stimulus, the CD11/CD18 expressed on the surface undergoes a change in its conformational state to an activated form that can recognize the endothelial ligand. This may also be associated with up-regulation and activation of the granular stores of CD11b/CD18.

The ligands for the neutrophil CD11/CD18 receptor on endothelial cells include the immunoglobulin superfamily member, ICAM-1 (28, 29, 62, 66). This molecule is constitutively expressed on the endothelium, as well as on many other cell types, and is up-regulated in response to cytokines, including IL-1 and TNF-α. This up-regulation in vitro is long lasting because it is still present 24 h after exposure to cytokines. ICAM-1 appears to mediate only part of CD11/CD18-mediated neutrophil-endothelial cell interactions and other, poorly characterized ligands are present. PECAM-1, another member of the immunoglobulin family that is important in neutrophil emigration, binds to itself, as well as to other adhesion molecules that are not identified (69). PECAM-1-mediated adhesion is likely to be important in transendothelial cell migration of neutrophils (69).

The third family of adhesion molecules, the selectins, have a lectin–binding domain at the N-terminus that is important in interactions with their ligands or receptors (5, 8, 18, 36, 55, 58, 60). The selectin family contains three members, L-selectin (CD62L), P-selectin (CD62P), and E-selectin (CD62E). L-selectin is expressed on the plasma membrane of neutrophils, primarily on the microvillar projections of quiescent neutrophils, and no granular pool has been identified (5, 60). It is shed from the surface within minutes after activation in vitro and prior to emigration. P-selectin is found in endothelial cells and in platelets (1, 37, 40, 77). It is stored in the Weibel-Palade bodies within endothelial cells, and its expression on the surface membrane can be rapidly increased by mobilization of these granules to the surface without requiring protein synthesis. It is up-regulated by histamine, thrombin, and oxidants. E-selectin is expressed on the surface of endothelial cells only after activation (5, 8). Its expression requires protein synthesis and can be induced by cytokines including IL-1 and TNF. Receptors for L-selectin, E-selectin, and P-selectin include sialyl Lewis X antigen (Sle^x), an oligosaccharide present on many proteins including L-selectin and CD11/CD18. Recently, CD11/CD18-dependent ICAM-1-independent binding appeared to occur through CD11/CD18-E-selectin interactions (36), although most E-selectin binding is not mediated through this pathway.

Both monocytes and eosinophils express the same adhesion molecules that are present on neutrophils, as well as a second member of the integrin family, VLA-4 (2, 8, 28, 29). This molecule recognizes VCAM-1, a member of the immunoglobulin superfamily (8, 29). Lymphocytes express VLA-4, L-selectin, and CD11a/CD18, but not CD11b/CD18 (28).

The paradigm for leukocyte emigration in the systemic circulation is based on data obtained from in vitro studies and in vivo videomicroscopy of the mesenteric and other systemic microvessels (1, 7, 21, 37, 40, 66, 71, 77). The initial step in this paradigm is a slowing of leukocyte transit through the injured site by reversible loose adhesion between leukocytes and endothelial cells that results in transient contacts and rolling of the leukocyte along the endothelium. This step is mediated through selectins, and a role for each (L-, P-, and E-selectin) has been described. The distribution of L-selectin on the microvilli of neutrophils places this molecule in an ideal position for initial interactions with the endothelium (60). The second step follows further activation of the leukocytes by chemotaxins and haptotaxins, which include IL-8, PAF, and complement protein fragments. Binding of these molecules to receptors on rolling neutrophils results in the up-regulation and activation of CD11/CD18 and the shedding of L-selectin. In the third step, leukocytes bind firmly to the endothelium through CD11/CD18-ICAM-1- or VLA-4/VCAM-1-mediated adhesion. This stable binding is required for leukocyte emigration. The trans-endothelial migration of leukocytes may require PECAM-1 (69), as well as CD11/CD18. The mechanisms by which the interactions required for adhesion are down-regulated to allow migration along the endothelium toward junctions and between endothelial cells into the tissue are not clear.

There are several reasons why this paradigm cannot be directly applied to the pulmonary circulation. First, the primary site of both leukocyte margination and migration is in capillaries, and the space constraints in these vessels do not allow the leukocytes to roll (13). Indeed, the requirement to deform to negotiate the restrictions in the pulmonary capillary bed ensures a close appo-sition of the circulating leukocytes and the capillary endothelial membranes that is unlikely to require receptor-ligand interactions. The pattern of blood flow and the expression of adhesion molecules that mediate leukocyte rolling in the postcapillary venules of the systemic circulation have not been ade-quately examined in the pulmonary circulation. Second, neutrophil emigration out of the pulmonary circulation appears to be mediated by two pathways, one that requires CD11/CD18 and one that does not (15), whereas all acute PMN migration from the systemic microvasculature appears to require CD11/CD18.

Effect of Stimuli Arising from Within the Vasculature

The infusion of inflammatory mediators including complement protein frag-ments and formyl methionine leucine proline peptide (fMLP) induces the sequestration of circulating PMNs within the microvasculature of all organs (12, 42, 76). The lungs are a major site of sequestration, and labeled PMNs accumulate there first, independently of whether they are injected into the systemic arteries or veins. Recent studies from one of our laboratories showed that isolated radiolabeled rabbit neutrophils depleted of L-selectin by treatment with chymotrypsin sequestered in response to infusion of complement fragments with the same rapidity and degree as PMNs expressing normal levels of L-selectin. This result contrasts with those in the systemic circulation where selectins play a major role in concentrating PMNs at an inflammatory site. Furthermore, the initial rapid sequestration that follows an intravascular stimulus does not require CD11/CD18-mediated adhesion (12, 42). However, CD11/CD18 adhesion does seem to be important in maintaining the sequestered PMNs within the pulmonary capillary bed for more than 4–7 min (12, 76).

An important mechanism for the initial sequestration of leukocytes in pulmonary microvessels is a stimulus-induced decrease in their deformability (34, 75). When inflammatory mediators including complement fragments bind to receptors on the neutrophil surface, neutrophil deformability decreases within 1 min, as measured by the pressure required to pass them through a filter containing 5 μm pores at a constant concentration and flow (34). This decrease in neutrophil deformability requires cytoskeletal changes that involve the polymerization of G-actin to F-actin, but not microtubule reassembly (34). This stiffening prevents neutrophils from deforming into the elongated shape required to negotiate the narrow capillaries and increases the time that the leukocytes are in close contact with endothelial cells. It is possible that this mechanically induced prolonged close application of neutrophils and endothelial cells can replace the L-selectin-mediated transient adhesion that occurs between leukocytes and postcapillary venules in the systemic circulation.

The Effect of Extravascular Stimuli

Leukocyte emigration also occurs in response to stimuli that arise in the airspace, which give rise to bronchitis, bronchiolitis, and pneumonia. Quantitative studies of the response of neutrophils to intrabronchial instillation of *Streptococcus pneumoniae* (14) showed that by 1 h, there was a small but significant increase in the number of intravascular neutrophils in the pneumonic region without migration of neutrophils into the alveoli. At 4 h, this intravascular number was further increased, and many neutrophils had migrated into the alveolar space. By 8 h, more neutrophils had emigrated, and the number of intravascular neutrophils was decreased. In the capillary bed of a comparable region of the uninfected contralateral lung, there was also a significant increase in the number of marginated neutrophils. However, none of these neutrophils migrated in the absence of a chemotactic stimulus.

Surprisingly, only 1–2% of the neutrophils delivered to the pneumonic region actually migrated into the air spaces over the time course of the experiment (14). This is in striking contrast to the results of in vitro studies by Smith et al, where 60–80% of the neutrophils that were adherent to the endothelium migrated across the endothelial barrier (66). The factors determining which neutrophils migrate and whether the migrating neutrophils represent a defined subset of the neutrophil population present in the circulation remain to be determined.

The neutrophil's ability to recognize the pro–adhesive site in the pneumonic region was determined by injecting radiolabeled neutrophils 10 min prior to the end of a 1, 2, 4, or 8 h exposure to *S. pneumoniae*. These studies showed that there was no increase in neutrophil retention in the pneumonic compared to the contralateral region at 1 h. However, when the pneumonia had developed over 2, 4, or 8 h, the neutrophil retention in the pneumonic region increased. These studies suggest that the neutrophils begin to recognize the infected site in the lung 1–2 h after the bacteria are deposited on the airway surface (14).

The pulmonary circulation is critical to neutrophil emigration into the pneumonic site because no PMN migration occurred when the pulmonary artery was ligated and the infected region was supplied exclusively by bronchial vessels. Furthermore, the pulmonary capillaries are the primary site of migration out of the pulmonary vessels (17, 45). This contrasts sharply with the systemic circulation where the postcapillary venules are the major site of neutrophil emigration.

The stiffening and decreased deformability that inflammatory mediators induce in neutrophils further increases their concentration with respect to RBCs in the pulmonary capillary blood (16, 25, 34, 65, 75). Several of the mediators associated with the endothelial cell surface at sites of inflammation including PAF, IL-8, and LTB_4 may activate intracapillary neutrophils (5, 16, 50, 65, 77) and delay them in the capillary bed. However, the reduction in deformability responsible for this delay is reversible by 15–20 min, even when the stimulus remains (59). This subsequent increase in deformability may facilitate the shape changes required for migration out of the vascular bed. Further studies will determine whether adhesion mediated by members of the selectin (CD62) family is important to leukocyte margination in pulmonary microvasculature.

The role of the CD11/CD18 adhesion complex in neutrophil emigration out of the pulmonary and systemic circulation has been determined by pretreating rabbits with an antibody that recognizes CD18, the common subunit of this complex, and blocks its function (15, 21). The response at the two sites was compared by instilling stimuli directly into the lung and inserting polyvinyl sponges saturated with the same stimulus into the abdominal wall. The results show that anti-CD18 antibody completely prevented neutrophil emigration initiated by *Escherichia coli* endotoxin and *S. pneumoniae* organisms at the systemic site. Although it also reduced, by 75%, the effect of *E. coli* endotoxin deposited in the lung, it had no effect on the leukocyte emigration induced by

S. pneumoniae. Subsequent studies (15, 21, 23) have shown that CD11/CD18 was required for neutrophil emigration during the acute response of the systemic vascular bed to virtually every stimulus. In contrast, *S. pneumoniae,* hydrochloric acid, or C5a deposited within the alveolar space resulted in CD18-independent neutrophil emigration. *E. coli* endotoxin, *E. coli* live organisms, IL-1α, or phorbol myristate acetate induced neutrophil emigration into the pulmonary parenchyma that was largely dependent on CD18. These data suggest that neutrophil adhesion within the lung differs from that in the systemic circulation in that leukocytes can migrate out of the lung capillaries independently of any interaction between CD11/CD18 and its endothelial ligands. Perhaps the most compelling evidence for a CD11/CD18-independent mechanism of emigration was provided from children with leukocyte adhesion deficiency, type 1, who have a genetic deficiency of CD11/CD18 on the surface of their leukocytes. Examination of autopsy tissue from one of these patients (15) showed that despite a complete genetic deficiency of this complex with no neutrophil emigration into infected appendiceal and skin lesions, many neutrophils emigrated into the alveolar space. This CD18-independent adhesion pathway may be induced by a factor produced by alveolar macrophages. Mileski et al (52) have shown that CD18-independent adhesion can be induced in the systemic circulation if the peritoneum is primed 1–2 days previously by instillation of thioglycolate. This CD18-independent adhesion required the presence of macrophages, which are potent producers of cytokines.

Mulligan et al (56, 57, 72) studied the role of adhesion molecules in modulating the acute inflammatory response to complement and neutrophil-dependent injury induced by cobra venom factor, neutrophil-dependent injury induced by IgG immune complexes, and macrophage-dependent injury induced by IgA immune complexes. They found that CD11/CD18 and ICAM-1 were required for lung injury induced by each stimulus. The selectins also played a role in injuries induced by cobra venom factor (L-selectin and P-selectin) and IgG immune complexes (L-selectin and E-selectin), but not IgA immune complex disease. However, inhibition of selectins reduced the injuries less than inhibition of CD11/CD18. The data of Horgan et al suggest that CD11/CD18 and ICAM-1 partially mediate ischemia/reperfusion injury in the lung (30, 31). However, Vedder et al found that antibodies against CD18 protected against reperfusion injury following hemorrhagic shock (70). Few studies have examined the function of adhesion molecules during chronic inflammation in the lungs, but Piguet et al reported that inhibition of either CD11a/CD18 or CD11b/CD18 reduced the collagen content and the accumulation of lymphocytes 15 days after bleomycin injury (61). Taken together, these studies suggest that adhesion molecules play an important role in the accumulation of leukocytes in acute and chronic inflammatory sites in the lung. However, more data are required before generalizations can be made about the contribution of each adhesion pathway from one inflammatory process to another.

Burns and colleagues (6) quantitated the expression of L-selectin, CD18, and ICAM-1 during CD18-dependent and CD18-independent adhesion using ultrastructural immunohistochemistry. The expression of these adhesion molecules was quantitated by counting the number of colloidal gold particles on the surface of neutrophils or endothelial cells, expressed as gold particle per/μm plasma membrane. Neutrophil emigration induced by *E. coli* endotoxin, a stimulus that elicits CD18-dependent neutrophil emigration, was compared to that induced by *S. pneumoniae,* which elicits CD18-independent emigration. In *E. coli* endotoxin-induced pneumonia, there was no significant up-regulation of CD18 or down-regulation of L-selectin when the neutrophils were within the microvasculature. Only after the neutrophils emigrated into the interstitium between the endothelial and epithelial cells was CD18 expression increased and L-selectin decreased (6). In contrast, neutrophils showed a marked up-regulation of CD18 and almost complete loss of L-selectin before they left the microvasculature, even though CD18 was not required for emigration. However, *S. pneumoniae* did not cause up-regulation of ICAM-1 during the time when neutrophils were emigrating, while CD18-dependent neutrophil emigration induced by *E. coli* endotoxin was associated with an up-regulation of ICAM-1 on the surface of endothelial cells. Subsequent studies showed that increases in ICAM-1 mRNA occurred later and were smaller during CD18-independent neutrophil emigration compared to CD18-dependent emigration, further confirming that ICAM-1 expression is not up-regulated on endothelial cells in response to stimuli that induce CD18-independent adhesion.

These data indicate that *E. coli* endotoxin, a stimulus that elicits CD18-dependent neutrophil emigration, did not alter the expression of L-selectin or CD18 on the surface of neutrophils, but did result in up-regulation of ICAM-1 expression on endothelial cells. In contrast, *S. pneumoniae,* a stimulus that elicits CD18-independent emigration, caused a decrease in L-selectin expression, an increase in CD18 expression, and no change in ICAM-1 expression. It is possible that if CD18 is up-regulated and L-selectin is lost early in the response, a CD18-independent mechanism of adhesion becomes important. However, the regulation of ICAM-1 expression by endothelial cells may be the critical step in determining whether CD18-dependent or -independent pathways of adhesion are used. Cytokines, particularly IL-1 and TNF, are important regulators of ICAM-1 expression on endothelial cells (57, 62, 68), and the selection of a particular adhesion pathway is likely to depend on the cytokines that are produced following the stimulus.

To date there have been few direct comparisons of the role of adhesion molecules in the bronchial and pulmonary circulation and few if any studies designed to determine if the bronchial submucosal capillary bed behaves differently from the capillaries outside the bronchial muscle (Figure 2). Descriptive studies of human bronchiolitis suggest that the inflammatory process focuses on the submucosal bronchial microvessels in some cases and on the peribronchial microvessels of the airways in others. Whether the mechanism of adhesion and migration of cells differs in the microvessels of these two regions of the bronchial wall is unknown.

Although the classic studies of Gowans et al (20) established that the majority of the lymphocytes recirculate from the blood into the lymph through the high endothelium of the postcapillary venules of the lymph nodes, there have been few direct studies of this process in the regional lymph nodes draining the lung. The clonal expansion of memory lymphocytes in regional lymph nodes following exposure to an antigen results in an increased number of lymphocytes leaving the node to drain into the systemic venous blood. Although the number of memory lymphocytes contributed to the 5-liter circulating blood volume by this mechanism may be small, the high levels of blood flow to the parenchyma and airways provide opportunities for these cells to re-enter a site of inflammation and recirculate through the tissue to the regional lymph nodes from which they arose. Selective adhesive interaction between the circulating memory cells and the microvessels at the site of the initial injury could serve to concentrate memory lymphocytes in the damaged tissue and its draining lymph nodes. Recent evidence suggests that there are separate ligands for L-selectin on the HEV of the lymph nodes and the microvessels supplying peripheral tissue (4) and that these ligands for L-selectin could concentrate memory lymphocytes in an injured region and its draining lymph nodes.

In contrast to the protein-dependent binding of the leukocyte integrins to their ligands, the selectins bind through a calcium-dependent recognition of carbohydrate ligands (lectins) in glycoproteins expressed on either the endothelium or the leukocyte (4). Leukocyte L-selectin recognizes sulfated glycoproteins of 50 and 90 kDa (Sgp50 and Spg90), and the interaction between recombinant L-selectin and Sgp50 and Sgp90 appears to exactly mimic that which occurs during L-selectin-mediated binding of lymphocytes to the postcapillary venules of peripheral lymph nodes. Recent studies (4) suggest that GlyCAM-1 (Sgp50) and CD34 (Sgp90) function as ligands for L-selectin and that there are differences in the tissue distribution of these molecules. GlyCAM-1 is expressed predominantly on HEVs of peripheral lymph nodes where its major function is to regulate lymphocyte homing. The CD34 molecule, on the other hand, has a much broader tissue distribution on the endothelial cells throughout the vascular system, and the data of Baumhuerter et al (4) suggest that appropriately glycosylated CD34 could function as the L-selectin ligand allowing leukocytes to return to a local inflammatory site.

Differences in the vascular distribution of the ligands for L-selectin could serve to concentrate memory lymphocytes in inflammatory sites supplied by either the bronchial or the pulmonary circulation. The direction of a specific type of tissue reaction to a particular vascular bed might help explain the pathogenesis of many forms of lung disease. For example, the distribution of the primary complex lesion of tuberculosis might result from the direction of a Th-1–type of response to the pulmonary microvessels of the infected lung and the lymph nodes that drain the tissue (9, 10). Similarly, the concentration of a Th-2 response in bronchial microvessels might explain the restriction of the inflammatory process associated with asthma to the wall and lumen of the bronchi and bronchioles (10, 25).

In summary, this brief review has outlined the important differences in leukocyte kinetics in the pulmonary and bronchial circulations of the lung. The concept of leukocyte margination, based on cells leaving the flowing stream of blood to roll on the endothelium of postcapillary venules, is not relevant to the pulmonary circulation because leukocytes normally come into very close contact with endothelium in the capillary bed. Furthermore, leukocyte migration occurs primarily out of capillaries in the pulmonary circulation, as opposed to postcapillary venules in the systemic circulation. Finally, there is growing evidence that the adhesion between CD11/CD18 that is required for PMN migration out of the systemic circulation is not required in some forms of lung inflammation. Although the threshold of our understanding of leukocyte adherence and migration has been raised in the recent past, much remains to be learned about differences in the nature and control of the inflammatory process in the pulmonary and bronchial vasculature. If the challenge of understanding these two different circulations is met, we should be rewarded with a better grasp of the pathogenesis of many forms of lung disease.

ACKNOWLEDGMENTS

The authors thank Erlene Upp and Kent Webb for the preparation of this manuscript and Stuart Green and Jenny Hards for preparation of the figures.

Literature Cited

1. Abbassi O, Lane CL, Krater SS, Kishimoto TK, Anderson DC, et al. 1991. Canine neutrophil margination mediated by lectin adhesion molecule-1 (LECAM-1) in vitro. *J. Immunol.* 147: 2107–15
2. Adams DH, Shaw S. 1994. Leukocyte endothelial interactions in regulation of leukocyte and migration. *Lancet* 343: 831–35
3. Barton BE, Jackson JV. 1993. Protective role of interleukin 6 in the lipopolysaccharide-galactosamine septic shock model. *Infect. Immun.* 61:1496–99

4. Baumhueter S, Singer MS, Henzel W, Hemmerich S, Renz M, et al. 1993. Binding of L-selectin to the vascular sialomucin CD34. *Science* 262:436–38
5. Bevilacqua MP, Nelson RM. 1993. Selectins. *J. Clin. Invest.* 91:379–87
6. Burns AB, Takei F, Doerschuk CM. 1994. ICAM-1 expression in mouse lung during pneumonia. *J. Immunol.* In press
7. Butcher EC. 1992. Leukocyte-endothelial cell adhesion as an active, multi-step process: a combinatorial mechanism for specificity and diversity in leukocyte targeting. In *Mechanisms of Lymphocyte Activation and Immune Regulation IV. Cellular Communications* pp. 181–94. New York: Plenum
8. Carlos T, Kovach N, Schwartz B, Rosa M, Newman B, et al. 1991. Human monocytes bind to two cytokine-induced adhesive ligands on cultured human endothelial cells: Endothelial-leukocyte adhesion molecule-1 and vascular cell adhesion molecule-1. *Blood* 77:2266–71
9. Cotran, RS, Kumar V, Robbins SL. 1989. *Pathologic Basis of Disease.* pp. 377–80. Philadelphia: Saunders. 4th ed.
10. Del Prete G, Maggi E, Romagnani S. 1994. Human Th-1 and Th-2 cells: functional properties, mechanisms of regulation and role in disease. *Lab. Invest.* 70:299–306
11. Dinarello CH, Wolff SM. 1993. The role of interleukin-1 in disease. *N. Engl. J. Med.* 328:106–13
12. Doerschuk CM. 1992. The role of CD18-mediated adhesion in neutrophil sequestration induced by infusion of activated plasma in rabbits. *Am. J. Respir. Cell Mol. Biol.* 7:140–48
13. Doerschuk CM, Beyers N, Coxson HO, Wiggs B, Hogg JC. 1993. Comparison of neutrophil and capillary diameters in relation to neutrophil sequestration in the lung. *J. Appl. Physiol.* 74:3040–45
14. Doerschuk CM, Markos J, Coxson HO, English D, Hogg JC. 1994. Quantitation of neutrophil migration in acute bacterial pneumonia in rabbits. *J. Appl. Physiol.* In press
15. Doerschuk CM, Winn RK, Coxson HO, Harlan JM. 1990. CD18-dependent and -independent mechanisms of neutrophil adherence in the pulmonary and systemic microvasculature of rabbits. *J. Immunol.* 114:2327–33
16. Downey GP, Worthen GS. 1988. Neutrophil retention in model capillaries: deformability, geometry, and hydrodynamic forces. *J. Appl. Physiol.* 65:1861–71
17. Downey GP, Worthen GS, Henson PM, Hyde DM. 1993. Neutrophil sequestration and migration in localized pulmonary inflammation: Capillary localization and migration across the interalveolar septum. *Am. Rev. Respir. Dis.* 147:168–76
18. Geng JG, Bevilacqua MP, Moore KL, McIntyre TM, Prescott SM, et al. 1990. Rapid neutrophil adhesion to activated endothelium mediated by GMP-140. *Nature* 343:757–60
19. Glazier JB, Hughes JMB, Maloney JE, West JB. 1969. Measurements of capillary dimensions and blood volume in rapidly frozen lungs. *J. Appl. Physiol.* 26:65–76
20. Gowans JL, Knight EJ. 1964. The route of recirculation of lymphocytes in the rat. *Proc. R. Soc. London Ser. B.* 159:257
21. Harlan JM, Winn RK, Vedder NB, Doerschuk CM, Rice CL. 1992. In vivo models of leukocyte adherence to endothelium. In *Adhesion: Its Role in Inflammatory Disease,* pp. 117–50. New York: Freeman
22. Harris P, Heath D. 1977. The human pulmonary circulation. In *The Measurement of Flow,* pp. 78–96. London/New York: Churchill Livingstone
23. Hellewell PG, Youn SK, Henson PM, Worthen GS. 1994. Disparate role of the β_2-integrin CD18 in the local accumulation of neutrophils in pulmonary and cutaneous inflammation in the rabbit. *Am. J. Respir. Cell Mol. Biol.* 10:391–98
24. Hogg, JC. 1987. Neutrophil kinetics and lung injury. *Physiol. Rev.* 67:1249–95
25. Hogg JC. 1987. Pathology. In *Bronchial Asthma. Mechanisms and Therapeutics,* ed. EB Weiss, M Stein, pp. 352–55. Boston/Toronto/London: Little Brown
26. Hogg JC, Coxson HO, Brumwell M-L, Beyers N, Doerschuk CM, et al. 1994. Erythrocyte and polymorphonuclear cell transit time and concentration in human pulmonary capillaries. *J. Appl. Physiol.* In press
27. Hogg JC, McLean T, Martin BA, Wiggs B. 1988. Erythrocyte transit and neutrophil concentration in the dog lung. *J. Appl. Physiol.* 65:1217–25
28. Hogg N. 1991. An integrin overview. *Chem. Immunol.* 50:1–12
29. Hogg N, Bates PA, Harvey J. 1991. Structure and function of intercellular adhesion molecule-1. *Chem. Immunol.* 50:98–115
30. Horgan MJ, Ge M, Gu J, Rothlein R, Malik AB. 1991. Role of ICAM-1 in neutrophil-mediated lung vascular injury after occlusion and reperfusion. *Am. J. Physiol.* 261:H1578–84
31. Horgan MJ, Wright SD, Malik AB.

1990. Antibody against leukocyte integrin (CD18) prevents reperfusion-induced lung vascular injury. *Am. J. Physiol.* 259:L315–19

32. Hornick DB. 1988. Pulmonary host defense: defects that lead to chronic inflammation of the airway. *Clin. Chest Med.* 9:669–78

33. Hubert AR, Kunkle SL, Todd RF Ill, Weiss SJ. 1991. Regulation of transendothelial neutrophil migration by endogenous interleukin 8. *Science* 254: 99–102

34. Inano H, English D, Doerschuk CM. 1992. Effect of zymosan-activated plasma on the deformability of rabbit polymorphonuclear leukocytes and the role of the cytoskeleton. *J. Appl. Physiol.* 73:1370–76

35. Johnson RL, Spicer WS, Bishop JM, Forster RE. 1960. Pulmonary capillary blood volume flow and diffusing capacity during exercise. *J. Appl. Physiol.* 15:893–902

36. Kotovuori P, Tontti E, Pigott R, Shepherd M, Kiso M, et al. 1993. The vascular E-selectin binds to the leukocyte integrins CD11/CD18. *Glycobiology* 3: 131–36

37. Lawrence MB, Springer TA. 1991. Leukocytes roll on a selectin at physiologic flow rates: distinction from and prerequisite for adhesion through integrins. *Cell* 65:859–73

38. Lefer AM, Ma XL, Weyrich AS, Scalia R. 1993. Mechanism of the cardioprotective effect of transforming growth factor β_1 in feline myocardial ischemia and reperfusion. *Proc. Natl. Acad. Sci. USA* 90:1018–22

39. Lewis BM, Forster RE, Beckman BL. 1958. Effect of inflation of a pressure site on pulmonary diffusing capacity in man. *J. Appl. Physiol.* 15:57–64

40. Ley K, Gaehtgens P, Fennie C, Singe MS, Lasky LA, Rosen SD. 1991. Lectin-like cell adhesion molecule 1 mediates leukocyte rolling in mesenteric venules in vivo. *Blood* 77:2553–55

41. Lien DC, Wagner Jr. WW, Kepon RL, Haslett C, Hansen WL, et al. 1987. Physiological neutrophil sequestration in the lung: visual evidence for location and capillaries. *J. Appl. Physiol.* 62:1236–43

42. Lundberg C, Wright SD. 1990. Relation of the CD11/CD18 family of leukocyte antigens to the transient neutropenia caused by chemoattractants. *Blood* 76: 1240–45

43. MacNee WB, Wiggs B, Belzberg A, Hogg JC. 1989. The effect of cigarette smoking on neutrophil kinetics in human lungs. *N. Engl. J. Med.* 321:924–28

44. Makristhathis A, Stauffer F, Feistauer SM, Georgopoulos A. 1993. Bacteria induce release of platelet-activating factor (PAF) from polymorphonuclear neutrophil granulocytes: possible role for PAF in pathogenesis of experimentally induced bacterial pneumonia. *Infect. Immunol.* 61:1996–2002

45. Marchesi VT. 1961. The site of leucocyte emigration during inflammation. *Q. J. Exp. Physiol.* 46:115–18

46. Marik P, Kraus P, Sribante J, Havlik I, Lipman J, Hohnson DW. 1993. Hydrocortisone and tumor necrosis factor in severe community-acquired pneumonia. *Chest* 104:389–92

47. Markos J, Doerschuk CM, English D, Wiggs BR, Hogg JC. 1993. Effect of positive end expiratory pressure on leukocyte transit in rabbit lungs. *J. Appl. Physiol.* 74:2627–33

48. Markos J, Hooper RO, Kavanagh-Gray D, Wiggs BR, Hogg JC. 1990. Effect of raised alveolar pressure on leukocyte retention in the human lung. *J. Appl. Physiol.* 69:214–21

49. Martin BA, Wiggs BR, Lee S, Hogg JC. 1987. Regional differences in neutrophil margination in dog lungs. *J. Appl. Physiol.* 63:1253–61

50. Martin TR, Pistorese BP, Chi EY, Goodman RB, Matthay MA. 1989. Effects of leukotriene B_4 in the human lung: recruitment of neutrophils into the alveolar spaces without a change in protein permeability. *J. Clin. Invest.* 84: 1609–19

51. Mayadas TN, Johnson RC, Rayburn H, Hynes RO, Wagner DD. 1993. Leukocyte rolling and extravasation are severely compromised in P selectin-deficient mice. *Cell* 74:541–54

52. Mileski W, Harlan J, Rice C, Winn R. 1990. *Streptococcus pneumoniae*-stimulated macrophages induce neutrophils to emigrate by a CD18-independent mechanism of adherence. *Circ. Shock* 31:259–67

53. Miller WS. 1943. The blood vessel. In *The Lung*, pp. 69–83. Springfield/Baltimore: Thomas

54. Moore KW, O'Garra A, de Waal Malefyt R, Vieira P, Mosmann TR. 1993. Interleukin-10. *Annu. Rev. Immunol.* 11:165–90

55. Muir AL, Cruz M, Martin BA, Thommassen H, Belzberg A, Hogg JC. 1984. Leukocyte kinetics in human lungs: role of exercise and catecholamines. *J. Appl. Physiol.* 57:711–19

56. Mulligan MS, Paulson JC, DeFrees S, Zheng ZL, Lowe JB, Ward PA. 1993. Protective effects of oligosaccharides in

P-selectin-dependent lung injury. *Nature* 364:149–51

57. Mulligan MS, Vaporciyan AA, Miyasaka M, Tamatani T, Ward PA. 1993. Tumor necrosis factor alpha regulates in vivo intrapulmonary expression of ICAM-1. *Am. J. Pathol.* 142:1739–49

58. Norgard-Sumnicht KE, Varki NM, Varki A. 1993. Calcium-dependent heparin-like ligands for L-selectin in nonlymphoid endothelial cells. *Science* 261:480–83

59. Pecsvarady Z, Fisher TC, Fabok A, Coates TD, Meiselman HJ. 1992. Kinetics of granulocyte deformability following exposure to chemotactic stimuli. *Blood Cells* 18:333–52

60. Picker LJ, Warnock RA, Burns AR, Doerschuk CM, Berg EL, Butcher EC. 1991. The neutrophil selectin LECAM-1 presents carbohydrate ligands to the vascular selectins ELAM-1 and GMP-140. *Cell* 66:921–33

61. Piguet PF, Rosen H, Vesin C, Grau GE. 1993. Effective treatment of the pulmonary fibrosis elicited in mice by bleomycin or silica with anti-CD11 antibodies. *Am. Rev. Respir. Dis.* 147:435–41

62. Pober JS. 1988. Cytokine-mediated activation of endothelium. *Am. J. Pathol.* 133:426–33

63. Rolfe MW, Kunkel SL, Standiford TJ, Chensue SW, Allen RM, et al. 1991. Pulmonary fibroblast expression of interleukin-8: A model for alveolar macrophage-derived cytokine networking. *Am. J. Respir. Cell Mol. Biol.* 5:493–501

64. Rot A. 1992. Endothelial cell binding of NAP-1/IL-8: role in neutrophil emigration. *Immunol. Today* 13:291–94

65. Selby C, Dorst E, Wraith PK, MacNee W. 1991. In vivo neutrophil sequestration within lungs of humans is determined by in vitro "filterability." *J. Appl. Physiol.* 71:1996–2003

66. Smith CW, Marlin SD, Rothlein R, Toman C, Anderson DC. 1989. Cooperative interactions of LFA-1 and Mac-1 with intercellular adhesion molecule-1 in facilitating adherence and transendothelial migration of human neutrophils in vitro. *J. Clin. Invest.* 83:2008–17

67. Staub NC, Schultz EL. 1968. Pulmonary capillary length in the dog, cat and rabbit. *Respir. Physiol.* 5:371–78

68. Strieter RM, Standiford T, Chensue SW, Kasahara K, Kunkel SL. 1991. Induction and regulation of interleukin-8 gene expression. *Adv. Exp. Med. Biol.* 305:23–30

69. Vaporciyan AA, DeLisser HM, Yan HC, Mendiguren II, Thom SR, et al. 1993. Involvement of platelet-endothelial cell adhesion molecule-1 in neutrophil recruitment in vivo. *Science* 262:1580–82

70. Vedder NB, Winn RK, Rice CL, Chi EY, Arfors KE, Harlan JM. 1988. A monoclonal antibody to the adherence-promoting leukocyte glycoprotein, CD18, reduces organ injury and improves survival from hemorrhage and resuscitation in rabbits. *J. Clin. Invest.* 81:939–44

71. Von Andrian UH, Chambers JD, McEvoy LM, Bargatze RF, Arfors KE, Butcher EC. 1991. Two-step model of leukocyte-endothelial cell interaction in inflammation: distinct roles for LECAM-1 and the leukocyte beta 2 integrins in vivo. *Proc. Natl. Acad. Sci. USA* 88:7538–42

72. Ward PA, Mulligan MS. 1993. Molecular mechanisms in acute lung injury. *Adv. Pharmacol.* 24:275–92

73. Weibel ER. 1963. *Morphometry of the Human Lung.* pp. 73–89. New York: Academic

74. Weiss L. 1983. Lymphatic vessels and lymph nodes. In *Histology,* pp. 527–43. New York/Amsterdam/Oxford: Elsevier Biomedical. 5th ed.

75. Worthen GS, Schwab B, Elson EL, Downey GP. 1989. Mechanics of stimulated neutrophils: cell stiffening induces retention in capillaries. *Science* 245:183–85

76. Yoder MC, Checkley LL, Giger U, Hanson WL, Kirk KR, et al. 1990. Pulmonary microcirculatory kinetics of neutrophils deficient in leukocyte adhesion-promoting glycoproteins. *J. Appl. Physiol.* 69:207–13

77. Zimmerman GA, Lorant DE, McIntyre TM, Prescott SM. 1993. Juxtacrine intercellular signaling: Another way to do it. *Am. J. Respir. Cell Mol. Biol.* 9:573–77

Annu. Rev. Physiol. 1995. 57:115–34

REGULATION OF PULMONARY VASCULAR TONE IN THE PERINATAL PERIOD

Jeffrey R. Fineman, Scott J. Soifer, and Michael A. Heymann

Cardiovascular Research Institute, University of California, San Francisco, California 94143–0106

KEY WORDS: persistent pulmonary hypertension of the newborn, nitric oxide, endothelium, transitional circulation, fetal blood flow

---

INTRODUCTION

In the fetus, gas exchange occurs in the placenta and not in the lung. Consequently, pulmonary vascular resistance is high, pulmonary blood flow is low (about 35 ml/min/kg fetal body wt in near–term fetal lambs), and right ventricular output is thereby directed through the ductus arteriosus toward the placenta for gas exchange. At the time of birth and the onset of ventilation, pulmonary vascular resistance falls, and pulmonary blood flow rapidly increases approximately tenfold (31). Failure of the pulmonary circulation to undergo this transition at birth results in persistent pulmonary hypertension of the newborn (PPHN), a condition that can result in significant morbidity and mortality. Many factors regulate pulmonary blood flow in this critical perinatal period: These include mechanical influences and the release of a variety of vasoactive substances. Recent evidence suggests that vasoactive mediators produced and released by the pulmonary vascular endothelium, either locally or into the circulation (paracrine or endocrine function), are central to many of these phenomena. This review discusses current knowledge dealing with the regulation of blood flow in the normal fetal, transitional, and postnatal pulmonary circulations, and possible aberrations in these regulatory mechanisms associated with PPHN. We place particular emphasis on newer information relating to the role of the pulmonary vascular endothelium in regulation

0066–4278/95/0315–0115$05.00

of the perinatal circulation. One must bear in mind that a great deal of our knowledge of fetal blood flow is based on animal studies. Obviously, data on human fetuses and newborns are lacking because invasive techniques would be necessary to obtain them. Therefore, the applicability of these animal studies to humans should be questioned. Historically, however, overlapping data on the pulmonary circulation obtained in animals and in humans have had excellent correlation.

MORPHOLOGIC DEVELOPMENT OF THE PULMONARY VASCULATURE

The morphologic development of the pulmonary circulation affects the physiological changes that occur in the perinatal period. In the fetus and immediate newborn, small pulmonary arteries of all sizes have a thicker muscular coat relative to external diameter than do similar arteries in the adult. This greater muscularity generally is held responsible, at least in part, for the increased vasoreactivity and the high pulmonary vascular resistance found in the fetus, particularly near term. In fetal lamb lungs fixed at perfusion pressures similar to those found normally in utero, the medial smooth muscle coat is most prominent in the smallest arteries (fifth and sixth generation arteries: external diameter 20–50 μm). During the latter half of gestation, the medial smooth muscle thickness remains constant in relation to the external diameter of the artery (41). Similar observations utilizing slightly different techniques have been made in human lungs (32, 54). After birth, particularly within the first several weeks, the medial smooth muscle involutes, and the thickness of the media of the small pulmonary arteries decreases rapidly and progressively (33).

Toward the periphery of the lung, the completely encircling smooth muscle of the media gives way to a region of incomplete muscularization (54). In these partially muscularized arteries, the smooth muscle is arranged in a spiral or helix. More peripherally, the muscle disappears from arteries that are still larger than capillaries (nonmuscularized small pulmonary arteries). In these nonmuscular, small pulmonary arteries, an incomplete pericyte layer is found within the endothelial basement membrane. In the nonmuscular portions of the partially muscular small pulmonary arteries, intermediate cells are found, i.e. cells intermediate in position and structure between pericytes and mature smooth muscle cells (43). These cells are precursor smooth muscle cells, and under certain conditions, such as hypoxia, they may rapidly differentiate into mature smooth muscle cells (43).

In the human, small pulmonary arteries are conveniently identified by their relationship to airways. Preacinar pulmonary arteries lie proximal to or with terminal bronchioli. Intra-acinar pulmonary arteries course with respiratory bronchioli or alveolar ducts, or within the alveolar walls. During the final quarter of gestation, only about half of the fetal pulmonary arteries associated with respiratory bronchioli (precapillary) are muscularized or partially muscularized, and the alveoli are free of muscular arteries (32). In the adult, complete circumferential muscularization extends peripherally along the intra–acinar arteries so that the majority of small pulmonary arteries in relationship to alveoli are completely muscularized. Between birth and puberty, the arteries undergo progressive peripheral muscularization; the adult pattern is reached about the time of puberty.

During fetal growth in lambs, the number of small arteries increases greatly, not only in absolute terms but also per unit volume of lung (41). In the human, the main preacinar pulmonary arterial branches that accompany the larger airways are developed by 16 weeks of gestation (32). However, the development of the intra–acinar circulation relates more closely to the alveolar development that occurs late in gestation and perhaps even predominantly after birth (33). As the alveoli multiply, so do the arteries, a process that is generally complete by 10 yr of age. In the early postnatal period (first 2 yr in humans), pulmonary arterial growth is more rapid than alveolar growth (33).

PHYSIOLOGY OF THE PULMONARY VASCULATURE

Determinants of Pulmonary Vascular Resistance

Pulmonary vascular resistance changes throughout gestation and after birth. The resistance of the pulmonary circulation at any one time is related to several factors and can be estimated by applying the resistance equation and the Poiseuille-Hagen relationship (57). The resistance equation (the hydraulic equivalent of Ohm's law) states that the resistance to flow between two points along a tube equals the decrease in pressure between the two points divided by the flow. For the pulmonary vascular bed, where Rp = pulmonary vascular resistance and Qp = pulmonary blood flow per min, the decrease in mean pressure is from the pulmonary artery (Ppa) to the pulmonary vein (Ppv):

$$Rp = (Ppa - Ppv)/Qp.$$

Therefore, pulmonary vascular resistance increases when pulmonary arterial pressure increases or when pulmonary blood flow decreases. Increases in pulmonary venous pressure cause pulmonary arterial pressure to increase in order to maintain the driving pressure across the lungs. This increase in pressure may also result in an increase in pulmonary vascular resistance.

Other factors that affect pulmonary vascular resistance can be defined by applying a modification of the Poiseuille-Hagen relationship, which describes the resistance (R) to flow of a Newtonian fluid through a system of round, straight glass tubes of constant cross-sectional area:

$$Rp = 8 \bullet l \bullet \eta / \pi r^4,$$

where l = length of the system of vessels, r = the internal radius of the system of vessels, and η = the viscosity of the fluid. According to this relationship, increasing the viscosity of blood perfusing the lungs or decreasing the radius of or the number of small pulmonary arteries increases pulmonary vascular resistance. Early in gestation, pulmonary vascular resistance is much higher than in the newborn or the adult because there are fewer small pulmonary arteries in the fetal lung and, therefore, a decreased cross-sectional area. Secondary to the growth of new pulmonary arteries and the increase in cross–sectional area of the pulmonary vascular bed, pulmonary vascular resistance decreases during fetal life. However, pulmonary vascular resistance is still much higher near term than after birth.

Because the above equations describe steady, laminar flow of a Newtonian fluid in rigid smooth tubes, differences between physical and biological systems should be considered. First, blood is not a Newtonian fluid. However, this is probably of little importance at normal hematocrits (3). The viscosity of blood is related to red cell number, fibrinogen concentration, and red cell deformability. An increased hematocrit (secondary to fetal hypoxemia, twin-to-twin or maternal-to-fetal blood transfusion, or delayed clamping of the umbilical cord) increases viscosity. Pulmonary vascular resistance increases logarithmically (not linearly) when the hematocrit increases. Second, pulmonary vessels are not rigid tubes. Their walls are deformable, and their size and shape are influenced by transmural pressure. For example, as pulmonary blood flow or left atrial pressure increases, vessel diameter may change, and/or the recruitment of new pulmonary vessels may occur. Therefore, the fall in calculated pulmonary vascular resistance with increases in pulmonary blood flow is nonlinear (15, 51, 61). However, the clinical importance of this nonlinearity is unclear, considering that the pressure-flow relationship remains quite linear with normal or increased flow (61). Third, blood flow through the pulmonary circulation is pulsatile, not laminar, and the small pulmonary arteries are branched, curved, and tapered, not straight. In addition, the small pulmonary arteries are in parallel, and the radii of these arteries may differ in different lung zones.

Despite these differences from physical models, the general effects of changes in physical factors, such as viscosity and radius, do apply. In fact, a change in luminal radius is the major factor responsible for maintaining a high pulmonary vascular resistance in the fetus (31). Consideration of these factors, particularly viscosity and cross–sectional area of the vascular bed, is important in evaluating the pathophysiology of persistent pulmonary hypertension of the newborn infant (see below).

The Normal Fetal Circulation

In the fetus, normal gas exchange occurs in the placenta, and pulmonary blood flow is low, essentially supplying only nutritional requirements for lung growth and performing some metabolic functions. Pulmonary blood flow in near–term lambs is about 100 ml/100 g wet lung wt per min, representing 8–10% of total output of the heart (62). Pulmonary blood flow is low despite the dominance of the right ventricle, which in the fetus ejects 55–65% of total cardiac output, depending on species. Most of the right ventricular output is diverted away from the lungs through the widely patent ductus arteriosus to the descending thoracic aorta, from which a large proportion reaches the placenta, through the umbilical circulation, for oxygenation. In young fetuses (at about 0.5 gestation), pulmonary blood flow is approximately 3–4% of the total combined left and right ventricular output of the heart (fetal cardiac output). This increases to about 6% at about 0.8 gestation, which corresponds temporally with the onset of the release of surface active material into lung fluid. This release is followed by another progressive, slow rise in pulmonary blood flow, reaching about 8–10% near term (62). Fetal pulmonary arterial pressure increases with advancing gestation. At term, mean pulmonary arterial pressure is about 50 mm Hg, generally exceeding mean descending aortic pressure by 1–2 mm Hg (59). Early in gestation, pulmonary vascular resistance is extremely high relative to that in the infant and adult, probably due to the paucity of small arteries. Pulmonary vascular resistance falls progressively during the last half of gestation, new arteries develop, and cross–sectional area increases; however, baseline pulmonary vascular resistance is still much higher than after birth (31, 59).

Regulation of Fetal Pulmonary Vascular Resistance

Many factors including mechanical effects, state of oxygenation, and the production of vasoactive substances regulate the tone of the fetal pulmonary circulation. In unventilated fetal lungs, fluid filling the alveolar space compresses the small pulmonary arteries, which increases pulmonary vascular resistance. In addition, high pulmonary vascular resistance is associated with the normally low oxygen tension (P_{O_2}) in pulmonary and systemic arterial blood in the fetus. In fetal lambs, pulmonary arterial blood P_{O_2} is 17–20 mm Hg, and femoral arterial blood P_{O_2} is 20–24 mm Hg. Reducing blood P_{O_2} to similar values in newborn lambs after birth produces a marked increase in pulmonary vascular resistance (59). Similarly, fetal pulmonary vascular resistance is increased by decreasing fetal blood P_{O_2} either by maternal hypoxia or by compression of the umbilical cord (50, 75). Conversely, fetal pulmonary vascular resistance is decreased by increasing blood P_{O_2} (80). The exact mechanism and site of hypoxic pulmonary vasoconstriction in the fetal pulmonary circulation remain unclear. In isolated fetal pulmonary arteries, oxygen modulates the production of both prostacyclin (PGI_2) and endothelium–derived nitric oxide (EDNO; previously called endothelium–derived relaxing factor: EDRF), two potent vasoactive substances that may mediate the responses to changes in oxygenation of the developing pulmonary circulation (72, 74). In the intact fetal lamb, oxygen–mediated fetal pulmonary vasodilation is regulated, at least in part, by the release of EDNO (45, 80). Oxygen–related changes in pulmonary vascular resistance are also affected by pH: Acidemia increases pulmonary vascular resistance and accentuates hypoxic vasoconstrictor responses (64).

In addition to the hypoxic environment, certain metabolites of arachidonic acid may be actively involved in the control of fetal pulmonary vascular resistance. Leukotrienes (LTs) C_4 and D_4 are potent pulmonary vasoconstrictors, synthesized in pulmonary arterial tissue from arachidonic acid by a 5'-lipoxygenase enzyme. Although their function as mediators of hypoxic pulmonary vasoconstriction in adults has been challenged, a role for them has been proposed in newborn lambs, and the possibility remains that they may be tonically active in utero (4, 68, 70). In fetal lambs, end–organ antagonism (receptor blockade) or synthesis inhibition of leukotrienes increases pulmonary blood flow about eightfold, i.e. to levels equivalent to those that accompany normal ventilation after birth (37, 76). These observations suggest a physiological role for leukotrienes in maintaining pulmonary vasoconstriction and, thereby, a low pulmonary blood flow in the fetus. Leukotrienes have also been isolated from tracheal fluid of near–term fetal lambs and from lung lavage fluid of newborns with the syndrome of persistent pulmonary hypertension, which further suggests that leukotrienes may contribute to maintaining the high pulmonary vascular resistance in the fetus (79, 81). However, nonselectivity of the leukotriene antagonists in animal studies has brought these conclusions into question, and the physiological role of leukotrienes remains unclear. In some systems, leukotriene effects may be mediated by inducing the production of thromboxane A_2. However, this does not seem to apply to the fetal lamb because inhibition of thromboxane synthesis does not affect pulmonary vascular resistance nor the response to leukotriene end–organ antagonism (12).

The fetal pulmonary circulation, in addition to producing vasoconstrictors, actively and continuously produces vasodilating substances that modulate the degree of vasoconstriction under normal conditions and that may play a more active role during periods of fetal stress. These substances are mainly endothelial derived and include EDNO and PGI_2. EDNO is synthesized by the oxidation of the guanidino nitrogen moiety of L-arginine (49). After stimulation by increased shear stress or the receptor binding of specific vasodilators (endothelium–dependent vasodilators, e.g. bradykinin), nitric oxide (NO) is synthesized and released from the endothelial cell by the activation of nitric oxide synthase. Once released from endothelial cells, NO diffuses into vascular smooth muscle cells and activates soluble guanylyl cyclase, the enzyme that catalyzes the production of guanosine-3′-5′-cyclic monophosphate (cGMP) from guanosine-5′-triphosphate. Activation of guanylyl cyclase increases the concentrations of cGMP, thus initiating a cascade that includes production of protein kinase G, and results in smooth muscle relaxation (Figure 1) (24). In the fetus, EDNO production is stimulated by receptor-mediated mechanisms and by activation of ATP–dependent K+ channels (10). The latter pathway is thought to be stimulated by stretch or by increased shear forces on the pulmonary vascular endothelium. In fetal lambs, inhibition of EDNO synthesis by N^{ω}-nitro-L-arginine, a competitive inhibitor of L-arginine, produces marked increases in resting fetal pulmonary vascular tone, which suggests that basal NO production, in part, mediates fetal

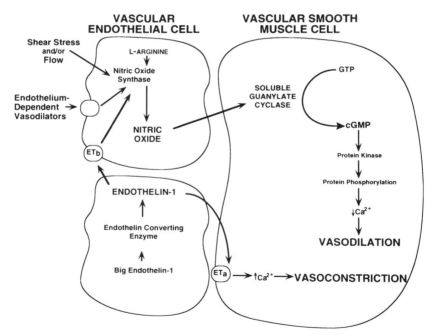

Figure 1   The binding of endothelium–dependent vasodilators to specific endothelial cell receptors, or changes in shear stress, initiate a series of events leading to the production of nitric oxide from L-arginine. Nitric oxide diffuses into the vascular smooth muscle, stimulates guanylyl cyclase, and initiates a cascade of events that produces vascular relaxation. Endothelin-1 may bind to receptors on the endothelial cell (ETb), which could result in vascular relaxation, in part by the production of nitric oxide. Endothelin-1 may also bind to receptors on the smooth muscle cell (ETa), which could result in vascular constriction.

tone (1, 45). PGI_2 is synthesized primarily in vascular endothelial cells and produces vasodilation by activating adenylyl cyclase via receptor G protein–coupled mechanisms. Activation of adenylyl cyclase results in increased adenosine $3',5'$-cyclic monophosphate (cAMP) concentrations, thus initiating a cascade that results in smooth muscle relaxation. A maturational increase in PGI_2 production throughout gestation parallels the decrease in pulmonary vascular resistance in the fetal third trimester (72). However, in vivo, prostaglandin inhibition does not change resting pulmonary vascular resistance consistently, thus calling into question the importance of basal PGI_2 activity in mediating resting fetal pulmonary vascular tone (47).

Endothelin-1 (ET-1), a 21–amino acid polypeptide also produced by vascular endothelial cells, has potent vasoactive properties (86). The hemodynamic effects of ET-1 are mediated by at least two distinctive receptor populations, ET_a and ET_b. ET_a receptors are located on vascular smooth muscle cells and are likely responsible for the vasoconstricting effects of ET-1, whereas the ET_b receptors may be located on endothelial cells and are likely responsible for the vasodilating effects of ET-1 (Figure 1) (5, 67). In the adult pulmonary circulation, exogenous ET-1 produces vasoconstriction, but it produces pulmonary vasodilation in both fetal and neonatal lambs (11, 85). In fetal lambs, selective ET_a receptor blockade produces small decreases in resting fetal pulmonary vascular resistance (84). This suggests a potential, minor role for basal ET-1–induced vasoconstriction in maintaining the high fetal pulmonary vascular resistance. However, this role, if any, requires further investigation.

Other vasoactive substances may also play a role in maintaining the high pulmonary vascular resistance in the fetus. Thromboxane A_2, synthesized from arachidonic acid by the cyclo-oxygenase enzymes, is a vasoconstrictor, as is platelet–activating factor. Both produce potent pulmonary vasoconstriction in newborn and adult animals. Several growth factors, particularly platelet–derived growth factor (PDGF), which are involved in vascular smooth muscle growth and proliferation, also have vasoconstrictor effects. Whether any of these compounds, or others yet to be defined, contribute to maintaining the high pulmonary vascular resistance in the fetus is unknown.

Animal studies suggest that the autonomic nervous system plays little or no role in mediating normal resting control of the fetal pulmonary vascular resistance, but when stimulated, it can alter pulmonary vascular resistance (8, 13, 63). The increased pulmonary vasomotor tone found in the fetus accentuates the responses to various stimuli. Whether these mechanisms are invoked during fetal stress or are involved in perinatal changes is not clear.

Changes in the Pulmonary Circulation at Birth

After birth, with initiation of ventilation by the lungs and the subsequent increase in pulmonary and systemic arterial blood P_{O_2}, pulmonary vascular resistance decreases and pulmonary blood flow increases eight- to tenfold to match systemic blood flow (300–400 ml/min/kg body wt) (31). This large increase in pulmonary blood flow increases pulmonary venous return to the left atrium, which increases left atrial pressure. Then the valve of the foramen ovale closes, thereby preventing any significant atrial right-to-left shunting of blood. In addition, the ductus arteriosus constricts and closes functionally within several hours after birth, which effectively separates the pulmonary and systemic circulations. Mean pulmonary arterial pressure decreases, and by 24 h after birth it is approximately 50% of mean systemic arterial pressure. Adult values are reached 2–6 weeks after birth (34, 60).

The decrease in pulmonary vascular resistance with ventilation and oxygenation at birth is regulated by a complex and incompletely understood interplay between metabolic and mechanical factors, which are triggered in turn by the

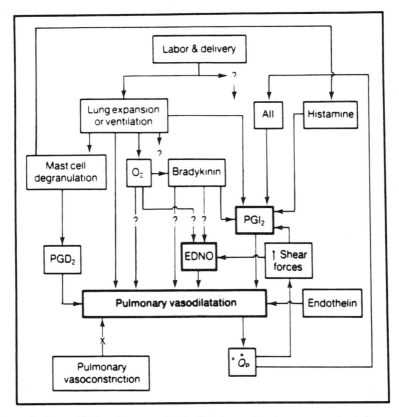

Figure 2 Factors likely to be responsible for the changes in pulmonary vascular resistance and pulmonary blood flow with oxygen ventilation at birth.

ventilatory and circulatory changes that occur at birth (Figure 2) (37). Physical expansion of the fetal lamb lung without changing blood P_{O_2} or P_{CO_2} increases fetal pulmonary blood flow and decreases pulmonary vascular resistance, but not to newborn values (18). A small proportion of this decrease relates to replacement of fluid in the alveoli with gas, which allows unkinking of the small pulmonary arteries, and to the changes in alveolar surface tension, which exert a negative dilating pressure on the small pulmonary arteries, thus maintaining their patency (20).

Physical expansion of the lung also releases vasoactive substances, such as PGI_2, that increase pulmonary blood flow and decrease pulmonary vascular resistance in the fetal goat and lamb (38, 39). There is also net production of PGI_2 by the lung with the initiation of ventilation at birth (39). Inhibitors of prostaglandin synthesis, such as indomethacin or meclofenamic acid, block PGI_2 production and also attenuate the increase in pulmonary blood flow and the decrease in pulmonary vascular resistance that occur with physical expansion of the fetal lung, although not the changes that occur with oxygenation (82). Therefore, PGI_2, or perhaps, but less likely, another cyclo-oxygenase metabolite of arachidonic acid, plays an important role in the increase in pulmonary blood flow and decrease in pulmonary vascular resistance in association with the mechanical component (stretch) of ventilation at birth. Other events that occur at the onset of ventilation may also play some role in stimulating PGI_2 production and, thus, pulmonary vasodilation. These include the release of bradykinin as well as the increased production of angiotensin II (AII) by pulmonary vascular endothelium.

Other prostaglandins may also play a role in these circulatory changes. In fetal lambs and goats, PGE_2, produced in the fetal vasculature and the placenta, maintains patency of the ductus arteriosus and decreases pulmonary vascular resistance. However, both PGI_2 and PGE_2 also produce systemic vasodilation in intact fetal animals at term, whereas systemic vascular resistance normally increases soon after ventilation begins (59). Therefore, they probably are not the only prostaglandins involved with pulmonary vasodilation. Among the other prostaglandins, PGD_2 has attracted particular interest. When given to newborn animals, PGD_2 produces greater pulmonary than systemic vasodilation (9, 77). This differential effect is lost by about 12–15 days of age, when PGD_2 produces pulmonary vasoconstriction. A similar pattern of response follows the administration of histamine, which is a modest pulmonary vasodilator in the immediate perinatal period, but subsequently becomes a pulmonary vasoconstrictor (27). Both PGD_2 and histamine are released from mast cells. In fetal rhesus monkeys, mast cell numbers increase in the lungs over the last portion of gestation; after birth, they decrease markedly (71). Therefore, the stimulus of lung expansion may cause mast cells to degranulate and release

PGD_2 and histamine, which contribute to the initial postnatal pulmonary vasodilation.

Bradykinin, another vasoactive agent, also appears to be a potent vasodilator in the fetus (30). After ventilating the lungs of fetal lambs with oxygen or exposing the fetuses to hyperbaric oxygen, the blood concentration of kininogen, the bradykinin precursor, decreases and the concentration of bradykinin increases (30). Bradykinin has been shown to stimulate PGI_2 production in intact fetal lungs and in pulmonary vascular endothelial cells in culture, which would enhance vasodilation (42). However, we have recently shown that bradykinin receptor blockade does not change the increase in pulmonary blood flow and the decrease in pulmonary vascular resistance that occur with oxygen ventilation of the fetal lamb (6). Therefore, the exact role of bradykinin in the transitional circulation is unclear. Although ET-1 is a potent fetal pulmonary vasodilator (84), and circulating levels of ET-1 are increased in the newborn period, the role of ET-1 in the transitional pulmonary circulation remains to be elucidated (11, 87).

Ventilation of the fetus without oxygenation produces partial pulmonary vasodilation, while ventilation with air or oxygen produces complete pulmonary vasodilation. The exact mechanisms of oxygen–induced pulmonary vasodilation during the transitional circulation also remain unclear. The increase in alveolar or arterial oxygen tension may decrease pulmonary vascular resistance, either directly by dilating the small pulmonary arteries, or indirectly by stimulating the production of vasodilator substances such as PGI_2 or bradykinin. Recently, EDNO has been implicated as an important mediator of the decrease in pulmonary vascular resistance at birth that is associated with increased oxygenation. For example, in fetal lambs, inhibition of NO synthesis attenuates the increase in pulmonary blood flow due to oxygenation induced either by ventilation with oxygen or by maternal hyperbaric oxygen exposure (14, 45, 80). In cultured fetal and newborn pulmonary endothelial cells, there is a maturational rise in NO production from late gestation to 4 weeks after birth (73). In addition, this NO production appears to be modulated by oxygen (74). Moreover, in the lamb, acute inhibition of NO synthesis prior to delivery significantly attenuates the normal increase in pulmonary blood flow at birth, further suggesting an important role for EDNO activity during the transitional circulation (1). Recently, we investigated the effects of chronic in utero NO inhibition on the transitional pulmonary circulation (22). In fetal lambs (gestational age 129 days; term = 145 days), we continuously infused low doses of N^{ω}-nitro-L-arginine, an inhibitor of EDNO synthesis, into the main pulmonary artery for at least 10 days. After the infusion period, the lambs were delivered by caesarean section and monitored for 3 h after birth. Those lambs with EDNO inhibition had persistent elevation of pulmonary arterial pressure,

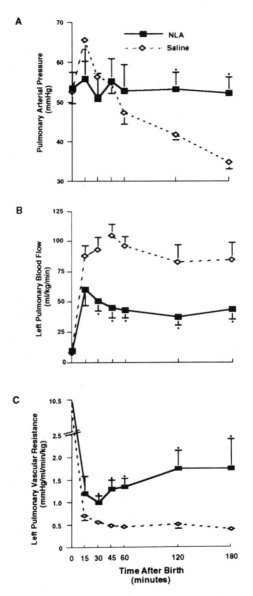

Figure 3   Changes in mean pulmonary arterial pressure (*A*), left pulmonary blood flow (*B*), and left pulmonary vascular resistance (*C*) after birth following in utero infusions of N^{ω}-nitro-L-arginine (NLA, *solid lines*; n = 6) or saline (*dashed lines*; n = 5). Values are mean ± SEM. * $P < 0.05$ vs saline–treated lambs.

and significant attenuation of the normal decrease in pulmonary vascular resistance as well as the increase in pulmonary blood flow throughout the study period (Figure 3). This further emphasizes the important role of NO activity in the development of the normal transitional pulmonary circulation.

Inhibition of NO activity attenuates the decrease in pulmonary vascular resistance after birth. However, the immediate decrease in pulmonary vascular resistance minutes after birth is not attenuated by NO inhibition. Therefore, the decrease in pulmonary vascular resistance with the initiation of ventilation and oxygenation has at least two components. First, there is partial pulmonary vasodilation caused by physical expansion of the lung and production of prostaglandins (PGI_2 and possibly PGD_2). This probably is independent of fetal oxygenation, and results in a modest increase in pulmonary blood flow and decrease in pulmonary vascular resistance. Next, there is a further maximal pulmonary vasodilation associated with fetal oxygenation, which is not necessarily dependent on prostaglandin production. This results in an increase in pulmonary blood flow and decrease in pulmonary vascular resistance to newborn values. This latter pulmonary vasodilation is likely caused by the synthesis of EDNO, although the exact stimulus, or stimuli, for EDNO production are not yet defined. Both components are necessary for successful transition to extrauterine life. An additional mechanism by which vasodilation occurs relates to the stimulation by increased shear forces of endothelial cells to produce both EDNO and PGI_2. It is possible that after the initial fall in pulmonary vascular resistance by a different mechanism, this particular mechanism acts to maintain pulmonary vasodilation.

Control of the perinatal pulmonary circulation, therefore, probably reflects a balance between factors producing pulmonary vasoconstriction (low O_2, leukotrienes, and other vasoconstricting substances) and those producing pulmonary vasodilation (high O_2, PGI_2, EDNO, and other vasodilating substances). The dramatic increase in pulmonary blood flow with the initiation of ventilation and oxygenation at birth reflects a shift from active pulmonary vasoconstriction in the fetus to active pulmonary vasodilation in the newborn.

Regulation of Postnatal Pulmonary Vascular Resistance

As stated above, mean pulmonary arterial pressure decreases to approximately 50% of mean systemic arterial pressure by 24 h after birth and reaches adult values by 2–6 weeks (34, 60). Therefore, after the immediate postnatal state, the pulmonary circulation is maintained in a dilated, low-resistance state. In fact, most pulmonary vasodilators cannot further dilate the resting newborn pulmonary circulation (61). Recent evidence suggests that basal release of NO, and the subsequent increase in smooth muscle cell concentrations of cGMP, partially mediates the low resting pulmonary vascular resistance of the newborn. For example, intravenous infusion of N^{ω}-nitro-L-arginine, an inhibitor of EDNO synthesis, produces significant increases in the resting pulmonary vascular resistance of newborn lambs (21). In addition, M&B 22948 (a cGMP–specific phosphodiesterase inhibitor that prevents the breakdown of endogenous cGMP) is one of the few agents that can further dilate the resting pulmonary circulation of the newborn lamb (7). In fact, the infusion of N^{ω}-nitro-L-arginine completely blocks M&B 22948–induced pulmonary vasodilation, which suggests that the majority of endogenous cGMP is generated from the basal release of NO. Other vasoactive substances including histamine, 5–hydroxytryptamine, bradykinin, and metabolites of arachidonic acid by the cyclo-oxygenase and lipoxygenase pathways have been implicated in mediating postnatal pulmonary vascular tone; however, their roles, if any, are not well elucidated. Prostaglandin inhibition following the infusion of meclofenamic acid does not alter resting pulmonary vascular tone of the newborn lamb, which minimizes the role of prostaglandins (23).

Two of the most important factors affecting pulmonary vascular resistance in the postnatal period are oxygen concentration and pH. Decreases in oxygen tension as well as in pH elicit pulmonary vasoconstriction of the resting pulmonary circulation (64). The pulmonary vasoconstriction in response to acute alveolar hypoxia is probably greater in the younger animal than in the adult (16). The mechanism of acute hypoxic pulmonary vasoconstriction remains unclear and is the subject of several extensive reviews (17). Acidosis potentiates hypoxic pulmonary vasoconstriction, and alkalosis reduces it (23). The exact mechanism of pH-mediated pulmonary vasoactive responses also remains incompletely understood, but appears to be independent of $PaCO_2$ (69).

Metabolic Function

Pulmonary vascular endothelium is capable of producing (e.g. PGI_2, EDNO, bradykinin, angiotensin II, ET-1) and removing (e.g. catecholamines, bradykinin, PGE_2, ET-1) many different vasoactive substances from the circulation. This activity, which is present in the fetus, changes at the time of transition to air breathing (35, 52, 65, 66). Concomitant with the increasing metabolic activity of the fetal lung (particularly increasing antioxidant enzyme and surfactant phospholipid synthesis) in the latter weeks of gestation, resting pulmonary blood flow increases (from about 4% of combined ventricular output to about 8%). After birth, and associated with the dramatic increase in pulmonary blood flow, pulmonary vascular metabolic capacity also increases markedly, to a large extent because of a significant increase in functional surface area of the pulmonary vascular endothelium. Conversion of angiotensin I to angiotensin II by the endothelial angiotensin–converting enzyme increases; the same enzyme is responsible for the metabolic breakdown of the vasoactive peptide bradykinin. Metabolic removal of PGE_2 also increases. Because PGE_2 is responsible for ductus arteriosus patency, this removal is an important component of the transition.

Failure of Pulmonary Vascular Resistance to Decrease at Birth

In a number of clinical conditions (e.g. respiratory distress syndrome, meconium aspiration, sepsis), pulmonary vascular resistance does not decrease normally at birth. As a result, pulmonary blood flow is reduced, and pulmonary arterial pressure remains high, at or near fetal levels. Associated with the persistent pulmonary hypertension, right-to-left shunting may occur across the ductus arteriosus, which remains patent in many of these infants. Right ventricular end-diastolic pressure is usually increased; consequently, right atrial pressure also is increased. As a result, right-to-left shunting generally occurs across the foramen ovale. The presence of tricuspid valve insufficiency, often associated with pulmonary hypertension and right ventricular dilation, may accentuate this shunting. The ultimate pathophysiologic effects are reduced pulmonary blood flow and reduced systemic oxygen delivery.

This syndrome of persistent pulmonary hypertension of the newborn accounts for approximately 1% of all admissions to newborn intensive care units. The clinical course is variable and treatment is supportive, consisting of administration of supplemental oxygen, mechanical hyperventilation, correction of metabolic abnormalities, infusion of nonspecific vasodilators to lower pulmonary arterial pressure, and infusion of cardiotonic drugs to improve cardiac function. Over the past 15 years, the use of extracorporeal membrane oxygenation (ECMO) has significantly reduced the mortality rate of this disorder. However, short– and long–term complications of this therapy can result in a high degree of morbidity, including neurological abnormalities (56).

Recently, exogenous, inhaled NO has been proposed as a potential therapy for infants with PPHN. Zapol and colleagues (25, 26) first investigated whether low levels of inhaled NO gas would produce selective pulmonary vasodilation in animals with pre-constricted pulmonary circulations. They reasoned that inhaled NO would produce pulmonary vasodilation without systemic effects because NO that diffused into the intravascular space would be bound to hemoglobin rapidly, and therefore would be inactive. They subsequently found, in sheep, that inhaled NO gas, in doses up to 80 ppm, completely and selectively reversed pulmonary vasoconstriction induced by acute alveolar hypoxia, infusion of U46619, or heparin-protamine interaction. Roberts et al (55) treated full-term infants with a clinical diagnosis of PPHN and severe systemic hypoxemia with 80 ppm of inhaled nitric oxide gas. Five of seven infants had a rapid and significant improvement in oxygenation following administration of NO. In addition, no patient developed systemic hypotension. Kinsella and co-workers (36) examined the effect of inhaling 20 ppm of NO on the course of infants with PPHN who were candidates for ECMO. They found that inhaled NO improved oxygenation in all infants without producing systemic hypotension. However, the potential toxicity of breathing low levels of NO, and whether the therapy will improve the clinical course of infants with PPHN, remain unclear. It is hoped that randomized, multicenter studies currently under way will answer these questions.

The pathophysiologic mechanisms preventing the normal pulmonary vasodilation and fall in pulmonary vascular resistance with ventilation and oxygenation at birth are not known. Haworth & Reid (29, 44, 48, 53) have described the pathologic changes in the pulmonary circulation of infants who die of PPHN. Endothelial cells swell and their luminal membranes thicken. There is an increase in the muscular thickness of the small pulmonary arteries and an extension of muscle to what generally would be nonmuscular arteries. This increase in muscle mass results from hypertrophy of existing muscle and differentiation and hyperplasia of smooth muscle cell precursors. The underlying mechanisms (such as alterations in smooth muscle growth-stimulating or inhibiting factors) producing these changes are unknown. In addition to structural changes, there may be functional alterations as well. There may be increased concentrations of or responsiveness to vasoconstricting substances (e.g. LTC_4, LTD_4, thromboxane A_2, or ET-1) or decreased concentrations of or responsiveness to vasodilating substances (PGI_2, PGD_2, EDNO, and increased O_2 tension). For example, elevated circulated plasma concentrations of ET-1 have been found in infants with PPHN (19). However, the role of ET-1, if any, in the pathophysiology of the disorder is unknown.

The structural changes take time to develop, which suggests that prolonged in utero events have altered the pulmonary circulation. Several investigators have studied the effects of intrauterine stress on the development of the pulmonary circulation as a potential model of PPHN. In animal studies, chronic fetal pulmonary hypertension induced by pharmacological or mechanical constriction or occlusion of the ductus arteriosus, or chronic fetal hypoxemia reproduces the physiological and pathological derangements of PPHN (2, 28, 40, 46, 58, 75, 83). Recently, we found that chronic in utero inhibition of NO synthesis reproduces the physiological derangements of PPHN without producing fetal pulmonary hypertension or the pathological derangements of PPHN (Figure 3) (22). In addition, the physiological derangements were completely reversible upon reversal of the NO inhibition. This study suggests that in utero events resulting in endothelial dysfunction and impaired NO activity may represent another etiology for PPHN. However, recent work by Stenmark and colleagues (78) suggests that postnatal remodeling alone, in response to noxious stimuli such as hypoxia, may be sufficient to produce significant pathophysiological changes.

Over the past 15 years, much new information has been obtained on the regulation of the perinatal pulmonary circulation. In particular, the potential role of mediators produced by the pulmonary vascular endothelium has been elucidated, which has resulted in a potential beneficial therapy for PPHN (i.e. inhaled NO). A better understanding of the normal and abnormal regulation of the perinatal pulmonary circulation will continue to result in improved treatment and possible prevention of pulmonary hypertensive disorders in childhood.

Any *Annual Review* chapter, as well as any article cited in an *Annual Review* chapter, may be purchased from the Annual Reviews Preprints and Reprints service.
1-800-347-8007; 415-259-5017; email: arpr@class.org

Literature Cited

1. Abman SH, Chatfield BA, Hall SL, McMurtry IF. 1990. Role of endothelium–derived relaxing factor during transition of pulmonary circulation at birth. *Am. J. Physiol.* 259(6 Pt 2): H1921–27
2. Abman SH, Shanley PF, Accurso FJ. 1989. Failure of postnatal adaptation of the pulmonary circulation after chronic intrauterine pulmonary hypertension in fetal lambs. *J. Clin. Invest.* 83(6):1849–58
3. Agarwal JB, Paltoo R, Palmer WH. 1970. Relative viscosity of blood at varying hematocrits in pulmonary circulation. *J. Appl. Physiol.* 29(6):866–71
4. Ahmed T, Oliver W Jr. 1983. Does slow–reacting substance of anaphylaxis mediate hypoxic pulmonary vasoconstriction? *Am. Rev. Respir. Dis.* 127(5): 566–71
5. Arai H, Hori S, Aramori I, Ohkubo H, Nakanishi S. 1990. Cloning and expression of a cDNA encoding an endothelin receptor. *Nature* 348(6303):730–32
6. Banarjee A, Heymann MA. 1992. Bradykinin receptor blockade does not affect oxygen mediated pulmonary vasodilation in fetal lambs. *Pediatr. Res.* 31:231A (Abstr.)
7. Braner DA, Fineman JR, Chang R, Soifer SJ. 1993. M&B 22948, a cGMP phosphodiesterase inhibitor, is a pulmonary vasodilator in lambs. *Am. J. Physiol.* 264(1 Pt 2):H252–58
8. Cassin S, Dawes GS, Mott JC, Ross BB, Strang LB. 1964. The vascular resistance of the foetal and newly ventilated lung of the lamb. *J. Physiol.* 171:61–79
9. Cassin S, Tod M, Philips J, Frisinger J, Jordan J, Gibbs C. 1981. Effects of prostaglandin D_2 on perinatal circulation. *Am. J. Physiol.* 240(5):H755–60
10. Chang J-K, Moore P, Fineman JR, Soifer SJ, Heymann MA. 1992. K^+ channel pulmonary vasodilatation in fetal lambs: role of endothelial derived nitric oxide. *J. Appl. Physiol.* 73(1):188–94
11. Chatfield BA, McMurtry IF, Hall SL, Abman SH. 1991. Hemodynamic effects of endothelin-1 on ovine fetal pulmonary circulation. *Am. J. Physiol.* 261(1 Pt 2):R182–87
12. Clozel M, Clyman RI, Soifer SJ, Heymann MA. 1985. Thromboxane is not responsible for the high pulmonary vascular resistance in fetal lambs. *Pediatr. Res.* 19(12):1254–57
13. Colebatch HJH, Dawes GS, Goodwin JW, Nadeau RA. 1965. The nervous control of the circulation in the foetal and newly expanded lungs of the lamb. *J. Physiol.* 178:544–62
14. Cornfield DN, Chatfield BA, McQueston JA, McMurtry IF, Abman SH. 1992. Effects of birth–related stimuli on L-arginine–dependent pulmonary vasodilation in ovine fetus. *Am. J. Physiol.* 262(5 Pt 2):H1474–81
15. Culver BH, Butler J. 1980. Mechanical influences on the pulmonary microcirculation. *Annu. Rev. Physiol.* 42:187–98
16. Custer JR, Hales CA. 1985. Influence of alveolar oxygen on pulmonary vasoconstriction in newborn lambs versus sheep. *Am. Rev. Respir. Dis.* 132(2): 326–31
17. Cutaia M, Rounds S. 1990. Hypoxic pulmonary vasoconstriction. Physiologic significance, mechanism, and clinical relevance. *Chest* 97(3):706–18
18. Dawes GS, Mott JC, Widdicombe JG, Wyatt DG. 1953. Changes in the lungs of the newborn lamb. *J. Physiol.* 121: 141–62
19. Drummond WH, Bissonnette JM. 1978.

Persistent pulmonary hypertension in the neonate: development of an animal model. *Am. J. Obstet. Gynecol.* 131(7): 761–63

20. Enhörning G, Adams FH, Norman A. 1966. Effect of lung expansion on the fetal lamb circulation. *Acta Paediatr. Scand.* 55(5):441–51

21. Fineman JR, Heymann MA, Soifer SJ. 1991. N^ω-nitro-L-arginine attenuates endothelium–dependent pulmonary vasodilation in lambs. *Am. J. Physiol.* 260 (29):H1299–1306

22. Fineman JR, Wong J, Morin FC, Wright L, Soifer SJ. 1994. Chronic nitric oxide inhibition in utero produces persistent pulmonary hypertension in newborn lambs. *J. Clin. Invest.* 93:2675–83

23. Fineman JR, Wong J, Soifer SJ. 1993. Hyperoxia and alkalosis produce pulmonary vasodilation independent of endothelium–derived nitric oxide in newborn lambs. *Pediatr. Res. 33(4 Pt* 1):341–46

24. Fiscus RR. 1988. Molecular mechanisms of endothelium–mediated vasodilation. *Semin. Thromb. Hemost. Suppl.* 14:12–22

25. Fratacci MD, Frostell CG, Chen TY, Wain JC Jr, Robinson DR, Zapol WM. 1991. Inhaled nitric oxide. A selective pulmonary vasodilator of heparin-protamine vasoconstriction in sheep. *Anesthesiology* 75(6):990–99

26. Frostell C, Fratacci MD, Wain JC, Jones R, Zapol WM. 1991. Inhaled nitric oxide. A selective pulmonary vasodilator reversing hypoxic pulmonary vasoconstriction. *Circulation* 83(6):2038–47

27. Goetzman BW, Milstein JM. 1980. Pulmonary vascular histamine receptors in newborn and young lambs. *J. Appl. Physiol.* 49(3):380–85

28. Goldberg SJ, Levy RA, Siassi B, Betten J. 1971. The effects of maternal hypoxia and hyperoxia upon the neonatal pulmonary vasculature. *Pediatrics* 48(4): 528–33

29. Haworth SG, Reid L. 1976. Persistent fetal circulation: newly recognized structural features. *J. Pediatr. 88(4Pt.* 1):614–20

30. Heymann MA, Rudolph AM, Nies AS, Melmon KL. 1969. Bradykinin production associated with oxygenation of the fetal lamb. *Circ. Res.* 25(5):521–34

31. Heymann MA, Soifer SJ. 1989. Control of the fetal and neonatal pulmonary circulation. In *Pulmonary Vascular Physiology and Pathophysiology,* ed. EK Weir, JT Reeves, pp. 33–50. New York: Dekker. 762 pp.

32. Hislop A, Reid LM. 1972. Intra–pulmonary arterial development during fetal life–branching pattern and structure. *J. Anat.* 113(1):35–48

33. Hislop A, Reid LM. 1973. Pulmonary arterial development during childhood: branching pattern and structure. *Thorax* 28(2):129–35

34. Iwamoto HS, Teitel D, Rudolph AM. 1987. Effects of birth–related events on blood flow distribution. *Pediatr. Res.* 22(6):634–40

35. Junod AF. 1975. Metabolism, production, and release of hormones and mediators in the lung. *Am. Rev. Respir. Dis.* 112(1):93–108

36. Kinsella JP, Neish SR, Shaffer E, Abman SH. 1992. Low–dose inhalation nitric oxide in persistent pulmonary hypertension of the newborn. *Lancet* 340 (8823):819–20

37. Le Bidois J, Soifer SJ, Clyman RI, Heymann MA. 1987. Piriprost: a putative leukotriene synthesis inhibitor increases pulmonary blood flow in fetal lambs. *Pediatr. Res.* 22(3):350–54

38. Leffler CW, Hessler JR, Green RS. 1984. Mechanism of stimulation of pulmonary prostacyclin synthesis at birth. *Prostaglandins* 28(6):877–87

39. Leffler CW, Hessler JR, Green RS. 1984. The onset of breathing at birth stimulates pulmonary vascular prostacyclin synthesis. *Pediatr. Res.* 18(10): 938–42

40. Levin DL, Mills LJ, Weinberg AG. 1979. Hemodynamic, pulmonary vascular, and myocardial abnormalities secondary to pharmacologic constriction of the fetal ductus arteriosus. A possible mechanism for persistent pulmonary hypertension and transient tricuspid insufficiency in the newborn infant. *Circulation* 60(2):360–64

41. Levin DL, Rudolph AM, Heymann MA, Phibbs RH. 1976. Morphological development of the pulmonary vascular bed in fetal lambs. *Circulation* 53(1):144–51

42. McIntyre TM, Zimmerman GA, Satoh K, Prescott SM. 1985. Cultured endothelial cells synthesize both platelet–activating factor and prostacyclin in response to histamine, bradykinin, and adenosine triphosphate. *J. Clin. Invest.* 76(1):271–80

43. Meyrick B, Reid L. 1978. The effect of continued hypoxia on rat pulmonary arterial circulation. An ultrastructural study. *Lab. Invest.* 38(2):188–200

44. Meyrick B, Reid L. 1979. Hypoxia and incorporation of ^{3}H-thymidine by cells of the rat pulmonary arteries and alveolar wall. *Am. J. Pathol.* 96(1):51–70

45. Moore P, Velvis H, Fineman JR, Soifer SJ, Heymann MA. 1992. EDRF inhibi-

tion attenuates the increase in pulmonary blood flow due to oxygen ventilation in fetal lambs. *J. Appl. Physiol.* 73(5): 2151–57

46. Morin FC III. 1989. Ligating the ductus arteriosus before birth causes persistent pulmonary hypertension in the newborn lamb. *Pediatr. Res.* 25(3):245–50

47. Morin FC III, Egan EA, Norfleet WT. 1988. Indomethacin does not diminish the pulmonary vascular response of the fetus to increased oxygen tension. *Pediatr. Res.* 24(6):696–700

48. Murphy JD, Rabinovitch M, Goldstein JD, Reid LM. 1981. The structural basis of persistent pulmonary hypertension of the newborn infant. *J. Pediatr.* 98(6): 962–67

49. Palmer RMJ, Ashton DS, Moncada S. 1988. Vascular endothelial cells synthesize nitric oxide from L-arginine. *Nature* 333(6174):664–66

50. Parker HR, Purves MJ. 1967. Some effects of maternal hyperoxia and hypoxia on the blood gas tensions and vascular pressures in the foetal sheep. *Q. J. Exp. Physiol.* 52(2):205–21

51. Permutt S, Caldini P, Maseri A, Palmer WA, Sasamori T, et al. 1969. Recruitment vs. distensibility in the pulmonary vascular bed. In *The Pulmonary Circulation and Interstitial Space,* ed. AP Fishman, HH Hecht, pp. 375–90. Chicago: Univ. Chicago Press. 432 pp.

52. Pitt BR. 1984. Metabolic functions of the lung and systemic vasoregulation. *Fed. Proc.* 43(11):2574–77

53. Reid L. 1979. The pulmonary circulation: remodelling in growth and disease. The 1978 J. Burns Amberson lecture. *Am. Rev. Respir. Dis.* 119(4):531–46

54. Reid LM. 1986. Structure and function in pulmonary hypertension. New perceptions. *Chest* 89(2):279–88

55. Roberts JD, Polaner DM, Lang P, Zapol WM. 1992. Inhaled nitric oxide in persistent pulmonary hypertension of the newborn. *Lancet* 340(8823):818–19

56. Roberts JD Jr, Shaul PW. 1993. Advances in the treatment of persistent pulmonary hypertension of the newborn. *Pediatr. Clin. North Am.* 40(5):983–1004

57. Roos A. 1962. Poiseuille's law and its limitations in vascular systems. *Med. Thorac.* 19:224–38

58. Rosenberg AA, Kennaugh J, Koppenhafer SL, Loomis M, Chatfield BA, Abman SH. 1993. Elevated immunoreactive endothelin-1 levels in newborn infants with persistent pulmonary hypertension. *J. Pediatr.* 123(1):109–14

59. Rudolph AM. 1979. Fetal and neonatal pulmonary circulation. *Annu. Rev. Physiol.* 41:383–95

60. Rudolph AM. 1985. Distribution and regulation of blood flow in the fetal and neonatal lamb. *Circ. Res.* 57(6):811–21

61. Rudolph AM, Auld PA. 1960. Physical factors affecting normal and serotonin-constricted pulmonary vessels. *Am. J. Physiol.* 198:864–72

62. Rudolph AM, Heymann MA. 1970. Circulatory changes during growth in the fetal lamb. *Circ. Res.* 26(3):289–99

63. Rudolph AM, Heymann MA, Lewis AB. 1977. Physiology and pharmacology of the pulmonary circulation in the fetus and newborn. In *Lung Biology in Health and Disease. Development of the Lung,* ed. WA Hodson, pp. 497–523. New York: Dekker. 646 pp.

64. Rudolph AM, Yuan S. 1966. Response of the pulmonary vasculature to hypoxia and H^+ ion concentration changes. *J. Clin. Invest.* 45(3):399–411

65. Ryan US, Ryan JW, Crutchley DJ. 1985. The pulmonary endothelial surface. *Fed. Proc.* 44(10):2603–9

66. Said SI. 1982. Metabolic functions of the pulmonary circulation. *Circ. Res.* 50(3):325–33

67. Sakurai T, Yanagisawa M, Takuwa Y, Miyazaki H, Kimura S, et al. 1990. Cloning of a cDNA encoding a non–isopeptide–selective subtype of the endothelin receptor. *Nature* 348(6303): 732–35

68. Schreiber MD, Heymann MA, Soifer SJ. 1985. Leukotriene inhibition prevents and reverses hypoxic pulmonary vasoconstriction in newborn lambs. *Pediatr. Res.* 19(5):437–41

69. Schreiber MD, Heymann MA, Soifer SJ. 1986. Increased arterial pH, not decreased Pa_{CO_2}, attenuates hypoxia–induced pulmonary vasoconstriction in newborn lambs. *Pediatr. Res.* 20(2): 113–17

70. Schuster DP, Dennis DR. 1987. Leukotriene inhibitors do not block hypoxic pulmonary vasoconstriction in dogs. *J. Appl. Physiol.* 62(5):1808–13

71. Schwartz LS, Osborn BI, Frick OL. 1974. An ontogenic study of histamine and mast cells in the fetal rhesus monkey. *J. Allergy Clin. Immunol.* 56:381–86

72. Shaul PW, Farrar MA, Magness RR. 1993. Oxygen modulation of pulmonary arterial prostacyclin synthesis is developmentally regulated. *Am. J. Physiol.* 265(2 Pt 2):H621–28

73. Shaul PW, Farrar MA, Magness RR. 1993. Pulmonary endothelial nitric oxide production is developmentally

regulated in the fetus and newborn. *Am. J. Physiol.* 265(4 Pt 2):H1056–63

74. Shaul PW, Farrar MA, Zellers TM. 1992. Oxygen modulates endothelium–derived relaxing factor production in fetal pulmonary arteries. *Am. J. Physiol.* 262(2 Pt 2):H355–64

75. Soifer SJ, Kaslow D, Roman C, Heymann MA. 1987. Umbilical cord compression produces pulmonary hypertension in newborn lambs: a model to study the pathophysiology of persistent pulmonary hypertension in the newborn. *J. Dev. Physiol.* 9(3):239–52

76. Soifer SJ, Loitz RD, Roman C, Heymann MA. 1985. Leukotriene end organ antagonists increase pulmonary blood flow in fetal lambs. *Am. J. Physiol.* 249(3 Pt 2):H570–76

77. Soifer SJ, Morin FC III, Kaslow DC, Heymann MA. 1983. The developmental effects of prostaglandin D_2 on the pulmonary and systemic circulations in the newborn lamb. *J. Dev. Physiol.* 5(4):237–50

78. Stenmark KR, Cook CL, Majack RA. 1993. Vascular growth. In *Perinatal and Pediatric Pathophysiology: A Clinical Perspective,* ed. PD Gluckman, MA Heymann, pp. 451–62. London: Arnold. 760 pp.

79. Stenmark KR, James SL, Voelkel NF, Toews WH, Reeves JT, Murphy RC. 1983. Leukotriene C_4 and D_4 in neonates with hypoxemia and pulmonary hypertension. *N. Engl. J. Med.* 309(2):77–80

80. Tiktinsky MH, Morin FC III. 1993. Increasing oxygen tension dilates fetal pulmonary circulation via endothelium-derived relaxing factor. *Am. J. Physiol.* 265(1 Pt 2):H376–80

81. Velvis H, Krusell J, Roman C, Soifer SJ, Riemer RK, Heymann MA. 1990. Leukotrienes C_4, D_4, and E_4 in fetal lamb tracheal fluid. *J. Dev. Physiol.* 14(1):37–41

82. Velvis H, Moore P, Heymann MA. 1991. Prostaglandin inhibition prevents the fall in pulmonary vascular resistance as a result of rhythmic distension of the lungs in fetal lambs. *Pediatr. Res.* 30(1):62–68

83. Wild LM, Nickerson PA, Morin FC III. 1989. Ligating the ductus arteriosus before birth remodels the pulmonary vasculature of the lamb. *Pediatr. Res.* 25(3):251–57

84. Wong J, Fineman JR, Heymann MA. 1994. The role of endothelin-1 (ET-1) and of endothelin receptor subtypes in regulation of fetal pulmonary vascular tone. *Pediatr. Res.* 35:664–70

85. Wong J, Vanderford PA, Fineman JR, Chang R, Soifer SJ. 1993. Endothelin-1 produces pulmonary vasodilation in the intact newborn lamb. *Am. J. Physiol.* 265(4 Pt 2):H1318–25

86. Yanagisawa M, Kurihara H, Kimura S, Tomobe Y, Kobayashi M, et al. 1988. A novel potent vasoconstrictor peptide produced by vascular endothelial cells. *Nature* 332(6163):411–15

87. Yoshibayashi M, Nishioka K, Nakao K, Saito Y, Temma S, et al. 1991. Plasma endothelin levels in healthy children: high values in early infancy. *J. Cardiovasc. Pharmacol. 17 Suppl.* 7:S404–5

Annu. Rev. Physiol. 1995. 57:135–50

EXTRACELLULAR METABOLISM OF PULMONARY SURFACTANT: The Role of a New Serine Protease[1]

Nicholas J. Gross

Departments of Medicine and Molecular and Cellular Biochemistry, Stritch School of Medicine, Loyola University of Chicago; Edward J. Hines, Jr., Veterans Affairs Hospital, Hines, IL 60141

KEY WORDS: lamellar bodies, tubular myelin, small vesicles, subtype conversion, surfactant convertase

INTRODUCTION

Lung surfactant, an organized complex of lipids and specific apoproteins that is responsible for maintaining alveolar stability, is a product of alveolar epithelial type II cells in which it is packaged for secretion in the form of lamellar bodies (LB) (41, 43, 44). Following its release from type II cells into the alveolar fluid-lining layer, surfactant undergoes a number of structural and metabolic changes. Ultimately, some of the extracellular surfactant is taken back into type II cells for recycling, and the remainder is probably removed by alveolar clearance mechanisms. The structural transformation that surfactant undergoes after its secretion from the type II cell includes at least one step requiring the action of a recently discovered enzyme. We review the evidence for enzymatic activity in this sequence, what is known of its role and actions, as well as some of the properties of the putative enzyme, which we call surfactant convertase.

[1]The US Government has the right to retain a nonexclusive, royalty-free license in and to any copyright covering this paper.

SUBTYPES OF EXTRACELLULAR SURFACTANT

The general scheme of the evolution of surfactant in its extracellular phase has been reviewed (1, 41, 43, 44). Four forms or subtypes of extracellular surfactant are well recognized. The first form, lamellar bodies, consists of concentric phospholipid membranes that after secretion rapidly become reoriented in the alveolar lining layer as tubular myelin (TM), the second subtype. This transformation seems to occur spontaneously, possibly as a result of changes in the calcium ion concentration in the environment of the alveolar lining layer (33). TM, in turn, is believed to supply the air-fluid interface with phospholipids that form a monomolecular layer, the third subtype, which lowers surface tension. At a later stage, surfactant is found as a uniform population of small vesicles (SV), presumed to be phospholipids that have been "squeezed out" of the monolayer during expiratory, surface area–reducing phases of respiratory cycles and have become reoriented in subsurface micellar structures, the fourth subtype. A moiety of each subtype is taken up by type II cells, probably by receptor–mediated endocytosis (45); the remainder is cleared by other mechanisms. All of the subtypes, including the monomolecular film, have been visualized in situ in the alveolar fluid lining layer, and their secular metabolic relationships have been firmly established by a wide variety of histologic, labeling, and in vitro methods.

In addition, each of the subtypes, with the exception of the monomolecular film, has been partially purified, and partially characterized in the lavage obtained from a variety of experimental animals, with use of either differential centrifugation (2, 26, 30, 32, 46) or isopycnic sucrose density gradient centrifugation (13, 14), e.g. Figure 1 top panel. The phospholipid compositions of the partially purified subtypes are similar, although small changes in the relative proportions of phospholipid species cannot be excluded. Less is known of the apoprotein composition of each subtype (see below) and their molecular structures (18). The proximate forms of surfactant, LB, and TM are surface active, whereas the SV form is only weakly surface active. Labeling studies have provided much of the evidence in favor of the above secular relationship of subtypes and for recycling (reviewed in 41, 43, 44), but there is other corroborative evidence. Spain et al, for example, examined the ultrastructure of surfactant lavaged from the lungs of fetal and newborn rats. Before the onset of air breathing, it consisted mainly of large aggregates of surfactant (TM) but little or no SV; after a few hours of air breathing, abundant SV was present (36). Baritussio et al (1) performed a similar experiment in fetal and newborn rabbits and analyzed the subtypes by centrifugation techniques. In term fetal rabbits, all of the phospholipid sedimented as LB; during the first 24 h increasing amounts were found at buoyant densities corresponding to TM and SV forms.

The in vivo turnover times of phospholipids of each of the subtypes is of the order of 1–3 h (data from adult rodents), which indicates rapid movement

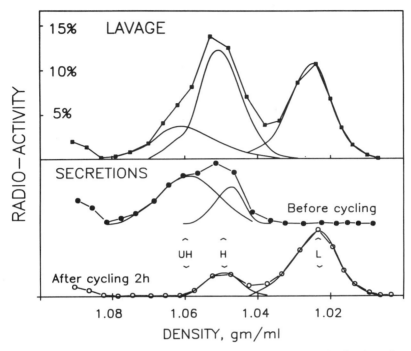

Figure 1 Profiles of radiolabeled surfactant phospholipids sedimented to equilibrium in continuous sucrose gradients. Top panel: alveolar lavage fluid of a mouse labeled with 10 μ Ci [³H]-choline 8 h previously. Each point represents a fraction. Filled squares, radioactivity in each fraction as percentage of total gradient activity. Continuous curves below profile, best–fit computer estimates of the three surfactant subtype components. Lower panel: secretions from pre–lavaged lungs that were incubated to release nascent secretions. One portion of the secretions was centrifuged without further processing (*closed circles*). The other portion was cycled for 2 h before centrifugation (*open circles*). For clarification, these two profiles have been displaced vertically. As in the top panel, computer analyses of subtype distributions are shown as continuous curves below the overall profiles. All plots have the same abscissa. Typical locations of the three subtypes are shown by arrowheads in the lower panel: UH, ultraheavy or predominantly LB form; H, heavy or predominantly TM form; L, light or small vesicular form (from Reference 16 with permission).

of phospholipids through the extracellular forms (41, 43). Less is known of the turnover times and recycling rates of the apoproteins, but existing data suggest that SPA turns over at rates that are comparable with but not identical to those of phospholipids (1, 47) and that SPB and SPC are turned over faster than the phosphatidylcholine component of alveolar surfactant (1, 4).

SUBTYPE CONVERSION IN VITRO

In order to study the steps in the extracellular metabolism of surfactant, we devised a method to reproduce this process in vitro (14). The LB form of surfactant was made by removing resident surfactant from the alveolar spaces of mice by lavage and then incubating the intact lungs at 38°C for 1–2 h. A small amount of buffer containing 10 μM isoproterenol (a surfactant secretagogue) was present in the alveolar spaces during incubation, and the same buffer was flushed into and out of the lungs at approximately 10-min intervals and harvested after 1–2 h. The lung secretions obtained, "nascent" surfactant, predominantly have the electron microscopic (EM) appearance of the LB form, with its buoyant density and surface activity. Most of these preparations also contain a minor component of TM. By prelabeling the animals with a phospholipid precursor, e.g. [³H]-choline, the conversion of one subtype into another during manipulations can readily be followed by either sucrose gradient analysis, as in Figure 1 lower panel, or by differential centrifugation to separate the relevant subtypes.

Conversion of nascent surfactant into its products in vitro was brought about by cyclic expansion and contraction of the surface area of a suspension of nascent surfactant in plastic tubes that were half filled and rotated end-over-end 40 times per min on a hematologic rotator (14), a process we call cycling. The medium for this manipulation generally contains isotonic saline and calcium ions (1–2 mM) buffered to pH 7.4. Cycling expands and contracts the surface area from about 1 to 9 cm² and back, 80 times per min. This is intended to imitate qualitatively, if not in magnitude, the cyclic expansion and contraction of the alveolar surface in vivo during ventilatory cycles. Cycling nascent secretion at 38°C resulted in stepwise, consecutive conversion of surfactant phospholipid from the buoyant density of the LB subtype (~ 1.060 gm/ml) to the buoyant density of the TM subtype (~ 1.050 gm/ml) to that of SV subtype (~ 1.025 gm/ml) in about 3 h, Figure 2. No phospholipid peaks of intermediate buoyant density were detected, suggesting quantal changes in structure from one form to another (14, 15).

Examination of the products of cycling by EM, phospholipid composition, and surface activity showed that they were essentially identical to the forms of similar buoyant densities found in alveolar lavage, thus suggesting that cycling mimics in vivo conversion (14, 15, 38). Indeed cyclic expansion and contraction of the surface appears to be important for the conversion of large aggregates to small aggregates in vivo as well as in vitro. The experiments of Baritussio et al (1) and Spain et al (36) are consistent with this notion. In addition, Nicholas et al (29) showed that increasing the tidal ventilation of rat lungs accelerated the conversion of large to small aggregates of surfactant in situ. Observations such as these suggest that cycling in vitro is not simply an artefactual way to bring about subtype conversion, but rather a simulation of the natural processes in vivo. This reasoning and the close similarity of the products of cycling in vitro with those found in vivo provide the basis for the use of in vitro cycling as a means of studying the details of surfactant subtype conversion under controlled conditions.

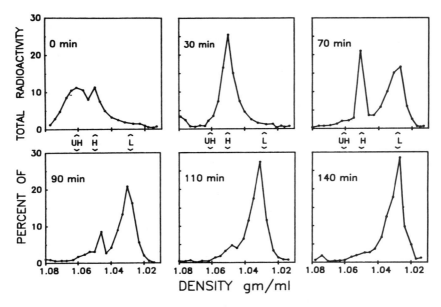

Figure 2   Effect of cycling in vitro on the profile of nascent secretion obtained from mice prelabeled with [³H]-choline. The sedimented and resuspended secretion was divided into aliquots that were cycled for the indicated times and centrifuged to equilibrium through continuous sucrose gradients. Arrowheads between panels indicate the typical buoyant densities of subtypes found in alveolar lavage as for Figure 1 (from Reference 15 with permission).

REQUIREMENTS FOR SUBTYPE CONVERSION IN VITRO

The conversion of LB to TM appears to occur spontaneously, even in the absence of an air-fluid interface (33, 40). Calcium ions may be required for this step. Using nascent surfactant as starting material, rapid conversion of LB to TM is also seen with cycling in vitro (14, 15), Figure 2. The in vitro conversion of TM to SV, however, has both physical and biochemical requirements.

Physical Requirements

The physical requirements include the absolute need for an air-fluid interface that is cyclically expanded and contracted. When suspensions of nascent surfactant were either (*a*) incubated at 38°C for 2 h without cycling, (*b*) incubated at 38°C for 2 h while stirred in a plastic beaker without changes in the surface area, or (*c*) cycled at 38°C in plastic tubes that were filled so that there was no air-fluid interface (a small stirring bar was included to ensure mixing), no conversion of TM to SV occurred (14). Moreover, the amount of SV that could be generated by cycling in a limited time was directly related to the surface area available: cycling in larger tubes generated more SV than cycling in smaller tubes (16). These results suggest that an air-fluid interface that is cyclically expanded and contracted plays an indispensable role at some step in the conversion of TM to SV.

Biochemical Requirements

When nascent secretion was cycled at 0–4°C, or even at 25°C, there was minimal generation of SV subtype, which suggests the possibility that enzyme activity is required (14). The nature of possible enzyme activity was explored further by including a variety of enzyme inhibitors in the cycling mix (15). These were typically added in various concentrations to the nascent secretion immediately before cycling at 38°C and remained in the mix through sucrose gradient analysis. Inclusion of any of a range of serine protease inhibitors (serpins) inhibited the conversion of TM to SV, and virtually all the phospholipid accumulated at the density corresponding to TM. These inhibitors include those relatively specific for trypsin-, chymotrypsin-, and elastase-like serine proteases, as well as diisopropylfluorophosphate (DFP), a universal and specific inhibitor of all enzymes that employ the serine–active site motif. Alpha-1 antitrypsin (α-1AT), a serpin that is normally present in the alveolar fluid-lining layer, also inhibited conversion. The inhibition brought about by DFP and α-1AT was dose dependent. Because inhibitors of other classes of proteases, e.g. metallo-, cysteine-, and acid-protease inhibitors, did not inhibit subtype conversion in vitro, the protease involved in subtype conversion appears to be of the serine protease family (15).

Further evidence of the need for an enzyme to convert TM to SV comes from recent experiments with reconstituted TM, (rTM). Barr et al (5) made rTM from purified SPA, SPB, SPC, and phospholipids. The reconstituted material had the same buoyant density, ultrastructure, and surface activity as native TM. Upon cycling, however, rTM was unable to convert to SV, whereas native TM (which contains endogenous convertase; see below) did generate SV. Unless rTM was defective in some unknown manner, this result suggests that conversion does not occur in the absence of enzyme activity and, therefore, that none of the SPs can be the source of convertase activity.

We explored the ability of several common serine proteases to promote the conversion of TM to SV in vitro. Nascent secretion, which contains convertase (16), was treated with DFP to inhibit its endogenous convertase activity; the DFP was subsequently washed out by sedimentation and resuspended in fresh buffer. Surfactant treated in this manner does not convert to SV on cycling in vitro (although conversion proceeds normally if DFP is omitted). Addition of a small amount of untreated unlabeled nascent secretion (as a source of active enzyme) restores the ability of DFP–treated surfactant to convert to SV on cycling. However, addition of each of several known serine proteases failed to promote conversion of DFP–treated surfactant. The known enzymes whose ability to promote subtype conversion was tested included porcine trypsin, chymotrypsin, elastase, human urokinase, and neutrophil elastase. In each case the enzyme failed to promote conversion; the labeled surfactant remained at the buoyant density of TM after cycling. Pancreatic phospholipase, even in low concentration, abolished the ability of surfactant to band in sucrose gradients, although the action of this enzyme was not explored in detail (NJ Gross, unpublished data). Consistent with this, additions of small amounts of either phospholipase A2 or C abolished the surface–active properties of surfactant (19). These findings suggest that the enzyme activity responsible for subtype conversion, surfactant convertase, cannot be substituted by common serine proteases or phospholipases and may be specific for surfactant subtype conversion. Its activity in vitro does not require calcium ions and has a broad pH range whose optimum is approximately pH 7.4 (16).

Two other potentially important aspects of convertase action have been reported. Firstly, convertase requires simultaneous surface area cycling in order express its activity. Thus exposing nascent surfactant to active convertase without cycling and then cycling the surfactant in the presence of a protease inhibitor does not generate SV . Similarly, cycling surfactant whose convertase had been inhibited followed by addition of active convertase without cycling also fails to generate SV. Only when cycling occurs in the presence of active enzyme does TM convert to SV (16, 38). It is concluded that convertase activity has the unusual requirement that the air-fluid interface be simultaneously cyclically expanded and contracted. The significance of this finding is discussed below.

Secondly, dose response studies of the effect of α-1AT as an inhibitor of conversion in vitro showed that its KI_{50} was about 5 μM (15). Previous studies have suggested that the concentration of α-1AT in the human alveolar fluid-lining layer is also 5 μM (8). Thus it is possible that α-1AT plays a role in controlling surfactant extracellular metabolism in addition to its well–known role in protecting the lung alveoli against autolytic digestion by serine proteases. Consistent with this is the alteration in subtype proportions found in a murine model of lung damage, radiation pneumonitis. In this condition, there is a substantial increase in the absolute amount of TM subtype in the alveolar lavage (11); this increase could be explained by an 18-fold increase in the amount of α-1AT found in the alveolar lavage fluid of mice with radiation pneumonitis (12), a concentration that would completely inhibit convertase activity in vitro, thereby leading to an accumulation of TM.

IDENTIFICATION AND PURIFICATION OF CONVERTASE

A DFP–binding protein was sought in alveolar lavage and nascent secretions using [^{3}H]-DFP (16). Both contained a [^{3}H]-DFP–binding protein of M_r 75 K (reducing conditions) on SDS-PAGE, M_r 80–85 K without reduction. Indeed, fractions of surfactant purified on sucrose gradients were found to contain this DFP–binding protein. Although quantitatively more was present in the high-speed supernatant of nascent secretions, the physical association of a DFP–binding protein with surfactant suggests the possibility that this protein is the serine protease that mediates surfactant subtype conversion. Serine proteases are involved in a great number of physiologic processes including complement activation, hemostasis, fibrinolysis, digestion, wound repair, and numerous other well–described functions. Most common serine proteases are of M_r 20–30 K, although exceptions, for example urokinase of M_r 54 K, occur. Thus a serine protease of M_r 75 K is somewhat unusual and suggests a unique protein. However, there is no conclusive evidence at present that the 75 K [^{3}H]-DFP–binding protein is surfactant convertase. [A previous publication (16) suggested that convertase was possibly membrane bound because it seemed to sediment from lung secretions at high-speed forces. Further experiments showed that this is incorrect; the enzyme is water soluble and present at highest concentration in the supernatant of high-speed centrifugation, and a sedimentable fraction is not required for subtype conversion (NJ Gross, unpublished data).]

Attempts to purify this protein showed that it is present in highest concentration in the nascent secretions of lungs incubated in vitro. Among a variety of column purification procedures that have been attempted (NJ Gross, unpublished data), only concanavalin-A affinity chromatography provided significant purification (five- to tenfold), which suggests that the enzyme is a glycoprotein. Indeed, treatment of the [^{3}H]-DFP labeled enzyme with a deglycosylating enzyme (N-glycosidase F) yielded several forms with M_r down to about 45 K, which suggests extensive glycosylation. By isoelectric focusing its Pi was 5.4.

Attempts to determine the amino acid sequence of this protein have been unsuccessful to date because its N-terminus is blocked.

It should be stated here that convertase may not be the only enzyme involved in the extracellular metabolism of surfactant. Phospholipases (34) and phospholipase activity (28) have been found in the alveolar lavage of rats and humans (reviewed in 44). Phospholipid transfer proteins have also been found in lavage material (25). Although the latter have a well–studied intracellular function in many tissues, their presence in the alveolus raises the possibility that they may be involved in the extracellular metabolism of surfactant (24), although this has apparently not been explored.

CELLULAR SOURCE OF CONVERTASE

Studies of convertase have been hampered by the fact that a convenient assay is lacking at present. Preparations that contain convertase activity (e.g. nascent secretion) do not hydrolyze any of a wide range of synthetic protease substrates (15). Therefore, attempts to identify or purify convertase must rely on its ability to promote the conversion of TM to SV, an assay that is tedious and semi-quantitative. Because the enzyme has not been purified in active form, it has not been possible to generate antibodies to the native enzyme for immunoassay. Polyclonal antibodies have been raised in rabbits to the SDS-PAGE-purified 75 K [^{3}H]-DFP–binding protein, but attempts to develop an affinity column with immobilized antibody have not been successful. Thus one must rely either on the presence of a 75 K [^{3}H]-DFP–binding protein as the most convenient, albeit uncertain, way of identifying the enzyme, or on the rather cumbersome cycling assay as the most convincing demonstration of convertase activity.

Convertase activity was found in a substantial amount in purified lamellar bodies and was released into secretions by lungs incubated in vitro together with nascent surfactant (16); therefore the possibility that its source was the alveolar type II cell was explored. Because type II cells rapidly tend to lose their typical secretory function in culture, the enzyme was sought instead in stable cell lines derived from human peripheral airway neoplasms. Lysates of two lung cell lines that express mRNAs of SPA and SPB were found to contain a [^{3}H]-DFP–binding protein of M_r 75 K, i.e. consistent with normal mouse lung tissue convertase. Other stable neoplastic human lung cell lines that lack type II cell features (as controls) did not contain a [^{3}H]-DFP–binding protein of M_r 75 K (16). All cell lines also contained [^{3}H]-DFP–binding proteins of M_r 20–30 K, the typical M_r of most serine proteases.

Additional evidence that the type II cell is the source of convertase was sought by comparing the release of surfactant phospholipids with the release of [^{3}H]-DFP–binding protein from lungs incubated in vitro in response to a range of agents that stimulate or inhibit surfactant secretion (9). Agents that promote phospholipid release, e.g. isoproterenol, phorbol myristate acetate, ionomycin, compound 48/80, also promote the release of the 75 K [^{3}H]-DFP–binding protein to approximately the same extent. Propanolol inhibited secretion of phospholipids and the [^{3}H]-DFP–binding protein. Although indirect, these results support the concept that convertase is a product of type II cells.

Immunohistochemical studies using a polyclonal antibody to SDS-PAGE-purified convertase also support the concept that convertase is a product of type II cells: In normal mouse lungs, staining was found in particulate structures in type II cells (possibly lamellar bodies) as well as along the alveolar lining layer. Lungs that were previously lavaged showed no staining along the alveolar surface, but the staining of particulate structures within type II cells persisted (10). This result supports the notion that convertase is packaged with phospholipids in alveolar type II cells and secreted from these cells into the alveolar fluid-lining layer.

However, the lung appears not to be the only organ that contains this enzyme. When several mouse organ homogenates were examined, an 83 K [^{3}H]-DFP–binding protein (nonreducing conditions) was found in substantial amounts in brain, heart, and to a lesser extent, in serum and kidney, as well as in lung. Moreover, the homogenate supernatants from these organs were capable of mediating surfactant subtype conversion on cycling in vitro (27).

At present it is reasonable to conclude that convertase is a product of lung type II cells, but that it may also be synthesized in other organs.

SUBSTRATE(S) OF CONVERTASE

Evidence presented above suggests that the enzyme that mediates the conversion of TM to SV is a serine protease, based largely on its inhibitability by serpins and DFP. Although it is plausible to conclude that the substrate of convertase is a protein or proteins, one should remember that DFP inhibits other enzymes including some lipases that use the serine-histidine-aspartic catalytic triad (e.g. 6, 23). The fact that lipases act at an interface may also be relevant. Nevertheless, the question of possible substrate(s) of convertase activity to date has focused on proteins, particularly surfactant–associated proteins. Clues to the substrate(s) of convertase action might be provided by examining the relative content of SPs in each of the surfactant subtypes (see below).

Wright and co-workers (42) showed that the more sedimentable forms of surfactant (equivalent to LB and TM forms) contained more total protein relative to phospholipid than did the less sedimentable forms (SV). They identified proteins by SDS-PAGE and found that the more sedimentable forms contained proteins of M_r 36 and 10 K; less sedimentable forms contained less of these proteins. Several groups have subsequently shown that the major surfactant–associated proteins, SPA, SPB, and SPC, are present in the more sedimentable forms of surfactant (reviewed in 18, 31, 39). Although most investigators analyzing for SPs were not concerned with the surfactant subtype, the methods they used to purify surfactant would have yielded mainly the more sedimentable subtypes. Few studies, even subsequent to that of Wright et al (42), have analyzed the SP content of purified surfactant subtypes. Where this has been attempted, determining the concentrations of these SPs relative to phospholipid has been complicated by the use of methods that are only semi–quantitative. This reservation applies particularly to the low M_r hydrophobic apoproteins SPB and SPC. A further caveat is that the large serine protease family includes many enzymes that are exoproteases. If convertase were an exoprotease, it might have large effects on the function of its substrate, but its action would be difficult to detect by techniques that typically employ anti-bodies that are not directed to the relevant epitope. Similarly, the small change in M_r brought about by an exoprotease action would be undetectable on SDS-PAGE. Consequently, it is not possible to obtain from the literature a comprehensive account of the SP content of surfactant subtypes that would strongly suggest a substrate for convertase. A recent report by Baritussio et al (1) goes some way towards filling this deficiency.

SPA appears to be more abundant relative to phospholipid in the LB and TM forms than in SV of alveolar lavage (42). SPA is abundant in the heavier surfactant lavaged from fetal and newborn rabbits and less abundant in the lighter fractions (SV form) that accumulate following air breathing (1). This finding suggests that a portion of the total of SPA found in lavage is not surfactant associated. Similarly, nascent surfactant from lungs incubated in vitro contains relatively more SPA before cycling than does the SV generated by cycling it in vitro (S Hawgood & NJ Gross, unpublished data). It is safe to conclude, therefore, that the SPA content of surfactant decreases as it evolves from proximate forms (e.g. LB) to more distal forms (e.g. SV), which may account, at least in part, for the progressive decrease in the buoyant density of subtypes as they evolve.

SPB is found in heavier subtypes and appears to be essential for their structure and surface activity (20, 21, 35). Recently, Baritussio et al (1) reported that more dense subtypes (fetal and neonatal rabbits) contained SPB (Western analysis), but that after 24 h of air breathing, the less dense subtype (SV) contained no SPB. Instead, SPB was found in dense fractions where no phos-pholipid was present and, therefore, was dissociated from surfactant phos-pholipid. Recently, Veldhuizen et al also provided evidence that although SPA was present in both large and small aggregates of dog surfactant, SPB was present only in large aggregates (38). Small aggregates generated by cycling large aggregates contained no detectable SPB (dot-blot analysis). Similar re-sults have been obtained in rodent surfactant (S Hawgood & NJ Gross, un-published data); after cycling, some SPB is found that is not associated with phos- pholipid bands. However, it is not clear whether the absence of SPB in SV truly represents degradation of SPB when TM converts to SV, or whether SPB, in either its native form or an enzymatically altered form, dissociates from surfactant during cycling, as seems likely. Degradation products of SPB in cycled surfactant have not been sought or found in these experiments.

SPC is more difficult to detect and quantitate. Although present in the more sedimentable forms of surfactant, it could not be detected in the less sediment-able form in two studies by Baritussio et al (1, 3). As with SPB, following the generation of SV after 24 h of air breathing, significant amounts of SPC were detected in high-density regions of sucrose gradients where little phospholipid was present, which again suggests that it had become dissociated from phospholipids.

From the available evidence, therefore, any of the three major surfactant–associated apoproteins could be a substrate for proteolytic action of convertase on the basis of a decrease in their apparent content in the SV form relative to more dense forms. However, this conclusion seems unjustified at present because of the evidence that all SPs may separate from phospholipids to greater or lesser extent during the conversion of TM to SV and appear in an immunoreactive form elsewhere. Balance studies using quantitative methods for the assay of SPs, together with the identification of SP degradation products or exoprotease–altered SPs, are needed to confirm which SPs are possible substrates for convertase.

PHYSIOLOGIC ACTION OF CONVERTASE

The precise role of convertase in surfactant physiology is uncertain. Evidence from cycling experiments cited above suggests that the enzyme mediates the conversion of TM to SV. However, the monomolecular film of surfactant at the air-fluid interface is widely assumed to be an intermediate between these two forms (and there may be other intermediate forms). This allows for at least two steps at which convertase might act in the conversion of TM to SV. One approach to determine which step convertase might mediate has been to explore whether convertase activity is required for the expression of surface activity by TM. The rationale is that if convertase were required for the step in which TM generates a monomolecular film, inhibiting its activity would impair surface tension reduction when TM is provided to an air-fluid system. Alternatively, if convertase acts at the step in which the monomolecular film is converted to SV, inhibiting convertase would not have any effect on the ability of TM to lower surface tension. When DFP–treated TM (to inhibit its endogenous convertase activity) was compared to TM that was not treated with DFP, no difference was detected, using either a teflon cup or the pulsating bubble methods, in the rate of film formation. Moreover, the minimum surface tension after 100 pulsations was not different, nor was there a detectable difference in the surface tension-surface area loops generated in a Wilhelmy balance (17). A fully defined, reconstituted surfactant containing all the SPs, but no convertase, was likewise able to reduce surface tension in the same way as native TM, despite its inability to convert to SV on cycling (5).

Although these experiments suggest that convertase activity might not be required for film formation, they cannot be considered as definitive proof. Additional experiments are called for, perhaps using other, novel methods to analyze the relationship between film formation and convertase activity. However, if these preliminary results are corroborated by further experiments, they would suggest that convertase acts at a stage that is distal to the monomolecular film, perhaps facilitating the reorientation of phospholipid from the surface into SV.

SPECULATIONS ABOUT THE ACTION AND ROLE OF CONVERTASE

Speculations about the enzymatic action of convertase (15, 16, 38) are stated tentatively and briefly because the evidence is fragmentary at present. The requirement for an air-fluid interface suggests that convertase acts on components of the surfactant film (or its immediate products) because other subtypes of surfactant, the film precursor (TM) and the film product (SV), exist in the subphase. The requirement for repeated expansion and contraction of the surface is consistent with the notion that film formation exposes limited amounts of the substrate(s) to convertase. Perhaps each expansion brings previously unexposed substrate sites into the surface film (e.g. by conversion of TM into the film), which enables convertase to act on the newly exposed set of substrate sites. Each subsequent compression of the surface may then allow the enzymatically altered portions of the film to be reoriented into the SV form. Alternatively, convertase may act on material that is squeezed out of the film during each compression of the surface.

One speculates that SPB is a likely substrate because this molecule appears to be oriented mainly within and parallel to the plane of phospholipids, unlike SPC, which appears to be oriented perpendicular to this plane (37). SPB might serve to stabilize the film of phospholipids at the air-fluid interface (22). Most of the SPB molecule appears to be buried in the hydrophobic environment within the phospholipid acyl chains (7, 39) and is probably not accessible to an enzyme in the surrounding aqueous phase. However, SPB contains some hydrophilic amino acid residues that are fairly regularly spaced in its sequence, and there is good evidence that these residues are associated with the polar head groups of the phospholipids (7). The peptide bonds around these residues might be accessible to a water-soluble protease. Possibly, lysis of these bonds, by removing the stabilizing effect of intact SPB, facilitates the regrouping of phospholipid molecules into vesicular structures that can leave the interface. According to this scheme, the role of convertase would be to facilitate the clearance of surfactant either from the film itself or, less likely, from material squeezed out of the film during expiratory phases of breathing cycles. Why such a function is required in the lung is obscure.

Clearly the study of surfactant convertase is in a preliminary stage. The field is particularly challenging because the highly unusual biophysical aspects of convertase activity and the intractable nature of its site of action and its possible substrates call for innovative experimental approaches. In addition to the basic research required to purify and sequence the enzyme, to study its molecular biology, to confirm its action, substrate, cellular origin, and physiologic role, the clinical importance in surfactant replacement therapy must be considered.

ACKNOWLEDGMENTS

Supported in part by grants from Veterans Administration and National Heart, Lung and Blood Institute HL-45782-01. I thank Richard M Schultz, Loyola University, for much helpful advice, and Vija Bublys and James D'Anza for expert technical support.

Literature Cited

1. Baritussio A, Alberti A, Quaglino D, Pettenazzo A, Dalzoppo D, et al. 1994. SP-A, SP-B, and SP-C in surfactant subtypes around birth: reexamination of alveolar life cycle around birth. *Am. J. Physiol.* 266:L436–47

2. Baritussio A, Bellina L, Carraro R, Rossi A, Enzi M, et al. 1984. Heterogeneity of alveolar surfactant in the rabbit: composition morphology and labeling of subfractions isolated by centrifugation of lung lavage. *Eur. J. Clin. Invest.* 14:24–29

3. Baritussio A, Benevento M, Pettenazzo A, Bruni R, Santucci A, et al. 1989. The life cycle of a low-molecular-weight protein of surfactant (SP-C) in 3-day-old rabbits. *Biochim. Biophys. Acta* 1006: 19–25

4. Baritussio A, Pettenazzo A, Benevento M, Alberti A, Gamba P. 1992. Surfactant protein C is recycled from the alveoli to the lamellar bodies. *Am. J. Physiol.* 263:L607–11

5. Barr F, Putz G, Hawgood S. 1993. Reconstituted surfactant–rich tubular myelin does not convert to vesicular forms with in vitro cycling. *Pediatr. Res.* 33: 317A (Abstr.)

6. Brady L, Brzozowski AM, Derewenda ZS, Dodson E, Dodson G, et al. 1990. A serine protease triad forms the catalytic center of a triacylglycerol lipase. *Nature* 343:767–70

7. Cochrane CG, Revak SD. 1991. Pulmonary surfactant protein B (SP-B): structure function relationships. *Science* 254: 566–68

8. Crystal RG, Brantly ML, Hubbard RC, Curiel DT, States DJ, Holmes MD. 1989. The alpha-1 antitrypsin gene and its mutations: clinical consequences and strategies for therapy. *Chest* 95:196–208

9. Dhand R, Bublys V, Gross NJ. 1993. Effect of modulators of surfactant secretion on "convertase" secretion. *Am. Rev. Respir. Dis.* 147:A143 (Abstr.)

10. Dhand R, Reyes C, Gross NJ. 1994. Localization of surfactant convertase in type II pneumocytes in mice. *Am. J. Rev. Respir. Crit. Care Med.* 149:A92 (Abstr.)

11. Gross NJ. 1991. Surfactant subtypes in experimental lung damage: radiation pneumonitis. *Am. J. Physiol.* 260:L302–10

12. Gross NJ. 1991. Inhibition of surfactant subtype convertase in the radiation model of adult respiratory distress syndrome. *Am. J. Physiol.* 260:L311–17

13. Gross NJ, Narine KR. 1989. Surfactant subtypes in mice: characterization and quantitation. *J. Appl. Physiol.* 66:342–49

14. Gross NJ, Narine KR. 1989. Surfactant subtypes of mice: metabolic relationships and conversion in vitro. *J. Appl. Physiol.* 67:414–21

15. Gross NJ, Schultz RM. 1990. Serine proteinase requirement for the extra–cellular metabolism of pulmonary surfactant. *Biochim. Biophys. Acta* 1044: 222–30

16. Gross NJ, Schultz RM. 1992. Requirements for extracellular metabolism of pulmonary surfactant: tentative identification of serine protease. *Am. J. Physiol.* 262:L446–53

17. Gross NJ, Veldhuizen R, Possmayer F.

1993. Surfactant convertase has little effect on surface–active properties of surfactant. *Am. Rev. Respir. Dis.* 147: A149 (Abstr.)

18. Hawgood S, Shiffer K. 1991. Structures and properties of the surfactant–associated proteins. *Annu. Rev. Physiol.* 53: 375–94

19. Holm BA, Keicher L, Liu M, Sokolowski J, Enhorning G. 1991. Inhibition of pulmonary surfactant function by phospholipases. *J. Appl. Physiol.* 71: 317–21

20. Kobayashi T, Nitta K, Takahashi R, Kurashima K, Robertson B, Suzuki Y. 1991. Activity of pulmonary surfactant after blocking the associated proteins SP-A and SP-B. *J. Appl. Physiol.* 71: 530–36

21. Kobayashi T, Robertson B, Grossman G, Nitta K, Curstedt T, Suzuki Y. 1992. Exogenous porcine surfactant (Curosurf) is inactivated by monoclonal antibody to the surfactant–associated hydrophobic protein SP-B. *Acta Paediatr.* 81:665–71

22. Longo ML, Bisagno AM, Zasadzinski JAN, Bruni R, Waring AJ. 1993. A function of lung surfactant protein SP-B. *Science* 261:453–56

23. Lowe ME. 1992. The catalytic site residues and interfacial binding of human pancreatic lipase. *J. Biol. Chem.* 267: 17069–73

24. Lumb RH. Phospholipid transfer proteins in mammalian lung. *Am. J. Physiol.* 257:L190–204

25. Lumb RH, Benson BJ, Clements JA. 1988. Transfer of phospholipids by a protein fraction obtained from canine pulmonary lavage. *Biochim. Biophys. Acta* 963:549–52

26. Magoon MW, Wright JR, Baritussio A, Williams MC, Goerke J, Clements JA. 1983. Subfractionation of lung surfactant: implications for metabolism and surface activity. *Biochim. Biophys. Acta* 750:18–31

27. Mazurek DA, Gross NJ. 1994. "Convertase" demonstrated in multiple mouse organs. *Am. J. Rev. Respir. Crit. Care Med.* 149:A94 (Abstr.)

28. Miles PR, Castranova V, Bowman L. 1985. Catabolism of rat surfactant disaturated phosphatidylcholines during incubation of alveolar lavage materials in vitro at 37°C. *Biochim. Biophys. Acta* 836:39–44

29. Nicholas TE, Power JHT, Barr HE. 1990. Effect of pattern of breathing on subfractions of surfactant in tissue and alveolar compartments of the adult rat lung. *Am. J. Respir. Cell. Mol. Biol.* 3:1251–58

30. Oulton M, MacDonald J, Janigan DT, Faulkner GT. 1993. Mouse alveolar surfactant: characterization of subtypes prepared by differential centrifugation. *Lipids* 28:715–20

31. Possmayer F. 1988. A proposed nomenclature for pulmonary surfactant–associated proteins. *Am. Rev. Respir. Dis.* 138:990–98

32. Power JHT, Barr HA, Jones ME, Nicholas TE. 1987. Changes in surfactant pools after a physiologic increase in alveolar surfactant. *J. Appl. Physiol.* 63: 1902–11

33. Sanders RL, Hassett RJ, Vatter AE. 1980. Isolation of lung lamellar bodies and their conversion to tubular myelin figures in vitro. *Anat. Rec.* 198:485–501

34. Sheehan PM, Stokes DC, Yeh Y-Y, Hughes WT. 1986. Surfactant phospholipids and lavage phospholipase A2 in experimental *Pneumocystis carinii* pneumonia. *Am. Rev. Respir. Dis.* 134: 526–31

35. Shiffer K, Hawgood S, Haagsman HP, Benson B, Clements JA, Goerke J. 1993. Lung surfactant proteins, SP-B and SP-C, alter the thermodynamic properties of phospholipid membranes: a differential calorimetry study. *Biochemistry* 32: 590–97

36. Spain CL, Silbajoris R, Young SL. 1987. Alterations of surfactant pools in fetal and newborn rat lungs. *Pediatr. Res.* 21:5–9

37. Van den Bussche G, Clercx A, Curstedt T, Johansson J, Jornvall H, Ruysschaert J-M. 1992. Structure and orientation of the surfactant-associated protein C in a lipid bilayer. *Eur. J. Biochem.* 203:201–9

38. Veldhuisen RAW, Inchley K, Hearn SA, Lewis JF, Possmayer F. 1993. Degradation of surfactant–associated protein B (SP-B) during in vitro conversion of large to small surfactant aggregates. *Biochem. J.* 295:141–47

39. Weaver TE, Whitsett JA. 1991. Function and regulation of expression of pulmonary surfactant–associated proteins. *Biochem. J.* 273:249–64

40. Williams MC. 1977. Conversion of lamellar body membranes into tubular myelin in alveoli of fetal rat lungs. *J. Cell Biol.* 72:260–77

41. Wright JR. 1990. Clearance and recycling of pulmonary surfactant. *Am. J. Physiol.* 259:L1–L12

42. Wright JR, Benson BJ, Williams MC, Goerke J, Clements JA. 1984. Protein composition of rabbit alveolar surfactant subfractions. *Biochim. Biophys. Acta* 791:320–32

43. Wright JR, Clements JA. 1987. Metabolism and turnover of lung surfactant. *Am. Rev. Respir. Dis.* 136: 426–44

44. Wright JR, Dobbs LG. 1991. Regulation of pulmonary surfactant secretion and clearance. *Annu. Rev. Physiol.* 53:359–414

45. Wright JR, Wager RE, Hamilton RL, Huang M, Clements JA. 1986. Uptake of lung surfactant subfractions into lamellar bodies of adult rat lungs. *J. Appl. Physiol.* 60:817–25

46. Yamada T, Ikegami M, Jobe AH. 1990. Effects of surfactant subfractions on preterm rabbit lung function. *Pediatr. Res.* 27:592–98

47. Young SL, Fram EK, Larson E, Wright JR. 1993. Recycling of surfactant lipid and apoprotein-A studied by electron microscopic autoradiography. *Am. J. Physiol.* 265:L19–26

Annu. Rev. Physiol. 1995. 57:151–70

CHEMICAL REGULATION OF PULMONARY AIRWAY TONE[1]

Jeffrey M. Drazen[2,3], Benjamin Gaston[4], and Stephanie A. Shore[3]
[2]Pulmonary and Critical Care Division, Brigham and Women's Hospital, 75 Francis Street, Boston, Massachusetts 02115; [3]Physiology Program, Harvard School of Public Health, Boston, Massachusetts 02115; [4]Pediatric Pulmonary Division, Naval Hospital, San Diego, California 92134

KEY WORDS: nitric oxide, leukotrienes, neuropeptides

INTRODUCTION

Airway tone is under active regulation by multiple effector systems, each with the capacity to modulate this tone. In this review, we focus on three distinct effector systems, namely the cysteinyl leukotrienes, neuropeptides, and nitrogen oxides (NO_x); we review specific aspects of our current understanding of each of these effector systems, with emphasis on progress made over the recent past. Special attention is paid to relationships among the various effector systems; examples are given from human asthma, a disease that illustrates the physiological significance of each of these systems in regulating airway tone.

INDIVIDUAL EFFECTOR SYSTEMS

Cysteinyl Leukotrienes

SYNTHESIS OF THE LEUKOTRIENES   The cysteinyl leukotrienes are derived from membrane phospholipids by the action of phospholipases that cleave arachidonic acid esterified in the *sn*-2 position from the triglyceride backbone. The liberated arachidonic acid is acted on twice in succession by 5-lipoxygenase to yield the unstable epoxide known as LTA_4; in the presence of LTC_4 synthase, glutathione is adducted at the C-6 position of LTA_4 to yield the molecule known as LTC_4. The LTC_4 is then exported from the cell cytosol to the extracellular microenvironment where the glutamic acid moiety is cleaved to form LTD$_4$. LTD$_4$ exerts its effects through action at specific receptors that transduce a variety of biological activities including constriction of airway smooth muscle. It is among the most potent airway contractile agonists identified to date. The removal of the glycine moiety from LTD$_4$ results in the formation of LTE$_4$, a molecule that has 30- to 100-fold less biopotency than LTD$_4$. Although this general schema (Figure 1) has been known for some time (63, 89), substantial progress has been made recently in elucidating the regu-

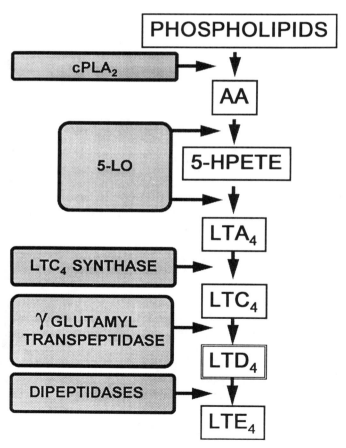

Figure 1 Block diagram of the steps in the metabolic transformation of membrane phospholipids to the cysteinyl leukotrienes. AA = arachidonic acid; 5-HPETE = 5-hydroxy-eicosatetraenoic acid; LT = leukotriene; 5-LO = 5-lipoxygenase; cPLA$_2$ = cytosolic PLA$_2$.

lation of the various steps involved in the production of the cysteinyl leuko-trienes and the role of these biomolecules in regulating airway tone in human asthma. Specific areas in which substantive progress has been made are re-viewed below.

Release of arachidonic acid from membrane phospholipids   The synthesis of LTC_4 is known to be an intracellular process, yet the process of cleavage of arachidonic acid from cell membrane phospholipids by secretory forms of phospholipase A_2 ($sPLA_2$) takes place in the extracellular microenvironment (18, 50, 109). In order to resolve this paradox, it was postulated that arachidonic acid diffused into target cells to serve as the substrate needed for generation of the cysteinyl leukotrienes. However, the discovery of a cytosolic form of phospholipase A_2 led to the understanding that the initial steps in leukotriene synthesis most likely all occur within target cells.

Cytosolic phospholipase A_2 ($cPLA_2$) is a 100- to 110-kDa (by sodium dodecyl sulfate–polyacrylamide gel electrophoresis) protein originally purified from the human monocytic cell line U937. It is distinguished from $sPLA_2$ by its molecular size, its dithiothreitol resistance, and its activity at calcium concentrations consistent with the intracellular microenvironment (15). The enzyme has been molecularly cloned; the isolated cDNAs encode a 749 amino acid protein, with a putative molecular mass of 85.2 kDa (14, 92). Studies of the protein derived from expression of the cDNA demonstrate that it contains structural elements homologous to the C2 region of protein kinase C, that it selectively cleaves arachidonic acid from membrane vesicles, and that it trans-locates from the cytosolic compartment to membrane vesicles in the presence of the concentrations of calcium found intracellularly after cell activation. Indeed, $cPLA_2$ phosphorylation, initiated by transmembrane signaling events, results in an up-regulation of the catalytic activity of the enzyme (55). Additional evidence for the uniqueness of this enzyme derives from the comparison of the responses of Chinese hamster ovary (CHO) cells transfected with a cDNA encoding either $cPLA_2$ or $sPLA_2$. Activation of these transfected cells by adenosine triphosphate (ATP) or thrombin results in enhanced catalytic activity only in the CHO cells transfected with the $cPLA_2$ cDNA (66). Furthermore, recent studies have shown that $cPLA_2$ is translocated to the perinuclear membrane upon cellular activation (83). This finding is of particular importance because, as outlined below, 5-lipoxygenase (5-LO) is also trans-located to the perinuclear membrane when mast cells are activated. Taken together this body of data strongly implicates $cPLA_2$ as the phospholipase that liberates arachidonic acid; the released arachidonate serves as the substrate for the various enzymes involved in the synthesis of the cysteinyl leukotrienes. The therapeutic use of agents that inhibit the action of $cPLA_2$ in disease states has yet to be studied.

Five-lipoxygenase activating protein (FLAP)   5-LO, the enzyme that catalyzes the formation of LTA$_4$ from arachidonic acid via the chemical intermediate 5-hydroperoxy eicosatetraenoic acid (5-HPETE), is also a cytosolic enzyme. Although it was known that 5-LO had to be translocated from the cytosol to a membrane compartment to be catalytically active, the mechanism by which this activation occurred was not clarified until the isolation of FLAP. FLAP is an 18–kDA integral membrane protein that binds 5-LO in the presence of Ca^{2+}.

The FLAP gene contains five small exons and four large introns; restriction maps of the FLAP gene confirm there is only a single FLAP gene. FLAP is highly conserved among species (108). The evolutionary conservation of FLAP structure is consistent with a functional role for leukotriene synthesis wherein FLAP activation exerts an important regulatory step (see below).

The importance of FLAP in regulating the synthesis of the leukotrienes was first demonstrated with osteogenic sarcoma cells, which possess neither 5-LO nor FLAP and hence are not capable of producing leukotrienes when activated. When these cells were transfected with a cDNA that encoded 5-LO, broken cell preparations were able to produce leukotrienes; however, intact cells did not produce leukotrienes when stimulated with the calcium ionophore A23187. When osteogenic sarcoma cells were cotransfected with FLAP and 5-LO, intact cells were able to synthesize leukotrienes when appropriately stimulated (21, 74). FLAP is present in all cells known to synthesize leukotrienes and absent from cells without that capacity (87).

We now have a reasonably clear idea of the mechanism of FLAP action (1, 68). FLAP, by virtue of its three hydrophobic membrane–spanning domains, integrates into plasma membranes. Data from immunoelectron microscopic localization studies have shown that FLAP is localized to the perinuclear membrane of human leukocytes, and when cells containing 5-LO and FLAP are activated, 5-LO also localizes to the perinuclear membrane (114). FLAP specifically binds radiolabeled L-739,059 (a photoaffinity-labeled analogue of arachidonic acid). The binding of L-739,059 and the inhibition of its binding by arachidonic acid suggest that FLAP binds arachidonic acid. FLAP activation also stimulates the utilization and efficiency of conversion of arachidonic acid to leukotrienes by 5-LO. Therefore, the colocalization of cPLA$_2$ and FLAP to the perinuclear membrane provides a physical locus where arachidonic acid can be cleaved from phospholipids by cPLA$_2$ and subsequently transferred to 5-LO.

BIOLOGICAL ACTIONS OF THE LEUKOTRIENES   Immediately after the the chemical structure of the leukotrienes was elucidated, it was noted that these molecules were potent airway contractile agonists and had the capacity to promote the leakage of intravascular tracers into the extravascular space. These biological properties have been reviewed in detail (84, 85); this review focuses on the potential role of leukotrienes in asthma.

Leukotrienes as prophlogistic molecules   Laitinen and co-workers (58) exposed four patients with asthma to aerosols generated from solutions of LTE$_4$ and analyzed bronchial biopsy specimens taken 4 h later. They found that the LTE$_4$ exposure was associated with an increase in the numbers of eosinophils and neutrophils in the lamina propria; there was no significant change in the number of lymphocytes, plasma cells, mast cells, or macrophages. These data are consistent with the hypothesis that recurrent exposure to leukotrienes, as may be produced endogenously in certain disease conditions, can alter the cellular composition of the airways.

Evidence for in vivo production of the leukotrienes   Measurable amounts of LTE$_4$ can be recovered from the urine of normal subjects, but the source of these leukotrienes and their biological role are not known. However, the importance of the cysteinyl leukotrienes as mediators of the abnormal physiological changes in certain diseases was substantially advanced by Taylor and co-workers (102), who observed that the quantity of LTE$_4$ in urine after an allergen challenge in susceptible individuals served as an index of the endogenous production of the cysteinyl leukotrienes. Sala and co-workers subsequently demonstrated (88) that approximately 30% of intravenously infused radiolabeled LTE$_4$ could be recovered in the urine, approximately half as intact LTE$_4$ and the remainder as more polar metabolites. Two predominant metabolites of LTE$_4$ were also recovered, namely, 14-carboxy-hexanor-LTE$_3$ and 16 carboxy-Δ13-tetranor-LTE$_4$. The intact LTE$_4$ appeared in the urine within 2 h, the more polar metabolites in the next 7 h. Recently, Westcott and colleagues (112) showed that radiolabeled LTC$_4$ infused into the airways by bronchoalveolar lavage could be recovered in the urine within 6 h of instillation. Thus urinary recovery of LTE$_4$ can be used as an index of endogenous production of the leukotrienes. Indeed, a number of investigators have used the urinary excretion of LTE$_4$ as such an index in various forms of induced asthma; specific examples are reviewed below.

In patients with exercise-induced asthma, the hyperpnea associated with exercise is followed by airway obstruction. Three different groups of investigators have reported the effects of exercise on the recovery of LTE$_4$ from the urine (51, 52, 97, 103). Kikawa and co-workers (51, 52) found a significant increase in the amount of LTE$_4$ recovered from the urine after exercise challenge, while Taylor and co-workers (103) and Smith and co-workers (97) were unable to document such an effect. A possible interpretation is that only a subset of patients with exercise-induced asthma produce cysteinyl leukotrienes; this hypothesis has not been subjected to direct test.

Seven investigative groups (57, 69, 96, 97, 101, 102, 111) have found that the excretion of urinary LTE_4 is increased after allergen challenge. All investigators have been able to show an elevation in urinary LTE_4 levels within a few hours of antigen exposure, and some show a positive correlation between airway responses to antigen challenge and the amount of urinary LTE_4 recovered. These data clearly indicate that allergen exposure, in susceptible individuals, is associated with enhanced production of the cysteinyl leukotrienes.

Evidence for a pathobiological role for leukotrienes in regulating airway tone in asthma   Investigators interested in the role of leukotrienes in spontaneous airway narrowing in asthma treated asthmatic patients who had not received their usual bronchodilator medications with agents that can either prevent the action of LTD_4 at its receptor or prevent the formation of leukotrienes by inhibition of 5-LO. This strategy was first tested in normal individuals and in patients with mild asthma (16, 43); in neither case was a change in airway tone observed after treatment with these agents. In contrast, when subjects with moderate asthma [forced expiratory volume in one second (FEV_1) approximately 65% of predicted] were given agents that inhibit the action of LTD_4 at its receptor, there was a 5–15% improvement in airflow rates as measured by FEV_1 (29, 40, 42, 59). It is noteworthy that in each of these studies, administration of an inhaled β-agonist resulted in further improvement in the FEV_1, which was additive to the increase in the FEV_1 resulting from the LTD_4 receptor antagonist. In this study, when 5-LO inhibitor was administered to patients with moderate asthma, an improvement in FEV_1 was seen; the onset of effect correlated well with the known kinetics of drug absorption. This observation provides evidence for the ongoing synthesis of the leukotrienes in patients with moderate asthma and more importantly for a biological role, i.e. the induction of airway narrowing, for these endogenously produced biomolecules. Because the patients studied in all the trials had stable asthma and were not given a provocational challenge, these data clearly implicate the leukotrienes as important endogenous mediators of airway obstruction.

Neuropeptides

NEURAL SYNTHESIS AND RELEASE   C-fibers are a class of small unmyelinated sensory neurons. In the airways, the terminal processes of these neurons are found underneath and between epithelial cells; near blood vessels, airway smooth muscle, and mucous glands; and around, but not in, parasympathetic ganglia. The cell bodies for the C-fibers innervating the lungs and airways are found in the nodose and jugular ganglia as well as in the upper thoracic dorsal root ganglia (3, 4). C-fiber neurons synthesize multiple neuropeptides including the tachykinins substance P (SP) and neurokinin A (NKA), which are products of the preprotachykinin I (*PPT-1*) gene. The *PPT-1* gene can be spliced to yield three different PPT-1 mRNAs: alpha, beta, and gamma. SP is produced by translation of all three forms of mRNA, whereas NKA is produced only by the beta and gamma forms (56). The third mammalian tachykinin, neurokinin B, is not expressed in pulmonary C-fibers. The peptides are transported in granules axoplasmically to the peripheral processes of these nerves where they can be released into the airway microenvironment following stimulation by inhaled irritants such as cigarette smoke and SO_2 gas, as well as by certain endogenous inflammatory mediators. Stimulation of the sensory nerves by inhaled irritants also results in the conduction of action potentials toward the central nervous system. For details on the distribution, synthesis, and release of tachykinins in the lungs and airways, see recent comprehensive reviews (3, 35, 64).

AIRWAY RESPONSES TO TACHYKININS   Tachykinins have multiple effects in the airways that include airway smooth muscle constriction, increased ion and water flux across the epithelium, cough, mucous secretion, increased airway blood flow, and increased airway vascular permeability. In vivo, tachykinins cause airway obstruction in many species, although the magnitude of the effect differs substantially. Initial studies with intravenously administered SP in humans did not demonstrate any effects on airway caliber (28), but recent experiments using changes in the partial flow-volume curve (46) indicate that inhaled NKA, and to a lesser extent SP, can each mediate airway obstruction. Using these methods, we now know that NKA is approximately 10–100 times more potent as a bronchoconstrictor in asthmatic than in normal humans (12, 13); this potency ratio is similar to that observed for other agonists.

While many factors may modulate the bronchoconstrictor potential of tachykinins, degradation of tachykinins by peptidases is among the most important (see 64). Both SP and NKA are rapidly degraded by neutral endopeptidase (NEP), an enzyme expressed in the airways in epithelial cells, in smooth muscle, and in submucosal connective tissue. Cleavage of SP and NKA by NEP results in fragments virtually devoid of bronchoconstrictor activity, and inhibition of NEP substantially increases the bronchoconstrictor activity of these agents including their ability to alter airflow in normal and asthmatic subjects (12, 13).

Tachykinin receptors   The effects of tachykinins in the airways are mediated by their interaction with specific receptors. At least three mammalian tachykinin receptors, NK_1, NK_2, and NK_3, have now been identified and molecularly cloned (72, 93, 115); subtypes of the NK_1 and NK_2 receptors have been proposed (see 67). SP has the highest affinity for the NK_1 receptor, NKA for the NK_2 receptor, and NKB for the NK_3 receptor, although each peptide can interact with all three receptors.

The tachykinin receptors are G protein–linked receptors with seven transmembrane domains. The seven membrane–spanning sequences, particularly transmembrane segment seven, and those portions of the cytoplasmic regions close to the transmembrane regions, show a high degree of homology among the three tachykinin receptors. Data obtained by expressing cDNAs encoding mutant or chimeric tachykinin receptors in COS or CHO cells indicate that the extracellular domains are important in binding of peptides to the receptors, but they are not the only domains that confer the specificity of the receptor because the transmembrane regions also appear to be involved in determining ligand–binding characteristics (26, 34, 77). It has now been established in numerous tissues that signal transduction via tachykinin receptors results in G protein–linked activation of phospholipase C and in phosphoinositide turnover, local synthesis of inositol 1,4,5-trisphosphate (IP_3), and consequent increases in intracellular calcium (77).

Anatomic localization of tachykinin receptors in human and guinea pig airways has been achieved by autoradiographic studies that show labeling of vascular smooth muscle, airway epithelium, submucosal glands, and airway smooth muscle from the trachea to small bronchioles (10, 39). Studies using stable and selective agonists and nonpeptide antagonists of the NK_1 and NK_2 receptors have allowed definition of which receptors contribute substantially to contraction of airway smooth muscle (67). In isolated human airway smooth muscle, NK_2 receptor-selective agonists mediate contraction, whereas agonists selective for the NK_1 or NK_3 only elicit contraction at high concentrations (24, 79). Contractile effects in this tissue mediated by all NK receptor agonists and by SP and NKA are not blocked by the NK_1 receptor antagonist CP96345 but are inhibited by NK_2-selective antagonists (24).

Thus NK_2 receptors are the predominant contractile tachykinin receptors present on human airway smooth muscle. In human subjects (either normal or asthmatic), administration of the NEP inhibitor thiorphan (12, 13) or the combined NK_1/NK_2 receptor antagonist FK224 (41) has no effect on baseline specific airway resistance (sRaw), which suggests that tachykinins do not contribute to the small degree of tone observed in normal human airways or the increased resistance observed in stable asthmatics. Similar results have been obtained in guinea pigs (94, 98). In contrast, tachykinins do appear to contribute to changes in airway tone or airway hyperresponsiveness caused by other agonists or agents in guinea pigs (64). In addition, a combined NK_1/NK_2 receptor antagonist attenuated airway obstruction caused by bradykinin in asthmatics, which suggests that tachykinins may also contribute to the bronchospasm induced by this peptide (41).

Interactions between C-fibers and mast cells   Histologic evidence shows that mast cells and C-fibers are colocalized in peripheral organs (95, 100) and in certain neural ganglia (105). Functional as well as structural evidence for innervation of mast cells by C-fibers also exists: Stimulation of the trigeminal nerve causes the histological appearance of degranulation in mast cells in the rat dura mater. This effect is abolished by neonatal capsaicin treatment, which suggests that the effect is mediated by C-fibers (20).

Tachykinin release by mast cell products   Substantial progress has been made in the last three years in understanding the functional interactions between mast cells and C-fibers in the airways. It appears that products of mast cells stimulate C-fibers and cause them to release tachykinins (95). In addition, tachykinins have the capacity to cause mast cell degranulation, at least in some species. These events may provide a potent pathway for amplifying broncho-constrictor responses (Figure 2).

Histamine and LTC_4 have been shown to increase the frequency of action potentials recorded from C-fibers innervating dog airways (17). These autocoids also cause membrane depolarization in some neurons in the guinea pig nodose ganglia with conduction velocities consistent with C-fibers (106). Products of mast cells including histamine, LTC_4/D_4, and platelet-activating factor (PAF) have also been shown to cause release of SP and NKA in the airways. Martins et al (70) measured increased levels of SP-like and NKA-like im-

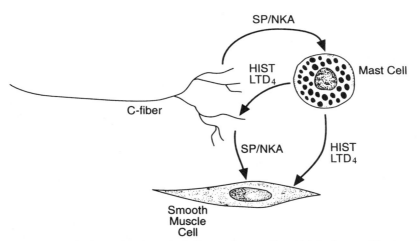

Figure 2   Potential interactions between C-fibers and mast cells, which lead to amplification of smooth muscle contraction. SP, substance P; NKA, neurokinin A; HIST, histamine; LTD_4, leukotriene D_4.

munoreactivity in the effluent of isolated tracheally perfused guinea pigs lungs after addition of histamine, LTC_4, or PAF to the perfusate. Addition of the NEP inhibitor thiorphan to the perfusate augmented peptide recovery, thereby indicating that the tachykinins were released in a locus that allowed them to be degraded by NEP. Bloomquist & Kream also reported that LTD_4 caused release of SP and NKA in isolated guinea pig trachea (7).

Tachykinins are not only released by mast cell products but, in some cases, appear to be involved in mediating the contractile responses or changes in airway responsiveness induced by these agents. Bronchoconstrictor responses to histamine decrease in anesthetized guinea pigs pretreated with large doses of capsaicin to deplete the lungs and airways of tachykinins (71). In isolated perfused guinea pig lungs, administration of the NEP inhibitor thiorphan increases the changes in airway opening pressure caused by histamine (70). Similarly, in guinea pig trachea, tachykinin receptor antagonists decrease and NEP inhibitors increase the contractile response to LTD_4 (7). Perretti et al reported that the airway hyperresponsiveness induced by PAF could be prevented if animals were pretreated with capsaicin to deplete the lungs and airways of tachykinins (82).

Tachykinin activation of mast cells   There is also evidence that tachykinins can cause activation and degranulation of mast cells. In rat peritoneal mast cells, SP causes release of histamine (27). This activity appears to be related to charged residues at the amino terminal of the molecule, rather than to an activity at tachykinin receptors because tachykinins such as eledoisin and SP4–11, which lack these charged moieties but can still activate receptors, did not cause histamine release. In rats, administration of either SP or NKA is associated with enhanced recovery of serotonin and histamine from bronchoalveolar lavage fluid (47). These effects of tachykinins appear to be receptor mediated because the NK_1 and NK_2 receptor antagonists reduced the concentrations of histamine and serotonin in bronchoalveolar fluid. Predegranulating mast cells by administration of compound 48/80 2 days before challenge with tachykinins prevented serotonin and histamine release, which suggests that mast cells were indeed the source of the amines recovered (47). Pretreatment with compound 48/80 or administration of a serotonin receptor antagonist also prevented the changes in pulmonary resistance induced by SP and NKA (47), thereby suggesting that stimulation of mast cells by tachykinins has important physiological consequences.

The importance of mast cell–sensory nerve interactions in human airways remains to be established. There are, to our knowledge, no data regarding the ability of mast cell products to stimulate C-fibers in human airways. Substance P does cause degranulation of human skin mast cells but not of mast cells isolated from human lung (60).

INTERACTIONS BETWEEN TACHYKININS AND LEUKOTRIENES   The physiological importance of tachykinin action on airway mast cells is not only related to their ability to cause release of amines. In isolated preparations of guinea pig bronchus containing an intact vagus nerve, stimulation of the nerve results in a biphasic contractile response (23). The first phase is cholinergically mediated, and the second phase is abolished by pretreatment with large doses of capsaicin, a fact indicating that it is C-fiber mediated. Ellis & Undem (23) have reported that the capsaicin-sensitive contraction is inhibited by three structurally unrelated sulfidopeptide leukotriene receptor antagonists. In their experiments, addition of exogenous LTD_4 potentiated the second-phase (i.e. noncholinergic) responses but did not alter response to exogenously administered SP or NKA, which suggests that LTD_4 augmented the release of tachykinins from C-fibers rather than their activity (23). One potential explanation for these results is that tachykinins released from C-fibers by nerve stimulation act on mast cells to cause release of leukotrienes which, in turn, enhance further release of tachykinins from the C-fibers. Such interactions may also explain the ability of tachykinin receptor antagonists (98) and leukotreine receptor antagonists (30) to attenuate the bronchospasm that occurs following eucapnic hyperventilation in guinea pigs. Indeed, the potential for complex interactions among effector systems is enhanced by the fact that in addition to their ability to synthesize SP and NKA, neurons in the nodose and jugular ganglia are immunoreactive for cNOS (25), consistent with the idea that NO may also modulate local neurotransmission.

Nitrogen Oxides (NO_x)

Oxides of nitrogen (NO_x) can be synthesized enzymatically. These compounds play a major role as functional effector molecules in the regulation of circulation and neurotransmission and are now acknowledged to be of importance in the regulation of airway tone.

BIOSYNTHESIS AND CHEMICAL CHARACTERISTICS OF LUNG NO_x Endogenously produced NO_x are present in the lung and have a major role in the chemical regulation of airway smooth muscle tone. Nitric oxide ($NO\bullet$) is produced by means of a five-electron transfer from the guanidino nitrogen of L-arginine to molecular oxygen (80). This transfer is catalyzed by a number of different enzymes known collectively as nitric oxide synthases (NOS); enzyme action results in the formation of $NO\bullet$ and citrulline from L-arginine. Several distinct isoforms of NOS, broadly classified as constitutive or inducible, have been identified, isolated, and cloned. Classically defined constitutive NOS (cNOS) isoforms, such as those found in endothelial cells and neuronal tissue, are rapidly activated by certain stimuli, e.g acetylcholine and bradykinin, that act through calcium-mediated calmodulin binding. Inducible isoforms (iNOS), on the other hand, such as those isolated from macrophages, are regulated at the level of transcription and are not dependent on calcium for activation. These latter isoforms are typically induced by cytokines and endotoxins; their synthesis is inhibited by glucocorticoids (48, 80). Nitric oxide synthases are found in a variety of pulmonary cell types (38, 53, 90) including epithelial cells (11), macrophages (48), neutrophils (116), mast cells (6), neurons (53, 90), fibroblasts (49), smooth muscle cells (78), and endothelial cells from arterial, venous, and lymphatic endothelium (53, 80). Several of these cell types including neutrophils (116) and airway epithelial cells (11) appear to have NOS with both constitutive and inducible properties.

EFFECTS OF NO_x ON AIRWAY TONE   Endogenous end-products of mammalian nitrogen oxidation include molecules such as S-nitrosothiols (RS-NO) capable of causing airway smooth muscle relaxation, or peroxynitrite ($OONO^-$) capable of causing tissue injury; the entities formed vary with the local redox conditions (33, 99). The highly reactive free radical NO• present in the expired air of humans, rabbits, and guinea pigs (8, 31, 37) has an established role as an airway smooth muscle relaxant (9, 22, 32, 33, 45, 117) but also has redox-dependent cytotoxic effects by virtue of its reactions with oxygen and superoxide to form NO_2• and $OONO^-$, as well as mutagenic effects mediated through nitrosamine formation (86, 113).

NO_x relax airway smooth muscle with potencies that vary depending on the species of origin of the contractile tissues, the airway size, and the integrity of the airway epithelium. The concentrations of NO_x required to achieve airway relaxation in guinea pig or human airways compare favorably with those of theophylline and isoproterenol (32, 45) (Figure 3). However, their relaxant potency varies with site of action (110). For example, bovine airway relaxations induced by the exogenous NO_x from nitroglycerin and nitroprusside are greater in proximal than in distal airway preparations (36). Further, NO_x in the form of RS-NO are more potent in relaxing guinea pig trachealis than in relaxing canine tracheal or human bronchial smooth muscle, an example of the marked species variability that is characteristic of the effects of these compounds (32, 45, 117). Finally, dissolved NO• relaxes guinea pig trachealis more potently in epithelium-denuded than in epithelium-intact preparations (76).

MECHANISMS OF ACTION

Guanylyl cyclase activation   Controversy exists concerning the mechanism by which NO_x relax airway smooth muscle. As in the case of vascular smooth muscle, evidence suggests that binding of NO• to guanylyl cyclase results in enzyme activation, which transduces at least some of the observed airway

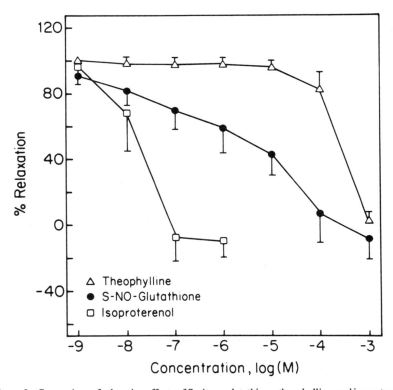

Figure 3   Comparison of relaxation effects of S-nitrosoglutathione, theophylline, and isoproterenol in human bronchi contracted with 7 µM methacholine. Concentration-effect relationships reveal an order of potency: isoproterenol (*open squares*) > S-nitrosoglutathione (*closed circles*) > theophylline (*open triangles*) (ANOVA; $p < 0.0005$). Results are presented as mean ± SEM.

relaxant effect. For example, in canine and guinea pig trachealis preparations, inhibitors of guanylyl cyclase partially inhibit RS-NO-induced relaxation (45, 117). Furthermore, in certain airway preparations, inhibition of cGMP phosphodiesterase enhances the relaxant activity of RS-NO, and 8-bromo cGMP causes modest airway relaxation (32). However, guanylyl cyclase inhibitors have little or no effect on the relaxant activity of RS-NO in human airways. Therefore, in distinct contrast to the situation with vascular smooth muscle, a solid case for a pivotal role of the activation of guanylyl cyclase in the mediation of NO_x-generated airway smooth muscle relaxation cannot be made.

Mechanisms of NO entry into cells   The hypothesis that diffusion of NO• across cell membranes precedes its subsequent intracellular actions has been challenged by Kowaluk & Fung (54), who demonstrated that the vascular smooth muscle relaxant response to various RS-NO species was not related to the spontaneous release of NO• from the molecule under study. Moreover, it has been shown in human smooth muscle airway preparations that hemoglobin, which binds NO•, does not inhibit the relaxant effect of RS-NO and that stable RS-NO, which spontaneously releases only small amounts of NO•, are equally potent or more potent than NO• itself (32). Furthermore, since macromolecular S-nitroso-albumin and low molecular weight RS-NO such as S-nitrosocysteine are of equal potency in relaxing human airway smooth muscle, intact uptake of RS-NO across cell membranes is likely not required for bioactivity. Instead, cell surface interactions (similar to ligand-receptor interactions) are proposed to be in part responsible for the NO_x-induced relaxant response (99).

PHYSIOLOGIC ROLE OF NO_x IN CONTROL OF AIRWAY SMOOTH MUSCLE   There are at least four distinct circumstances in which the airway relaxant properties of NO_x appear to be of physiologic importance: (*a*) maintenance of basal airway tone, (*b*) mediation of inhibitory nonadrenergic-noncholinergic (i-NANC) bronchodilation, (*c*) modulation of bronchoconstrictor effects, and (*d*) non-neuronal cell–cell signaling.

Maintenance of basal airway tone   Luminal perfusion of guinea pig tracheal tube preparations with inhibitors of NOS results in an increase in basal tone, which suggests that there is NOS activity in these preparations without specific stimulation (81). Superfusates from normal guinea pig lungs contain NO_x in concentrations sufficient to relax guinea pig trachealis (65). This constellation of findings is consistent with the role of NO_x and their stabilized congeners in regulating baseline airway tone. Indeed, the endogenous bronchodilator S-nitrosoglutathione (S-NO-GLU) is present in normal human airway lining fluid in concentrations of 250 µM, which are sufficient to mediate relaxation of human airway smooth muscle (33).

Inhibitory NANC (i-NANC) bronchodilator response   Vasoactive intestinal peptides (VIP) containing neurons and NOS are colocalized in lung tissues (19). i-NANC responses are thought to be mediated in part by VIP (2, 73, 107). Recent supporting evidence shows that pretreatment of tissue preparations with proteolytic enzymes capable of inactivating VIP decreases the magnitude of induced i-NANC relaxation of airway smooth muscle (2, 5, 104). Belvisi et al (5) have shown that the "proteolytic enzyme resistant" component of the i-NANC response can be abolished by treatment with NOS inhibitors. It is reasoned, therefore, that NOS stimulated by i-NANC neurotransmission accounts for at least part of the non-VIP component of the response. Furthermore, there is reason to believe that NO_x mediate the airway smooth muscle relaxant effects of VIP itself in the isolated perfused guinea pig lung (65) because NOS inhibitors partially prevent relaxation induced by VIP, but not that induced by isoproterenol. A significant and appropriately timed increase in the NO_x content of lung perfusion fluid can be measured in response to VIP. These data support the conclusion that VIP-NO_x interactions mediate a substantial component of i-NANC transmission.

Modulation of bronchoconstriction   Atropine–sensitive electric field stimulation (EFS)–induced bronchoconstrictor responses are enhanced by NOS inhibitors, but not by α-chymotrypsin (91, 110). There is also evidence that NO_x modulate the effects of noncholinergic bronchoconstrictors. Histamine stimulation of H_1 receptors in the guinea pig lung is associated with NOS activation (62). Furthermore, guinea pig and human airway smooth muscle contractions caused by histamine and leukotriene D_4 are reversed by RS-NO (32, 45). Finally, NANC bronchoconstrictor effects induced by certain frequencies of EFS in vitro are potentiated by NOS inhibitors and by α-chymotrypsin (61).

Nonneuronal cell–cell signaling   There is evidence that generation of NO_x, such as NO• or S-NO-GLU, may represent a means by which nonneuronal airway cells signal nearby smooth muscle tissues to relax. For example, during states of immune activation or inflammation, S-NO-GLU can be recovered from human airways at concentrations sufficient to cause over 50% relaxation of precontracted human bronchial smooth muscle (33). Immunohistochemical analysis shows that in asthma epithelial NOS is activated (38); such activation may explain the elevated concentrations of NO• recovered from the expirate of asthma patients (31). Epithelially derived NO_x may act as counterregulatory bronchodilators in pathologic states of bronchoconstriction and, hence, serve a homeostatic function. Alternatively, activation of epithelial and other NOS isoforms may have a prophlogistic role and actually induce or perpetuate airway injury. For example, it is known that NOS inhibitors prevent pulmonary capillary leak caused by macrophage and neutrophil activation, probably through prevention of $OONO^-$ formation (75). Whether NO_x are predominantly homeostatic or prophlogistic in asthma remains to be established.

SUMMARY

Over the past three years, substantial progress has been made in dissecting out the role of each of these individual effector systems, namely, the leukotrienes, neuropeptides, and nitrogen oxides. The next major challenge is to understand how they function in an integrated fashion.

Literature Cited

1. Abramovitz M, Wong E, Cox ME, Richardson CD, Li C, Vickers PJ. 1993. 5-Lipoxygenase-activating protein stimulates the utilization of arachidonic acid by 5-lipoxygenase. *Eur. J. Biochem.* 215: 105–11

2. Bai TR, Bramley AM. 1993. Effect of an inhibitor of nitric oxide synthase on neural relaxation of human bronchi. *Am. J. Physiol.* 264:L425–30

3. Barnes PJ, Baraniuk JN, Belvisi MG. 1991. Neuropeptides in the respiratory tract, Part I. *Am. Rev. Respir. Dis.* 144: 1187–98

4. Barnes PJ, Baraniuk JN, Belvisi MG. 1991. Neuropeptides in the respiratory tract, Part II. *Am. Rev. Respir. Dis.* 144: 1391–99

5. Belvisi MG, Stretton CD, Yacoub M, Barnes PJ. 1992. Nitric oxide is the endogenous neurotransmitter of bronchodilator nerves in humans. *Eur. J. Pharmacol.* 210:221–22

6. Bissonnette EY, Hogaboam CM, Wallace JL, Befus AD. 1991. Potentiation of tumor necrosis factor-alpha-mediated cytotoxicity. *J. Immunol.* 147: 3060–65

7. Bloomquist EI, Kream RM. 1990. Release of substance P from the guinea pig trachea (by) leukotriene D_4. *Exp. Lung Res.* 16:645–59

8. Borl C, Cox Y, Higenbottam T. 1993. Measurement of exhaled nitric oxide in man. *Thorax* 48:1160–62

9. Buga GM, Gold ME, Wood KS, Chaudhuri G, Ignarro LJ. 1989. Endothelium-derived nitric oxide relaxes nonvascular smooth muscle. *Eur. J. Pharmacol.* 161:61–72

10. Castairs JR, Barnes PJ. 1986. Autoradiographic mapping of substance P receptors in lung. *Eur. J. Pharmacol.* 127:295–96

11. Chee C, Gaston B, Gerard C, Loscalzo J, Kobzik L, et al. 1993. Nitric oxide is produced by a human epithelial cell line. *Am. Rev. Respir. Dis.* 147:A433

12. Cheung D, Bel EH, den Hartigh J, Dijkman JH, Sterk PJ. 1992. The effect of an inhaled neutral endopeptidase inhibitor, thiorphan, on airway responses to neurokinin A in normal humans in vivo. *Am. Rev. Respir. Dis.* 145:1275–80

13. Cheung D, Timmers MC, Zwinderman AH, den Hartigh J, Dijkman JH, Sterk PJ. 1993. Neutral endopeptidase activity and airway hyperresponsiveness to neurokinin A in asthmatic subjects in vivo. *Am. Rev. Respir. Dis.* 148:1467–73

14. Clark JD, Lin LL, Kriz RW, Ramesha CS, Sultzman LA, et al. 1991. A novel arachidonic acid-selective cytosolic PLA_2 contains a Ca^{2+}-dependent translocation domain with homology to PKC and GAP. *Cell* 65:1043–51

15. Clark JD, Milona N, Knopf JL. 1990. Purification of a 110-kilodalton cytosolic phospholipase A_2 from the human monocytic cell line U937. *Proc. Natl. Acad. Sci. USA* 87:7708–12

16. Cloud ML, Enas GC, Kemp J, Platts-Mills T, Altman LC, et al. 1989. A specific LTD_4/LTE_4-receptor antagonist improves pulmonary function in patients with mild, chronic asthma. *Am. Rev. Respir. Dis.* 140:1336–39

17. Coleridge JC, Coleridge HM. 1984. Afferent vagal C fibre innervation of the lungs and airways and its functional significance. *Rev. Physiol. Biochem. Pharmacol.* 99:1–110

18. Dennis EA, Rhee SG, Billah MM, Hannun YA. 1991. Role of phospholipase in generating lipid second messengers in signal transduction. *FASEB J.* 5:2068–77

19. Dey RD, Mayer B, Said SI. 1993. Colocalization of vasoactive intestinal peptide and nitric oxide synthase in neurons of the ferret trachea. *Neuroscience* 54: 839–43

20. Dimitriadou V, Buzzi MG, Moskowitz MA, Theoharides TC. 1991. Trigeminal sensory fiber stimulation induces morphological changes reflecting secretion in rat dura mater mast cells. *Neuroscience* 44:97–112

21. Dixon RA, Diehl RE, Opas E, Rands E, Vickers PJ, et al. 1990. Requirement of a 5-lipoxygenase-activating protein for leukotriene synthesis. *Nature* 343: 282–84

22. Dupuy PM, Shore SA, Drazen JM, Frostell C, Hill WA, Zapol WM. 1992. Bronchodilator action of inhaled nitric oxide in guinea pigs. *J. Clin. Invest.* 90:421–28

23. Ellis JL, Undem BJ. 1991. Role of peptidoleukotrienes in capsaicin-sensitive sensory fibre–mediated responses in guinea-pig airways. *J. Physiol.* 436:469–84

24. Ellis JL, Undem BJ, Kays JS, Ghanekar SV, Barthlow HG, Buckner CK. 1993. Pharmacological examination of receptors mediating contractile responses to tachykinins in airways isolated from human, guinea pig, and hamster. *J. Pharmacol. Exp. Ther.* 267:95–101

25. Fischer A, Mundel P, Mayer B, Preissler

U, Philippin B, Kummer W. 1993. Nitric oxide synthase in guinea pig lower airway innervation. *Neurosci. Lett.* 149: 157–60

26. Fong TM, Huang RR, Yu H, Strader CD. 1993. Mapping the ligand binding site of the NK$_1$ receptor. *Regul. Pept.* 46:43–48

27. Foreman J, Jordan C. 1983. Histamine release and vascular changes induced by neuropeptides. *Agents Actions* 13: 105–16

28. Fuller RW, Maxwell DL, Dixon CM, McGregor GP, Barnes VF, et al. 1987. Effect of substance P on cardiovascular and respiratory function in subjects. *J. Appl. Physiol.* 62:1473–79

29. Gaddy JN, Margolskee DJ, Bush RK, Williams VC, Busse WW. 1992. Bronchodilation with a potent and selective leukotriene D$_4$ (LTD$_4$) antagonist (MK-571) in patients with asthma. *Am. Rev. Respir. Dis.* 146:358–63

30. Garl A, Jordan JE, Ray DW, Spaethe SM, Alger L, Solway J. 1993. Role of eicosanoids in hyperpnea-induced airway responses in guinea pigs. *J. Appl. Physiol.* 75:2797–2804

31. Gaston B, Drazen J, Chee CBE, Wohl MEB, Stamler JS. 1993. Expired nitric oxide (NO) concentrations are elevated in patients with reactive airways disease. *Endothelium* 1:87

32. Gaston B, Drazen JM, Jansen A, Sugarbaker D, Loscalzo J, Stamler JS. 1994. Relaxation of human bronchial muscle by S-nitrosothiols in vitro. *J. Pharmacol. Exp. Ther.* 268:978–94

33. Gaston B, Reilly J, Drazen JM, Fackler J, Ramdev P, et al. 1993. Endogenous nitrogen oxides and bronchodilator S-nitrosothiols in human airways. *Proc. Natl. Acad. Sci. USA* 90:10957–61

34. Gether U, Johansen TE, Schwartz TW. 1993. Chimeric NK1 (substance P)/NK$_3$ (neurokinin B) receptors. Identification of domains determining the binding specificity of tachykinin agonists. *J. Biol. Chem.* 268:7893–98

35. Gordon RE, Case BW, Kleinerman J. 1983. Acute NO$_2$ effects on penetration and transport of horseradish peroxidase in hamster respiratory epithelium. *Am. Rev. Respir. Dis.* 128:528–33

36. Gruetter CA, Childers CE, Bosserman MK, Lemke SM, Ball JG, Valentovic MA. 1989. Comparison of relaxation induced by glyceryl trinitrate, isosorbide dinitrate, and sodium nitroprusside in bovine airways. *Am. Rev. Respir. Dis.* 139:1192–97

37. Gustafsson LE, Leone AM, Persson MG, Wiklund NP, Moncada S. 1991. Endogenous nitric oxide is present in the exhaled air of rabbits, guinea pigs, and humans. *Biochem. Biophys. Res. Commun.* 181:852–57

38. Hamid Q, Springall DR, Riverosmoreno V, Chanez P, Howarth P, et al. 1993. Induction of nitric oxide synthase in asthma. *Lancet* 342:1510–13

39. Hoover DB, Hancock JC. 1987. Autoradiographic localization of substance P binding sites in guinea-pig airways. *J. Auton. Nerv. Syst.* 19:171–74

40. Hui KP, Barnes NC. 1991. Lung function improvement in asthma with a cysteinyl-leukotriene receptor antagonist. *Lancet* 337:1062–63

41. Ichinose M, Nakajima N, Takahashi T, Yamauchi H, Inoue H, Takishima T. 1992. Protection against bradykinin-induced bronchoconstriction in asthmatic patients by neurokinin receptor antagonist. *Lancet* 340:1248–51

42. Impens N, Reiss TF, Teahan JA, Desmet M, Rossing TH, et al. 1993. Acute bronchodilation with an intravenously administered leukotriene-D$_4$ antagonist, MK-679. *Am. Rev. Respir. Dis.* 147: 1442–46

43. Israel E, Dermarkarian R, Rosenberg M, Sperling R, Taylor G, et al. 1990. The effects of a 5-lipoxygenase inhibitor on asthma induced by cold, dry air. *N. Engl. J. Med.* 323:1740–44

44. Israel E, Rubin P, Kemp JP, Grossman J, Pierson I, et al. 1993. The effect of inhibition of 5-lipoxygenase by zileuton in mild to moderate asthma. *Ann. Int. Med.* 119:1059–66

45. Jansen A, Drazen J, Osborne JA, Brown R, Loscalzo J, Stamler JS. 1992. The relaxant properties in guinea pig airways of S-nitrosothiols. *J. Pharmacol. Exp. Ther.* 261:154–60

46. Joos G, Pauwels R, van der Straeten M. 1987. Effect of inhaled substance P and neurokinin A on the airways of normal and asthmatic subjects. *Thorax* 42:779–83

47. Joos GF, Pauwels RA. 1993. The in vivo effect of tachykinins on airway mast cells of the rat. *Am. Rev. Respir. Dis.* 148:922–26

48. Jorens PG, van Overveed FJ, Bult H, Vermeire PA, Herman AG. 1991. L-arginine-dependent production of nitrogen oxides by rat pulmonary macrophages. *Eur. J. Pharmacol.* 200:205–9

49. Jorens PG, van Overveed FJ, Vermeire PA, Bult H, Herman AG. 1992. Synergism between interleukin-1 beta and interferon-gamma, an inducer of nitric-oxide synthase in rat lung fibroblasts. *Eur. J. Pharmacol.* 224:7–12

50. Kaiser E, Chiba P, Zaky K. 1990. Phospholipases in biology and medicine. *Clin. Biochem.* 23:349–70

51. Kikawa Y, Hosoi S, Inoue Y, Saito M, Nakai A, et al. 1991. Exercise-induced urinary excretion of leukotriene-E_4 in children with atopic asthma. *Pediatr. Res.* 29:455–459

52. Kikawa Y, Miyanomae T, Inoue Y, Saito M, Nakai A, et al. 1992. Urinary leukotriene E_4 after exercise challenge in children with asthma. *J. Allerg. Clin. Immunol.* 89:1111–19

53. Kobzik L, Bredt DS, Lowenstein CJ, Drazen J, Gaston B, et al. 1993. Nitric oxide synthase in human and rat lung—immunocytochemical and histochemical localization. *Am. J. Respir. Cell. Mol. Biol.* 9:371–77

54. Kowaluk EA, Fung HL. 1990. Spontaneous liberation or nitric oxide cannot account for in vitro vascular relaxation by S-nitrosothiols. *J. Pharmacol. Exp. Ther.* 255:1256–64

55. Kramer RM, Roberts EF, Manetta JV, Hyslop PA, Jakubowski JA. 1993. Thrombin-induced phosphorylation and activation of Ca^{2+}-sensitive cytosolic phospholipase A_2 in human platelets. *J. Biol. Chem.* 268:26796–26804

56. Krause JE, Chirgwin JM, Carter MS, Xu ZS, Hershey AD. 1987. Three rat preprotachykinin mRNAs encode the neuropeptides substance P and neurokinin A. *Proc. Natl. Acad. Sci. USA* 84:881–85

57. Kumlin M, Dahlen B, Bjorck T, Zetterstrom O, Granstrom E, Dahlen SE. 1992. Urinary excretion of leukotriene-E_4 and 11-dehydro–thromboxane-B_2 in response to bronchial provocations with allergen, aspirin, leukotriene-D_4, and histamine in asthmatics. *Am. Rev. Respir. Dis.* 146:96–103

58. Laitinen LA, Laitinen A, Haahtela T, Vilkka V, Spur BW, Lee TE. 1993. Leukotriene-E_4 and granulocytic infiltration into asthmatic airways. *Lancet* 341:989–90

59. Lammers JW, van Daele P, van den Elshout FM, Decramer M, Buntinx A, et al. 1992. Bronchodilator properties of an inhaled leukotriene D_4 antagonist (verlukast–MK-0679) in asthmatic patients. *Pulm. Pharmacol.* 5:121–25

60. Lawrence ID, Warner JA, Cohan VL, Hubbard WC, Kagey-Sobotka AI, Lichtenstein LM. 1987. Purification and characterization of human skin mast cells. Evidence for human mast cell heterogeneity. *J. Immunol.* 139:3062–69

61. Lei YH, Barnes PJ, Rogers DF. 1993. Regulation of NANC neural broncho-constriction in vivo in the guinea-pig: involvement of nitric oxide, vasoactive intestinal peptide and soluble guanylyl cyclase. *Br. J. Pharmacol.* 108:228–35

62. Leurs R, Brozius MM, Jansen W, Bast A, Timmerman H. 1991. Histamine H1-receptor-mediated cyclic GMP production in guinea-pig lung tissue is an L-arginine-dependent process. *Biochem. Pharmacol.* 42:271–77

63. Lewis RA, Austen KF, Soberman RJ. 1990. Leukotrienes and other products of the 5-lipoxygenase pathway. Biochemistry and relation to pathobiology in human diseases. *N. Engl. J. Med.* 323:645–55

64. Lilly CM, Drazen JM, Shore SA. 1993. Peptidase modulation of airway effects of neuropeptides. *Proc. Soc. Exp. Biol. Med.* 203:388–404

65. Lilly CM, Stamler JS, Gaston B, Meckel C, Loscalzo J, Drazen JM. 1993. Modulation of vasoactive intestinal peptide pulmonary relaxation by NO in tracheally superfused guinea pig lungs. *Am. J. Physiol.* 265:L410–15

66. Lin LL, Lin AY, Knopf JL. 1992. Cytosolic phospholipase A_2 is coupled to hormonally regulated release of arachidonic acid. *Proc. Natl. Acad. Sci. USA* 89:6147–51

67. Maggi CA. 1993. Tachykinin receptors and airway pathophysiology. *Eur. Respir. J.* 6:735–42

68. Mancini JA, Abramovitz M, Cox ME, Wong E, Charleson S, et al. 1993. 5-Lipoxygenase-activating protein is an arachidonate binding protein. *FEBS Lett.* 318:277–81

69. Manning PJ, Rokach J, Malo JL, Ethier D, Cartier A, et al. 1990. Urinary leukotriene E_4 levels during early and late asthmatic responses. *J. Allerg. Clin. Immunol.* 86:211–20

70. Martins MA, Shore SA, Drazen JM. 1991. Release of tachykinins by histamine, methacholine, PAF, LTD_4, and substance-P from guinea pig lungs. *Am. J. Physiol.* 261:L449–55

71. Martling CR, Saria A, Andersson P, Lundberg JM. 1984. Capsaicin pretreatment inhibits vagal cholinergic and noncholinergic. *Naunyn Schmiedebergs Arch. Pharmacol. Exp. Pathol.* 325:343–48

72. Masu Y, Nakayama K, Tamaki H, Harada Y, Kuno M, Nakanishi S. 1987. cDNA cloning of bovine substance-K receptor through oocyte expression system. *Nature* 329:836–38

73. Matsuzaki Y, Hamasaki Y, Said SI. 1980. Vasoactive intestinal peptide: a possible transmitter of nonadrenergic re-

laxation of guinea pig airways. *Science* 210:1252–53

74. Miller DK, Gillard JW, Vickers PJ, Sadowski S, Leveille C, et al. 1990. Identification and isolation of a membrane protein necessary for leukotriene production. *Nature* 343:278–81

75. Mulligan MS, Warren JS, Smith CW, Anderson DC, Yeh CG, et al. 1992. Lung injury after deposition of IgA immune complexes. Requirements for CD18 and L-arginine. *J. Immunol.* 148: 3086–92

76. Munakata M, Masaki Y, Sakuma I, Ukita H, Otsuka Y, et al. 1990. Pharmacological differentiation of epithelium-derived relaxing factor. *J. Appl. Physiol.* 69:665–70

77. Nakanishi S, Nakajima Y, Yokota Y. 1993. Signal transduction and ligand-binding domains of the tachykinin receptors. *Regul. Pept.* 46:37–42

78. Nakayama DK, Geller DA, Lowenstein CJ, Davies P, Pitt BR, et al. 1992. Cytokines and lipopolysaccharide induce nitric oxide synthase in cultured rat pulmonary artery smooth muscle. *Am. J. Respir. Cell Mol. Biol.* 7:471–76

79. Naline E, Devillier P, Drapeau G, Toty L, Bakdach H, et al. 1989. Characterization of neurokinin effects and receptor selectivity in human isolated bronchi. *Am. Rev. Respir. Dis.* 140:679–86

80. Nathan C. 1992. Nitric oxide as a secretory product of mammalian cells. *FASEB J.* 6:3051–64

81. Nijkamp FP, van der Linde HJ, Folkerts G. 1993. Nitric oxide synthesis inhibitors induce airway hyperresponsiveness in the guinea pig in vivo and in vitro. Role of the epithelium. *Am. Rev. Respir. Dis.* 148:727–34

82. Perretti F, Manzini S. 1993. Activation of capsaicin-sensitive sensory fibers modulates PAF-induced bronchial hyperresponsiveness in anesthetized guinea pigs. *Am. Rev. Respir. Dis.* 148: 927–31

83. Peters-Golden M, McNish RW. 1993. Redistribution of 5-lipoxygenase and cytosolic phospholipase A_2 to the nuclear fraction upon macrophage activation. *Biochem. Biophys. Res. Commun.* 196:147–53

84. Piper PJ. 1984. Formation and actions of leukotrienes. *Physiol. Rev.* 64:744–61

85. Piper PJ. 1989. Leukotrienes and the airways. *Eur. J. Anaesthesiol.* 6:241–55

86. Radi R, Beckman JS, Bush KM, Freeman BA. 1991. Peroxynitrite oxidation of sulfhydryls. The cytotoxic potential of superoxide and nitric oxide. *J. Biol. Chem.* 266:4244–50

87. Reid GK, Kargman S, Vickers PJ, Mancini JA, Leveille C, et al. 1990. Correlation between expression of 5-lipoxygenase-activating protein, 5-lipoxygenase, and cellular leukotriene synthesis. *J. Biol. Chem.* 265:19818–23

88. Sala A, Voelkel N, Maclouf J, Murphy RC. 1990. Leukotriene E_4 elimination and metabolism in normal human subjects. *J. Biol. Chem.* 265:21771–78

89. Samuelsson B. 1983. Leukotrienes: mediators of immediate hypersensitivity reactions and inflammation. *Science* 220: 568–75

90. Schmidt HH, Gagne GD, Nakane M, Pollock JS, Miller MF, Murad F. 1992. Mapping of neural nitric oxide synthase in the rat suggests frequent colocalization with NADPH diaphorase but not with soluble guanylyl cyclase, and novel paraneural functions for nitrinergic signal transduction. *J. Histochem. Cytochem.* 40:1439–56

91. Sekizawa K, Fukushima T, Ikarashi Y, Maruyama Y, Sasaki H. 1993. The role of nitric oxide in cholinergic neurotransmission in rat trachea. *Br. J. Pharmacol.* 110:816–20

92. Sharp JD, White DL, Chiou XG, Goodson T, Gamboa GC, et al. 1991. Molecular cloning and expression of human Ca^{2+}-sensitive cytosolic phospholipase A_2. *J. Biol. Chem.* 266:14850–53

93. Shigemoto R, Yokota Y, Tsuchida K, Nakanishi S. 1990. Cloning and expression of a rat neuromedin K receptor cDNA. *J. Biol. Chem.* 265:623–28

94. Shore SA, Stimler-Gerard NP, Coats SR, Drazen JM. 1988. Substance P-induced bronchoconstriction in the guinea pig. Enhancement by inhibitors of neutral metalloendopeptidase and angiotensin-converting enzyme. *Am. Rev. Respir. Dis.* 137:331–36

95. Skofitsch G, Savitt JM, Jacobowitz DM. 1985. Suggestive evidence for a functional unit between mast cells and substance P fibers in the rat diaphragm and mesentery. *Histochemistry* 82:5–8

96. Sladek K, Dworski R, Fitzgerald GA, Buitkus KL, Block FJ, et al. 1990. Allergen-stimulated release of thromboxane A_2 and leukotriene E_4 in humans. Effect of indomethacin. *Am. Rev. Respir. Dis.* 141:1441–45

97. Smith CM, Christie PE, Hawksworth RJ, Thien F, Lee TH. 1991. Urinary leukotriene-E_4 levels after allergen and exercise challenge in bronchial asthma. *Am. Rev. Respir. Dis.* 144:1411–13

98. Solway J, Kao BM, Jordan JE, Gitter B, Rodger IW, et al. 1993. Tachykinin receptor antagonists inhibit hyperpnea-

induced bronchoconstriction in guinea pigs. *J. Clin. Invest.* 92:315–23

99. Stamler JS, Singel DJ, Loscalzo J. 1992. Biochemistry of nitric oxide and its redox-activated forms. *Science* 258: 1898–1902
100. Stead RH, Tomioka M, Quinonez G, Simon GT, Felten SY, Bienenstock J. 1987. Intestinal mucosal mast cells in normal and nematode-infected rat intestines are in intimate contact with peptidergic nerves. *Proc. Natl. Acad. Sci. USA* 84:2975–79
101. Tagari P, Rasmussen JB, Delorme D, Girard Y, Eriksson LO, et al. 1990. Comparison of urinary leukotriene E_4 and 16-carboxytetranordihydro leukotriene E_4 excretion in allergic asthmatics after inhaled antigen. *Eicosanoids* 3:75–80
102. Taylor GW, Taylor I, Black P, Maltby NH, Turner N, et al. 1989. Urinary leukotriene E_4 after antigen challenge and in acute asthma and allergic rhinitis. *Lancet* 1:584–88
103. Taylor IK, Wellings R, Taylor GW, Fuller RW. 1992. Urinary leukotriene-E_4 excretion in exercise-induced asthma. *J. Appl. Physiol.* 73:743–48
104. Thompson DC, Diamond L, Altiere RJ. 1990. Enzymatic modulation of vasoactive intestinal peptide and nonadrenergic noncholinergic inhibitory responses in guinea pig tracheas. *Am. Rev. Respir. Dis.* 142:1119–23
105. Undem BJ, Hubbard W, Weinreich D. 1993. Immunologically induced neuromodulation of guinea pig nodose ganglion neurons. *J. Auton. Nerv. Syst.* 44: 35–44
106. Undem BJ, Weinreich D. 1993. Electrophysiological properties and chemosensitivity of guinea pig nodose ganglion neurons in vitro. *J. Auton. Nerv. Syst.* 44:17–33
107. Venugopalan CS, Said SI, Drazen JM. 1984. Effect of vasoactive intestinal peptide on vagally mediated tracheal pouch relaxation. *Respir. Physiol.* 56: 205–16
108. Vickers PJ, O Neill GP, Mancini JA, Charleson S, Abramovitz M. 1992.

Cross-species comparison of 5-lipoxygenase-activating protein. *Mol. Pharmacol.* 42:1014–19
109. Waite M. 1990. Phospholipases, enzymes that share a substrate class. *Adv. Exp. Med. Biol.* 279:1–22
110. Ward JK, Belvisi MG, Fox AJ, Miura M, Tadjkarimi S, et al. 1993. Modulation of cholinergic neural bronchoconstriction by endogenous nitric oxide and vasoactive intestinal peptide in human airways in vitro. *J. Clin. Invest.* 92:736–42
111. Westcott JY, Smith HR, Wenzel SE, Larsen GL, Thomas RB, et al. 1991. Urinary leukotriene-E_4 in patients with asthma—Effect of airways reactivity and sodium cromoglycate. *Am. Rev. Respir. Dis.* 143:1322–28
112. Westcott JY, Voelkel NF, Jones K, Wenzel SE. 1993. Inactivation of leukotriene C_4 in the airways and subsequent urinary leukotriene E_4 excretion in normal and asthmatic subjects. *Am. Rev. Respir. Dis.* 148:1244–51
113. Wink DA, Kasprzak KS, Maragos CM, Elespuru RK, Misra M, et al. 1991. Deaminating ability and genotoxicity of nitric oxide and its progenitors. *Science* 254:1001–4
114. Woods JW, Evans JF, Ethier D, Scott S, Vickers PJ, et al. 1993. 5-Lipoxygenase and 5-lipoxygenase activating proteins are localized in the nuclear envelope of activated human leukocytes. *J. Exp. Med.* 178:1935–46
115. Yokota Y, Sasai Y, Tanaka K, Fujiwara T, Tsuchida K, et al. 1989. Molecular characterization of a functional cDNA for rat substance P receptor. *J. Biol. Chem.* 264:17649–52
116. Yui Y, Hattori R, Kosuga K, Eizawa H, Hiki K, et al. 1991. Calmodulin-independent nitric oxide synthase from rat polymorphonuclear neutrophils. *J. Biol. Chem.* 266:3369–71
117. Zhou H-L, Torphy TJ. 1991. Relationship between cyclic guanosine monophosphate accumulation and relaxation of canine trachealis induced by nitrovasodilators. *J. Pharmacol. Exp. Ther.* 258:972–78

Annu. Rev. Physiol. 1995. 57:171–89

ENDOTHELIUM AS AN ENDOCRINE ORGAN[1]

Tadashi Inagami[2], Mitsuhide Naruse[3], and Richard Hoover[4]

Departments of [2]Biochemistry, [2]Medicine and [4]Pathology and Cell Biology,
Vanderbilt University School of Medicine, Nashville, Tennessee 37232;
[3]Department of Medicine, Institute of Clinical Endocrinology, Tokyo Women's
Medical College, Tokyo, Japan

KEY WORDS: endothelin, endothelium-derived relaxing factor, nitric oxide, natriuretic
               peptide, crosstalk

INTRODUCTION

Recent findings that endothelial cells are capable of producing numerous vasoactive substances have placed the thin unicellular layer endothelium in a unique position as an endocrine, paracrine, and even autocrine organ with multiple functions, in addition to its role as a permeable and physical barrier protecting vascular smooth muscle cells (VSMC) from adhesion of leukocytes and platelets. The endothelium's protective function involves the elaboration and release of paracrine substances such as prostacycline (PGI_2) and nitric oxide (NO) and the production of endothelin (ET) and growth factors in response to damage. These substances, which are intended to be protective, may also trigger responses with harmful sequelae.

However, the endothelium's major role is not that of a traditional endocrine

---

[1]Abbreviations used in text: Ach, acetylcholine; Ang, angiontensin; ANP, atrial natriuretic peptide; BNP, brain natriuretic peptide; CNP, C-type natriuretic peptides; bFGF, basic fibroblast growth factor; EDRF, endothelium-derived relaxing factor; EDHF, endothelium-derived hyperpolarization factor; ECE, endothelin-converting enzyme; ET-1, -2, -3: endothelin-1, -2, -3; ET_A, ET_B, endothelin receptor A and B; IFN, interferon; IL, interleukin; IP_3, inositol-1,4,5-trisphosphate; JG, juxtaglomerular; NO, nitric oxide; NOS, nitric oxide synthase (b, brain; c, constitutive; e, endothelial; i, inducible); NP-A, -B, -C, natriuretic peptide type A, B, C (for receptors); PGI_2, prostaglandin I_2; PKC, protein kinase C; P450-11β, P450-11β-hydroxylase; RT-PCR, reverse transcription–polymerase chain reaction; TGF-β, transforming growth factor-β; TNF, tumor necrosis factor; VSMC, vascular smooth muscle cells.

0066–4278/95/0315–0171$05.00

gland; rather its regulatory role lies in the production of endothelium-derived vasoactive substances that arise from the endothelium's strategic location between the blood and the vascular tunica media. In this position, endothelium can sense not only changes in humoral substances but also changes in flow rate through shear stress, changes in blood pressure through stretch, as well as contacts with other cells. Thus the endothelium can integrate and respond to signals from chemical receptors and mechano-receptors in regulating the production of vasoactive substances that play a role in blood pressure regulation and vascular growth. These substances appear to affect the functions of cells in the immediate vicinity. The large number of regulatory substances produced from the endothelium include prostaglandins, endothelium-derived relaxing factor (EDRF), hyperpolarization factor (EDHF), ET, natriuretic peptides, steroids, and receptors for numerous substances. Interactions of these substances are complex because many of these products have only been observed in cultured endothelial cells, in which gene expression has been drastically altered from the naturally functioning cells. Therefore, caution should be exercised in translating these in vitro results to in vivo situations. Also, endothelial cells do not contain typical secretory granules that are characteristic of endocrine cells. Diverse regulatory steps are involved, including transcriptional and translational control as well as proteolytic activation of prohormones. Readers are referred to numerous reviews on many of these factors and their products and functions, as cited in the sections below.

ENDOTHELIN

ETs are a family of potent and long-acting vasopressor peptides (ET-1, ET-2, and ET-3) consisting of 21 amino acid residues and two disulfide bridges (51, 95). A close resemblance in structure among these peptides suggests similar mechanisms of action through related receptor isoforms (see 51, 83, for recent reviews).

Although ETs are produced in various tissues, vascular endothelial cells produce ET-1, but not ET-2 or ET-3. The ETs are synthesized in their preproforms (5, 28). In cultured endothelial cells, proendothelin is proteolytically cleaved to form big ET that, in turn, is activated by a neutral metallo-endopeptidase, endothelin-converting enzyme (ECE), to form the mature and active ET-1 (69). An ECE recently purified from porcine aortic endothelial membranes is a 120 kDa peptidase inhibitable by phosphoramidon and shows preference for big ET-1 (66), which is in agreement with the fact that the endothelial cells produce ET-1. The cDNA of the endothelial enzyme has recently been cloned (94).

ET is secreted by a constitutive pathway (59); thus ET synthesis and release from endothelial cells is largely regulated at a transcriptional step rather than during secretory processes. Endothelial cells have the unique ability to sense changes in blood flow, blood pressure, and presumably oxygen tension by unknown mechanisms and are subject to regulation by a variety of hormones.

Analysis of the structure and promotor functions of the ET-1 gene (28, 45) indicates that upstream of a typical TATAA box and proximal CAAT sequence are AP-1 sites that are activated by the protooncogene products (c-Fos and c-Jun), a GATA sequence for GATA-2 binding as a determinant of tissue specificity, and a NF-1 sequence, which is activated by TGF-β. Gene expression of ET-1 is stimulated by numerous factors, including phorbol esters, thrombin, Ang II, vasopressin, and epinephrine, which may be mediated by the AP-1 site. Stimulation by various growth factors, cytokines (i.e. IL-1, TNF-α), insulin, and physical stimuli (e.g. shear stress, hypoxia) have also been reported (28, 95).

Involvement of the calcium-dependent protein kinase C (PKC)–c-Jun–c-Fos mechanism in the ET-1 gene activation by vasopressors is supported by the inhibition of the activation by a PKC inhibitor, and a cytosolic calcium ion chelator (18). This mechanism (28, 45) is further supported by the observation that ET-1 mRNA is increased in cultured endothelial cells cotransfected with the ET-1, *c-fos*, and *c-jun* genes (45). ET-1 gene expression is stimulated by PKC, in contrast to renin gene expression and secretion, which are inhibited by an increase in cytosolic Ca^{2+} and PKC activity. By contrast, ET-1 gene expression is down-regulated by factors such as nitric oxide (7) and natriuretic peptides, which elevate cytosolic cGMP and presumably suppress PKC (17).

Hemodynamic shear stress is an important factor affecting the structure and function of the endothelium. Shear stress changes actin filaments to stress fibers, which contain myosin, tropomyosin, and α-actinin. In addition to these cytoskeletal changes, shear stress is involved in changes of endothelial function that produce vasoactive substances. The exact mechanism involved in shear stress–dependent regulation of ET-1 production is controversial. It was first shown that hemodynamic shear stress in the physiological range stimulates ET gene expression in porcine endothelial cells (98). Under conditions of low shear (5 dyn/cm^2), endothelial cell shape undergoes a change in which the cells line up longitudinally in the direction of flow, with subsequent disruption of the cytoskeleton, ET-1 gene expression, and ET-1 secretion (57). Structural changes precede the functional changes. In sharp contrast, ET-1 production is decreased in human endothelial cells at higher flow rates and increased shear stress (20 dyn/cm^2) (82). However, other investigators (50) have shown that the exposure of bovine endothelial cells to shear stress (8 $dyne/cm^3$) causes a down-regulation of ET-1 mRNA and decreased secretion of ET-1. These changes occurred in a shear force–dependent manner, which exhibits saturation above 15–20 dyn/cm^2. The reasons for the disparity between these studies are not clear; however, they may be attributed to species difference and the particular passage of the cultured cells and, in part, by the influence of secondary changes in intracellular cGMP production by nitric oxide. The shear stress–induced changes in the ET-1 gene do not depend on PKC or cAMP but on an up-stream *cis* element (49); thus basal and shear stress–induced changes of the ET-1 gene are regulated by different mechanisms.

Two isoforms of ET receptors ET_A and ET_B have been cloned (3, 79). ET_A is specific for ET-1 and ET-2, with a low affinity to ET-3, and is distributed in tissues such as VSMC, heart, lung, and gut, whereas ET_B binds all three ETs equally well and is located in endothelial cells, as well as in the brain, lung, and kidney. For vascular tissues, ET_A in VSMC mediates paracrine vasoconstrictor effects of ET-1, whereas ET_B on the endothelial cells mediates autocrine functions of ET-1 that result in the release of EDRF (78). Recently, ET_B was found in VSMC and shown to contribute to vasoconstriction (81).

ET_A and ET_B are seven-membrane-spanning domain-type receptors (3, 79). The primary actions at nanomolar ET concentrations are the activation of phospholipase C, inducing the formation of inositol trisphosphate, and a transient increase in cytosolic Ca^{2+} concentration. This step is followed by a long sustained vascular contraction and elevation of cytosolic Ca^{2+} (95). The sustained response, but not the initial transient phase, is inhibited by pertussis toxin or removal of calcium from the medium (58, 95). These observations indicate that the G protein–dependent opening of calcium channels is important for the ET-mediated contraction (33). The calcium channel opening was observed at subnanomolar and even picomolar concentrations of ET without being preceded by the transient phosphoinositol turnover (4, 33).

ET_A and ET_B have opposing effects on adenylyl cyclase; ET_A markedly stimulates adenylyl cyclase presumably via G_s protein, and ET_B is coupled negatively to adenylyl cyclase presumably via G_i protein (16). Thus cAMP produced in VSMC by the action of ET_A may blunt contraction. The autocrine stimulation of ET_B in the endothelial cells results in the release of NO and contributes to vasorelaxation, which demonstrates that ETs can elicit diverse biological responses in target tissues. However, the cell-specific localization of ET_A in VSMC is neither rigid nor permanent because switching from ET_A to ET_B occurs in highly passaged cells (14). Although the pathophysiological significance of the in vitro phenomenon remains unknown, the development of ET_B in senescent cells could be more harmful than that of ET_A because the former does not stimulate adenylyl cyclase.

In addition to vasoconstrictor and vasorelaxing activities, ETs possess diverse biological actions on cardiovascular, neural, renal, endocrine, metabolic, gastrointestinal, and genitourinary systems; however, the physiological significance of these effects remains to be clarified. In addition to the vasoconstrictor functions that activate the G_q-mediated Ca^{2+}-PKC system, ET-1 promotes proliferation of vascular endothelial cells, VSMC, and fibroblasts (25), which may result in structural changes of the vascular wall. The presence of the ET_B

receptor on endothelial cells where ET is produced suggests that function and structure of endothelial cells are under the control of the same or adjacent endothelial cells (autocrine) or other nonendothelial cells (paracrine) located in the vessels (26, 89).

Although it is tempting to speculate that potent vasoconstrictor ET is involved in the pathogenesis of cardiovascular degenerative or proliferative disease, details of in vivo pathogenic mechanisms are far from being understood primarily because of the diversity of ET actions. The vasoconstrictive action of ET can be modified by its counteracting mechanisms at the vascular level (i.e. vasorelaxation via ET_B on the endothelial cells) and at the systemic levels by stimulation of ANP secretion, suppression of renin secretion, Na^+-K^+ ATPase activity (99), and vasopressin action in the kidney (68). In addition, the plasma ET levels do not accurately reflect the local production of ET because most ET is secreted on the abluminal side (93). Interestingly, chronic infusion of ET-1 over a period of 4 weeks in normal rats was associated with a normalization of the once elevated blood pressure despite the sustained elevation of the plasma ET-1 levels (63). In agreement with this, transgenic rats harboring the human ET-2 gene do not show any hypertension despite the elevation of plasma ET-2 levels (73), which suggests that a minor increase in the plasma levels of ET does not lead to chronic hypertension.

There are several clinical settings where increased plasma ET levels do suggest a pathogenic role: essential hypertension, hypertension following erythropoietin therapy in patients under chronic hemodialysis (61), cyclosporine-induced hypertension (54), atherosclerosis (46), and renal failure (38). Whether the increased plasma ET-1 levels in disease states are central to the pathogenesis or merely a phenomenon secondary to the vascular lesion remains unclear.

Limited but significant effects of anti-ET antiserum (67) or ET_A receptor antagonist (65) on blood pressure and renal function in animal models of hypertension suggest some pathological roles for ET. A recently developed orally active ET receptor antagonist capable of blocking ET_A and ET_B (11) was shown to decrease blood pressure in sodium-depleted monkeys and to prevent renal vasospasm after renal ischemia and cerebral vasospasm following subarachnoid hemorrhage, which suggests that ET_B as well as ET_A are potentially important in pathological conditions.

Recent studies in which the ET-1 gene in the mouse was knocked out by homologous recombination showed that heterozygotic mice with one allele of the ET-1 gene eliminated displayed lower ET-1 in plasma but had clearly elevated blood pressure (42). This suggests that ET-1 may act as a vasodilator, presumably through the ET_B receptor on the endothelial cells, under physiological conditions. At higher pathological concentrations, the vasoconstrictor action of ET_A and ET_B receptors becomes dominant. An imbalance in the effects of ET on endothelium and VSMC may lead to a pathological condition.

ENDOTHELIUM-DERIVED RELAXING FACTOR AND NITRIC OXIDE

Vasorelaxation factors produced by the endothelium consist of both nonpeptide substances including EDRF (21), PGI_2, and EDHF, and a peptide substance, C-type natriuretic peptide (CNP). The finding that vasorelaxation and inhibition of platelet aggregation by EDRF are in parallel with the secretion of NO provides strong evidence for NO as EDRF (71, 77); however, whether EDRF is only NO itself or includes other similar compounds such as S-nitrosocysteine remains unknown.

NO is a free radical gas generated by NO synthase (NOS) through the oxygenation of one of the guanidino nitrogen atoms of L-arginine (L-Arg). The NO has a half-life of seconds. It is inactivated by oxygen, hemoglobin, and reductants like methylene blue and potentiated by a free radical scavenger like superoxide dismutase. Acetylcholine (Ach) produces endothelium-dependent increases in membrane potential of VSMC. The Ach-induced hyperpolarization is blocked by ouabain, a $Na^+K^+ATPase$ inhibitor. Ach also produces normal vasorelaxation in atherosclerotic arteries without a significant increase in cGMP. These observations support the hypothesis that the endothelium produces EDHF, which causes hyperpolarization of VSMC (19). More recently, however, it was shown that NO can directly activate a Ca^{2+}-dependent K^+ channel and cause hyperpolarization of VSMC by a cGMP-independent mechanism (6).

The NOS gene family is composed of three isoforms: brain NOS (bNOS); endothelial NOS (eNOS); and inducible NOS (iNOS). bNOS and eNOS are classified as constitutive NOS (cNOS) because of their constitutive expression. eNOS exists in the membrane-bound particulate fraction of cells, whereas bNOS and iNOS exist in the soluble fraction. cDNA of three isoforms were cloned, and all were shown to be products of different genes. The molecular mass of the eNOS protein deduced from nucleotide sequence was 144 kDa in human (32) and 133 kDa in bovine (44). The amino acid sequences of NOSs show 50–60% identity with each other.

All three isoforms share a basically identical primary molecular structure consisting of a cytochrome P450-heme–binding domain sequence in the N-terminal portion, a calmodulin-binding domain in the mid portion, and binding sequences for NADPH, FAD, and FMN as cofactors in the C-terminal portion. In addition, there is a sequence for phosphorylation by the cAMP-dependent protein kinase in the N-terminal portion of the cNOS. The presence of a sequence for N-terminal myristoylation supports the membrane-bound localization of the eNOS.

The activity of eNOS increases within seconds in response to the activation of specific cell surface receptors with various vasoactive substances (i.e. Ach, bradykinin, Ang II, vasopressin, histamine, norepinephrine, serotonin, ET, thrombin) and shear stress. After binding of the agonists to their specific G protein–coupled receptors, they activate phospholipase C to produce IP_3 and diacylglycerol; the former in turn increases the cytosolic Ca^{2+} concentration and then activates calmodulin, which results in the activation of eNOS. The rapid increase in the enzyme activity does not require protein synthesis (32, 44). In addition, the activity of cNOS is attenuated through phosphorylation by protein kinase A. It was shown that the phosphorylation process reversibly regulates intracellular localization and hence the biological activity of eNOS (53).

NO shows diverse biological actions. Endothelium-derived NO induces vascular smooth muscle relaxation and suppresses platelet functions including aggregation and secretion of vasoconstrictive substances into the vascular lumen; however, the NO action appears to be limited to a small area because of its rapid adsorptive loss to hemoglobin. Administration of NOS inhibitors shows a quick and significant increase in blood pressure, which indicates that sustained secretion of eNOS-derived NO from resistance vessels regulates blood flow and blood pressure under steady-state conditions (76). In addition, activation of eNOS plays a key role in the endothelium-dependent vasorelaxation associated with vasoactive substances. Since NO inhibits mitogenesis and proliferation of VSMC (24), NO from endothelial cells may regulate the tone and structural remodeling of the vascular wall.

Endothelial cell-derived NO activates soluble guanylate cyclase in the VSMC. NO binds to Fe-heme at its active site and converts GTP to cGMP as a second messenger. It is thought that the NO-induced relaxation of VSMC is mediated by the cGMP-dependent modification of several intracellular processes. However, NO seems to activate calcium-dependent potassium channels without significant changes in cGMP production in VSMC (6). The effects are inhibited by a specific inhibitor of calcium-dependent K^+ channel and NOS inhibitors.

Immunohistochemical staining demonstrates that bNOS is localized in neuronal tissues (i.e. cerebrum, cerebellum, posterior pituitary, and adrenal medulla) (8, 80), and in the macula densa of the juxtaglomerular (JG) apparatus (80). In addition, nonadrenergic, noncholinergic nerve fibers and ganglions, which express bNOS, are distributed in the gastrointestinal tract, perivascular tissue, VSMC, and the conduction system of the heart (8, 91). The bNOS-derived NO in the central nervous system and the noncholinergic, nonadrenergic nerve fibers may serve as a neurotransmitter.

iNOS does not exist unless induced by cytokines and lipopolysaccharides, which indicates that the enzyme is primarily regulated at the level of transcription. Induction takes 3–4 h and requires protein synthesis. The activity of the iNOS does not depend on calcium for regulation because it tightly binds calmodulin. IFN-γ is a potent inducer of the iNOS gene, whereas TNF-α, IL-6, IL-1, or EGF produce weaker responses individually. However, more pronounced responses can be induced when more than one of these substances is present. In contrast, glucocorticoids suppress iNOS gene expression. It is noteworthy that the amount of NO produced by the iNOS reaches a level about 1000 times as high as that produced by cNOS and, therefore, could have a strong impact on systemic circulation under pathological conditions (for review, see 56). iNOS is inducible in the macrophage, polymorphonuclear leukocytes, renal mesangial cells, fibroblasts, VSMC, JG cells, endothelial cells, and liver, lung, and spleen. NO induced in these cells is related to tumor cytotoxicity, microbiostasis, and inhibition of growth and/or injury of various cells including those in the vascular wall. A large amount of NO released into the circulation during endotoxin shock could play a major role in severe hypotension.

The pathophysiological significance of NO in cardiovascular diseases presents two different aspects: deficiency of eNOS-derived NO and excess of iNOS-derived NO. As described above, eNOS-derived NO plays an important role in maintaining the integrity of vascular function and structure. Therefore, injured endothelium and atherosclerotic foci of vessels are closely associated with pathological states arising from impaired endothelial functions, dominance of the actions of various vasoconstrictor substances, and facilitation of blood coagulation and thrombus formation, which would accelerate atherosclerosis and trigger angina pectoris and acute myocardial infarction through coronary vasospasm (52).

Attenuated endothelium-dependent vasorelaxation is demonstrated in various animal models of hypertension and in human hypertension (72). Reversibility after treatment suggests that the attenuated function is the secondary result of hypertension.

A similar phenomenon is also seen in atherosclerosis and in disease states with vascular lesions such as diabetes mellitus. Although the attenuated endothelium-dependent relaxation may not be necessarily attributed to NO deficiency alone, an exaggerated blood pressure lowering effect of exogenous L-Arg and diminished inhibition of Ach-induced vasorelaxation by NOS inhibitors suggest that the impairment of NO production under basal and stimulated conditions is one of the major factors in hypertension. Lack of L-Arg as a substrate, a defect in signal transduction systems of the endothelial cell membrane, and/or accelerated degradation of NO by superoxide anion have been postulated as mechanisms for NO deficiency; however, no direct in vivo evidence for NO deficiency is presently available.

An excess production of NO, especially by the iNOS, may directly induce pathological conditions. One example is septic shock. Lipopolysaccharides from anaerobic bacteria induce iNOS in VSMC, macrophages, and/or endothelial cells, with the resulting excess of NO causing intractable hypotension. Effectiveness of NOS inhibitors, but not catecholamine, supports an important pathological role of NO (74). Clinical efficacy of glucocorticoids, which inhibit iNOS gene expression, also supports this concept. Furthermore, lipopolysaccharide or IFN-γ added to cultured endothelial cells leads to cell injury and death, which is prevented by NOS inhibitors (70). This indicates that endotoxin produces NO by inducing iNOS in endothelial cells and causes its own injury. Similar cytotoxic effects of iNOS-derived NO are also suggested in reperfusion injury following myocardial ischemia.

These data support pathological roles for iNOS-derived NO. However, a possible compensatory role of iNOS-derived NO in remedying the hypoperfusion associated with shock cannot be excluded. A critical question relevant to this issue is how NO derived from eNOS and iNOS can be differentially recognized by target cells and whether they show different biological actions. A similar question is relevant to the action of NO in the JG apparatus. NO was shown to suppress renin secretion and to modulate glomerular hemodynamics (31); however, NO may be derived from endothelial cells located on the luminal side of the JG cells, from the macula densa with bNOS, and from the iNOS induced inside the JG cells. Therefore, NO from three different sources may be encountered in the same cells. The relative significance of NO from different sources may depend on the nature of stimuli, the amount produced, and/or the molecular species of NO-related products. It is an intriguing and important question to be answered.

VASCULAR NATRIURETIC PEPTIDE (NP) SYSTEM

The natriuretic peptide family consists of three distinct gene products: ANP, BNP (for review, see 60), and CNP (55, 86, 90). ANP is mainly synthesized in the cardiac atrium and secreted into circulation. Although BNP and CNP were initially cloned from the brain, BNP is now well established as a circulating hormone produced in the cardiac ventricle. In addition, more recent studies have disclosed that CNP is produced by endothelial cells (87) and macrophages (30). This finding provides an exciting new aspect to vascular biology research.

ANP is composed of 28 amino acids residues and has a ring structure involving a disulfide bond between Cys^7 and Cys^{23}; BNP has a similar structure to ANP with a different length of the N-terminal extension. CNP has been isolated from the brain as the third member of the NP family and exists in two isopeptide forms of different molecular size, CNP-53 and CNP-22. Although the CNP molecule shares the ring structure common to other NP families, it characteristically lacks the C-terminal tail. The amino acid sequence of CNP is highly conserved, whereas that of BNP is more variable among species.

Plasma ANP and BNP levels reflect the hemodynamic overloads to the atrium and ventricle, respectively, and show a significant increase in various disease states (62). By contrast, CNP is thought to be a neuropeptide or neurotransmitter in the central nervous system because CNP contents in the central nervous system tissues such as the hypothalamus, thalamus, cerebellum, and pituitary gland are about tenfold higher than that of ANP and BNP. However, recently it was shown that the cultured endothelial cells of bovine carotid arteries produce CNP (87). Using Northern blot analysis and/or RT-PCR, the CNP gene transcript has been demonstrated in cultured endothelial cells and vascular walls (41). In addition, CNP was found in human plasma (85). These in vitro and in vivo findings suggest that the vascular endothelial cells synthesize and secrete CNP into the circulation. In addition, human monocytic leukemia cells were also found to express CNP mRNA and secrete CNP after phorbol-ester treatment of macrophages (30). CNP produced in the endothelial cells and macrophage is secreted rapidly by a constitutive pathway, similar to that of ET, and not stored inside cells.

Secretion of CNP from the cultured endothelial cells is significantly augmented by various factors including bFGF, TGF-β, cGMP, cAMP, vasopressin, thrombin, IL-1, TNF-α, and endotoxin (87). Of these factors, TGF-β and TNF-α provide the most pronounced stimulation. The magnitude of increase in CNP secretion by TGF-β, TNF-α, and endotoxin is much greater than the increase of ET production, which indicates that these stimuli are more specific for CNP. CNP mRNA expression is also markedly stimulated by TGF-β. Because most of these factors are derived from platelet and macrophage, CNP could be one of the factors involved in cell-cell communication between blood cells and vascular wall cells. In addition, it was recently found that CNP production is markedly stimulated by ANP (E Levin et al, personal communication).

Physiological stimuli for CNP production have not been identified; however, analysis of the 5'-flanking region of the CNP gene demonstrates the presence of a sequence compatible with a cAMP-responsive element. This suggests that CNP gene expression might be regulated by various factors that activate protein kinase A.

Three different NP receptor isoforms have been cloned: NP-A, NP-B, and NP-C (for review, see 10). NP-A and NP-B receptors are single transmembrane-types, with a molecular mass of ~120–140 kDa, and are particulate guanylate cyclases that contain the protein kinase domain and the guanylate cyclase domain in their intracellular portions. The biological action of these receptors is mediated by the production of cGMP. Studies on the binding affinity and the production of cGMP showed that ANP and BNP have a higher affinity with the NP-A receptor than does CNP, whereas CNP has a higher affinity with the NP-B receptor than do ANP and BNP (40, 86). The NP-C receptor is a homodimer consisting of two 60–70-kDa subunits. Although the extracellular domain shows a high homology to NP-A and NP-B receptors, the intracellular domain is short and acts as a clearance receptor. There is evidence that this receptor is also coupled to adenylyl cyclase-cAMP through a G_i protein and could be of biological significance (1, 47).

VSMC exist in the contractile phenotype in mature normal vessels; however, they assume a synthetic phenotype with proliferation and migration in atherosclerotic foci and neointima following vascular injury. Suga et al (88) demonstrated that the NP-A receptor is the dominant form in the adult rat vascular media, which indicates a contractile phenotype, whereas the NP-B receptor is the major form expressed in cultured VSMC with a synthetic phenotype. These observations suggest that switching of the NP receptor subtype is associated with the phenotypic modulation of the VSMC. In support of this concept, increased expression of the NP-B receptor has been demonstrated in the intima after air-dry vascular injury (22).

In contrast to that of ANP and BNP, details of the biological action of CNP remain unknown. Intravenous administration of CNP decreases blood pressure, cardiac output, urinary volume, and sodium excretion (84). CNP relaxes the vein more than the artery in vitro. Although the vasorelaxation and hypotensive activity of CNP is less pronounced than ANP and BNP in vivo, as well as in vitro, it strongly stimulates cGMP production and inhibits cell proliferation and DNA synthesis in VSMC (23). CNP inhibits DNA synthesis stimulated by various growth factors (75), thereby suggesting that CNP may be involved more intimately with regulation of vascular structure than vascular tone.

The proximity of CNP production in endothelial cells and macrophage to its specific receptor NP-B receptor in VSMC suggests a paracrine mode of CNP action in vascular walls that constitutes a "vascular natriuretic peptide system" (87). Furuya et al (22) demonstrated that CNP markedly stimulates cGMP production in arteries with intimal thickening after air-dry injury but not in intact arteries. CNP dramatically improves the intimal thickening following vascular injury. Therefore, CNP is expected to have a therapeutic potential in preventing re-stenosis following coronary angioplasty.

CNP production is stimulated by cytokines and endotoxin and is significantly elevated in endotoxin shock (27), which suggests its pathophysiological role in shock. Whether the vasorelaxant peptide aggravates shock or alleviates it by maintaining microcirculation is a challenging question that is also asked concerning the rise in NO production in shock.

ENDOTHELIAL STRUCTURE-FUNCTION RELATIONSHIP

Cytoskeletal organization is involved in the shear stress–induced stimulation of ET-1. Cytochalasin, which disrupts the actin filaments, also increases ET-1 mRNA levels. Thrombin also stimulates ET-1 production, presumably through phosphorylation of myosin light chain kinase and the resulting formation of filamentous actin and myosin (36). Apparently the configuration of actin and myosin into their filamentous structures facilitates the transport of ET-1 vesicles to the outside of the cells. Effects of ET-1 on endothelial synthesis of PGI_2 and NO (13, 20) are also indirectly related to cell stretching (9).

ET-3 causes leakiness of venules, presumably through ET_B, in the endothelial cells (43). Phalloidin, which stabilizes the actin filament and maintains the filamentous state of the cytoskeleton, prevents leakiness. These data support an important role for the cytoskeletal organization in the regulation of endothelial function including the production of ET-1.

CROSSTALK NETWORK BETWEEN ENDOTHELIUM-DERIVED SUBSTANCES

Endothelial cells communicate with blood cells and VSMC by various humoral factors (48, 92) and by contact-mediated mechanisms through myoendothelial gap junctions (12). Here we focus on the interactions among ET, NO, and NP within the endothelium and between the endothelial and nonendothelial cells.

Cell-cell contact exerts a profound effect on endothelial cell function. It was recently shown that microvascular endothelial cells from rat ventricle, which do not express ET mRNA by themselves, began to express the mRNA when incubated with adult rat myocytes (64). Cell contact is apparently necessary because conditioned media from the myocytes had no effect, whereas conditioned media from cultures of myocytes and endothelial cells mimicked the physical contact experiments. It is also interesting to note that TGF-β gene transcripts were increased early. The addition of TGF-β alone increased the ET-1 mRNA levels, and antibodies to TGF-β blocked the increase; thus TGF-β appears to have an important role in cell-cell contact.

ANP and BNP suppress thrombin– and/or Ang II–induced ET release from human endothelial cells (39). ANP and BNP activate particulate guanylate cyclase A, produce cGMP, and activate protein kinase G. These cGMP-dependent processes suppress the agonist-induced changes in inositol trisphosphate formation and intracellular Ca^{2+} concentration, which results in an inhibition of prepro ET-1 gene expression (17). CNP shows a strong inhibition of ET-1 secretion in porcine endothelial cells (37). Thus NP with a vasorelaxing activity may counteract vasoconstriction by suppressing ET production. Furthermore, intracellular increases in cGMP were shown to down-regulate the NP-C receptor (34). This mechanism can potentiate the biological action of NP. Endothelium-derived NO also inhibits ET production via a cGMP-dependent mechanism through activation of soluble guanylyl cyclase (7). PGI_2 produces cAMP via activation of adenylyl cyclase and inhibits ET production

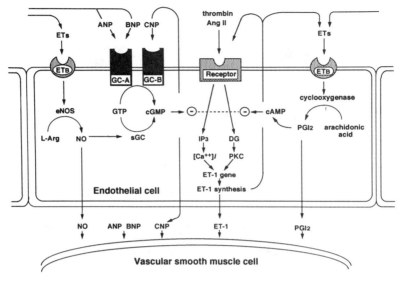

Figure 1 Schematic diagram showing the putative interactions between nonpeptide (NO, PGI₂) and peptide (ANP, BNP, CNP) vasorelaxing factors and ETs in endothelial cells. sGC, soluble guanylyl cyclase; DG, diacylglycerol; PKC, protein kinase C.

(96). These results indicate that the EDRFs such as NP and NO counterregulates ET at the level of endothelial cells (Figure 1).

Interaction among these factors also occurs in VSMC. NP and NO decrease vascular tone by a cGMP/guanylyl cyclase–dependent pathway, whereas ET increases vascular tone via Ca^{2+}/calmodulin– and PKC–dependent pathways. In addition, NP-induced cGMP, especially by CNP, up-regulates ET_B receptor mRNA expression in cultured VSMC (15). Although the function of the ET_B receptor in VSMC remains unclear, it could be involved in contraction and proliferation (14). Therefore, NP may indirectly enhance the effects of ET in VSMC (2). NO is expected to show a similar up-regulation of the ET_B receptor. By contrast, ET_A receptor mRNA expression in VSMC is up-regulated by cAMP, which is increased by a β-adrenergic agonist and PGI₂ (14). Up-regulation of the ET_A receptor potentiates the action of ET. Taken together, nonpeptidic and peptidic EDRF may potentiate the ET action by up-regulating ET receptors on the VSMC (Figure 2).

In addition, there is an interaction between biologically active NP receptors and the NP-C receptor. Because CNP down-regulates the expression of the NP-C receptor, the NP-B receptor is thought to be involved in the regulation

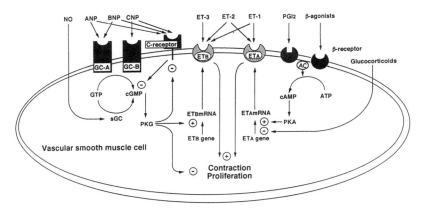

Figure 2 Schematic diagram showing the putative interactions between various vasoactive substances and ET receptors in the vascular smooth muscle cells. GC-A, guanylyl cyclase A; GC-B, guanylyl cyclase B; C-receptor, clearance receptor of natriuretic peptides; AC, adenylyl cyclase; PKG, protein kinase G; PKA, protein kinase A; +, up-regulation; −, down-regulation.

of the NP-C receptor (35). On the other hand, the NP-C receptor regulates cGMP production by ANP through the NP-A and NP-B receptors (29); thus the interaction between NP receptors is reciprocal.

CONCLUDING REMARKS

It is clear that the endothelium, owing to its strategic position, plays an exceedingly important role in regulating the vascular system by integrating diverse mechanical and biochemical signals and by responding to them through the release of vasoactive substances, cytokines, and growth factors. However, the functions of these substances are not limited to the control of local vascular tone. These substances also have profound effects on the hypertrophic and hyperplastic growth of VSMC. It should be emphasized that the endothelium is the major source of the only known anti-mitogen, cGMP, via NO or CNP. It appears that the complexity of the regulatory mechanism of this cell type may even exceed that of many other endocrine cells. The endothelium is undoubtedly the organ of the 1990s. It is, therefore, our hope that this review, by delineating the complexity of the endothelial functions, will assist with identifying areas of further exciting research.

Literature Cited

1. Ananda-Srivastava MB, Sairam MR, Cantin M. 1990. Ring-deleted analogs of atrial natriuretic factor inhibit adenylate cyclase/cAMP system. *J. Biol. Chem.* 265:8566–72

2. Appel RG. 1992. Growth-regulatory properties of atrial natriuretic factor. *Am. J. Physiol.* 31:F911–18

3. Arai H, Hori S, Aramori I, Ohkubo H, Nakanishi S. 1990. Cloning and expression of a cDNA encoding an endothelin receptor. *Nature* 348:730–32

4. Badr KF, Murray JJ, Breyer MD, Takahashi K, Inagami T, et al. 1989. Mesangial cell, glomerular and renal vascular responses to endothelin in the rat kidney—elucidation of signal transduction pathway. *J. Clin. Invest.* 83:336–42

5. Bloch KD, Friedlich SP, Lee ME, Eddy RL, Shows TB, et al. 1989. Structural organization and chromosomal assignment of the gene encoding endothelin. *J. Biol. Chem.* 264:10851–57

6. Bolotina VM, Najibi S, Palacino JJ, Pagano PJ, Cohen RA. 1994. Nitric oxide directly activates calcium-dependent potassium channels in vascular smooth muscle. *Nature* 368:850–53

7. Boulanger C, Lüscher TF. 1990. Release of endothelin from the porcine aorta. Inhibition by endothelium derived nitric oxide. *J. Clin. Invest.* 85:587–90

8. Bredt DS, Hwang PM, Snyder SH. 1990. Localization of nitric oxide synthase indicating a neural role for nitric oxide. *Nature* 347:768–70

9. Carosi JA, Eskin SG, McIntire LV. 1992. Cyclical strain effects on production of vasoactive materials in cultured endothelial cells. *J. Cell. Physiol.* 151:29–36

10. Chinkers M, Garbers DL. 1991. Signal transduction by guanylyl cyclases. *Annu. Rev. Biochem.* 60:553–75

11. Clozel M, Breu V, Burri K, Cassal JM, Fischli W, et al. 1993. Pathophysiologic role of endothelin revealed by the first orally active endothelin receptor antagonist. *Nature* 365:759–61

12. Davis PF, Olesen SP, Clapham DE, Morrel EM, Schoen FJ. 1988. Endothelial communication. *Hypertension* 11:563–72

13. DeNucci D, Thomas R, D'Orleans-Juste P, Antumes E, Walder E, et al. 1988. Pressor effects of circulating endothelin are limited by its removal in the pulmonary circulation and by release of prostacyclin and endothelial-derived relaxing factor. *Proc. Natl. Acad. Sci. USA* 85:9797–800

14. Eguchi S, Hirata Y, Imai T, Kanno K, Marumo F. 1994. Phenotypic changes of endothelin receptor subtype in cultured rat vascular smooth muscle cells. *Endocrinology* 134:222–28

15. Eguchi S, Hirata Y, Imai T, Marumo F. 1994. C-type natriuretic peptide up–regulates endothelin type B receptor in cultured rat vascular smooth muscle cells. *Hypertension* 23(part 2):936–40

16. Eguchi S, Hirata Y, Imara M, Yano M, Marumo F. 1992. A novel ETA antagonist BQ-123 inhibits endothelin-1-induced phosphoinositide breakdown and DNA synthesis in rat vascular smooth muscle cells. *FEBS Lett.* 302:243–46

17. Emori T, Hirata Y, Imai T, Eguchi S, Kanno K, et al. 1993. Cellular mechanism of natriuretic peptides induced inhibition of endothelin-1 biosynthesis in rat endothelial cells. *Endocrinology* 133:2474–80

18. Emori T, Hirata Y, Ohta K, Kano K, Eguchi S, et al. 1991. Cellular mechanism of endothelin-1 release by angiotensin and vasopressin. *Hypertension* 18:165–70

19. Feletou M, Vanhoutte PM. 1988. Endothelium-dependent hyperpolarization of canine coronary smooth muscle. *Br. J. Pharmacol.* 93:515–24

20. Filep J, Battistini B, Cote Y, Beaudoin A, Sirois P. 1991. Endothelin-1 induces prostacyclin release from bovine aortic endothelial cells. *Biochem. Biophys. Res. Commun.* 177:171–77

21. Furchgott RF, Zawadzki JV. 1980. The obligatory role of endothelial cells in the regulation of arterial smooth muscle by acetylcholine. *Nature* 288:373–76

22. Furuya M, Aisaka K, Miyazaki T, Honbou N, Kawashima K, et al. 1993. C-type natriuretic peptide inhibits intimal thickening after vascular injury. *Biochem. Biophys. Res. Commun.* 193:248–53

23. Furuya M, Takehisa M, Minamitake Y, Kitajima Y, Hayashi Y, et al. 1990. Novel natriuretic peptide, CNP, potently stimulates cyclic GMP production in rat cultured vascular smooth muscle cells. *Biochem. Biophys. Res. Commun.* 170:201–8

24. Garg UC, Hassid A. 1989. Nitric oxide–generating vasodilators and 8-bromo-cyclic GMP inhibit mitogenesis and proliferation of cultured rat vascular

smooth muscle cells. *J. Clin. Invest.* 83:1774–77

25. Golfman LS, Hata T, Beamish RE, Dhalla NS. 1993. Role of endothelin in heart function in health and disease. *Can. J. Cardiol.* 9:635–53

26. Hahn AW, Resink TJ, Scott-Burden T, Powell J, Dohi Y, et al. 1990. Stimulation of endothelin mRNA and secretion in rat vascular smooth muscle cells: a novel autocrine function. *Cell Regul.* 1:649–59

27. Hama N, Itoh H, Shirakami G, Suga S, Komatsu Y, et al. 1994. Detection of C-type natriuretic peptide in human circulation and marked increase of plasma CNP level in septic shock patients. *Biochem. Biophys. Res. Commun.* 198: 1177–82

28. Inouye A, Yanagisawa M, Takuwa Y, Mitsui Y, Kobayashi M, et al. 1989. The human preproendothelin-1 gene: complete nucleotide sequence and regulation of expression. *J. Biol. Chem.* 264:14954–59

29. Ishido M, Fujita T, Shimonaka M, Saheki T, Ohuchi S, et al. 1989. Inhibition of atrial natriuretic peptide-induced cyclic GMP, accumulation in the bovine endothelial cells with anti-atrial natriuretic peptide receptor antiserum. *J. Biol. Chem.* 264:641–45

30. Ishizuka Y, Kangawa K, Minamino N, Ishii K, Takano S, et al. 1992. Isolation and identification of C-type natriuretic peptide in human monocytic cell line, THP-1. *Biochem. Biophys. Res. Commun.* 189:697–704

31. Ito S, Ren Y-L. 1993. Evidence for the role of nitric oxide in macular densa control of glomerular hemodynamics. *J. Clin. Invest.* 92:1093–98

32. Janssens SP, Shimouchi A, Quertermous T, Bloch DB, Bloch KD. 1992. Cloning and expression of a cDNA encoding human endothelium–derived relaxing factor/nitric oxide synthase. *J. Biol. Chem.* 267:14519–22

33. Kasuya Y, Takuwa Y, Yanagisana M, Masaki T, Goto K. 1992. A pertussis toxin–sensitive mechanism of endothelium action in porcine coronary artery smooth muscle. *Br. J. Pharmacol.* 107: 456–62

34. Kato J, Lanier-Smith KL, Currie MG. 1991. Cyclic GMP downregulates atrial natriuretic peptide receptors on cultured vascular endothelial cells. *J. Biol. Chem.* 266:14681–85

35. Kishimoto I, Nakao K, Suga S, Hosoda K, Yoshimasa T, et al. 1993. Down-regulation of C-receptor by natriuretic peptides via ANP-B receptor in vascular

smooth muscle cells. *Am. J. Physiol.* 265: H1373–79

36. Kitazumi K, Tasaka K. 1992. Thrombin stimulated phosphorylation of myosin light chain and its possible involvement in endothelin-1 secretion from porcine aortic endothelial cells. *Biochem. Pharmacol.* 43:1701–9

37. Kohno M, Horio T, Yokokawa K, Kurihara N, Takeda T. 1992. C-type natriuretic peptide inhibits thrombin-and angiotensin II–stimulated endothelin release via cyclic guanosine 3′,5′-monophosphate. *Hypertension* 19: 320–25

38. Kohno M, Yasunari K, Murakawa KI, Yokokawa K, Hori T, et al. 1990. Plasma immunoreactive endothelin in essential hypertension. *Am. J. Med.* 88: 614–18

39. Kohno M, Yasunari K, Yokokawa K, Murakawa K, Horio T, et al. 1991. Inhibition by atrial and brain natriuretic peptide of endothelin-1 secretion after stimulation with angiotensin II and thrombin of cultured human endothelial cells. *J. Clin. Invest.* 87:1999–2004

40. Koller KJ, Lowe DG, Bennett GL, Minamino N, Kangawa K, et al. 1991. Selective activation of the B natriuretic peptide receptor by C-type natriuretic peptide (CNP). *Science* 252:120–23

41. Komatsu Y, Nakao K, Itoh H, Suga SI, Ogawa Y, Imura H. 1992. Vascular natriuretic peptide. *Lancet* 340:622

42. Kurihara Y, Kurihara H, Suzuki H, Kodama T, Yazaki Y, et al. 1994. Elevated blood pressure and craniofacial abnormalities in mice deficient in endothelin. *Nature* 368:703–10

43. Kurose I, Miura S, Fukumura D, Tsuchiya M. 1993. Mechanism of endothelin-induced macromolecular leakage in microvascular beds of rat mesentery. *Eur. J. Pharmacol.* 250:85–94

44. Lamus S, Marsden PA, Li GK, Tempst P, Michel T. 1992. Endothelial nitric oxide synthase: molecular cloning and characterization of a distinct constitutive enzyme isoform. *Proc. Natl. Acad. Sci. USA* 89:6348–52

45. Lee ME, Phadly MS, Temizer DH, Clifford JA, Yoshizumi M, et al. 1991. Regulation of endothelin-1 gene expression by *fos* and *jun*. *J. Biol. Chem.* 266:19034–39

46. Lerman A, Edwards BS, Hallett JW, Heublein DM, Sondberg SM, et al. 1991. Circulating and tissue endothelin immunoreactivity in advanced atherosclerosis. *N. Engl. J. Med.* 325:997–1001

47. Levin ER, Frank HJL. 1991. Natriuretic

peptides inhibit rat astroglial proliferation: mediation by C receptor. *Am. J. Physiol.* 261:R453–57

48. Lüscher TF. 1990. Imbalance of endothelium-derived relaxing and contracting factors. A new concept in hypertension. *Am. J. Hypertens.* 3:317–30
49. Malek AM, Greene AL, Izumo S. 1993. Regulation of endothelin-1 gene by fluid shear stress is transcriptionally mediated and independent of protein kinase C and cAMP. *Proc. Natl. Acad. Sci. USA* 90: 5999–6003
50. Malek A, Izumo S. 1992. Physiological fluid shear stress causes down regulation of endothelin-1 mRNA in bovine aortic endothelial cells. *Am. J. Physiol.* 32: C389–96
51. Masaki T. 1993. Endothelins: homeostatic and compensatory actions in the circulatory and endocrine systems. *Endocrine Rev.* 14:256–68
52. Meredith IT, Yeung AC, Weidinger FF, Anderson TJ, Uehata A, et al. 1993. Role of impaired endothelium-dependent vasodilation in ischemic manifestations of coronary artery disease. *Circulation* 87(Suppl. V):V56–66
53. Michel T, Li GK, Busconi L. 1993. Phosphorylation and subcellular translocation of endothelial nitric oxide synthase. *Proc. Natl. Acad. Sci. USA* 90: 6252–56
54. Mihatsch MJ, Bach JF, Coovadia HF, Forre O, Moutsopoulos HM, et al. 1988. Cyclosporin-associated nephropathy in patients with autoimmune diseases. *Klin. Wochenschr.* 66:43–47
55. Minamino N, Kangawa K, Matsuo H. 1990. N–terminally extended form of C-type natriuretic peptide (CNP-53) identified in porcine brain. *Biochem. Biophys. Res. Commun.* 170: 973–79
56. Moncada S, Palmer RM, Higgs EA. 1991. Nitric oxide: physiology, pathophysiology, and pharmacology. *Pharmacol. Rev.* 43:109–42
57. Morita T, Kurihara H, Maemura K, Yoshizumi M, Yazaki Y. 1993. Disruption of cytoskeletal structures mediates shear stress–induced endothelin-1 gene expression in cultured porcine aortic endothelial cells. *J. Clin. Invest.* 92:1706–12
58. Muldon LL, Endlen H, Rodland KD, Magun BE. 1992. Stimulation of Ca²⁺ influx by endothelin-1 is subject to negative feedback by elevated intracellular Ca²⁺. *Am. J. Physiol.* 260:C1273–81
59. Nakamura S, Naruse M, Naruse K, Demura H, Uemura H. 1990. Immunocytochemical localization of endothelin

in cultured bovine endothelial cells. *Histochemistry* 94:475–77
60. Nakao K, Ogawa Y, Suga S, Imura H. 1992. Molecular biology and biochemistry of the natriuretic peptide system: natriuretic peptides. *J. Hypertens.* 10: 907–12
61. Naruse M, Nakamura N, Naruse K, Kubo K, Kato M, et al. 1992. Plasma immunoreactive endothelin levels are increased in hemodialysis patients with hypertention following erythropoietin therapy. *Hypertens. Res.* 15:11–16
62. Naruse M, Tanabe A, Naruse K, Takeyama Y, Hiroshige J, et al. 1994. Atrial and brain natriuretic peptides in cardiovascular diseases. *Hypertension* 23(Suppl. I):I-231–34
63. Naruse M, Zeng Z-P, Naruse K, Tanabe A, Yoshimoto T, et al. 1993. Is chronic elevation of plasma endothelin levels a cause of hypertension? *Hypertens. Res.* 16:247–51
64. Nishida M, Springhorn JP, Kelly RA, Smith TW. 1993. Cell-cell signaling between rat ventricular myocytes and cardiac microvascular endothelial cells in heterotypic primary culture. *J. Clin. Invest.* 91:1934–41
65. Nishikibe M, Ikeda M, Tsuchida S, Fukuroda T, Shimamoto K, et al. 1992. Antihypertensive effect of a newly synthesized endothelin antagonist, BQ-123, in genetic hypertension models. *J. Hypertens.* 10(Suppl. 4) p. 53 (Abstr.)
66. Ohnaka K, Takayanagi R, Nishikawa M, Haji M, Nawata M. 1993. Purification and characterization of a phosphoramidon-sensitive endothelin-converting enzyme in porcine aortic endothelium. *J. Biol. Chem.* 268:26759–66
67. Ohno A, Naruse M, Kato S, Hosaka M, Naruse K, et al. 1992. Endothelin-specific antibodies decrease blood pressure and increase glomerular filtration rate and renal plasma flow in spontaneously hypertensive rats. *J. Hypertens.* 10:781–85
68. Oishi R, Nonoguchi H, Tomita K, Marumo F. 1991. Endothelin-1 inhibits AVP-stimulated osmotic water permeability in rat inner medullary collecting duct. *Am. J. Physiol.* 261: F951–56
69. Okada K, Miyazaki Y, Takeda J, Matsuyama K, Yamaki T, et al. 1990. Conversion of big endothelin-1 by membrane-bound metalloendopeptidase in cultured bovine endothelial cells. *Biochem. Biophys. Res. Commun.* 171: 1192–98
70. Palmer RMJ, Bridge L, Foxwell NA, Moncada S. 1992. The role of nitric oxide in endothelial cell damage and its

inhibition by glucocorticoids. *Br. J. Pharmacol.* 105:11–12

71. Palmer RMJ, Ferrigo AG, Moncada S. 1987. Nitric oxide release accounts for the biological activity of endothelium-derived relaxing factor. *Nature* 327:524–25

72. Panza JA, Casino PR, Kilcoyne CM, Quyyumi AA. 1993. Role of endothelium–derived nitric oxide in the abnormal endothelium-dependent vascular relaxation of patients with essential hypertension. *Circulation* 87:1468–74

73. Paul M, Retting R, Talsness CE, Zintz M, Yanagisawa M. 1994. Transgenic rats expressing human endothelin-2 gene: a new model to study endothelin regulation in vivo. *J. Hypertens.* 12 (Suppl. 3):S72 (Abstr.)

74. Petros A, Bennett D, Vallance P. 1991. Effects of nitric oxide synthase inhibitors on hypotension in patients with septic shock. *Lancet* 338:1557–58

75. Porter JG, Catalano R, McEnroe G, Lewicki JA, Protter AA. 1992. C-type natriuretic peptide inhibits growth factor-dependent DNA synthesis in smooth muscle cells. *Am. J. Physiol.* 263(5 Pt 1):C1001–6

76. Rees DD, Palmer RMJ, Moncada S. 1989. Role of endothelium-derived nitric oxide in the regulation of blood pressure. *Proc. Natl. Acad. Sci. USA* 86:3375–78

77. Sakuma I, Stuehr DJ, Gross SS, Nathan C, Levi R. 1988. Identification of arginine as a precursor of endothelium-derived relaxing factor. *Proc. Natl. Acad. Sci. USA* 85:8664–67

78. Sakurai T, Yanagisawa M, Masaki T. 1992. Molecular characterization of endothelin receptors. *Trends Pharmacol. Sci.* 13:103–8

79. Sakurai T, Yanagisawa M, Takuwa K, Miyazaki H, Kimura S, et al. 1990. Cloning of a cDNA encoding a nonisopeptide-selective subtype of the endothelin receptor. *Nature* 348:732–35

80. Schmidt HH, Gagne GD, Nakane M, Pollock JS, Miller MF, et al. 1992. Mapping of neural nitric oxide synthase in the rat suggests frequent co-localization with NADPH diaphorase but not with soluble guanylyl cyclase, and novel paraneural functions for nitrinergic signal transduction. *J. Histochem. Cytochem.* 40:1439–56

81. Seo BG, Tschudl MR, Lüscher TF. 1994. Both ETA- and ETB-receptors mediate endothelin-induced contractions in human blood vessels. *J. Hypertens.* 12(Suppl. 3):S127 (Abstr.)

82. Sharefkin JB, Diamond SL, Eskin SG, McIntire LV, Dieffenbach CW. 1991. Fluid flow decreases preproendothelin-1 peptide release in cultured human endothelial cells. *J. Vasc. Surg.* 14:1–9

83. Simonson MS, Dunn MJ. 1993. Endothelin peptides and the kidney. *Annu. Rev. Physiol.* 55:249–65

84. Stingo AJ, Clavell AL, Heublein DM, Wei CM, Pittelkow MR, et al. 1992. Presence of C-type natriuretic peptide in cultured human endothelial cells and plasma. *Am. J. Physiol.* 263:H1318–21

85. Sudoh T, Minamino N, Kangawa K, Matsuo H. 1990. C-type natriuretic peptide (CNP): a new member of natriuretic peptide family identified in porcine brain. *Biochem. Biophys. Res. Commun.* 168:863–70

86. Suga S, Nakao K, Hosoda K, Mukoyama M, Ogawa Y, et al. 1992. Receptor selectivity of natriuretic peptide family, atrial natriuretic peptide, brain natriuretic peptide, and C-type natriuretic peptide. *Endocrinology* 130:229–39

87. Suga S, Nakao K, Itoh H, Komatsu Y, Ogawa Y, et al. 1992. Endothelial production of C-type natriuretic peptide and its marked augmentation by transforming growth factor-β. Possible existence of "vascular natriuretic peptide system." *J. Clin. Invest.* 90:1145–49

88. Suga S, Nakao K, Kishimoto I, Hosoda K, Mukoyama M, et al. 1992. Phenotype-related alteration in expression of natriuretic peptide receptor in aortic smooth cells. *Circ. Res.* 71:34–39

89. Takagi Y, Fukase M, Tanaka S, Yoshizumi H, Tokunaga O, et al. 1990. Autocrine effect of endothelin on DNA synthesis in human vascular endothelial cells. *Biochem. Biophys. Res. Commun.* 168:537–43

90. Tawaragi Y, Fuchimura K, Tanaka S, Minamino N, Kangawa K, et al. 1991. Gene and precursor structures of human C-type natriuretic peptide. *Biochem. Biophys. Res. Commun.* 175:645–51

91. Toda N, Okamura T. 1990. Possible role of nitric oxide in transmitting information from vasodilator nerve to cerebroarterial muscle. *Biochem. Biophys. Res. Commun.* 170:308–13

92. Vanhoutte PM. 1989. Endothelium and control of vascular function. *Hypertension* 13:658–67

93. Wagner OF, Christ G, Wojta J, Vierhapper H, Parzer S, et al. 1992. Polar secretion of endothelin-1 by cultural endothelial cells. *J. Biol. Chem.* 267:16066–88

94. Yanagisawa M. 1994. Plenary lecture.

15th Sci. Sess, Int. Soc. Hypertens. Melbourne, Australia

95. Yanagisawa M, Kurihara H, Kimura S, Tomobe Y, Kobayashi Y, et al. 1988. A novel potent vasoconstrictor peptide produced by vascular endothelial cells. *Nature* 332:411–15

96. Yokokawa K, Kohno M, Yasunari K, Murakami K, Takeda T. 1991. Endothelin-3 regulates endothelin-1 production in cultured human endothelial cells. *Hypertension* 18:304–15

97. Yokokawa K, Tahara H, Kohno M, Murakawa K, Yasunari K, et al. 1991. Hypertension associated with en-dothelin-secreting malignant heman-gioendothelioma. *Ann. Intern. Med.* 114: 213–15

98. Yoshizumi M, Kurihara H, Sugiyama T, Takaku F, Yanagisawa M, et al. 1989. Hemodynamic shear stress stimulates endothelin production by cultured endo-thelial cells. *Biochem. Biophys. Res. Commun.* 161:859–64

99. Zaidel ML, Brady HR, Kone BC, Gullans SR, Brenner BM. 1989. En-dothlein, a peptide inhibitor of Na$^+$-K$^+$-ATPase in intact renal tubular epithelial cells. *Am. J. Physiol.* 257: C1101–7

Annu. Rev. Physiol. 1995. 57:191–218

REGULATION OF GLUCOSE FLUXES DURING EXERCISE IN THE POSTABSORPTIVE STATE

David H. Wasserman

Department of Molecular Physiology and Biophysics, Vanderbilt University School of Medicine, Nashville, Tennessee 37232

KEY WORDS: liver, muscle, gluconeogenesis, glycogenolysis, hormones

---

INTRODUCTION

Research conducted in the 1920s and 1930s described the glycemic response to a variety of exercise conditions (20, 21, 27, 74). It was demonstrated that despite a marked increase in carbohydrate oxidation, glucose homeostasis was generally maintained during moderate-intensity exercise provided that carbohydrate reserves were adequate (27). On the other hand, glucose levels were shown to increase during high-intensity exercise (20), and extreme hypoglycemia was shown to be a frequent occurrence at the latter stage of a marathon when the carbohydrate reserves were exhausted (74). Classic work from the Harvard Fatigue Laboratory illustrated the importance of circulating glucose as a fuel by showing that glucose ingestion during prolonged, glycogen-depleting exercise increased endurance in dogs by more than threefold (21). Research in the area of glucose metabolism and exercise was further advanced by Swedish studies that used techniques for obtaining splanchnic and limb arteriovenous differences and muscle biopsies to characterize aspects of substrate fluxes during muscular work (4, 7, 28, 122, 123). The next major step in understanding the regulation of glucose fluxes during exercise followed the development of sensitive hormone assay techniques. This allowed for the effects of exercise on known and putative glucoregulatory hormone levels in arterial blood, as well as those of the sympathetic neurotransmitter norepinephrine, to be comprehensively described (32), which paved the way for recent

191

investigations designed to elucidate the endocrine and neural mechanisms involved in the control of glucose fluxes during exercise.

This review focuses on studies that comprise our current understanding of factors that control glucose fluxes during exercise in the postabsorptive state. The emphasis is on three critical aspects: (a) the mechanisms that stimulate muscle glucose uptake and metabolism; (b) the importance of the endocrine system for the increase in hepatic glucose production; and (c) the signals that inform the endocrine and nervous systems, and ultimately the liver, that an individual is engaged in physical exercise.

REGULATION OF GLUCOSE UTILIZATION BY THE WORKING MUSCLE

Cellular Bases for Contraction-Stimulated Muscle Glucose Utilization

In healthy, postabsorptive individuals, glucose uptake from the blood satisfies 15 to 30% of the energy requirement of the working muscle during moderate-intensity exercise (122), which can increase to ~40% during high-intensity exercise. The work rate–dependent increase in glucose uptake is disproportionately greater at intensities greater than ~50% of the maximum VO_2 (16, 122). Kinetic analyses of muscle glucose uptake (in vivo; 145) (Figure 1) and transport (in vitro; 39, 61, 86, 93, 111) indicate that the maximal velocity (V_{max}) for this process is increased by moderate exercise generally without affecting the Michaelis-Menton constant (K_m). The K_m for glucose uptake across the working limb of the dog engaged in sustained moderate exercise (145) is equal to that for insulin-mediated glucose uptake across the human leg (26), which suggests that plasma membrane transport by the insulin-regulatable glucose transport protein GLUT4 is rate limiting for glucose uptake, at least under these exercise conditions. The K_m for glucose oxidation by the working dog limb is the same as that for glucose uptake, which implies that both processes are rate limited by the same step (145). If one assumes that transport is limiting under these conditions, the increase in V_{max} for glucose uptake and oxidation without a change in K_m suggests that exercise increases the number, turnover, and/or availability of active glucose transporters without a change in their affinity for glucose. This is consistent with the demonstration that prior exercise increases transporter number (24, 25, 31, 38, 45, 90, 93) and turnover (39, 61) in plasma membranes prepared from rat skeletal muscle. The increased transporter number comes specifically from an increase in plasma membrane GLUT4 because plasma membrane GLUT1, the other isoform found in muscle, is unaffected (25, 37). The increase in plasma membrane transporters in response to exercise, similar to that from insulin stimulation, is

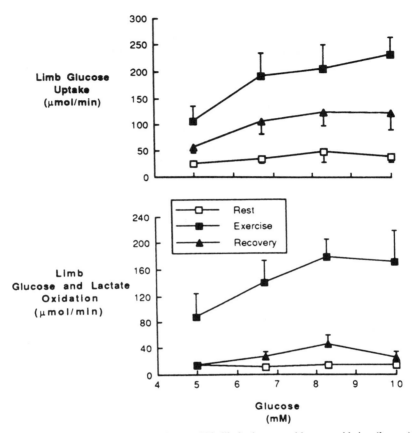

Figure 1 Hindlimb glucose uptake (*top*) and hindlimb glucose and lactate oxidation (*bottom*) vs plasma glucose concentration during rest, exercise, and recovery in dogs. The glucose clamp technique was used to maintain glucose at one of four glucose levels. Exercise and recovery samples were obtained during the last 40 of 90 min periods. Insulin levels were fixed at basal using somatostatin and intraportal insulin replacement. n = 5 at a glucose level of 5.0 mM, and n = 4 for all other glucose levels. Data are mean±SE (modified from Reference 145).

the result of an increase in translocation from an intracellular pool because a concurrent decrease in transporters in an intracellular microsomal fraction has been reported (31, 37). However, exercise and insulin most likely recruit GLUT4 from different intracellular pools (24, 25, 93). The presence of distinct intracellular glucose transporter pools for insulin and exercise stimulation, along with the demonstration that these two stimuli are additive, support the concept that exercise and insulin signal translocation by separate mechanisms (86, 90, 91, 92, 101, 125, 149).

In addition to glucose transport, glucose phosphorylation is necessary for glucose utilization. This reaction is catalyzed in skeletal muscle by hexokinase (HK) II. Although glucose uptake is probably rate limited by glucose transport at rest and during moderate, steady-state exercise, there is evidence that under some conditions glucose phosphorylation may become rate limiting. This could result if glucose transport is stimulated to a critically high level or if glucose 6-phosphate, an inhibitor of hexokinase, accumulates. The onset of exercise (60) and heavy exercise (59) are conditions in which intracellular glucose accumulates and may reflect instances when glucose phosphorylation is limiting for glucose uptake. This observation is consistent with findings indicating that phosphorylation, and not transport, is limiting in skeletal muscle in situations characterized by elevated glucose uptake rates (30, 70, 97). In contrast to the extensive work assessing exercise and glucose transport, little is known about the effects of exercise on HKII and glucose phosphorylation. Chronic, low-frequency stimulation can lead to a redistribution of muscle HK activity, thus more of the enzyme exists in its more active form in an insoluble fraction (140). In support of this observation, acute exercise is shown to result in a small increase in the percent of muscle HK activity associated with mitochondria (115). Moreover, O'Doherty and colleagues showed that skeletal muscle HKII mRNA is stimulated two- to threefold by just 30 min of exercise (89) and that this increase is due to an increase in gene transcription (88). Further studies find that HKII mRNA in the rat tibialis anterior is increased by 3 h of chronic, low-frequency stimulation (48). Interestingly, increases in HKII gene transcription (87, 88), mRNA (48, 89), and protein synthesis (48) precede and are larger than those for GLUT4. The fact that HKII synthesis is stimulated more rapidly and is more pronounced has been used to argue that muscle glucose utilization is rate limited by phosphorylation during sustained contractile activity (48). Because the exercise-induced increase in HKII activity lags behind the increase in HKII gene expression (48, 89), it is likely that this effect is more important to the persistent increase in insulin action following exercise or the adaptations that occur with training than it is during acute exercise.

Insulin-Independent Glucose Utilization in the Contracting Muscle

There is evidence, as noted above, that contraction- and insulin-stimulated glucose transport occur through the activation of different pathways. The insulin-independent nature of contraction-mediated glucose uptake is further exemplified by the demonstration that muscle contraction increases plasma membrane glucose transporter protein (40) and glucose uptake (49) in vitro even when no insulin is present. In the whole organism, glucose utilization is increased by exercise although insulin levels decrease. This finding supports studies conducted in isolated muscle preparations and highlights the importance of insulin-independent mechanisms in the regulation of glucose utilization during exercise in vivo. Nevertheless, despite the potent effects of contraction on muscle glucose uptake, exercise in the chronic absence of insulin is inadequate for the increase in glucose uptake seen in the whole organism. This is evidenced by the failure of tracer-determined glucose clearance to increase normally with exercise in insulin-deficient depancreatized dogs (8, 121, 126). The increase in glucose utilization in insulin-deficient depancreatized dogs is only ~25 to 50% of the response present during 150 min of exercise when insulin is replaced (126). The importance of insulin in this setting is also supported by the observation that the percent of substrate oxidation due to glucose metabolism is impaired during rest and exercise in depancreatized dogs deprived of insulin (52).

An hypothesis for the inability of contraction alone to fully stimulate glucose utilization in the whole organism is that metabolic events antagonistic to glucose uptake occur under these conditions (e.g. enhanced nonesterified fatty acid oxidation, catecholamine action). If this is so, insulin-independent mechanisms are sufficient to stimulate glucose utilization in vivo if characteristics of the diabetic state are minimized. Consistent with this hypothesis, β-adrenergic blockade suppresses lipolysis and normalizes the impaired increase in glucose utilization present in alloxan-diabetic dogs (135). To determine whether insulin is required for the exercise-induced increase in muscle carbohydrate metabolism when circulating glucose and nonesterified fatty acids are normal, somatostatin (SRIF) was infused in dogs to suppress endogenous insulin and glucagon release with or without simulated intraportal insulin replacement (136). The advantage of using SRIF to obtain an insulin-deficient state is that if glucagon is withheld, an interval exists during which the animal can be studied in the absence of hyperglycemia and hyperlipidemia. Under these conditions, the contribution of insulin-independent mechanisms to the exercise-induced increase in tracer-determined glucose utilization is ~ twofold more than in the depancreatized dog. In this model of insulin-deficiency, insulin-independent glucose utilization comprises ~70% of the total response. Furthermore, over 60% of the increase in limb glucose uptake and oxidation occurs despite SRIF-induced insulinopenia (Figure 2). A second approach for estimating the contribution of insulin-independent mechanisms in the absence of characteristics of the diabetic state is by extrapolating metabolic data obtained during hyperinsulinemic (>90 μU/ml) euglycemic clamps in healthy subjects to a theoretical insulin value of zero (128). Estimates of insulin-independent glucose uptake and carbohydrate oxidation using this approach show that 84 and 98% of the total rates and virtually the entire exercise-induced responses occur independently of insulin action. Taken together, in vivo and

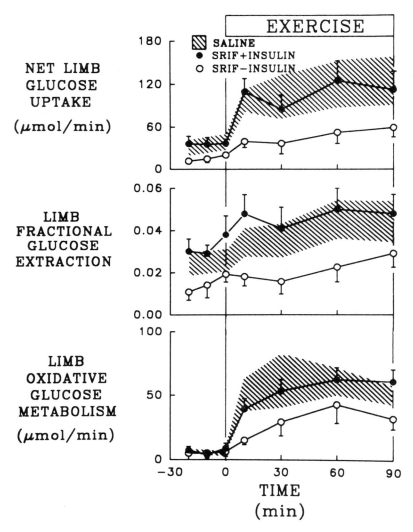

Figure 2 Effect of exercise alone (n = 9) and exercise plus somatostatin with (n = 8) and without
(n = 6) insulin replacement on (*top*) limb glucose uptake, (*center*) fractional extraction, and (*bottom*)
oxidation in dogs. Data are mean±SE. The shaded area represents the mean±SE for saline control
animals (modified from Reference 136).

in vitro experiments are consistent in showing that muscular work is a potent stimulus for insulin-independent glucose uptake and metabolism. Furthermore, these experiments support the conclusion that glucose utilization is impaired in the insulin-deficient diabetic state as a result of accompanying metabolic abnormalities.

The increase in insulin-independent glucose uptake during exercise may relate to some aspect of metabolic changes in the working muscle. Excessive increments in glucose uptake occur when O_2 availability is limited, such as exercise under anemic conditions (41, 134), or when breathing a hypoxic gas mixture (17), even when energy expenditure is no greater. Elevated rates of glucose uptake occur under these circumstances even though insulin levels are no higher and catecholamines, which may be antagonistic to glucose uptake, are greater (17, 41, 134). These findings are consistent with studies conducted in perfused (51, 124) or isolated (96) rat skeletal muscle, which show the close relationship of hypoxia, and the consequent metabolic state, to glucose uptake. The mechanism that links muscle metabolism to glucose uptake remains to be identified.

Insulin Action at the Working Muscle

In addition to the increase in insulin-independent glucose utilization, insulin action is increased by acute exercise (18, 73, 86, 100, 116, 128). Studies conducted in humans show that exercise and insulin stimulate glucose utilization and carbohydrate oxidation synergistically over a range of insulin doses as judged by the effects on both the ED_{50} of insulin and V_{max} of these pathways (128) (Figure 3). The effects of this increase in insulin action are probably most important in the postprandial state and in the intensively treated diabetic state, when insulin levels can be higher than those that normally accompany exercise. There is, nevertheless, an increased sensitivity of glucose uptake to the sub-basal insulin levels present during exercise in the postabsorptive state (126). Exercise also has a potent effect on the intracellular pathway for insulin-stimulated muscle glucose metabolism. The primary route of insulin-mediated glucose metabolism at rest (144) and in the post-exercise state (9) is nonoxidative metabolism. Acute exercise, however, shifts the route of insulin-stimulated glucose disposal so that all the glucose consumed by the muscle is oxidized (Figure 3) (128).

Several mechanisms have been proposed to explain how exercise enhances insulin action. Hemodynamic adjustments, which cause an increased blood flow to the working muscle, increase the exposure of this insulin-sensitive tissue to circulating insulin and glucose. A strong positive correlation does exist between insulin delivery to the working muscle and insulin action (18). Moreover, insulin action in specific muscles correlates to their blood flow even in the resting state (54). A role for muscle blood flow is consistent with studies

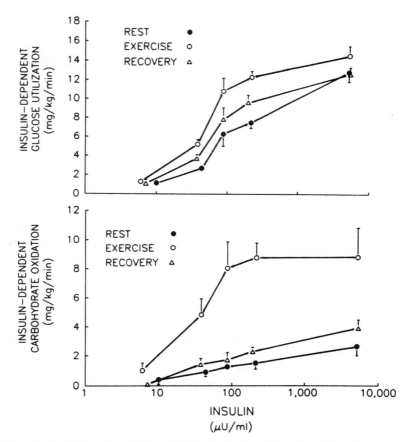

Figure 3 Insulin-dependent glucose utilization (*top*) and carbohydrate oxidation (*bottom*) over a range of insulin concentrations during rest, exercise, and recovery in humans. Insulin-dependent rates are calculated as described previously (128). Exercise and recovery samples were obtained during the last 40 of 100 min periods. n = 5 at each insulin level. Data are mean±SE (modified from Reference 128).

examining the post-exercise state, after basal hemodynamics are largely re-stored, which show that the increase in insulin-dependent glucose uptake is reduced compared to exercise (128). Insulin action does, nevertheless, remain elevated above basal during recovery (83). It has been proposed that trans-endothelial insulin transport is rate limiting for insulin action (2). If this is the case, the hemodynamic adjustments that result in increased capillary surface area in the working muscle may enhance insulin action by increasing insulin transport across the endothelium. Exercise may also increase insulin-stimulated glucose utilization by a mechanism secondary to insulin's suppressive effect on nonesterified fatty acid (NEFA) availability. The absolute magnitude of the insulin-induced suppression of plasma NEFA levels and fat oxidation is greater during exercise. The $ED_{50}s$ for stimulation of total carbohydrate and suppression of fat oxidation occur at similar insulin levels during exercise, which suggests that the greater stimulation of carbohydrate oxidation may be an essential response to a primary suppression of lipolysis (128).

Based on studies that showed an increase in insulin binding to monocytes in exercised subjects (68), it was hypothesized that an increase in insulin binding to skeletal muscle explains the increased action of this hormone during exercise. Studies in humans (10) and rats (10, 82, 112, 148) generally indicate, however, that insulin-binding affinity to skeletal muscle is unaffected by moderate exercise. An increase in insulin-stimulated glucose uptake after exercise in the absence of an increase in insulin binding to muscle suggests that a step distal to binding must be altered (148). Although this may be the case, studies of muscle insulin receptor kinase activity show that exercise does not alter this step (112). A post-receptor modification has been proposed as the link to the glycogen-depleting effect of exercise (9). Although glycogen depletion may be partially involved, insulin action can be stimulated at the onset of exercise before glycogen is depleted (18). Moreover, the improved effect of insulin on glucose uptake can persist after exercise, even when pre-exercise glycogen levels have been restored (34). Conversely, glucose uptake can return to basal even if muscle glycogen remains depleted (91). One recent study showed that the ability of muscle contraction to enhance insulin-stimulated glucose uptake and transport in the perfused rat hindquarter was eliminated by adenosine receptor blockade (116). Adenosine receptor blockade had no effect during contraction in the absence of insulin, which suggests that the increased adenosine production that occurs in response to muscular work (1) plays a role in facilitating insulin action.

ROLE AND REGULATION OF HEPATIC GLUCOSE PRODUCTION DURING EXERCISE

Maintaining adequate blood glucose supply is critical during exercise because it constitutes an appreciable fraction of the fuel for the working muscle and, as is the case at rest, supplies virtually all the fuel for the central nervous system. Were it not for the increase in hepatic glucose production that occurs with exercise of just moderate intensity, the increased rate of muscle glucose uptake would cause overt hypoglycemia in ~ 30 min. Hepatic glucose production does increase, however, and hypoglycemia does not occur, at least until hepatic glycogen stores begin to exhaust. It is a testament to the rigorous nature of the glucoregulatory system that not only is the increase in glucose production effective in preventing hypoglycemia, but during moderate exercise, it increases with dynamics so similar to muscle glucose utilization that only small deviations in arterial glucose levels can be detected. During high-intensity exercise, the glucoregulatory response resembles a response more characteristic of a stress condition. The result is that the increase in glucose production exceeds the increase in glucose utilization and circulating glucose rises.

Magnitude and Mechanisms of the Hepatic Glycogenolytic and Gluconeogenic Responses

The contributions of hepatic glycogenolysis and gluconeogenesis are determined by specific characteristics of the type of exercise in which one is engaged (e.g. prolonged, high intensity) and specific conditions of the participating individual (e.g. absorptive state, health). In overnight-fasted humans and dogs (both of whom are postabsorptive but have substantial liver glycogen), the initial increment in hepatic glucose production during the early stages of exercise is due almost entirely to accelerated glycogenolysis (122, 139). By combining dual isotope methods with hepatic arteriovenous gluconeogenic precursor differences in the dog, minimum and maximum estimates of hepatic gluconeogenesis can be obtained; hepatic gluconeogenesis is a minimum of 5 and 18% and a maximum of 15 and 22% of the increase in glucose production at 30 and 150 min of moderate treadmill exercise (127). Gluconeogenesis becomes increasingly more important with more prolonged exercise as hepatic glycogen stores decrease. Net splanchnic gluconeogenic balance measurements in exercising humans suggest that 45% of the glucose production rate is derived from gluconeogenesis at 4 h of moderate exercise in overnight-fasted humans (4), if one assumes that all the precursors extracted by the splanchnic bed are channeled into glucose. Essentially all the glucose produced gluconeogenically during prolonged exercise in the dog is released by the liver because neglible radioactivity of ^{14}C-alanine incorporated into ^{14}C-glucose is detectable in glycogen (139). The increase in gluconeogenesis during prolonged exercise delays the depletion of liver and muscle glycogen by transforming the energy provided by hepatic fat oxidation to glucose synthesis. The important role that gluconeogenesis plays is apparent from the more rapid liver and muscle glycogen depletion and the reduced endurance time present when this pathway is inhibited in rats with use of mercaptopicolinic acid (58, 113).

The increase in hepatic glucose production is greater with more strenuous work (16, 122). This is particularly the case at work rates above the lactate threshold (~50% maximum VO_2) (16). Stringent isotopic methods have shown that exercise to exhaustion at 100% maximum VO_2 leads to a sevenfold rise in glucose production in as quickly as 10 to 15 min (79). The mechanism for this rapid increase is unclear. Because a reduced O_2 supply stimulates glucose fluxes, it has been hypothesized that the added increase during heavy exercise is due to an O_2 supply-and-demand imbalance (17, 41, 134). The added increment in glucose production that occurs with heavy exercise is generally due to an increase in hepatic glycogenolysis (122). Nevertheless, measurements of splanchnic gluconeogenic precursor uptake indicate that if heavy exercise can be sustained, gluconeogenesis will become important more rapidly because the finite glycogen stores will deplete faster and hormone signals will be greater (3, 4).

The regulatory factors that acutely affect hepatic glycogenolysis act through allosteric modification of glycogen phosphorylase and synthetase within the liver (43). In contrast, gluconeogenesis is regulated by diverse mechanisms that act at many different sites. Gluconeogenesis is regulated by mechanisms that influence the delivery and extraction of gluconeogenic precursors and the efficiency of conversion to glucose within the liver (127). Exercise stimulates all three processes. Hepatic gluconeogenic precursor delivery is enhanced by the mobilization of amino acids, glycerol, lactate, and pyruvate from extrahepatic sites. The hepatic fractional extraction of gluconeogenic amino acids is increased in response to exercise, which indicates that amino acid transport systems are stimulated (28, 129, 139). Evidence that intrahepatic gluconeogenic mechanisms are stimulated by muscular work is twofold. First, gluconeogenic enzyme activities [e.g. phosphoenolpyruvate carboxykinase (PEPCK), fructose-1,6-bisphosphatase, glucose-6-phosphatase] are elevated (22, 23, 50), whereas the activity of the glycolytic enzyme phosphofructokinase is diminished (22) in rats. Second, the intrahepatic gluconeogenic efficiency, measured by the fraction of ^{14}C-alanine that is extracted by the liver and channeled into ^{14}C-glucose, is increased in dogs (139). Following exercise, gluconeogenesis remains elevated as increases in gluconeogenic precursor uptake (3, 139) and intrahepatic gluconeogenic efficiency (139) persist. The mechanism for the increase in intrahepatic gluconeogenic mechanisms during prolonged exercise and exercise recovery may be the result, in part, of increases in the transcription of genes that encode key gluconeogenic enzymes. After only 30 min of exercise, PEPCK gene transcription leading to a threefold rise in liver PEPCK mRNA, is increased in mice (29). There are parallel increases in the transcription of the genes for the nuclear proteins CCAAT/enhancer–binding protein B and C-jun, both of which stimulate transcription of the PEPCK gene (29). It is unlikely, however, that sufficient synthesis of these activators has taken place during the early stages of exercise to account for the rapid increase in PEPCK gene transcription.

Regulation of Hepatic Glucose Production

Exercise can result in a decrease in insulin secretion and increases in glucagon, norepinephrine, epinephrine, and cortisol secretion. The magnitude of these changes generally increases at greater exercise durations and intensities. The role these hormones play in the stimulation of glucose fluxes has been the subject of considerable interest in recent years. The existence of basal glucagon levels is clearly required during exercise and at rest to attain typical glucose production rates (53, 133). Glucagon suppression with SRIF during moderate treadmill exercise in the dog results in a reduction in glucose production and a fall in circulating glucose that is normalized by glucagon replacement (53). Clamping arterial glucose levels in the presence of glucagon suppression in the dog has permitted the role of this hormone to be assessed without the confounding effects of the excess counterregulation that results if glucose is allowed to fall (133). Under these conditions, glucagon is necessary for over 60% of the total glucose production during exercise. This is similar to the percent observed at rest in dogs (15) and humans (75). However, because hepatic glucose production is much greater during exercise than rest, the absolute role of glucagon is more. Subsequent studies assessed the importance of the exercise-induced increase in glucagon in the exercising dog model using arteriovenous differences and isotopic techniques to distinguish between effects on hepatic glycogenolysis and gluconeogenesis. The role of the exercise-induced increase in glucagon was determined selectively by suppressing endogenous pancreatic hormone release, using SRIF with glucagon replaced at either basal or exercise-simulated rates (137). Insulin was replaced intraportally to simulate its fall during exercise. Circulating glucose levels were clamped to prevent the effects of hypoglycemic counterregulation. These studies showed that the exercise–induced increase in glucagon controls ~60% of the exercise–induced increase in glucose production. It was further determined that the rise in glucagon is necessary for the full increment in both hepatic glycogenolysis and gluconeogenesis. The stimulatory effect of glucagon on gluconeogenesis results from a greater gluconeogenic precursor extraction by the liver and increased channeling of precursor to glucose within the liver.

The importance of the exercise-induced fall in insulin was elucidated by infusing insulin intraportally in the dog at a rate that prevented an insulin decrease during exercise with arterial glucose clamped (132). In the absence of the fall in insulin, the exercise-induced increase in glucagon was attenuated and the increases in hepatic glycogenolysis and gluconeogenesis were impaired. The role of the fall in insulin was isolated by restoration of exercise-induced glucagon levels with an intraportal infusion. It was calculated from the results of this study that the fall in insulin controls 55% of the increase in glucose production and it does so by stimulation of hepatic glycogenolysis. It was subsequently shown that SRIF-induced suppression of biologically active glucagon eliminates the stimulatory effect of the exercise-induced fall in insulin on glucose production (146), which suggests that the fall stimulates glucose production during exercise by potentiating glucagon action.

Despite the compelling data obtained by experiments in the dog, the im-

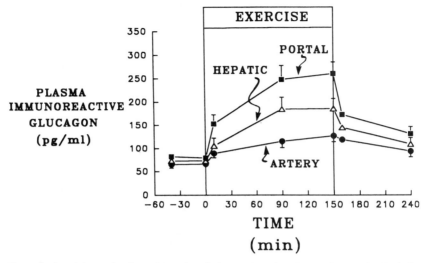

EXERCISE

PLASMA
IMMUNOREACTIVE
GLUCAGON
(pg/ml)

PORTAL
HEPATIC
ARTERY

TIME
(min)

Figure 4   Arterial, portal vein, and hepatic vein immunoreactive plasma glucagon levels during rest, exercise, and recovery. Data are mean±SE; n = 5 (from Reference 130).

portance of changes in glucagon and insulin during moderate exercise in humans has been questioned. This skepticism has been based primarily on two observations. First, an increase in arterial or peripheral vein plasma glucagon is frequently undetectable during exercise in humans. Second, insulin-infused insulin-dependent diabetics, in whom insulin levels are constant during rest and exercise, are often able to maintain blood glucose constant thus suggesting that the fall of insulin level is unnecessary (114, 147). With regard to the first observation, one should note that glucagon levels in the peripheral circulation do not necessarily reflect levels in the portal vein particularly out of steady state (94, 109). A study in the dog showed a tenfold increase in the arterial to portal vein glucagon gradient in response to exercise (Figure 4) (130). The second observation arises from the fact that insulin is delivered in a peripheral vein to these individuals and not via its physiologic entry site, the portal vein. Alternatively, there may be some other inherent difference in diabetic subjects (e.g. hepatic insulin resistance). Nevertheless, more recent studies support work in the dog showing that changes in glucagon and insulin are important for glucose homeostasis during exercise in humans. When glucagon and insulin levels are fixed at basal by infusing SRIF to suppress their endogenous release, and then replacing these hormones in a peripheral vein to recreate basal arterial levels, the increase in glucose production is attenuated and plasma glucose falls by ~25 to 50 mg/dl within 60 min of moderate exercise despite a large compensatory increase in the catecholamines (44, 63, 143). Selective deletion of either the exercise-induced fall in insulin or rise in glucagon using SRIF and pancreatic hormone replacement has been shown to lead to a 30 mg/dl fall in plasma glucose within 60 min (44).

Most of the literature indicates that epinephrine is unimportant for the increase in hepatic glucose production, at least during moderate exercise of < 120 min duration (127). Although adrenodemedullation in the rat has been shown to reduce hepatic glycogenolysis (98) and total glucose production (110) during exercise in some experiments, most studies in this model show that the absence of epinephrine has no effect on the liver (5, 14, 36, 77, 141, 142). Studies conducted in humans, adrenalectomized for treatment of Cushing's disease or bilateral pheochromocytoma, support findings in the rat. These patients have a normal increase in glucose production during 60 min of moderate exercise (47). Similarly, hepatic glucose production is equivalent in adrenalectomized dogs for the first 120 min of exercise regardless of whether they are receiving basal or exercise-simulated epinephrine replacement (85). The rise in epinephrine, however, controls a significant portion of the increase in glucose output after 120 min of exercise. This late stimulatory effect of epinephrine occurs even though glucagon and insulin responses are similar in the presence and absence of the increase in this hormone. Because epinephrine stimulates glucose production during prolonged exercise when gluconeogenesis is high and coincides with a diminished arterial lactate response, one can speculate that the effect of epinephrine is to facilitate gluconeogenic precursor mobilization from peripheral sites. This hypothesis is supported by the importance of epinephrine for glucoregulation in fasted rats highly reliant on gluconeogenesis (141).

Sympathetic innervation of the liver has been proposed to play an important function in the stimulation of hepatic glucose production during exercise based on two premises. First, increases in phosphorylase a activity (42, 106) and hepatic glycogenolysis (33, 42, 71) occur with direct hepatic nerve stimulation. Second, the exercise-induced increase in glucose production is more rapid than changes in arterial glucagon, insulin, and epinephrine levels (32) [albeit portal vein glucagon may increase more rapidly (130)]. Despite the circumstantial evidence that implicates the sympathetic nerves, no role during exercise has been demonstrated. Combined α- and β-adrenergic blockade does not attenuate glucose production in exercising humans (46, 78, 108), which implies that sympathetic drive is unimportant to this process. Another study in humans showed that blocking sympathetic nerve activity to the liver and adrenal medulla with local anesthesia of the celiac ganglion, while controlling the pancreatic hormone responses (SRIF with insulin and glucagon replacement), did not impair the increase in glucose production during exercise (63). Further supporting the lack of a role for hepatic innervation is the demonstration that liver-transplanted human subjects have a normal increase in glucose production with exercise (64). Animal studies that fail to show an important role for hepatic innervation during exercise are consistent with studies in humans. A general sympathectomy with 6-OH dopamine has no effect on hepatic glycogen breakdown in exercising rats (99, 105), and surgical hepatic denervation has no effect on the increment in glucose production in rats (110) or dogs (138).

The role of glucocorticoids is considered to be small within a single bout of exercise because the effects of this hormone generally take hours to be manifested. Nevertheless, evidence suggests that glucocorticoids play a role in the increase in intrahepatic gluconeogenic efficiency during prolonged exercise. Transgenic mice carrying a gene consisting of the PEPCK promotor linked to a reporter gene for bovine growth hormone (bGH) exhibit nearly a fivefold increase in hepatic bGH mRNA in response to exercise (29). However, transgenic mice with a deletion in the PEPCK gene glucocorticoid regulatory element show no change. This observation is supported by the finding that the exercise-induced increase in PEPCK mRNA is markedly attenuated in adrenalectomized mice and dexamethasone corrects the impairment (29). An increased gluconeogenic capacity may explain the improved endurance of corticosterone-replaced adrenalectomized rats compared to those that are corticosterone deficient (104).

Most investigations into the regulation of hepatic function during exercise have addressed mechanisms that are operative at moderate intensities (~50% maximum VO_2). Figure 5 summarizes the hormonal regulation of hepatic glucose production during moderate exercise in the dog (85, 132, 137). Glucoregulation during heavy exercise may be much different. The main identifiable difference in glucoregulation during high-intensity exercise (> ~75% maximum VO_2) is that the increase in glucose production no longer matches, but exceeds, the rise in glucose utilization, resulting in an increase in arterial glucose that continues after exercise (12, 59, 80, 122). It has been postulated based on several lines of evidence that the increase in catecholamines, and not changes in glucagon and insulin, are important for the increase in hepatic glycogenolysis during high-intensity exercise. First, during heavy exercise, catecholamines may increase by 10- to 15-fold, while arterial glucagon may increase, remain the same, or even decrease (32). Second, circulating glucose often increases with heavy exercise, and this may prevent the fall or even lead to an increase in insulin levels (32, 80). This effect may be important because insulin suppresses glucagon's stimulatory effect on glucose production but has much less effect on catecholamine action (19, 102). Finally, epinephrine-deficient adrenodemedullated rats appear to have decreased liver glycogen breakdown during high-intensity exercise but generally not during exercise of lesser intensities (77). The glucagon response to high-intensity exercise was attenu-

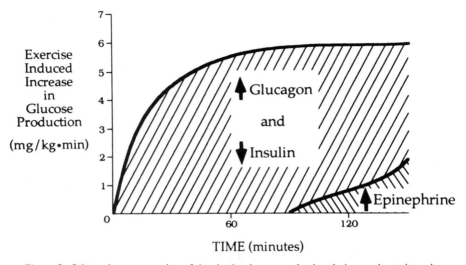

Figure 5 Schematic representation of the rise in glucose production during moderate-intensity exercise and the impact of the fall in insulin and the rise in glucagon and the role of the increase in epinephrine on this response (modified from Reference 127).

ated in these studies and may have led to the impairment in liver glycogen breakdown (77). Although the evidence cited above is consistent with the possibility that catecholamines are important during heavy exercise, studies in humans have been negative. Attenuation of sympathetic nerve activity to the liver and adrenal medulla using anesthesia of the celiac ganglion does not affect glucose production during high-intensity exercise (~75% maximum VO_2) (63). A second study showed that liver transplant patients (presumably free of hepatic innervation) have a normal glucose production response to high-intensity exercise (~82% maximum VO_2) (64). Moreover, β-adrenergic blockade actually results in an exaggerated increase in glucose production during exercise at 100% maximum VO_2 in healthy subjects (107).

LINKING ENDOCRINE, NEURAL, AND HEPATIC RESPONSES TO MUSCLE CONTRACTION

It is apparent that substantial progress has been made in understanding the regulation of glucose fluxes during exercise. The facet of glucoregulatory response probably the least understood is the nature of the initial signal informing the effector systems (endocrine and nervous systems), and ultimately the liver, that the body is engaged in muscular work. The signal that activates glucoregulatory processes during exercise may be feedback or feedforward in nature, and it may be transmitted by neural or vascular channels. Research delineating the pathways that may comprise the signals initiating the glucoregulatory response to exercise is summarized below.

Feedback Mechanisms

Thin group III and IV afferent nerves from the working limb are sensitive to mechanical and chemical stimuli in the muscle and may participate in the regulation of the cardiovascular and pulmonary responses to exercise (81, 94). It does not appear, however, that these afferent nerves play a role in signaling the glucoregulatory response (67). Epidural blockade at the third and fourth lumbar vertebrae was used to abolish afferent neural feedback during cycling in humans. Despite the apparent block of sensory feedback from the working limbs, pancreatic hormone, catecholamine, and growth hormone levels were normal. Only the ACTH and β-endorphin responses, which are probably not of great importance to hepatic glucose production during exercise, were attenuated. Consistent with the endocrine response, glucose production and circulating glucose were unaffected by epidural blockade. The investigators were cautious in their report and expressed the possibility that the epidural blockade of the thin afferents was not complete, information may have been transmitted by thicker myelinated fibers not targeted by the epidural blockade (62), or an alternate mechanism may have compensated in the presence of epidural blockade (67). In a second study, epidural blockade during static exercise diminished the catecholamine response, which suggests that a neural reflex may activate sympathoadrenergic mechanisms (66).

Hepatic glucose production generally increases in parallel with the increase in muscle glucose utilization during exercise, thus it seems likely that a feedback signal somehow transmits information proportional to the added quantity of glucose that is utilized by the working muscle. One possible mechanism by which glucose production may be linked to the increase in glucose utilization during moderate exercise is through changes in blood glucose levels. The hypothesis is that an initial increase in glucose utilization causes a deviation in blood glucose that leads to the increase in glucose production. A corollary to the existence of a blood glucose signal is that glucoregulatory mechanisms are so responsive to changes in blood glucose that they exceed or come close to exceeding the ability to detect them analytically. It has been demonstrated that glucoregulatory mechanisms during exercise are, in fact, highly sensitive to blood glucose or some closely related variable. Studies in humans (56) and dogs (6) demonstrated that the exercise-induced increase in glucose production is completely attenuated by a glucose infusion that mimics the increase in glucose flux. In humans, this attenuation occurs even though no statistical differences in arterial glucose

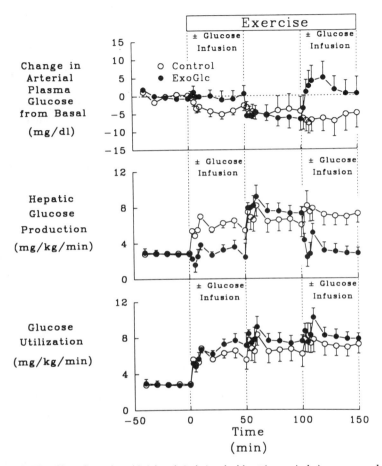

Figure 6   The effect of exercise with (*closed circles*) and without (*open circles*) exogenous glucose on the change in arterial plasma glucose from basal levels (*top*) and hepatic glucose production (*center*). Basal plasma glucose values in control and ExoGlc are 103 ± 3 and 109 ± 3 mg/dl, respectively. Data are mean±SE; n = 5 in each group (modified from Reference 6).

and pancreatic hormone levels are detectable. However, the existence of a transient or subtle blood glucose signal or pancreatic hormone response could not be excluded. In the dog, rapid sampling and measurements of arterial and portal vein blood were employed to maximize the likelihood of detecting changes (Figure 6). In control experiments, plasma glucose fell by ~2 to 6 mg/dl and glucose production rose by threefold. When exogenous glucose was delivered to mimic exercise-induced increases in glucose flux, the fall in glucose and the increment in glucose production were eliminated. Removal of exogenous glucose during subsequent 50 min of exercise restored the small decrease in plasma glucose and the increment in glucose production. Glucagon levels were increased both with and without exogenous glucose. More frequent sampling and measurement of portal vein blood showed, however, that exogenous glucose resulted in transient increases in arterial and portal vein insulin. These studies showed that the pancreatic β-cell and liver are sufficiently sensitive to an imbalance in glucose supply-and-demand to regulate the increase in glucose production during moderate exercise. They also demonstrated that the transient insulin increase and/or the absence of the small exercise-induced fall in plasma glucose completely negate the normally potent effects of the rise in glucagon on glucose production.

The extraordinary sensitivity of the glucoregulatory system to glucose was also shown by studies in dogs exercised when the normal fall in insulin was prevented with an intraportal infusion, with and without glucose levels clamped (131). Preventing the fall in insulin attenuated the rise in glucose production by over 50% when arterial glucose was clamped. Despite the importance of the fall in insulin to glucose production, only a gradual fall in plasma glucose resulted when glucose levels were not clamped. Under these conditions, a plasma glucose error signal (i.e. the difference in plasma glucose levels in glucose clamped and unclamped dogs) of ~5 mg/dl elicited a compensatory increase in glucose production of ~5 mg/kg•min, the result of stimulation of the glycogenolytic and gluconeogenic pathways. Thus a greater fall in plasma glucose was prevented by a highly sensitive counterregulatory response.

The information presented above demonstrates the high sensitivity of coun-terregulatory mechanisms to a glucose supply-and-demand imbalance and supports the hypothesis that small changes in arterial glucose or some related variable trigger the appropriate glucoregulatory responses. Glucose sensors exist at the liver, and there is evidence that this organ may be important in monitoring blood glucose during exercise (69, 72). An important role for portal vein/hepatic sensors was suggested by the attenuation of the exercise-induced reduction in insulin and increase in glucagon following hepatic vagotomy in the rat (72). A role for portal vein/hepatic sensors was also suggested from a study in the dog that showed an intraportal glucose infusion of ~2.3 mg/kg•min resulted in a twofold increase in insulin, an attenuated norepinephrine response (other counterregulatory factors were not measured), and a reduction in blood glycerol during moderate intensity exercise compared to exercise with an equivalent peripheral vein glucose infusion (69). Since portal vein glucose and hepatic glucose delivery were not measured, it could not be determined with certainty whether the effect of intraportal glucose was the result of simply over-replacing glucose or whether it was associated with some physiologic signal. Furthermore, the scope of the measurements made in this study were limited and shed little light on how portal vein glucose levels were affecting glucose fluxes. Nevertheless, these findings contrast with the observations that chronic hepatic denervation of experimental animals (110, 138) and liver transplantation in humans (64) (both procedures presumably remove afferent nerves) do not impair the glucoregulatory response to exercise. It is still possible that other mechanisms adapt and become important following total hepatic denervation or that the removal of sympathetic nerves compensate for the absence of parasympathetic nerves.

Two factors indicate that blood glucose is not the sole signal for the increase in glucose production with exercise. First, a fall in glucose is often not observed with exercise because, in some instances, the changes are small and coupled with measurement limitations. During heavy exercise, blood glucose may, nevertheless, rise (12, 20, 79, 80, 122). It has been proposed that glucoregulation may be different during heavy exercise, and the mechanisms for the increase in glucose production during moderate exercise may not apply to this condition (79, 80). A second factor indicating that blood glucose may not be the primary signal is that a deficit in substrates other than blood glucose [circulating NEFAs (11), muscle glycogen (118)] may also stimulate glucose fluxes during exercise even though changes in blood glucose are undetectable (11, 118). These studies suggest that an important event in triggering the increase in glucose production may be a more general, substrate deficit. This is consistent with the hypothesis that changes in blood glucose are important because they reflect larger deficits in metabolically active tissue (6). Alternatively, it is possible that information regarding the muscle metabolic state is transmitted by a metabolite other than glucose that is released in the blood and subsequently sensed (119).

Feedforward Mechanisms

Zuntz & Geppert proposed, over 100 years ago, that regions in the brain produce a command signal capable of driving not only locomotion, but also respiration (150). This concept was then applied to explain the circulatory response to exercise (57). In more recent years, feedforward mechanisms have been hypothesized to be involved in glucoregulation during exercise (62). Several studies have shown the potential for feedforward mechanisms to exist. One such study utilized the neuromuscular blocker tubocurare to decrease muscle strength and increase the voluntary effort required to perform exercise of a given work intensity (65). Even though VO_2 was equivalent in the presence and absence of neuromuscular blockade, the increased effort required to overcome the decrease in muscle strength with tubocurare resulted in an increase in catecholamine and pituitary hormone responses and a more rapid rise in glucose production. Added support for central control of glucoregulatory processes was provided by a study showing that electrical stimulation of hypothalamic centers associated with locomotion elicits a hormonal response and an increase in glucose production in paralyzed and decorticated cats that is similar to the response observed with exercise (117). Consistent with these observations is the finding that rats have a reduced catecholamine and glucose production response to exercise following administration of the local anesthetic bupivacaine to the ventromedial hypothalamus (120).

It is apparent that there are numerous mechanisms that may activate glucoregulatory processes during exercise. One of the main difficulties in deciphering the contributions of feedback and feedforward regulation is that more than one mechanism may act simultaneously. As a consequence, the effect of an absence of one mechanism, whether it is abolished experimentally or through disease or injury, may be difficult to identify because of compensation from an alternate pathway.

Neural Control of the Endocrine Pancreas

Neural input to the pancreas probably comprises a component of the effector system that regulates the pancreatic hormone response to exercise. Certainly the known effects of pancreatic nerve stimulation (increase in glucagon release and decrease in insulin release) are consistent with neural mediation (103). One study showed that partial denervation of the canine pancreas (the extent of denervation was not determined) does not affect the insulin response to exercise but blunts the glucagon reponse, which suggests that the α-cell, but not the β-cell, response to exercise is under neural control (35). It is possible that complete pancreatic denervation may have disrupted the insulin response as well. Insulin levels in long-term islet cell autografted dogs, presumably lacking neural input, were actually increased by exercise compared to controls, despite a greater fall in plasma glucose (95). Other studies have shown that α- and β-adrenergic blockade can prevent the insulin (55) and glucagon (76) responses to exercise, respectively. Adrenalectomy does not affect the pancreatic hormone response in human subjects; thus it appears that the effects of adrenergic blockers are a result of preventing the actions of sympathetic nerves (47, 55). In short, the known effects of pancreatic nerve stimulation, supported by the literature addressing the role of these nerves during exercise, suggest that sympathetic nerves play a role in mediating the exercise response.

SUMMARY

The increase in glucose utilization by the working muscle would lead to hypoglycemia were it not accompanied by an increase in hepatic glucose production. Although the increase in glucose uptake is normally driven by mechanisms that are primarily independent of the action of insulin and other hormones, the response of the liver appears to be closely controlled by the endocrine system. Although considerable progress has been made in understanding the bases for the increases in glucose utilization and production, the means by which these two processes are coordinated to form the exercise response are unclear (e.g. feedback or central feedforward control). Work intensity affects the mechanisms by which glucose fluxes are regulated. For example, during moderate-intensity exercise, the glucoregulatory response resembles glucoregulation in the basal state in that under both conditions, glucose release from the liver is controlled by glucagon and insulin, and blood glucose levels are tightly controlled. The response to high-intensity exercise, on the other hand, takes on characteristics of the stress response, as described by Cannon (13). That is, the catecholamine response increases disproportionately for a given increment in work intensity, and glucose levels are no longer closely regulated, but increase. The specific factors that turn exercise into stress at higher work intensities are not well defined.

Determining factors involved in the regulation of glucose fluxes are limited in some respects because the body is more sensitive than are experimental detection methods to various stimuli (glucose, hormones, neurotransmitter release). More complete delineation of mechanisms involved in the regulation of glucose fluxes will require the development of improved techniques and unique experimental models. The trend in the physiological sciences is for more study at the level of the gene. Technical limitations will be overcome or circumvented as knowledge of gene regulation and the development of genetically engineered animal models provide new avenues with which to address basic questions regarding the control of glucose fluxes during exercise.

Literature Cited

1. Achike FI, Ballard HJ. 1993. Influence of stimulation parameters on the release of adenosine, lactate, and CO_2 from contracting dog gracilis muscle. *J. Physiol.* 463:107–21

2. Ader M, Bergman RN. 1990. Peripheral effects of insulin dominate suppression of fasting hyperglycemia. *Am. J. Physiol.* 258:E1029–32

3. Ahlborg G, Felig P. 1982. Lactate and glucose exchange across the forearm, legs, and splanchnic bed during and after prolonged leg exercise. *J. Clin. Invest.* 69:45–54

4. Ahlborg G, Felig P, Hagenfeldt L, Hendler R, Wahren J. 1974. Substrate turnover during prolonged exercise in man. *J. Clin. Invest.* 53:1080–90

5. Arnall DA, Marker JC, Conlee RK, Winder WW. 1986. Effect of infusing epinephrine on liver and muscle glycogenolysis during exercise. *Am. J. Physiol.* 250:E641–49

6. Berger CM, Sharis PJ, Bracy DP, Lacy DB, Wasserman DH. 1994. Sensitivity of the exercise-induced increments in hepatic glycogenolysis and gluconeogenesis to glucose supply and demand. Implications for the mechanism of coupling of glucose production to utilization. *Am. J. Physiol.* 267:E411–21

7. Bergstrom J, Hermansen L, Hultman E,

Saltin B. 1967. Diet, muscle glycogen and physical performance. *Acta Physiol. Scand.* 71:140–50

8. Bjorkman O, Miles P, Wasserman DH, Lickley L, Vranic M. 1988. Muscle glucose uptake during exercise in total insulin deficiency: no effect of beta-adrenergic blockade. *J. Clin. Invest.* 81: 1759–67
9. Bogardus C, Thuillez P, Ravussin E, Vasquez B, Narimiga M, Azhar S. 1983. Effect of muscle glycogen depletion on in vivo insulin action in man. *J. Clin. Invest.* 72:1605–10
10. Bonen A, Hood DA, Tan MH, Sopper MM, Begin-Heik N. 1985. Effects of exercise on insulin binding to human muscle. *Am. J. Physiol.* 248: E403–8
11. Bracy DP, Zinker BA, Lacy DB, Jacobs J, Wasserman DH. 1994. Regulation of muscle carbohydrate metabolism during exercise by free fatty acid availability. *FASEB J.* 8:A699
12. Calles J, Cunningham JJ, Nelson L, Brown N, Nadel E, et al. 1983. Glucose turnover during recovery from intensive exercise. *Diabetes* 32:734–38
13. Cannon WB. 1939. *The Wisdom of the Body.* New York: Norton
14. Carlson KI, Marker JC, Arnall DA, Terry ML, Yang HT, et al. 1985. Epinephrine is unessential for stimulation of liver glycogenolysis during exercise. *J. Appl. Physiol.* 58:544–48
15. Cherrington AD, Liljenquist JE, Shulman GI, Williams PE, Lacy WW. 1979. Importance of hypoglycemia-induced glucose production during isolated glucagon deficiency. *Am. J. Physiol.* 236:E263–71
16. Cooper DM, Barstow TJ, Bergner A, Lee WP. 1989. Blood glucose turnover during high- and low-intensity exercise. *Am. J. Physiol.* 257:E405–12
17. Cooper DM, Wasserman DH, Vranic M, Wasserman K. 1986. Glucose turnover in response to exercise during high- and low-FiO$_2$ breathing in humans. *Am. J. Physiol.* 14:E209–14
18. Defronzo RA, Ferrannini E, Sato Y, Felig P, Wahren J. 1981. Synergistic interaction between exercise and insulin on peripheral glucose uptake. *J. Clin. Invest.* 68:1468–74
19. Deibert DC, Defronzo RA. 1980. Epinephrine-induced insulin resistance in man. *J. Clin. Invest.* 65:717–21
20. Dill DB, Edwards HT, Mead S. 1935. Blood sugar regulation in exercise. *Am. J. Physiol.* 111:21–30
21. Dill DB, Edwards HT, Talbott JH. 1932. Studies in muscular activity. VII. Factors limiting the capacity to work. *J. Physiol.* 77:49–62

22. Dohm GL, Kasperek GJ, Barakat HA. 1985. Time course of changes in gluconeogenic enzyme activities during exercise and recovery. *Am. J. Physiol.* 249: E6–11
23. Dohm GL, Newsholme EA. 1983. Metabolic control of hepatic gluconeogenesis during exercise. *Biochem. J.* 212: 633–39
24. Douen AG, Ramlal T, Cartee GD, Klip A. 1989. Exercise-induced increase in glucose transporters of plasma membranes of rat skeletal muscle. *Endocrinology* 124:449–54
25. Douen AG, Ramlal T, Rastogi S, Bilan PJ, Cartee G, et al. 1990. Exercise induces recruitment of the insulin responsive glucose transporter. Evidence for distinct intracellular insulin– and exercise–recruitable transporter pools in skeletal muscle. *J. Biol. Chem.* 265: 13427–30
26. Edelman SV, Laakso M, Wallace P, Brechtel G, Olefsky JM, Baron AD. 1990. Kinetics of insulin-mediated and non-insulin-mediated glucose uptake in humans. *Diabetes* 39:955–64
27. Edwards HT, Margaria R, Dill DB. 1934. Metabolic rate, blood sugar and the utilization of carbohydrate. *Am. J. Physiol.* 108:203–9
28. Felig P, Wahren J. 1971. Amino acid metabolism in exercising man. *J. Clin. Invest.* 50:2703–11
29. Friedman JE. 1994. Role of glucocorticoids in activation of hepatic PEPCK gene transcription during exercise. *Am. J. Physiol.* 266:E560–66
30. Furler SM, Jenkins AB, Storlien LH, Kraegen EW. 1991. In vivo location of the rate-limiting step of hexose uptake in muscle and brain tissue of rats. *Am. J. Physiol.* 261:E337–47
31. Fushiki T, Wells JA, Tapscott EB, Dohm GL. 1989. Changes in glucose transporters in muscle in response to exercise. *Am. J. Physiol.* 256:E580–87
32. Galbo H. 1983. *Hormonal Adaptations to Exercise.* New York: Thieme-Stratton
33. Garceau D, Yamaguchi N, Goyer R, Guitard F. 1984. Correlation between endogenous noradrenaline and glucose released from the liver upon hepatic sympathetic nerve stimulation in anesthetized dogs. *Can. J. Physiol. Pharmacol.* 62:1086–91
34. Garetto LP, Richter EA, Goodman MN, Ruderman NB. 1984. Enhanced muscle glucose metabolism after exercise in the rat: the two phases. *Am. J. Physiol.* 246:E471–75

35. Girardier L, Seydoux J, Berger M, Veicsteinas A. 1978. Selective pancreatic nerve section. An investigation of neural control of glucagon release in the conscious unrestrained dog. *J. Physiol.* 74:731–35

36. Gollnick PD, Soule RG, Taylor AW, Williams C, Ianuzzo CD. 1970. Exercise-induced glycogenolysis and lipolysis in the rat: hormonal influences. *Am. J. Physiol.* 219:729–33

37. Goodyear LJ, Hirshman MF, Horton ES. 1991. Exercise-induced translocation of skeletal muscle glucose transporters. *Am. J. Physiol.* 261:E795–99

38. Goodyear LJ, Hirshman MF, King PA, Thompson CM, Horton ED, Horton ES. 1990. Skeletal muscle plasma membrane glucose transport and glucose transporters after exercise. *J. Appl. Physiol.* 68: 193–98

39. Goodyear LJ, Hirshman MF, Smith RJ, Horton ES. 1991. Glucose transporter number, activity, and isoform content in plasma membranes of red and white skeletal muscle. *Am. J. Physiol.* 261: E556–61

40. Goodyear LJ, King PA, Hirshman MF, Thompson CM, Horton ES. 1990. Contractile activity increases plasma membrane glucose transporters in absence of insulin. *Am. J. Physiol.* 258:E667–72

41. Gregg SG, Kern M, Brooks GA. 1989. Acute anemia results in an increased glucose dependence during sustained exercise. *J. Appl. Physiol.* 66:1874–80

42. Hartmann H, Beckh K, Jungermann K. 1982. Direct control of glycogen metabolism in the perfused rat liver by the sympathetic innervation. *Eur. J. Biochem.* 123:521–26

43. Hems DA, Whitton PD. 1980. Control of hepatic glycogenolysis. *Physiol. Rev.* 60:1–50

44. Hirsh IB, Marker JC, Smith LJ, Spina R, Parvin CA, et al. 1991. Insulin and glucagon in the prevention of hypoglycemia during exercise in humans. *Am. J. Physiol.* 260:E695–704

45. Hirshman MF, Goodyear LJ, Wardzala LJ, Horton ED, Horton ES. 1988. Acute exercise increases the number of plasma membrane glucose transporters in rat skeletal muscle. *FEBS Lett.* 238:235–39

46. Hoelzer DR, Dalsky GP, Clutter WE, Shah SD, Holloszy JO, Cryer PE. 1986. Glucoregulation during exercise: hypoglycemia is prevented by redundant glucoregulatory systems, sympathochromaffin activation, and changes in islet hormone secretion. *J. Clin. Invest.* 77:212–21

47. Hoelzer DR, Dalsky GP, Schwartz NS, Clutter WE, Shah SD, et al. 1986. Epinephrine is not critical to prevention of hypoglycemia during exercise in humans. *Am. J. Physiol.* 251:E104–10

48. Hofmann S, Pette D. 1994. Low-frequency stimulation of rat fast-twitch muscle enhances the expression of hexokinase 11 and both the translocation and expression of glucose transporter 4 (GLUT4). *Eur. J. Biochem.* 219:307–15

49. Holloszy JO, Constable SH, Young DA. 1986. Activation of glucose transport in muscle by exercise. *Diabetes Metab. Rev.* 1:409–23

50. Huston RL, Weiser PC, Dohm GL, Askew EW, Boyd JB. 1975. Effect of training, exercise, and diet on muscle glycogenolysis and liver gluconeogenesis. *Life Sci.* 17:369–76

51. Idstrom JP, Subramanian VH, Chance B, Schersten T, Bylund-Fellinius AC. 1985. Oxygen dependence of energy metabolism in contracting and recovering rat skeletal muscle. *Am. J. Physiol.* 248:H40–48

52. Issekutz B, Paul P, Miller H. 1967. Metabolism in normal and pancreatectomized dogs during steady-state exercise. *Am. J. Physiol.* 213:857–62

53. Issekutz B, Vranic M. 1980. Significance of glucagon in the control of glucose production during exercise. *Am. J. Physiol.* 238:E13–2O

54. James DE, Burleigh KM, Storlien LH, Bennett P, Kraegen EW. 1986. Heterogeneity of insulin action in muscle: influence of blood flow. *Am. J. Physiol.* 251:E422–30

55. Jarhult J, Holst JJ. 1979. The role of the adrenergic innervation to the pancreatic islets in the control of insulin release during exercise in man. *Pflügers Arch.* 383:41–45

56. Jenkins AB, Chisholm DJ, Ho KY, Kraegen EW. 1985. Exercise induced hepatic glucose output is precisely sensitive to the rate of systemic glucose supply. *Metabolism* 34:431–34

57. Johansson JE. 1893. Uber die Einwirkung der Muskeltatigkeit auf die Atmung und die Herztatigkeit. *Skand. Arch. Physiol.* 5:20–66

58. John-Adler HB, McAllister RM, Terjung RL. 1986. Reduced running endurance in gluconeogenesis-inhibited rats. *Am. J. Physiol.* 251:R137–42

59. Katz A, Broberg S, Sahlin K, Wahren J. 1986. Leg glucose uptake during maximal dynamic exercise in humans. *Am. J. Physiol.* 251:E65–70

60. Katz A, Sahlin K, Broberg S. 1991. Regulation of glucose utilization in human skeletal muscle during moderate

dynamic exercise. *Am. J. Physiol.* 260: E411–15

61. King PA, Hirshman MF, Horton ED, Horton ES. 1989. Glucose transport in skeletal muscle membrane vesicles from control and exercised rats. *Am. J. Physiol.* 257:C1128–34

62. Kjaer M. 1992. Regulation of hormonal and metabolic responses during exercise in humans. *Exerc. Sports Sci. Rev.* 20: 161–84

63. Kjaer M, Engered K, Fernandez A, Secher N, Galbo H. 1993. Regulation of hepatic glucose production during exercise in humans: role of sympathoadrenergic activity. *Am. J. Physiol.* 265:E275–83

64. Kjaer M, Engered K, Galbo H, Sonne B, Rasmussen K, Keiding S. 1991. Hepatic glucose production during exercise in liver-transplanted subjects. *Scand. J. Gastroenterol.* 26(Suppl.):46A (Abstr.)

65. Kjaer M, Secher NH, Bach FW, Galbo H. 1987. Role of motor center activity for hormonal changes and substrate mobilization in humans. *Am. J. Physiol.* 253:R687–95

66. Kjaer M, Secher NH, Bach FW, Galbo H, Reeves DR, Mitchell JH. 1991. Hormonal, metabolic, and cardiovascular responses to static exercise in man: influence of epidural anesthesia. *Am. J. Physiol.* 261:E214–20

67. Kjaer M, Secher NH, Bach FW, Sheikh S, Galbo H. 1989. Hormonal and metabolic responses to exercise in humans: effect of sensory nervous blockade. *Am. J. Physiol.* 257:E95–101

68. Koivisto VA, Soman VR, Conrad P, Hendler R, Nadel E, Felig P. 1979. Insulin binding to monocytes in trained athletes: changes in the resting state and after exercise. *J. Clin. Invest.* 64:1011–15

69. Kozlowski S, Nazar K, Brzezinska Z, Stephens D, Kaciuba-Uscitko H, Kobryn A. 1983. Mechanism of sympathetic activation during prolonged physical exercise in dogs. *Pflügers Arch.* 399:63–67

70. Kubo K, Foley JE. 1966. Rate-limiting steps for insulin-mediated glucose uptake into perfused rat hindlimb. *Am. J. Physiol.* 250:E100–2

71. Lautt WW, Wong C. 1978. Hepatic glucose balance in response to direct stimulation of sympathetic nerves in the intact liver of cats. *Can. J. Physiol. Pharmacol.* 56:1022–28

72. Lavoie JM, Cardin S, Doiron B. 1989. Influence of hepatic vagus nerve on pancreatic hormone secretion. *Am. J. Physiol.* 257:E855–59

73. Lawrence RH. 1926. The effects of exercise on insulin action in diabetes. *Br. Med. J.* 1:648–52

74. Levine SA, Burgess G, Derick CL. 1924. Some changes in the chemical constituents of the blood following a marathon race. With special reference to the development of hypoglycemia. *J. Am. Med. Assoc.* 82:1778

75. Liljenquist JE, Mueller GL, Cherrington AD, Keller U, Chiasson JL, et al. 1977. Evidence for an important role of glucagon in the regulation of hepatic glucose production in normal man. *J. Clin. Invest.* 59:369–74

76. Luyckx AS, Lefebvre PJ. 1974. Mechanisms involved in the exercise-induced increase in glucagon secretion in rats. *Diabetes* 23:81–93

77. Marker JC, Arnall DA, Conlee RK, Winder WW. 1986. Effect of adrenodemedullation on metabolic responses to high-intensity exercise. *Am. J. Physiol.* 251:R552–59

78. Marker JC, Hirsh IB, Smith LJ, Parvin CA, Holloszy JO, Cryer PE. 1991. Catecholamines in prevention of hypoglycemia during exercise in humans. *Am. J. Physiol.* 260:E705–12

79. Marliss EB, Purdon C, Halter JB, Sigal RJ, Vranic M. 1992. Glucoregulation during and after intense exercise in control and diabetic subjects. In *Diabetes Mellitus and Exercise*, ed. JT Devlin, M Vranic, ES Horton, pp. 173–90. London: Smith-Gordon

80. Marliss EB, Simantirakis E, Purdon C, Gougeon R, Field CJ, et al. 1991. Glucoregulatory and hormonal responses to repeated bouts of intense exercise in normal male subjects. *J. Appl. Physiol.* 71:924–33

81. McClosky DI, Mitchell JH. 1972. Reflex cardiovascular and respiratory responses originating in exercising muscle. *J. Physiol.* 224:173–86

82. Michel G, Vocke T, Fiehn W, Weicker H, Schwarz W, Bieger WP. 1964. Bidirectional alteration of insulin receptor affinity by direct forms of physical activity. *Am. J. Physiol.* 246:E153–59

83. Mikines KJ, Sonne B, Farrell PA, Tronier B, Galbo H. 1988. Effect of physical exercise on sensitivity and responsiveness to insulin in man. *Am. J. Physiol.* 254:E248–59

84. Mitchell JH, Reardon WC, McClosky DI. 1977. Reflex effects on circulation and respiration from contracting skeletal muscle. *Am. J. Physiol.* 233:H374–78

85. Moates JM, Lacy DB, Cherrington AD, Goldstein RE, Wasserman DH. 1988. The metabolic role of the exercise-in-

duced increment in epinephrine. *Am. J. Physiol.* 255:E428–36

86. Nesher R, Karl I, Kipnis D. 1985. Dissociation of effects of insulin and contraction on glucose transport in rat epitrochlearis muscle. *Am. J. Physiol.* 249:C226–32

87. Neufer PD, Dohm GL. 1993. Exercise induces a transient increase in transcription of the GLUT-4 gene in skeletal muscle. *Am. J. Physiol.* 265:C1597–603

88. O'Doherty RM, Bracy DP, Granner DK, Wasserman DH. 1994. Hexokinase II gene transcription is increased by acute exercise in rat skeletal muscle. *Med. Sci. Sports Exerc.* 26(Suppl.):S90

89. O'Doherty RM, Bracy DP, Osawa H, Wasserman DH, Granner DK. 1994. Rat skeletal muscle hexokinase II mRNA and activity are increased by a single bout of acute exercise. *Am. J. Physiol.* 266:E171–78

90. Ploug T, Galbo H, Ohkuwa T, Tranum-Jensen J, Vinten J. 1992. Kinetics of glucose transport in rat skeletal muscle membrane vesicles: effects of insulin and contractions. *Am. J. Physiol.* 262:E700–11

91. Ploug T, Galbo H, Vinten J, Jorgensen M, Richter EA. 1987. Kinetics of glucose transport in rat muscle: effect of insulin and contractions. *Am. J. Physiol.* 259:E12–20

92. Ploug T, Stallknecht B, Pedersen O, Kahn B, Ohkuwa T, et al. 1990. Effect of endurance training on glucose transport capacity and glucose transporter expression in rat skeletal muscle. *Am. J. Physiol.* 259:E778–86

93. Ploug T, Wojtaszewski J, Kristiansen S, Hespel P, Galbo H, Richter EA. 1993. Glucose transport and transporters in muscle giant vesicles: differential effects of insulin and contractions. *Am. J. Physiol.* 264:E270–78

94. Polonsky K, Jaspan J, Pugh W, Dhorajiwala J, Abraham M, et al. 1981. Insulin and glucagon breakthrough of somatostatin suppression. Importance of portal vein hormone measurements. *Diabetes* 30:664–69

95. Portis AJ, Warnock GL, Finegood DT, Belcastro AN, Rajotte RV. 1990, Glucoregulatory response to moderate exercise in long–term islet cell autografted dogs. *Can. J. Physiol. Pharmacol.* 68:1308–12

96. Randle PJ, Smith GH. 1958. Regulation of glucose uptake by muscle. 1. The effects of insulin, anaerobiosis, and cell poisons on the uptake of glucose and release of potassium by isolated rat diaphragm. *Biochem. J.* 70:490–500

97. Ren JM, Adkins-Marshall B, Gulve EA, Gao J, Johnson DW, et al. 1993. Evidence from transgenic mice that glucose transport is rate limiting for glycogen deposition and glycolysis in skeletal muscle. *J. Biol. Chem.* 268:16113–15

98. Richter EA, Galbo H, Christensen NJ. 1981. Control of exercise-induced muscular glycogenolysis by adrenal medullary hormones in rats. *J. Appl. Physiol.* 50:21–26

99. Richter EA, Galbo H, Holst JJ, Sonne B. 1981. Significance of glucagon for insulin secretion and hepatic glycogenolysis during exercise in rats. *Horm. Metab. Res.* 13:323–26

100. Richter EA, Garetto LP, Goodman MN, Ruderman NB. 1982. Muscle glucose metabolism following exercise in the rat. Increased sensitivity to insulin. *J. Clin. Invest.* 69:785–93

101. Richter EA, Garetto LP, Goodman MN, Ruderman NB. 1984. Enhanced muscle glucose metabolism after exercise: modulation by local factors. *Am. J. Physiol.* 246:E476–82

102. Sacca L, Eigler N, Cryer PE, Sherwin RS. 1979. Insulin antagonistic effects of epinephrine and glucagon in the dog. *Am. J. Physiol.* 237:E487–92

103. Samols E, Weir GC. 1979. Adrenergic modulation of pancreatic A, B, and D cells. *J. Clin. Invest.* 63:230–38

104. Sellers TL, Jaussi AW, Yang HT, Heninger RW, Winder WW. 1988. Effect of the exercise-induced increase in glucocorticoids on endurance in the rat. *J. Appl. Physiol.* 65:173–78

105. Sembrowich WL, Ianuzzo CD, Saubert CW, Shepherd RE, Gollnick PD. 1974. Substrate mobilization during prolonged exercise in 6-hydroxydopamine treated rats. *Pflügers Arch.* 349:57–62

106. Shimazu T, Usami M. 1982. Further studies on the mechanism of phosphorylase activation in rabbit liver in response to splanchnic nerve stimulation. *J. Physiol.* 329:231–42

107. Sigal RJ, Purdon C, Bilinski D, Vranic M, Halter JB, Marliss EB. 1994. Glucoregulation during and after intense exercise: effects of beta-blockade. *J. Clin. Endocrinol. Metab.* 78:359–66

108. Simonson DC, Koivisto VA, Sherwin RS, Ferrannini E, Hendler R, Defronzo RA. 1984. Adrenergic blockade alters glucose kinetics during exercise in insulin-dependent diabetics. *J. Clin. Invest.* 73:1648–58

109. Sirek A, Vranic M, Sirek OV, Vigas M, Policova Z. 1979. Effect of growth hor-

mone on acute glucagon and insulin release. *Am. J. Physiol.* 237:E107–12

110. Sonne B, Mikines KJ, Richter EA, Christensen NJ, Galbo H. 1985. Role of liver nerves and adrenal medulla in glucose turnover of running rats. *J. Appl. Physiol.* 59:1650–56

111. Sternlicht E, Barnard RJ, Grimditch GK. 1989. Exercise and insulin stimulate skeletal muscle glucose transport by different mechanisms. *Am. J. Physiol.* 256:E227–30

112. Treadway JL, James DE, Burcel E, Ruderman NB. 1989. Effect of exercise on insulin receptor binding and kinase activity in skeletal muscle. *Am. J. Physiol.* 256:E138–44

113. Turcotte LP, Rovner AS, Roark RR, Brooks GA. 1990. Glucose kinetics in gluconeogenesis-inhibited rats during rest and exercise. *Am. J. Physiol.* 258:E203–11

114. Tuttle KR, Marker JC, Dalsky GP, Schwartz NS, Shah SD, et al. 1988. Glucagon, not insulin, may play a secondary role in defense against hypoglycemia. *Am. J. Physiol.* 254:E713–19

115. Vanhouten DR, Davis JM, Meyers DM, Durstine JL. 1992. Altered cellular distribution of hexokinase in skeletal muscle after exercise. *Int. J. Sports Med.* 13:436–38

116. Vergauwen L, Hespel P, Richter EA. 1994. Adenosine receptors mediate synergistic stimulation of glucose uptake and transport by insulin and by contractions in rat skeletal muscle. *J. Clin. Invest.* 93:974–81

117. Vissing J, Iwamoto GA, Rybicki KJ, Galbo H, Mitchell JH. 1989. Mobilization of glucoregulatory hormones and glucose by hypothalamic locomotor centers. *Am. J. Physiol.* 257:E722–28

118. Vissing J, Lewis SF, Galbo H, Haller RG. 1992. Effect of deficient muscular glycogenolysis on extramuscular fuel metabolism in exercise. *J. Appl. Physiol.* 72:1773–79

119. Vissing J, Sonne B, Galbo H. 1988. Role of metabolic feedback regulation in glucose production of running rats. *Am. J. Physiol.* 255:R400–6

120. Vissing J, Wallace JL, Scheurink AJW, Galbo H, Steffens AB. 1989. Ventromedial hypothalamic regulation of hormonal and metabolic responses to exercise. *Am. J. Physiol.* 256:R1019–26

121. Vranic M, Kawamori R, Pek S, Kovacevic N, Wrenshall G. 1976. The essentiality of insulin and the role of glucagon in regulating glucose utilization and production during strenuous exercise in dogs. *J. Clin. Invest.* 57:245–55

122. Wahren J, Felig P, Ahlborg G, Jorfeldt L. 1971. Glucose metabolism during leg exercise in man. *J. Clin. Invest.* 50:2715–25

123. Wahren J, Hagenfeldt L, Felig P. 1975. Splanchnic and leg exchange of glucose, amino acids, and free fatty acids during exercise in diabetes mellitus. *J. Clin. Invest.* 55:1303–14

124. Walker PM, Idstrom JP, Schersten T, Bylund-Fellenius AC. 1982. Glucose uptake in relation to metabolic state in perfused rat hindlimb at rest and during exercise. *Eur. J. Appl. Physiol.* 48:163–76

125. Wallberg-Henriksson H, Constable SH, Young DA, Holloszy JO. 1988. Glucose transport into rat skeletal muscle: interaction between exercise and insulin. *J. Appl. Physiol.* 65:909–13

126. Wasserman DH, Bupp JL, Johnson JL, Bracy D, Lacy DB. 1992. Glucoregulation during rest and exercise in depancreatized dogs: role of the acute presence of insulin. *Am. J. Physiol.* 262:E574–82

127. Wasserman DH, Cherrington AD. 1991. Hepatic fuel metabolism during exercise: role and regulation. *Am. J. Physiol.* 260:E811–24

128. Wasserman DH, Geer RJ, Rice DE, Bracy D, Flakoll PJ, et al. 1991. Interaction of exercise and insulin action in man. *Am. J. Physiol.* 260:E37–45

129. Wasserman DH, Geer RJ, Williams PE, Lacy DB, Abumrad NN. 1991. Interaction of gut and liver in nitrogen metabolism during exercise. *Metabolism* 40:307–14

130. Wasserman DH, Lacy DB, Bracy DP. 1993. Relationship between arterial and portal vein immunoreactive glucagon during exercise. *J. Appl. Physiol.* 75:724–29

131. Wasserman DH, Lacy DB, Colburn CA, Bracy DP, Cherrington AD. 1991. Efficiency of compensation for the absence of the fall in insulin during exercise. *Am. J. Physiol.* 261:E587–97

132. Wasserman DH, Lacy DB, Goldstein RE, Williams PE, Cherrington AD. 1989. Exercise-induced fall in insulin and hepatic carbohydrate metabolism during exercise. *Am. J. Physiol.* 256:E500–8

133. Wasserman DH, Lickley HLA, Vranic M. 1984. Interactions between glucagon and other counterregulatory hormones during normoglycemic and hypoglycemic exercise in dogs. *J. Clin. Invest.* 74:1404–13

134. Wasserman DH, Lickley HLA, Vranic M. 1985. Effect of hematocrit reduction on hormonal and metabolic responses

to exercise. *J. Appl. Physiol.* 58:1257–62

135. Wasserman DH, Lickley HLA, Vranic M. 1985. The role of beta-adrenergic mechanisms during exercise in poorly controlled diabetes. *J. Appl. Physiol.* 59:1282–89

136. Wasserman DH, Mohr T, Kelly P, Lacy DB, Bracy D. 1992. The impact of insulin-deficiency on glucose fluxes and muscle glucose metabolism during exercise. *Diabetes* 41:1229–38

137. Wasserman DH, Spalding JS, Lacy DB, Colburn CA, Goldstein RE, Cherrington AD. 1989. Glucagon is a primary controller of the increments in hepatic glycogenolysis and gluconeogenesis during exercise. *Am. J. Physiol.* 257:E108–17

138. Wasserman DH, Williams PE, Lacy DB, Bracy D, Cherrington AD. 1990. Hepatic nerves are not essential to the increase in hepatic glucose production during muscular work. *Am. J. Physiol.* 259:E195–203

139. Wasserman DH, Williams PE, Lacy DB, Green DR, Cherrington AD. 1988. Importance of intrahepatic mechanisms to gluconeogenesis from alanine during prolonged exercise and recovery. *Am. J. Physiol.* 254:E518–25

140. Weber FE, Pette D. 1990. Changes in free and bound forms and total amount of hexokinase isozyme II of rat muscle in response to contractile activity. *Eur. J. Biochem.* 191:85–90

141. Winder WW, Terry ML, Mitchell VM. 1985. Role of plasma epinephrine in fasted exercising rats. *Am. J. Physiol.* 248:R302–7

142. Winder WW, Yang HT, Jaussi AW, Hopkins CR. 1987. Epinephrine, glucose, and lactate infusion in exercising adrenomedullated rats. *J. Appl. Physiol.* 62:1442–47

143. Wolfe RR, Nadel ER, Shaw JHF, Stephenson LA, Wolfe M. 1986. Role of changes in insulin and glucagon in glucose homeostasis in exercise. *J. Clin. Invest.* 77:900–7

144. Young AA, Bogardus C, Stone K, Mott DM. 1988. Insulin response of components of whole-body and muscle carbohydrate metabolism in humans. *Am. J. Physiol.* 254:E231–36

145. Zinker BA, Bracy D, Lacy DB, Jacobs J, Wasserman DH. 1993. Regulation of glucose uptake and metabolism during exercise: an in vivo analysis. *Diabetes* 42:956–65

146. Zinker BA, Mohr T, Kelly P, Namdaran K, Bracy DP, Wasserman DH. 1994. Exercise-induced fall in insulin: mechanism of action at the liver and effect on skeletal muscle glucose metabolism. *Am. J. Physiol.* 266:E683–89

147. Zinman B, Murray FF, Vranic M, Albisser AM, Leibel BS, et al. 1977. Glucoregulation during moderate exercise in insulin-treated diabetics. *J. Clin. Endocrinol. Metab.* 45:641–52

148. Zorzano A, Balon TW, Garetto LP, Goodman MN, Ruderman NB. 1985. Muscle alpha-aminoisobutyric acid transport after exercise: enhanced stimulation by insulin. *Am. J. Physiol.* 248:E546–52

149. Zorzano A, Balon TW, Goodman MN, Ruderman NB. 1986. Additive effects of prior exercise and insulin on glucose and AIB uptake by rat muscle. *Am. J. Physiol.* 251:E21–26

150. Zuntz N, Geppert J. 1886. Uber die Natur der normalen Atemreize und den Ort ihrer Wirkung. *Arch. Ges. Physiol.* 38:337–38

Annu. Rev. Physiol. 1995. 57:219–44

INHIBIN, ACTIVIN AND THE FEMALE REPRODUCTIVE AXIS

Teresa K. Woodruff and Jennie P. Mather

Discovery Research, Genentech, Inc. South San Francisco, California 94080

KEY WORDS: ovary, pituitary, FSH, LH, receptors

INTRODUCTION

Identification of Inhibin

The history of inhibin is intermingled with the emergence of endocrinology as a discipline and the concept that factors produced in regulating organs impact distal target tissues. In 1932, McCullagh assigned the name inhibin to a nonsteroidal activity of testicular origin that regulated the histologic appearance of the pituitary gland (73). The timeline of inhibin achievement was next marked in the late 1960s by the development of the radioimmunoassay (RIA), specifically a RIA for follicle-stimulating hormone (FSH). The RIA provided a tool to measure the effects of testicular and ovarian factors on a distinct pituitary index, hormone secretion. The definition of inhibin activity was subsequently refined to a nonsteroidal activity of gonadal origin that specifically suppresses serum FSH concentration (18).

Attempts to purify the activity were met with frustration and little progress until the development of a pituitary cell bioassay and identification of ovarian follicular fluid as an enriched and easily obtainable source of the material (21). Simultaneous purification and characterization of bovine and porcine inhibin were described in 1985 (14, 24, 34, 133, 151). Inhibins are dimeric, disulfide-linked, glycoproteins consisting of generically labeled α- and β-subunits. Recently, human and rat forms of inhibin A have been purified from follicular fluid, and human inhibin A (rh-inhibin A) has been produced using recombinant DNA techniques (42, 64, 129). Additionally, inhibin subunits have been isolated as free monomers from follicular fluid (102, 104). The sequelae of events immediately following the identification of the inhibin protein were

0066–4278/95/0315–0219$05.00

expected (cloning of the subunits from a variety of sources) and unexpected (member of a conserved and emerging growth and differentiation superfamily). The latter resulted in several paradigm shifts for the inhibin community that are described throughout this review.

Identification of Activin

The first and most profound new finding was introduced in 1986 when proteins capable of stimulating pituitary FSH release were purified as dimers of disulfide-linked β-subunits (133). The molecules were labeled activin. Two closely related forms of the activin molecule were characterized, differing by a few amino acids, and subsequent cloning efforts confirmed that two forms of the β-subunit (β_A and β_B) exist. The combinatorial hetero- and homodimeric assembly of α- and β-subunits results in two forms of inhibin and three forms of activin, all of which occur naturally. The nomenclature for the family members is as follows: inhibin A = α-β_A; inhibin B = α-β_B; activin A = β_A-β_A; activin B = β_B-β_B; and activin AB = β_A-β_B (16).

Inhibin/Activin Subunit Characterization

The cloning of inhibin/activin subunit cDNAs and genes provided additional novel insights. First, the β-subunit is highly conserved between species (mature β_A is 100% conserved between human, cow, rat, and sheep; mature β_B differs by one amino acid), which suggests an important function and evolutionary pressure to maintain the molecular integrity of inhibin family members (132). Second, the inhibin/activin protein and the individual β-subunits are similar in structure and sequence to the growth and differentiation factor transforming growth factor-beta (TGFβ) (63). TGFβ is the prototype of factors involved in a vast number of cellular processes that include cellular death, proliferation, and differentiation (65). Third, the subunits are products of separate genes, and the transcription elements controlling the expression of the independent subunit genes differ (62, 121). Current studies examining cAMP response elements, transcription factor AP2-binding sites, the translation initiation sequence TATA, as well as tissue-specific domains are underway for each subunit promoter (10, 31, 85, 92). The heterogeneity in gene response elements may account for the complex control of individual inhibin/activin isoform synthesis in a tissue-, hormone-, or species-specific manner. Finally, activin A is able to induce inhibin subunit production in cultured rat granulosa cells and is also capable of stimulating β_A- and β_B-subunit transcription in the *Xenopus* embryo (2, 125, 126). The ability to direct assembly of protein dimers or auto-induce transcription is a profoundly refined mechanism for the control of functional diversity.

Identification of Follistatin

A third member of the FSH-modulating family was characterized in 1987 (26). Follistatin, similar to inhibin, inhibits pituitary FSH release; however, the molecule is biochemically unrelated to inhibin and activin. Further studies demonstrated that follistatin is an inhibin/activin-binding protein and bioneutralizes the activity of activin in many tissues. Follistatin may also regulate granulosa cell function independently of its role as an inhibin/activin-binding factor (32).

Inhibin, Activin, and Follistatin Outside the Reproductive Axis

The hypothesis that inhibin and activin are exclusive participants in the ovarian-pituitary axis was reexamined when the expression of subunit mRNA in tissues other than the ovary was noted. Meunier et al provide the most complete survey of inhibin/activin subunit mRNA localization in reproductive and nonreproductive tissues (83). Moreover, activin A has been purified from several sources including human leukemia cells (29), bone (91), and amniotic fluid (23).

Activin and inhibin act as functional antagonists in many cellular systems; however, it is clear that they should be classified separately. The β-subunit mRNA and activin protein are made in a variety of tissues and have numerous growth and differentiation activities (including mesoderm determination, hormone regulation, cellular death, erythroid cell differentiation, and neuronal survival) (26). Moreover, activin and its receptor (described below) bear remarkable resemblance to TGFβ. Inhibin, on the other hand, appears to participate primarily in the endocrine regulation of pituitary FSH. Additionally, it is produced by the ovary in a cycle-dependent manner and may regulate local gonadal functions. Activin has been described as a paracrine (68) or autocrine (126) hormone, as well as a growth and differentiation factor (26), and most recently as a cytokine (30). Molecules such as activin that breach classical definitions of activity can be classified broadly as "multicrine," i.e. of multiple activity.

Similar to the expression of inhibin/activin subunits, the expression and translation of follistatin mRNA and protein is prevalent outside the reproductive axis (26). However, expression of this molecule (described below) is not always coincident with activin or inhibin expression, and examples exist in which all members of the inhibin family are produced, but follistatin mRNA is not detected (e.g. testes of male rodent fetus at term) (100). Conversely, under certain circumstances, follistatin is expressed independently of inhibin/activin mRNA (kidney, artherosclerotic plaques, and the implantation site of rat embryos) (53, 57, 114). Taken together, these data indicate that follistatin may have functions unrelated to inhibin/activin-binding duties in some tissue types.

THE DEVELOPMENT OF INHIBIN, ACTIVIN, AND FOLLISTATIN ASSAYS

Inhibin and Activin Bioassays

The measurement of hormones or multicrine factors in serum identifies the total physiological load or material available to target tissues. Assays are tools used to measure the factor under normal circumstances, following physiological perturbations, and in disease states. Often, the physiology of a factor is defined by the circulating profile of that factor relative to a known parameter (e.g. the normal menstrual cycle). Obviously the value of the measurement relative to a single axis is most useful when the factor participates solely in that axis.

The complex biochemistry of the inhibin/activin family strains currently available assay technology. The conservation of sequence and structure and the presence of free subunits, binding proteins, and precursor forms of inhibin and activin are important considerations in assay development and interpretation of data (68). The classic method for measuring biologically relevant forms of any circulating hormone is a bioassay. Two inhibin/activin bioassays have been developed and used primarily to purify the respective activities. The dispersed pituitary cell bioassay, in which inhibin suppresses and activin stimulates FSH release, was used to purify inhibin, activin, and follistatin and to measure inhibin-like activity in human and rat serum (131, 133). A second bioassay was established to measure modulators of erythroid-stem cell differentiation using a human leukemia cell line (K562) (29, 110). In the K562 bioassay, activin stimulates hemoglobin production and inhibin antagonizes activin-stimulated hemoglobin production. Unfortunately, neither bioassay format distinguishes opposing biological activities contained within serum or tissue samples and both measure only the net activity present in the sample (60, 67).

The Inhibin Radioimmunoassay

The most widely used and reported assay for immunoreactive-inhibin (ir-inhibin) is the Monash RIA, using a polyclonal antibody designated 1989, which recognizes epitopes on the inhibin α-subunit (14, 79). The Monash RIA was initially characterized using reagents that were in low abundance and often partially purified. Cross-reactivity to the free subunits was examined using α- and β-subunits obtained following reduction and alkylation of native inhibin (78, 79). Moreover, inhibin/activin-binding proteins had not been discovered at that time; thus the interference of these moieties in the assay was untested. Nevertheless, this assay has provided the basis for the current understanding of inhibin physiology.

The profile of ir-inhibin measured in the inhibin RIA during the normal menstrual cycle has been reviewed elsewhere (7, 14, 15, 35); however, several technical points have made interpretation of the data unclear. These issues have been resolved largely by second generation assays, and a summary of the issues and an interpretation of the ir-inhibin levels measured during the normal menstrual cycle is described below.

Inhibin Measured During the Normal Menstrual Cycle, Perimenopausal Period, and Postmenopausal Period

Ir-inhibin has been evaluated in serum from women with normal menstrual cycles. The cycle is characterized by low ir-inhibin during the early- and mid-follicular phases, with a rise and peak coincident with the preovulatory gonadotropin surges (74, 79). A slight fall in ir-inhibin levels then precedes a LH-induced, mid-luteal phase surge and plateau (75, 119). The luteal phase serum concentration of ir-inhibin reaches levels two to three times higher than those found during the periovulatory time. Ir-inhibin serum concentration falls during the late luteal phase presumably to allow the intercycle FSH rise required for follicular recruitment.

The secretory pattern of inhibin and the hormones that regulate its production differ between human and rat. In the rat, luteinizing hormone (LH) causes a rapid decrease in inhibin production (serum and mRNA levels) (82, 137, 140, 141). Moreover, the corpus luteum of the rat (normal cycle and pregnancy) does not express inhibin subunit mRNA (142, 149). Conversely, the primate corpus luteum is the source of luteal inhibin, as demonstrated by in situ hybridization (36, 101), immunohistochemistry (20, 38), ovarian vein ir-inhibin measurements (51), and an increase in FSH following lutectomy [surgical: (9); hormonal ablation: (37, 50, 75, 119)]. Indeed, human follicular fluid is a poor source of dimeric inhibin because it has <2% the activity that is present in bovine follicular fluid (42). Consistent with other species, FSH induces inhibin during the follicular phase of the normal human menstrual cycle (46). Moreover, ir-inhibin correlates positively with follicle development when measured in women undergoing in vitro fertilization protocols (IVF) (48).

The perimenopausal time of reproductive life is characterized by inconsistent cycle length and variable (elevated) FSH levels (81). Ir-inhibin is not detected during cycles in which FSH is elevated, yet it is in the normal range for follicular and luteal phases during cycles in which FSH is within the normal menstrual cycle range (45). Furthermore, in cross-sectional studies of women approaching menopause, ir-inhibin decreases progressively in both serum and follicular fluid (27, 61). Finally, postmenopausal women do not have measurable ir-inhibin (79). The lack of negative feedback from the ovary (both estradiol and inhibin) is therefore responsible for the unopposed elevation of FSH following ovarian senescence.

Impetus to Develop New Inhibin Assays

The inverse correlation of (presumptive) ovarian inhibin and pituitary FSH under many normal physiological conditions suggests that the Monash RIA detects a biologically active fraction of human inhibin. Additional immuno-reactive-nonbioactive fractions are also detected based on several lines of evidence. Robertson et al evaluated the biological:immunological (B:I) ratios during the menstrual cycle (105). They found that the B:I ratio correlated well during the follicular phase; however, there was a twofold decrease in the ratio during the luteal phase that suggested immunodetection of an FSH-irrelevant form of inhibin. However, the bioassay measures the interaction of any number of FSH-regulating bioactivities and, therefore, efforts to relate this ratio specifically to inhibin activity in the female are difficult. Knight and colleagues developed a two-site inhibin assay for macaque ir-inhibin and compared the serum levels of ir-inhibin measured in a RIA (single epitope) and ELISA (dual epitope α-β) formats (58). The group reported that the RIA measured ir-inhibin in great excess over dimeric inhibin and concluded that the macaque makes excess free α-subunit relative to dimeric inhibin A. The correlate conclusion drawn was that the single epitope RIA is an inadequate tool to measure functional inhibin in the macaque.

Despite the plethora of papers describing ir-inhibin serum concentration by RIA and the consistent physiological correlation of biological and immunological activity, questions regarding the single epitope RIA format, the complexity of the inhibin family structure (e.g. precursors and free subunits), and physiology (binding-protein complexed forms) led to the development of second generation assays. Reagents to address questions of specificity (purified precursor, mature hormone, free subunits, and follistatin) are now available, thus profiles of cross-reactivity and interference can be examined. Nonetheless, it should be recognized that inhibin physiology (as monitored by circulating levels), the relative interference of various binding proteins (60), presence of α-subunit or other inhibin-related molecules (108), the production of non-gonadal inhibin (80, 83, 98), and the circulating level of activin may differ between species.

Second-Generation Inhibin Assays

Several laboratories developed antibody catalogs that include peptide-directed antibodies and polyclonal and monoclonal antibodies raised against native inhibin and activin in novel host species (e.g. hypogonadal mice and chickens) (8, 40, 107, 118, 135, 138). Intense efforts were mounted to produce individually pure recombinant reagents required to investigate interference and cross reactivity. Novel two-site ELISA formats were the result. Two groups, those of Groome and Franchimont, have reported assays that measure the 32-kDa form of inhibin in human serum (41, 97). Baly et al also generated an inhibin ELISA that measures 32-kDa inhibin A (it does not cross-react with inhibin B) (8). This assay, although not as sensitive as the Groome ELISA, is vital to the production of inhibin reagents (8). Groome reports assay sensitivity of 2 pg/ml and Baly reports assay sensitivity of 78 pg/ml (8, 41). The Franchimont assay does not use recombinant inhibin as standard, therefore a direct comparison with this assay is not currently available.

The overall profile of inhibin measured during the human menstrual cycle in the Monash RIA and in the Groome ELISA is similar (41; see Figure 1). Dimeric ir-inhibin is low during the early follicular phase and rises 3 days prior to the LH surge. The Monash RIA does not detect this subtle rise in ir-inhibin. Both assays detect ir-inhibin at mid-cycle and during the luteal phase, and the correlation of ir-inhibin with the gonadotropins and steroids of the menstrual cycle are identical between assays. While the overall pattern of putative inhibin measured between assays is similar, the absolute quantitation differs (Monash RIA quantitates greater ir-inhibin than does the Groome ELISA). The Monash assay likely measures free α-subunit in addition to dimeric inhibin A. Additional possibilities for the difference between assays include technical differences between the antigen measured (oxidation of inhibin is required for recognition of the epitope in the Groome two-site assay but not in the Monash assay), format differences (ELISA vs RIA), or specificity differences (cross-reactivity to free α-subunit or inhibin B). Precursor forms of inhibin A and inhibin B are also candidates for ir-inhibin in both assays. It is unlikely that measurement of precursor plus mature inhibin will alter the interpretation of the biological activity because Hasegawa et al have shown that precursor forms of human dimeric inhibin isolated from follicular fluid are biologically active in the pituitary cell bioassay (42).

Future Assay Development

The pattern of ir-inhibin measured during the normal menstrual cycle in a RIA and two-site ELISA is similar. The RIA overestimates ir-inhibin (relative to ELISA) and the likely ir-candidate is a free α-subunit. The physiology of the free α-subunit produced during the normal menstrual cycle may be to ensure inhibin production over activin production. While this may be true for the female, the quantitative abundance of the free subunits relative to dimeric inhibin may differ between species, between men and women, and in disease states. This fact should be kept in mind when choosing an ir-inhibin assay and when interpreting the profiles generated in the various assays.

Considerable progress has been made in the establishment of reliable and

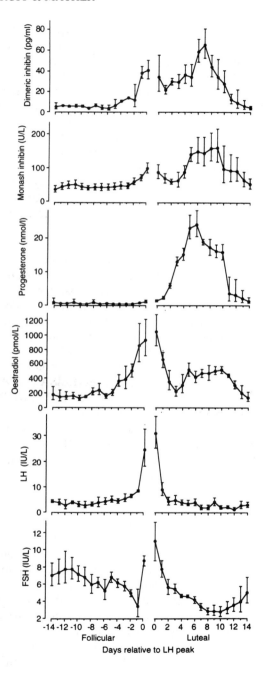

Days relative to LH peak

sensitive inhibin immunoassays. Additional progress will be made when individual forms of inhibin, activin, and follistatin are purified and compared simultaneously in all available assays. Robertson et al and Hasagawa et al have begun an exhaustive purification of inhibin forms from human female serum and ovarian extracts (42, 103). The isolated inhibin forms are evaluated by RIA and bioassay to establish the B:I ratio of each inhibin form present in serum. A myriad of forms have been identified and, as anticipated, not all fractions have equivalent bioactivity (42, 103). The availability of all inhibin forms will provide the reagents required to move forward in delineating new assays. When the receptors for inhibin and activin are identified, radio-receptor assays will be generated that are sensitive and that reflect a biologically active component of various samples. Until this type of assay is available, RIAs and ELISAs will be used to measure immunoreactive-inhibin (ir-inhibin) and immunoreactive-activin and (ir-activin).

MEASUREMENT OF ACTIVIN DURING THE NORMAL MENSTRUAL CYCLE AND DURING PREGNANCY

Activin Assay Development

Similar to that of inhibin assays, activin assay development has been difficult largely due to the near 100% conservation of the molecule between species and the sequence similarity between the two β-subunits. Wong et al, using hypogonadal mice as host species, were able to generate a panel of monoclonal antibodies that were evaluated for their utility in generating specific, sensitive, and independent activin A and activin B two-site assays (138). Assays were developed to detect ir-activin in human, monkey, rat, and mouse serum (123, 138; T Woodruff, unpublished data). The ELISAs for activin A and activin B detect free hormone and not follistatin-bound forms of activin (138, 139). The association of activin with follistatin renders the complex bioinactive in many instances. Therefore, the assays measure a predominantly biologically relevant form of activin action on granulosa cells (86); action on K562 cells (60); in vivo inhibition of erythropoiesis (116); and inhibition of mesoderm induction (3).

A RIA for activin has been reported; however, the assay has significant cross reactivity to inhibin A (25, 117). Several laboratories are developing follistatin, activin:follistatin complex, and inhibin:follistatin complex assays. A follistatin RIA has been reported by Sugawara et al (124). Further work will

←——————————————————————————————

Figure 1   The geometric mean concentration of (reading from top to bottom): dimeric human inhibin; Monash inhibin; progesterone; oestradiol; LH; and FSH during the follicular and luteal phases of the female menstrual cycle. Data are aligned around the succeeding LH peak in the follicular phase and preceding LH peak in the luteal phase (printed with permission from Reference 41).

be required to determine if there is any interference by activin or if the assay measures activin:follistatin or inhibin:follistatin complexes.

Circulating ir-Activin A and ir-Activin B Measured During Normal Human Pregnancy

We have been unable to detect ir-activin A or ir-activin B during the normal human menstrual cycle; however, both molecules are present in various compartments during pregnancy (94). Ir-activin A is present in maternal serum samples, cord blood serum, and amniotic fluid, while ir-activin B is primarily confined to fetal-derived fluids. During the first two trimesters of pregnancy, ir-activin A is low but detectable in maternal serum samples. It increases dramatically approaching parturition. Indeed, the highest maternal serum concentrations are found coincident with labor. Ir-activin A serum concentration then declines to prepregnancy (less than standard in our current assay) within 30 min of parturition (preliminary pharmacokinetic studies of activin decay following parturition suggests a <10-min half-life; T Woodruff, F Petraglia, unpublished observation). In the pathophysiological condition of pre-term labor, activin A increases 48 h prior to delivery, which suggests that activin A may participate in the process of parturition.

Ir-activin B was not detected in maternal serum; however, amniotic fluid and cord blood serum have relatively high concentrations of ir-activin B (94). Interestingly, ir-activin B is elevated in cord blood at term but is rapidly eliminated such that it is undetectable during delivery. Ir-activin B is also present in amniotic fluid at all times examined (second trimester, third trimester, and during labor).

Ir-activin A measured in maternal serum may be the product of the ovary, placenta, or fetus (95). β_A-subunit mRNA is present in the ovary of pregnancy, placenta, and developing embryo (93, 95, 96). Activin B subunit mRNA is also known to be produced by ovarian follicles, although expression during pregnancy has not been evaluated (82). β_B-subunit mRNA is exclusively expressed in the epithelial layer of the amnion (suggesting a source for amniotic-derived activin B) and in the developing fetus (93).

The the target tissue(s) sites (pituitary, ovary, placenta, or fetus) also remain to be clarified, as does the functional significance of elevated levels of these hormones. Several levels of control may be operational in the maternal, fetal, and placental environment that require these hormones. First, by analogy to amphibian early development in which activin is involved in inducing dorsal mesoderm structures (notochord and somites) and ventral mesoderm structures, one could hypothesize that activin participates in the early development and cell determination of mammalian embryos (128). Alternatively, circulating activin A is known to cause ovarian quiescence (described below) when administered exogenously, and it is possible that activin maintains follicular inactivity during pregnancy (123, 147). The rapid decline in activin after parturition may allow resumption of follicular growth. Lastly, activin may be one of the cascade of factors required to initiate the processes of parturition. In this regard, levels of activin are induced prior to normal labor but do not increase where labor is not a part of delivery, and activin has been shown to induce prostaglandin E2α (93, 93a).

Circulating ir-inhibin has been examined during pregnancy and has a serum profile similar to that of activin (measured in rats, monkeys, and humans) (89, 152, 153). Ir-inhibin is low during the first two trimesters and rises progressively, reaching a peak coincident with parturition. The source of inhibin may be the ovary, placenta, or adrenal gland (71, 77, 89, 152, 153). Clearly the requirements and function of inhibin and activin in the process of fetal recognition, implantation, and development, and/or maternal gonadotropin regulation, ovarian function, stress management, or nutrition remain to be fully elucidated.

INHIBIN/ACTIVIN SUBUNIT AND RECEPTOR LOCALIZATION

Inhibin, Activin, and Follistatin mRNA and Protein Localization in the Ovary

Inhibin/activin subunit mRNA localization has provided the field with crucial guideposts for evaluating the role(s) of the hormones in a variety of different tissues. Specifically, in situ hybridization (82, 140), S1-RNA analysis assays (83), and in situ ligand binding (56, 59, 144) have provided information regarding the timing of inhibin and activin subunit expression and the tissues in which the hormones may exert action. Biscak et al demonstrated that the transcription and translation of the inhibin/activin subunits are linked; therefore, inhibin/activin mRNA measurement are reflective of the protein (11). Unfortunately, the translation of follistatin mRNA to protein is uncoupled in some cells. Nakatani and colleagues have shown that follistatin mRNA exists in atretic follicles, but there is no detectable protein (87). However, both protein and mRNA are found in healthy follicles. Transcription and translation correlates have not been reported for activin receptor transcripts. Because the type II receptor may bind activin, but may not be active without a type I receptor, in situ ligand-binding data likewise must be interpreted cautiously (52), as should the interpretation of follistatin and receptor mRNA data.

The expression of inhibin subunit mRNA in the rat ovary has been reviewed extensively elsewhere (149). Recent studies have extended the early localization studies to additional species, including human, rhesus monkey, cow, and chicken (35, 54, 101, 112). The hormone transcripts are produced in similar stages of follicle maturation and cellular compartments. α- and β-subunit mRNAs are expressed in common sites in the granulosa cells of recruited follicles of all species examined. Little or no expression of α- and β-subunit mRNA is found in the theca cells of rats, cows, and chickens; however, human theca cells express α-subunit mRNA in small and large follicles. The β_A-subunit mRNA is found in the theca of dominant follicles (35, 54, 101, 112). Bovine granulosa cells in follicles of all sizes and health express the β_B-subunit constitutively (54). This expression contrasts with β_B-subunit expression in the primate and rat (35, 101). Granulosa cells of the dominant follicle class in the human and monkey do not express β_B-subunit mRNA but do express α- and β_A-subunit mRNA (35, 101). Expression of the subunit mRNA in the corpus luteum varies with the species. Rodents do not express the subunit mRNAs within the corpus luteum; however, corpus luteum from human and macaque ovaries express the α- and β_A-subunit and follistatin (35, 54, 101, 112, 149).

Localization of Inhibin/Activin-Binding Sites in the Ovary

In situ ligand binding has also been used to identify sites of labeled ligand binding to receptor (membrane-bound or shed) or cell surface–binding proteins (144). The pattern of inhibin binding in the rat ovary is restricted to the antral granulosa cells, cells that do not express α- or β-subunit mRNA. Activin binding is more generalized, both in terms of cell types (granulosa cells, theca cells, and luteal cells) and cycle dependency (144). During the early follicular phase, the ligand binds the granulosa cells of developing follicles. Preceding ovulation, ^{125}I rh-activin A binds to theca cells. Ligand also binds follicular fluid, suggesting the presence of shed receptor or binding protein in this compartment. Curiously, in situ ligand binding to rat oocytes on each day of the cycle failed to demonstrate specific binding, whereas the mRNA for type II receptor was expressed during this time (17). It is likely that receptor mRNA expression precedes receptor translation and expression on the oocyte cell surface. Alternatively, a second receptor subunit(s) (type I or III or both) or cofactor is required to allow binding of activin to receptors available on oocytes. Following ovulation (and resumption of meiosis), activin specifically binds the oocyte-cumulus complex.

The ovarian distribution of ^{125}I rh-activin A and ^{125}I rh-inhibin A in immature female rats (intravenous bolus administration) was primarily to the theca cells with a slow internalization of labeled ligand into the granulosa compartment and ultimately into the follicular fluid (143). The divergence of activin and inhibin binding, when delivered systemically, compared to binding sites on tissue sections (free of binding proteins and compartmentalization) demonstrates that the ability of inhibin and activin to affect a variety of cellular responses may depend entirely on the route of administration (143, 144). Indeed, the measurement of physiological parameters following the exogenous delivery of inhibin and activin probably does not mimic true in vivo activities.

Rather, similar to that of an in vitro bioassay, the response reflects the sum of endogenous activity and exogenous test material.

IN VIVO EFFECTS OF INHIBIN AND ACTIVIN

Pituitary and Ovarian Response to Systemically Administered Inhibin and Activin

Most published experiments using partially purified ovarian follicular fluid and rh-inhibin A describe the role of inhibin in regulating pituitary function. The conclusion of numerous elegant and classic studies is that systemic administration of inhibin inhibits pituitary FSH. Moreover, serum FSH levels increase in passively immunized animals (33). Indeed, immuno-elimination of circulating inhibin can result in superovulation in some domestic animals (33). Injection of rh-activin A into immature or adult rats (multiple days of the cycle) or monkeys increases circulating FSH (28, 62, 99, 111, 123, 146). These data confirm the hypothesis that activin stimulates basal or GnRH-stimulated FSH synthesis and release. Activin also regulates a variety of pituitary and ovarian hormones (26, 122). In female rhesus monkeys, rh-activin A administration causes a rapid and robust increase in circulating LH during the early follicular phase with no change in either estradiol or FSH (123). Estradiol and FSH increase eventually, lagging behind LH by 12 to 36 h, following chronic (7 day) administration of activin. Conversely, activin administration during the late luteal phase causes a rapid (<8 h) decline in LH and progesterone (to follicular phase levels) and immediate menses (122). Direct luteal infusions of rh-activin does not alter luteal hormones or length of phase, which suggests that the target tissue of activin in the late luteal phase is likely the pituitary. This dramatic impact of activin on the primate ovarian-pituitary axis is not completely unprecedented. Modest effects of activin on pituitary hormones, including GnRH-stimulated LH synthesis and release, were found in the pituitary cell bioassay (133). Moreover, injection of activin into a GnRH-primed male monkey causes an increase in LH (76). Additionally, activin stimulates estradiol production in immature granulosa cells in culture (84).

The experimental results described above raise intriguing questions and avenues for further study. First, a direct effect of activin on FSH secretion has not been demonstrated in the female primate. The sequence of hormonal response (LH followed by estradiol and FSH) suggests that exogenous activin may not regulate FSH in the primate (the surge levels of estradiol are sufficient to be causative in the FSH release) (123). Second, rat LH is largely unperturbed by exogenous activin administration (99, 146). However, activin can stimulate LH mRNA in rodent pituitary cells and production in the GnRH-primed pituitary bioassay (4). The species specificity and requirement for additional factors in the hypothalamic-pituitary-ovarian axis response merits further study. Third, LH is stimulated by activin during the follicular phase and negatively regulated during the luteal phase in the adult rhesus monkey (122, 123). The cycle-dependent effect may simply represent the response of the pituitary to the combination of activin and other regulating molecules, or reflect a true differential effect of activin on the pituitary (suggesting cycle-dependent mechanisms of action controlled by receptor conformation or binding protein availability). Last, if biologically active activin is produced during the late luteal phase, it may stimulate the intercycle FSH rise (perhaps in tandem with falling inhibin) and/or signal luteolysis (pituitary-derived activin would be the likely source for these putative activities).

Modulation of Follicular Maturation by Inhibin

In addition to endocrine effects on the pituitary, in vitro data suggest that inhibin and activin may act directly on the ovary (32, 68). The paracrine effect of inhibin on follicular maturation was evaluated by injecting rh-inhibin A directly into immature rat ovaries (147). Follicle maturation, as indicated by follicle size, increased in the rh-inhibin A–treated group. Interestingly, inhibin-stimulated follicles were found in the medulla and around the cortex. Inhibin may regulate follicular maturation, particularly in immature follicles, by stimulating theca cell androgen production (47, 125, 132). The dose, time, and route of drug administration, stage of follicular maturation, presence of neutralizing binding proteins, availability of specific receptors, and relative ratio of activin:inhibin contribute to the dynamics of the cellular response to inhibin.

Inhibin and Cancer

The logical antithesis to the observation that local inhibin is involved in normal follicular function is that aberrant production of hormone or the inappropriate regulation of receptor may be causative in a pathophysiological condition. One disease with which inhibin seems to be linked is ovarian cancer. Healy et al examined serum ir-inhibin in postmenopausal women with ovarian cancer, and 82% of women with mucinous carcinomas (tumors of the ovary with masses resembling endocervix tissue) had elevated serum levels (44). Ir-inhibin was elevated in 17% of women with serous carcinomas (tumors resembling fallopian tissue). Ir-inhibin serum concentration declines following surgical ablation of the tumor, which suggests that the tumors themselves are the source of the material. Ir-inhibin did not correlate with FSH in either serous or mucinous ovarian carcinomas in the study described by Healy et al. However, a second study reports that the ir-inhibin is inversely correlated with serum FSH in patients with ovarian tumors (13). Moreover, 60% of the women with malignant ovarian tumors had increased ir-inhibin (mucinous and serous-type tumors were not separated, and the samples were measured in the Medginix two-site α-inhibin assay). A 5.3-fold improvement in life expectancy is reported for women with ovarian carcinoma and high ir-inhibin serum concentration (4.6 years survival) vs low ir-inhibin serum concentration (0.9 years survival). Obviously, further work will be required to confirm and extend these findings.

The pathophysiology of a mouse line deficient in the inhibin α-subunit (therefore, inhibin A and inhibin B) (70) has been described. Within 3 weeks (time of puberty) the α-subunit-deficient homozygous mice develop goandal tumors. When the ovarian tumors or ovaries are removed, adrenal tumors arise. Matzuk et al hypothesize that the α-subunit acts as a tumor suppresser gene. This could be accounted for either because there is a lack of free α-subunit inhibin, or because the α-subunit is a binding molecule for β-subunits. Ir-activin A is extremely high in the α-subunit-deficient animals and may participate, directly or indirectly, in the genesis of the tumors (M Matzuk, personal communication).

Although the mechanism of inhibin (interpret as free α-subunit, elevated activin, or inhibin) action in the etiology of ovarian cancer in humans or in the mouse model is not known, the value of the inhibin assay as a diagnostic tool and potential novel molecular handle on the genesis of ovarian tumors is intriguing.

A somewhat new role for inhibin in local tissue growth is suggested by Russo et al who demonstrated that mammary epithelial cells produce inhibin in response to human chorionic gonadotropin (hCG) (106). Human CG and pregnancy are known to protect rat mammary gland from tumor growth, and inhibin is one of the products that is upregulated in response to hCG. Thus inhibin may participate in the control of cell proliferation in this tissue and protect it from tumorogenesis. Further studies are required; however, this is a novel role for inhibin and fits with the hypothesis that it acts as a tumor suppresser molecule.

Role of Activin in Modulating Follicular Maturation

Activin, a multicrine factor, participates in a variety of regulatory pathways; thus the effect of activin on local ovarian function was examined. Rh-activin A was administered locally to immature PMSG-injected rat and follicular phase rhesus monkey ovaries (147). Activin caused widespread atresia in this rat model and a temporary interruption of follicular maturation in the primate model. It is clear that activin is involved in the regulation of cellular homeostasis and, in these models, could initiate mechanisms leading to apoptosis. Subsequent to the original correlation of activin with general apoptosis in the ovary, activin has been shown to regulate programmed cell death in numerous cells (49, 113). Schwall et al reported a profound and immediate loss of liver weight following high-dose rh-activin A administration in an immature female rat model (113). Histological analysis revealed hepatic cell death via apoptosis. Several other cell types, including myeloma (U26631) and hybridoma (B9) cell lines, respond to activin by undergoing programmed cell death, whereas a mouse lymphoma (EL-4) does not respond to activin (88). In both models the effect was specific (inhibition of activity in the presence of follistatin) and TGFβ independent. The ability of activin to participate in the processes of terminal cellular differentiation may be dose and route dependent and confirms the fundamental role activin plays in cellular homeostasis.

Animal Models of Activin A and Activin B Deficiency

In vivo immunoneutralization of endogenous activin A has not been evaluated because a specific, high-affinity neutralizing antibody has not been generated. Activin A germ line–deficient animals have been generated and preliminary reports indicate that homozygote animals die at birth (M Matzuk, personal communication). The cause of mortality in these animals is currently under investigation, but certainly activin must be required for juvenile survival.

Immunoneutralizing antibodies to activin B have been generated and injected into rats (12, 19). Potential sites of activin B production are pituitary and ovary, and immunoneutralization resulted in decreased FSH secretion (19). Based on this experiment, it has been hypothesized that activin B participates in a short-loop-controlling pathway regulating pituitary FSH synthesis and secretion. However, a β_B-deficient mouse line has recently been generated, and surprisingly, founder homozygous animals develop normally (134). Offspring of homozygous females die in utero at the time of parturition, and the reasons for the inability to carry the fetus to term are under investigation. Clearly, however, the lack of inhibin B, activin B, activin AB, and the β_B-subunit does not effect overt FSH regulation, which allows follicular maturation, selection, and ovulation in the β_B-deficient mouse. The hypothesis that activin B participates in the pituitary may be true under normal physiological circumstances, but activin B also may be one of a redundant group of factors important in the fine tuning of cyclical FSH patterns.

BINDING PROTEINS AND RECEPTORS FOR INHIBIN, ACTIVIN, AND RELATED PROTEINS

Inhibin/Activin-Binding Proteins

Follistatin was identified as an inhibin/activin-binding protein by Nakamura et al (86). Follistatin is also able to bind inhibin (e.g. filter assay, HPLC analysis of purified material, follicular fluid and human serum, and in vivo association of iodinated ligand following infusion in the rat) (60, 109, 115, 145). In the course of analysis of biological fluid protein association with iodinated inhibin and activin, a second binding protein was identified as alpha2 macroglobulin (60). This broad-spectrum protease inhibitor is known to bind a variety of growth factors, including TGFβ. Both inhibin and activin bind alpha2 macroglobulin in a low-affinity, high-capacity manner, contrasting with the high-affinity, low-capacity binding of both ligands to follistatin. The actions of the binding proteins when found in serum may include bioneutralization, altered clearance, or specific tissue targeting (for activity or elimination). Both follistatin and alpha2 macroglobulin are produced and regulated in a hormonally dependent fashion in the gonads and therefore may participate in the bioavailability of inhibin and activin to local actions (39, 87). Nakatani et al reported that follistatin protein is made in developing follicles but not in atretic follicles (87). Extending earlier studies demonstrating that activin can induce atresia, Erikson suggests that follistatin protects the follicles destined to ovulate from the apoptotic action of activin, whereas the lack of follistatin in atretic follicles allows such activity.

Activin/TGFβ Receptors

A group of membrane proteins has been identified that binds activin and/or related TGFβ family members (66, 69). The three membrane-derived binding moieties are named generically, based on their molecular weight: Type I (55 K); type II (70–85 K); type III (200–400 K). Cellular transduction of TGFβ activity to cells may require the combinatorial assembly of at least two distinct receptor subunits (52, 150).

The activin type II receptor was first identified by expression cloning (69). Several related activin A–specific and TGFβ-specific type II receptors were subsequently identified by degenerate PCR cloning (6). The type II receptors have a highly conserved serine-threonine kinase domain and bind TGFβ or activin A with a variety of affinities that may contribute to the narrow concentration dependence of activin effects on different cell types. For example, the fate of the *Xenopus* blastomere greatly differs when exposed to different concentrations (1.5-fold differences) of activin A (as discussed above). Activin and TGFβ have distinct type II receptors that bind the ligands but do not signal intracellular responses. For transmission of signal, the type II:ligand complex may require binding of a type I receptor (150).

The type I receptor family was identified and, similar to the type II class receptor, is a single transmembrane-spanning molecule with an intracellular serine/threonine kinase domain (5). Specific, promiscuous, and orphan type I receptors have been identified from a variety of species (43, 127). Specific type I receptors allow the cellular discrimination of TGFβ and activin activity, whereas, promiscuous type I receptors provide minimal gene requirements for maximal cellular response (or redundant mechanisms). Orphan type I receptors have been identified based on source tissue (e.g. a presumptive Müllerian inhibiting substance type I half receptor was isolated from the urogenital ridge) (43). Obviously, the inability to bind ligand in the absence of an appropriate type II component confounds the identification of these receptor subunits.

The TGFβ type III receptor was first identified as a beta-glycan present on the surface of most cells and having no signaling motif (136). It is postulated that this cell surface–binding protein binds various TGFβ isotypes on the cell surface and makes the ligand readily available to the type I:type II receptor complex (136). An analogous activin type III receptor has been identified by cross-linking studies, and evidence that ligand is bound by a heterotrimeric receptor (requiring type I, type II, and type III) was recently reported (72). Whether the activin type III and TGFβ type III are homologous is currently under investigation.

The TGFβ/activin receptors are intriguing in that two transmembrane kinases interact in a cooperative manner. The mechanism for signaling has not been completely established; however, several possibilities exist. Each of the kinases may have independent substrates, or a common substrate may undergo phosphorylation at different sites. Alternatively, one receptor kinase may act on the other thereby generating the first step in the signaling cascade within the receptor complex itself. Binding of ligand to the type II receptor subunit may cause activation of transcription or translation products associated with production or trafficking of the type I receptor subunit to the cell surface. At the cell surface, the type II:ligand complex binds type I and signals cell growth or differentiation pathways. This two-step controlling mechanism may allow the variety of cellular responses reported for the TGFβ/activin family.

Inhibin receptors have not yet been identified. The activin receptors may be high-capacity, low-affinity inhibin receptors, but a separate inhibin receptor(s) must exist because of its high-affinity interaction with the pituitary cell. The high-capacity, low-affinity interaction with the activin receptor may, however, explain the ability of inhibin to antagonize the action of activin in some cells (for example in K562 cells).

Embryonic Expression of Inhibin, Activin, Follistatin, and Receptor mRNA

Interest in identifying the sites of hormone production has extended to the developing embryo. Roberts has evaluated the expression pattern of the α-, β_A-, β_B-subunit and follistatin mRNA during embryogenesis (100). The most broadly distributed member of the family is follistatin. During development, it is expressed in all tissues examined, with the exception of testis, somites, heart, and placenta. This broad distribution suggests that follistatin may participate in actions in addition to the mediation of activin activity if the mRNA is translated to protein. The tissues that produce β_A-subunit mRNA are also prevalent and diverse. The potential to produce all inhibin/activin isoforms exists in the testis and ovary exclusively. Activin A and B may be produced together in the brain, and activin B is the sole inhibin family member that can be produced by the salivary gland.

An evaluation of the developmental and adult expression of the known activin type II and IIB receptors has been reported (17). It is important to note that the type II receptor can bind ligand but requires a type I receptor (and possibly a type III receptor) to signal intracellular responses. In the embryo, the type II receptor mRNA is restricted to neuronal tissues. It is present in the brain, spinal cord, dorsal root ganglia, and eye. The neuronal sites of receptor mRNA localization are preserved in the adult. All stages of immature ooctyes express the type II receptor mRNA. Contrasting with the discreet localization of the type II receptor is the broad distribution of the type IIB receptor mRNA in the embryo. Type IIB mRNA is expressed in neuronal tissue, gonadal tissue, ear, kidney, and lung (113).

FINAL THOUGHTS

Gaps in information and interpretation of data may occur because of the constant increase in knowledge and the appropriate reevaluation of previously gathered data. With reference to the inhibin and activin field, the reader is reminded of the words of Francis Bacon, "the subtlety of nature, the secret recesses of truth, the obscurity of things, the difficulty of experiment, the implication of causes and the infirmity of [wo]man's discerning power...." The inhibin and activin communities look forward to the next decade of research with the anticipation that it will be as exciting as the past ten years.

ACKNOWLEDGMENTS

The authors thank the entire Genentech, Inc. Inhibin/Activin team including Roger Pai, Wai-Lee Wong, Debbie Baly, Lynne Krummen, and Ralph Schwall for their commitment to this project. The work of Dr. Richard Stouffer, Oregon Regional Primate Research Center, is also gratefully acknowledged.

Literature Cited

1. Deleted in proof
2. Asashima M, Nakano H, Uchiyama H, Sugino H, Nakamura T, et al. 1991. Presence of activin (EDF) in unfertilized eggs and blastulae of *Xenopus laevis*. *Proc. Natl. Acad. Sci. USA* 88:6511–14

3. Asashima M, Nakano H, Uchiyama H, Sugino H, Nakamura T, et al. 1991. Follistatin inhibits the mesoderm-inducing activity of activin A and the vegetalizing factor from chicken embryo. *Roux's Arch. Dev. Biol.* 200:4–7

4. Attardi B, Klatt B, Miklos J, Winters S. 1994. Regulations of FSH synthesis and secretion by inhibin, activin, and follistatin. In *Frontiers in Endocrinology.* Vol. 3: *Inhibin and Inhibin-Related Proteins,* ed. H Burger, J Findlay, D Robertson, D deKretser, F Petraglia, pp. 101–13. Rome: Ares-Serono Symposia

5. Attisano L, Carcamo J, Ventura F, Weis F, Massagué J, Wrana J. 1993. Identification of human activin and TGFβ type I receptors that forms a heteromeric complex with the TGFβ type II receptor. *Cell* 75:681–92

6. Attisano L, Wrana J, Cheifetz S, Massagué J. 1992. Novel activin receptors: distinct genes and alternative mRNA splicing generate a repertoire of serine/threonine kinase receptors. *Cell* 68:97–108

7. Baird DT, Smith KB, Illingworth PJ, Millar MR, Hilliar SG. 1994. Endocrine and paracrine action of inhibin/activins in women. See Ref. 4, pp. 179–90

8. Baly D, Allison D, Krummen L, Woodruff T, Soules M, et al. 1993. Development of a specific and sensitive two-site enzyme-linked immunosorbent assay (ELISA) for measurement of inhibin A in serum. *Endocrinology* 132:2099–108

9. Basseti SG, Winters SJ, Keeping HS, Zeleznik AJ. 1990. Serum immunoreactive inhibin levels before and after lutectomy in the cynomologus monkey (*Macaca fascicularis*). *J. Clin. Endocrinol Metab.* 70:590–94

10. Bhasin S, Rosenberg LA, Strathearn M, Sod-Moriah UA, Krummen L, Burger H. 1994. Transcriptional regulation of inhibin alpha and beta subunit genes by 3′, 5′, cyclic-adenosine monophosphate. See Ref. 4, pp. 209–22

11. Bicsak TA, Cajander SG, Bale W, Hsueh A. 1988. Inhibin: studies of stored and secreted forms by biosynthetic labeling and immunodetection in cultured rat granulosa cells. *Endocrinology* 122:741–48

12. Bilezikjian L, Corrigan A, Vale W. 1994. Activin-B, inhibin-B and follistatin as autocrine/paracrine factors of the rat anterior pituitary. See Ref. 4, pp. 81–99

13. Blaakaer J, Micic S, Morris I, Hording U, Bennett P, Toftager-Larsen K. 1993. Immunoreactive inhibin production in post-menopausal women with malignant epithelial ovarian tumors. *Eur. J. Obstet. Gynecol. Reprod. Biol.* 52:105–10

14. Burger HG. 1992. Inhibin. *Reprod. Med. Rev.* 1:1–20

15. Burger HG. 1993. Evidence for a negative feedback role of inhibin in follicle stimulating hormone regulation in women. *Hum. Reprod.* 8(Suppl. 2):129–32

16. Burger HG, Igarashi M. 1988. Inhibin: definition and nomenclature including related substances. *J. Clin. Endocrinol. Metab.* 66:885–86

17. Cameron V, Nishimura E, Mathews L, Lewis K, Sawchendo P, Vale W. 1994. Hybridization histochemical localization of activin receptor subtypes in rat brain, pituitary, ovary, and testis. *Endocrinology* 134:799–808

18. Channing CP, Gordon WL, Liu W-K, Ward DN. 1985. The physiology and biochemistry of ovarian inhibin. *Proc. Soc. Exp. Biol. Med.* 178:339–61

19. Corrigan AZ, Bilezikjian M, Carroll RS, Bald LN, Schmelzer CH, et al. 1991. Evidence for an autocrine role of activin B within rat anterior pituitary cultures. *Endocrinology* 128:1682–84

20. Davis SR, Krozowski Z, McLachlan RI, Burger HG. 1987. Inhibin gene expression in the human corpus luteum. *J. Endocrinol.* 115:R21–R23

22. deJong FH. 1988. Inhibin. *Physiol. Rev.* 68:555–607

21. deJong FH, Robertson DM. 1985. Inhibin: 1985 update on action and purification. *Mol. Cell. Endocrinol.* 42:95–103

23. deKretser DM, Foulds LM, Hancock M, McFarlane J, Goss N. 1994. The isolation of activin from human amniotic fluid. *Endocrinology* 134:1231–37

24. deKretser DM, Robertson DM. 1989. The isolation and physiology of inhibin and related proteins. *Biol. Reprod.* 40:33–47

25. Demura T, Suzuki T, Tajima S, Mitsuhashi S, Odagiri E, et al. 1992. Competitive protein binding assay for activin A/EDF using follistatin determination of activin levels in human plasma. *Biochem. Biophys. Res. Commun.* 185:1148–54

26. DePaolo L, Bicsak T, Erickson G, Shimasaki S, Ling N. 1991. Follistatin and activin: potential intrinsic regulatory system within diverse tissues. *Proc. Soc. Exp. Biol. Med.* 198:500–12

27. Dionyssiou-Asteriou A, Drakakis P, Loutradis D. 1993. Follicular fluid inhibin levels in relation to age in patients in an in vitro fertilization and embryo transfer program. *Eur. J. Obst. Gynecol. Reprod. Biol.* 51:55–61

28. Doi M, Igarashi M, Hasegawa Y, Eto Y, Shibai H, et al. 1992. In vivo action of activin A on pituitary-gonadal system. *Endocrinology* 130:139–44

29. Eto Y, Tsuji T, Takezawa M, Takano

S, Yokogawa Y, Shibai H. 1987. Purification and characterization of erythroid differentiation factor (EDF) isolated from human leukemia cell line THP-1. *Biochem. Biophys. Res. Commun.* 42: 1095–1103

30. Fann M-F, Patterson P. 1994. Neuropoietic cytokines and activin A differentially regulate the phenotype of cultured sympathetic neurons. *Proc. Natl. Acad. Sci. USA* 91:43–47

31. Feng Z-M, Li Y-P, Chen C-LC. 1989. Analysis of the 5'-flanking regions of rat inhibin alpha and beta B subunit genes suggests two different regulatory mechanisms. *Mol. Endocrinol.* 3:1914–25

32. Findlay J. 1993. An update on the roles of inhibin, activin, and follistatin as local regulators of folliculogenesis. *Biol. Reprod.* 48:15–23

33. Findlay JK, Doughton BW, Tonis CG, Brown RW, Hungerford JW, et al. 1993. Inhibin as a fecundity vaccine. *Anim. Reprod. Sci.* 33:325–43

34. Franchimont P, Hazee-Hagelstein M, Jaspar J, Charlet-Renard C, Demoulin A. 1989. Inhibin and related peptides: mechanisms of action and regulation of secretion. *J. Steroid Biochem.* 32:193–97

35. Fraser HM. 1994. Physiology of inhibin in female primates. See Ref. 4, pp. 163–77

36. Fraser HM, Lunn SF, Cowen GM, Saunders PT. 1993. Localization of inhibin activin subunit messenger-RNAs during the luteal-phase in the primate ovary. *J. Mol. Endocrinol.* 10: 245–57

37. Fraser HM, Robertson DM, deKretser DM. 1989. Immunoreactive inhibin concentrations in serum throughout the menstrual cycle of the macaque: suppression of inhibin during the luteal phase after treatment with an LHRH antagonist. *J. Endocrinol.* 121:107–13

38. Fraser HM, Smith KB, Lunn SF, Crowen GM, Morris K, McNeilly A. 1992. Immunoneutralization and immunocytochemical localization of inhibin alpha subunit during the mid-luteal phase in the stump-tailed macaque. *J. Endocrinol.* 133:341–47

39. Gaddy-Kurten D, Hickey G, Fey G, Gauldie J, Richards J. 1989. Hormonal regulation and tissue-specific localization of a2-macroglobulin in rat ovarian follicles and corpora lutea. *Endocrinology* 125:2985–95

40. Groome N. 1991. Ultrasensitive two-site assays for inhibin A and activin A using monoclonal antibodies raised to synthetic peptides. *J. Immunol. Methods* 145:65–69

41. Groome NP, Illingworth M, O'Brien I, Cooke T, Ganessa S, Baird D. 1994. Detection of dimeric inhibin throughout the human menstrual cycle by 2–site enzyme immunoassay. *Clin. Endocrinol.* 6:717–23

42. Hasegawa Y, Miyamoto K, Sugino H, Takio K, Inoue M, Ibuki Y. 1994. Progress with human and rat inhibin characterization. See Ref. 4, pp. 5–24

43. He W, Gustagson S, Hirobe S, Donahoe P. 1993. Developmental expression of four novel serine/threonine kinase receptors homologs to the activin/transforming growth factor-beta type II receptor family. *Dev. Dyn.* 196:133–42

44. Healy DL, Burger HG, Mamers P, Jobling T, Bangah M, et al. 1993. Elevated serum inhibin concentrations in postmenopausal women with ovarian tumors. *N. Engl. J. Med.* 329:1539–42

45. Hee J, MacNaughton J, Bangah M, Burger HG. 1993. Perimenopausal patterns of gonadotropins, immunoreactive inhibin, oestradiol, and progesterone. *Maturitas* 18:9–20

46. Hee JP, MacNaughton J, Bangah M, Zissimos M, McCloud PJ, et al. 1993. FSH induces dose-dependent stimulation of immunoreactive inhibin secretion during the follicular phase of the human menstrual cycle. *J. Clin. Endocrinol. Metab.* 76:1340–43

47. Hsueh AJ, Dahl KD, Vaughan J, Tucker E, Rivier J, et al. 1987. Heterodimers of inhibin subunits have different paracrine actions in the modulation of LH-stimulated androgen production. *Proc. Natl. Acad. Sci. USA* 84:5082–86

48. Hughes EG, Tovertson DM, Handelsman DJ, Hayward S, Healy DL, deKretser DM. 1990. Inhibin and estradiol responds to ovarian hyper stimulation: effects of age and predictive value for in vitro fertilization outcome. *J. Clin. Endocrinol. Metab.* 70:358–64

49. Hully J, Chang R, Schwall R, Widmer H, Terrell T, Gillett N. 1994. Induction of apoptosis in the murine liver with recombinant human activin A. *Hepatology.* 20:854–61

50. Illingworth PJ, Reddi K, Smith KB, Baird DT. 1990. Pharmacological "rescue" of the corpus luteum. *Clin. Endocrinol.* 33:323–32

51. Illingworth PJ, Reddi K, Smith KB, Baird DT. 1991. The source of inhibin secretion during the human menstrual cycle. *J. Clin. Endocrinol. Metab.* 73: 667–73

52. Inagaki M, Moustaka A, Lin H, Lodish

H, Carr B. 1993. Growth inhibition by transforming growth factor type I receptor is restored in TGF-β-resistant hepatoma cells after expression of TGF-β receptor type II cDNA. *Proc. Natl. Acad. Sci. USA* 90:5359–63

53. Inoue S, Orimo A, Hosoi T, Matsuse T, Hashimoto M, Yamada, R, et al. 1993. Expression of follistatin, an activin-binding protein, in vascular smooth muscle cells and arteriosclerotic lesions. *Arterioscler. Thromb.* 13:1859–64

54. Ireland J, Ireland JL. 1994. Changes in expression of inhibin/activin α, βA, and βB subunit messenger ribonucleic acids following increases in size and during different stages of differentiation or atresia of non-ovulatory follicles in cows. *Biol. Reprod.* 50:492–501

55. Itoh M, Igarahi M, Yamada K, Hasegawa Y, Seki M, et al. 1990. Activin A stimulates meiotic maturation of the rat ooctye in vitro. *Biochem. Biophys. Res. Commun.* 166:1479–84

56. Jakeman L, Mather J, Woodruff T. 1992. In vitro ligand binding of ^{125}I-recombinant human activin A to the female rat brain. *Endocrinology* 131:3117–19

57. Kaiser M, Gibori G, Mayo KE. 1990. The rat follistatin gene is highly expressed in decidual tissue. *Endocrinology* 126:2768–70

58. Knight PG, Muttukrishna S, Groome N, Webley GE. 1992. Evidence that most of the radioimmunoassayable inhibin secreted by the corpus luteum of the common marmoset is of a non-dimeric form. *Biol. Reprod.* 47:554–60

59. Krummen L, Woodruff T, Covello R, Taylor R, Working P, Mather J. 1994. In situ localization of inhibin and activin binding sites in the adult testis by in situ ligand binding and radio-immunohistochemistry. *Biol. Reprod.* 50: 734–44

60. Krummen L, Woodruff T, DeGuzman L, Cox E, Baly D, et al. 1993. Identification and characterization of binding proteins for inhibin and activin in human serum and follicular fluids. *Endocrinology* 132:431–43

61. MacNaughton J, Bangah M, McCloud P, Hee J, Burger H. 1992. Age related changes in follicle stimulating hormone, luteinizing hormone, oestradiol and immunoreactive inhibin in women of reproductive age. *Clin. Endocrinol.* 36: 339–45

62. Mason A, Berkemeir LM, Schmelzer CH, Schwall RH. 1989. Activin B precursor sequences, genomic structures and in vivo activities. *Mol. Endocrinol.* 3:1352–58

63. Mason A, Hayflick JS, Ling M, Esch F, Ueno N, et al. 1985. Complementary DNA sequences of ovarian follicular fluid inhibin show precursor homology with transforming growth factor-β. *Nature* 318:659–63

64. Mason AJ, Schwall RH, Renz M, Rhee LM, Nikolics K, Seeburg P. 1987. Human inhibin and activin: structure and recombinant expression in mammalian cells. See Ref. 4, pp. 77–88

66. Massagué J. 1990. The transforming growth factor-β family. *Annu. Rev. Cell Biol.* 6:597–641

65. Massagué J. 1992. Receptors for the TGF-β family. *Cell* 69:1067–70

67. Mather J, Krummen L, Roberts P, Gibson U, Mann E, Stocks D. 1994. Progress with human and rat inhibin characterization. See Ref. 4, pp. 223–31

68. Mather J, Woodruff T, Krummen L. 1992. Paracrine regulation of reproductive function by inhibin and activin. *Proc. Soc. Exp. Biol. Med.* 201:1–15

69. Mathews L, Vale W. 1991. Expression cloning of an activin receptor, a predicted transmembrane kinase. *Cell* 65: 973–82

70. Matzuk M, Ginegold M, Su J, Hsueh A, Bradley A. 1992. α-inhibin is a tumour-suppressor gene with gonadal specificity in mice. *Nature* 360:313–19

71. Mayo KE, Cerelli GM, Spiess J, Rivier J, Rosenfeld MG, et al. 1986. Inhibin A-subunit complementary DNA species from porcine ovary and human placenta. *Proc. Natl. Acad. Sci. USA* 83:5849–53

72. McCarthy S, Bicknell R. 1994. Activin-A binds to a heterotrimeric receptor complex on the vascular endothelial cell surface: evidence for a type 3 activin receptor. *J. Biol. Chem.* 269:3909–12

73. McCullagh DR. 1932. Dual endocrine activity of the testes. *Science* 76:19–20

74. McLachlan RI, Cohen NL, Dahl KD, Bremner WL, Soules MR. 1990. Serum inhibin levels during the periovulatory interval in normal women: relationship with sex steroid and gonadotropin levels. *Clin. Endocrinol.* 32:39–48

75. McLachlan RI, Cohen NL, Vale WW, Rivier JE, Burger HG, et al. 1989. The importance of LH in the control of inhibin and progesterone secretion by the human corpus luteum. *J. Clin. Endocrinol. Metab.* 68:1078–85

76. McLachlan RI, Dahl KD, Bremner WJ, Schall R, Schmelzer CH, et al. 1989. Recombinant human activin-A stimulates basal FSH and GnRH-stimulated FSH and LH release in the adult male macaque, *Macaca fascicularis*. *Endocrinology* 125:2787–89

77. McLachlan RI, Healy DL, Lutjen PJ, Findlay JK, deKretser D, Burger HG. 1987. The maternal ovary is not the source of circulating inhibin levels during human pregnancy. *Clin. Endocrinol.* 27:663–68

78. McLachlan RI, Robertson DM, Burger HG, deKretser DM. 1986. The radioimmunoassay of bovine and human follicular fluid and serum inhibin. *Mol. Cell. Endocrinol.* 46:175–85

79. McLachlan RI, Robertson DM, Healy DL, Burger HG, deKretser DM. 1987. Circulating immunoreactive inhibin levels during the normal menstrual cycle. *J. Clin. Endocrinol. Metab.* 65:954–61

80. McNeilly AS, Brooks AN, Baxter G, Webb R. 1994. Sheep adrenal inhibin. See Ref. 4, pp. 261–69

81. Metcalf MG, Donald RA, Livesey JH. 1981. Pituitary-ovarian function in normal women during the menopause transition. *Clin. Endocrinol.* 14:245–55

82. Meunier H, Cajander S, Roberts V, Rivier C, Sawchenko P, et al. 1988. Rapid changes in the expression of inhibin α, βA, and βB subunits in ovarian cell types during the rat estrous cycle. *Mol. Endocrinol.* 2:1352–63

83. Meunier H, Rivier C, Evans R, Vale W. 1988. Gonadal and extragonadal expression of inhibin α-, β_A-, and β_B-subunits in various tissues predicts diverse functions. *Proc. Natl. Acad. Sci. USA* 85: 247–51

84. Miro F, Smyth CD, Hillier SG. 1991. Development-related effects of recombinant activin on steroid synthesis in rat granulosa cells. *Endocrinology* 129: 3388–94

85. Najmabadi H, Rosenberg LA, Yuan QX, Reyaz G, Bhasin S. 1993. Transcriptional regulation of inhibin beta b mRNA levels in TM.4 or primary Sertoli cells by 8-bromo-cAMP. *Mol. Endocrinol.* 7:561–69

86. Nakamura T, Takio K, Eto Y, Shibai H, Titani K, Sugino H. 1990. Activin-binding protein from rat ovary is follistatin. *Science* 247:836–38

87. Nakatani A, Shimasaki S, DePaolo L, Erickson G, Ling N. 1991. Cyclic changes in follistatin messenger RNA and its protein in the rat ovary during the estrous cycle. *Endocrinology* 129: 603–11

88. Nishihara T, Okahashi N, Ueda N. 1993. Activin A induces apoptotic cell death. *Biochem. Biophys. Res. Commun.* 197: 985–91

89. Nozaki M, Watanabe G, Taya K, Katakai Y, Wada I, Sasamoto S. 1990. Changes in circulating inhibin levels during pregnancy and early lactation in the Japanese monkey. *Biol. Reprod.* 43: 444–49

90. Deleted in proof

91. Ogawa Y, Schmidt D, Nathan R, Armstrong R, Miller K, Sawamura S. 1992. Bovine bone activin enhances bone morphogenetic protein-induced ectopic bone formation. *J. Biol. Chem.* 267: 14233–37

92. Pei L, Schoderbek W, Maurer RA, Mayo KE. 1991. Regulation of the alpha gene by cyclic adenosine 3'-5'-monophosphate after transfection in rat granulosa cells. *Mol. Endocrinol.* 5:521–34

93. Petraglia F, Anceschi M, Calza L, Garuti GC, Fusaro P, et al. 1993. Inhibin and activin in human fetal membranes: evidence for a local effect on prostaglandin release. *J. Clin. Endocrinol. Metab.* 77: 542–48

93a. Petraglia F, Gallinelli A, DeVita D, Lewis K, Matthews L, Vale W. 1994. Activin at parturition: changes of maternal serum levels and evidence of binding sites in placenta and fetal membranes. *Obst. Gynecol.* 84:278–82

94. Petraglia F, Garg S, Florio P, Sadick M, Gallinelli A, et al. 1993. Free activin A and free activin B measured in maternal serum, cord blood serum, and amniotic fluid during human pregnancy. *Endocrine J.* 1:323–27

95. Petraglia F, Volpe A, Genazzani A, Rivier J, Sawchenko P, Vale W. 1990. Neuroendocrinology of the human placenta. *Front. Neuroendocrinol.* 11:6–37

96. Petraglia F, Woodruff TK, Botticelli G, Botticelli A, Genazzani A-R, et al. 1992. Gonadotropin-releasing hormone, inhibin, and activin in human placenta: evidence for a common cellular localization. *J. Clin. Endocrinol. Metab.* 74: 1184–88

97. Poncelet E, Franchimont P. 1994. Two site enzymo-immunoassays of inhibin. See Ref. 4, pp. 45–54

98. Rabinovici J, Spencer SJ, Doldi N, Jaffe RB. 1994. Localization and actions of activin in the human ovary and adrenal gland. See Ref. 4, pp. 191–97

99. Rivier C, Vale W. 1991. Effect of recombinant activin-A on gonadotropin secretion in the female rat. *Endocrinology* 129:2463–65

100. Roberts V, Barth S. 1994. Expression of messenger ribonucleic acids encoding the inhibin/activin system during mid- and late-gestation rat embryogenesis. *Endocrinology* 134:914–23

101. Roberts V, Barth S, El-Roeiy A, Yen S. 1993. Expression of inhibin/activin subunits and follistatin messenger ribo-

nucleic acids and proteins in ovarian follicles and the corpus luteum during the human menstrual cycle. *J. Clin. Endocrinol. Metab.* 77:1402–10

102. Robertson DM, Foulds LM, Prisk M, Hedger MP. 1992. Inhibin/activin β-subunit monomer: isolation and characterization. *Endocrinology* 130:1680–87

103. Robertson D, Sullivan J, Watson M, Cahir N. 1994. Forms of inhibin: biological and immunological characterization. See Ref. 4, pp. 25–32

104. Robertson DM, Giacometti M, Foulds LM, Lahnstein J, Goss NH, et al. 1989. Isolation of inhibin α-subunit precursor proteins from bovine follicular fluid. *Endocrinology* 125:2141–49

105. Robertson DM, Tsonis CG, McLachlan RI, Handelsman DJ, Leask R, et al. 1988. Comparison of inhibin immunological and in vitro biological activities in human serum. *J. Clin. Endo- crinol. Metab.* 67:438–43

106. Russo I, Russo J. 1994. Role of hCG and inhibin in breast cancer. *Int. J. Oncol.* 4:297–306

107. Saito S, Roche PC, McCormick DJ, Ryan RJ. 1989. Synthetic peptide segments of inhibin alpha- and beta-subunits preparation and characterization of polyclonal antibodies. *Endocrinology* 125:898–905

108. Schneyer A, Mason A, Burton L, Ziegner J, Crowley W. 1990. Immunoreactive inhibin alpha-subunit in human serum: implication for radioimmunoassay. *J. Clin. Endocrinol. Metab.* 70:1208–12

109. Schneyer A, O'Neil D, Crowley W. 1992. Activin binding proteins in human serum and follicular fluid. *J. Clin. Endocrinol. Metab.* 74:1320–24

110. Schwall R, Lai C. 1991. Erythroid differentiation assays for activin. In *Peptide Growth Factors,* Part C, ed. D Barnes, JP Mather, GH Sato, 198:347–58 San Diego: Harcourt Brace Jovanovich

111. Schwall R, Schmelzer CH, Matsuyama E, Mason AJ. 1989. Multiple actions of recombinant activin A in vivo. *Endocrinology* 125:1420–23

112. Schwall RH, Mason AJ, Wilcox JN, Bassett SG, Zeleznik AJ. 1990. Localization of inhibin/activin subunit mRNAs within the primate ovary. *Mol. Endocrinol.* 4:75–79

113. Schwall RH, Robbins K, Jardieu P, Chang L, Mason AJ, Lai C, Terrell T. 1993. Activin induces cell death in hepatocytes in vivo and in vitro. *Hepatology* 18:347–56

114. Shimasaki S, Koga M, Buscaglia M, Simmons D, Bicsak T, Ling M. 1989. Follistatin gene expression in the ovary and extragonadal tissues. *Mol. Endocrinol.* 3:651–59

115. Shimonaka M, Inouye S, Shimasaki S, Ling N. 1991. Follistatin binds to both activin and inhibin through the common beta-subunit. *Endocrinology* 128:3313–15

116. Shiozaki M, Sakai R, Tabuchi M, Nakamura T, Sugino K, et al. 1992. Evidence for the participation of endogenous activin A (erythroid differentiation factor) in the regulation of erythropoiesis. *Proc. Natl. Acad. Sci. USA* 89:1553–56

117. Shitani Y, Takada Y, Tamasaki T, Saito S. 1991. Radioimmunoassay for activin A/EDF levels in various biological material. *J. Immunol. Methods* 137:267–74

118. Sinosich MJ, Sieg S, Zakher A, Ling M, Saunders DM, et al. 1991. Radioimmunoassay of inhibin based on synthetic human inhibin alpha chain peptides. *Clin. Chem.* 37:40–46

119. Smith KB, Fraser HM. 1991. Control of progesterone and inhibin secretion during the luteal phase in the macaque. *J. Endocrinol.* 128:107–13

120. Deleted in proof

121. Stewart A, Miborrow H, Ring J, Crowther C, Forage R. 1986. Human inhibin genes: genomic characterization and sequencing. *FEBS Lett.* 206:329–34

122. Stouffer R, Dahl K, Hess D, Woodruff T, Mather J, Molkness T. 1994. Systemic and intraluteal infusion of inhibin A and activin A in rhesus monkeys during the luteal phase of the menstrual cycle. *Biol. Reprod.* 50:888–95

123. Stouffer R, Woodruff T, Dahl K, Hess D, Mather J, Molkness T. 1993. Human recombinant activin-A alters pituitary luteinizing hormone and follicle-stimulating hormone secretion, follicular development, and steroidogenesis during the menstrual cycle in rhesus monkeys. *J. Clin. Endocrinol. Metab.* 77:241–48

124. Sugawra M, DePaolo L, Nakatani A, DiMarzo, SJ, Ling N. 1990. Radioimmunoassay of follistatin: application for in vitro fertilization procedures. *J. Clin. Endocrinol. Metab.* 71:1672–74

125. Sugino H, Nakamura T, Hasegawa Y, Miyamoto K, Abe Y, et al. 1988. Erythroid differentiation factor can modulate follicular granulosa cell functions. *Biochem. Biophys. Res. Commun.* 153:281–88

126. Suzuki A, Nagai T, Nishimatsu S, Sugino H, Eto Y, et al. 1994. Autoinduction of activin genes in early *Xenopus* embryos. *Biochem. J.* 298:275–80

127. ten Dijke P, Ichijo H, Franzen P, Schulz P, Saras J, et al. 1993. Activin recep-

tor-like kinases: a novel subclass of cell-surface receptors with predicted serine/threonine kinase activity. *Oncogene* 8:2879–87

128. Thomsen G, Woolf T, Whitman M, Sokol S, Vaughan J, et al. 1990. Activins are expressed early in Xenopus embryogenesis and can induce axial mesoderm and anterior structures. *Cell* 63:485–93

129. Tierney ML, Goss NH, Tomkins SM, Kerr DB, Pitt DE, et al. 1990. Physiochemical and biological characterization of recombinant human inhibin A. *Endocrinology* 126:3268–70

130. Deleted in proof

131. Vale W, Grant G, Amoss M, Backwell R, Guillemin R. 1972. Culture of enzymatically dispersed pituitary cells: functional validation of a method. *J. Clin. Endocrinol. Metab.* 91:562–72

132. Vale W, Hsueh A, Rivier C, Yu J. 1990. The inhibin/activin family of hormones and growth factors. In *Handbook of Experimental Pharmacology,* ed. MB Sporn, AB Roberts, 95:211–48. Heidleberg: Springer-Verlag

133. Vale W, Rivier C, Hsueh A, Campen C, Meunier H, Bicsak T. 1988. Chemical and biological characterization of the inhibin family of protein hormones. *Recent Prog. Horm. Res.* 44:1–34

134. Vassalli A, Matzuk M, Lee K, Jaenisch R. 1994. Activin/inhibin βb subunit gene disruption leads to defects in eyelid development and female reproduction. *Genes Dev.* 8:414–27

135. Vaughan JM, Rivier J, Corrigan AZ, McClintock R, Campen DA, et al. 1989. Detection and purification of inhibin using antisera generated against synthetic peptide fragments. *Methods Enzymol.* 168:588–617

136. Wang X, Lin E, Ng-Eaton E, Downward J, Lodish H, Weinberg R. 1991. Expression cloning and characterization of the TGF-beta type III receptor. *Cell* 67:797–805

137. Watanabe G, Taya K, Sasamoto S. 1990. Dynamics of ovarian inhibin secretion during the oestrus cycle of the rat. *J. Endocrinol.* 126:151–57

138. Wong W, Garg S, Bald L, Fendly B, Woodruff T, Lofgren J. 1993. Monoclonal antibody based ELISAs for measurement of activins in biological fluids. *J. Immunol. Methods* 165:1–10

139. Woodruff T, Krummen L, Baly D, Garg S, Allison D, et al. 1993. Quantitative two-site enzyme-linked immunosorbent assays for inhibin A, activin A, and activin B. *Hum. Reprod.* 8:133–37

140. Woodruff TK, D'Agostino J, Schwartz

N, Mayo KE. 1988. Dynamic changes in inhibin messenger RNAs in rat ovarian follicles during the reproductive cycle. *Science* 239:1296–99

141. Woodruff TK, D'Agostino J, Schwartz N, Mayo KE. 1989. Decreased inhibin gene expression in preovulatory follicles requires primary gonadotropin surges. *Endocrinology* 124:2193–99

142. Woodruff TK, Kaiser ML, Rahl J, Ackland J, Schwartz N, Mayo KE. 1991. Expression of ovarian inhibin during pregnancy in the rat. *Endocrinology* 128:1647–54

143. Woodruff TK, Krummen L, Chen SA, Lyon R, Hansen SE, et al. 1993. Pharmacokinetic profile of recombinant human inhibin A and activin A in the immature rat II. Tissue distribution of ^{125}I-rh-inhibin A and ^{125}I-rh-activin A in immature female and male rats. *Endocrinology* 132:725–34

144. Woodruff TK, Krummen L, McCray G, Mather JP. 1993. In situ ligand binding of ^{125}I-rh-activin A and ^{125}I-rh-inhibin A to the adult rat ovary. *Endocrinology* 133:2998–3006

145. Woodruff TK, Krummen LA, Chen S, DeGuzman G, Lyon R, et al. 1993. Pharmacokinetic profile of recombinant human inhibin A and activin A in the immature rat I. Serum profile of rh-inhibin A and rh-activin A in the immature female rat. *Endocrinology* 132:715–24

146. Woodruff TK, Krummen LA, Lyon RJ, Stocks DL, Mather JP. 1993. Recombinant human inhibin A and recombinant human activin A regulate pituitary and ovarian function in the adult female rat. *Endocrinology* 132:2332–41

147. Woodruff TK, Lyons RJ, Hansen SE, Rice GC, Mather JP. 1990. Inhibin and activin regulate rat ovarian folliculogenesis. *Endocrinology* 127:3196–205

148. Deleted in proof

149. Woodruff TK, Mayo KE. 1990. Regulation of inhibin synthesis in the rat ovary. *Annu. Rev. Physiol.* 52:807–21

150. Wrana J, Tran J, Attisano L, Arrora K, Childs S, et al. 1994. Two distinct transmembrane serine-threonine kinases from *Drosophila melanogaster* form an activin receptor complex. *Mol. Cell. Biol.* 14:944–50

151. Ying S-Y. 1987. Inhibins and activins: chemical properties and biological activity. *Proc. Soc. Exp. Biol. Med.* 186:253–64

152. Yohkaichiya T, O'Connor A, deKretser DM. 1991. Circulating immunoreactive inhibin, gonadotropin, and prolactin lev-

els during pregnancy, lactation and post weaning estrous cycle in the rat. *Biol Reprod.* 44:6–12

153. Yohkaichiya T, Polson D, O'Connor A, Bishop S, Mamers P, McLachlan RI. 1991. Concentrations of immunoreactive inhibin in serum during human pregnancy: evidence for an ovarian contribution. *Reprod. Fertil. Dev.* 3: 671–78

Annu. Rev. Physiol. 1995. 57:245–62

THE ROLE OF REACTIVE OXYGEN METABOLITES IN GLOMERULAR DISEASE

Sudhir V. Shah

Department of Medicine, Division of Nephrology, University of Arkansas for Medical Sciences, 4301 W. Markham, Slot 501, Little Rock, Arkansas 72205

KEY WORDS: free radicals, glomerulonephritis, oxidants, glomerular function

INTRODUCTION

A large body of evidence accumulated over the last decade indicates that partially reduced oxygen metabolites are important mediators of ischemic, toxic, and immune-mediated tissue injury (7, 19, 30, 32, 52, 82). Numerous studies have examined the role of reactive oxygen metabolites in leukocyte-dependent and -independent models and the biological effects these metabolites have in glomerular pathophysiology (9, 21, 73, 74). In this review, I define the term reactive oxygen metabolites, briefly recount the sequence of events that led to the consideration of these metabolites as important mediators of tissue injury, and present the available evidence in support of the role of reactive oxygen metabolites in glomerular disease, including the recent studies in which the role of intrinsic antioxidant defenses are beginning to be delineated.

Oxygen normally accepts four electrons and is converted directly to water. However, partial reduction of oxygen can and does occur in biological systems, which leads to the generation of partially reduced and potentially toxic reactive oxygen intermediates (33, 53). Thus sequential reduction of oxygen along the univalent pathway leads to the generation of superoxide anion, hydrogen peroxide, hydroxyl radical, and water (33, 53).

oxygen→superoxide→hydrogen peroxide→hydroxyl radical→water.
(free radical)   (free radical)

245

Superoxide and hydrogen peroxide appear to be the primary species generated; they may play a role in the generation of additional and more reactive oxidants, including the highly reactive hydroxyl radical (or a related highly oxidizing species) in which iron salts act as a catalyst in a reaction commonly referred to as the metal-catalyzed Haber-Weiss reaction (36).

$$Fe^{3+} + O_{2-} \rightarrow Fe^{2+} + O_2$$

$$\frac{Fe^{2+} + H_2O_2 \rightarrow Fe^{3+} + \cdot OH + OH^-}{O_{2-} + H_2O_2 \rightarrow O_{2+} + \cdot OH + OH}$$

Additional reactive oxygen metabolites are formed as a result of the metabolism of hydrogen peroxide by neutrophil-derived myeloperoxidase (MPO) (the enzyme responsible for the green color of pus) to produce highly reactive toxic products, including hypochlorous acid. MPO reacting with hydrogen peroxide forms an enzyme substrate complex that can oxidize various halides to produce highly reactive toxic products. Because of the wide distribution of chloride ion in biologic systems, the formation of hypochlorous acid (HOCl, the active ingredient in Clorox bleach) is probably the most significant product (30, 46, 47, 84).

$$H_2O_2 + Cl^- \xrightarrow{MPO} HOCl + H^+.$$

Other hypohalous acids may also be generated. For example, Weiss et al recently reported the generation of hypobromous acid by eosinophils (86). In addition, human neutrophils have been reported to generate long-lived (half-life approximately 18 h) oxidants with characteristics similar to N-chloramines (83). These oxygen metabolites, including the free radical species superoxide and hydroxyl radical and other metabolites such as hydrogen peroxide and hypohalous acids, are often collectively referred to as reactive oxygen metabolites (ROM).

It is now well-established that oxidants generated by leukocytes have bactericidal activity, which indicates at least one functional role for ROM (3, 46). The notion that ROM are important in inflammation was first suggested by McCord. He reasoned that because phagocytizing neutrophils, the effector cells of the acute inflammatory response, release large amounts of superoxide extracellularly and because superoxide dismutase, an enzyme that scavenges superoxide possesses anti-inflammatory activity, superoxide anion and other oxygen metabolites could be important chemical mediators of the inflammatory process (51). This hypothesis has received considerable support from numerous studies in which the effect of ROM produced either by an enzymatic–generating system such as xanthine-xanthine oxidase or by activated leukocytes has been examined in a variety of biological systems, as well as in vivo studies, where scavengers of ROM appear to be protective.

ROLE OF ROM IN GLOMERULAR DISEASE

The evidence implicating ROM in glomerular injury may be addressed by three broad questions. What are the sources of ROM that may participate in glomerular injury? What are the biological effects of ROM relevant to glomerular pathophysiology? How well has the role of ROM been demonstrated in animal models of glomerular disease?

Sources of ROM

Neutrophils and monocytes/macrophages exhibit a burst of oxidative metabolism (respiratory burst), with a marked increase in oxygen uptake and the generation of ROM in response to plasma membrane perturbation by a variety of soluble and particulate stimuli (30). Phagocytosis per se is not essential to trigger the oxidative burst; perturbation of the plasma membrane appears to be the critical event. In in vitro studies, a variety of soluble and particulate stimuli, many of them relevant to glomerular injury, enhance the generation of ROM by neutrophils and monocytes. Of particular interest is the demonstration that several immune reactants such as serum-treated zymosan (a C_3b receptor stimulus), heat-aggregated IgG (Fc receptor stimulus), immune complexes, and complement components have been shown to trigger the oxidative burst (30). Anti-neutrophil cytoplasmic autoantibodies (ANCA) present in the circulation of patients with pauci-immune necrotizing vasculitis and pauci-immune crescentic glomerulonephritis have been shown to significantly increase the generation of superoxide by neutrophils (29). Thus stimulated neutrophils or monocytes are potential sources of ROM in leukocyte-dependent glomerular injury.

More direct evidence supporting this concept has been given by Poelstra et al, who used cytochemical techniques to demonstrate the presence of superoxide anion and hydrogen peroxide–generating leukocytes in anti-Thy-1 and anti-glomerular basement membrane (GBM)-induced glomerulonephritis (59). Similarly, enhanced generation of ROM by macrophages isolated from glomeruli of rabbits with anti-GBM antibody disease and by macrophages isolated from nephritic glomeruli in the anti-thymocyte serum model has been demonstrated (14, 57). Thus stimulated neutrophils or monocytes may serve as sources of ROM in proliferative and exudative glomerulonephritides (Table 1a,b).

Ample evidence supports the concept that resident glomerular cells serve as sources of ROM in the noninflammatory forms of glomerular disease (Table 1a,b). Because phagocyte-like cells are present in the glomerulus (particularly

Table 1a   Sources of ROM for glomerular injury

Leukocytes

In vitro studies
   A wide variety of soluble and particulate stimuli, including immune complexes, complement components, and ANCA (29, 30)

In vivo studies
   Cytochemical detection of the presence of superoxide and hydrogen peroxide generating leukocytes in anti-Thy-1 and anti-GBM–induced GN (59)
   Enhanced superoxide and hydroxyl radical generated by macrophages isolated from glomeruli of rabbits with anti-GBM antibody disease (14)
   Enhanced superoxide generated by macrophages isolated from nephritic glomeruli (anti-thymocyte serum) (57)

Table 1b   Sources of ROM for glomerular injury

Resident glomerular cells	
Isolated glomeruli	In vitro: phorbol myristate acetate, zymosan, trypsin, chymotrypsin, (73); adriamycin (80) In vivo: (35)
Mesangial cells	PAF, immune complexes, MAC, TNF, interleukin-1 (9, 73) (61)
Glomerular epithelial cells	Puromycin aminonucleoside (43)

mesangial cells), it was postulated that glomerular cells, like other phagocytic cells, would also generate ROM in response to plasma membrane pertubation. In response to phorbol myristate acetate, a plasma membrane perturbing agent, rat glomeruli showed a marked chemiluminescence response, a sensitive measure of ROM generated by phagocytic cells (70). In a subsequent study, chymotrypsin or trypsin markedly increased light emission from the glomeruli. Neutral proteases from infiltrating leukocytes and/or renal tissue are released in glomerular diseases, which suggests a potential mechanism for the production of ROM in glomerular diseases. In vivo generation of hydrogen peroxide by normal glomeruli has been demonstrated (35) utilizing aminotriazole-induced inactivation of catalase as a measure of intracellular generation of hydrogen peroxide. Adriamycin, an agent that induces nephrotic syndrome, has been shown to enhance the intracellular generation of ROM by freshly isolated glomeruli in vitro (80).

These studies with isolated glomeruli are amply supported by studies utilizing cultured glomerular cells. Mesangial cells have enhanced generation of superoxide and hydrogen peroxide in response to a variety of stimuli, including opsonized zymosan, immune complexes, membrane attack complex, and platelet–activating factor (9, 61, 73). In a recent study, Radeke et al have shown that human glomerular mesangial cells express low potential cytochrome b_{558} α- and β-subunits, a 45- or 66-kDa flavo protein, and a 47-kDa phospho-protein, the three essential components of a plasma membrane–associated NADPH oxidase system, in a manner similar to that described in neutrophils (60). Finally, glomerular epithelial cells appear to be the target of injury in many of the noninflammatory forms of glomerular disease, including the nephrotic syndrome induced by the injection of puromycin aminonucleoside. In response to puromycin aminonucleoside, cultured glomerular epithelial cells enhance the generation of hydrogen peroxide (43). The ability of glomerular cells to generate ROM appears to be well established (Table 1). Therefore, either leukocytes in inflammatory glomerular diseases or resident glomerular cells in noninflammatory diseases serve as sources for ROM.

Effects of ROM Relevant to Glomerular Disease

The major manifestations of glomerular disease are proteinuria, altered glo-merular filtration rate (GFR), and depending on the type of glomerular disease, morphological changes (Figure 1). The biological effects of ROM have been divided into three general areas: those that are most relevant to the occurrence of proteinuria, those that are most relevant to altered GFR, and those that are most relevant to morphological changes.

It is generally accepted that leukocytes cause proteinuria (a hallmark of glomerular diseases) by damaging the GBM, which serves as the major ultra-filtration barrier to restrict the entry of proteins into the urinary space. The degradation of the GBM by stimulated neutrophils is caused by the activation of a latent metalloenzyme (most likely gelatinase) by hypochlorous acid or a similar oxidant generated by the myleoperoxidase-hydrogen peroxide-halide system (Table 2) (75). Other studies have shown that oxidants could contribute to GBM damage by increasing its susceptibility to proteolytic damage (81) and by inactivating the alpha1-proteinase inhibitor (the primary regulator of neutrophil elastase) (15, 16, 18, 85), thus allowing the released elastase to more readily inflict damage to the extracellular matrix. A recent study reports

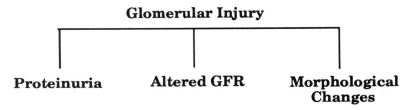

Glomerular Injury

Proteinuria   **Altered GFR**   **Morphological Changes**

Figure 1   The role of ROM in glomerular disease. The major manifestations of glomerular disease.

Table 2 Effects of ROM relevant in glomerular pathophysiology

Effects of ROM relevant to the occurrence of proteinuria
ROM participate in GBM degradation (75, 81)
Lipid peroxide induces enhanced generation of gelatinase by mesangial cells (41)
ROM decrease de novo synthesis of glomerular proteoglycans (42)
Infusion of phorbol myristate acetate, an activator of neutrophils, results in proteinuria (63) and
   a fall in GFR (88). These effects are prevented by catalase
Hydrogen peroxide infused directly into the renal artery causes massive transient proteinuria by
   inducing a molecular size selectivity defect (89)
Infusion of myleoperoxidase-hydrogen peroxide induces proteinuria (38)

Effect of ROM relevant to altered GFR
Reactive oxygen metabolites generated enzymatically or by stimulated neutrophils:
   Increase glomerular eicosanoid synthesis (1, 10, 69)
   Increase glomerular cyclic AMP content (6, 71)
   Induce a reduction in glomerular and mesangial cell planar surface and myosin light chain
      phosphorylation. These effects appear to be mediated by PAF (26)
ROM have an effect on release and inactivation of TNF (8, 9)
Infusion of 8-epi-PGF$_2\alpha$, a novel prostanoid produced by non-cyclooxygenase mechanism
   involving lipid peroxidation (56), results in a marked fall in GFR and RPF (77)

Role of ROM in the morphological changes
Infusion of myleoperoxidase-hydrogen peroxide causes significant proteinuria, marked influx
   of platelets, endothelial cell swelling, and epithelial cell foot process effacement. Four to ten
   days later a marked proliferative glomerular lesion develops (38, 39)
Scavengers of ROM prevent the reduction in glomerular ADPase activity and increase in
   platelet aggregation in anti-Thy-1 and anti-GBM antibody disease models (59)
Rats immunized with myleoperoxidase and perfused with lysosomal enzyme extract and
   hydrogen peroxide develop a proliferative glomerulonephritis (27)

that lipid peroxide (linoleic acid hydroperoxide) enhanced the production of gelatinase by mesangial cells, and thus enhanced generation of matrix-degrading proteinase may contribute to proteinuria (41). Prevention of proteinuria by catalase in neutrophil-dependent glomerulonephritides (vide infra) suggests that the oxidative mechanism for GBM degradation described above may be relevant to leukocyte-dependent glomerular injury.

In contrast to the increased degradation suggested by these studies, Kanwar et al suggest that synthesis of glomerular heparan sulfate proteoglycans (HSPGs) is highly susceptible to oxidant injury (42). A drastic dose-dependent decrease in the de novo synthesis of proteoglycans, in response to xanthine-xanthine oxidase (a system that generates ROM), was demonstrated using an isolated perfused kidney model. The synthesis of type IV collagen and laminin was decreased only slightly (~15%). Morphological studies revealed a 14-fold decrease in the [^{34}S]sulfate–associated autoradiographic grains overlying the GBM. Thus the nascent core peptide appears to be highly susceptible to selective direct damage from ROM during de novo synthesis of HSPGs necessary to maintain integrity of the GBM and normal glomerular ultrafiltration.

Direct in vivo effects of ROM on glomerular function have been examined in several studies (Table 2). Infusion of phorbol myristate acetate (a potent activator of leukocytes) or of cobra venom factor in the renal artery caused significant proteinuria that was prevented by catalase (which destroys hydrogen peroxide) and neutrophil depletion (63, 65, 88). Recently it was shown that hydrogen peroxide infused directly into the renal artery caused massive transient proteinuria with no effect on GFR and renal plasma flow (89). Fraction clearances of graded-size neutral dextrans of larger molecular radii, an index of glomerular size selectivity, were significantly and substantially elevated after hydrogen peroxide infusion.

These studies indicate that hydrogen peroxide and/or its metabolites generated by neutrophils can cause proteinuria. Johnson et al reasoned that hydrogen peroxide–mediated injury involves the myeloperoxidase-hydrogen peroxide-halide system. The postulate is particularly attractive in view of the high cationic nature of myleoperoxidase with an isoelectric point of >10. Johnson et al demonstrated that infusion of myeloperoxidase followed by hydrogen peroxide in a chloride-containing solution into the renal artery in rats results in significant proteinuria (38) and, 4 to 10 days later, development of a marked proliferative glomerular lesion (39) (Table 2). In addition, halogenation (as measured by the incorporation of [^{125}I]) of glomeruli and GBM was demonstrated in an in situ model of neutrophil-mediated immune complex glomerulonephritis (40). These studies indicate that the myeloperoxidase-hydrogen peroxide-halide system is activated in a model of neutrophil-mediated immune complex glomerulonephritis and that the myeloperoxidase-hydrogen peroxide-halide system is capable of inducing glomerular injury that results in proteinuria.

Increased production of prostaglandins and thromboxane has been demonstrated in various human and experimental glomerulopathies, and these agents have been implicated as important mediators that cause proteinuria and/or a fall in GFR in experimental models of glomerular disease, including anti-GBM antibody disease, adriamycin-induced nephrotic syndrome in rats, and complement-mediated glomerular injury (20, 50, 66). Because the most dramatic effect of these autocoids is on glomerular hemodynamics, they are further discussed under the effects of ROM that are relevant to altered GFR. It has been demonstrated that ROM generated either enzymatically or by stimulated neutrophils increase the synthesis of prostaglandin E_2, $PGF_2\alpha$, $6_{keto}PGF_1\alpha$, the stable metabolite of prostacyclin, and thromboxane B_2 (Table 2) (1, 10, 69). Thus some of the observed effects of ROM may be mediated through their effect on prostaglandin and thromboxane synthesis.

Roberts et al recently identified a series of prostaglandin F_2-like compounds that are produced in vivo in humans by a non-cyclooxygenase mechanism involving free radical–catalyzed peroxidation of arachidonic acid (56). Intrarenal arterial infusion of small amounts (0.5 μg/kg/min) of 8-epi-PGF$_2$α resulted in a dose-dependent reduction in GFR and renal plasma flow (RPF) (77). The changes were completely reversed by thromboxane A_2 receptor antagonist, which indicates that 8-epi-PGF$_2$α is a potent preglomerular vasoconstrictor acting principally through thromboxane A_2 receptor activation. This finding suggests that in those glomerular injuries where free radical mechanisms, including lipid peroxidation, have been implicated, the formation of novel prostanoids plays an important role in the fall in the GFR and the alterations in RPF (see Table 2).

Infusion of dibutryl cAMP and several hormones that increase cAMP content in glomeruli cause a fall in the glomerular ultrafiltration coefficient (28). In addition, the cAMP content in glomeruli is altered most strikingly by several local mediators of inflammation such as serotonin, histamine, and prostaglandins, which suggests that, as in other systems, cyclic nucleotides modulate inflammatory and/or immune response in glomerular disease (24, 25). It has been shown that xanthine-xanthine oxidase increases cAMP content in freshly isolated glomeruli, and the responsible metabolite appears to be hydrogen peroxide (71). Similarly cell free supernatants from stimulated neutrophils increase cAMP content in freshly isolated glomeruli, and this effect appears to be mediated by hydrogen peroxide and hypochlorous acid, the product of the myleoperoxidase-hydrogen peroxide-halide system (6).

In a recent study, the xanthine-xanthine oxidase system induced a reduction in the glomerular and mesangial cell planar surface and an increase in myosin light chain phosphorylation, a biochemical marker of contraction (26). Interestingly, these effects were completely blocked by a platelet–activating factor antagonist, which suggests that the effects of ROM are mediated by platelet-activating factor. Duque et al suggest that ROM, particularly hydrogen peroxide, could modulate the surface area of mesangial cells, modifying the ultrafiltration coefficient, and this change could explain the decrease in the GFR in those pathological conditions characterized by a fall in GFR.

Recent work has implicated platelets in glomerular injury. As mentioned above, infusion of myleoperoxidase and hydrogen peroxide causes a marked influx of platelets, endothelial cell swelling, and epithelial cell foot process effacement followed by a marked proliferative glomerular lesion (39). In addition, low doses of hydrogen peroxide stimulate the proliferation of cultured rat mesangial cells (27). These findings indicate that ROM are capable of inducing morphological changes that are similar to those seen in models of immune complex glomerulonephritis and anti-GBM antibody disease.

It has been suggested that glomerular ADPase is of major importance in preventing intraglomerular thrombus formation in experimental glomerulonephritis (59). Membrane-associated enzymes are apparently highly susceptible to ROM (4). There is a marked decrease in the activity of these enzymes in two models of glomerulonephritis (anti-GBM and anti-Thy1) that is characterized by influx of polymorphonuclear neutrophils (59). Scavengers of oxygen metabolites prevent the decrease in glomerular ADPase, which suggests that ROM acts in the reduction of glomerular ADPase activity (Table 2) (59).

Necrotizing crescentic glomerulonephritis associated with anti-MPO antibodies is part of ANCA-associated glomerulonephritis and is characterized by segmental fibrinoid necrosis of the GBM and marked infiltration of neutrophils and mononuclear cells. The close association of pauci-immune necrotizing glomerulonephritis and anti-MPO antibodies suggests a pathogenetic role for anti-MPO–directed immune response. Rats immunized with MPO and perfused with lysosomal enzyme extract and hydrogen peroxide developed glomerular intracapillary thromboses, followed by a proliferative glomerulonephritis that was characterized by glomerular capillary wall necrosis, extracapillary cell proliferation, infiltration of neutrophils and monocytes, and vasculitis (27). These studies indicate that the ROM are capable of inducing many of the functional and morphological changes that are observed in glomerular diseases.

ROM have usually been regarded as toxic metabolites with cytotoxic properties. However, at low concentrations they seem to play a significant regulatory role without inducing cell death. The effects of ROM in altering the cAMP levels has been described above. In addition, regulated generation of low concentrations of ROM may serve as intracellular signals for gene activation involving specific transcription factors such as NF-κB (67, 68, 79) and may represent a second messenger system for generation of cytokines involved in tissue injury and repair. Recently a number of monocyte-specific cytokines have been described that include the monocyte colony–stimulating factor (CSF-1) and the monocyte chemoattractant protein (MCP-1). MCP-1 has been identified as a product of a gene belonging to the small, inducible cytokine family, known in the murine system as the JE gene. CSF-1 is a cytokine required for proliferation, maturation, and activation. Expression of the JE/MCP-1 and CSF-1 genes can be rapidly induced by a number of agents, including tumor necrosis factor. Satriano et al have shown that scavengers of free radicals attenuate the increase in the mRNA level in response to TNF-α and aggregated IgG. Generation of superoxide anion by xanthine oxidase and hypoxanthine increase the mRNA levels of these genes. They concluded that the generation of reactive oxygen species, possibly by NADPH-dependent oxidase, is involved in the induction of the JE/MCP-1 and CSF-1 genes by TNF-α and IgG complexes. Local generation of ROM could represent a factor responsible for the expression of JE/MCP-1 in immune-mediated increased expression of monocyte chemoattractant protein in glomeruli from rats with anti-Thy-1 glomerulonephritis (76).

Tumor necrosis factor is able to generate ROM, superoxide anion, and hydrogen peroxide in glomerular mesangial cells. There is also in vitro evidence of effects of ROM on the release of TNF-α from lipopolysaccharide-activated mesangial cells (8, 9). Although the role of these cytokines has not been adequately defined in glomerular diseases, these results indicate important interactions between other mediators and reactive oxygen species. For additional examples of such interactions, the reader is referred to a recent review (2).

Effects of Scavengers of ROM in Animal Models of Glomerular Disease

One of the best-characterized models of complement- and neutrophil-dependent glomerular injury is the heterologous phase of anti-GBM antibody disease. In this model, treatment with catalase markedly reduced the proteinuria, whereas superoxide dismutase had no protective effect (64) (Table 3). In another study, dimethylthiourea, a potent hydroxyl radical scavenger, or deferoxamine, an iron chelator, significantly attenuated proteinuria in the complement- and neutrophil-dependent heterologous phase of anti-GBM antibody disease in rabbits (13). Although the role of iron is not completely understood, the protective effect of iron chelators has generally been taken as evidence for the participation of hydroxyl radical in tissue injury because iron is critical in the generation of hydroxyl radical (via the Haber-Weiss reaction).

The ability of glomerular cells to generate ROM suggests that they may be important mediators of glomerular injury in glomerular diseases that lack infiltrating leukocytes (Table 3). A single intravenous injection of puromycin aminonucleoside (PAN) results in marked proteinuria and glomerular morphological changes that are similar to minimal change disease in humans. Diamond et al reported that allopurinol (an inhibitor of xanthine oxidase) and superoxide dismutase were protective in PAN-induced nephrotic syndrome, which suggests a role for xanthine oxidase–generated superoxide anion in this model of minimal change disease (22). Beaman et al confirmed the protective effect of

Table 3 Evidence for the role of ROM in animal models of glomerular injury

Scavengers of reactive oxygen metabolites reduce proteinuria in
  Complement and neutrophil-dependent heterologous phase of anti-GBM antibody disease (13, 64)
  Puromycin aminonucleoside model of minimal change disease (11, 22, 78)
  Adriamycin model of minimal change disease (58)
  Passive Heymann nephritis model of membranous nephropathy (72)
  Cationized gamma globulin-induced immune complex GN (62)

superoxide dismutase and in addition reported that proteinuria was significantly reduced in rats receiving polyethylene glycol (PEG) catalase, which suggested a role for hydrogen peroxide and superoxide anion in this model of glomerular disease (11). Superoxide anion and hydrogen peroxide may interact (with iron as a catalyst) to generate the hydroxyl radical. Several studies have, in fact, shown that enhanced generation of hydrogen peroxide and superoxide anion is accompanied by enhanced generation of a hydroxyl radical (or a similar highly oxidizing species). Thakur et al reported the protective effects of two hydroxyl radical scavengers and an iron chelator, further implicating hydroxyl radical in PAN-induced nephrotic syndrome (78).

A single intravenous injection of adriamycin (an anthracycline antibiotic used in cancer chemotherapy) causes nephrotic syndrome in rats (73) with morphological and functional changes similar to those seen in minimal change disease in humans. Adriamycin undergoes a one-electron reduction to a free radical, a semi-quinone species catalyzed by microsomes, sarcosomes, mitochondria, nuclei, and cytoplasm (73). Thus adriamycin-induced nephrotic syndrome appears to be a good model to demonstrate the concept that ROM generated intracellularly by glomerular cells can cause glomerular injury resulting in proteinuria. However, the evidence from scavenger studies is somewhat controversial. There is one study that showed the protective effect of superoxide dismutase (Table 3) (58), whereas another study did not find any protective effects of scavengers of ROM (12).

Passive Heymann nephritis, induced by a single intravenous injection of anti-Fx1A, is a complement-dependent and neutrophil-independent model of glomerular disease that resembles membranous nephropathy in humans. Shah reported that superoxide dismutase or catalase (native or PEG-coupled) did not affect the anti-Fx1A–induced proteinuria. In contrast, scavengers of hydroxyl radical and deferoxamine markedly reduced the proteinuria (72). The protective effects of the hydroxyl radical scavengers and iron chelator suggests that the hydroxyl radical plays a part in passive Heymann nephritis. Similarly, Rahman et al reported that two hydroxyl radical scavengers significantly reduced the proteinuria in the cationized gamma globulin–induced immune complex glomerulonephritis, a complement- and neutrophil-independent model of membranous nephropathy (62). Taken together these studies suggest an important role for hydroxyl radical in animal models of membranous nephropathy. Thus it appears that leukocytes or resident glomerular cells serve as sources for ROM. In vitro and in vivo studies indicate that ROM have many effects that are relevant to the functional and morphological changes observed in glomerular injury, and data on scavengers of ROM document the importance of ROM in glomerular injury. While most studies have emphasized enhanced generation of ROM, antioxidant defenses are likely to be equally important as determinants of injury.

ROLE OF ANTIOXIDANT DEFENSES IN GLOMERULAR INJURY

A multilayered system of defense has evolved in respiring cells to counter the threat from the reactive intermediates generated by the univalent reduction of oxygen. The first defense is simply avoidance of the univalent pathway. Thus most of the oxygen consumed (~90%) by respiring cells is utilized by cytochrome oxidase, which can accomplish a tetravalent reduction of oxygen to water without releasing either superoxide or hydrogen peroxide (Figure 2) (34). Despite this, in respiring cells, at least, some reduction of oxygen occurs via the univalent path. In in vitro studies, the ability of microsomes and mitochondria to generate superoxide and hydrogen peroxide (17, 31) has been demonstrated. Precisely how much univalent reduction occurs in vivo is less certain (estimated to be ~2–5%) but not insignificant, as evidenced by the ubiquity of superoxide dismutase in mammalian cells.

Two superoxide dismutases have been identified in mammalian tissues: a cytoplasmic copper-zinc and a mitochondrial manganese–dependent enzyme. The enzymatic mechanisms for cellular detoxification of hydrogen peroxide are catalase and glutathione peroxidase (30, 34, 82). Catalase, a heme enzyme, catalyzes the divalent reduction of hydrogen peroxide to water. Glutathione peroxidase is a seleno enzyme that catalyzes the reaction

Glutathione peroxidase
$$2GSH + H_2O_2 \rightarrow GSSG + 2H_2O.$$

The reaction accomplishes the reduction of hydrogen peroxide to water at the expense of oxidation of glutathione to the corresponding disulfide. In order for the enzyme to continue to reduce a flux of hydrogen peroxide, the GSSG

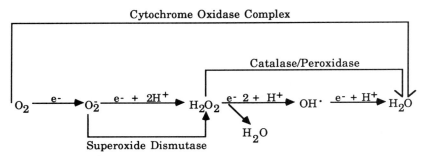

Figure 2 Schema shows reactive oxygen metabolites generated as a result of the sequential reduction of oxygen to water along the univalent pathway and the enzymatic defenses against superoxide and hydrogen peroxide.

must be reduced back to GSH by the NADPH-dependent enzyme GSSG reductase.

$$\text{GSSG} + \text{NADPH} + \text{H}^+ \xrightarrow{\text{GSSG reductase}} 2\text{GSH} + \text{NADP}^+.$$

In turn, the NADPH can be regenerated from the NADP$^+$ via the hexose monophosphate shunt (HMPS). Glutathione peroxidase can also act upon lipid hydroperoxides, thus countering the toxicity of a wide range of peroxides (34, 48). Recently, a selenium-independent glutathione peroxidase activity that can detoxify organic peroxides, but not metabolize hydrogen peroxide, has been identified (49).

In contrast to superoxide and hydrogen peroxide, no enzymes are known to directly regulate the concentration of hydroxyl radical. Indeed, the primary stratagem of the cell is to use superoxide dismutase, catalase, and glutathione peroxidase to prevent superoxide and hydrogen peroxide from participating in reactions that generate more reactive oxidants (34, 82). Under normal conditions, these defenses serve to protect the cells from superoxide and hydrogen peroxide and from hydroxyl radical or other oxidizing species by removing its precursors. It has been shown, for example, that endothelial cells are able to degrade hydrogen peroxide generated by neutrophils or glucose-glucose oxidase, and only after this rate of hydrogen peroxide is exceeded is there evidence of cytotoxicity (23).

The importance of endogenous antioxidant defenses in glomerular injury has been delineated by demonstrating that augmentation of the defenses results in diminished injury and that reduction in defenses results in enhanced injury (Table 4). It was shown that subjecting rat kidneys to ischemia-reperfusion injury resulted in augmented antioxidant enzymes and these enhanced enzyme activities protected against hydrogen peroxide–induced fall in GFR and proteinuria (87). Similarly, it was reported that glucocorticoid administration resulted in an increase in the activity of superoxide dismutase (but not glutathione peroxidase or catalase), and this was accompanied by protection against PAN-induced and hydrogen peroxide–induced proteinuria (44). In contrast, feeding rats a selenium-deficient diet resulted in marked diminution of glutathione peroxidase. Additionally, a marked increase in urinary protein occurred following PAN injection, which together suggest an important role of glutathione peroxidase in this model of glomerular disease (5). It was also reported that inhibition of superoxide dismutase led to an aggravation of PAN-induced proteinuria (37). These studies not only demonstrate the importance of endogenous antioxidant defenses but also provide additional support for the role of ROM in these models of glomerular injury.

These studies imply that regulation of the antioxidant enzymes contributes

Table 4   Role of intrinsic antioxidant enzymes in glomerular injury

Feeding selenium-deficient diet results in marked diminution of glutathione peroxidase accompanied by increase in PAN- and anti-Fx1A-induced proteinuria (5)
Inhibition of SOD[a] by diethyldithiocarbonate results in increase in PAN-induced proteinuria (37)
Induction of AOE[b] by ischemia-reperfusion injury protects against hydrogen peroxide–induced proteinuria (87)
Induction of AOE by glucocorticoids protects against PAN-induced proteinuria (44)

[a] Superoxide dismutase, [b] antioxidant enzymes

to renal disease. Indeed, in in vitro studies it has been shown that exposure of cultured mesangial cells to hydrogen peroxide induces mRNA and Mn-superoxide dismutase activity but not Cu Zn-superoxide dismutase activity (90). Similarly, glucocorticoids induce mRNA and Mn-superoxide dismutase activity in cultured glomerular endothelial cells (45). The mechanisms regulating antioxidant enzymes in mammalian cells are the focus of current intense investigation, and it is likely that we will learn not only about the regulation but also about the role of antioxidant defenses in various forms of injury in this decade.

GSH, a tripeptide, occurs in high concentrations in virtually all mammalian cells and is the most prevalent intracellular thiol (54) with many diverse functions. In addition to participation of GSH in the defense against ROM-mediated injury via the glutathione redox cycle (because thiols are easily oxidized), it may be preferentially (and non-enzymatically) oxidized by ROM, thereby protecting the tissues from oxidative damage. There is limited information on the importance of GSH in glomerular injury. However, a preliminary report shows that depletion of glutathione results in aggravation of PAN-induced proteinuria (55).

CONCLUSIONS

Sufficient in vitro and in vivo information exists to postulate that ROM are important mediators in glomerular pathophysiology. Nonetheless, the multifaceted nature of tissue injury makes it almost a certainty that the cooperative and sometimes complex interactions between different injurious mechanisms are important in the final expression of injury.

Literature Cited

1. Adler S, Stahl RAK, Baker PJ, Chen YP, Pritzl PM, Couser WG. 1987. Biphasic effect of oxygen radicals on prostaglandin production by rat mesangial cells. *Am. J. Physiol.* 252:F743–49
2. Ardaillou R, Baud L. 1991. Interactions between glomerular autocoids. *Sem. Nephrol.* 11:340–45
3. Babior BM. 1978. Oxygen-dependent microbial killing by phagocytes (second of two parts). *N. Engl. J. Med.* 298:721–25
4. Bakker WW, Baller JFW, Hardonk MJ. 1987. Decrease of glomerular ATPase activity induced by adriamycin is mediated by oxygen free radical species. *Kidney Int.* 31:1045–46
5. Baliga R, Baliga M, Shah SV. 1992. Effect of selenium deficient diet in experimental glomerular disease. *Am. J. Physiol.* 263:F214–21
6. Basci A, Wallin JD, Shah SV. 1987. Effect of stimulated neutrophils on cyclic nucleotide content in isolated rat glomeruli. *Am. J. Physiol.* 252:F429–36
7. Baud L, Ardaillou R. 1986. Reactive oxygen species: production and role in kidney. *Am. J. Physiol.* 251:F765–76
8. Baud L, Fouqueray B, Philippe C, Amrani A. 1992. Tumor necrosis factor alpha and mesangial cells. *Kidney Int.* 41:600–3
9. Baud L, Fouqueray B, Philippe C, Ardaillou R. 1992. Reactive oxygen species as glomerular autocoids. *J. Am. Soc. Nephrol.* 2:S132–38
10. Baud L, Nivez M-P, Chansel D, Ardaillou R. 1981. Stimulation by oxygen radicals of prostaglandin production by rat renal glomeruli. *Kidney Int.* 20:332–39
11. Beaman M, Birtwistle R, Howie AJ, Michael J, Adu D. 1987. The role of superoxide anion and hydrogen peroxide in glomerular injury induced by puromycin aminonucleoside in rats. *Clin. Sci.* 73:329–32
12. Bertolatus JA, Klinzman D, Bronsema DA, Ridnour L, Oberley LW. 1991. Evaluation of the role of reactive oxygen species in doxorubicin hydrochloride nephrosis. *J. Lab. Clin. Med.* 118:435–45
13. Boyce NW, Holdsworth SR. 1986. Hydroxyl radical mediation of immune renal injury by desferrioxamine. *Kidney Int.* 30:813–17
14. Boyce NW, Tipping PG, Holdsworth SR. 1989. Glomerular macrophages produce reactive oxygen species in experimental glomerulonephritis. *Kidney Int.* 35:778–82
15. Carp H, Janoff A. 1979. In vitro suppression of serum elastase–inhibitory capacity by reactive oxygen species generated by phagocytosing polymorphonuclear leukocytes. *J. Clin. Invest.* 63:793–97
16. Carp H, Janoff A. 1980. Phagocyte-derived oxidants suppress the elastase-inhibitory capacity of alpha1-proteinase inhibitor in vitro. *J. Clin. Invest.* 66:987–95
17. Chance B, Sies H, Boveris A. 1979. Hydroperoxide metabolism in mammalian organs. *Physiol. Rev.* 59:527–604
18. Clark RA, Stone PJ, El Hag A, Calore JD, Franzblau C. 1981. Myeloperoxidase-catalyzed inactivation of alpha1-protease inhibitor by human neutrophils. *J. Biol. Chem.* 256:3348–53
19. Cross CE, Halliwell B, Borish ET, Pryor WA, Ames BN, et al. 1987. Oxygen radicals and human disease. *Ann. Intern. Med.* 107:526–45
20. Cybulsky AV, Lieberthal W, Quigg RJ, Rennke HG, Salant DJ. 1987. A role for thromboxane in complement-mediated glomerular injury. *Am. J. Pathol.* 128:45–51
21. Diamond JR. 1992. The role of reactive oxygen species in animal models of glomerular disease. *Am. J. Kidney. Dis.* 19:292–300
22. Diamond JR, Bonventre JV, Karnovsky MJ. 1986. A role for oxygen free radicals in aminonucleoside nephrosis. *Kidney Int.* 29:478–83
23. Dobrina A, Patriarca P. 1986. Neutrophil-endothelial cell interaction. Evidence for and mechanisms of the self-protection of bovine microvascular endothelial cells from hydrogen peroxide–induced oxidative stress. *J. Clin. Invest.* 78:462–71
24. Dousa TP. 1979. Cyclic nucleotides in renal pathophysiology. In *Contemporary Issues in Nephrology,* ed. BM Brenner, JH Stein, pp. 251–85. New York: Churchill Livingstone
25. Dousa TP, Shah SV, Abboud HE. 1980. Potential role of cyclic nucleotides in glomerular pathophysiology. In *Advances in Cyclic Nucleotide Research,* ed. P Hamet, H Sands, pp. 285–99. New York: Raven. 461 pp.
26. Duque I, Garcia-Escribano C, Rodri-

guez-Puyol M, Diez-Marques ML, Lopez-Novoa JM, et al. 1992. Effects of reactive oxygen species on cultured rat mesangial cells and isolated rat glomeruli. *Am. J. Physiol.* 263:F466–73

27. Duque I, Puyol MR, Ruiz P, Gonzalez-Rubio M, Marques MLD, Puyol DR. 1993. Calcium channel blockers inhibit hydrogen peroxide–induced proliferation of cultured rat mesangial cells. *J. Pharmacol. Exp. Ther.* 267:612–16

28. Dworkin LD, Ichikawa I, Brenner BM. 1983. Hormonal modulation of glomerular function. *Am. J. Physiol.* 244:F95–104

29. Falk RJ, Terrell RS, Charles LA, Jennette JC. 1990. Anti–neutrophil cytoplasmic autoantibodies induce neutrophils to degranulate and produce oxygen radicals in vitro. *Proc. Natl. Acad. Sci. USA* 87:4115–19

30. Fantone JC, Ward PA. 1982. Role of oxygen-derived free radicals and metabolites in leukocyte-dependent inflammatory reactions. *Am. J. Pathol.* 107: 397–418

31. Forman HJ, Boveris A. 1982. Superoxide radical and hydrogen peroxide in mitochondria. In *Free Radicals in Biology,* ed. WA Pryor, 5:65–90. New York: Academic

32. Freeman BA, Crapo JD. 1982. Biology of disease. Free radicals and tissue injury. *Lab. Invest.* 47:412–26

33. Fridovich I. 1978. The biology of oxygen radicals. The superoxide radical is an agent of oxygen toxicity; superoxide dismutases provide an important defense. *Science* 201:875–79

34. Fridovich I, Freeman B. 1986. Antioxidant defenses in the lung. *Annu. Rev. Physiol.* 48:693–702

35. Guidet BR, Shah SV. 1989. In vivo generation of hydrogen peroxide by rat kidney cortex and glomeruli. *Am. J. Physiol.* 256:F158–64

36. Halliwell B, Gutteridge JMC. 1990. Role of free radicals and catalytic metal ions in human disease: an overview. *Meth. Enzymol.* 186:1–85

37. Hara T, Miyai H, Iida T, Futenma A, Nakamura S, Kato K. 1990. Aggravation of puromycin aminonucleoside (PAN) nephrosis by the inhibition of endogenous superoxide dismutase (SOD). *Proc. XIth Int. Congr. Nephrol., Jpn.* p. 442A

38. Johnson RJ, Couser WG, Chi EY, Adler S, Klebanoff SJ. 1987. New mechanism for glomerular injury. *J. Clin. Invest.* 79:1379–87

39. Johnson RJ, Guggenheim SJ, Klebanoff SJ, Ochi RF, Wass A, et al. 1988. Morphologic correlates of glomerular oxidant injury induced by the myeloperoxidase-hydrogen peroxide-halide system of the neutrophil. *Lab. Invest.* 5:294–301

40. Johnson, RJ, Klebanoff SJ, Ochi RF, Adler S, Baker P, et al. 1987. Participation of the myeloperoxidase-H_2O_2-halide system in immune complex nephritis. *Kidney Int.* 32:342–49

41. Kakita N, Sasaguri Y, Kato S, Morimatsu M. 1993. Induction of gelatinolytic neutral proteinase secretion by lipid peroxide in cultured mesangial cells. *Nephron* 63:94–99

42. Kashihara N, Watanabe Y, Makino H, Wallner EI, Kanwar YS. 1992. Selective decreased de novo synthesis of glomerular proteoglycans under the influence of reactive oxygen species. *Proc. Natl. Acad. Sci. USA* 89:6309–13

43. Kawaguchi M, Yamada M, Wada H, Okigaki T. 1992. Roles of active oxygen species in glomerular epithelial cell injury in vitro caused by puromycin aminonucleoside. *Toxicology* 72:329–40

44. Kawamura T, Yoshioka T, Bills T, Fogo A, Ichikawa I. 1991. Glucocorticoid activates glomerular antioxidant enzymes and protects glomeruli from oxidant injuries. *Kidney Int.* 40:291–301

45. Kawamura T, Yoshioka T, Moore-Jarrett T, Hoover RL, Ichikawa I. 1990. Glucocorticoid raises antioxidant enzyme activity and attenuates hydrogen peroxide generation in glomerular endothelial cells. *J. Am. Soc. Nephrol.* 1:528 (Abstr.)

46. Klebanoff SJ. 1980. Oxygen metabolites and the toxic properties of phagocytes. *Ann. Intern. Med.* 93:480–89

47. Lampert MB, Weiss SJ. 1983. The chlorinating potential of the human monocyte. *Blood* 62:645–51

48. Lawrence RA, Burk RF. 1976. Glutathione peroxidase activity in selenium-deficient rat liver. *Biochem. Biophys. Res. Commun.* 71:952–58

49. Lawrence RA, Burk RF. 1978. Species, tissue and subcellular distribution of non-Se-dependent glutathione peroxidase activity. *J. Nutr.* 108:211–15

50. Lianos EA, Andres GA, Dunn MJ. 1983. Glomerular prostaglandin and thromboxane synthesis in rat nephrotoxic serum nephritis. *J. Clin. Invest.* 72: 1439–48

51. McCord JE, Wong K, Stokes SH, Petrone WF, English D. 1980. Superoxide and inflammation: a mechanism for the anti-inflammatory activity of superoxide dismutase. *Acta Physiol. Scand.* 492:25–30

52. McCord JM. 1985. Oxygen-derived free

radicals in postischemic tissue injury. *N. Engl. J. Med.* 312:159–63

53. McCord JM, Fridovich I. 1978. The biology and pathology of oxygen radicals. *Ann. Intern. Med.* 89:122–27

54. Meister A. 1983. Selective modification of glutathione metabolism. *Science* 22: 472–78

55. Miyai H, Hara T, Yamada K, Nakamura S, Futenma A, Kato K. 1990. Aggravation of puromycin aminonucleoside nephrosis by glutathione–depleting agent. See Ref. 37, p. 442A

56. Morrow JD, Hill KE, Burk RF, Nammour TM, Badr KF, Roberts LJ. 1990. A series of prostaglandin F$_2$-like compounds are produced in vivo in humans by a non-cyclooxygenase, free radical–catalyzed mechanism. *Proc. Natl. Acad. Sci. USA* 87:9383–87

57. Oberle GP, Niemeyer J, Thaiss F, Schoeppe W, Stahl RAK. 1992. Increased oxygen radical and eicosanoid formation in immune-mediated mesangial cell injury. *Kidney Int.* 42:69–74

58. Okasora T, Takikawa T, Utsunomiya Y, Senoh I, Hayashibara H, et al. 1992. Suppressive effect of superoxide dismutase on adriamycin nephropathy. *Nephron* 60:199–203

59. Poelstra K, Hardonk MJ, Koudstaal J, Bakker WW. 1990. Intraglomerular platelet aggregation and experimental glomerulonephritis. *Kidney Int.* 37: 1500–8

60. Radeke HH, Cross AR, Hancock JT, Jones OTG, Nakamura M, et al. 1991. Functional expression of NADPH oxidase components (α- and β-subunits of cytochrome b$_{558}$ and 45-kDa flavoprotein) by intrinsic human glomerular mesangial cells. *J. Biol. Chem.* 266: 21025–29

61. Radeke HH, Meier B, Topley N, Floge J, Habermehl GG, Resch K. 1990. Interleukin 1-α and tumor necrosis factor-α induce oxygen radical production in mesangial cells. *Kidney Int.* 37:767–75

62. Rahman MA, Emancipator SS, Sedor JR. 1988. Hydroxyl radical scavengers ameliorate proteinuria in rat immune complex glomerulonephritis. *J. Lab. Clin. Med.* 112:619–26

63. Rehan A, Johnson KJ, Kunkel RG, Wiggins RC. 1985. Role of oxygen radicals in phorbol myristate acetate–induced glomerular injury. *Kidney Int.* 27:503–11

64. Rehan A, Johnson KJ, Wiggins RC, Kunkel RG, Ward PA. 1984. Evidence for the role of oxygen radicals in acute nephrotoxic nephritis. *Lab. Invest.* 51: 396–403

65. Rehan A, Wiggins RC, Kunkel RG, Till GO, Johnson KJ. 1986. Glomerular injury and proteinuria in rats after intrarenal injection of cobra venom factor. *Am. J. Pathol.* 123:57–66

66. Remuzzi G, Imberti L, Rossini M, Morelli C, Carminati C, et al. 1985. Increased glomerular thromboxane synthesis as a possible cause of proteinuria in experimental nephrosis. *J. Clin. Invest.* 75:94–101

67. Schreck R, Baeuerle PA. 1991. A role for oxygen radicals as second messengers. *Trends Cell Biol.* 1:39–42

68. Schreck R, Rieber P, Baeuerle PA. 1991. Reactive oxygen intermediates as apparently widely used messengers in the activation of the NF-κB transcription factor and HIV-1. *EMBO J.* 10:2247–58

69. Sedor JR, Abboud HE. 1986. Hydrogen peroxide stimulates PGE2 synthesis by cultured rat mesangial cells. *Kidney Int.* 29:291 (Abstr.)

70. Shah SV. 1981. Light emission by isolated rat glomeruli in response to phorbol myristate acetate. *J. Lab. Clin. Med.* 98:46–57

71. Shah SV. 1984. Effect of enzymatically generated reactive oxygen metabolites on the cyclic nucleotide content in isolated rat glomeruli. *J. Clin. Invest.* 74:393–401

72. Shah SV. 1988. Evidence suggesting a role for hydroxyl radical in passive Heymann nephritis in rats. *Am. J. Physiol.* 254:F337–44

73. Shah SV. 1989. Role of reactive oxygen metabolites in experimental glomerular disease. *Kidney Int.* 35:1093–106

74. Shah SV. 1991. Oxidant mechanisms in glomerulonephritis. *Sem. Nephrol.* 11: 320–26

75. Shah SV, Baricos WH, Basci A. 1987. Degradation of human glomerular basement membrane by stimulated neutrophils. Activation of a metalloproteinase/s by reactive oxygen metabolites. *J. Clin. Invest.* 79:25–31

76. Stahl R, Disser M, Hora K, Schlondorff D. 1992. Increased expression of monocyte chemoattractant protein in glomeruli from rats with anti-Thy-1 glomerulonephritis. *J. Am. Soc. Nephrol.* 3: 616a (Abstr.)

77. Takahashi K, Nammour TM, Fukunaga M, Ebert J, Morrow JD, et al. 1992. Glomerular actions of a free radical–generated novel prostaglandin, 8-epi-prostaglandin F$_{2\alpha}$ in the rat. *J. Clin. Invest.* 90:136–41

78. Thakur V, Walker PD, Shah SV. 1988. Evidence suggesting a role for hydroxyl radical in puromycin aminonucleoside–

induced proteinuria. *Kidney Int.* 34:494–99

79. Toledano MB, Leonard WJ. 1991. Modulation of transcription factor NF-κB binding activity by oxidation-reduction in vitro. *Proc. Natl. Acad. Sci. USA* 88:4328–32

80. Ueda N, Guidet B, Shah SV. 1994. Measurement of intracellular generation of hydrogen peroxide by rat glomeruli in vitro. *Kidney Int.* 45:788–93

81. Vissers MCM, Winterbourn CC. 1986. The effect of oxidants on neutrophil-mediated degradation of glomerular basement membrane collagen. *Biochim. Biophys. Acta* 889:277–86

82. Weiss SJ. 1986. Oxygen, ischemia and inflammation. *Acta Physiol. Scand.* 548:9–37

83. Weiss SJ, Lampert MB, Test ST. 1983. Long-lived oxidants generated by human neutrophils: characterization and bioactivity. *Science* 222:625–28

84. Weiss SJ, LoBuglio AF. 1982. Biology of disease. Phagocyte-generated oxygen metabolites and cellular injury. *Lab. Invest.* 47:5–18

85. Weiss SJ, Regiani S. 1984. Neutrophils degrade subendothelial matrices in the presence of alpha1-proteinase inhibitor. Cooperative use of lysosomal proteinases and oxygen metabolites. *J. Clin. Invest.* 73:1297–303

86. Weiss SJ, Test ST, Eckmann CM, Roos D, Regiani S. 1986. Brominating oxidants generated by human eosinophils. *Science* 234:200–3

87. Yoshioka T, Bills T, Moore-Jarrett T, Greene HL, Burr IM, Ichikawa I. 1990. Role of intrinsic antioxidant enzymes in renal oxidant injury. *Kidney Int.* 38:282–88

88. Yoshioka T, Ichikawa I. 1989. Glomerular dysfunction induced by polymorphonuclear leukocyte–derived reactive oxygen species. *Am. J. Physiol.* 257:F53–59

89. Yoshioka T, Ichikawa I, Fogo A. 1991. Reactive oxygen metabolites cause massive, reversible proteinuria and glomerular sieving defect without apparent ultra-structural abnormality. *J. Am. Soc. Nephrol.* 2:902–12

90. Yoshioka T, Takeda M, Burr IM, Meyrick BO, Ichikawa I. 1992. Hydrogen peroxide can activate the Mn-superoxide dismutase gene in glomerular mesangial cells (GMC). *J. Am. Soc. Nephrol.* 3:718 (Abstr.)

Annu. Rev. Physiol. 1995. 57:263–78

PROGRESSION OF RENAL DISEASE AND RENAL HYPERTROPHY

Thomas H. Hostetter

Division of Renal Diseases and Hypertension, Department of Medicine, University of Minnesota, Minneapolis, Minnesota 55455

KEY WORDS: glomerulus, renal failure, renal growth

INTRODUCTION

Growth of residual renal tissue in response to loss of other renal tissue is usually termed compensatory hypertrophy. This process occurs not only when unilateral nephrectomy is performed with the contralateral organ increasing its mass but also when undamaged nephrons within a kidney undergo enlargement as other nephron units in that same kidney are destroyed either by natural disease or experimentally (34, 41, 49, 51). Although compensatory hypertrophy is a standard term for this phenomenon, it deserves some further clarification. Hyperplasia (often experimentally defined as an increase in DNA content) as well as hypertrophy (often defined as an increase of protein/DNA ratio) underlie compensatory hypertrophy. Although the compensatory nature of the response seems obvious, the exact physiologic functions of the kidney targeted for compensation are undefined. Furthermore, it is possible that compensatory growth and associated functional alterations, despite mitigating the fall in renal function for the organism, have long-term deleterious consequences for these residual nephrons.

Along with structural enlargement, the residual nephrons take on a large number of functional adaptations, most notably, an increase in single-nephron filtration rate and net reabsorption of solutes and water (32). Other metabolic processes presumably associated with heightened transport, such as oxygen consumption, increase in remaining nephrons as do synthetic pathways such as ammoniagenesis (32, 40, 56). Undoubtedly, structural growth and functional

263

adaptations are closely related. However, the precise temporal sequence and the possible causal links between these two phenomena are less than definite.

This review examines the data regarding the process of compensatory renal growth and attempts to place it in the context of chronic progressive renal disease. The roles of compensatory growth and functional adaptations in promoting further renal injury are also assessed.

COMPENSATORY RENAL GROWTH

Most studies of this process have focused on removal of a single kidney or on ablating its function. Following contralateral nephrectomy, the extant kidney eventually increases its mass by approximately 50% (51, 73). This growth, in most instances, is achieved through an increase in the size of the constituent nephrons. Nephron number does not increase in adult animals. However, in a few species (mice and rats), nephron number has been reported to rise following nephrectomy in very young animals (4, 7). In mice and rats, nephrogenesis is incomplete at birth, and perhaps this idiosyncrasy provides a plasticity that, in turn, permits an increase in nephron number. However, even in these species, increases in nephron number do not occur after nephrectomy in adulthood.

The degree of renal growth and its character are also conditioned by age; specifically, younger animals demonstrate more dramatic growth of residual renal tissue than older ones, and hyperplasia plays a larger role in the younger animals (18, 38). Using DNA and protein as the indices of hyperplasia vs hypertrophy, adult rats demonstrate an increase of only about 20% in renal cells, whereas in young animals the increase in DNA content is more pronounced (8, 51).

After nephrectomy, the remaining glomeruli increase in volume by approximately 50%, whether in the deep or superficial cortex (51, 60). Within the glomerulus, the cells and extracellular matrix and capillary lumen expand to similar degrees (60). However, the resulting relative numbers of mesangial, endothelial, and epithelial populations are uncertain. The length and number of capillaries appear to increase (60). The functional process subserved by glomerular growth is likely that of increased single-nephron filtration rate, a regular accompaniment of structural enlargement (32). Because the glomerular ultrafiltration coefficient (K_f) is usually considered a product of the filtering surface area (S) and its hydraulic conductivity (k), the expansion of S by glomerular enlargement should allow for a greater K_f, k remaining constant. Morphometric measures of the capillary surface subtended by the visceral epithelial cells demonstrate an increase (60, 70). However, calculations of K_f from micropuncture measurements of glomerular pressures and flows usually demonstrate no increase in K_f following substantial losses of renal mass, even those greater than simple unilateral nephrectomy (35). [This constancy of K_f

is in the face of substantial increases in single-nephron glomerular filtration rate (GFR).] The apparent paradox may result from morphometric measures of filtering surface area that are flawed or from a reduction in k. The latter situation might derive from local hormonal effects and/or changes in the epithelial cell foot processes. Indeed, a fall in the fraction of glomerular surface covered by their intercellular junctions, the slit pores, has been inferred (51, 70). Because the slit pores are the sites of filtration, such a diminution could limit k. The possibility of a hormonal effect is also supported by the observation that pharmacologic blockade of the renin-angiotensin system in rats with extreme degrees of partial renal ablation leads to elevation of the ultrafiltration coefficient along with other hemodynamic changes (see below) (50). Because angiotensin II can lower K_f in normal rats, the inference that heightened angiotensin II activity limits the K_f in renal ablation is logical (3). The resulting ultrafiltration coefficient after angiotensin II blockade in residual nephrons is more nearly commensurate with the degrees of glomerular structural growth measured microscopically (50).

Tubular growth following nephrectomy follows *pari passu* with glomerular growth, although a causal association is uncertain. Increases of approximately 30% in both cross-sectional area and length have been observed in the proximal tubule (33). Transporters and metabolically crucial components of the proximal tubule also increase. The Na-K-ATPase activity increases as does mitochondrial volume in measured mitochondrial enzyme activities (67). Glucose and amino acid transport measured by in vivo clearance techniques and in vitro vesicle methodology increases in proportion to the mass of the tubule (51). As emphasized by Meyer et al, several other functions of the proximal tubule increase out of proportion to its overall enlargement (51). The enzymes responsible for ammoniagenesis increase in rough proportion to the acid excretory requirements of a nephron following uninephrectomy, i.e. twofold augmentation (69). By contrast, the increase in Na-H exchange activity is greater than accounted for by increments in proximal bicarbonate reabsorption (29). The physiologic processes served by this latter effect are uncertain. The distal tubule and loop of Henle seem to grow but proportionately less than the glomeruli and proximal tubules. However, these segments have been less extensively studied (51).

Compensatory renal growth begins promptly following contralateral nephrectomy. The earliest biochemical changes of choline incorporation into membranes occur within 5 min (72). Augmentation of RNA synthesis has been observed within the first 4 h (62). The increments in total RNA abate after about 2 days, presumably as the largest fraction of net protein production has been achieved (47). Levels of DNA rise somewhat after those of RNA, but mitosis returns to a basal level by about 2 weeks (18). Although increases in total renal weight, both wet and dry, have been reported by 24 h, the total increase of about 50% in mass following unilateral nephrectomy is not achieved for 2 to 4 weeks (18, 47, 51, 73). The degree of loss of renal mass is a key determinant of compensatory growth. For example, partial ablation of one kidney leads to less growth than complete unilateral nephrectomy, and greater ablative procedures such as nephrectomy coupled with partial infarction or resection of the residual kidney yield more growth and greater augmentation of residual nephron function (32). Thus the extent of compensatory growth and hyperfunction is directly related to the amount of functioning mass lost.

Whether alterations in transport functions, especially GFR, precede, follow, or occur concurrently with accretion of renal mass is not known. This dilemma lies near the root of the larger question of whether renal growth is caused by increases in renal transport work. Glomerular filtration and renal blood flow rise soon after nephrectomy. Indeed, nearly instantaneous renal vasodilatation has been reported in the dog, and heightened GFR occurs by 90 min in some studies of the rat (42, 63). The precise timing of these events may be hampered by methodologic issues such as fluid volume losses attendant to surgery, i.e. surgery for renal extirpation and that often required for subsequent hemodynamic measurements. The work hypothesis states that the increases in transport occasioned by increases in filtration rate provide a signal, of unspecified molecular nature, to trigger renal growth (51, 62). The absence of a firmly described temporal sequence of these events and the difficulties in achieving such a description reduce the force of this hypothesis. However, the rapidity of the earliest reported biochemical changes (by 5 min) and its occurrence during the anesthesia and surgical procedure speak against the likelihood that increases in filtration rate and thereby transport are necessary to begin renal growth (72).

The circulating stimuli to renal growth have been often sought but still elude identification. That a circulating signal initiates the process seems likely in view of parabiotic experiments demonstrating initiation of hypertrophy following nephrectomy in one pair of cross-circulating animals (43, 73). Reduction in net renal tissue is not necessary because unilateral ureteral obstruction leads to growth of the unobstructed kidney (24). The possibility that retention of products normally excreted in the urine signal the residual kidney to grow has been examined in two ways. First, surgical diversion of one ureter into the peritoneum, circulation, or gut has been performed (51). Although many of these studies conclude that this experimental situation does not provoke renal growth, the surgical complexity of the procedures coupled with the nonspecific but likely growth inhibitory effects of surgery, such as inflammation and poor feeding, make interpretation of these experiments difficult. Second, intravenous re-infusion of half of the daily urine production is another method for assessing the proposition that some urine component(s) might signal renal growth. This technique causes renal growth to a degree similar to that of unilateral nephrectomy (30). Confirmation of the result and specification of the responsible urinary components are needed. However, some obvious components of urine have been excluded. Urea supplementation does not suffice (51, 73). Even though large degrees of acid loading have been reported to cause hypertrophy, the absence of associated increases in GFR with acidemia, the large acid loads required, and the inability to blunt compensatory renal growth by alkali suggest that an initial fall in net acid excretion is an unlikely stimulus to the process (29, 46, 51).

Although no particular metabolic product has been singled out as the instigator of compensatory renal growth, numerous well-characterized substances are capable of inducing growth in renal tissue in vivo and renal cells in vitro (19, 27). However, no alteration has been found sufficiently early in compensatory growth in the circulatory levels and/or renal sensitivity to any of these substances to be considered the proximate signal. Thus no truly renotrophic hormone has been identified. Renal innervation is also not necessary for hypertrophy to occur (51, 73). Worthy of comment are the observations that certain manipulations such as hypophysectomy, when performed concurrently with unilateral nephrectomy, result in a remaining kidney not significantly larger than the one initially removed (48). However, pituitary ablation causes renal regression; thus when nephrectomy is performed on the background of prior hypophysectomy, the remaining kidney grows in comparison to the one removed, which indicates that an intact pituitary is not essential to compensatory renal expansion (16). Removal of other endocrine glands such as the thyroid and adrenal also does not prevent hypertrophy as long as the smaller renal size of such endocrine-deficiency states is taken into account.

Several growth factors may be produced within the kidney during compensatory growth (19, 27). Insulin-like growth factor 1 (IGF-1) levels rise within the residual kidney and administration of exogenous IGF-1 causes renal growth and elevations in GFR (19). However, some reports have found elevated intrarenal levels of the peptide only after substantial renal growth has already occurred (27). Similarly, intrarenal epidermal growth factor (EGF) levels are augmented after hypertrophy (19, 27). Renal expression of hepatocyte growth factor (HGF) has been proposed as an early feature of compensatory growth, but its role awaits further exploration (36). Almost certainly, multiple intrarenal pathways for promoting, sustaining, and coordinating compensatory renal growth will be identified. However, the circulating, systemic signal-generated consequence to the loss of functioning kidney tissue, which engages these pathways within the residual nephrons, remains elusive.

MECHANISMS OF PROGRESSIVE RENAL DISEASE

For more than 60 years, the deleterious effects of severe experimental reductions in renal mass have been recognized. Chanutin & Ferris described progressive hypertension, proteinuria, and uremic death in rats after reductions in renal mass achieved by unilateral nephrectomy and partial ablation of the remaining tissue (the subtotal ablation or remnant kidney model) (9). Following the initial reduction in renal mass, growth in residual nephrons is dramatic, but the functional aberrations supervene, and structural damage to these remnant nephrons accumulates. Specifically, glomeruli develop sclerotic lesions characterized by loss of the filtering capillary loops that are replaced by extracellular mesangial matrix (71). It is the progressive obliteration of filtering capillary units that likely underlies the eventual decay in function of these initially hyperfunctioning nephrons. Based on these observations, it was hypothesized that the hemodynamic adaptations driving the increased single-nephron GFR in residual nephrons, when extreme, are damaging. To investigate this hypothesis, micropuncture studies were performed in rats subjected to subtotal nephrectomy produced by unilateral nephrectomy and partial infarction of the remaining kidney (35). These investigations demonstrated that within 7 to 10 days following the ablative maneuver, single-nephron GFR had nearly doubled in residual nephron units compared to sham-operated controls with two kidneys. This increase in single-nephron GFR rested on alterations of two hemodynamic determinants of glomerular filtration. First, single-nephron plasma flow increased because of reductions in both afferent and efferent vascular resistances. Second, the glomerular transcapillary hydrostatic gradient, ΔP, also rose by approximately 10 to 45 mmHg. The resulting increase in ΔP was due to the associated systemic arterial hypertension and a relatively greater reduction in afferent vascular resistance than in efferent resistance. As noted above, the K_f was not measurably different. Associated with the increases in single-nephron GFR, single-nephron plasma flow, and ΔP were early structural disruptions. Glomerular epithelial cells had begun to demonstrate blebbing and detachment from the underlying basement membrane; protein reabsorption droplets were visible in glomerular and tubular epithelial cells coincident with urinary protein excretory rates that had increased by more than tenfold per residual nephron. Studies of the glomerular permeability characteristics for macromolecules conducted at this same early stage demonstrated disturbances of size- and charge-selective properties to neutral and sulfated dextran macromolecules (61). Morphologic evaluations at later intervals revealed the expected glomerular obliterative sclerosis as well as mononuclear cell infiltrates and expansion of the interstitial compartment. To test the role of the hemodynamic alterations in the changes in permeability to macromolecules and progressive structural damage, animals with subtotal ablation were placed on a very low protein diet (6% protein compared to 24% protein) because this diet has long been known to ameliorate experimental renal diseases as well as influence renal hemodynamics in normal animals (35). The low protein diet prevented the increases in single-nephron GFR, plasma flow, and ΔP. Associated with these diminutions in the adaptive hyperfiltration, there was a marked blunting of the progressive sclerotic changes in the kidney and a substantial attenuation of the impairment of permselective properties such that proteinuria was greatly reduced. Furthermore, other disease models including diabetes, post-salt hypertension, experimental glomerulonephritis, experimental nephrotic syndrome, and mineralocorticoid-salt hypertension were investigated with regard to their glomerular hemodynamic pattern (59). In all cases, glomerular pressures were noted to be elevated. The use of low protein diets in several of these experimental diseases not only attenuated the pathologic changes but also reduced glomerular capillary pressures, whereas in some instances there was little or no influence on plasma flows or single-nephron GFR (59). From these comparisons, the initial hypothesis was narrowed to suggest that increases in glomerular capillary pressure per se were deleterious to the glomerulus.

Further support for the notion that elevations in glomerular capillary pressure were maladaptive derives from investigations of angiotensin-converting enzyme inhibition in many of these same models including that of subtotal renal ablation. These agents, which block the conversion of angiotensin I to angiotensin II, proved not only to reduce the systemic hypertension of the subtotal ablation model, but also to reduce glomerular capillary pressures (50). In the course of these investigations, other antihypertensive regimens (reserpine, hydralazine, thiazide) lowered arterial pressure but did not reduce glomerular capillary pressure. In the absence of an effect on capillary pressure, these regimens also failed to attenuate proteinuria and glomerular injury (1). The efficacy of blockade of the renin-angiotensin system has been more recently extended to the angiotensin II receptor blocker losartan (44). The effects of angiotensin-converting enzyme inhibition on capillary pressure, proteinuria, and sclerosing glomerular damage have been extended to a range of experimental models (59, 66). These pharmacological studies, like those of dietary protein restriction studies, support the hypothesis that increases in glomerular capillary pressure are injurious.

The investigations with angiotensin II blockers further suggest that heightened activity of the renin-angiotensin system either within the kidney or systemically is critical to the hemodynamic alterations with severe reduction in renal mass and subsequent glomerular injury (66). However, in the case of the subtotal ablation model, plasma renin activity is normal or even depressed, which suggests no clear activation of this key element on the renin-angiotensin system, at least systemically (66). Intrarenal renin content for the remnant kidney is also not generally increased (10, 64, 65). However, renin levels do rise in the areas adjacent to the infarcted scar, a residual of the initial ablative maneuver, and to a lesser extent within the mesangium (10, 64, 65). Whether other elements of the system within the kidney are increased has not been extensively investigated; however, mRNA for angiotensinogen, similar to renin, is not uniformly augmented (10). Although the heightened glomerular pressure in the remnant kidney model is blunted by pharmacologic alteration of this system, the structural enlargement of the glomerulus and the increases in single-nephron GFR and plasma flow are not notably modified (1, 44, 66). Thus these flows and early compensatory growth are not absolutely dependent on an intact renin-angiotensin system despite the profound effects that drugs interfering with its operation have on the glomerular capillary pressure and subsequent structural and functional damage.

Several mechanisms have been proposed to explain how increases in glomerular pressure lead to structural changes, specifically the generation of the excess extracellular matrix that replaces glomerular capillaries and the provocation of permselective defects to macromolecules. One proposal suggests that stretch of mesangial cells brought about by increases in ΔP causes them to proliferate and increase the production of various components of the mesangial matrix (11, 31). In vitro studies show that stretch does indeed lead to these cellular responses (11, 31). Whether the nature of the stretch produced in vitro is comparable to that in vivo is, of course, uncertain, but this process represents an attractive possibility whereby the mechanical effects of heightened glomerular pressures are translated into structural changes within the glomerulus. Second, it is possible that altered pressures lead directly to injury, particularly to endothelial cells, and result in a process generally analogous to that of atherosclerosis in large vessels (15, 20). The reparative process following endothelial injury involves deposition of platelets and macrophages and their various products as an early phase of atherogenesis and by analogy to glomerular sclerosis. Lastly, the suggestion has been made that with altered glomerular capillary dynamics, macromolecules, particularly lipoproteins, may be deposited to a greater degree within the glomerular mesangium (26, 39). This possibility is to an extent a corollary of the atherogenesis analogy and places emphasis on pathological mesangial expansion as a consequence of some toxic or proliferative effect of circulating macromolecules accumulating in the mesangium. However, the normal mesangial permeability to macromolecules is poorly defined but appears to be quite substantial (39). Thus accumulation of such macromolecules likely would depend on altered egress as well as enhanced access.

The view that glomerular capillary hypertension is maladaptive has been extended more generally to suggest that other compensatory adjustments, both structural and functional, may have long-term deleterious effects in renal diseases. Augmentation of ammoniagenesis occurs with nephron mass reduction and results in increments in the cortical levels of total and free-base ammonia (6, 58, 69). However, free-base ammonia is highly reactive with the internal thiolester of the third component of the complement protein system,

C3, and may have adverse consequences (58). The resulting product, an amidated C3, interacts with leukocyte receptors and provokes their release of inflammatory intermediates. Amidated C3 also has the capacity to generate the membrane attack complex of the terminal complement cascade. Experiments designed to diminish the heightened levels of ammonia in the remnant kidney model by bicarbonate supplementation to the diet demonstrate associated reduction in tubular-interstitial inflammation (58). These investigations support the hypothesis that the compensatory elevations in ammonia production may be another change with long-term maladaptive consequences. In addition to increased ammonia production, the oxygen consumption of residual nephrons increases (28, 56). Such an augmentation of oxygen consumption would be predicted on the basis of an increased filtered load of solutes with consequent requirement for energy expenditure in solute reclamation along the length of the tubule. However, the increases in oxygen consumption are out of proportion to tubular sodium reabsorption (56). Whether this exaggerated oxygen consumption rests on a less efficient sodium reabsorption (for example, greater distal delivery with more reabsorption by the energy-expensive processes of the distal nephron) or from some nontransport-related process or processes is uncertain. However, pathologic consequences of increased oxygen consumption have been proposed. Specifically, a small component of the normal flow of the electron transport chain (estimated at less than 10%) escapes and generates free radical species within the cell. Of course, these species are largely contained through a variety of scavenging molecules and enzyme systems. The possibility that the exaggerated rate of oxygen consumption entails a greater absolute generation of free radicals, put forth with some experimental support, holds that an additional consequence of the hyperfiltration of residual nephrons would be an increase in generation of free radical species with damage to various cellular components by these toxic metabolites (28, 56). Thus at least two components of the tubular-metabolic adaptation to loss of functioning renal mass may entail long-term costs to the structure of those initially adapting nephrons.

ROLE OF GROWTH IN PROGRESSIVE RENAL DISEASE

That compensatory growth might be a cause and not simply a consequence of loss of renal mass follows by analogy from the general ideas raised in the previous section. Just as hemodynamic and metabolic hyperfunction of residual nephrons may prove injurious over time, the structural enlargement of such a nephron may also eventually prove maladaptive. This latter proposition has focused largely on glomerular rather than tubular expansion and posits that the larger glomeruli are predisposed to undergo degeneration through sclerosis (13, 17, 22, 45).

In multiple clinical situations, glomerular hypertrophy is associated with glomerular sclerosis (21). One of the most extreme, albeit rare, of such conditions is oligomeganephronia, in which individuals are congenitally endowed with a dramatically reduced nephron number, but the nephrons are markedly enlarged. These individuals eventually develop renal disease due to progressive sclerosis of the glomeruli. Other less extreme clinical examples of the association between glomerular enlargement and ultimate sclerosis, and in individuals presumably beginning with a normal mass of nephrons, include sickle cell anemia, cyanotic heart disease, diabetes, reflux nephropathy, AIDS nephropathy, and extreme obesity (21). Also, several experimental diseases demonstrate this link, e.g. subtotal nephrectomy, dietary protein excess, chemically induced diabetes, and some apparently genetic entities (21). Of course, the causal flow of this connection is impossible to establish from the mere presence of an association.

A first step toward demonstrating a causal relationship has been that glomerular enlargement often precedes the pathological process of sclerosis, and this temporal sequence has been made clear in several disease models. In the case of the experimental diseases, remnant kidney, diabetes, and high dietary protein intake, the growth occurs first (21, 45, 51). One of the strongest pieces of evidence tying early growth and later injury derives from a retrospective analysis of clinical kidney biopsy material reported by Fogo et al (21). These investigators measured glomerular size by morphometric techniques in biopsies obtained in children with a type of nephrotic syndrome known as minimal change disease; the term denotes the normal glomerular structure seen by light microscopy. Most patients with this disease do not progress to renal failure, but some do, and in this subgroup the developing glomerular lesion is sclerosis. When the sizes of the glomeruli at the original biopsy were compared with the course of the disease, a separation based on glomerular dimensions was noted. Glomeruli of normal size (compared with controls from autopsy samples) were associated with the benign course, whereas large glomeruli were associated with later sclerotic changes. These authors concluded that glomerular hypertrophy was a risk factor for sclerosis. Many experimental studies have sought to assess the role of glomerular growth in subsequent sclerotic change. A greater resistance to sclerosis has been noticed in the PVG/c rat strain, following unilateral nephrectomy, compared with the Wistar strain (25). The resistance is associated with a lesser increase in glomerular volume in the PVG/c strain. In addition to the apparent genetic limit on size and sclerosis, numerous maneuvers have been imposed alone or in the setting of partial renal ablation in attempts to alter glomerular size and determine the subsequent effects on pathological course. In many but not all cases, the degree of glomerular hypertrophy was greatest when eventual sclerosis proved greatest (21, 45, 50, 75).

The glomerular hydraulic pressure gradient, ΔP, is a well-established determinant of the progression of glomerular injury as noted above, and the role of this factor independent of glomerular size has not always been considered. Yoshida et al attempted to dissociate these two factors by comparing the standard subtotal nephrectomy model with one in which one kidney was partially ablated and its contralateral partner remained in situ with its ureter diverted into the peritoneum (74). In both models glomerular pressure rose, but only in the single subtotal nephrectomy kidney did early glomerular enlargement and later sclerosis develop. Daniels & Hostetter reported that higher dietary salt intakes in the remnant kidney model were associated with greater glomerular growth than lower salt diets, but glomerular capillary pressures were uninfluenced across the range of dietary salt. The higher salt diet also provoked more sclerosis and more proteinuria (13). These two studies, with others of generally similar design, are consistent with the hypothesis that glomerular growth perhaps in conjunction with glomerular hypertension promotes progressive sclerotic injury (13, 17, 21).

If glomerular hypertrophy represents a risk for the development of glomerular injury, it does not seem to be sufficient in itself to precipitate such a course of events, or even to sustain it in the absence of other factors, nor is it always a necessary factor. Evidence for this view derives from several observations of glomerular growth without notable subsequent structural deterioration and also from the finding that in some circumstances glomerular enlargement does not by itself predict the presence of later degenerative disease (45, 50, 75). For example, effective interruption of damage in the remnant kidney model by pharmacologic blockade of the renin-angiotensin system has been well established but without large or even statistically detectable diminution in the size of the hypertrophied glomeruli (44, 45). Although reduction in glomerular size of modest degree has been associated with such therapy in some studies, glomerular capillary pressures have been more consistently reduced. The late failure of the kidney allograft in humans, also a progressive degenerative process including the sclerosis of glomeruli, has no clear relationship to earlier glomerular hypertrophy (37). Likewise, Schmidt et al reported that glomerular volume in Pima Indians, while substantially greater than that in Caucasian subjects, was not clearly related to the degree of glomerulosclerosis in this population predisposed to progressive diabetic renal disease (68). The impossibility of measuring glomerular capillary pressures directly in humans clouds the interpretation of these latter reports. The observations are nevertheless consistent with the notion that glomerular expansion alone may not be sufficient for sclerosing injury. Not surprisingly, some progressive experimental renal diseases can occur without notable initial glomerular enlargement. Puromycin or adriamycin administration causes a nephrotic syndrome in rats followed by a progressive glomerular sclerosis, but glomerular enlargement has not been detected early in this process (2, 14, 45, 53). However, the possibility of a more heterogeneous growth as diseases progress and a contribution of adaptive hypertrophy later in the course of adriamycin nephrosis and other diseases is difficult to exclude. Moreover, the late phase destructive process accelerates greatly when partial renal ablation (and therefore glomerular growth and capillary hypertension) is superimposed on adriamycin nephrosis (53).

The potential mechanisms whereby glomerular growth could enhance susceptibility to degenerative destruction are several. Dilation of the preglomerular vasculature and certainly that of the glomerular capillaries is likely due, in part, to the structural growth of those elements. This dilation would reduce vascular resistance and bring about greater blood flow, which, depending upon the systemic pressure and efferent resistance, could elevate glomerular capillary pressure. Such falls in resistance based on enlargement of the caliber of the vessels should be of greatest impact in the preglomerular vasculature because the normal glomerular capillary circuit is thought to contribute little to overall renal vascular resistance. The increase in the radius of glomerular capillaries and of the entire glomerular sphere may enhance their wall tension via the La Place relation, even at a constant transmural pressure gradient (13). In accord with the interaction of distending pressure and radius, glomerular hypertrophy and elevated glomerular pressure act synergistically to increase injury. For example, the combination of unilateral nephrectomy and chronic angiotensin II infusion causes much greater sclerosis and albuminuria than either maneuver alone and even greater than the sum of their individual effects (52). Nagata et al have suggested that an increase in wall tension may have as one of its consequences an exhaustion of normally contractile mesangial cells (54). In their view mesangial cells ordinarily function as tethers through their attachments to the glomerular basement membrane at the nonfiltering face of the capillary. Failure of this cellular system could allow capillary expansion to microaneurysmal proportions, an observed pathology, with consequences to glomerular permeability. Trapping of circulating macromolecules within the extracapillary space of the mesangium has been suggested as a potential consequence of glomerular growth, with obvious analogies to the insudation of lipoprotein and other macromolecule into the walls of larger vessels with atherosclerotic consequences, as noted above (26, 39). Evidence also supports the possibility that glomerular enlargement perhaps due to the mechanical stresses of wall tension and mesangial cell dysfunction outstrips the capacity of the visceral epithelial cell coat to match the augmented underlying surface area (23, 53). Morphometric examinations have demonstrated that extreme enlargement of glomerular volume is accompanied by loss of the epithelial covering, which leaves areas of denuded glomerular basement membrane (23, 53). The measured extent of the bare areas has been relatively small, but in view of the critical role of the epithelial cells in determining glomerular permeability for macromolecules, even small areas are quantitatively sufficient to account for massive protein leak into the urinary space (12). The relatively long life of glomerular epithelial cells and their limited ability to proliferate are proposed to be the underlying cellular basis for such "podocyte insufficiency" (23, 53, 64a). Alterations in adhesion of the podocytes to the underlying basement membrane must contribute both in the setting of glomerular growth and other pathological states characterized by these findings. The aneurysmal expansion of capillaries would presumably only exacerbate this tendency to epithelial denudation. Finally, glomerular sclerosis could be defined equally as disproportionate growth or remodeling of the capillary wall. Thus some of those stimuli giving rise to the earlier more proportional growth probably continue to play roles in the more clearly disadvantageous pathologic progression that constitutes glomerular sclerosis, mesangial cell proliferation, excess production of mesangial matrix, and collapse or occlusion of capillary lumina (5, 19, 20).

The growth of tubular epithelium most likely is linked to the compensatory augmentation of metabolic and transport functions. Some of these functions such as ammoniagenesis and oxidative metabolism may, at the extreme, represent adverse responses, as noted above (55). However, plausible mechanisms have not been proposed whereby increases in cell volume and/or number are harmful. Presumably cells have optimal size, and this size does not appear to vary much across species of widely differing size. It seems likely that chronic cellular expansion beyond that optimum might carry some disadvantage whose exact biochemical or cellular basis is not apparent.

In summary, nephronal growth occurs with loss of functioning mass. The stimulus (stimuli) to that growth is (are) not well defined. Enhanced growth occurs in conjunction with compensatory hyperfunction of the glomerulus and tubule. Some of these increased functions may, in the extreme, or in combination with other events, damage the residual nephrons. Likewise, the structural expansion of the remaining glomerulus may contribute to its accelerated degenerative destruction.

Literature Cited

1. Anderson S, Rennke H, Brenner B. 1986. Therapeutic advantage of converting enzyme inhibitors in arresting progressive renal disease associated with systemic hypertension in the rat. *J. Clin. Invest.* 77:1993–2000

2. Bertani T, Poggi A, Pozonni R, Delaini F, Sacchi G, et al. 1982. Adriamycin-

induced nephrotic syndrome in rats. Sequence of pathologic events. *Lab. Invest.* 46:16–23

3. Blantz RC, Konnen KS, Tucker BJ. 1976. Angiotensin II effects upon the glomerular microcirculation and ultrafiltration coefficient of the rat. *J. Clin. Invest.* 57:419–34

4. Bonvalet JP. 1978. Evidence of induction of new nephrons in immature kidneys undergoing hypertrophy. *Yale J. Biol. Med.* 51:315–19

5. Border WA, Ruoslahti E. 1992. Transforming growth factor β in disease: the dark side of tissue repair. *J. Clin. Invest.* 90:1–7

6. Buerkert J, Martin D, Trigg D, Simon E. 1983. Effect of reduced renal mass on ammonium handling and net acid formation by the superficial and juxtamedullary nephron of the rat. Evidence of impaired re–entrapment rather than decreased production of ammonium in the acidosis of uremia. *J. Clin. Invest.* 71:1661–75

7. Canter CE, Goss RJ. 1975. Induction of extra nephrons in unilaterally nephrectomized immature rats (38525). *Proc. Soc. Exp. Biol. Med.* 148:294–96

8. Celsi G, Jakobsson B, Aperia A. 1986. Influence of age on compensatory renal growth in rats. *Pediatr. Res.* 20:347–50

9. Chanutin A, Ferris EB. 1932. Experimental renal insufficiency produced by partial nephrectomy. 1. Control diet. *Arch. Intern. Med.* 49:767–87

10. Correa-Rotter R, Hostetter TH, Manivel JC, Rosenberg ME. 1992. Renin expression in renal ablation. *Hypertension* 20:483–90

11. Cortes P, Riser B, Zhao X, Narins RG. 1994. Glomerular volume expansion and mesangial cell mechanical strain: mediators of glomerular pressure injury. *Kidney Int. Suppl.* 45:S11–16

12. Daniels BS, Deen WM, Mayer G, Meyer TW, Hostetter TH. 1993. Glomerular permeability barrier in the rat: functional assessment by in vitro methods. *J. Clin. Invest.* 92:929–36

13. Daniels BS, Hostetter TH. 1990. Adverse effects of growth in the glomerular microcirculation. *Am. J. Physiol.* 258: F1409–16

14. Diamond JR, Karnovsky MJ. 1986. Focal and segmental glomerulosclerosis following a single intravenous dose of puromycin aminonucleoside. *Am. J. Pathol.* 122:481–87

15. Diamond JR, Karnovsky MJ. 1988. Focal and segmental glomerulosclerosis: analogies to atherosclerosis. *Kidney Int.* 33:917–24

16. Dicker SE, Greenbaum AL, Morris CA. 1977. Compensatory renal hypertrophy in hypophysectomized rats. *J. Physiol.* 273:241–53

17. Dworkin LD, Feiner HD, Parker M, Tolisent E. 1991. Effects of nifedipine and enalapril on glomerular structure in uninephrectomized SHR. *Kidney Int.* 39: 1112–17

18. Fine LG. 1986. The biology of renal hypertrophy. *Kidney Int.* 29:619

19. Fine LG, Hammerman MR, Abboud HE. 1992. Evolving role of growth factors in the renal response to acute and chronic disease. *J. Am. Soc. Nephrol.* 2:1163–70

20. Floege J, Burns MW, Alpers CE, Yoshimura A, Pritzl P, et al. 1992. Glomerular cell proliferation and PDGF expression precede glomerulosclerosis in the remnant kidney model. *Kidney Int.* 41:297–309

21. Fogo A, Ichikawa I. 1992. Glomerular growth promoter: the common channel to glomerulosclerosis. In *The Progressive Nature of Renal Disease,* ed. WE Mitch, pp. 23–54. New York: Churchill-Livingstone

22. Fogo A, Ichikawa I. 1991. Evidence for a pathogenic linkage between glomerular hypertrophy and sclerosis. *Am. J. Kidney Dis.* 17:666–69

23. Fries JWU, Sandstrom DJ, Meyer TW, Rennke HG. 1989. Glomerular hypertrophy and epithelial cell injury modulate progressive glomerulosclerosis in the rat. *Lab. Invest.* 60:205–17

24. Goss RJ. 1978. The physiology of renal growth. In *The Physiology of Growth,* pp. 299–328. New York: Academic

25. Grond J, Bankers JB, Schilthuis MS, Werning JJ, Elema JD. 1986. Analysis of renal structural and functional differences in two rat strains with different susceptibility to glomerular sclerosis. *Lab. Invest.* 54:77–83

26. Grond J, Schilthuis MS, Koudstaal J, Elema JD. 1982. Mesangial function and glomerular sclerosis in rats after unilateral nephrectomy. *Kidney Int.* 22:338–43

27. Hammerman MR, O'Shea M, Miller SB. 1993. Role of growth factors in regulation of renal growth. *Annu. Rev. Physiol.* 55:305–21

28. Harris DC, Chan L, Schrier RW. 1988. Remnant kidney hypermetabolism and progression of chronic renal failure. *Am. J. Physiol.* 254:F267–76

29. Harris RC, Seifter JL, Brenner BM. 1984. Adaptation of Na⁺-H⁺ exchange in renal microvillus membrane vesicles: the role of dietary protein and uni-

nephrectomy. *J. Clin. Invest.* 74:1979–87

30. Harris RH, Best CF. 1977. Circulatory retention of urinary factors as a stimulus to renal growth. *Kidney Int.* 12:305–12

31. Harris RL, Akai Y, Yasuda T, Homma T. 1994. The role of physical forces in alterations of mesangial cell function. *Kidney Int. Suppl.* 45:S17–21

32. Hayslett JP. 1979. Functional adaptation to reduction in renal mass. *Physiol. Rev.* 59:137–69

33. Hayslett JP, Kashgarian M, Epstein FH. 1968. Functional correlates of compensatory renal hypertrophy. *J. Clin. Invest.* 47:774–82

34. Hostetter TH, Brenner BM. 1981. Glomerular adaptations to renal injury. In *Contemporary Issues in Nephrology, Chronic Renal Failure,* ed. BM Brenner, JH Stein, 7:1. New York: Churchill-Livingstone

35. Hostetter TH, Olson JL, Rennke HG, Venkatachalam MA, Brenner BM. 1981. Hyperfiltration in remnant nephrons: a potentially adverse response to renal ablation. *Am. J. Physiol.* 241:F85–93

36. Ishibashi K, Sasaki S, Sakamoto H, Nakamura T, Marumo F. 1991. Expression of hepatocyte growth factor and its receptor mRNA in kidney after ischemia or unilateral nephrectomy. *J. Am. Soc. Nephrol.* 2:648. (Abstr.)

37. Kasiske BL, Kalil RSN, Lee HS, Rao KV. 1991. Histopathologic findings associated with a chronic, progressive decline in renal allograft function. *Kidney Int.* 40:514–24

38. Kaufman JM, Hardy R, Hayslett JP. 1975. Age-dependent characteristics of compensatory renal growth. *Kidney Int.* 8:21–26

39. Keane WF, Raij L. 1965. Relationship among altered glomerular barrier permselectivity, angiotensin II, and mesangial uptake of macromolecules. *Lab. Invest.* 52:599–604

40. Klahr S, Schwab SJ, Stokes TJ. 1986. Metabolic adaptations of the nephron in renal disease. *Kidney Int.* 29:80–89

41. Kramp RA, MacDowell M, Gottschalk CW, Oliver JR. 1974. A study by microdissection and micropuncture of the structure and function of the kidneys and the nephrons of rats with chronic renal damage. *Kidney Int.* 5:147–76

42. Krohn AG, Perry BBK, Antell HI, Stein S, Waterhouse K. 1970. Compensatory renal hypertrophy: the role of immediate vascular changes in its production. *J. Urol.* 103:564–68

43. Kurnick NB, Lindsay PA. 1968. Compensatory renal hypertrophy in parabiotic mice. *Lab. Invest.* 19:45–48

44. Lafayette RA, Mayer G, Park SK, Meyer TW. 1992. Angiotensin II receptor blockade limits glomerular injury in rats with reduced renal mass. *J. Clin. Invest.* 90:766–71

45. Lafferty HM, Brenner BM. 1990. Are glomerular hypertension and "hypertrophy" independent risk factors for progression of renal disease? *Sem. Nephrol.* 10:294–304

46. Lotspeich WD. 1965. Renal hypertrophy in metabolic acidosis and its relation to ammonia excretion. *Am. J. Physiol.* 208:1135–42

47. Malt R. 1969. Compensatory growth of the kidney. *N. Engl. J. Med.* 280:1446–59

48. McQueen-Williams M, Thompson KW. 1940. The effect of ablation of the hypophysis upon the weight of the kidney of the rat. *Yale J. Biol. Med.* 12:531–41

49. Meyer TW, Anderson S, Rennke HG, Brenner BM. 1987. Reversing glomerular capillary hypertension stabilizes established glomerular injury. *Kidney Int.* 31:752–59

50. Meyer TW, Rennke HG. 1988. Progressive glomerular injury after limited renal infarction in the rat. *Am. J. Physiol.* 254:F856–62

51. Meyer TW, Schooley TW, Brenner BM. 1991. Nephron adaptation to renal injury. In *The Kidney,* ed. BM Brenner, FC Rector Jr., pp. 1871–1908. Philadelphia: Saunders. 4th ed.

52. Miller PL, Rennke HG, Meyer TW. 1991. Glomerular hypertrophy accelerates hypertensive glomerular injury in rats. *Am. J. Physiol.* 261:F459–65

53. Miller PL, Scholey JW, Rennke HG, Meyer TW. 1990. Glomerular hypertrophy aggravates epithelial injury in nephrotic rats. *J. Clin. Invest.* 85:1119–26

54. Nagata M, Scharer K, Kriz W. 1992. Glomerular damage after uninephrectomy in young rats. *Kidney Int.* 72:136–47

55. Nath KA. 1992. Tubulointerstitial changes as a major determinant in the progression of renal disease. *Am. J. Kidney Int.* 20:1–17

56. Nath KA, Croatt AJ, Hostetter TH. 1990. Oxygen consumption and oxidant stress in surviving nephrons. *Am. J. Physiol.* 258:F1354–62

57. Deleted in proof

58. Nath KA, Hostetter MK, Hostetter TH. 1985. Pathophysiology of chronic tubulo-interstitial disease in rats. Interactions of dietary acid load, ammonia,

and complement component C3. *J. Clin. Invest.* 76:667–75

59. Neuringer JR, Anderson S, Brenner BM. 1992. The role of systemic and intraglomerular hypertension. See Ref. 21, pp. 1–21

60. Olivetti G, Anuensa P, Melissari M, Loud AV. 1980. Morphometry of the renal corpuscle during postnatal growth and compensatory hypertrophy. *Kidney Int.* 17:438–54

61. Olson JL, Hostetter TH, Rennke HG, Brenner BM, Venkatachalam MA. 1982. Mechanisms of altered glomerular permselectivity and progressive glomerulosclerosis following extreme ablation of renal mass. *Kidney Int.* 22:112–26

62. Ouellette AJ, Moonka R, Zelenetz AD, Malt RA. 1987. Regulation of ribosome synthesis during compensatory renal hypertrophy in mice. *Am. J. Physiol.* 253:C506–13

63. Potter DE, Leumann EP, Sakai T, Holliday MA. 1974. Early responses of glomerular filtration rate to unilateral nephrectomy. *Kidney Int.* 5:131–36

64. Pupilli C, Chevalier RL, Carey RM, Gomez A. 1992. Distribution and content of renin and renin mRNA in remnant kidney of adult rat. *Am. J. Physiol.* 263:F731–38

64a. Rennke HG. 1994. How does glomerular epithelial cell injury contribute to glomerular damage? *Kidney Int. Suppl.* 45:S558–63

65. Rosenberg ME, Correa-Rotter R, Inagami T, Kren SM, Hostetter TH. 1991. Glomerular renin synthesis and storage in the remnant kidney. *Kidney Int.* 40:677–83

66. Rosenberg ME, Smith LJ, Correa-Rotter R, Hostetter TH. 1994. The paradox of the renin angiotensin system in chronic renal disease. *Kidney Int.* 45:403–10

67. Salehmoghaddam S, Bradley T, Mikhail N, Badie-Dezfooly B, Nord EP, et al. 1985. Hypertrophy of basolateral Na-K pump activity in the proximal tubule of the remnant kidney. *Lab. Invest.* 53:443–52

68. Schmidt K, Pesce C, Liu Q, Nelson RG, Bennett PH, et al. 1992. Large glomerular size in Pima Indians: lack of change with diabetic nephropathy. *J. Am. Soc. Nephrol.* 3:229–35

69. Schoolwerth AC, Sandler RS, Hoffsten PM, Klahr S. 1975. Effects of nephron reduction and dietary protein content on renal ammoniagenesis in the rat. *Kidney Int.* 7:397–404

70. Shea SM, Raskova J, Morrison AB. 1978. A stereologic study of glomerular hypertrophy in the subtotally nephrectomized rat. *Am. J. Path.* 90:201–10

71. Shimamura T, Morrison AB. 1975. A progressive glomerulosclerosis occurring in partial five-sixths nephrectomized rats. *Am. J. Pathol.* 79:95–106

72. Toback FG, Smith PD, Lowenstein LM. 1974. Phospholipid metabolism in the initiation of renal compensatory growth after acute reduction of renal mass. *J. Clin. Invest.* 54:91–97

73. Wesson LG. 1989. Compensatory growth and other growth responses of the kidney. *Nephron (editorial)* 51:149–84

74. Yoshida Y, Fogo A, Ichikawa I. 1989. Glomerular hemodynamic changes vs. hypertrophy in experimental glomerular sclerosis. *Kidney Int.* 35:654–60

75. Zatz R, Fujihara CK. 1994. Glomerular hypertrophy and progressive glomerulopathy. Is there a definite pathogenetic connection? *Kidney Int. Suppl.* 45:S27–29

Annu. Rev. Physiol. 1995. 57:279–95

TRANSFORMING GROWTH FACTOR-β AND ANGIOTENSIN II: The Missing Link from Glomerular Hyperfiltration to Glomerulosclerosis?

Markus Ketteler, Nancy A. Noble, and Wayne A. Border

Division of Nephrology and Hypertension, University of Utah Health Sciences Center, Salt Lake City, Utah 84132

KEY WORDS: ACE-inhibitors, cytokines, extracellular matrix, fibrosis, tissue renin angiotensin system

INTRODUCTION

The mechanism responsible for progression of kidney diseases to end-stage renal failure is still unknown. Glomerular and tubulointerstitial fibrosis characterized by excessive accumulation of extracellular matrix represent the morphological equivalent of kidney failure and appear to occur independently of the primary underlying disorder. In numerous studies of experimental and human kidney diseases, transforming growth factor-β (TGF-β) has been identified as a key mediator of glomerulosclerosis. TGF-β is a potent fibrogenic cytokine, and its transient expression promotes matrix accumulation in normal wound healing. Sustained TGF-β expression underlies the development of chronic progressive tissue fibrosis, but the factors that cause TGF-β overexpression in chronic fibrosis are incompletely understood. Glomerular hyperfiltration is another mechanism known to be involved in the progression of renal failure. Angiotensin II causes hyperfiltration and elevated intraglomerular pressure by mediating vasoconstriction predominantly of the efferent glomerular arterioles. Administration of angiotensin-converting enzyme (ACE) inhibitors appears to exert beneficial effects on the course of progressive

279

kidney diseases. Recent studies have demonstrated that angiotensin II is also capable of inducing TGF-β gene expression and that angiotensin II effects on cell growth and matrix protein expression are mediated by TGF-β. These findings may represent the "missing link" between altered hemodynamics and the development of glomerulosclerosis and may also explain the superior effects of ACE inhibition vs other antihypertensive drugs in progressive kidney disease.

TGF-β: Basic Biology and Fibrogenic Properties

Biology of TGF-β

TGF-βs are homodimeric peptide growth factors with a molecular weight of 25 kDa (70,71). Three distinct isoforms (TGF-β1, 2, and 3) have been characterized, and most cells lines respond identically to stimulation with any isoform of TGF-β (70, 71). The three genes encoding these isoforms are located on different chromosomes (70). TGF-β1 is most abundant in mammalian species. TGF-βs are released as latent, biologically inactive peptides, and activation can be achieved in vitro by acidification and alkalinization, and by proteases (57). Activation involves cleavage of the mature, dimeric TGF-β from the latency-associated peptide, which remains after processing of a larger TGF-β precursor (57). In vivo mechanisms of TGF-β activation are incompletely understood.

The TGF-β1 precursor gene is ~ 100 kb in size and is encoded by seven exons (70). One of two characterized promoter regions of the gene, the positive regulatory region of the upstream promoter, contains binding sites for several transcription factors (70). Among these transcription factors is AP-1, which is thought to mediate the potential of TGF-β1 to autoinduce its own expression (48). Autoinduction is thought to be of major importance in maintaining TGF-β1 overexpression in chronic disease states.

The biological effects of TGF-β are mediated by binding to specific cell membrane receptors (29, 52, 57, 85). TGF-β receptors I and II are serine-threonine kinases, and their interaction is responsible for most of the biological actions of TGF-β (29, 52). Both receptors have a significantly higher affinity for TGF-β1 than for the other isoforms. The TGF-β receptor III, also termed betaglycan, is a membrane-bound proteoglycan (85). This receptor has no signaling complex and probably serves as a binding reservoir for TGF-β in tissues.

Fibrogenesis and TGF-β

TGF-β is a multifunctional cytokine with potent effects on development, cell growth, chemotaxis, and immune function. However, one of the most important biological properties of TGF-β is the induction of extracellular matrix accumulation in tissues, which is achieved by three distinct mechanisms: (a) TGF-β induces transcription, synthesis, and secretion of matrix proteins. (b) TGF-β decreases synthesis of proteases and increases synthesis of protease inhibitors leading to decreased matrix degradation. (c) TGF-β increases transcription and membrane expression of receptors of cell adhesion proteins (integrins) that regulate matrix assembly (17, 70). Matrix proteins shown to be directly induced by TGF-β include collagens I, III, IV, and VI, fibronectin, tenascin, and some proteoglycans (70).

Studies of wound healing have confirmed the importance of TGF-β as a mediator of extracellular matrix accumulation. TGF-β administration leads to increased collagen deposition and increased tensile breaking strength of wounds in animals and humans (71). Acceleration of wound healing by TGF-β has been demonstrated in studies of healing-impaired models including radiation-exposed and glucocorticoid-treated animals (8, 9). TGF-β thus plays a key role for mediating matrix synthesis following injury and is needed in physiological repair processes. However, in chronic progressive fibrosis, sustained TGF-β expression may mediate organ damage by excessive induction of extracellular matrix deposition.

TGF-β EXPRESSION IN KIDNEY DISEASE

TGF-β Effects on Renal Cells in Vitro

Mesangial, glomerular epithelial, and proximal tubule cells stimulated with TGF-β respond with increased synthesis of matrix proteins in vitro (15, 39, 59). This was shown for proteoglycans, fibronectin, laminin, and collagen IV. Other cytokines including platelet-derived growth factor (PDGF) and tumor necrosis factor-α (TNF-α) had no effect on matrix protein synthesis by mesangial and epithelial cells.

TGF-β also regulates mesangial cell growth in a differential manner. A recent study showed that TGF-β inhibits cell growth within the first 36 h of culture and then promotes cell proliferation by induction of PDGF protein and receptor expression (36). In another study, TGF-β caused hypertrophy by inhibiting cell proliferation but increasing overall protein and collagen synthesis in cultured mesangial cells (23). This effect may have been amplified by autocrine secretion of TGF-β.

TGF-β in Experimental Glomerulonephritis

Studies were conducted on the role of TGF-β in glomerular extracellular matrix accumulation in a rat model of acute mesangioproliferative glomerulonephritis. Glomerulonephritis was induced by antithymocyte serum (ATS) recognizing a Thy-1-like antigen on the mesangial cell surface (62, 93). Following ATS injection, complement-dependent mesangial cell lysis occurred, which was subsequently followed by mesangial cell proliferation and pronounced matrix protein accumulation in the glomeruli starting at about 5 days after disease induction.

TGF-β was shown to induce matrix protein synthesis, especially proteoglycan synthesis, in this animal model (62). Proteoglycan production of cultured nephritic glomeruli and extracellular matrix accumulation in glomeruli in vivo could be prevented by administration of a TGF-β-neutralizing antibody, thereby implicating TGF-β as a key mediator of glomerular fibrosis (16). Decorin, a TGF-β-binding proteoglycan, also prevented matrix deposition in vivo (14). Thus decorin has potential as an anti-fibrotic drug.

In addition to the direct induction of matrix protein expression, TGF-β mediates extracellular matrix accumulation in ATS-induced glomerulonephritis by inhibition of matrix degradation and by induction of integrin receptors (45, 83). TGF-β is shown to reduce plasminogen activator activity and increase plasminogen activator inhibitor-1 (PAI-1) activity in glomerulonephritic rats (83). The increase in PAI-1 activity can be blocked by a TGF-β-neutralizing antibody in vivo (83). In another study, TGF-β specifically induces glomerular expression of β1-integrins (α1β1, α5β1) (45). These integrins play an important role as collagen and fibronectin receptors in matrix assembly. Taken together, these results indicate that TGF-β displays each of its three fibrogenic properties in experimental glomerulonephritis in vivo: increased matrix protein synthesis, decreased matrix degradation, and increased synthesis of integrin receptors.

TGF-β in Chronic Models of Kidney Disease

Although acute models are helpful in identifying mechanisms of disease, results obtained from such studies do not necessarily explain mechanisms of chronic progressive disease. Since chronic renal failure is a process of progressive glomerular and tubulointerstitial sclerosis, studies in models of chronic renal disease are needed to confirm the suggestion that TGF-β overexpression is a key mediator of unterminated tissue fibrosis.

Diabetic nephropathy is the leading cause of end-stage renal failure in the human, and streptozotocin-induced diabetes in the rat is a suitable animal model for studies of diabetic complications (54). In this model, development of nephropathy histologically resembles human disease very closely (54). We have reported increased TGF-β expression in the progression of diabetic nephropathy in the rat, which correlates with increased glomerular deposition of matrix proteins including fibronectin and biglycan (91). TGF-β is also responsible for increased glomerular collagen synthesis in this model (13).

Recently, we also investigated TGF-β expression in a rat model of chronic glomerulonephritis induced by two ATS injections given 1 week apart (92).

Whereas one injection of ATS causes an acute and self-limiting mesangioproliferative glomerulonephritis, two injections transform disease into chronic progressive glomerulosclerosis. Sustained TGF-β expression is associated with progressive extracellular matrix accumulation in this model (92). In the first weeks after disease induction, TGF-β overexpression is limited to the glomeruli but expands to the tubulointerstitium by 18 weeks (92). Increasing tubulointerstitial fibrosis is also a hallmark of later stages in progressive kidney disease in the human and is closely correlated with the loss of kidney function (60). Our findings in this chronic disease model implicate TGF-β as a major mediator of tubulointerstitial fibrosis. However, the questions of why TGF-β overexpression is terminated in acute but not in chronic disease and why TGF-β overexpression expands from the glomerulus to the tubulointerstitium are not yet answered. The ability of TGF-β to induce its own synthesis through both autocrine and paracrine mechanisms may play a role here.

TGF-β in Human Kidney Disease

To evaluate the relevance of TGF-β for the progression of chronic fibrotic diseases in the human, studies were performed to detect TGF-β expression in diseased tissues. Kidney biopsy tissues obtained from patients with diabetic nephropathy were stained with TGF-β antibody using immunofluorescence (91). Increased TGF-β protein staining in glomeruli was detected in diabetic glomeruli, and the staining intensity closely correlated with the severity of glomerulosclerosis (91). Yoshioka and co-workers found highly increased TGF-β expression using immunohistochemistry and in situ hybridization in glomeruli from patients with focal segmental glomerulosclerosis and progressive IgA-nephropathy (94). No TGF-β was detectable in glomeruli from normal kidneys, and from biopsy samples obtained from patients with minimal- change and thin-basement membrane disease, which served as control in both studies. Recent evidence shows that TGF-β overexpression may be involved in the development of HIV nephropathy and chronic kidney transplant rejection (18, 81). In both diseases, TGF-β staining was strongly increased in the kidney as compared with control and was associated with severe glomerular and interstitial fibrosis. Because other human studies also implicate TGF-β in the progression of chronic fibrotic diseases of other organ systems including liver cirrhosis, pulmonary fibrosis and scleroderma, understanding of TGF-β regulation may lead to novel and potent therapies targeting progressive tissue fibrosis.

THE RENIN-ANGIOTENSIN SYSTEM

Biology of Angiotensin II

The renin-angiotensin system (RAS) is a complex regulatory system generating the octapeptide angiotensin II, the biologically active product. Signals for angiotensin II activation, including decreases in glomerular blood flow and in plasma sodium concentration, lead to renin release from the juxtaglomerular apparatus of the kidney into the circulation, where renin acts as a protease targeting angiotensinogen (6). Renin represents the rate-limiting step of angiotensin II synthesis (6). Angiotensinogen, an oligopeptide synthesized mainly in the liver, is transformed to angiotensin I by renin-mediated proteolytic cleavage of four amino acids. Angiotensin I is then converted to angiotensin II by the action of angiotensin converting enzyme (ACE), a large acidic glycoprotein metalloenzyme present in the plasma. The mechanism is a further cleavage of two amino acids. Angiotensin II has only a short plasma half-life, in the range of a few minutes, and is further metabolized by aminopeptidase A to the less active angiotensin III, which is finally processed to inactive peptide fragments (6).

The cellular actions of angiotensin II are mediated via specific binding to cell surface receptors (10). Two major subtypes termed AT_1 and AT_2 are identified (10). Receptors are present in many tissues including CNS, liver, kidney, and in adrenal glands (10). Vascular receptors are located on the vascular smooth muscle cells (6, 10). Receptor down-regulation represents one important control mechanism of the action of angiotensin II. Receptor binding initiates intracellular signaling events that include G proteins, phospholipase C, and adenylate cyclase (1, 6, 7, 61). 1, 4, 5-inositol trisphosphate and diacylglycerol increase in cells and levels of cAMP and cGMP decrease. This is followed by a rapid rise in intracellular Ca^{2+} concentration and an activation of membrane-associated protein kinase C (1, 6, 22). These events are associated with contraction of vascular smooth muscle cells and mesangial cells, augmentation of steroid synthesis in the adrenal gland, and mitogenesis in some cells (5, 6, 22, 95). However, the exact regulation of molecular events leading to biological actions, which may also include induction of growth factors and early response genes, is still incompletely understood.

Physiological Action

The main physiological actions of angiotensin II involve regulation of renal hemodynamics and salt homeostasis. Angiotensin II is a potent, systemic vasoconstrictor and acts in the kidney predominantly on the efferent arteriole of the glomerulus thereby increasing glomerular filtration pressure (6). This mechanism restores glomerular filtration when mean systemic blood pressure decreases due to volume depletion or a fall in peripheral vascular resistance.

Angiotensin II also regulates aldosterone synthesis and secretion. Adrenal glomerulosa cells are directly stimulated by angiotensin II, which leads to release of aldosterone into the circulation. Aldosterone increases distal tubule sodium transport, and thereby sodium reabsorption, and also increases tubular potassium secretion (6). Angiotensin II may have aldosterone-independent effects on sodium retention by enhancing proximal tubular sodium reabsorption (37).

Angiotensin II also exerts effects on the CNS. Infusion into the cerebral vasculature leads to an increase of systemic blood pressure, although angiotensin II does not reach the peripheral circulation (6, 82), which suggests that angiotensin II participates in blood pressure regulation at the level of the CNS. Angiotensin II also mediates thirst and salt appetite (6). Therefore, the RAS is a key regulator of volume and salt homeostasis and acts on kidney, vasculature, and CNS.

Tissue Renin Angiotensin System

Whereas growth factors exert their biological effects in tissues in a paracrine-autocrine fashion, the RAS was considered to be a typical endocrine system. However, this view is being revised because components of the RAS (angiotensinogen, ACE, renin, angiotensin II receptors) have been found in a number of cell types and organs (27, 28, 65, 78). Under pathophysiological conditions of cardiac hypertrophy, and in vascular smooth muscle cells following balloon angioplasty, expression of tissue RAS components are increased (26, 84). In the absence of exogenous RAS components, shear stress leads to angiotensin II synthesis in cultured cardiac myocytes, which suggests that these cells can manufacture all components of the RAS (76). The tissue RAS thus exists independently of the systemic RAS.

In studies including ours, angiotensin II induced hypertrophic and mitogenic responses in vitro, effects reminiscent of those induced by growth factors including TGF-β and PDGF (2, 6, 23, 31, 34, 95). Studies investigating the mechanisms of angiotensin II/growth factor interactions indicate that angiotensin II is a potent inducer of TGF-β and PDGF and that some of its reported effects are directly mediated by expression of these growth factors (35, 44, 58, 87). Details of these studies and their impact on the understanding of chronic progressive renal disease are summarized below.

ROLE OF ANGIOTENSIN II IN PROGRESSIVE RENAL FAILURE

Because angiotensin II is a potent vasoconstrictor capable of causing systemic and glomerular hypertension, increased angiotensin II has long been a suspected contributor to progressive renal disease. Over 40 years ago, using the Goldblatt model, it was demonstrated that clamping of one renal artery leads to angiotensin II-mediated hypertension and glomerular and tubulointerstitial injury in the contralateral kidney (86). Intravenous infusion of angiotensin II in rats causes progressive glomerular and tubulointerstitial damage including proliferative changes and excessive fibrosis (43, 56). It is not clear how angiotensin II-mediated glomerular hypertension leads to progressive glomerular damage, although hypertension-induced mechanical stretching of mesangial cells has been proposed as one mechanism. Mesangial cell stretching induces TGF-β, a potent inducer of matrix protein expression, and synthesis of matrix proteins (68, 69). Thus matrix production probably results from TGF-β expression and not from the shear force itself. Another mechanism may be that the elevated glomerular filtration pressure defect in glomerular permselectivity allows potentially damaging macromolecules to leave the circulation and deposit in the glomerulus (55, 67).

However, measurement of the systemic components of the RAS, for example plasma renin activity, do not always suggest a major activation of the RAS in experimental or human kidney diseases, a paradox recently reviewed by Rosenberg et al (74). On the other hand, treatment with ACE-inhibitors such as captopril and enalapril, shows beneficial effects on the course of many renal diseases including glomerulonephritis and diabetic nephropathy (11, 21, 24, 33, 47, 67, 74, 96). Treatment with ACE-inhibitors rather consistently slows the deterioration of renal function and reduces the degree of proteinuria in experimental models and in patients. In animal models, amelioration of glomerular injury and fibrosis has been observed. Comparable effects have been demonstrated using angiotensin II receptor antagonists in experimental studies (50, 74).

ACE-inhibitors block the endogenous synthesis of angiotensin II and thereby decrease systemic and glomerular blood pressure. Renal hemodynamics are affected in the following way: A selective vasodilation of the efferent glomerular arteriole leads to significant reduction of glomerular filtration pressure but maintains or improves glomerular perfusion. Because reduced numbers of functioning nephrons in later stages of progressive kidney diseases cause hyperfiltration of the remaining nephrons, this action of ACE-inhibitors is thought to be particularly beneficial (19). Some studies comparing the effect of ACE-inhibitors to those of other antihypertensive drugs (β-blocker, Ca^{2+} antagonists, diuretics) on the course of renal disease have, indeed, documented superior effects of ACE inhibition, although observation periods or number of subjects under investigation were not always sufficient in these studies (12, 21, 73, 74).

Recently it was proposed that ACE-inhibitors exert effects independently of their antihypertensive properties. Lewis et al reported results from a randomized, controlled trial showing that deterioration of renal function is significantly ameliorated by captopril in patients with diabetic nephropathy (51). Blood pressure was equal in patients with either captopril or placebo treatment, but only patients treated with captopril showed a 50% risk reduction for decline of renal function. ACE inhibition also causes regression of cardiac hypertrophy (26, 79). This effect may be the result of afterload reduction because ACE-inhibitors decrease arterial blood pressure, but again the results seem to be superior to those obtained with other antihypertensive agents. Since ACE-inhibitors modulate prostaglandin and bradykinin synthesis, some of their effects may follow an interaction with those autacoids (25, 40, 49, 66, 77). Another challenging hypothesis is that ACE inhibition reduces the activity of a tissue RAS and thereby blocks autocrine angiotensin II effects on cell growth and possibly tissue fibrosis independently of its antihypertensive effects. This view is strongly supported by a number of recent studies indicating that angiotensin II is an inducer of TGF-β and PDGF, which possess potent fibrogenic and mitogenic properties, respectively (35, 44, 58, 87).

INTERPLAY OF TGF-β AND ANGIOTENSIN II: The Missing Link Between Hyperfiltration and Glomerulosclerosis?

TGF-β plays a pivotal role in the extracellular matrix accumulation observed in chronic progressive tissue fibrosis (17, 71). PDGF is important for cell proliferation (31, 41). Overexpression of both growth factors is now documented in a large number of experimental and human kidney diseases and associated with progression of disease (14, 16, 17, 31, 41, 62, 91, 92, 94). Angiotensin II infusion causes glomerulosclerosis, and decreasing angiotensin II synthesis by ACE-inhibitors slows the progression of chronic renal disease and significantly ameliorates histopathological changes including glomerulosclerosis, tubulointerstitial injury, and hypertrophic and proliferative responses in experimental models (11, 12, 21, 24, 33, 43, 47, 51, 56, 74, 96). Recent studies suggest a possible connection between the beneficial effect of ACE-inhibitors and the action of angiotensin II on growth factor and especially TGF-β overexpression.

The first study to show that angiotensin II induces TGF-β expression in vitro was published by Gibbons et al (35). Using cultured vascular smooth muscle cells, they showed that angiotensin II leads to increased TGF-β mRNA and protein expression and also promotes conversion of latent to active TGF-β through a protein kinase C–dependent pathway (35). This autocrine active TGF-β appeared to be an important mediator of cell growth leading to cell hypertrophy (35). A subsequent study by Itoh et al suggested that the antiproliferative effect of autocrine TGF-β is due to inhibition of mitogenic growth factors including basic fibroblast growth factor (bFGF) and PDGF, which are also directly induced by angiotensin II in vitro (42, 58).

Studies from Wolf et al have documented the importance of angiotensin II on the development of tubular hypertrophy (88, 89), which is an adaptive response of the kidney in a variety of processes (19, 30). This hypertrophy is observed in the contralateral kidney in response to uninephrectomy, but also under pathophysiological conditions including early diabetes and glomerulo-

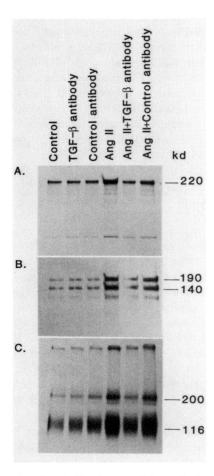

Figure 1 Coincubation of angiotensin II and a neutralizing antibody to TGF-β: effect on matrix protein synthesis in supernatants from cultured rat mesangial cells. (*A*) immunoprecipitation of 35S-methionine–labeled fibronectin; (*B*) immunoprecipitation of 35S-methionine–labeled collagen I; (*C*) SDS-PAGE of 35S-sulfate–labeled proteoglycans. The increased matrix protein production following angiotensin II stimulation can be specifically blocked by a neutralizing antibody to TGF-β (figure from Reference 44).

nephritis. The same group of investigators recently identified angiotensin II-induced TGF-β synthesis as the major mediator of proximal tubular cell hypertrophy because a neutralizing TGF-β antibody abolished the hypertrophic effect of angiotensin II and led to proliferation (87).

Glomerular hypertrophy and mesangial cell proliferation are frequently observed in the course of progressive renal diseases and are suspected to contribute to glomerulosclerosis (10, 30, 49). TGF-β is an important growth modulator for mesangial cells in vitro, mediating hypertrophic and proliferative changes (23, 36). Anderson et al recently showed that angiotensin II mediates mesangial cell hypertrophy (2). Since TGF-β is the key mediator of extracellular matrix accumulation in vitro and in vivo, we asked whether angiotensin II also directly increases matrix protein synthesis in cultured mesangial cells via induction of TGF-β synthesis. In this study, angiotensin II caused hypertrophy and induced TGF-β, collagen I, fibronectin, and biglycan mRNA and protein synthesis in a dose-dependent manner in cultured mesangial cells (44). Angiotensin II also increased conversion of the endogenously produced, latent TGF-β to its biologically active form (44). These effects could be blocked by saralasin, an angiotensin II receptor blocker. The increased matrix protein synthesis could be inhibited by saralasin, as well as by a TGF-β-neutralizing antibody (Figure 1). In vivo administration of angiotensin II by osmotic minipumps releasing angiotensin II subcutaneously led to increased glomerular TGF-β and collagen I mRNA expression in rats within 1 week (44). Thus angiotensin II may directly cause glomerulosclerosis by induction of TGF-β overexpression independently of its vasoconstrictive effect on renal hemodynamics or of mechanical stretching of mesangial cells. This action indicates a potentially important role of a tissue RAS in the progression of renal disease.

Unilateral ureteral obstruction in rats causes tubulointerstitial fibrosis. The contralateral kidney of animals serves as control in this model. Recently it was shown that TGF-β is a major factor associated with interstitial fibrotic changes in the animal model (46). TGF-β expression and fibrosis can be ameliorated by using enalapril, an ACE-inhibitor, in vivo (46). This finding is particularly interesting because glomerular hemodynamics are not primarily altered following unilateral ureteral obstruction and, therefore, the data may indirectly support the hypothesis that pressure-independent interactions of angiotensin II and TGF-β contribute to the pathophysiology of kidney disease.

The course of diabetic nephropathy is especially sensitive to the beneficial effects of ACE-inhibitors (12, 21, 33, 51, 74, 96). Increased glomerular filtration pressure is a characteristic pathophysiological change occurring in the kidney in early diabetes (38). A recent study showed that intrarenal renin protein content and renin and angiotensinogen mRNA expression are increased in diabetic rats (3). In renal tubular cells cultured under hyperglycemic conditions, there is an increase in angiotensin II receptors associated with a hypertrophic response (90). We have shown that sustained glomerular TGF-β overexpression also occurs in experimental and human diabetic nephropathy and is closely related to the severity of glomerulosclerosis (91). A recent study showed that increased glomerular TGF-β gene expression is present in early diabetes, which suggests an association with hypertrophic changes at this stage

Table 1   Interaction of TGF-β and angiotensin II (AngII) in vitro studies

Cell type	Observation	Biological effects	Reference
Mesangial cells	AngII $\Rightarrow$ TGF-β expression	Hypertrophic growth, matrix protein synthesis	44
Vascular smooth muscle cells	AngII $\Rightarrow$ TGF-β expression	Hypertrophic growth, modulation of cytokine effects (PDGF, bFGF)	34, 42
Proximal tubular cells	AngII $\Rightarrow$ TGF-β expression	Hypertrophic growth	38
Juxtaglomerular cells	TGF-β $\Rightarrow$ renin secretion	(?)	2

of the disease (80). Thus the beneficial effects of ACE inhibition on diabetic nephropathy may be in part related to a suppression of TGF-β overexpression.

A low-protein diet represents another therapeutic strategy that effectively slows the progressive course of many renal diseases (20, 75). Decreased activity of the RAS is observed with dietary protein restriction, although it is unclear whether this finding contributes to its beneficial effects, and some contradictory results exist (53, 64, 72). We and others have shown that low protein suppresses TGF-β expression in ATS-induced glomerulonephritis and in puromycin aminonucleoside nephrosis, respectively (32, 63). One might speculate that the effects of protein restriction also involve a mechanism of angiotensin II/TGF-β interaction.

Finally, TGF-β may also be involved in the regulation of the RAS. TGF-β1 and 2 are expressed in the macula densa and are stimulants of renin release from cultured juxtaglomerular cells at picomolar concentrations (4). Prostaglandins may be involved in mediating this effect because renin release can be blocked by cyclooxygenase inhibitors. Table 1 summarizes studies that have identified interactions of TGF-β and the RAS.

SUMMARY

Both angiotensin II and TGF-β are key mediators of glomerular and tubulo-interstitial injury and fibrosis in progressive kidney diseases. It was thought that angiotensin II damages the kidney by increasing glomerular filtration pressure, whereas autocrine TGF-β overexpression occurs from unidentified mechanisms. Recent studies reveal that angiotensin II is a potent inducer of TGF-β synthesis in a variety of cells and that this mechanism exerts important biological effects including extracellular matrix accumulation, cell proliferation, and hypertrophy. Because these studies were performed in vitro, there is clear evidence that the biological effects were observed independently of the vasoconstrictive properties of angiotensin II. Although it is difficult to study angiotensin II-mediated effects in vivo without influencing systemic and glomerular blood pressure, further studies are needed to evaluate the ability of ACE-inhibitors and angiotensin II receptor blockers to suppress TGF-β overexpression in selected models of chronic progressive kidney disease.

Literature Cited

1. Alexander RW, Brock TA, Gimbrone MA Jr, Rittenhouse SE. 1985. Angiotensin increases inositol trisphosphate and calcium in vascular smooth muscle cells. *Hypertension* 7:447–51
2. Anderson PW, Do YS, Hsueh WA. 1993. Angiotensin II causes mesangial cell hypertrophy. *Hypertension* 21:29–35
3. Anderson S, Jung FF, Ingelfinger JR. 1993. Renal renin-angiotensin system in diabetes: functional, immunohistochemical, and molecular biology correlations. *Am. J. Physiol.* 265:F477–86
4. Antonipillai I, Le TH, Soceneantu L, Horton R. 1993. Transforming growth factor-β is a renin secretagogue at picomolar concentrations. *Am. J. Physiol.* 265:F537–41
5. Ausiello DA, Kreisberg JI, Roy C, Karnovsky MJ. 1980. Contraction of cultured rat glomerular cells of apparent mesangial origin after stimulation with angiotensin II and arginine vasopressin. *J. Clin. Invest.* 65:754–60
6. Ballermann BJ, Zeidel ML, Gunning ME, Brenner BM. 1991. Vasoactive peptides and the kidney. In *The Kidney* ed. BM Brenner, FC Rector, Jr, pp. 510–83. Philadelphia/London/Toronto: Saunders
7. Baukal AJ, Balla T, Hunyadi L, Hausdorff W, Guillemette G, Catt KJ. 1988. Angiotensin II and guanine nucleotides stimulate formation of inositol 1,4,5-trisphosphate and its metabolites in permeabilized adrenal glomerulosa cells. *J. Biol. Chem.* 263:6087–92
8. Beck LS, DeGuzman L, Lee WP, Xu Y, McFatridge LA, Amento EP. 1991. TGF-β1 accelerates wound healing: reversal of steroid-impaired healing in rats and rabbits. *Growth Factors* 5:295–304
9. Bernstein EF, Harisiadis L, Salomon D, Norton J, Sollberg S, et al. 1991. Transforming growth factor-β improves healing of radiation-impaired wounds. *J. Invest. Dermatol.* 97:430–34
10. Bernstein KE, Berk BC. 1993. The biology of angiotensin II receptors. *Am. J. Kidney Dis.* 22:745–54
11. Bjoerck S, Mulec H, Johnsen SA, Norden G, Aurell M. 1992. Renal protective effect of enalapril in diabetic nephropathy. *Br. Med. J.* 304:339–43
12. Bjoerck S, Mulec H, Johnsen SA, Nyberg G, Aurell M. 1986. Contrasting effects of enalapril and metoprolol on proteinuria in diabetic nephropathy. *Br. Med. J.* 293:471–74
13. Bollineni JS, Reddi AS. 1993. Transforming growth factor-β1 enhances glomerular collagen synthesis in diabetic rats. *Diabetes* 42:1673–77
14. Border WA, Noble NA, Yamamoto T, Harper J, Yamaguchi Y, et al. 1992. Natural inhibitor of transforming growth factor-β protects against scarring in experimental kidney disease. *Nature* 360:361–64
15. Border WA, Okuda S, Languino LR, Ruoslahti E. 1990. Transforming growth factor-β regulates production of proteoglycans by mesangial cells. *Kidney Int.* 37:689–95
16. Border WA, Okuda S, Languino LR, Sporn MB, Ruoslahti E. 1990. Suppression of experimental glomerulonephritis by antiserum against transforming growth factor-β1. *Nature* 346:371–74
17. Border WA, Ruoslahti E. 1992. Transforming growth factor-β in disease: the dark side of tissue repair. *J. Clin. Invest.* 90:1–7
18. Border WA, Yamamoto T, Noble NA, Gold L, Nast C, Cohen A. 1993. HIV-associated nephropathy is linked to TGF-β and matrix protein expression in human kidney. *J. Am. Soc. Nephrol.* 4:675 (Abstr.)
19. Brenner BM. 1985. Nephron adaptation

to renal injury or ablation. *Am. J. Physiol.* 249:F324–37

20. Brenner BM, Meyer TW, Hostetter TH. 1982. Dietary protein intake and the progressive nature of kidney disease: the role of hemodynamically mediated glomerular injury in the pathogenesis of progressive glomerular sclerosis in aging, renal ablation and intrinsic renal disease. *N. Engl. J. Med.* 307:652–59

21. Brunner HR. 1992. ACE inibitors in renal disease. *Kidney Int.* 42:463–79

22. Capponi AM, Lew PD, Jornot L, Valloton MB. 1984. Correlation between cytosolic free Ca^{2+} and aldosterone production in bovine adrenal glomerulosa cells. *J. Biol. Chem.* 259: 8863–69

23. Choi ME, Kim EG, Huang Q, Ballermann BJ. 1993. Rat mesangial cell hypertrophy in response to transforming growth factor-β1. *Kidney Int.* 44:948–58

24. Diamond JR, Anderson S. 1990. Irreversible tubulointerstitial damage associated with chronic aminonucleoside nephrosis. Amelioration by angiotensin I converting enzyme inhibition. *Am. J. Pathol.* 137:1323–32

25. Dworkin LD, Ichikawa I, Brenner BM. 1983. Hormonal modulation of glomerular function. *Am. J. Physiol.* 244:F95–104

26. Dzau VJ. 1987. Evolution of the clinical management of hypertension. *Am. J. Med.* 82:36–43 (Suppl.)

27. Dzau VJ, Burt DW, Pratt RE. 1988. Molecular biology of the renin-angiotensin-system. *Am. J. Physiol.* 255: H563–73

28. Dzau VJ, Ellison KE, Brody T, Ingelfinger J, Pratt RE. 1987. A comparative study of the distribution of renin and angiotensinogen messenger ribonucleic acids in rat and mouse tissues. *Endocrinology* 120:2334–38

29. Ebner R, Chen RH, Shum L, Lawler S, Zioncheck TF, et al. 1993. Cloning of a type I TGF-β receptor and its effect on TGF-β binding to the type II receptor. *Science* 260:1344–48

30. Fine LG. 1986. The biology of renal hypertrophy. *Kidney Int.* 29:619–34

31. Floege J, Eng E, Young BA, Johnson RJ. 1993. Factors involved in the regulation of mesangial cell proliferation in vitro and in vivo. *Kidney Int.* 43:S47–54 (Suppl.)

32. Fukui M, Nakamura T, Ebihara I, Nagaoka I, Tomino Y, Koide H. 1993. Low-protein diet attenuates increased gene expression of platelet-derived growth factor and transforming growth factor-β in experimental glomerular sclerosis. *J. Lab. Clin. Med.* 121:224–34

33. Geiger H, Bahner U, Vaaben W, Dammrich J, Heidland A, Luft FC. 1992. Effects of angiotensin-converting enzyme inhibition in diabetic rats with reduced renal function. *J. Lab. Clin. Med.* 120:861–68

34. Geisterfer AAT, Peach MJ, Owens GK. 1988. Angiotensin II induces hypertrophy, not hyperplasia, of cultured rat aortic smooth muscle cells. *Circ. Res.* 62:749–56

35. Gibbons GH, Pratt RE, Dzau VJ. 1992. Vascular smooth muscle cell hypertrophy vs. hyperplasia: autocrine transforming growth factor-β1 expression determines growth response to angiotensin II. *J. Clin. Invest.* 90:456–61

36. Haberstroh U, Zahner G, Disser M, Thaiss F, Wolf G, Stahl RAK. 1993. TGF-β stimulates rat mesangial cell proliferation in culture: role of PDGF β-receptor expression. *Am. J. Physiol.* 264: F199–205

37. Hall JE. 1986. Control of sodium excretion by angiotensin II: intrarenal mechanism and blood pressure regulation. *Am. J. Physiol.* 250:R960–72

38. Hostetter TH, Troy JL, Brenner BM. 1981. Glomerular hemodynamics in experimental diabetes mellitus. *Kidney Int.* 19:410–15

39. Humes HD, Nakamura T, Cieslinski DA, Miller D, Emmons RV, Border WA. 1993. Role of proteoglycans and cytoskeleton in the effects of TGF-β1 on renal proximal tubule cells. *Kidney Int.* 43:575–84

40. Hura CE, Kunau RT Jr. 1988. Angiotensin II-stimulated prostaglandin production by canine renal afferent arterioles. *Am. J. Physiol.* 254:F734–38

41. Iida H, Seifert R, Alpers CE, Gronwald RGK, Philips PE, et al. 1991. Platelet-derived growth factor (PDGF) and PDGF receptor are induced in mesangial proliferative nephritis in the rat. *Proc. Natl. Acad. Sci. USA* 88:6560–64

42. Itoh H, Mukoyama M, Pratt RE, Gibbons GH, Dzau VJ. 1993. Multiple autocrine growth factors modulate vascular smooth muscle cell growth response to angiotensin II. *J. Clin. Invest.* 91:2268–74

43. Johnson RJ, Alpers CE, Yoshimura A, Lombardi D, Pritzl P, et al. 1992. Renal injury from angiotensin II-mediated hypertension. *Hypertension* 19:464–74

44. Kagami S, Border WA, Miller DA, Noble NA. 1994. Angiotensin II stimulates extracellular matrix protein synthesis through induction of transforming

growth factor-β expression in rat glomerular mesangial cells. *J. Clin. Invest.* 93:2431–37

45. Kagami S, Border WA, Ruoslahti E, Noble NA. 1993. Coordinated expression of β1 integrins and TGF-β1-induced matrix proteins in glomerulonephritis. *Lab. Invest.* 69:68–76

46. Kaneto H, Morrissey J, Klahr S. 1993. Increased expression of TGF-β1 in the obstructed kidney of rats with unilateral ureteral ligation. *Kidney Int.* 44:313–21

47. Keane WF, Anderson S, Aurell M, de Zeeuw D, Narins RJ, Povar G. 1989. Angiotensin converting enzyme inhibitors and progressive renal insufficiency. *Ann. Int. Med.* 111:503–16

48. Kim SJ, Angel P, Lafyatis R, Hattori K, Kim KY, et al. 1990. Autoinduction of transforming growth factor β1 is mediated by the AP-1 complex. *Mol. Cell. Biol.* 10:1492–97

49. Klahr S, Schreiner G, Ichikawa I. 1988. The progression of renal disease. *N. Engl. J. Med.* 318:1657–66

50. Lafayette RA, Mayer G, Park SK, Meyer TW. 1992. Angiotensin II receptor blockade limits glomerular injury in rats with reduced renal mass. *J. Clin. Invest.* 90:766–71

51. Lewis EJ, Hunsicker LJ, Bain RP, Rohde RD. 1993. The effect of angiotensin-converting-enzyme inhibition on diabetic nephropathy. *N. Engl. J. Med.* 329:1456–62

52. Lin HY, Wang XF, Ng-Eaton E, Weinberg RA, Lodish HF. 1992. Expression cloning of the TGF-β type II receptor, a functional transmembrane serine/threonine kinase. *Cell* 68:775–85

53. Martinez-Maldonado M, Benabe JE, Wilcox JN, Wang S, Luo C. 1993. Renal renin, angiotensinogen, and ANG I-converting enzyme gene expression: influence of dietary protein. *Am. J. Physiol.* 264:F981–88

54. Mauer SM, Steffes MW, Michael AF, Brown DM. 1976. Studies of diabetic nephropathy in animals and in man. *Diabetes* 25:850–57

55. Mayer G, Lafayette RA, Oliver J, Deen WM, Myers BD, Meyer TW. 1993. Effects of angiotensin II receptor blockade on remnant glomerular permselectivity. *Kidney Int.* 43:346–53

56. Miller PL, Rennke HG, Meyer TW. 1991. Glomerular hypertrophy accelerates hypertensive glomerular injury in rats. *Am. J. Physiol.* 261: F459–65

57. Miyazono K, Ichijo H, Heldin CH. 1993. Transforming growth factor-β: latent forms, binding and receptors. *Growth Factors* 8:11–22

58. Naftilan AJ, Pratt RE, Dzau VJ. 1989. Induction of platelet-derived growth factor A-chain and *c-myc* gene expressions by angiotensin II in cultured rat vascular smooth muscle cells. *J. Clin. Invest.* 83:1419–24

59. Nakamura T, Miller D, Ruoslahti E, Border WA. 1992. Production of extracellular matrix by glomerular epithelial cells is regulated by transforming growth factor-β1. *Kidney Int.* 41:1213–21

60. Nath KA. 1992. Tubulointerstitial changes as a major determinant in the progression of renal damage. *Am. J. Kidney Dis.* 20:1–17

61. Nishizuka Y. 1988. The molecular heterogeneity of protein kinase C and its implications for cellular regulation. *Nature* 334:661–65

62. Okuda S, Languino LR, Ruoslahti E, Border WA. 1990. Elevated expression of transforming growth factor-β and proteoglycan production in experimental glomerulonephritis. *J. Clin. Invest.* 86: 453–62

63. Okuda S, Nakamura T, Yamamoto T, Ruoslahti E, Border WA. 1991. Dietary protein restriction rapidly reduces transforming growth factor-β1 expression in experimental glomerulonephritis. *Proc. Natl. Acad. Sci. USA* 88: 9765–69

64. Paller MS, Hostetter TH. 1986. Dietary protein increases plasma renin and reduces pressor reactivity to angiotensin II. *Am. J. Physiol.* 251:F34–39

65. Paul M, Wagner J, Dzau VJ. 1993. Gene expression of the renin-angiotensin system in human tissues. *J. Clin. Invest.* 91:2058–64

66. Quilley J, Duchin KL, Hudes EM, McGiff JC. 1987. The antihypertensive effect of captopril in essential hypertension: relationship to prostaglandins and the kallikrein-kinin system. *J. Hypertens.* 5:121–28

67. Remuzzi A, Puntorieri S, Battaglia C, Bertani T, Remuzzi G. 1990. Angiotensin converting enzyme inhibition ameliorates glomerular filtration of macromolecules and water and lessens glomerular injury in the rat. *J. Clin. Invest.* 85:541–49

68. Riser BL, Cortes P, Zhao X, Bernstein J, Dumler F, Narins RG. 1992. Intraglomerular pressure and mesangial stretching stimulate extracellular matrix formation in the rat. *J. Clin. Invest.* 90:1932–43

69. Riser BL, Grondin JM, Cortes P, Patterson D, Narins RG. 1993. Mesangial cell stretch stimulates the secretion and activation of transforming growth factor

beta 1 (TGF-β1), but not TGF-β2/TGF-β3. *J. Am. Soc. Nephrol.* 4:663 (Abstr.)

70. Roberts AB, Sporn MB. 1990. The transforming growth factor-βs. In *Handbook of Experimental Pharmacology: Peptide Growth Factors and Their Receptors, I* ed. MB Sporn, AB Roberts, 95:419–72. Berlin/Heidelberg/New York: Springer Verlag

71. Roberts AB, Sporn MB. 1993. Physiological actions and clinical applications of transforming growth factor-β (TGF-β). *Growth Factors* 8:1–9

72. Rosenberg ME, Chmielewski D, Hostetter TH. 1990. Effect of dietary protein on rat renin and angiotensinogen gene expression. *J. Clin. Invest.* 85:1144–49

73. Rosenberg ME, Hostetter TH. 1990. Comparative effects of antihypertensives on proteinuria: angiotensin-converting enzyme inhibitor vs α1-antagonist. *Am. J. Kidney Dis.* 16: 118–25

74. Rosenberg ME, Smith LJ, Correa-Rotter R, Hostetter TH. 1994. The paradox of the renin-angiotensin system in chronic renal disease. *Kidney Int.* 45:403–10

75. Rosman JB, Meijer S, Sluiter WJ, Ter Wee PMT, Piers-Becht TPH, Donker AJM. 1984. Prospective randomized trial of early dietary protein restriction in chronic renal failure. *Lancet* ii:1291–96

76. Sadoshima J, Xu Y, Slayter HS, Izumo S. 1993. Autocrine release of angiotensin II mediates stretch induced hypertrophy of cardiac myocytes in vitro. *Cell* 75:977–84

77. Salvetti A, Abdel-Haq B, Magagna A, Pedrinelli R. 1987. Indomethacin reduces the antihypertensive action of enalapril. *Clin. Exp. Hypertens.* A9: 559–67

78. Sawa H, Tokushi F, Mochizuki N, Endo Y, Furuta Y, et al. 1992. Expression of the angiotensinogen gene and localization of its protein in the human heart. *Circulation* 86:138–46

79. Sen S, Tarazi RC, Bumpus FM. 1980. Effect of converting enzyme inhibitor (SQ 14,225) on myocardial hypertrophy in spontaneously hypertensive rats. *Hypertension* 2:169–76

80. Shackland SJ, Scholey JW. 1994. Expression of transforming growth factor β1 during diabetic renal hypertrophy. *Kidney Int.* 46:430–42

81. Shihab F, Yamamoto T, Nast C, Cohen A, Gold L, et al. 1993. Acute and chronic allograft rejection in human kidney correlate with the expression of TGF-β and extracellular matrix proteins. *J. Am. Soc. Nephrol.* 4:918 (Abstr.)

82. Sweet CS, Kadowitz PJ, Brody MJ. 1971. Arterial hypertension elicited by prolonged intracerebral infusion of angiotensin II in conscious dogs. *Am. J. Physiol.*221:1640–44

83. Tomooka S, Border WA, Marshall BC, Noble NA. 1992. Glomerular matrix accumulation is linked to inhibition of the plasmin protease system. *Kidney Int.* 42:1462–69

84. Viswanathan M, Stroemberg C, Seltzer A, Saavedra JM. 1992. Balloon angioplasty enhances the expression of angiotensin II AT1 receptors in neointima of rat aorta. *J. Clin. Invest.* 90:1707–12

85. Wang XF, Lin HY, Ng-Eaton E, Downward J, Lodish HF, Weinberg RA. 1991. Expression cloning and characterization of the TGF-β type III receptor. *Cell* 67:797–805

86. Wilson C, Byrom FB. 1940. The vicious circle in chronic Bright's disease: experimental evidence from the hypertensive rat. *Q. J. Med.* 10:65–96

87. Wolf G, Mueller E, Stahl RAK, Ziyadeh F. 1993. Angiotensin II-induced hypertrophy of cultured murine proximal tubular cells is mediated by endogenous transforming growth factor-β. *J. Clin. Invest.* 92:1366–72

88. Wolf G, Neilson EG. 1991. Molecular mechanisms of tubulointerstitial hypertrophy and hyperplasia. *Kidney Int.* 39: 401–20

89. Wolf G, Neilson EG. 1993. Angiotensin II as a hypertrophogenic cytokine for proximal tubular cells. *Kidney Int.* 43: S100–7 (Suppl.)

90. Wolf G, Neilson EG, Goldfarb S, Ziyadeh FN. 1991. The influence of glucose concentration on angiotensin II-induced hypertrophy of proximal tubular cells in culture. *Biochem. Biophys. Res. Commun.* 176:902–9

91. Yamamoto T, Nakamura T, Noble NA, Ruoslahti E, Border WA. 1993. Expression of transforming growth factor β is elevated in human and experimental diabetic nephropathy. *Proc. Natl. Acad. Sci. USA* 90:1814–18

92. Yamamoto T, Noble NA, Miller DE, Border WA. 1994. Sustained expression of transforming growth factor-β1 underlies development of progressive kidney fibrosis. *Kidney Int.* 45:916–27

93. Yamamoto Y, Wilson CB. 1987. Quantitative and qualitative studies of antibody-induced mesangial cell damage in the rat. *Kidney Int.* 32:514–25

94. Yoshioka K, Takemura T, Murakami K, Okada M, Hino S, et al. 1993. Transforming growth factor-β protein and

mRNA in glomeruli in normal and diseased human kidneys. *Lab. Invest.* 68:154–63

95. Zachary I, Wolf PJ, Rozengurt E. 1987. A role for neuropeptides in the control of cell proliferation. *Dev. Biol.* 124:295–308

96. Zatz R, Dunn BR, Meyer TW, Anderson B, Rennke HG, Brenner BM. 1986. Prevention of diabetic glomerulopathy by pharmacological amelioration of glomerular capillary hypertension. *J. Clin. Invest.* 77:1925–30

Annu. Rev. Physiol. 1995. 57:297–309

ROLE OF PLATELET-DERIVED GROWTH FACTOR IN RENAL INJURY

Hanna E. Abboud

Department of Medicine, The University of Texas Health Science Center at San Antonio, and the Audie L. Murphy VA Hospital, San Antonio, Texas 78284–7882

KEY WORDS: cytokines, kidney, glomerulonephritis, diabetes, signaling

INTRODUCTION

Platelet-derived growth factor (PDGF) is one of many cytokines that is involved in mediating and modulating the complex biologic processes that occur during renal tissue injury (1, 6, 7, 23, 25). Thus far the role ascribed to PDGF in the kidney is one of a phlogistic mediator, based on temporal association of enhanced expression of PDGF and/or its receptors with renal pathology. However, this presumption is premature and a potential beneficial effect of PDGF in promoting tissue remodeling and repair, as has been suggested during wound repair, remains possible (37). These divergent actions should be strongly considered so that experimental strategies can focus on augmenting the beneficial effect of PDGF and/or neutralizing its pathogenic effects, depending on the experimental or clinical setting.

BIOLOGY OF PDGF

Synthesis and Release

PDGF is a family of closely related proteins that are synthesized as approximately 30-kDa disulfide-bonded dimers of A and B chains, PDGF AA, PDGF AB, or PDGF BB (19, 40, 41). The A and B chains, which share 60% homology in their amino acid sequence, are encoded by separate genes located on human chromosomes 7 and 22, respectively (19, 40, 41). The initial observation that PDGF B chain was almost identical to a part of p28 sis, the transforming

297

protein of simian sarcoma virus (SSV), provided the first link between growth factors and oncogenes and suggested a mechanism whereby oncogene products are involved in cell transformation and growth (19). PDGF is stored in platelets and is synthesized by many transformed as well as primary cells in culture when cells are activated (40, 41). PDGF isoforms act locally in an autocrine or paracrine manner because PDGF released into the systemic circulation is rapidly inactivated by binding to α2 macroglobulin (41). The relative expression of PDGF chains is cell specific. The assembly of the two monomer peptides is a random process dictated by the concentration of each chain (19). There is recent evidence for cell compartmentalization of PDGF dimers (27, 38). A sequence present in the B chain and a spliced variant of the A chain may also mediate interaction with heparan sulfate proteoglycans present in matrix. Precise localization of the PDGF isoforms and their spatial and temporal relationship to PDGF receptors should help characterize the role of this cytokine in mediating the functional and structural changes that accompany its increased expression.

PDGF Receptors and Signaling Proteins

The levels and types of PDGF receptors expressed by a particular target cell are some of the major factors that determine response to PDGF (1, 7). Two distinct types of PDGF receptors have been cloned and characterized (7, 18), and a soluble form of the PDGF receptor has recently been identified (43). PDGF-α receptor recognizes both chains of PDGF and binds all three isoforms, whereas PDGF-β receptor recognizes predominantly the B chain and binds with high affinity to the BB homodimer (7, 11, 19). Both receptors transduce similar but not identical signals and mediate similar biologic effects. However, actin reorganization and chemotaxis are mediated by the β receptor (19). Binding of PDGF dimers to the extracellular part of the receptor induces dimerization of the receptor subunits, which results in autophosphorylation and provides attachment sites for substrate proteins (7, 31). A conserved motif in these substrates designated src homology region 2 (SH2) mediates the interaction with the phosphorylated sites in the receptor (31, 44). PDGF receptor associates with several SH2 domain-containing substrates for protein tyrosine kinases. These include phosphatidylinositol-3 kinase (PI-3-K), GTPase-activating protein (GAP), phospholipase C gamma (PLC-γ), and src. It is not clear how these signaling proteins mediate the biologic effects of PDGF such as cell growth and chemotaxis (44). At least one pathway appears to converge on the *ras* oncogene and ultimately on transcription factor AP-1 (8, 31). More recently, a direct signaling pathway was described that involves the tyrosine phosphorylation of cytoplasmic proteins such as p91, which subsequently translocates to the nucleus. This new pathway may define key intermediates in growth factor–dependent transcription and clarify the convergent and divergent mechanism of action of various cytokines including PDGF (8). Sustained activation of various signal transducing proteins in response to the expression of cytokines and cytokine receptors in renal tissue in vivo may result in the diverse pathobiologic processes that contribute to renal injury. Therefore, in vitro studies delineating the mechanism of signaling in response to PDGF receptors should be combined with in vivo studies to establish the temporal association between activation of signal-transducing proteins and pathobiologic processes that occur during renal injury. Such studies could provide an excellent chance to identify the most relevant signaling protein targets for therapeutic intervention. It is equally important to identify mechanisms by which the signals are terminated. One potential shut-off mechanism of PDGF is dephosphorylation of autophosphorylation sites of the receptor through the action of protein tyrosine phosphatases (19, 45). Another mechanism is proteolytic degradation of the receptor in the cytoplasm prior to fusion of the endocytic vesicle with lysosomes (19), which may be facilitated by ubiquitin (19, 33). PDGF receptors can be upregulated or downregulated by other cytokines or surrounding matrix (17, 32). Several agents reported to block the biologic activities of PDGF include trapidil, simvastatin, and pentoxyphyllin (15). These agents deserve additional testing in experimental animals in spite of their limited specificity.

Sources of PDGF in the Kidney

The normal adult kidney expresses relatively small amounts of PDGF protein and PDGF receptors. However, PDGF and PDGF-β receptors in the embryonic mammalian kidney and in diseased kidneys are markedly upregulated, which suggests a role for PDGF in renal development and kidney disease (1, 3, 4, 6, 7, 24–27). Immunohistochemical and in situ hybridization studies in the normal adult kidney localize faint PDGF expression in the glomerular mesangium and, to a lesser extent, in the parietal epithelial cells, interstitium, and proximal and collecting duct cells (1, 7, 23, 25, 26). PDGF-β receptor is also expressed in the mesangium and parietal epithelial cells at low abundance, but higher levels of expression are found in cortical and medullary interstitial cells (4, 14). PDGF-β receptor is also expressed in renal vascular smooth muscle cells. The relatively high expression of PDGF-β receptor expression described recently in the interstitium of normal kidney tissue is explained by the fact that the tissue was obtained from older subjects because carcinoma was the indication for nephrectomy (14). Some degree of interstitial fibrosis may be present in older patients.

The principal cells producing PDGF are cultured primary mesangial, glomerular, and microvascular endothelial cells; collecting duct cells; and vascular smooth muscle cells. Glomerular epithelial cells in culture also produce PDGF (12). In addition, mesangial cells, interstitial fibroblasts, and smooth muscle

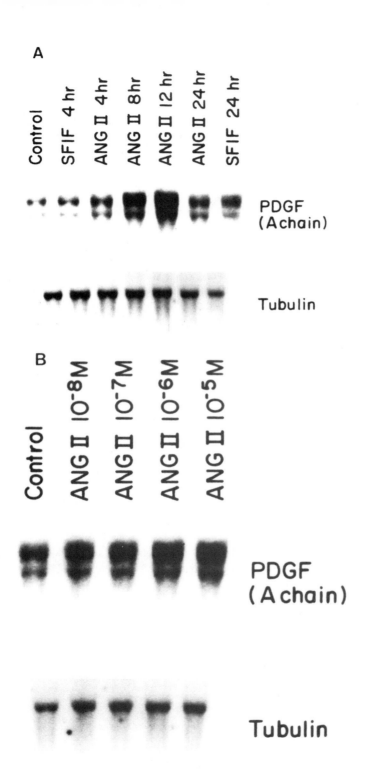

A

Control
SFIF 4 hr
ANG II 4 hr
ANG II 8 hr
ANG II 12 hr
ANG II 24 hr
SFIF 24 hr

PDGF
(A chain)

Tubulin

B

Control
ANG II 10⁻⁸M
ANG II 10⁻⁷M
ANG II 10⁻⁶M
ANG II 10⁻⁵M

PDGF
(A chain)

Tubulin

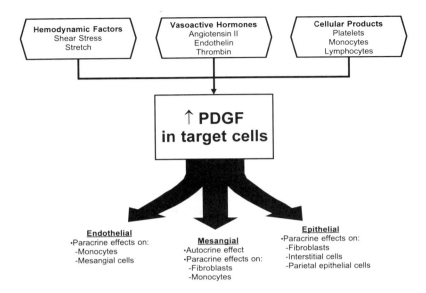

Figure 2   Mechanisms of PDGF release and cellular targets.

cells express PDGF receptors. In disease states, infiltrating inflammatory cells (e.g. monocytes and platelets) are a major source of cytokines including PDGF (1, 23, 25, 26). PDGF, like many other cytokines, is subject to regulation by numerous biologically active agents. Exposure of mesangial cells in vitro to several cytokines, products of inflammatory cells, and platelets results in a coordinate induction of PDGF A and B chain mRNAs and release of the protein (1, 42). Vasoactive compounds such as Ang II have recently been shown to induce PDGF and transforming-growth factor β (TGF-β) in smooth muscle cells. In mesangial cells, endothelin (21) and Ang II stimulate PDGF A chain (Figure 1) and TGF-β expression. Lipid mediators and lipoproteins also stimulate PDGF expression in mesangial cells (16). Ang II synergizes with lipid mediators to promote DNA synthesis and PDGF gene induction. Changes in local hemodynamics may also influence PDGF production. High shear stress has been reported to induce PDGF in endothelial cells via a specific response element in the PDGF-β chain gene (39, 40). These in vitro observations have correlates in vivo. The protective effect of Ang II receptor(s) blockade or

Figure 1   Effect of Ang II on PDGF A chain mRNA levels in human mesangial cells. (*A*) Time course in response to 10^{-6} M Ang II. (*B*) Dose response to Ang II at 8 h.

angiotensin-coverting enzyme inhibition against progression of renal injury may be mediated, at least in part, by a reduction in the expression of PDGF or TGF-β (6).

Both PDGF A and B chains are also induced in human renal microvascular endothelial cells by exposure to thrombin and TGF-β (7). Bovine glomerular endothelial cells also respond to thrombin with an increase in PDGF B chain, but not A chain, mRNA levels. On the other hand, EGF and TGF-α increase PDGF A chain levels in these cells (G Grandaliano et al, unpublished observations). Cultured glomerular epithelial cells, as well as bovine glomerular and human renal microvascular endothelial cells, do not express PDGF receptors and, therefore, are not responsive to any of the PDGF isoforms. The biologic significance of the differential induction of PDGF chains in endothelial cells is not known. These data also indicate that somatic parenchymal renal cells respond to various forms of injury by releasing PDGF. Because PDGF induces its own expression, in responsive cells an amplification loop is created that helps to sustain PDGF expression. PDGF released at sites of tissue injury acts via autocrine or paracrine mechanisms on somatic renal cells or on adherent and infiltrating monocyte/macrophages (Figure 2). The relevance of many of these in vitro observations is demonstrated in several in vivo studies (1, 6, 7, 22–26).

PDGF AND KIDNEY DISEASE

Actions of PDGF in the Kidney

Cytokines contribute to the functional and structural changes seen in diseased organs including the diseased kidney. Cytokines induce the expression and release of other cytokines and potentiate or inhibit their effect, thereby creating a complex network. Thus it is often difficult to attribute a pathologic process to an individual cytokine or even to understand how individual cytokines affect different cells. The use of pure populations of cultured cells combined with in vivo studies attempting to determine precise localization of cytokines and their effects in situ would help characterize the role of a particular cytokine. The role of PDGF in renal injury, therefore, is defined in the context of a cytokine network where the primacy of a particular cytokine manifests itself at a particular stage of the pathologic process or disease entity. The most relevant consequences of renal injury are a reduction in glomerular filtrate rate and irreversible destruction of renal parenchyma, i.e. fibrosis. PDGF is a vasoconstrictor and thus a candidate for causing severe reduction in renal blood flow and glomerular filtration rate upon in vivo release in the injured kidney. Vascular beds, whose endothelial cells express PDGF receptors, vasodilate in response to PDGF. However, no such PDGF receptors are present in cultured renal endothelial cells. Furthermore, infusion of PDGF in vivo into the rat kidney results in marked reduction in renal blood flow, glomerular filtration rate, and ultrafiltration coefficient, consistent with the contractile effect of PDGF on smooth muscle and mesangial cells (1). In addition to its hemodynamic effect, PDGF may contribute to renal pathology through its chemotactic, mitogenic, and other cell-activating functions including stimulation of release of other cytokines (1) and inhibition of nitric oxide (36).

PDGF and Human Kidney Disease

Increased expression of PDGF and PDGF receptors in renal tissue from patients with a variety of renal diseases provided early evidence for a role of this cytokine in kidney disease (1, 6, 7, 14, 23–26, 47). Increased PDGF-β receptor expression was demonstrated, using an immunohistochemical technique, in renal tissue obtained from patients with proliferative glomerulonephritis and transplant rejection (1, 7, 23–26). PDGF-β receptor immunoreactivity was localized in the glomerular mesangial region, intimal smooth muscle cells, and fibroblast-like cells in the renal interstitium (1, 6, 7, 23–26). Additional studies applying immunohistochemical and in situ hybridization techniques to human renal tissue demonstrated increased expression of PDGF and PDGF receptor mRNAs and proteins in patients with IgA nephropathy and other proliferative forms of human glomerulonephritis including lupus nephritis, membranoproliferative glomerulonephritis, vasculitis with crescents, and proliferative forms of light-chain deposition disease (1, 6, 7, 22–26). Gesualdo et al (14) recently studied the expression of PDGF-α and -β receptors by immunohistochemical and in situ hybridization techniques. PDGF-β receptor mRNA and protein were upregulated in the glomerular mesangium, interstitial areas, and diseased vessels in patients with IgA nephropathy and lupus nephritis, but not in patients with minimal change or membranous nephropathy. Intensity of expression correlated with histologic lesions. PDGF-α receptor was slightly upregulated in interstitial areas, most likely in fibroblasts, because this cell type expresses a significant number of α receptors (2).

Role of PDGF in Animal Models of Renal Disease

The pattern of distribution of PDGF in the diseased kidney implicates this cytokine in glomerular, vascular, and interstitial pathology. There are excellent experimental models of immune and non-immune-mediated renal diseases. The role of cytokines and, in particular, PDGF and TGF-β has been best characterized in a rat model of mesangioproliferative glomerulonephritis induced by the injection of a complement fixing antibody to the Thy-1 antigen present on rat mesangial cell membrane (1, 23, 25). The initial phase of the disease is characterized by an acute complement-dependent lysis of mesangial cells followed shortly by platelet and monocyte infiltration. A proliferative phase then follows that is characterized by hypercellularity arising from an influx of monocytes and a proliferation of smooth muscle-like mesangial cells that is associated with matrix expansion. The disease appears to be self-limiting because resolution of cell proliferation and matrix expansion occurs spontaneously. The severity of the disease, i.e. mesangiolysis and subsequent proliferation and matrix expansion, is dependent on the type and amount of the anti-Thy-1 antibody administered. Iida and colleagues (20) found a marked increase in the expression of PDGF A and B chain mRNAs and protein as well as in PDGF-β receptor expression in isolated glomeruli, which corresponded to the course of mesangial cell proliferation. Administration of a neutralizing antibody to PDGF resulted in reduction of hypercellularity and matrix expansion that occurred 4, but not 2, days after induction of the disease (26). The importance of PDGF as a mediator of cell proliferation in vivo was also confirmed by its ability to cause mesangial cell proliferation when infused into the renal artery of rats treated with subnephritogenic doses of anti-Thy-1 serum (11) or after PDGF gene delivery through a liposome system injected into the renal artery (21). It is interesting that other investigators using a similar model found that neutralization of TGF-β-1 by antibody or by the proteoglycan decorin, which neutralizes three isoforms of TGF-β, prevented the development of hypercellularity, matrix expansion, and proteinuria (1, 6, 7, 46). The role of these two cytokines in this model illustrates how cytokines act in a network: One cytokine regulates the expression and perhaps the effect of another cytokine and results in pathology. Evidence generated in models of wound healing indicates expression of PDGF, which results in and is followed by TGF-β expression (37). In vitro studies have shown that exposure of human mesangial cells to the cytokines PDGF or EGF results in induction of TGF-β, which suggests that sequential expression and activation of cytokines takes place in the kidney (5). In a rat model of glomerular injury induced by Habu snake venom, expression of PDGF and TGF-β corresponds with hypercellularity and matrix expression within focal glomerular lesions (5). When PDGF expression subsided, strong TGF-β expression associated with type IV collagen staining was sustained. Based on these in vitro and in vivo studies, it appears that the relative expression of growth-promoting cytokines, e.g. PDGF, EGF, or FGF, vs cytokines that promote matrix expansion, e.g TGF-β, may determine the nature of the glomerular lesion proliferation or sclerosis and that release of cytokines, particularly TGF-β, by somatic renal cells occurs at later phases of renal injury. Recent reports of sustained and delayed expression of TGF-β and PDGF by somatic renal cells in two different models of progressive renal injury support this contention (10, 46).

Enhanced PDGF and/or PDGF receptor gene expression has also been reported in other models of renal disease including Heymann nephritis, lupus nephritis, and puromycin aminonucleotide nephrosis (12, 13, 34). Low-protein diet or glucocorticoid treatment, which afford renal protection, decreases the expression of PDGF (13, 34). Additional studies have also shown that enhanced PDGF expression occurs in non-immunologic forms of progressive renal injury. In the remnant kidney model in which progressive glomerulo-sclerosis develops after subtotal nephrectomy, PDGF B chain and receptor mRNAs and protein expression were increased several days after the nephrectomy and persisted for several weeks during which cell proliferation, macrophage infiltration, and matrix expansion occur (10). Genetic manipulation of cytokines in these models will provide valuable insights into their role in renal pathology.

PDGF and Diabetic Nephropathy

Data suggest that PDGF is also involved in mediating diabetic nephropathy. Increased expression of PDGF-β chain mRNA has been demonstrated in glomeruli 3 weeks after the induction of diabetes (6, 35). The expression of other cytokines, together with monocyte infiltration, has also been reported in kidneys and glomeruli of rats with diabetes induced by streptozotocin (6). Because many cytokines including PDGF are induced by activation of protein kinase C (PKC) in vitro (29), it is likely that in vivo activation of PKC by hyperglycemia is responsible for increased cytokine expression (45). There is indirect evidence that PDGF may be involved in increased matrix in diabetes (9). Exposure of mesangial cells to advanced glycosylated products results in increased synthesis of collagen. This effect is inhibited by an antibody to PDGF (9). The enhanced expression of cytokines with tyrosine kinase receptors such as PDGF, IGF-1, and FGF in diabetic glomeruli may have major therapeutic implications (45). There is evidence that altered activity of tyrosine phosphatases may contribute to insulin resistance seen in diabetic states. Indeed, the phosphatase inhibitor vanadate has insulin-like effects and corrects hyperglycemia in insulin-dependent and insulin-independent animal models of diabetes. For these reasons, vanadate administration has been advocated as a therapeutic modality for diabetes (45). We recently found that vanadate activates mesangial cells in vitro, stimulating sustained DNA synthesis and PDGF gene expression (45). If vanadate exerts a similar effect in vivo, increased expression of certain cytokines or potentiation of the effect of cytokines by vanadate may have a detrimental effect and contribute to the progression of glomerular injury. Therefore, in vivo studies are warranted to determine the expression of cytokines, their biologic effect, and the potential implication of vanadate therapy in diabetes.

PDGF and Interstitial Disease

While most studies thus far have focused on the glomerulus and glomerular cells as potential sources and targets for PDGF, there is evidence that PDGF is likely involved in mediating vascular and interstitial injury in the kidney (1,

6, 7, 23). Vascular endothelial and smooth muscle cells are potential sources of PDGF, and injury to the endothelium may result in increased production of PDGF that stimulates smooth muscle cell proliferation (7, 40, 41). It is also known that proliferating smooth muscle cells produce large amounts of PDGF (40, 41). Therefore, local release of PDGF by these cells, as well as by infiltrating monocytes or macrophages, may result in the progression of arterial and arteriolar lesions within the renal vasculature. It was recently demonstrated that the administration of cyclosporine to rats results in increased expression of PDGF in the afferent arteriole and renin-secreting cells. An additional mechanism by which PDGF contributes to interstitial fibrosis is through its ability to stimulate fibroblast proliferation (2, 30). In addition to infiltrating inflammatory cells, particularly monocytes, in the interstitium, inner medullary-collecting duct cells are an important source of PDGF (30). Cocultures of inner medullary-collecting duct epithelial cells and interstitial fibroblasts were undertaken (30) to examine the role of tubulointerstitial cell interactions in the regulation of fibroblast cell growth. Inner medullary-collecting duct epithelial cells or conditioned medium from these cells stimulated DNA synthesis in isolated papillary fibroblasts. The effect was specific for this cell type because proximal tubular epithelial cells had no effect on the proliferation of fibroblasts. Inner medullary-collecting duct cells also produced PDGF, and the effect of these cells on DNA synthesis in papillary fibroblasts was inhibited by an antibody to PDGF. Of interest is the fact that the papillary fibroblasts were more responsive to PDGF than were cortical fibroblasts. This paracrine system may be important in the pathogenesis of interstitial fibrosis of the kidney. Johnson and colleagues (24) also infused angiotensin II for several weeks in the rat and found that the interstitial fibrosis is associated with increased expression of PDGF.

ROLE OF PDGF IN RENAL TISSUE DEVELOPMENT

There is increasing evidence that cytokines are involved in mammalian renal development (3, 7). PDGF B chain immune reactivity localizes to epithelial cells of the glomerular vesicle, whereas PDGF-β receptor immunoreactivity is present in undifferentiated metanephric blastema, vascular structures, and interstitial cells. This specific, temporal pattern of expression suggests that PDGF in the developing glomerulus may be responsible for recruitment of mesangial and perhaps endothelial cell precursors to the glomerular vesicle. Studies in transgenic mice support an important role for PDGF in the development of mesenchymal structures. These studies also suggest that the chemotactic activity of PDGF toward mesenchymal cells that express PDGF receptors represents a biologic activity of major importance in renal tissue development (48, 49).

SUMMARY

Evidence indicates that PDGF is a major cytokine that impacts on the biology of renal cells and the pathogenesis of renal disease. The biologic effects of PDGF on cells and tissue, whether contraction, proliferation, matrix expansion, or cell migration, can result in beneficial or injurious consequences depending on the particular setting. Although expression of PDGF and PDGF receptors is required for glomerular development, their overexpression can be detrimental in renal disease. The chemotactic and mitogenic effects of PDGF are beneficial in recruitment and repopulation by mesangial cells in focal or diffuse necrotizing diseases. On the other hand, a sustained proliferative response can be detrimental to renal function. There is much to understand about PDGF's role in the cytokine network during renal development and renal injury. Understanding the mechanism of action of PDGF and, specifically, the signaling molecules transduced by the PDGF receptor may lead to the development of new therapeutic strategies to offset the detrimental effect of PDGF. Methods of targeting PDGF to hypocellular or necrotic areas to effect tissue remodeling and repair are a desirable goal (28). On the other hand, promotion of fibroblast proliferation and smooth muscle cell proliferation is a detrimental effect of PDGF that contributes to interstitial and perhaps periglomerular fibrosis as well as atherosclerosis. Ultimately, understanding the role of PDGF and other cytokines in renal development and organogenesis will provide the means to treat glomerular pathology without residual scarring.

Literature Cited

1. Abboud HE. 1993. Growth factors in glomerulonephritis. *Kidney Int.* 43:252–57

2. Abboud HE, Pinzani M, Knauss T, Pierce GF, Hsieh P, et al. 1994. Actions of platelet-derived growth factor isoforms in mesangial cells. *J. Cell. Physiol.* 158:140–50

3. Alpers CE, Seifert RA, Hudkins KL, Johnson RJ, Bowen-Pope DF. 1992. Developmental patterns of PDGF B-chain, PDGF-receptor, and α-actin expression in human glomerulogenesis. *Kidney Int.* 42:390–99

4. Alpers CE, Seifert RA, Hudkins KL, Johnson RJ, Bowen-Pope DF. 1993. PDGF-receptor localizes to mesangial, parietal epithelial, and interstitial cells in human and primate kidneys. *Kidney Int.* 43:286–94

5. Barnes JL, Abboud HE. 1993. Temporal expression of autocrine growth factors corresponds to morphologic features of mesangial proliferation in Habu snake venom–induced glomerulonephritis. *Am. J. Pathol.* 143:1366–76

6. Couser WG, Johnson RJ. 1994. Mechanisms of progressive renal disease in glomerulonephritis. *Am. J. Kidney Dis.* 23:193–98

7. Daniel TO, Kumjian DA. 1993. Platelet-derived growth factor in renal development and disease. *Semin. Nephrol.* 13:87–95

8. Darnell JE, Kerr IM, Stark GR. 1994. Jak-STAT pathways and transcriptional

activation in response to IFNs and other extracellular signaling proteins. *Science* 264:1415–21

9. Doi T, Vlassara H, Kirstein M, Yamada Y, Striker GE, Striker LJ. 1992. Receptor-specific increase in extracellular matrix production in mouse mesangial cells by advanced glycosylation end products is mediated via platelet-derived growth factor. *Proc. Natl. Acad. Sci. USA* 89: 2873–77

10. Floege J, Burns MW, Alpers CE, Yoshimura A, Pritzl P, et al. 1992. Glomerular cell proliferation and PDGF expression precede glomerulosclerosis in the remnant kidney model. *Kidney Int.* 42:297–309

11. Floege J, Eng E, Young BA, Alpers CE, Barrett TB, et al. 1993. Infusion of platelet-derived growth factor or basic fibroblast growth factor induces selective glomerular mesangial cell proliferation and matrix accumulation in rats. *J. Clin. Invest.* 92:2952–62

12. Floege J, Johnson RJ, Alpers CE, Fatemi-Nainie S, Richardson C, et al. 1993. Visceral glomerular epithelial cells can proliferate in vivo and synthesize PDGF B-chain. *Am. J. Pathol.* 142: 637–50

13. Fukui M, Nakamura T, Ebihara I, Nagaoka I, Tomino Y, et al. 1993. Low-protein diet attenuates increased gene expression of platelet-derived growth factor and transforming growth factor-beta in experimental glomerular sclerosis. *J. Lab. Clin. Med.* 121:224–34

14. Gesualdo L, DiPaolo S, Milani M, Grappone C, Raieri E, et al. 1994. Expression of platelet-derived growth factor receptors in normal and diseased human kidney. *J. Clin. Invest.* 94:50–58

15. Grandaliano G, Biswas P, Ghosh Choudhury G, Abboud HE. 1993. Simvastatin inhibits PDGF-induced DNA synthesis in human mesangial cells. *Kidney Int.* 44:503–8

16. Gröne HJ, Abboud HE, Höhne M, Walli AK, Gröne E, et al. 1992. Action of lipoproteins in culture human mesangial cells: modulation by mitogenic vasoconstrictors. *Am. J. Physiol.* 263:F686–96

17. Haberstroh U, Zahner G, Disser M, Thaiss F, Stahl RA, et al. 1993. TGF-beta stimulates rat mesangial cell proliferation in culture: role of PDGF beta-receptor expression. *Am. J. Physiol.* 264:F199–205

18. Heidaran MA, Beeler JF, Yu J-C, Ishibashi T, LaRochelle WJ. 1993. Differences in substrate specificities of α and β platelet-derived growth factor (PDGF) receptors. *J. Biol. Chem.* 268: 9287–95

19. Heldin CH. 1992. Structural and functional studies on platelet-derived growth factor. *EMBO J.* 11:4251–59

20. Iida H, Seifert R, Alpers CE, Gronwald RG, Phillips PE, et al. 1991. Platelet-derived growth factor (PDGF) and PDGF receptor are induced in mesangial proliferative nephritis in the rat. *Proc. Natl. Acad. Sci. USA* 88:6560–64

21. Isaka Y, Fujiwara Y, Ueda N, Kaneda Y, Kamada T, Imai E. 1993. Glomerulosclerosis induced by in vivo transfection of TGF-β or PDGF gene into the rat kidney. *J. Clin. Invest.* 92:2597–601

22. Jaffer F, Knauss T, Poptic E, Abboud HE. 1990. Endothelin stimulates DNA synthesis and PDGF secretion in mesangial cells. *Kidney Int.* 38:1193–98

23. Johnson RJ. 1994. The glomerular response to injury: progression or resolution? *Kidney Int.* 45:1769–82

24. Johnson RJ, Alpers CE, Yoshimura A, Lombardi D, Pritzl P, et al. 1992. Renal injury from angiotensin II-mediated hypertension. *Hypertension* 19:464–74

25. Johnson RJ, Floege J, Couser WG, Alpers CE. 1993. Role of platelet-derived growth factor in glomerular disease. *J. Am. Soc. Nephrol.* 4:119–28

26. Johnson RJ, Raines EW, Floege J, Yoshimura A, Pritzl P, et al. 1992. Inhibition of mesangial cell proliferation and matrix expansion in glomerulonephritis in the rat by antibody to platelet-derived growth factor. *J. Exp. Med.* 175:1413–16

27. Kelly JL, Sanchez A, Brown GS, Chesterman CN, Sleigh MJ. 1993. Accumulation of PDGF B and cell-binding forms of PDGF A in the extracellular matrix. *J. Cell. Biol.* 121:1153–63

28. Kitamura M, Taylor S, Unwin R, Burton S, Shimizu F, Fine LG. 1994. Gene transfer into the rat renal glomerulus via a mesangial cell vector: site specific delivery, in situ amplification, and sustained expression of an exogenous gene in vivo. *J. Clin. Invest.* 94:497–505

29. Knauss TC, Jaffer F, Abboud HE. 1990. Phosphatidic acid modulates DNA synthesis, phospholipase C and PDGF mRNAs in mesangial cells. *J. Biol. Chem.* 265:14457–63

30. Knecht A, Fine LG, Kleinman KS, Rodemann HP, Muller GA, et al. 1991. Fibroblasts of rabbit kidney in culture. II. Paracrine stimulation of papillary fibroblasts of PDGF. *Am. J. Physiol.* 261: F292–99

31. Marra F, Ghosh Choudhury G, Bhandari B, Abboud HE. 1994. Biology and reg-

ulation of platelet-derived growth factor. In *Falk Symposium 71, Fat-Storing Cells and Liver Fibrosis*, ed. C Surrenti, A Casini, S Milani, M Pinzani, pp. 209–21. Hingham, MA: Kluwer

32. Marx M, Daniel TO, Kashgarian M, Madri JA. 1993. Spatial organization of the extracellular matrix modulates the expression of PDGF-receptor subunits in mesangial cells. *Kidney Int.* 43:1027–41

33. Mori S, Heldin CH, Claesson-Welsh L. 1993. Ligand-induced ubiquitination of the platelet-derived growth factor β-receptor plays a negative regulatory role in its mitogenic signaling. *J. Biol. Chem.* 268:577–83

34. Nakamura T, Ebihara I, Nagaoka I, Tomino Y, Koide H. 1992. Renal platelet-derived growth factor gene expression in NZB/W F1 mice with lupus and ddY mice with IgA nephropathy. *Clin. Immunol. Immunopathol.* 63:173–81

35. Nakamura T, Fukui M, Ebihara I, Osada S, Nagaoka I, et al. 1993. mRNA expression of growth factors in glomeruli from diabetic rats. *Diabetes* 42:450–56

36. Pfilschifter J. 1991. Platelet-derived growth factor inhibits cytokine induction of nitric oxide synthase in rat renal mesangial cells. *Eur. J. Pharmacol.* 208:339–40

37. Pierce GF, Vandeberg J, Rudolf R, Tarpley J, Mustoe TA. 1991. Platelet-derived growth factor-BB and transforming growth factor beta 1 selectively modulate glycosaminoglycans, collagen, and myofibroblasts in excisional wounds. *Am. J. Pathol.* 138(3):629–46

38. Raines EW, Ross R. 1992. Compartmentalization of PDGF on extracellular binding sites dependent on exon-6-encoded sequences. *J. Cell. Biol.* 116:533–43

39. Resnick N, Collins T, Atkinson W, Bonthron DT, Dewey CF Jr, Gimbrone MA Jr. 1993. Platelet-derived growth factor B chain promoter contains a *cis*-acting fluid shear-stress element. *Proc. Natl. Acad. Sci. USA* 90:4591–95

40. Ross R. 1993. The pathogenesis of atherosclerosis: a perspective for the 1990s. *Nature* 362:801–9

41. Ross R, Raines EW, Bowen-Pope DF. 1986. The biology of platelet-derived growth factor. *Cell* 46:155–69

42. Silver BJ, Jaffer FE, Abboud HE. 1989. Platelet-derived growth factor (PDGF) synthesis in mesangial cells: induction by multiple peptide mitogens. *Proc. Natl. Acad. Sci. USA* 86:1056–60

43. Tiesman J, Hart CE. 1993. Identification of a soluble receptor for platelet-derived growth factor in cell-conditioned medium and human plasma. *J. Biol. Chem.* 268:9621–28

44. Valius M, Kazlauskas A. 1993. Phospholipase C-γ1 and phosphatidylinositol 3 kinase are the downstream mediators of the PDGF receptor's mitogenic signal. *Cell* 73:321–34

45. Wenzel U, Fouqueray B, Biswas P, Grandaliano G, Ghosh Choudhury G, Abboud HE. 1994. Activation of mesangial cells by the phosphatase inhibitor vandate: potential implications for diabetic nephropathy. *J. Cin. Invest.* In press

46. Yamamoto T, Nobel NA, Miller DE, Border WA. 1994. Sustained expression of TGFβ1 underlies development of progressive kidney fibrosis. *Kidney Int.* 45:916–27

47. Yoshimura A, Gordon K, Alpers CE, Floege J, Pritzl P, et al. 1991. Demonstration of PDGF B-chain mRNA in glomeruli in mesangial proliferative nephritis by in situ hybridization. *Kidney Int.* 40:470–76

ADDED IN PROOF

48. Levéen P, Pekny M, Gebre-Medhin S, Swolin B, Larsson E, et al. 1994. Mice deficient for PDGF B show renal, cardiovascular, and hematological abnormalities. *Genes Dev.* 8:1875–87

49. Soriano P. 1994. Abnormal kidney development and hematological disorders in PDGF β-receptor mutant mice. *Genes Dev.* 8:1888–96

Annu. Rev. Physiol. 1995. 57:311–32

PHYSIOLOGIC MECHANISMS OF POSTISCHEMIC TISSUE INJURY

D. Neil Granger and Ronald J. Korthuis

Department of Physiology, Louisiana State University Medical Center, School of Medicine, Shreveport, Louisiana 71130

KEY WORDS: ischemia, reperfusion, oxygen radicals, leukocytes, preconditioning

INTRODUCTION

Early restitution of blood flow to ischemic tissues is essential to halt the progression of cellular injury associated with decreased oxygen and nutrient delivery. Recognition of this fact provides the basis for the traditional view that minimizing ischemic time is the only important intervention for diminishing the extent of ischemic injury. However, it is now clear that reperfusion of ischemic tissues initiates a complex series of reactions that paradoxically injures tissues. Although several mechanisms have been proposed to explain the pathogenesis of ischemia/reperfusion (I/R) injury, most attention has focused on a role for reactive oxygen metabolites and inflammatory leukocytes. This work has led to the proposal that free radical ablation or inhibition of postischemic neutrophil infiltration may prove useful for therapeutic intervention in I/R. In addition to these mechanisms, recent evidence suggests that prior exposure to brief periods of ischemia (ischemic preconditioning) prevents the development of cellular injury induced by a subsequent prolonged interruption in blood flow. By elucidating the cellular events underlying preconditioning, additional mechanisms contributing to the pathogenesis of I/R may become apparent. This review summarizes the evidence supporting the view that oxidants and leukocytes contribute to the pathogenesis of reperfusion injury and discusses the mechanisms underlying the protective actions of ischemic preconditioning.

311

MECHANISMS OF POSTISCHEMIC TISSUE INJURY

Ischemic vs Reperfusion Injury

Several lines of evidence support the concept that reperfusion can paradoxically injure ischemic tissues: (*a*) Brief periods of reperfusion are associated with little histologic evidence of injury, while longer periods of reperfusion are associated with progressive injury (26, 57). (*b*) Less injury is induced by 4 h of intestinal ischemia than by 3 h ischemia and 1 h of reperfusion (121). (*c*) Therapeutic interventions that are initiated at the onset of reperfusion are as effective in attenuating I/R injury as treatments introduced during the preischemic period (20, 49, 68, 108). (*d*) Ischemic tissues must be exposed to molecular oxygen on reperfusion to manifest tissue injury (57, 58, 80, 130, 163, 170). The implication of these studies is that reperfusion initiates a series of cytotoxic events that are associated with the return of oxygenated blood. It now appears that the cytotoxic events initiated upon reperfusion involve the formation of reactive metabolites of oxygen.

Reactive Oxygen Metabolites

The term reactive oxygen metabolites (ROM) or species (ROS) refers to any compound derived from molecular oxygen that has acquired less than four electrons (47, 50, 54). For example, the superoxide anion radical, hydrogen peroxide, and the hydroxyl radical are considered ROM because they have been reduced by one, two, and three electrons, respectively. Although superoxide can spontaneously dismutate to form hydrogen peroxide, the enzyme superoxide dismutase (SOD) greatly accelerates the rate ($\sim 10^4$ times) of this reaction (104). While superoxide and hydrogen peroxide can spontaneously interact to form hydroxyl radicals, the rate of this reaction is too slow to be of physiologic significance. However, the rate of this reaction can be substantially enhanced by the presence of trace amounts of transition metals (e.g. iron) or metal chelates (e.g. ADP-Fe^{3+}), which act as catalysts (47, 54). Alternative mechanisms that may account for the formation of hydroxyl radicals under physiologic conditions but do not depend on the presence of iron include the possibility that the free radical nitric oxide (NO an endothelial–derived relaxing factor) interacts with superoxide to form peroxynitrite, which decomposes at physiologic pH to yield hydroxyl radicals and nitrogen dioxide (9). It has also been suggested that neutrophil–derived hypochlorous acid can interact with superoxide to form hydroxyl radicals by a mechanism that is iron independent (133).

The observation that the reintroduction of molecular oxygen at reperfusion is required to produce postischemic cellular injury and dysfunction is consistent with the view that I/R injury may result from the generation of reactive oxygen metabolites. More compelling support for this concept is derived from the following lines of evidence. First, the production of oxidant species in post-ischemic tissues has been detected by use of electron spin resonance (ESR) spectroscopy and ESR spin trapping (15, 16, 28, 81, 100, 181). The demonstration that by–products of oxidant–induced lipid peroxidation (e.g. malondialdehyde, lipid hydroperoxides, and conjugated dienes) are formed in postischemic tissues has also been used as evidence of radical production during reperfusion (94, 137–139). Second, exposure of tissues to exogenous oxidant–generating systems in the absence of ischemia and reperfusion produces structural and functional changes that are reminiscent of those noted in postischemic tissues (19, 53, 123, 132, 157). Third, treatment with agents that limit oxidant production (e.g. xanthine oxidase inhibitors such as allopurinol) or effectively scavenge reactive oxygen metabolites after they are produced (e.g. superoxide dismutase, catalase, dimethyl sulfoxide, mercaptopropionylglycine) attenuates I/R injury (32, 42, 76–78, 88, 134, 146, 180). The findings that administration of hydroxyl radical scavengers or iron chelators/binding proteins are as effective as superoxide dismutase and catalase in reducing postischemic tissue dysfunction suggest that the secondarily derived hydroxyl radical may contribute to the pathogenesis of I/R (42, 60, 77, 78, 145).

Although there are several potential sources of reactive oxygen species in postischemic tissues, most attention has focused on xanthine oxidase, an enzyme found in parenchymal cells and endothelium, and neutrophilic NADPH oxidase (42, 48, 122, 164). Both enzymes produce superoxide. H_2O_2 may be produced directly by xanthine oxidase or indirectly by both enzymes through the spontaneous dismutation of superoxide (47, 54, 122). Activated neutrophils also secrete myeloperoxidase (MPO), an enzyme that catalyzes the formation of hypochlorous acid (HOCl) from H_2O_2 and chloride ions (48, 164). The hydrogen peroxide that fuels this reaction is derived from the spontaneous dismutation of neutrophil NADPH oxidase–derived superoxide. HOCl is a potent oxidizing and chlorinating agent that can react with primary amines to yield N-chloramines. The observation that xanthine oxidase inhibition, depletion, or immunoneutralization reduces postischemic tissue injury supports the concept that xanthine oxidase–derived oxidants contribute to the pathogenesis of I/R (46, 122, 146, 153). On the other hand, the fact that neutrophil depletion reduces lipid peroxidation and prevents cellular dysfunction and necrosis in postischemic tissues suggests that neutrophilic oxidant production may contribute to reperfusion injury (2, 137–139).

The generation of reactive oxygen species during reperfusion may directly contribute to the pathogenesis of I/R by oxidatively modifying the entire array of biomolecules found in tissues, thereby altering cellular function (2, 47, 54). The molecular pathology that results from oxidant generation includes DNA nicking and other abnormalities, membrane lipid peroxidation, and cross-linking and degradation of proteins (54, 76). These oxidant–induced alterations in molecular structure can decimate cellular function by interfering with the activity of structural, contractile, and transport proteins, enzymes, receptors, membrane glycolipids, glycosaminoglycans, and nucleic acids.

In addition to direct cytotoxic effects, reactive oxygen species may act by attracting and activating inflammatory phagocytes; these, in turn, induce tissue injury by directing their cytotoxic arsenal against host tissue. For example, oxidants can interact with specific components of extracellular fluid to generate substances that are chemotactic for neutrophils. Petrone and co-workers (131) demonstrated that chemotactic activity is generated in plasma treated with an oxidant–generating system (hypoxanthine-xanthine oxidase). This effect was attenuated by superoxide dismutase but not catalase (131). Moreover, injection of superoxide–treated plasma or hypoxathine-xanthine oxidase into the dermis induced massive neutrophil infiltration, effects that were blocked by superoxide dismutase (131). These observations support the concept that superoxide interacts with certain substances in extracellular fluid to produce a potent chemoattractant. However, this result cannot be extrapolated across species because superoxide–dependent chemoattractants are not formed in cat plasma exposed to an oxidant–generating system (178).

Hydrogen peroxide (H_2O_2) may also contribute to the formation of chemo-attractants in extracellular fluid. H_2O_2 concentrations as low as 70 µM in normal human serum (activated neutrophils can produce H_2O_2 concentrations that approach 300 µM) result in the generation of chemotactic activity for human neutrophils (143). The fact that the chemotactic activity of plasma exposed to H_2O_2 is reduced by the addition of antibodies directed against C5, coupled with the observation that the addition of purified C5 to H_2O_2 generates chemotactic activity, suggests that H_2O_2 generates a C5a-like chemotactic factor through hydrolysis of C5 (143, 161). The ability of H_2O_2 to activate complement and generate a chemotactic agent in plasma is enhanced by the presence of catalytically active iron (e.g. Fe EDTA, hemoglobin) (178), which suggests that the process of complement activation is not brought about by H_2O_2 per se, but by an oxidant derived from H_2O_2. The ability of heme-iron to enhance H_2O_2–mediated formation of chemotactic agents in plasma may be important in conditions (e.g. I/R of large muscle masses) that are associated with hemolysis or rhabdomyolysis and the associated liberation of hemoglobin or myoglobin into extracellular fluid (120).

Oxidant formation during reperfusion may also contribute to the expression of adhesive structures on the surface of neutrophils and endothelial cells, thereby promoting leukocyte adhesion in postischemic tissue. For example, incubation of naive neutrophils with hydrogen peroxide or monochloramine (NH_2Cl) increases the expression of CD11/CD18 (149), whereas exposure of unactivated endothelial cells to H_2O_2 induces the expression of P-selectin (124) and intercellular adhesion molecule-1 (ICAM-1) (18, 95). Moreover, H_2O_2 and NH_2Cl, at concentrations produced by activated neutrophils, promote leukocyte adhesion to postcapillary venules (149). Since these effects were blocked by administration of antibodies directed against CD18, it appears that H_2O_2 can promote leukocyte adhesion to endothelial cells at physiologically relevant concentrations by a mechanism that involves up–regulation of CD11/CD18 (149). Similarly, P-selectin or ICAM-1 immunoneutralization prevents neutrophil adhesion to peroxide–treated endothelial cell monolayers (18, 95, 124).

Although this evidence provides compelling support for the concept that reactive oxygen metabolites play an essential role in the pathogenesis of I/R, the notion remains controversial for many organs, most notably the heart. While the bulk of available evidence indicates that reactive oxygen species contribute to the myocardial stunning induced by short periods (<15 min) of ischemia (88, 180), the role of oxidants in the production of myocardial injury induced by longer periods of ischemia that give rise to irreversible injury is less clear (32, 134). The discrepant results regarding the role of oxidants in myocardial injury induced by prolonged ischemia appear to be related to many factors including the possibility that tetrazolium staining may be an unreliable indicator of infarct size, the lack of standardized ischemic insults, and the failure to measure collateral blood flow (32, 134). In addition, the short plasma half-lives of superoxide dismutase and catalase and the dose or manner in which these antioxidant enzymes are administered has complicated the interpretation of many studies (79, 158). Despite these complications, the preponderance of evidence appears to support the notion that oxidants play an important role in reperfusion injury.

Leukocytes

Numerous reports implicate leukocytes in the pathobiology of I/R injury. The view that leukocytes participate in this injury process is largely based on three lines of evidence: (a) Granulocytes accumulate in tissues exposed to ischemia and reperfusion. (b) Depletion of circulating neutrophils significantly reduces the microvascular and parenchymal cell dysfunction associated with I/R. (c) Agents that prevent neutrophil activation and/or leukocyte–endothelial cell adhesion effectively blunt I/R–induced tissue injury. Thus leukocytes are implicated in I/R injury in the heart (74, 96, 110, 136), small intestine (61), skeletal muscle (20, 138), brain (73, 142), stomach (147), lung (1), and kidneys (58a, 59).

Because postischemic tissues appear to generate large quantities of leukotriene B_4 (LTB$_4$), platelet–activating factor (PAF), C5a, and other chemoattractants, it is not surprising that this condition is associated with an infiltration of neutrophils. Several strategies have been used to quantify the flux of leukocytes in ischemic and postischemic tissues, among them: monitoring the appearance of radiolabeled leukocytes (36) or granulocyte–specific enzymes (20, 177, 178), and histological assessment of specific leukocyte populations (116). The technique of intravital videomicroscopy has also been used to quantify the leukocyte–endothelial cell adhesive interactions that are elicited in postcapillary venules by I/R (43). The latter approach affords the opportunity to obtain continuous, real–time estimates of leukocyte accumulation within the microvasculature (adherent or trapped), as well as in the surrounding interstitial compartment (emigrated cells). The data derived from the use of these techniques indicate that the intensity of leukocyte accumulation elicited by I/R is determined by the magnitude and duration of the ischemic insult. Complete arterial inflow occlusion followed by reperfusion is associated with a more profound leukocyte infiltration than that elicited by partial arterial occlusion (low flow ischemia) and subsequent reperfusion (38, 43, 92, 116). The number of leukocytes adhering in postcapillary venules increases up to 35-fold following reperfusion in complete arterial occlusion models (38, 92), with 4- to 10-fold increases noted in low flow (80% reduction in flow) ischemia models (43, 116).

The leukocyte–endothelial cell interactions observed in postcapillary venules exposed to I/R can be mimicked in in vitro models wherein monolayers of cultured endothelial cells are exposed to anoxia followed by reoxygenation (106, 125, 174). These monolayers exhibit a hyperadhesive surface for neutrophils. Supernatants recovered from endothelial cells exposed to anoxia/reoxygenation (A/R) enhance neutrophil adhesion to naive monolayers, which indicates that a stable inflammatory mediator is produced by posthypoxic endothelial cells (45). Inasmuch as PAF receptor antagonists are effective in attenuating the hyperadhesive state of endothelial cell monolayers exposed to A/R, the phospholipid appears to be a likely candidate for the inflammatory mediator (106, 174).

Although leukocyte–endothelial cell adhesion in postcapillary venules appears to be largely responsible for the leukosequestration observed in some postischemic tissues, the physical restriction or trapping of leukocytes within capillaries may significantly contribute to the leukocyte accumulation observed in postischemic myocardium, liver, brain, kidney, and skeletal muscle (4, 8, 27, 31, 35–37, 51). Because the entrapped leukocytes occlude the capillary lumen, leukocyte–capillary plugging may contribute to the development of the "no-reflow phenomenon" in postischemic tissues. Indeed, the strong correlation between the percent of capillaries exhibiting no-reflow and the percent of capillaries that contain granulocytes in postischemic tissues (8, 31, 35–37) suggests that trapping of leukocytes with the consequent restriction of capillary perfusion represents a tenable mechanism for the no-reflow phenomenon. The leukocyte trapping may result from ischemia–induced leukocyte deformability as well as the swelling of endothelial cells and neutrophils (2, 27, 75, 169). An alternative explanation for the no-reflow phenomenon is that the accumulation of interstitial fluid (edema) in postischemic tissues acts to compress the microvasculature thereby impeding the movement of blood elements within capillaries (65, 75). The latter explanation is more likely to apply to tissues that cannot readily expand as fluid accumulates within the interstitial compartment, i.e. the brain, kidney, and muscles surrounded by tight fascial sheaths. Compelling evidence that leukocytes contribute to I/R–induced no-reflow is provided by reports that demonstrate virtual elimination of the phenomenon in animals that are either rendered neutropenic (8, 20, 67) or that receive antibodies that interfere with leukocyte–endothelial cell adhesion in postcapillary venules and the subsequent interstitial edema (20, 68, 66, 107).

The leukocyte accumulation that occurs during ischemia resulting from partial arterial occlusion has been attributed to low shear rates that favor leukocyte–endothelial cell adhesion in postcapillary venules (129). Indeed, reductions in venular shear rate over a range of 800–50 s^{-1} led to an increased number of rolling and adherent leukocytes (11–13, 129). Furthermore, the number of adherent leukocytes that are recruited by an inflammatory mediator such as PAF is far greater at low than at normal shear rates (13), which suggests that it is easier for leukocytes to create strong adhesive bonds with venular endothelial cells at low shear rates. A dependence of leukocyte adherence on shear forces has also been demonstrated using in vitro models that employ isolated neutrophils and monolayers of cultured endothelial cells (89, 144); however, much lower shear stresses (3 vs 15 dynes/cm^2) are needed to dislodge an adherent leukocyte in vitro.

The recruitment of adherent leukocytes that is observed in postcapillary venules exposed to low shear rates has been attributed to a reduced washout of inflammatory mediators that are normally produced by endothelial and/or parenchymal cells (12). At low shear rates, these mediators accumulate within microvessels to elicit the activation and/or increased expression of leukocyte adhesion molecules. Support for this view is provided by studies that demonstrate an attenuated recruitment of adherent leukocytes in mesenteric venules at low shear rates following administration of either an LTB$_4$ (but not a PAF) receptor antagonist or a 5-lipoxygenase inhibitor, which suggests that LTB$_4$ accumulation contributes to the recruitment of adherent leukocytes at low shear rates. LTB$_4$–mediated recruitment of leukocytes at low shear rates has been estimated to account for a significant fraction (>50%) of the leukocyte adherence observed in postcapillary venules during low flow ischemia (44).

Several factors, in addition to shear rate, may contribute to the modulation of leukocyte–endothelial cell adhesion in postcapillary venules exposed to I/R. These include electrostatic cell surface charges, adhesion glycoproteins, and reactive species produced by activated neutrophils and/or endothelial cells. Cationic proteins (lactoferrin, elastase) released from activated neutrophils are known to promote the adhesion of neutrophils to endothelial cell monolayers and in postcapillary venules (17, 119). This effect has been attributed to neutralization of negative surface charges on leukocytes and endothelial cells that tend to promote cell separation through electrostatic repulsion (55). However, the results of a recent study indicate that the ability of lactoferrin to elicit leukocyte adherence in postcapillary venules is unrelated to its positive electrical charge (6). Cationic proteins (histone, chymotrypsinogen A) with net electrical charges exceeding that of lactoferrin do not cause leukocyte adhesion. Furthermore, the leukocyte adhesion in mesenteric venules elicited by lactoferrin is largely prevented by treatment with either diamine oxidase or a histamine H_1-antagonist, which suggests that lactoferrin promotes leukocyte–endothelial cell adhesion through histamine release rather than an electrostatic charge neutralization effect (6). It appears equally unlikely that the pro–adhesive effect of elastase is related to electrostatic charge since agents that inhibit elastase activity without modifying its charge properties are able to significantly attenuate I/R–induced leukocyte adherence in postcapillary venules (177).

It is now well recognized that the adhesion of leukocytes to endothelial cells is mediated by various coordinately regulated adhesion glycoproteins expressed on the surface of leukocytes (CD11/CD18, L-selectin) and endothelial cells (P- and E-selectin) (56, 72, 75). The CD11/CD18 glycoprotein complex on leukocytes consists of three heterodimers, each of which contains an immunologically distinct α-subunit (CD11) that is linked to a common β-subunit (CD18). Each heterodimer is classified according to its unique α-subunit; i.e. CD11a/CD18, CD11b/CD18, and CD11c/CD18. Inflammatory mediators such as LTB_4 and PAF induce the rapid (1–2 min) expression of CD11b/CD18 on neutrophils, thereby allowing for rapid adhesion to endothelial cells (56, 75). L-selectin, another adhesion molecule, is found on circulating leukocytes where it participates in the weak adhesive interactions that are manifested as leukocyte rolling (72). Two other members of the selectin family of adhesion molecules (P- and E-selectin) are found on activated endothelial cells (56, 75). Neither molecule is constitutively expressed on endothelial cells but can be mobilized to the cell surface in response to specific stimuli. P-selectin is rapidly (<10 min) expressed on endothelial cells exposed to histamine, thrombin, and hydrogen peroxide, while E-selectin expression is induced by cytokines and requires several hours for maximal expression (105). Both P- and E-selectin can interact with distinct oligosaccharides (e.g. sialyl Lewis X) on leukocytes to promote adhesion (rolling). ICAM-1 is another endothelial cell adhesion molecule, but unlike P- and E-selectin, it is constitutively expressed on endothelial cells. ICAM-1 serves as a ligand for CD11a/CD18 and CD11b/CD18 on leukocytes. Cytokines also induce an increased expression of ICAM-1 over a period of several hours (148). The interaction between ICAM-1 and CD11/CD18 appears to mediate firm adhesion and emigration of leukocytes in postcapillary venules (44).

The contribution of different adhesion molecules to I/R–induced leukocyte adherence and emigration in postcapillary venules has recently been determined. In cat mesenteric venules exposed to 60 min of low flow ischemia followed by 60 min of reperfusion, pretreatment with a CD18–specific monoclonal antibody (MAb) reduced reperfusion–induced leukocyte adherence and emigration by about 95% (151). The same MAb was less effective in reducing the adhesive interactions elicited by I/R of a similar magnitude and duration induced by hemorrhage-reperfusion (128), which suggests that other adhesion molecules make a greater contribution to the leukocyte–endothelial cell interactions caused by whole body I/R. MAbs directed against the α-subunits CD11a and CD11b reduce I/R–induced leukocyte adherence by approximately 50% each, while an ICAM-1 MAb reduces adherence by 40% (45). In rat mesenteric venules exposed to 20 min of complete arterial occlusion followed by 30 min of reperfusion, MAbs directed against either CD11b or CD18 nearly abolish the reperfusion–induced recruitment of adherent and emigrated leukocytes, whereas an ICAM-1–specific MAb reduces leukocyte adherence and emigration by more than 50% (85). MAbs directed against P- and E-selectin were ineffective in altering the leukocyte–endothelial cell interactions elicited by I/R in rat mesentery. However, an L-selectin–specific MAb did attenuate the initial leukocyte adherence response observed following reperfusion. Although there are quantitative differences in the contributions of different adhesion molecules to I/R–induced leukocyte adhesion in cat and rat mesenteric venules, the findings in both models are generally consistent with a major role for CD11/CD18 interactions with ICAM-1 and other substrates on the endothelial cell surface in mediating firm adherence and emigration of leukocytes. This pattern of involvement of adhesion molecules is similar to that observed in rat mesenteric venules exposed to either PAF or LTB_4 (179), as well as to the neutrophil adhesion observed on endothelial cell monolayers exposed to anoxia/reoxygenation (174). The molecular determinants of the leukocyte rolling responses induced by I/R remain unclear; however, P- and L-selectin are more likely to make a contribution than E-selectin in most of the I/R models used to date, given the durations of ischemia and reperfusion studied.

The critical role of leukocyte adhesion in the pathogenesis of I/R injury is best exemplified by studies that demonstrate protection against microvascular and/or parenchymal cell dysfunction or necrosis in postischemic tissues. For example, monoclonal antibodies directed against CD11/CD18 attenuate I/R–induced myocardial necrosis (41, 98, 141), alterations in endothelium–dependent coronary vascular reactivity (98), skeletal muscle contractile dysfunction

(165), reexpansion edema in atelectatic lungs (40), neurological deficits related to spinal cord ischemia (22), gut mucosal injury (139), and microvascular permeability in intestine (61), mesentery (85), lung (1), and skeletal muscle (20). Although CD18–specific MAbs generally yield the most impressive protective effects in different models of I/R injury, MAbs directed against endothelial cell adhesion molecules also afford protection in some models of I/R injury. Immunoneutralization of ICAM-1 leads to an attenuation of I/R–induced pulmonary edema (62), reduces infarct size in reperfused myocardium (97, 141), and blunts coronary endothelium–dependent vasoregulatory dysfunction (97). Similarly, P-selectin MAbs have been shown to protect the myocardium against I/R injury, which is manifested as a reduction in infarct size and preservation of nitric oxide production by coronary vascular endothelium (167). The increased pulmonary vascular permeability elicited by reperfusion of the ischemic intestine also appears to be attenuated by a P-selectin MAb (21). The protective effects of anti–adhesion interventions in different conditions associated with I/R (e.g. transplantation, circulatory shock, cardiopulmonary bypass) have recently been summarized (75).

The reactive oxygen metabolites released by activated leukocytes and endothelial cells have also been implicated in I/R–induced leukocyte accumulation. Exposure of postcapillary venules to exogenous hydrogen peroxide (151) or superoxide (30, 39) promotes leukocyte–endothelial cell adhesion. Furthermore, both superoxide dismutase and catalase attenuate the leukocyte adherence observed in mesenteric venules exposed to I/R (43, 150, 151). The two reactive oxygen metabolites appear to promote leukocyte adhesion via different mechanisms. The pro–adhesive effect of H_2O_2 can be significantly attenuated by PAF receptor antagonists as well as CD18–specific MAbs (151), which suggests that the oxidant elicits the formation of PAF, which in turn, induces the up–regulation of CD11/CD18 on neutrophils. Support for such a mechanism is provided by data from endothelial cell monolayers exposed to anoxia/reoxygenation (174). Both catalase and a PAF receptor antagonist are effective in blunting the increased neutrophil adhesion normally elicited by A/R.

The mechanism(s) involved in superoxide–mediated leukocyte adherence remain unclear; however, nitric oxide may contribute to this response (84). Nitric oxide, which reacts avidly with superoxide, is normally produced by vascular endothelium. Inhibition of NO production with analogues of L-arginine [e.g. nitro-L-arginine methyl ester (L-NAME), nitro-L-NG-monomethyl-arginine (L-NMMA)] results in an intense leukocyte adherence response in mesenteric venules (5, 84, 86), which suggests that NO is an endogenous inhibitor of leukocyte–endothelial cell adhesion. Consequently, one would predict that conditions associated with an enhanced formation of superoxide (e.g. I/R) should lead to increased leukocyte adherence by virtue of superoxide's ability to render nitric oxide biologically inactive. The contention that nitric oxide attenuates leukocyte–endothelial cell adhesion is supported by reports that demonstrate a reduced adhesion response to different inflammatory mediators following the administration of nitric oxide donors (39, 87, 90). Endothelial cell production of nitric oxide appears to fall following I/R (87, 99), and agents that spontaneously release NO appear to attenuate the increased albumin leakage in mesenteric venules exposed to I/R (87) and to reduce the myocardial necrosis and neutrophil accumulation following I/R (24, 90, 91). In the intestine, inhibition of NO synthesis elicits most of the microvascular and mucosal alterations normally observed in the postischemic state, i.e. leukocyte adherence and emigration, platelet–leukocyte aggregation, vascular protein leakage, mast cell degranulation, and mucosal barrier dysfunction (82, 86). Nitric oxide donors largely prevent these alterations (87, 127). Although the beneficial effects of NO donors have been attributed to their ability to attenuate I/R–induced leukocyte–endothelial cell adhesion (24, 87), there is evidence that NO directly abrogates hydrogen peroxide–mediated cytotoxicity (168) and serves to ensure mast cell stabilization (83).

A large body of evidence also suggests that NO promotes (rather than protects against) I/R injury. It is well known that nitric oxide contributes to the microbicidal and tumoricidal activities of macrophages (10). Although the deleterious effect of macrophage–derived NO has been attributed to the larger fluxes of NO produced by these cells (as compared to endothelium), some reports indicate that endothelial cell–derived NO may also be cytotoxic. Several reports indicate that the production of NO and subsequent activation of guanylate cyclase contribute to the increased permeability of postcapillary venules exposed to elevated shear rates or to agents such as ADP, leukotriene C_4, and bradykinin (102, 103, 176). Furthermore, there are studies that demonstrate diminished neutrophil recruitment and protection against immune complex–induced vascular injury in animals treated with inhibitors of NO synthesis (111). Similarly, NO synthase inhibitors have been shown to limit neutrophil accumulation and vascular protein leakage in postischemic lung and skeletal muscle (140), as well as reduce the contractile dysfunction and lipid peroxidation normally associated with myocardial I/R (101). Because oxygen free radical scavengers are as effective as NO synthase inhibitors in reducing tissue injury and organ dysfunction in these models of I/R injury, the product of the interaction between superoxide and NO, i.e. the peroxynitrite anion and/or hydroxyl radical (10), is proposed to be the injurious agent. A definitive explanation for the apparent contradictory role of NO in different models of I/R does not yet exist. However, resolution of this issue awaits a better understanding of the relative rates of production of NO and superoxide, as well as the level of dependence of injury on leukocytes, mast cells, and macrophages in different tissues and experimental models of I/R.

Ischemic Preconditioning

In addition to the potential for inhibition of leukocyte adherence to postcapillary venular endothelium as a novel approach to the treatment of reperfusion injury, an emerging body of evidence suggests that ischemic preconditioning (IPC) may be effective in reducing postischemic tissue injury. IPC refers to a phenomenon in which a tissue is rendered resistant to the deleterious effects of prolonged ischemia and reperfusion by prior exposure to brief periods of vascular occlusion (112). IPC has been shown to improve contractile function and reduce the extent of necrosis in skeletal muscles and hearts that were subsequently subjected to prolonged ischemia followed by reperfusion (33, 52, 64, 112, 126, 152, 159, 162, 166). Also, preconditioning exerts pronounced antiarrythmic effects and preserves endothelium–dependent vasodilatory responses in postischemic myocardium (29, 152, 160).

Although the mechanisms underlying the protective actions of IPC have not been elucidated in most tissues, this issue has been the subject of intensive investigation in the heart. The bulk of the available experimental evidence suggests that it is unlikely that the protective actions of IPC can be attributed to altered myocardial collateral blood flow (23), attenuation of oxidant generation (63, 118), myocardial stunning (109), altered glycolytic flux (113, 162), activation of an endogenous mitochondrial ATPase inhibitor (162), or increased prostacyclin (93) or nitric oxide synthesis (172). In addition, a role for the induction of heat shock proteins has been excluded because protein synthesis inhibitors do not reduce the protective actions of IPC (154).

A growing body of evidence suggests that preconditioning induces the release of adenosine. Not only does adenosine reduce tissue injury induced by prolonged ischemia and reperfusion (33, 34), it is well established that adenosine receptor activation reduces leukocyte adhesion to postcapillary venules in tissues subjected to prolonged I/R (49). It is also clear that adenosine modulates neutrophilic oxidative metabolism and inhibits platelet aggregation and microthrombi formation (25). This evidence has been linked to IPC by Downey and co-workers (33), who demonstrated that the protective actions of preconditioning are blocked by prior administration of adenosine A_1-receptor, but not adenosine A_2-receptor, antagonists. Moreover, these investigators demonstrated that the limitation of infarct size induced by IPC or adenosine A_1-receptor activation is sustained over a 3 day reperfusion period (33). This observation provides strong support for the notion that IPC or adenosine treatment reduces postischemic tissue injury rather than merely delaying its development.

There is also evidence that ATP–sensitive potassium (K_{ATP}) channels may be involved in mediating the effects of IPC. For example, administration of K_{ATP} channel inhibitors (e.g. glybenclamide or 5-hydroxydecanoate) reverses the protective actions of IPC in postischemic canine myocardium and murine skeletal muscle (3, 52, 172). Similarly, we have demonstrated that glybenclamide reverses the protective effect of IPC on microvascular patency in postischemic canine gracilis muscles (67). These studies suggest that K_{ATP} channels play an important role in preconditioning and that K_{ATP} channel activators may prove beneficial in the treatment of postischemic tissue injury. Indeed, the protective actions of IPC are mimicked by administration of K_{ATP} channel activators (e.g. pinacidil or cromakalim) in canine myocardium and in rat, mouse, and canine skeletal muscle subsequently exposed to prolonged I/R (3, 52, 67, 172). However, it does not appear that a role for K_{ATP} channel activation can be extrapolated to all species since glybenclamide administration does not reverse the protective effect of IPC in rabbit myocardium (156).

The results of several recent studies suggest that the participation of adenosine receptors and K_{ATP} channels in IPC may be linked. For example, Kirsch et al (70) have shown that adenosine A_1-receptor activation opens K_{ATP} channels in rat neonatal ventricular myocytes. Recent reports indicate that adenosine–induced limitation of postischemic myocardial injury can be abolished by K_{ATP} channel blockade with glybenclamide (7, 159, 173). These latter results suggest that activation of myocardial K_{ATP} channels by adenosine mediates preconditioning, at least in some models.

Adenosine A_1-receptors are coupled to G_i-proteins; thus it has been postulated that adenosine A_1-receptor activation opens K_{ATP} channels via a G protein (7, 70, 115, 159, 173). According to this scenario, inhibition of G proteins would be expected to attenuate the protective effects of adenosine and IPC. This notion is supported by the observation that administration of pertussis toxin attenuates the protective actions of both adenosine and IPC in postischemic myocardium (155). Inasmuch as G proteins are also essential signal transduction elements regulating the activity of membrane phospholipases (14) and adenosine A_1-receptor activation activates phospholipase C (115), it is possible that phospholipase C–mediated events contribute to IPC. For example, activation of phospholipase C leads to the production of diacylglycerol and inositol 1,4,5-trisphosphate. Diacylglycerol activates protein kinase C (PKC) which, in turn, can modify cellular proteins by phosphorylation (71). A role for PKC in the preconditioning phenomenon is supported by the observation that inhibition of PKC with staurosporin or polymyxin B abolishes the protective effects of IPC (175). Furthermore, exogenous PKC activation with phorbol myristate acetate or a diacylglycerol analogue mimics IPC and protects the myocardium from the deleterious effects of prolonged ischemia and reperfusion (175).

Although the above–mentioned studies support the hypothesis that activation of myocardial K_{ATP} channels by adenosine mediates preconditioning by a mechanism that involves activation of G proteins and PKC, the mechanism whereby these events protect postischemic tissues is not clear. However, because IPC slows cellular metabolism in preconditioned hearts, it has been suggested that preservation of ATP or reduced accumulation of toxic metabolites is responsible for preconditioning in the myocardium (69, 113). This hypothesis is supported by the observation that increased potassium efflux induced by K_{ATP} channel activation is associated with reduced action potential duration and hyperpolarization (114). As a consequence, the time that voltage–dependent calcium channels are open is reduced, which in turn, decreases intracellular calcium and contractile activity, thereby preserving myocardial ATP.

Adenosine may also act via several other mechanisms to produce IPC. For example, adenosine has been shown to increase myocardial energy production during ischemia by promoting glucose transport (171). In addition, IPC may reduce myocardial oxygen demand during ischemia by reducing norepinephrine release from sympathetic nerve terminals (135). Finally, adenosine has been shown to inhibit neutrophilic oxidative metabolism and adhesion to postcapillary venules (25, 49). However, these latter effects appear to be mediated by A_2-receptors, whereas a role for adenosine in IPC involves A_1-receptor activation.

Recent reports indicate that IPC reduces the extent of postischemic capillary no-reflow and attenuates leukocyte adherence and emigration in muscles subjected to subsequent prolonged I/R by a mechanism that involves adenosine receptor and K_{ATP} channel activation (3, 66). These observations, when coupled with the fact that neutrophil adhesion and emigration are prerequisites for the production of reperfusion injury, suggest an additional novel mechanism for the beneficial effects of IPC. That is, the protective actions of IPC may be in part related to preservation of capillary perfusion (i.e. reduced postischemic capillary no-reflow) and decreased leukocyte adhesion and emigration during reperfusion.

ACKNOWLEDGMENTS

This work was supported by grants from the National Institutes of Health (HL-26441, DK-43785, HL-36069, and HL-48646).

Literature Cited

1. Adkins WK, Taylor AE. 1990. Role of xanthine oxidase and neutrophils in ischemia–reperfusion injury in rabbit lung. *J. Appl. Physiol.* 69:2012–18

2. Akimitsu T, Gute DC, Jerome SN, Korthuis RJ. 1994. Reactive oxygen metabolites and their consequences. In *Ischemia–Reperfusion of Skeletal Mus-*

cle, ed. GA Fantini pp. 5–31. Austin, Tex.: Landes

3. Akimitsu T, Gute DC, Korthuis RJ. 1994. Ischemic preconditioning attenuates postischemic leukocyte adhesion and emigration: role of adenosine and ATP–sensitive potassium channels. *Circulation.* In press

4. Ames A, Wright LW, Kowada M, Thurston JM, Majno G. 1968. Cerebral ischemia: II. The no-reflow phenomenon. *Am. J. Pathol.* 52:437–53

5. Arndt H, Smith CW, Granger DN. 1993. Leukocyte–endothelial cell adhesion in spontaneously hypertensive and normal rats. *Hypertension* 21:667–73

6. Asako H, Kurose I, Wolf RE, Granger DN. 1994. Mechanisms of lactoferrin–induced leukocyte–endothelial cell adhesion in postcapillary venules. *Microcirculation* 1:27–34

7. Auchampach JA, Gross GJ. 1993. Adenosine A_1 receptors, K_{ATP} channels, and ischemic preconditioning in dogs. *Am. J. Physiol.* 264:H1327–36

8. Barroso-Arranda J, Schmid-Schonbein GW, Zweifach BW, Engler RL. 1988. Granulocytes and the no-reflow phenomenon in irreversible hemorrhagic shock. *Circ. Res.* 63:437–47

9. Beckman JS, Beckman TW, Chen J. 1990. Apparent hydroxyl radical production by peroxynitrite: implications for endothelial injury from nitric oxide and superoxide. *Proc. Natl. Acad. Sci. USA* 87:1620–24

10. Beckman JS, Crow JP. 1993. Pathological implications of nitric oxide, superoxide and peroxynitrite formation. *Biochem. Soc. Trans.* 21:330–34

11. Bienvenu K, Granger DN. 1993. Molecular determinants of shear rate–dependent leukocyte adhesion in postcapillary venules. *Am. J. Physiol.* 264:H1504–8

12. Bienvenu K, Russell J, Granger DN. 1992. Leukotriene B_4 mediates shear rate–dependent leukocyte adhesion in mesenteric venules. *Circ. Res.* 71:906–11

13. Bienvenu K, Russell J, Granger DN. 1993. Platelet–activating factor promotes shear rate–dependent leukocyte adhesion in postcapillary venules. *J. Lipid Mediators* 8:95–103

14. Birnbaumer L. 1990. G proteins in signal transduction. 1990. *Annu. Rev. Pharmacol. Toxicol.* 30:675–706

15. Bolli R, Jeroudi MO, Patel BS, DuBose CM, Lai EK, et al. 1989. Direct evidence that oxygen–derived free radicals contribute to post ischemic myocardial dysfunction in the intact dog. *Proc. Natl. Acad. Sci. USA* 86:4695–99

16. Bolli R, Patel BS, Jeroudi MO, Lai EK, McKay PB. 1988. Demonstration of free radical generation in "stunned" myocardium of intact dogs with the use of the spin trap α-phenyl-N-tert-butyl nitrone. *J. Clin. Invest.* 82:476–85

17. Boxer LA, Bjorksten B, Bjork J, Yang HH, Allen JM. 1982. Neutropenia induced by systemic infusion of lactoferrin. *J. Lab. Clin. Med.* 99:866–72

18. Bradley JR, Johnson DR, Pober JS. 1993. Endothelial activation by hydrogen peroxide. Selective increases of intercellular adhesion molecule-1 and major histocompatibility complex class 1. *Am. J. Pathol.* 142:1598–609

19. Burton KP. 1988. Evidence of direct toxic effects of free radicals on the myocardium. *Free Rad. Biol. Med.* 4:15–24

20. Carden DL, Smith JK, Korthuis RJ. 1990. Neutrophil–mediated microvascular dysfunction in postischemic canine skeletal muscle: role of granulocyte adherence. *Circ. Res.* 66:1436–44

21. Carden DL, Young JA, Granger DN. 1993. Pulmonary microvascular injury following intestinal ischemia/reperfusion: role of P-selectin. *J. Appl. Physiol.* 75:2529–34

22. Clark WM, Madden KP, Rothlein R, Ziven JA. 1991. Reduction of central nervous system ischemic injury in rabbits using leukocyte adhesion antibody treatment. *Stroke* 22:877–83

23. Cohen MV, Liu GS, Downey JM. 1991. Preconditioning causes improved wall motion as well as smaller infarcts after transient coronary occlusion in rabbit. *Circulation* 84:341–49

24. Cooke JP, Tsao PS. 1993. Cytoprotective effects of nitric oxide. *Circulation* 88:2451–54

25. Cronstein BN, Levin RI, Belanoff J, Weissmann G, Hirschhorn R. 1986. Adenosine: an endogenous inhibitor of neutrophil-mediated injury to endothelial cells. *J. Clin. Invest.* 78:760–70

26. Dahlback LO, Rais O. 1966. Morphological changes in striated muscle following ischemia: immediate postischemic phase. *Acta Chir. Scand.* 131:430–40

27. Dahlgren MD, Peterson MA, Engler RL, Schmid-Schonbein GW. 1984. Leukocyte rheology in cardiac ischemia. In *White Cell Mechanics, Basic Science and Clinical Aspects,* Kroc. Found. Ser. (16):271–83. New York: Liss

28. Davies MJ. 1989. Direct detection of radical production in the ischaemic and reperfused myocardium: current status. *Free Rad. Res. Commun.* 7:275–84

29. DeFily DV, Chilian WM. 1993. Preconditioning protects coronary arteriolar endothelium from ischemia-reperfusion injury. *Am. J. Physiol.* 265:H700–6

30. Del Maestro RF, Planker M, Arfors KE. 1982. Evidence for the participation of superoxide anion radical in altering the adhesive interaction between granulocytes and endothelium in vivo. *Int. J. Microcirc. Clin. Exp.* 1:105–20

31. del Zoppo GJ, Schmid-Schonbein GW, Mori E, Copeland BR, Chang CM. 1991. Polymorphonuclear leukocytes occlude capillaries following middle cerebral artery occlusion and reperfusion in baboons. *Stroke* 22:1276–83

32. Downey JM. 1990. Free radicals and their involvement during long–term myocardial ischemia and reperfusion. *Annu. Rev. Physiol.* 52:487–504

33. Downey JM, Liu GS, Thornton JD. 1993. Adenosine and the anti–infarct effects of preconditioning. *Cardiol. Res.* 27:3–8

34. Ely SW, Berne RM. 1992. Protective effects of adenosine in myocardial ischemia. *Circulation* 85:893–904

35. Engler RL, Dahlgren MD, Morris DD, Peterson MA, Schmid-Schonbein GW. 1986. Role of leukocytes in response to acute myocardial ischemia and reflow in dogs. *Am. J. Physiol.* 251:H314–23

36. Engler RL, Dahlgren MD, Peterson MA, Dobbs A, Schmid-Schonbein GW. 1986. Accumulation of polymorphonuclear leukocytes during 3-h experimental myocardial ischemia. *Am. J. Physiol.* 251:H93–100

37. Engler RL, Schmid-Schonbein GW, Pavelec RS. 1983. Leukocyte capillary plugging in myocardial ischemia and reperfusion in the dog. *Am. J. Pathol.* 111:98–111

38. Erlansson M, Bergqvist D, Persson, NH, Svensjo E. 1991. Modification of postischemic increase of leukocyte adhesion and vascular permeability in the hamster by iloprost. *Prostaglandins* 41:157–68

39. Gaboury J, Anderson DC, Kubes P. 1994. Molecular mechanisms involved in superoxide–induced leukocyte–endothelial cell interactions in vivo. *Am. J. Physiol.* 266(2 Pt. 2):H637–42

40. Goldman G, Welbourn R, Rothlein R, Valeri CR, Shepro D, et al. 1992. Adherent neutrophils mediate permeability after atelectasis. *Ann. Surg.* 216:372–80

41. Gomoll AW, Lekich RF, Grove RI. 1991. Efficacy of a monoclonal antibody (MoAb 603) in reducing myocardial injury resulting from ischemia/reperfusion in the ferret. *J. Cardiovasc. Pharmacol.* 17:873–78

42. Granger DN. 1988. Role of xanthine oxidase and granulocytes in ischemia–reperfusion injury. *Am. J. Physiol.* 255:H1269–75

43. Granger DN, Benoit JN, Suzuki M, Grisham MB. 1989. Leukocyte adherence to venular endothelium during ischemia-reperfusion. *Am. J. Physiol.* 257:G683–88

44. Granger DN, Kubes P. 1994. The microcirculation and inflammation: modulation of leukocyte–endothelial cell adhesion. *J. Leuk. Biol.* 55:662–75

45. Granger DN, Kvietys PR, Perry MA. 1993. Leukocyte-endothelial cell adhesion induced by ischemia and reperfusion. *Can. J. Physiol. Pharmacol.* 71:67–75

46. Granger DN, McCord JM, Parks DA, Hollwarth MA. 1986. Xanthine oxidase inhibitors attenuate ischemia–induced vascular permeability changes in the cat intestine. *Gastroenterology* 90:80–84

47. Grisham MB. 1993. *Reactive Metabolites of Oxygen and Nitrogen in Biology and Medicine.* Austin, Tex.: Landes

48. Grisham MB, Granger DN. 1989. Metabolic sources of reactive oxygen metabolites during oxidant stress and ischemia and reperfusion. *Clin. Chest Med.* 10:71–81

49. Grisham MB, Hernandez LA, Granger DN. 1989. Adenosine inhibits ischemia–reperfusion–induced leukocyte adherence and extravasation. *Am. J. Physiol.* 257:H1334–39

50. Grisham MB, McCord JM. 1986. Chemistry and cytotoxicity of reactive oxygen metabolites. In *Physiology of Oxygen Radicals,* ed. AE Taylor, S Matalon, PA Ward, pp. 1–18. Bethesda: Am. Physiol. Soc.

51. Grogaard B, Schurer L, Gerdin B, Arfors KE. 1989. Delayed hypoperfusion after incomplete forebrain ischemia in the rat: the role of polymorphonuclear leukocytes. *J. Cereb. Blood Flow Metab.* 9:500–5

52. Gross GJ, Auchampach JA. 1992. Role of ATP dependent potassium channels in myocardial ischaemia. *Cardiol. Res.* 26:1011–16

53. Gupta M, Singhal P. 1989. Time course of structure, function, and metabolic changes due to an exogenous source of oxygen metabolites in the rat heart. *Can. J. Physiol. Pharmcol.* 67:1549–59

54. Halliwell B, Gutteridge JMC. 1989. *Free Radicals in Biology and Medicine.* Oxford: Clarendon

55. Harlan JM. 1985. Leukocyte–endothelial cell interactions. *Blood* 65:513–25

56. Harlan JM, Liu DY. 1992. *Adhesion: Its Role in Inflammatory Disease.* New York: Freeman

57. Hearse DJ. 1977. Reperfusion of ischemic myocardium. *J. Mol. Cell Cardiol.* 9:605–15

58. Hearse DJ, Humphrey RM, Chain EB. 1973. Abrupt reoxygenation of the anoxic potassium arrested rat heart: a study of myocardial enzyme release. *J. Mol. Cell Cardiol.* 5:395–407

58a. Hellberg A, Kallskog OT, Ojteg G, Wolgast M, et al. 1990. Peritubular capillary permeability and intravascular RBC aggregation after ischemia: effects of neutrophils. *Am. J. Physiol.* 258: F1018–25

59. Hellberg POA, Kallskog O, Wolgast M. 1988. Effects of neutrophil granulocytes on the inulin barrier of renal tubular epithelium after ischaemic damage. *Acta Physiol. Scand.* 134:313–15

60. Hernandez LA, Grisham MB, Granger DN. 1987. A role for iron in oxidant–mediated ischemic injury to intestinal microvasculature. *Am. J. Physiol.* 253: G49–53

61. Hernandez LA, Grisham MB, Twohig B, Arfors KE, Harlan JM. 1987. Role of neutrophils in ischemia/reperfusion-induced microvascular injury. *Am. J. Physiol.* 253:H699–703

62. Horgan MJ, Ge M, Gu J, Rothlein R, Malik AB. 1991. Role of ICAM-1 in neutrophil–mediated lung vascular injury after occlusion and reperfusion. *Am. J. Physiol.* 261:H1578–84

63. Iwamoto T, Miura T, Adachi T, Noto T, Ogawa T, et al. 1991. Myocardial infarct size–limiting effect of ischemic preconditioning was not attenuated by oxygen free–radical scavengers in the rabbit. *Circulation* 83: 1015–22

64. Jennings RB, Murry CE, Reimer KA. 1991. Preconditioning myocardium with ischemia. *Cardiovasc. Drugs Ther.* 5: 933–38

65. Jerome SN, Akimitsu T, Korthuis, RJ. 1994. Leukocyte adhesion, edema, and the development of postischemic capillary no-reflow. *Am. J. Physiol.* 267: H1329–36

66. Jerome SN, Dore M, Paulson JC, Smith CW, Korthuis RJ. 1994. P-selectin and ICAM-1 dependent adherence reactions: role in the genesis of postischemic capillary no-reflow. *Am. J. Physiol.* 266: H1316–21

67. Jerome SN, Korthuis RJ. 1994. Ischemic preconditioning attenuates postischemic

capillary no-reflow: role of ATP–sensitive potassium channels. *FASEB J.* 8:A129 (Abstr.)

68. Jerome SN, Smith CW, Korthuis RJ. 1993. CD18–dependent adherence reactions play an important role in the development of the no-reflow phenomenon. 1993. *Am. J. Physiol.* 263: H1637–42

69. Kida M, Fujiwara H, Ishida M, Kawai C, Ohura M, et al. 1991. Ischemic preconditioning preserves creatine phosphate and intracellular pH. *Circ. Res.* 84:2595–603

70. Kirsch GE, Codina J, Birnbaumer L, Brown AM. 1990. Coupling of ATP–sensitive K^+ channels to A_1 receptors by G proteins in rat ventricular myocytes. *Am. J. Physiol.* 259:H820–26

71. Kishimoto A, Takai Y, Mori T. 1990. Activation of calcium and phospholipid–dependent protein kinase by diacylglycerol, its possible relation to phosphatidylinositol turnover. *J. Biol. Chem.* 255:2273–76

72. Kishimoto TK, Jutila MA, Berg EL, Butcher EC. 1991. Neutrophil Mac-1 and MEL-14 adhesion proteins are inversely regulated by chemotactic factors. *Science* 245:1238–41

73. Kochanek PM, Hallenbeck JM. 1992. Polymorphonuclear leukocytes and monocytes/macrophages in the pathogenesis of cerebral ischemia and stroke. *Stroke* 23:1367–79

74. Kofsky ER, Julia PL, Buckberg GD, Quillen JE, Acar C. 1991. Studies of controlled reperfusion after ischemia. XXII. Reperfusate composition: effects of leukocyte depletion of blood and blood cardioplegic reperfusates after acute coronary occlusion. *J. Thor. Cardiovasc. Surg.* 101:350–59

75. Korthuis RJ, Anderson DC, Granger DN. 1994. Role of neutrophil–endothelial cell adhesion in inflammatory disorders. *J. Crit.* 9:47–71

76. Korthuis RJ, Granger DN. 1993. Reactive oxygen metabolites, neutrophils, and the pathogenesis of ischemic-tissue/reperfusion. *Clin. Cardiol.* 16:119–26

77. Korthuis RJ, Granger DN. 1992. Cellular dysfunction induced by ischemia/reperfusion: role of reactive oxygen metabolites and granulocytes. In *Biological Consequences of Oxidative Stress: Implications for Cardiovascular Disease and Carcinogenesis,* ed. L Spatz, AD Bloom, pp. 50–77. New York: Oxford Univ. Press

78. Korthuis RJ, Granger DN. 1986. Ischemia–reperfusion injury: role of oxy-

gen–derived free radicals. See Ref. 50, pp. 217–50

79. Korthuis RJ, Kubes P, Tso P, Perry M, Granger DN. 1991. Transport kinetics for superoxide dismutase and catalase between the plasma and interstitial fluid in the rat small intestine. *Free Rad. Biol. Med.* 11:293–98

80. Korthuis, RJ, Smith, JK, Carden, DL. 1989. Hypoxic reperfusion attenuates postischemic microvascular injury. *Am. J. Physiol.* 256:H315–19

81. Kramer JH, Arroyo CM, Dickens BF, Weglicki WB. 1987. Spin–trapping evidence that graded myocardial ischemia alters postischemic superoxide production. *Free Rad. Biol. Med.* 3:153–59

82. Kubes P. 1993. Ischemia–reperfusion in feline small intestine: a role for nitric oxide. *Am. J. Physiol.* 264:G143–49

83. Kubes P, Kanwar S, Niu X-F, Gaboury J. 1993. Nitric oxide synthesis inhibition induces leukocyte adhesion via superoxide and mast cells. *FASEB J.* 7:1293–99

84. Kubes P, Suzuki M, Granger DN. 1991. Nitric oxide: an endogenous modulator of leukocyte adhesion. *Proc. Natl. Acad. Sci. USA* 88:4651–55

85. Kurose I, Anderson DC, Miyasaka M, Tamatani T, Paulson JC, et al. 1994. Molecular determinants of reperfusion–induced leukocyte adhesion and vascular protein leakage. *Circ. Res.* 74(2): 336–43

86. Kurose I, Kubes P, Wolf RE, Anderson, DC, Paulson JC, et al. 1993. Inhibition of nitric oxide production: mechanisms of vascular albumin leakage. *Circ. Res.* 73:164–71

87. Kurose I, Wolf R, Grisham MB, Granger DN. 1994. Modulation of ischemia/ reperfusion–induced microvascular dysfunction by nitric oxide. *Circ. Res.* 74: 376–82

88. Kusuoka H, Marban E. 1992. Cellular mechanisms of myocardial stunning. *Annu. Rev. Physiol.* 54:243–56

89. Lawrence MB, McIntire LV, Eskin SG. 1987. Effect of flow on polymorphonuclear leukocyte/endothelial cell adhesion. *Blood* 70:1284–90

90. Lefer AM, Siegfried MR, Ma X-l. 1993. Protection of ischemia–reperfusion injury by sydnonimine NO donors via inhibition of neutrophil–endothelium interaction. *J. Cardiol. Pharm.* 22:S27–33

91. Lefer DJ, Nakanishi K, Johnston WE, Vinten-Johansen J. 1993. Antineutrophil and myocardial protecting actions of a novel nitric oxide donor after acute myocardial ischemia and reperfusion in dogs. *Circulation* 88:2337–50

92. Lehr HA, Guhlmann A, Nolte D, Messmer K. 1991. Leukotrienes as mediators in ischemia–reperfusion injury in a microcirculation model in the hamster. *J. Clin. Invest.* 87:2036–41

93. Li Y, Kloner RA. 1992. Cardioprotective effects of ischemia preconditioning are not mediated by prostanoids. *Cardiol. Res.* 26:226–31

94. Lindsay T, Walker P, Mickle D, Romaschin A. 1988. Measurement of hydroxy conjugated dienes after ischemia/ reperfusion in canine skeletal muscle. *Am. J. Physiol.* 254:H578–83

95. Lo SK, Janakidevi K, Lai L, Malik AB. 1993. Hydrogen peroxide–induced increase in endothelial adhesiveness is dependent on ICAM-1 activation. *Am. J. Physiol.* 264:L406–12

96. Lucchesi BR, Mickelson JK, Homeister JW, Jackson CV. 1987. Interaction of formed elements of blood with the coronary vasculature in vivo. *Fed. Proc.* 46:63–72

97. Ma X-L, Lefer DJ, Lefer AM, Rothlein R. 1993. Coronary endothelial and cardiac protective effects of a monoclonal antibody to intercellular adhesion molecule-1 in myocardial ischemia and reperfusion. *Circulation* 86:937–46

98. Ma X-L, Tsao PS, Lefer AM. 1991. Antibody to CD-18 exerts endothelial and cardiac protective effects in myocardial ischemia and reperfusion. *J. Clin. Invest.* 88:1237–43

99. Ma X-L, Weyrich AS, Lefer DJ, Lefer, AM. 1993. Diminished basal nitric oxide release after myocardial ischemia and reperfusion promotes neutrophil adherence to coronary endothelium. *Circ. Res.* 72:403–12

100. Mason RP, Morehouse M. 1989. Electron spin resonance investigations of oxygen–centered free radicals in biological systems. In *Oxygen Radicals in Biology and Medicine*, ed. MG Simic, KA Taylor, JF Ward, C von Sonntag 49:75–79. New York: Plenum

101. Matheis G, Sherman MP, Buckberg GD, Haybron DM, Young HH, Ignarro LJ. 1992. Role of L-arginine-nitric oxide pathway in myocardial reoxygenation injury. *Am. J. Physiol.* 262:H616–20

102. Mayhan WG. 1993. Role of nitric oxide in leukotriene C4–induced increases in microvascular transport. *Am. J. Physiol.* 265:H409–14

103. Mayhan WG. 1992. Role of nitric oxide in modulating permeability of hamster cheek pouch in response to adenosine 5′-diphosphate and bradykinin. *Inflammation* 16:No. 4

104. McCord JM, Fridovich I. 1969. Super-

oxide dismutase. An enzymic function for erythrocuprein (hemocuprein). *J. Biol. Chem.* 244:6049–55

105. McEver RP. 1991 Selectins: novel receptors that mediate leukocyte adhesion during inflammation. *Thromb. Haemostasis* 65:223–28

106. Milhoan KA, Lane TA, Bloor CM. 1992. Hypoxia induces endothelial cells to increase their adherence for neutrophils: role of PAF. *Am. J. Physiol.* 263:H956–62

107. Mori E, del Zoppo GJ, Chambers JD, Copeland BR, Arfors KE. 1992. Inhibition of polymorphonuclear leukocyte adherence suppresses no-reflow after focal cerebral ischemia in baboons. *Stroke* 23:712–18

108. Morris JB, Haglund U, Bulkley GB. 1987. The protection from postischemic injury by xanthine oxidase inhibition: blockade of free radical generation or purine salvage. *Gastroenterology* 92:1542–47

109. Miura T, Goto M, Uraki K, Endoh A, Shimamoto K, Iimura O. 1991. Does myocardial stunning contribute to infarct size reduction limitation by ischemic preconditioning? *Circulation* 84:2504–12

110. Mullane KM, Read N, Salmon JA. 1984. Role of leukocytes in acute myocardial infarction in anesthetized dogs: relationship to myocardial salvage by anti–inflammatory drugs. *J. Pharmacol. Exp. Therap.* 228:510–22

111. Mulligan MS, Hevel JM, Marletta MA, Ward PA. 1991. Tissue injury caused by deposition of immune complexes is L-arginine–dependent. *Proc. Natl. Acad. Sci. USA* 88:6338–42

112. Murry CE, Jennings RB, Reimer KA. 1986. Preconditioning with ischemia: a delay of lethal cell injury in ischemic myocardium. *Circulation* 74:1124–36

113. Murry CE, Richard VJ, Reimer KA, Jennings RB. 1990. Ischemic preconditioning slows energy metabolism and delays ultrastructural damage during a sustained ischemic episode. *Circ. Res.* 66:913–31

114. Noma A. 1983. ATP–regulated K⁺ channels in cardiac muscle. *Nature* 205:147–48

115. Olah ME, Stiles GL. 1992. Adenosine receptors. *Annu. Rev. Physiol.* 54:211–25

116. Oliver MG, Specian RD, Perry MA, Granger DN. 1991. Morphologic assessment of leukocyte–endothelial cell interactions in mesenteric venules subjected to ischemia and reperfusion. *Inflammation* 15:331–46

117. Deleted in proof

118. Osada M, Sato T, Komori S, Tamura K. 1991. Protective effect of preconditioning on reperfusion induced ventricular arrhythmias of isolated rat heart. *Cardiovasc. Res.* 25:441–44

119. Oseas R, Yang H, Baener RL. 1981. Lactoferrin: a promoter of polymorphonuclear leukocyte adhesiveness. *Blood* 57:939–45

120. Paller MS. 1988. Hemoglobin– and myoglobin–induced acute renal failure in rats: role of iron in nephrotoxicity. *Am. J. Physiol.* 255:F539–44

121. Parks DA, Granger DN. 1986. Contributions of ischemia and reperfusion to mucosal lesion formation. *Am. J. Physiol.* 250:G749–53

122. Parks DA, Granger DN. 1986. Xanthine oxidase: biochemistry, distribution, and physiology. *Acta Physiol. Scand.* 548:87–100

123. Parks DA, Shah AK, Granger DN. 1984. Oxygen radicals: effects on intestinal vascular permeability. *Am. J. Physiol.* 247:G167–70

124. Patel KM, Zimmerman GA, Prescott SM, McEver RP, McIntyre TM. 1991. Oxygen radicals induce human endothelial cells to express GMP-140 and bind neutrophils. *J. Cell Biol.* 112:749–59

125. Paully O, Morliere L, Gris JC, Bonne C, Modat G. 1992. Hypoxia/reoxygenation stimulates endothelium to promote neutrophil adhesion. *Free Rad. Biol. Med.* 13:21–30

126. Pang CH, Forrest CR, Mounsey R. 1993. Pharmacologic intervention in ischemia–induced reperfusion injury in the skeletal muscle. *Microsurgery* 14:176–82

127. Payne D, Kubes P. 1993. Nitric oxide donors reduce the rise in reperfusion–induced intestinal mucosal permeability. *Am. J. Physiol.* 265:G189–95

128. Perry MA, Granger DN. 1992. Leukocyte adhesion in local versus hemorrhage–induced ischemia. *Am. J. Physiol.* 263:H810–15

129. Perry MA, Granger DN. 1991. Role of CD11/CD18 in shear rate–dependent leukocyte–endothelial cell interactions in cat mesenteric venules. *J. Clin. Invest.* 87:1798–804

130. Perry MA, Wadhaw SS. 1988. Gradual reintroduction of oxygen reduces reperfusion injury in cat stomach. *Am. J. Physiol.* 254:366–72

131. Petrone WF, English DK, Wong K, McCord JM. 1980. Free radicals and inflammation: superoxide–dependent activation of a neutrophil chemotactic factor

in plasma. *Proc. Natl. Acad. Sci. USA* 77:1150–63

132. Przyklenk K, Whittaker P, Kloner RA. 1990. In vivo infusion of oxygen free radical substrates causes myocardial systolic, but not diastolic, dysfunction. *Am. Heart J.* 119:807–15

133. Ramos CL, Pou S, Britigan BE, Cohen MS, Rosen GM. 1992. Spin trapping evidence for myeloperoxidase–dependent hydroxyl radical formation by human neutrophils and monocytes. *J. Biol. Chem.* 267:8307–12

134. Reimer KA, Murray CE, Richard VJ. 1989. The role of neutrophils and free radicals in the ischemic–reperfused heart: why the confusion and controversy? *J. Mol. Cell Cardiol.* 21:1225–39

135. Richardt G, Wass W, Kranzhofer R, Mayer E, Schomig A. 1987. Adenosine inhibits exocytotic release of endogenous noradrenaline in rat heart: a protective mechanism in early myocardial ischemia. *Circ. Res.* 61:117–23

136. Romson JL, Hook BG, Kunkel SL, Abrams GD, Schork MA. 1983. Reduction of the extent of ischemic myocardial injury by neutrophil depletion in the dog. *Circulation* 67:1016–23

137. Rubin BB. 1991. *Mechanisms of prolonged skeletal muscle reperfusion injury.* PhD thesis. Univ. Toronto

138. Rubin BB, Chang G, Liauw S, Young A, Romaschin A, Walker PM. 1992. Phospholipid peroxidation deacylation and remodeling in postischemic skeletal muscle. *Am. J. Physiol.* 263:H1695–702

139. Schoenberg MH, Poch B, Younes M, Schwarz A, Baczako K. 1991. Involvement of neutrophils in postischaemic damage to the small intestine. *Gut* 32:905–12

140. Seekamp A, Mulligan MS, Till GO, Ward PA. 1993. Requirements for neutrophil products and L-arginine in ischemia–reperfusion injury. *Am. J. Pathol.* 142:1–10

141. Seewaldt-Becker E, Rothlein R, Dammgen JW. 1989. CD18 dependent adhesion of leukocytes to endothelium and its relevance for cardiac reperfusion. In *Leukocyte Adhesion Molecules,* ed. T Springer, DC Anderson, A Rosenthal, R Rothlein, pp. 138–48. New York: Springer-Verlag

142. Shiga Y, Onodera H, Kogure K, Yamasaki Y, Yashima Y. 1991. Neutrophil as a mediator of ischemic edema formation in the brain. *Neurosci. Lett.* 125:110–12

143. Shingu M, Nobunaga M. 1984. Chemotactic activity generated in human serum from the fifth component of complement

by hydrogen peroxide. *Am. J. Pathol.* 117:201–6

144. Smith CW, Marlin SD, Rothlein R, Lawrence MB, McIntire LV, Anderson DC. 1990. Role of ICAM-1 in the adherence of human neutrophils to human endothelial cells in vitro. In *Leukocyte Adhesion Molecules: Structure, Function, and Regulation,* ed. TA Springer, DC Anderson, AS Rosenthal, R Rothlein, pp. 170–89. New York: Springer-Verlag

145. Smith JK, Carden DL, Grisham MB, Granger DN, Korthuis RJ. 1989. Role of iron in postischemic microvascular injury. *Am. J. Physiol.* 256:H1472–77

146. Smith JK, Carden DL, Korthuis RJ. 1989. Role of xanthine oxidase in postischemic microvascular injury in skeletal muscle. *Am. J. Physiol.* 257:H1782–89

147. Smith SM, Holm-Rutili LH, Perry MA, Grisham MB, Arfors KE. 1987. Role of neutrophils in hemorrhagic shock–induced gastric mucosal injury in the rat. *Gastroenterology* 93:466–71

148. Springer T. 1990. Adhesion receptors of the immune system. *Nature* 346:425–34

149. Suzuki M, Asako H, Kubes P, Jennings S, Grisham MB, Granger DN. 1991. Neutrophil–derived oxidants promote leukocyte adherence in postcapillary venules. *Microvasc. Res.* 42:125–38

150. Suzuki M, Grisham MB, Granger DN. 1991. Leukocyte–endothelial cell interactions: role of xanthine oxidase–derived oxidants. *J. Leuk. Biol.* 50:488–94

151. Suzuki M, Inauen W, Kvietys PR, Grisham MB, Meininger C, et al. 1989. Superoxide mediates reperfusion–induced leukocyte–endothelial cell interactions. *Am. J. Physiol.* 257:H1740–45

152. Tan HL, Mazon P, Verberne HJ, Sleeswijk ME, Coronel R, et al. 1993. Ischaemic preconditioning delays ischaemia–induced cellular electrical coupling in rabbit myocardium by activation of ATP–sensitive potassium channels. *Cardiol. Res.* 27:644–51

153. Terada LS, Dormish JJ, Shanley PF, Leff J, Anderson BO, Repine JE. 1992. Circulating xanthine oxidase mediates lung neutrophil sequestration after intestinal ischemia-reperfusion. *Am. J. Physiol.* 263:L394–401

154. Thornton J, Striplin S, Liu GS, Swafford A, Stanley AWH, et al. 1990. Inhibition of protein synthesis does not block myocardial protection afforded by preconditioning. *Am. J. Physiol.* 259: H1822–25

155. Thornton JD, Liu GS, Downey JM.

1993. Pretreatment with pertussis toxin blocks the protective effects of preconditioning: evidence for a G-protein mechanism. *J. Mol. Cell Cardiol.* 25:311–20

156. Thornton JD, Thornton CS, Sterling DL, Downey JM. 1993. Blockade of ATP–sensitive potassium channels increases infarct size but does not prevent preconditioning in rabbit hearts. *Circ. Res.* 72:44–49

157. Tsushima RG, Moffat MP. 1990. Differential effects of purine/xanthine oxidase on the electrophysiologic characteristics of ventricular tissues. *J. Cardiovasc. Pharmacol.* 16:50–58

158. Turren JF, Crapo JD, Freeman BA. 1984. Protection against oxygen toxicity by intravenous injection of liposome–entrapped catalase and superoxide dismutase. *J. Clin. Invest.* 73:87–95

159. Van Winkle DM, Chien GL, Wolff RA, Soifer BE, Kuzume K, Davis RF. 1994. Cardioprotection provided by adenosine receptor activation is abolished by blockade of the K_{ATP} channel. *Am. J. Physiol.* 266:H829–39

160. Vegh A, Papp JG, Szekeres L, Parratt JR. 1993. Are ATP sensitive potassium channels involved in the pronounced antiarrhythmic effects of preconditioning? *Cardiol. Res.* 27:638–43

161. Vogt W, von Zabern I, Hesse D, Nolte R, Haller Y. 1987. Generation of activated form of human C5 (C6b-like C5) by oxygen radicals. *Immunol. Lett.* 14:209–15

162. Walker DM, Yellon DM. 1992. Ischaemic preconditioning: from mechanisms to exploitation. *Cardiol. Res.* 26:734–39

163. Walker PM, Lindsay TF, Labbe R, Mickle DA, Romaschin AD. 1987. Salvage of skeletal muscle with free radical scavengers. *J. Vasc. Surg.* 5:68–75

164. Weiss SJ. 1989. Tissue destruction by neutrophils. *N. Engl. J. Med.* 320:365–76

165. Weselcouch EO, Grove RI, Demusz CD, Baird AJ. 1991. Effect of in vivo inhibition of neutrophil adherence on skeletal muscle function during ischemia in ferrets. *Am. J. Physiol.* 261:H1178–83

166. Weselcouch EO, Sargent C, Wilde MW, Smith MA. 1993. ATP–sensitive potassium channels and skeletal muscle function in vitro. *J. Pharm. Exper. Therap.* 267:410–16

167. Weyrich AS, Ma X, Lefer DJ, Albertine KH, Lefer AM. 1993. In vivo neutralization of P-selectin protects feline heart and endothelium in myocardial ischemia and reperfusion injury. *J. Clin. Invest.* 91:2620–29

168. Wink DA, Hanbauer I, Krishna MC, DeGraff W, Gamson J, Mitchell JB. 1993. Nitric oxide protects against cellular damage and cytotoxicity from reactive oxygen species. *Proc. Natl. Acad. Sci. USA* 90:9813–17

169. Worthen GS, Schwab B, Elson EL, Downey GP. 1989. Cellular mechanics of stimulated neutrophils: stiffening of cells induces retention in pores in vitro and lung capillaries in vivo. *Science* 245:183–86

170. Wright JG, Fox D, Kerr JC, Valeri CR, Hobson RW. 1988. Rate of reperfusion blood flow modulates reperfusion injury in skeletal muscle. *J. Surg. Res.* 44:754–59

171. Wyatt DA, Edmunds MC, Rubio R, Berne RM, Lasley RD. 1989. Adenosine stimulates glycolytic flux in isolated perfused rat hearts by A_1 adenosine receptors. *Am. J. Physiol.* 254:H1952–57

172. Yao Z, Gross GJ. 1993. Role of nitric oxide, muscarinic receptors, and the ATP–sensitive K^+ channel in mediating the effects of acetylcholine to mimic preconditioning in dogs. *Circ. Res.* 73: 1193–201

173. Yao Z, Gross GJ. 1993. Glibenclamide antagonizes adenosine A_1 receptor–mediated cardioprotection in stunned canine myocardium. *Circulation* 88: 235–44

174. Yoshida N, Granger DN, Anderson DC, Kvietys PR. 1992. Anoxia/reoxygenation induced neutrophil adherence to cultured endothelial cells. *Am. J. Physiol.* 262:H1891–98

175. Ytrehus K, Liu Y, Downey JM. 1994. Preconditioning protects ischemic rabbit heart by protein kinase C activation. *Am. J. Physiol.* 266:H1145–52

176. Yuan Y, Granger HJ, Zawieja DC, Chilian WM. 1992. Flow modulates coronary venular permeability by a nitric oxide–related mechanism. *Am. J. Physiol.* 263:H641–46

177. Zimmerman BJ, Granger DN. 1990. Reperfusion–induced leukocyte infiltration: role of elastase. *Am. J. Physiol.* 259:H390–94

178. Zimmerman BJ, Grisham MB, Granger DN. 1990. Role of oxidants in ischemia/reperfusion–induced granulocyte infiltration. *Am. J. Physiol.* 258:G185–90

179. Zimmerman BJ, Holt JW, Paulson JC, Anderson DC, Miyasaka M, et al. 1994. Molecular determinants of lipid mediator–induced leukocyte adherence and emigration in rat mesenteric venules. *Am. J. Physiol.* 266:H847–53

180. Zughaib M, Xiao YL, Jeroudi MO,

Hartley CJ, Bolli R. 1993. Oxidative stress in the pathogenesis of postischemic ventricular dysfunction (myocardial "stunning"). In *Oxygen Free Radicals in Tissue Damage,* ed. M Tarr, F Samson, pp. 211–49. Boston: Birkhauser

181. Zweier JL, Flaherty JT, Weisfeldt ML. 1987. Direct measurement of free radical generation following reperfusion of ischemic myocardium. *Proc. Natl. Acad. Sci. USA* 84:1404–7

Annu. Rev. Physiol. 1995. 57:333–53

MECHANOSENSITIVE CHANNELS

Henry Sackin

Department of Physiology and Biophysics, Cornell University Medical College, New York, NY 10021

KEY WORDS: stretch, volume regulation, ion channels, channel regulation

---

INTRODUCTION

Mechanosensitive or stretch-activated (SA) channels respond to membrane stress by changes in open probability. These channels exist in auditory cells, stretch receptors, muscle spindles, vascular endothelium, and other neurosensory tissues where their physiological function seems readily apparent. It is less obvious why nonexcitable cells such as those of blood and epithelial tissues need channels that respond to mechanical stimuli, although all cells must cope with the dual problems of volume regulation and electrolyte homeostasis. Regulation of cell growth may also require specific mechanotransducers that detect physical changes in cell size and shape. Thus the abnormal growth of cancer cells could involve a breakdown of such a mechanotransduction system.

In an attempt to group SA channels into logical categories, a functional rather than phylogenetic scheme is stressed, with an emphasis on volume regulation and electrolyte homeostasis. The properties that characterize SA channels are considered and the various hypotheses for electro-mechanical transduction reviewed. Finally, the important question of how SA channels might be involved in the physiological regulation of transport and volume is addressed. This treatment of SA channels is not intended to be all–inclusive, and the reader is referred to reviews that deal more extensively with the growing family of mechanosensitive channels (35, 52, 66).

333

FUNCTIONAL CLASSIFICATION OF SA CHANNELS

SA Cation Channels

SA or mechanosensitive cation channels have been identified in choroid plexus (11), corneal epithelium (14), neuroblastoma cells (23), osteoblasts (20), Ehrlich ascites tumor cells (35), opossum kidney cells (82), *Xenopus* oocytes (85), aortic endothelial cells (45), amphibian smooth muscle cells (43), frog diluting segments (39), basolateral membrane of frog proximal tubule (38), and apical membrane of *Necturus* renal proximal tubule (24).

Despite diverse tissues of origin, these SA cation channels share a number of characteristics. They are consistently cation selective with single channel conductance ranging from 25 to 35 pS (in Na, K solutions). They display significant permeability to divalent cations, which allows measurable Ca influx into cells during stretch. They are consistently blocked by micromolar concentrations of the trivalent lanthanide gadolinium (24, 85).

CELL VOLUME REGULATION   The significant calcium permeability of the SA cation channel raises the possibility that Ca functions as a second messenger for translating mechanical stress into regulation of ion transport, which would be particularly appropriate for volume regulation. In the choroid plexus, hypotonic shock activates Ca-dependent maxi K channels, possibly by stimulation of SA cation channels (11) and conseqent Ca influx, resulting in elevation of cytosolic Ca to micromolar levels near the membrane.

The SA cation channel is also implicated in hypotonic activation of two epithelial K channels: a small conductance (15 pS) Ca-dependent K channel in opossum kidney cells (81), and a large conductance (150 pS) K channel in cultured renal, medullary thick ascending limb cells (80). Stretch and osmotic activation of both channels appear to depend on extracellular Ca.

Although calcium appears to be important for normal regulatory volume decrease (RVD) in a number of epithelial preparations (33, 56, 84), fluorescence measurements of cytosolic Ca in rabbit proximal tubule during cell swelling suggest that the changes in free intracellular Ca during swelling are too small to activate Ca–dependent maxi K channels (4).

Another problem with the SA cation channel as a volume regulator is that cation-selective channels allow Na influx as well as K efflux. Any significant entry of Na offsets the volume regulatory effect of Ca-dependent K efflux. One way around this problem would be for the cell to use Ca as a biological amplifier so that a relatively small influx of Ca gates a large efflux of K. The steep Ca dependence of the maxi K channel makes it a possible candidate for an amplification scheme. However, such a volume control system would also require Na levels in the cell to be under tight regulation by an independent

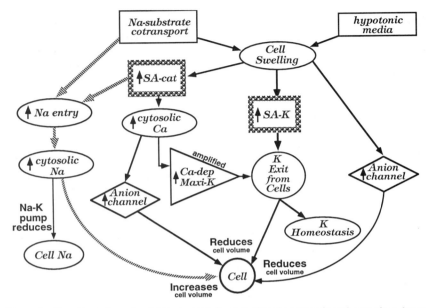

Figure 1   Hypothesis for role of SA channels in electrolyte homeostasis and osmotic volume regulation. See text for explanation of pathways. Solid arrows denote paths for regulatory volume decrease; dashed arrows denote a parallel path that could interfere with volume and electrolyte homeostasis.

system. Figure 1 is a flow chart of a hypothetical scheme for how SA cation channels and SA-K channels might be involved in volume regulation and K homeostasis.

Calcium permeation through SA cation channels may also regulate chloride currents essential for hypotonic volume regulation. The finding of several types of Ca-activated chloride currents in *Xenopus* oocytes (2, 6, 10) raises the possibility that oocyte volume regulation is mediated by swelling-induced Ca permeation through SA channels.

MORPHOGENESIS   In contrast to the oocytes of freshwater animals, the oocytes of ocean-dwelling ascidians (like the sea squirt *Boltenia villosa*) are not subjected to the hypotonic stress of freshwater ovulation. The existence of the same SA cation channels in oocytes of both freshwater *Xenopus* and saltwater ascidians suggests that mechanosensitive channels may have functions besides volume regulation (50). Specifically, mechanosensitive channels may be important in the cytokinetic events associated with morphogenesis and embryonic development. The dramatic changes in cell shape that occur during cleavage cycles of the early embryo could produce sufficient increases in membrane tension to induce Ca influx via these SA cation channels. This influx of Ca coupled with release of Ca from intracellular stores could trigger active contraction of cytoskeletal elements essential for the morphogenic movements associated with gastrulation. For example, there is evidence that Ca entry via SA cation channels stimulates a propagated stretch-activated contraction that causes neural tube closure in developing oocytes (55).

The relative high density of SA channels would not only favor significant influx of Ca during cytokinesis but might also depolarize the oocyte sufficiently to allow further entry of Na and Ca via voltage-gated channels (50). Because the SA cation channel persists from pre-fertilization through the early stages of morphogenesis, it may help to orchestrate the complex pattern of appearance and disappearance of Na, Ca, and K currents during embryogenesis.

CAPILLARY ENDOTHELIUM   The SA cation channel may also be involved in mechanotransduction of shear stress forces in blood vessels. Studies on cultured endothelial cells from pig aorta reveal a cation-selective channel with a single channel conductance that varies from 39 pS in physiological saline solutions to 19 pS in solutions where calcium is the primary current-carrying ion (45). Similar SA cation channels have been reported in cells isolated from pig coronary arteries where single channel conductance varied from 36 pS in normal K solutions to 11 pS in high Ca solutions (17). This raises the possibility that changes in blood pressure and shear stress associated with flow over the capillary endothelium are sufficient to turn on SA cation channels. The relatively high selectivity of these channels ($P_{Ca}/P_{Na} = 6$) (45) could permit sufficient entry of Ca to stimulate synthesis and release of endothelial relaxing factor and subsequent vascular vasodilation.

OSTEOBLASTS AND LENS   Osteoblasts at the surface of bone matrix are instrumental in synthesizing bone matrix proteins. Clonal UMR-106 cells derived from rat osteogenic sarcoma possess an 18 pS SA channel capable of conducting barium and calcium into the cell (20). This channel is voltage insensitive, but its susceptibility to membrane tension suggests a role in volume regulation or as a stimulus for bone metabolism in response to mechanical stress. The finding of three types of SA channels in human osteoblast osteosarcoma G292 cells (16) lends weight to this suggestion.

A mechanosensitive channel has also been seen in amphibian lens preparations (14). Its ion selectivity is similar to SA cation selectivity, but it has a slightly higher single channel conductance, 50 pS compared with the 20–30 pS of other SA cation channels. Because it is the only channel in the lens that appears to be stretch sensitive, it is distinguished by the label CAT-50. This channel could play a role in cataract formation because any increase in lens pressure would activate CAT-50s and allow abnormal amounts of Na, Ca, and water to enter the cell. The influx of Na would also depolarize the lens, which would produce a greater driving force for K exit. An increase in Na and decrease in K are, indeed, observed in many types of cataracts.

PLANT CELLS   An interesting variety of SA cation channels is found in plant and fungus cells. Opening of SA ion channels may play a crucial role in the geotrophic response of plants by selectively permitting Ca entry into cells responsible for root orientation. The finding that micromolar concentrations of gadolinium block this trophic response suggests that the SA channels of plant cells are similar to the SA cation channels of animal cells (49).

A much larger conductance SA cation channel has been reported in membrane patches of the fungus *Uromyces* (86). This mechanosensitive channel is permeable to divalent ions like Ca, blocked by low concentrations of gadolinium, but has a single channel conductance of 600 pS, a value more than 20 times the conductance of most SA cation channels in animal cells. This mechanosensitive channel does not seem to be involved in volume regulation but does seem to be essential for allowing the fungus to gain entry into wheat and bean plants. SA plant channels are more involved in transducing topographical and geotropic signals than in maintaining cell homeostasis. In higher plants, mechanosensitive channels may transduce mechanical (i.e. gravitational) signals into elevations in cytoplasmic Ca, thereby causing membrane kinases to selectively phosphorylate specific transporters of gravitropic hormones (62, 63).

SA Potassium Channels

In addition to the large SA cation family of mechanosensitive channels, there are smaller families of mechanosensitive channels that are less widely distributed among species but are more selective for particular ions. SA channels displaying a predominant selectivity for K are labeled SAKs and can be grouped into two broad classes based on their sensitivity to Ca.

Ca-INSENSITIVE SAKS   A flickery K-selective SA channel with two open and three closed states has been reported in molluscan heart cells (73). The spontaneous activity of this ventricular SAK, in the absence of applied stretch, raises the possibility that it contributes to the normal resting potential. Application of pipette suction up to 25 mmHg dramatically increased the P_o of this channel without altering its selectivity or its 33 pS single channel conductance.

Two types of SAK channels were found at the basolateral membrane of *Necturus* proximal tubule: (*a*) a short open-time flickery SAK with conductance of about 45 pS and mean open-time on the order of 1.5 ms (25, 68); and (*b*) a longer open-time SAK with conductance of about 30 pS and mean open-time between 40 and 50 ms (25, 40). In addition to being activated by pipette suction, these K channels were also sensitive to osmotic swelling. Hyposmotic solutions increased P_o without changes in conductance or channel selectivity in K depolarized cells (69) as well as cells maintained in Na-Ringer solutions (25). Since hypotonic volume regulation depends on an efflux of cellular cations, any channel with a significant selectivity for K over Na would be useful in restoring cell volume.

Ca-SENSITIVE SAKS   A number of preparations exist in which what appear to be maxi K channels also display a direct sensitivity to stretch. The channels retain their characteristic steep dependence on voltage and Ca sensitivity but also respond directly to increases in membrane tension, even when Ca concentrations are tightly controlled. Maxi K channels have been identified at the apical membrane of rat and rabbit cortical collecting tubule (CCT) that react independently to the three variables: voltage, cytosolic Ca, and membrane stretch (61).

Mechanosensitive K(Ca) channels have also been reported in osteoblast cell lines (15) and pulmonary smooth muscle (42). In pulmonary smooth muscle experiments, four distinct types of stimuli were effective in increasing the P_o of this large conductance K channel: cytosolic Ca, cell depolarization, membrane stretch, and exogenous fatty acids, where the effect of stretch does not seem to be mediated by calcium. This was elegantly demonstrated by applying pipette suction to a series of excised (inside-out) patches with 5 mM EGTA and no added Ca on both sides of the patch. It is interesting that these channels were also activated by fatty acids via a mechanism that did not seem to involve formation of biologically active metabolites, phosphorylation, or Ca. This effect raises the possibility that increases in membrane tension stimulate a membrane–bound phospholipase to release endogenous fatty acids that then activate the channel.

SA Anion Channels

Mechanosensitive anion channels are not as prevalent as SA cation or SAK channels. Most mechanosensitive anion channels are large (>300 pS) and often subject to regulation by specific chemical mediators as well as by stretch. For example, a 305–pS mechanosensitive anion–selective channel has been described in a cell line (RCCT-28A) that has the phenotype of α-intercalated renal CCT cells. Both pipette suction and hyposmotic solutions activated this channel, which suggests that it might be involved in hyposmotic volume regulation (76). In addition, exposing these cells to dihydrocytochalasin B dramatically increased the stretch sensitivity of the channel (77).

Of particular importance is the identification and reconstitution of two bacterial mechanosensitive ion channels from *Escherichia coli* spheroblasts

(78, 79): a large conductance (3000 pS) nonselective channel, referred to as *MscL*, and a smaller conductance (900 pS) anion-selective channel with nomenclature *MscS*. The latter is similar to the 650–970 pS mechanosensitive channel that may be important in *E. coli* volume regulation (47). *MscS* also appears to be activated by amphipathic compounds via a mechanism that may be related to its mechanosensitivity (46).

The *MscL* channel was cloned and identified as a relatively small (136 amino acids) protein that retained its mechanosensitive activity when reconstituted into liposomes. Hence, the protein itself appears to contain the complete machinery for translating membrane tension into changes in open probability. This could pave the way for understanding the unique structural requirements for mechanosensitivity in a variety of SA channel types.

Stretch-Activated Nonselective Channels and Stretch-Inactivated Channels

Truly nonselective channels (SA non), which exhibit little discrimination between anions and cations, are relatively rare in eukaryotic cells. Perhaps the best example of a nonselective mechanosensitive channel in higher animals is the 22 pS mechanosensitve channel found in opossum kidney cells (81, 82). This channel was activated equally well by either pipette suction or hypotonic shock and exhibited a significant permeability to Ca as well as small monovalent ions. It may play an important role in renal cell volume regulation.

Nonselective channels are more common in bacteria and yeast. The very large conductance (3000 pS) *MscL E. coli* channel (see above) can be contrasted with the much smaller (36 pS) nonselective channel in yeast plasma membrane that has been studied at both the whole cell and single channel level (31). Although this yeast channel is blocked by 10 µM gadolinium, its inability to select between cations and anions and its kinetic response to suction distinguish it from the SA cation family of mechanosensitive channels.

Stretch-inactivated channels (SI) are also relatively rare. However, they have now been identified in dystrophic muscle from *mdx* mice (27), toad gastric smooth muscle (34), astrocytes (18), snail neurons (54), and atrial myocytes (83). Their presence in dystrophic muscle is particularly intriguing because normal muscle contains a high proportion of SA channels and almost no SI channels (2%), whereas dystrophic muscle contains a much higher proportion of SI channels. The significant P_0 and Ca permeability of SI channels in dystrophic muscle could account for the elevated Ca seen in *mdx* myotubes (26).

The coexistence of SA and SI channels in the same preparation functions as a "notch filter," where the effective P_0 of both channels reaches a minimum within a narrow region of membrane tension. For example, in snail neuron, K-selective SA and SI channels together produce a minimum K cell permeability in a region of intermediate membrane tension (54). Within this region, the cell is sufficiently depolarized to render voltage-gated Ca channels hyper-excitable. This might have important consequences for neuronal growth cone motility (52).

THE MECHANICS OF STRETCH ACTIVATION

Properties Common to SA Channels

Despite profound differences in kinetics, ion selectivity, and stretch sensitivity, there are a surprising number of properties common to the different classes of SA channels. In all SA channels studied to date, mechanical stimuli induce an increase in open probability without significant changes in either single chan-nel conductance or ion selectivity. This preservation of selectivity and con-ductance reinforces the notion that membrane stretch gates the channel. At high levels of suction, "breakdown currents" do occur, but these can be readily distinguished from discrete openings that characterize channel currents.

Stretch activation is a membrane or membrane-cytoskeleton phenomenon. It does not seem to involve soluble cytosolic messengers or insertion of pre-existing cytoplasmic channels. The principal evidence for this comes from the repeated observation that mechanosensitive channels can be stretch activated in cell–free excised patches. This effectively rules out mediators like Ca, ATP, etc, provided the excised patch is near the tip of the pipette. Nonetheless, a variable amount of cytoskeleton often remains attached to excised patches, and the stimulus for an increase in P_o may be more complicated than simply membrane tension. The reconstitution of fully functional bacterial SA channels in artificial liposomes suggests that tension is transduced to mechanosensitive channels directly via the lipid bilayer (79).

A COMMON KINETIC SCHEME   In addition to gross similarities in their general mode of activation, mechanosensitive channels also display subtle similarities in the kinetics of their activation. Most SA channels activate in bursts of flickery openings, although the extent of flicker seems to be greater in SAKs than SA cations. Figure 2A (taken from work on chick skeletal muscle) illustrates the general effect of suction on mechanosensitive cation currents (28).

The basic kinetic scheme for mechanosensitive channels was proposed by Sachs and others to explain the rapid bursting between sustained periods of inactivity. In the model of Figure 2B, there is one open state, with a mean open-time that is relatively unaffected by stretch (28). Three closed states are arranged in a linear fashion, where only the rate constant governing transitions

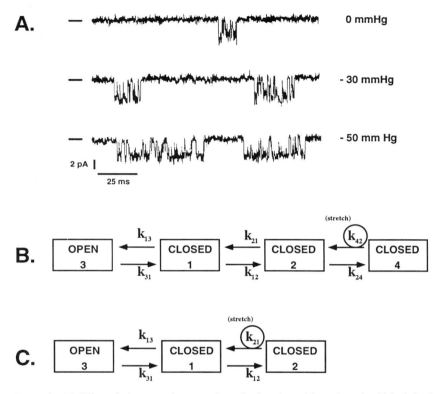

Figure 2 (*A*) Effect of pipette suction on cation-selective channel in embryonic chick skeletal muscle. Inward currents (down deflections) from an excised (inside-out) patch with 150 mM K in the pipette and normal saline in the bath. Pipette potential was + 50 mV with respect to the bath (reproduced from Figure 1, Reference 28). (*B*) Possible kinetic scheme for stretch activation of chick skeletal muscle cells. The mechanosensitive rate constant governs the transitions out of the longest closed state. (*C*) Variation of model B that is appropriate for amphibian preparations, in which the mechanosensitive rate constant governs transitions between the interburst closed state (2) and the flickery closed state (1).

out of the longest closed state is stretch sensitive. Mechanosensitive channels from amphibian proximal tubule have a similar kinetic scheme (Figure 2C), except that only two distinct closed states can be resolved (69). As with the first model, the predominant effect of pipette suction is to increase the rate constant (K_{21}) governing transitions out of the longest closed state.

SIGMOIDAL DEPENDENCE OF OPEN PROBABILITY   Early models for mechanosensitive gating relied on a strict application of Hooke's law to the elastic elements of the membrane with the result that the free energy of gating was dependent on the square of applied tension (21, 28, 52). This model predicted a sigmoid dependence similar to that of Equation 1, where K is a pressure independent constant, θ is the stretch sensitivity of the membrane, and T is the applied tension. Although Equation 1 has an empirical basis, and it is usually possible to obtain a good fit for the parameters K and θ, the underlying assumptions of a T^2 dependence are incomplete (67).

$$P_o = \frac{P_{max}}{1+K \cdot \exp\left[-\theta \cdot T^2\right]} \qquad 1.$$

A better representation for open probability can be derived by assuming that the free energy available for gating is linearly (rather than quadratically) related to applied tension T (37). Open probability, P_o, will still be a sigmoid function of tension, but the curve will have a slightly different shape and obey the equation

$$P_o = \frac{P_{max}}{1 + k_{eq} \cdot \exp\left[\dfrac{-T\Delta A - q \cdot V}{k\, T_k}\right]} \qquad 2.$$

where k_{eq} is the equilibrium constant for channel opening in the absence of stretch, ΔA is the increase in channel cross-sectional area during opening (where $\Delta A > 0$), q is the total gating charge (in coulombs) moving across the potential field during channel opening ($q > 0$), k is the Boltzman constant, and T_k is the absolute temperature in degrees Kelvin. The best representation is actually one that includes both a linear and quadratic dependence on membrane tension (T): where the linear term arises from the change in area associated with opening, and the quadratic dependence arises from the elastic energy stored in the channel (67).

ADAPTATION   Several varieties of SA channels exhibit a time-dependent decrease in P_o upon exposure to a constant or repeated pipette suction. This adaptation can be distinguished from inactivation because the channel remains sensitive to mechanical stimuli but with a reduced stretch sensitivity. Adaptation has been reported in *Xenopus* oocyte (32), yeast (31), and higher plants (63). It is independent of Ca and is evident at both the single channel (32) and whole cell level (29). Adaptation occurs at negative cell membrane potentials and is virtually abolished when the potential is clamped to a positive value. Since adaptation, but not mechanosensitivity, is easily abolished after strong suction, the mechanism of adaptation may involve membrane-cytoskeleton interactions that can be decoupled by mechanical stress (32).

Theories of Mechanosensitive Channel Activation

TENSION VS PRESSURE   Early studies of mechanosensitive channels often contained tacit assumptions about the equivalence of hydrostatic pressure and membrane tension. In thin-walled spheres, hydrostatic pressure (P) and wall tension (T) are related by Laplace's law, where d_c is the diameter of the sphere:

$$T = \frac{P \cdot d_c}{4} \hspace{4cm} 3.$$

The issue of pressure vs tension was addressed in whole cell clamps on yeast spheroblasts of various sizes (31). Whereas plots of mechanosensitive current vs applied pressure exhibited a clear dependence on spheroblast diameter, plots of current vs tension (calculated by Laplace's law) were independent of diameter. These studies indicate that membrane tension is the relevant parameter that controls SA channel activity.

IDEAL SPHERICAL CELL   If SA channels play a role in volume regulation, then it is reasonable to ask whether physiological changes in cell volume can produce sufficient membrane tension to activate mechanosensitive channels. Although many cell types possess elaborate infoldings that, by lowering the apparent elasticity coefficient, would minimize changes in membrane tension during swelling, it is still instructive to apply Laplace's law (Equation 3) as if the membrane were an ideal elastic system.

In this case, the additional membrane tension on a cell-attached patch (ΔT_p) that is associated with a relative increase in patch surface area $\Delta A/A$ can be described by a two-dimensional form of Hooke's law (28):

$$\Delta T = K_A (\Delta A / A) \hspace{4cm} 4.$$

where K_A is the area elasticity coefficient. This latter parameter can be estimated, given certain assumptions, from the hydrostatic pressure that produces lysis (22, 44). Similarly, a cell that increases its surface area during swelling would undergo a uniform increase in membrane tension as described by Equation 4.

The elasticity coefficient K_A is determined empirically, and the cell's $\Delta A/A$ is related to the relative change in cell volume $\Delta V/V$ by the surface/volume relation for an ideal sphere, Equation 5:

$$\left(\frac{\Delta A}{A}\right)_c = \left(1 + \frac{\Delta V}{V}\right)^{2/3} - 1 \hspace{3cm} 5.$$

Combining Equations 4 and 5, the increment in cell membrane tension associated with a given relative increase in cell volume $(\Delta V/V)$ is

$$\Delta T_c = K_A \cdot \left[\left(1 + \frac{\Delta V}{V} \right)^{2/3} - 1 \right]$$ 6.

We can use Equation 6 to estimate the increase in cell volume needed to generate sufficient membrane tension, T_c, to activate SA channels. If a cell is hypotonically swollen by 1% (i.e. $\Delta V/V = 0.01$), the relative volume factor in Equation 6 becomes

$$\left[\left(1 + \frac{\Delta V}{V} \right)^{2/3} - 1 \right] = (1.01)^{2/3} - 1 = 0.007$$ 7.

Assuming an elasticity coefficient K_A for the whole cell on the order of 12 dyne/cm (22, 44), the increase in membrane tension T_c that would occur in a cell subjected to a 1% increase in cell volume is, from Equations 6 and 7,

$$\Delta T_c = 12 \text{ dyne/cm} \cdot 0.007 = 0.09 \text{ dyne/cm}$$ 8.

It turns out that this tension is sufficient to activate at least some classes of SA channels. For example, the tension developed in a patch of membrane 0.5 μm in diameter that is subjected to a negative pressure of 6 cm H_2O is given by Equation 9. Prior studies have indicated that this amount of pipette suction activates amphibian SAK channels (69).

$$T = \frac{P \cdot d}{4} = \frac{6 \times 980 \text{ dyne-cm}^{-2} \times 0.5 \times 10^{-4}}{4} = 0.07 \text{dyne/cm.}$$ 9.

Hence, the cell membrane tension (T_c) of 0.09 dyne/cm that is generated by only a 1% increase in cell volume (Equation 8) could be sufficient to turn on SA channels in this preparation.

If this is the case, why is it usually necessary to swell cells by about 50% in order to detect significant increases in P_o? This apparent paradox arises from the mismatch between the diameter of the cell-attached patch and the diameter of the cell. If it were possible to form gigaohm seals on half the cell, a 1% increase in cell volume would produce sufficient tension in this "super patch" to activate mechanosensitive channels.

In practice, pipette tips larger than 1 μm fail to form stable high-resistance seals on most cells. The giant patches that have been formed on cardiac myocytes are an important exception (13). It is not clear if the giant patch technique can be applied to epithelial cells; however, it is worth considering because it would favorably increase the ratio of patch to cell diameter (d_p/d_c). When single channel currents are recorded from patches whose area is small compared with the cell surface area, the mechanical constraints at the tight seal reduce the tension in the cell-attached patch (T_p) in proportion to the ratio (d_p/d_c), which can be as small as 0.5/30 μm = 0.017. This situation is expressed by Equation 10, which follows from Laplace's law and the requirement that both the unclamped region of the cell and the section of membrane within the pipette must experience the same hydrostatic pressure (P), where the subscript(s) c denotes cell and p denotes patch.

$$P = \frac{T_c}{d_c} = \frac{T_p}{d_p} \qquad\qquad 10.$$

Combining Equations 6 and 10, one can compute the actual increase in tension that a cell-attached patch experiences from a 60% increase in cell volume $(\Delta V/V)$:

$$\Delta T_p = \frac{d_p}{d_c} K_A \cdot \left[\left(1 + \frac{\Delta V}{V}\right)^{2/3} - 1\right] = \frac{0.5}{30} \times 12 \text{ dyne/cm } [(1 + 0.6)^{2/3} - 1]$$

$$= 0.08 \text{ dyne/cm} \qquad\qquad 11.$$

In other words, a 60% increase in relative cell volume is required to produce sufficient tension (>0.07 dyne/cm) in a cell-attached patch to turn on SA channels to the same extent as a direct application of 6 cm H_2O suction to the patch (see Equation 9).

NON-IDEAL MEMBRANE MECHANICS   Although the above calculations are instructive, it is a considerable simplification to assume that the shape of the membrane at the tip of the patch pipette is an ideal hemisphere. The spherical portion of the patch often occurs quite far from the pipette tip so that the patch assumes an "omega shape," with a long straight section of membrane in close contact with the glass wall of the pipette (75). Presumably this straight section is the site of the gigaohm seal. Light microscopic observations (75), as well as electron microscopy (64), reveal cytoplasmic and cytoskeletal material within the patch pipette. This material often persists even after the patch is excised.

In some cases, suction completely distorts the shape of the membrane; whereas in other cases, suction simply decreases the radius of curvature of the domed portion of membrane spanning the inside of the pipette, while the straight section of membrane, attached to the glass, remains unchanged (74). Hence, some of the basic concepts of ideal hemispherical patches considered in the above section could still be applied to the spherical portion of membrane spanning the pipette. However, the presence of a viscous cytoplasm within the pipette and different estimates of K_A resulting from the omega shape of the patch could alter some of the predictions about how cell swelling affects membrane tension.

High-resolution video microscopy indicates that pipette suction proportionately increases apparent patch area and patch capacitance so that the specific capacitance of the patch remains relatively unchanged (75). Hence, patch area is increased at nearly constant membrane thickness. Consequently, the increase in patch surface area during stretch does not arise from membrane thinning but apparently from an influx of lipid recruited from the walls of the patch pipette. Release of suction causes retraction of the patch, which probably arises from elastic restoring forces of the underlying cytoskeleton.

Despite movement of lipid along the wall, the membrane itself remains rigidly attached to the glass in both excised and cell-attached patches (75). This suggests that the membrane-glass attachment involves specific proteins that bind to the glass, whereas surface glycoproteins provide a high-resistance "sucrose gap" between the outer membrane leaflet and the glass pipette. In such a model, suction could produce real increases in patch area via lipid flow without pulling new channel proteins into the patch.

LIPID SOLUBLE MEDIATORS   The process of stretch activation may mimic normally occurring physiological regulators. For example, endogenous fatty acids seem to augment the open probability of certain SA channels in a fashion similar to membrane stretch and by processes that do not depend on arachidonic acid pathways. Activation of mechanosensitive channels by free fatty acids was observed in a large conductance, Ca–dependent K channel from pulmonary artery smooth muscle (42) and in a lower conductance K channel in toad stomach muscle (43, 58, 60).

One hypothesis for fatty acid mediation of mechanotransduction is that physical deformation of the patch activates membrane-bound phospholipases, thereby releasing fatty acids from the bilayer that could then directly gate the channel protein (59). The mechanism may involve binding of the fatty acid to the channel via a process similar to fatty acid activation of purified protein kinase C (48, 51, 71). It is equally possible that endogenous fatty acids, released by stretch or cell swelling, indirectly affect P_o by altering either membrane fluidity or the lipid environment of the channel (59).

A clue to the process of fatty acid channel activation is the finding that lipid-soluble amphipaths activate mechanosensitive channels of *E. coli* by a mechanism that appears to alter the curvature of the bilayer (46). Following a model originally proposed by Sheetz & Singer to explain drug–erythrocyte interactions (72), Martinac et al suggested that amphipathic compounds would preferentially insert into the inner or outer leaflet of the bilayer (46). This would expand one monolayer relative to the other and produce a microscopic bending of the bilayer that transmits tension to mechanosensitive receptors on the channel protein or cytoskeleton. In this model, hydrophobic cations would insert into the relatively negatively charged inner leaflet, causing a concave bending (as seen in red cells). Conversely, hydrophobic anions would insert into the less negative outer leaflet, expanding it and creating a convex region of the cell membrane. This bilayer couple model may be important in transducing membrane tension into changes in channel open probability.

CYTOSKELETON   Given the intimate association between channels and the cytoskeleton (5, 7), it would not be surprising if suction forces were coupled to SA channels via the cytoskeletal network. Early studies by Guharay & Sachs found dramatic increases in the stretch sensitivity (θ) of mechanosensitive channels after treatment with a class of cytochalasins known to disrupt actin filaments (28). At the time, these results were interpreted as indicating a network of cytoskeletal strands funneling membrane strain into widely spaced nodal points (65). The increased sensitivity to stretch after cytochalasin would then be consistent with disruption of the elastic elements in parallel with the channel because this would increase the effective stress on the individual channel proteins.

The proximity of an actin-based cytoskeleton to Na channels in A6 cells (8) suggests that the cytoskeletal network is essential for the proper regulation of at least some types of channels. These structural data were reinforced by observations that anything that increased the relative amount of short actin filaments (cytochalasin D, exogenous actin + ATP, or gelsolin) increased Na channel open probability in A6 cells (8). However, the reconstitution of a completely functional mechanosensitive bacterial channel into liposomes implies that membrane tension can be directly transferred to the channel via the lipid bilayer independently of an underlying cytoskeletal network. However, in intact cells, the cytoskeleton may modulate the response to membrane tension.

DO MECHANOSENSITVE CHANNELS MEDIATE CELLULAR CURRENTS?

It was recently proposed that the process of gigaseal formation artificially sensitizes channels to mechanical stimuli (53). This hypothesis arose from experiments demonstrating a lack of correlation between activation of single mechanosensitive channels and changes in macroscopic currents (53).

A number of investigators have reexamined this issue by comparing single channel and whole cell currents in the same preparation. For example, inflating yeast spheroblasts with positive pressure elicited macroscopic currents of a magnitude consistent with the expected total current from individual SA channels (30). Stretched smooth muscle cells exhibited a net inward current that could be attributed to microscopic SA channels (17). In liver cells, hyposmotic stress activated Ca-permeable SA channels concomitant with an increase in cytosolic calcium (3). In the intestinal cell line I407, hyposmotic stress produced large gadolinium-sensitive inward currents that were correlated with Ca influx (57). Unfortunately, gadolinium is not a totally specific blocker for mechanosensitive channels. There is some evidence that it also blocks N-type Ca channels in neuroblastoma cells (19) and volume-activated Cl currents in *Xenopus* oocytes (1).

In order to circumvent the absence of highly specific blockers for SA channels, we have used the amphibian proximal tubule, where all of the demonstrable K conductance seems to be mechanosensitive (9, 24, 25, 38, 40, 41, 68, 69). Even the large conductance, Ca-dependent K channel at the apical membrane is indirectly activated by stretch-induced increases in local Ca concentration via adjacent SA cation channels (24, 41). Since all the amphibian K channels are also blocked by 5 mM barium (Ba), changes in barium-sensitive whole cell conductance (in the region of negative membrane potential) reflect activation of individual SAKs (9).

In one set of experiments, the effects of Na-glucose and Na-phenylalanine coupled transport on cell volume and whole cell current were examined using whole cell voltage clamps on isolated frog proximal tubule cells (9). Isosmotic addition of 40 mM glucose to the bathing solution increased cell volume by $23 \pm 4\%$ and increased barium-sensitive (i.e. K) conductance by $40 \pm 10\%$ in 11 isolated cells. Similar results were obtained for isosmotic addition of phenylalanine and for addition of cotransported, nonmetabolized glucose analogues (9). In all cases, the swelling associated change in Ba-sensitive conductance occurred without a change in reversal potential, which implies that channel selectivity was unchanged.

In another series of experiments, *Necturus* proximal tubule cells were electrically uncoupled with 0.6 mM octanol and then subjected to an abrupt change in bath osmolarity while recording whole cell currents. Decreasing bath osmolarity at constant ionic strength (by removal of sucrose) caused a significant increase in the barium-sensitive whole cell conductance. Because barium-sensitive SAK channels have been identified at the basolateral membrane of these cells (41, 68, 69, 70), the increase in macroscopic barium-sensitive conductance can tentatively be attributed to osmotic activation of these stretch channels.

In all these studies, the temporal association between cell swelling and the increase in gadolinium- or barium-sensitive conductance does not conclusively prove that changes in macroscopic conductance are caused by mechanosensitive channels. However, at least for the case of amphibian K channels, one can invoke the following line of reasoning. Because all K channels observed in amphibian proximal tubule cells are stretch activated and barium sensitive, both the glucose- and osmotic-induced barium-sensitive macroscopic currents can be attributed to SAKs.

Use of a conventional whole cell technique in these experiments, rather than the permeabilized patch procedure (36), effectively washes out diffusable intracellular mediators that might link substrate transport to increased

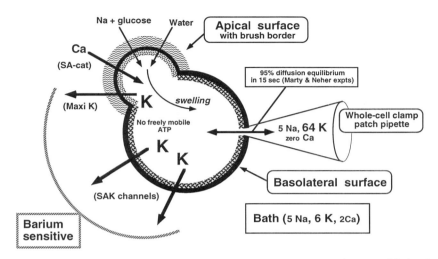

Figure 3 Hypothetical model of substrate-induced increase in the K conductance of isolated proximal tubule cells. Stippled regions within the cell denote possible unstirred layers where osmolarity transiently exceeds that of the bulk cytosol. The cross-hatched region denotes a sub-membranous cytoskeletal network that may be altered by cell swelling. SA cation refers to stretch-activated, cation-selective channels found at the apical membrane. Maxi K refers to Ca-dependent, high conductance K channels at the apical surface, and SAK refers to stretch-activated K channels (re-drawn from Figure 14, Reference 9).

K conductance (Figure 3). Even when high concentrations of ATP (>5 mM) were placed in the pipette, there was no attenuation of the swelling associated increase in barium-sensitive conductance (9). Therefore, this increase in G_K probably arises from either a deformation of the sub-membrane cytoskeleton or a direct change in membrane tension. In this regard, mechanosensitive K channels would be the microscopic correlates of the macroscopic change in G_K.

The above experiments, together with the independent finding that mechanosensitivity is an intrinsic property of certain channels that can be reconstituted into different lipid environments (78, 79), argue against the hypothesis (53) that mechanosensitivity is an artifact of the patch-clamp technique. On the other hand, certain SA channels exhibit adaptive responses to suction that are only seen with gentle sealing (32). Seals formed with more vigorous suction abolish the adaptation and possibly increase the stretch sensitivity of the channel. Hence, it is conceivable that SA currents are not always seen in the whole cell model because these currents would adapt (shut down) quickly, whereas single channels in cell-attached patches, formed with enough suction to destroy adaptation, would remain sensitive to membrane tension.

ACKNOWLEDGMENTS

The author gratefully acknowledges the assistance and advice of Larry G Palmer (Cornell) and Fred Sachs (SUNY Buffalo). This work was supported in part by a grant from the National Institute of Diabetes and Digestive and Kidney Diseases, grant R01-DK38596.

Literature Cited

1. Ackerman MJ, Wickman KD, Clapham DE. 1994. Hypotonicity activates a native chloride current in *Xenopus* oocytes. *J. Gen. Physiol.* 103:153–79
2. Barish ME. 1983. A transient calcium-dependent chloride current in the immature *Xenopus* oocyte. *J. Physiol.* 342: 309–25
3. Bear CE. 1990. A nonselective cation channel in rat liver cells is activated by membrane stretch. *Am. J. Physiol.* 258: C421–28
4. Beck JS, Breton S, Laprade R, Giebisch G. 1991. Volume regulation and intracellular calcium in the rabbit proximal convoluted tubule. *Am. J. Physiol.* 260: F861–67
5. Bennett V. 1985. The membrane skeleton of human erythrocytes and its implications for more complex cells. *Annu. Rev. Biochem.* 54:273–304
6. Boton R, Dascal N, Gillo B, Lass Y. 1989. Two calcium-activated chloride conductances in *Xenopus laevis* oocytes permeabilized with the ionophore A23187. *J. Physiol.* 408:511–34
7. Branton D. 1981. Membrane cytoskeletal interactions. *Cold Spring Harbor Symp. Quant. Biol.* 46:1–5
8. Cantiello HF, Stow JL, Prat AG, Ausiello DA. 1991. Actin filaments regulate Na channel activity. *Am. J. Physiol.* 261:C882–88
9. Cemerikic D, Sackin H. 1993. Substrate activation of mechanosensitive, whole-cell currents in renal proximal tubule. *Am. J. Physiol.* 264:F697–714
10. Chen JG, Chen Y, Kempson SA, Yu L. 1993. Hypotonicity potentiates chloride currents in *Xenopus* oocytes. *Biophys. J.* 64:A389
11. Christensen O. 1987. Mediation of cell volume regulation by Ca influx through stretch-activated channels. *Nature* 330: 66–68
12. Deleted in proof
13. Collins A, Somlyo AV, Hilgemann DW. 1992. The giant cardiac membrane patch method: stimulation of outward Na-Ca exchange current by MgATP *J. Physiol.* 454:27–57
14. Cooper KE, Tang JM, Rae JL, Eisenberg RS. 1986. A cation channel in frog lens epithelia responsive to pressure and calcium. *J. Membr. Biol.* 93:259–69
15. Davidson R. 1993. Membrane stretch activates a high conductance K channel in G292 osteoblastic-like cells. *J. Membr. Biol.* 131:81–92
16. Davidson R, Tatakis D, Auerbach A. 1990. Multiple forms of mechanosensitive ion channels in osteoblast-like cells. *Pflügers Arch.* 416:646–51
17. Davis MJ, Donovitz JA, Hood JD. 1992. Stretch-activated single-channel and whole cell currents in vascular smooth muscle cells. *Am. J. Physiol.* 262: C1083–88
18. Ding JP, Bowman CL, Sokabe M, Sachs F. 1989. Mechanical transduction in glial cells: SACs and SICs. *Biophys. J.* 55:244a
19. Docherty RJ. 1988. Gadolinium selectively blocks a component of calcium current in rodent neuroblastoma x glioma hybrid (NG108–15) cells. *J. Physiol.* 398:33–47
20. Duncan R, Misler S. 1989. Voltage-activated and stretch-activated Ba^{2+} conducting channels in an osteoblast-like cell line (UMR 106). *FEBS Lett.* 251: 17–21
21. Erxleben C. 1989. Stretch-activated current through single ion channels in the abdominal stretch receptor organ of the crayfish. *J. Gen. Physiol.* 94:1071–83
22. Evans EA, Waugh R, Melnik L. 1976. Elastic area compressibility modulus of red cell membrane. *Biophys. J.* 16:585–95

23. Falke LC, Misler S. 1989. Activity of ion channels during volume regulation by clonal N1E115 neuroblastoma cells. *Proc. Natl. Acad. Sci. USA* 86:3919–23

24. Filipovic D, Sackin H. 1991. A calcium-permeable stretch-activated cation channel in renal proximal tubule. *Am. J. Physiol.* 260:F119–29

25. Filipovic D, Sackin H. 1992. Stretch and volume activated channels in isolated proximal tubule cells. *Am. J. Physiol.* 262:F857–70

26. Fong P, Turner PR, Denetclaw WF, Steinhardt R. 1990. Increased activity of calcium leak channels in myotubes of Duchenne human and *mdx* mouse origin. *Science* 250:673–76

27. Franco A, Lansman JB. 1990. Calcium entry through stretch–inactivated ion channels in *mdx* myotubes. *Nature* 344:670–73

28. Guharay F, Sachs F. 1984. Stretch-activated single ion channel currents in tissue-cultured embryonic chick skeletal muscle. *J. Physiol.* 352:685–701

29. Gustin MC. 1992. Mechanosensitive ion channels in yeast. Mechanisms of activation and adaptation. In *Advances in Comparative and Environmental Physiology,* ed. F Ito, 10:19–38. Berlin: Springer-Verlag

30. Gustin MC, Sachs F, Sigurdson W, Ruknudin A, Bowman C, et al. 1991. Single-channel mechanosensitive currents. *Science* 253:800–2

31. Gustin MC, Zhou X, Martinac B, Kung C. 1988. A mechanosensitive ion channel in the yeast plasma membrane. *Science* 242:762–65

32. Hamill OP, McBride DW. 1992. Rapid adaptation of single mechanosensitive channels in *Xenopus* oocytes. *Proc. Natl. Acad. Sci. USA* 89:7462–66

33. Hazama A, Okada Y. 1988. Ca sensitivity of volume-regulatory K and Cl channels. *J. Physiol.* 402:687–702

34. Hisada T, Walsh JV Jr, Singer J. 1993. Stretch-inactivated cationic channels in single smooth muscle cells. *Pflügers Arch.* 422:393–96

35. Hoffmann EK, Kolb H-A. 1991. Volume and osmolality control in animal cells. In *Comparative and Environmental Physiology,* ed. R. Gilles, EK Hoffmann, L Bolis, 9:140–85. Berlin: Springer-Verlag

36. Horn D. 1988. Muscarinic activation of ionic currents measured by a new whole-cell recording method. *J. Gen. Physiol.* 92:145–59

37. Howard J, Roberts WM, Hudspeth AJ. 1988. Mechanoelectrical transduction by hair cells. *Annu. Rev. Biophys. Biophys. Chem.* 17:99–124

38. Hunter M. 1990. Stretch-activated channels in the basolateral membrane of single proximal cells of frog kidney. *Pflügers Arch.* 416:448–53

39. Hurst AM, Hunter M. 1990. Stretch-activated channels in single early distal tubule cells of the frog. *J. Physiol.* 430:13–24

40. Kawahara K. 1990. A stretch-activated K channel in the basolateral membrane of *Xenopus* kidney proximal tubule cells. *Pflügers Arch.* 415:624–29

41. Kawahara K, Hunter M, Giebisch G. 1987. Potassium channels in *Necturus* proximal tubule. *Am. J. Physiol.* 253:F488–94

42. Kirber MT, Ordway RW, Clapp LH, Walsh JV Jr, Singer JJ. 1991. Both membrane stretch and fatty acids directly activate large conductance Ca-activated K channels in vascular smooth muscle cells. *FEBS Lett.* 297:24–28

43. Kirber MT, Walsh JV, Singer JJ. 1988. Stretch-activated ion channels in smooth muscle: a mechanism for the initiation of stretch-induced contraction. *Pflügers Arch.* 412:339–45

44. Kwok R, Evans E. 1981. Thermoelasticity of large lecithin bilayer vesicles. *Biophys. J.* 35:637–52

45. Lansman JB. 1987. Single stretch-activated ion channels in vascular endothelial cells as mechanotransducers. *Nature* 325:811–13

46. Martinac B, Adler J, Kung C. 1990. Mechanosensitive ion channels of *E. coli* activated by amphipaths. *Nature* 348:261–63

47. Martinac B, Buechner M, Delcour A, Adler J, Kung C. 1987. Pressure-sensitive ion channel in *Escherichia coli. Proc. Natl. Acad. Sci. USA* 84:2297–301

48. McPhail LC, Snyderman R. 1984. A potential second messenger role for unsaturated fatty acids: activation of Ca-dependent protein kinase. *Science* 224:622–25

49. Millet B, Pickard BG. 1988. Gadolinium ion is an inhibitor suitable for testing the putative roles of stretch-activated ion channels in geotropism and thigmotropism. *Biophys. J.* 53:155a

50. Moody WJ, Bosma MM. 1989. A nonselective cation channel activated by membrane deformation in oocytes of the ascidian *Boltenia villosa. J. Membr. Biol.* 107:179–88

51. Morimoto YM. 1988. Activation of protein kinase C by fatty acids and its dependency on Ca and phospholipid. *Cell Struct. Funct.* 13:45–49

52. Morris CE. 1990. Mechanosensitive ion channels. *J. Membr. Biol.* 113:93–107

53. Morris CE, Horn R. 1991. Failure to elicit neuronal macroscopic mechanosensitive currents anticipated by single-channel studies. *Science* 251:1246–49

54. Morris CE, Sigurdson WJ. 1989. Stretch-inactivated ion channels coexist with stretch-activated ion channels. *Science* 243:807–9

55. Odell GM, Oster G, Alberch P, Burnside B. 1981. The mechanical basis of morphogenesis. I. Epithelial folding and invagination. *Dev. Biol.* 85:446–62

56. Okada Y, Hazama A. 1989. Volume-regulatory ion channels in epithelial cells. *News Physiol. Sci.* 4:238–42

57. Okada Y, Hazama A, Yuan WL. 1990. Stretch-induced activation of Ca permeable ion channels is involved in the volume regulation of hypotonically swollen epithelial cells. *Neurosci. Res.* 12:S5–13

58. Ordway RW, Petrou S, Kirber MT, Walsh JV Jr, Singer JJ. 1992. Two distinct mechanisms of ion channel activation by membrane stretch: evidence that endogenous fatty acids mediate stretch activation of K channels. *Biophys. J.* 61:A391 (Abstr.)

59. Ordway RW, Singer JJ, Walsh JV Jr. 1991. Direct regulation of ion channels by fatty acids. *Trends Neurosci.* 14:96–100

60. Ordway RW, Walsh JV Jr, Singer JJ. 1989. Arachidonic acid and other fatty acids directly activate potassium channels in smooth muscle cells. *Science* 244:1176–78

61. Pacha J, Frindt G, Sackin H, Palmer L. 1991. Apical maxi K channels in intercalated cells of CCT. *Am. J. Physiol.* 261:F696–705

62. Pickard BG, Ding JP. 1992. Gravity sensing in higher plants. See Ref. 29, pp. 81–110

63. Pickard BG, Ding JP. 1993. The mechanosensory calcium-selective ion channel: key component of a plasmalemmal control centre? *Aust. J. Plant Physiol.* 20:439–59

64. Ruknudin A, Song MJ, Sachs F. 1989. The ultrastructure of patch-clamped membranes: a study using high voltage electron microscopy. *Biophys. J.* 112:125–34

65. Sachs F. 1987. Baroreceptor mechanisms at the cellular level. *Fed. Proc.* 46:12–16

66. Sachs F. 1989. Ion channels as mechanical transducers. In *Cell Shape: Deter-*

minants, Regulation and Regulatory Role, ed. F Bonner, W Stein, pp. 63–92. New York: Academic

67. Sachs F, Lecar H. 1991. Stochastic models for mechanical transduction. *Biophys. J.* 59:1143–45

68. Sackin H. 1987. Stretch-activated potassium channels in renal proximal tubule. *Am. J. Physiol.* 253:F1253–62

69. Sackin H. 1989. A stretch-activated potassium channel sensitive to cell volume. *Proc. Natl. Acad. Sci. USA* 86:1731–35

70. Sackin H, Palmer LG. 1987. Basolateral potassium channels in renal proximal tubule. *Am. J. Physiol.* 253:F476–87

71. Seifert R, Schächtele C, Roenthal W, Schultz G. 1988. Activation of protein kinase C by *cis*- and *trans*-fatty acids and its potentiation by diacylglycerol. *Biochem. Biophys. Res. Commun.* 154:20–26

72. Sheetz MP, Singer SJ. 1974. Biological membranes as bilayer couples. A molecular mechanism of drug-erythrocyte interactions. *Proc. Natl. Acad. Sci. USA* 71:4457–61

73. Sigurdson WJ, Morris CE, Brezden BL, Gardner DR. 1987. Stretch activation of a K channel in molluscan heart cells. *J. Exp. Biol.* 127:191–209

74. Sokabe M, Sachs F. 1990. The structure and dynamics of patch-clamped membranes: a study using differential interference contrast light microscopy. *J. Cell Biol.* 111:599–606

75. Sokabe M, Sachs F, Jing Z. 1991. Quantitative video microscopy of patch-clamped membranes: stress, strain, capacitance, and stretch activation. *Biophys. J.* 59:722–28

76. Stanton BA, Dietl P, Schwiebert E. 1990. Cell volume regulation in the cortical collecting duct: stretch activated Cl channels. *J. Am. Soc. Nephrol.* 1:692 (Abstr.)

77. Stanton BA, Mills JA, Schwiebert EM. 1991. Role of the cytoskeleton in regulatory volume decrease in cortical collecting duct cells in culture. *J. Am. Soc. Nephrol.* 2:751 (Abstr.)

78. Sukharev SI, Blount P, Martinac B, Blattner FR, Kung C. 1994. A large-conductance mechanosensitive channel in *E. coli* encoded by *mscL* alone. *Nature* 368:265–68

79. Sukharev SI, Martinac B, Arshavsky VY, Kung C. 1993. Two types of mechanosensitive channels in the *Escherichia coli* cell envelope: solubilization and functional reconstitution. *Biophys. J.* 65:177–83

80. Taniguchi J, Guggino WB. 1989. Membrane stretch: a physiological stimulator of Ca-activated K channels in thick ascending limb. *Am. J. Physiol.* 257:F347–52

81. Ubl J, Murer H, Kolb H-A. 1988. Hypotonic shock evokes opening of Ca-activated K channels in opossum kidney cells. *Pflügers Arch.* 412:551–53

82. Ubl J, Murer H, Kolb H-A. 1988. Ion channels activated by osmotic and mechanical stress in membranes of opossum kidney cells. *J. Membr. Biol.* 104:223–32

83. Wagoner DRV. 1991. Mechanosensitive ion channels in atrial myocytes. *Biophys. J.* 59:546a

84. Wong SM, DaBell MC, Chase H. 1990. Cell swelling increases intracellular free [Ca] in cultured toad bladder cells. *Am. J. Physiol.* 258:F292–96

85. Yang X, Sachs F. 1989. Block of stretch-activated ion channels in *Xenopus* oocytes by gadolinium and calcium ions. *Science* 243:1068–71

86. Zhou X, Stumpf M, Hoch H, Kung C. 1991. A mechanosensitive channel in whole cells and in membrane patches of the fungus *Uromyces*. *Science* 253:1415–17

Annu. Rev. Physiol. 1995. 57:355–85

MOLECULAR PATHOLOGY OF THE SKELETAL MUSCLE SODIUM CHANNEL

Robert L. Barchi

Mahoney Institute of Neurological Sciences and the Departments of Neuroscience and Neurology, University of Pennsylvania School of Medicine, Philadelphia, Pennsylvania 19104

KEY WORDS: ion channels, muscle disease, periodic paralysis, myotonia, paramyotonia congenita

---

INTRODUCTION

Although the primary role of skeletal muscle is to do work, muscle contraction can only take place when signals arriving at the neuromuscular junction are successfully coupled to the release of Ca^{2+} from the sarcoplasmic reticulum. This coupling requires the spread of an action potential across the muscle fiber surface membrane and into the T tubule system. Should this signal fail, muscle paralysis will result in spite of normal neuromuscular junction and contractile protein function.

The muscle action potential, like that in nerve, is initiated by the opening of membrane voltage–dependent sodium channels (1, 39). It has recently become evident that abnormalities in muscle membrane–sodium channel function can produce clinical disease (9, 40, 82); sodium channels that are too easily activated can produce repetitive membrane electrical activity or myotonia, while channels that resist activation can result in periodic weakness or paralysis.

The molecular characterization of muscle sodium channels and the genes that encode them has provided the tools necessary to explore the relationship between sodium channels and diseases of human skeletal muscle. The nature of this relationship has now been defined for a number of diseases, and several mutations in the sodium channel gene have been identified. These sodium channel disorders, although rare, are important not only for what they tell us

355

about the pathophysiology of disease but also for the insights they provide into structure and function relationships in the normal channel.

This article briefly reviews our concepts of muscle sodium channel structure and function and the role that abnormal sodium channels play in producing human muscle disease.

SKELETAL MUSCLE SODIUM CHANNELS

Voltage–dependent sodium channels comprise a large multigene family of closely related isoforms (7). A comprehensive survey of sodium channel structure and function, beyond the scope of this article may be found in several recent review articles (18, 19, 47, 99, 105). Although similar in most aspects of structure and kinetics, sodium channel isoforms show subtle variations that optimize their function for a particular location or cell type. In some species like *Drosophila*, different isoforms may arise from differential splicing of exons within a single gene (102). In mammalian muscle, however, each isoform is encoded on a separate gene. Mammalian skeletal muscle expresses two forms of sodium channel that differ in their sensitivity to various toxins (10, 92). The sodium channel in adult skeletal muscle (designated SkM1) is tetrodotoxin (TTX) sensitive and has a single-channel conductance of 25–30 pS (106, 110), while that in embryonic and denervated muscle and in heart (SkM2) is relatively insensitive to TTX and has a lower single-channel conductance of 10–15 pS (29, 48). The expression of the adult phenotype requires the interaction of muscle fibers with active motor neurons (6, 36, 74, 86, 108, 111).

Skeletal muscle sodium channels contain one large glycoprotein α-subunit of ~260 kDa and a second, smaller β-subunit of 38 kDa that is noncovalently associated with the α-subunit in a 1:1 stoichiometry (54, 91). Both subunits undergo extensive posttranslational modification (25, 68, 91, 104).

The complete primary sequence of the SkM1 and SkM2 skeletal muscle sodium channel α-subunit isoforms in rat and human muscle have been deduced from molecular cloning of their cognate cDNAs (29, 31, 48, 106). These cDNAs range in size from 8.5 to 9.5 kb and hybridize with mRNA transcripts of 8.5 to 9.0 kb (Figure 1). Open reading frames for the rat and human SkM1 isoform encode 1840 and 1836 amino acids (aa), respectively, corresponding to a predicted core M_r of ~208,500 K. The SkM2 isoform is slightly larger in both species [2018 aa in rat, 2016 aa in human] with a predicted core M_r of ~ 227,000 K.

Skeletal muscle α-subunits resemble all other known sodium channels in containing four large internal repeat domains (231 to 327 aa) that exhibit strong sequence homology at the amino acid level (see 47 for a detailed review and references). About half of the residues are either identical or conservatively substituted among these domains in each channel, and each domain contains

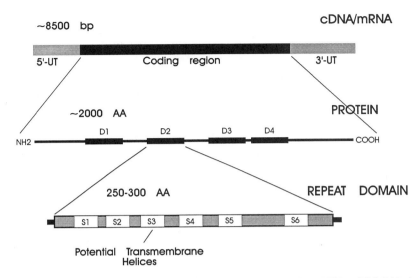

Figure 1 Skeletal muscle sodium channel α-subunits are encoded by mRNAs of 8.5–9 kb that contain a single open reading frame encompassing ~1800–2000 aa. Within the primary sequence are four large regions of internal homology (D1–D4), each containing 250–325 residues; the sequence in these regions most likely arose from duplication of a common primordial genetic element. Analysis of each domain suggests six regions with high likelihood of transmembrane helical structure (S1–S6); the fourth putative helix in each domain contains a unique series of positive charges in a repeating $(R/K-X-X)_n$ motif.

six segments in comparable locations that are capable of forming membrane-spanning helices. Two of these hydrophobic segments contain no charged residues (S5 and S6), three have several charged residues and are weakly amphipathic (S1, S2, and S3), and one (S4) is unique in containing a positively charged lysine or arginine at every third position with two intervening, non-polar amino acids. When this S4 segment is folded into an α-helix, positive charges form a spiral band along an otherwise neutral surface (19). The repeating tripeptide motif (R/K-X-X) occurs four times in D1-S4, five times in D2-S4 and D3-S4, and eight times in D4-S4. The 22 positive charges in the S4 segments are invariant in all sodium channels in this large family, and most of the hydrophobic residues in these segments are conserved as well.

The carboxy and amino terminal sequences and that of the regions joining the repeat domains [interdomains (IDs)] are quite divergent among species and isoforms (47). The ID 3–4 region, however, is a striking exception, exhibiting nearly complete sequence conservation. This 53 aa segment plays a key role in inactivation gating (77, 100, 109).

Although most of the loops that join the proposed transmembrane helices in each domain are short and variable in sequence, the segment between helices S5 and S6 in each repeat domain bears particular comment. It is much longer than the other interhelical segments and in D1 contains insertions or deletions and N-glycosylation sites near its amino terminal end that differentiate various channel isoforms. However, the carboxy-terminal end of the S5-S6 loop has two contiguous regions designated SS1 and SS2 that are highly conserved at the amino acid level among all sodium channels. Similar regions of homology are found in the S5-S6 interhelical loop in voltage-gated potassium channels. Evidence from mutagenesis experiments supports a role for these SS1-SS2 regions in ion selectivity and suggests that they form the lining of the channel pore.

The adult muscle sodium channel β-subunit has an apparent molecular mass of 38 kDa on SDS-PAGE; the core M_r after deglycosylation is 23 (91). The comparable glycosylated and deglycosylated rat brain sodium channel β_1-subunits have apparent molecular masses of 36 and 23 kDa (68). cDNA encoding the β_1-subunit of the rat brain sodium channel was sequenced first and encodes a 218 aa protein with a predicted molecular mass of ~23 kDa (43). Using polymerase chain reaction (PCR) methods, Bennett et al (12) then obtained cDNAs encoding a β-subunit from rat heart. This proved to be identical at the nucleotide level with the brain β_1 protein. Yang et al (112) subsequently cloned an identical sequence from rat skeletal muscle. cDNA from human brain or skeletal muscle encodes a closely related beta protein that exhibits 96% homology with the rat brain β_1 and has extensive homology in the 3'-untranslated region as well (62, 65). Analysis of the β_1 sequence suggests a single transmembrane domain (between aa 142–163) with an extracellular N-terminus (43). A single gene on human chromosome 19 encodes the β_1-subunit expressed in brain, heart, and skeletal muscle (63).

The current model of channel tertiary structure, incorporating biochemical, immunological, physiological, and molecular biological data, organizes the four repeat domains compactly within the plane of the membrane in a pseudosymmetrical fashion around a central ion pore (Figure 2). The pore itself is formed by contributions from each of the four domains, including in part, the SS1 and SS2 regions of each S5-S6 interhelix loop. The amino and carboxy termini and the interdomain regions are all on the cytoplasmic side of the membrane. While the α-subunit alone forms a functional channel, the muscle β-subunit binds to its perimeter, perhaps by interaction of its transmembrane helix with one or more of the repeat domains.

Functional Expression of Muscle Sodium Channels

Functional skeletal muscle sodium channels have been expressed in oocytes using synthetic cRNA encoding only α-subunits (31, 48, 106, 110). However,

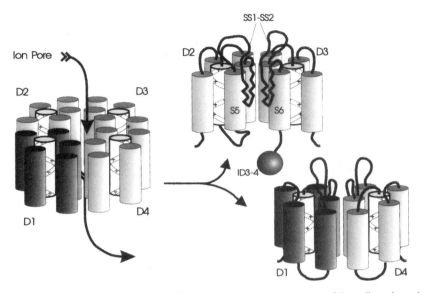

Figure 2   Although few data are available concerning the tertiary structure of the sodium channel, a consensus view has emerged in which each of the four repeat domains, with its transmembrane helices arranged in compact units within the plane of the membrane, surround and contribute to the formation of a central ion pore. The extended interhelical loops connecting S5 and S6 in each domain form part of the pore lining and contribute to its ion selectivity and conductance properties. The amino and carboxyl termini (not shown here to scale) are on the cytoplasmic surface of the protein. The segment joining D3 and D4 (ID3–4) plays a unique role in channel inactivation, perhaps by folding inward after channel opening to bind to a receptor site on the cytoplasmic surface and block ion flow.

the properties of channels from SkM1 α cRNA are not completely normal; the time course of inactivation is much slower than for channels expressed from total mRNA in mammalian cells or studied in vivo (45, 53, 71, 106). This slow inactivation of macroscopic currents reflects the increased frequency with which individual channels shift from the normal fast-inactivation kinetic mode to a second mode characterized by late openings or reopenings (116). This shifting, or modal gating, is seen in vivo in skeletal (75, 76) and cardiac muscle (70) but at a much lower probability.

The slow inactivation of SkM1 expressed in oocytes is corrected by coexpression with either the rat or human β_1-subunit (12, 16, 44) (Figure 3), in agreement with earlier coexpression studies with β_1- and the rat brain IIa α-subunit isoform (43). The acceleration in the kinetics of the macroscopic currents produced by β_1 coexpression can be accounted for by a shift in the equilibrium between the two gating modes induced by β_1 binding.

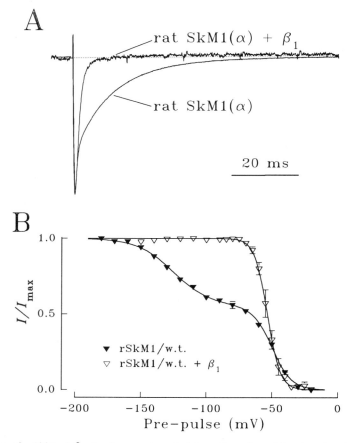

Figure 3 Although β-subunits are not required for sodium channel function, they do modify the properties of the expressed α-subunit. (*A*) Rat SkM1 α channels expressed in oocytes show bimodal inactivation kinetics dominated by a slow component. Coexpression of SkM1 α with skeletal muscle β-subunit restores the rapid inactivation kinetics associated with this channel in vivo. (*B*) The two kinetic modes of inactivation for SkM1 α are interconvertible and have different voltage dependence; coexpression with muscle β-subunit strongly favors the inactivation kinetic mode having the less-hyperpolarized $V_{1/2}$ for inactivation and the more rapid kinetics [adapted from Ji et al (44) with permission].

cRNAs encoding the rat or human SkM2 muscle α-subunit direct the expression of sodium channels with normal inactivation kinetics in oocytes (29, 110). Unlike SkM1, SkM2 channels do not show late openings at the single-channel level during depolarizing pulses. The SkM2 α isoform may contain structural features within it that stabilize the normal kinetic mode of channel inactivation, or that mode may be stabilized by interactions with oocyte proteins that bind uniquely to this isoform.

Structure-Function Correlations

CHANNEL ACTIVATION: S4 HELIX   Mutational analysis of sodium and potassium channels supports the involvement of the S4 helices in the voltage-sensing mechanism for channel activation (61, 73, 100). In general, reducing the number of positive charges decreases the voltage-dependence of channel activation (100). However, the complexity of the activation process is reflected in the observation that mutations of some neutral residues affect activation nearly as much as those that remove a conserved positive charge, and some mutants produce significant but unpredictable shifts in the midpoint of the activation curve as well as in its steepness. Activation probably does not depend simply on the net charge on a protein dipole, but also reflects the contributions of interactions among nonpolar residues between helices to the conformational energy of the closed, intermediate, and open states. Such nonelectrostatic interactions may have little tolerance for change if coordinated charge movements are to be retained.

CHANNEL INACTIVATION   Mutations introducing breaks in ID3–4 greatly reduce channel inactivation (100), and it has been proposed that this cytoplasmic region folds inward after channel activation to block ion movement. Although mutations that neutralize the charge on 11 of 12 basic amino acids in ID3–4 and on all three acidic residues do not affect inactivation, a triple mutation (IFM — QQQ) centered on F1489 of the RB-II channel completely eliminates fast inactivation (69, 77). The single mutation (F1489Q) alone removes most of the fast inactivation (109). These mutations have a comparable effect on the SkM1 channel. The ID3–4 region in sodium channels may play a role comparable to that of the amino terminus of fast-inactivating potassium channels, i.e. acting as a "ball" to plug the inner mouth of the ion pore to produce inactivation (4, 42, 115).

PERMEATION: PORE STRUCTURE AND BLOCKERS   Tetrodotoxin (TTX) blocks ion flow through sodium channels by binding to and occluding the external opening of the pore (90). Therefore, identification of the TTX-binding site in the muscle channel helps to localize portions of the channel structure that form this critical region. Since earlier studies suggested that modification of a channel pore carboxy group altered sensitivity to TTX, investigators first examined the consequences of removing carboxylate groups in the S5-S6 loop of each repeat domain on the binding of this highly specific toxin. Neutralizing the charge of a single glutamic acid residue (E387), located in the S5-S6 loop of D1, greatly reduced TTX sensitivity and also reduced the conductance of a sodium channel expressed in oocytes (72). While this effect could be produced by conformational changes acting at a distance, it seems more likely that E387 is in close proximity to the mouth of the channel and is involved either directly or indirectly in toxin binding and ion permeation.

Mutations of homologous residues were introduced into the S5-S6 loop of each repeat domain in the rat brain II channel. Many of these mutations produced changes in TTX affinity (101), thereby suggesting that portions of all four S5-S6 loops contribute to the formation of the TTX–binding site. In addition, several mutations caused marked reductions in channel conductance without affecting gating currents, which suggests that the loops contribute to the formation of the ion pore (52, 101). Two of the mutants, K1422E(D3) and A1714E(D4), demonstrated reduced selectivity for Na+, and bi-ionic reversal experiments with K1422E and the double mutant showed behavior much like voltage-dependent calcium channels (38).

However, when the sequence of the TTX-insensitive SkM2 sodium channels from rat (48) and human (29) heart and rat denervated muscle was compared with those of TTX-sensitive channels, virtually all the negatively charged residues targeted in the above mutatants were found to be conserved, which indicates that the difference in affinity between TTX-sensitive and -insensitive channels has not been identified. Another approach to localizing the physiologically relevant residues takes advantage of the low sensitivity of the SkM2 muscle isoform to this toxin ($K_d > 1 \times 10^{-3}$ mM) by creating chimeras in which selected regions of SkM1 and SkM2 are interchanged. Studies using this approach ultimately localized the difference in TTX sensitivity between the isoforms to a single amino acid residue, namely Y401 (TTX-S) to C374 (TTX-I) in SkM1 and the reciprocal mutation C374 (TTX-I) to Y401 (TTX-S) in SkM2/rH1 (5, 21, 98). An aromatic amino acid (Y or F) in the carboxy-terminal region of the S5-S6 loop of domain 1 confers the TTX-S SkM1 phenotype, whereas a cysteine at this position yields a TTX-I SkM2 sodium channel. A favorable interaction between aromatic side chains and the cationic TTX molecule, similar to interactions proposed for tetra-ethylammonium in K+ channels (114), is postulated to account for the increased affinity for TTX in TTX-S channels (21). The presence of cysteine at this site also is associated with sensitivity to Cd^{2+} block (5).

Chromosomal Localization of Sodium Channel Genes

The human cardiac (hH1) and skeletal muscle (hSkM1) sodium channels have now been cloned, sequenced, and functionally expressed (29, 31). The separate genes encoding each of these isoforms have been localized using species- and subtype-specific probes in hamster-human somatic cell hybrid lines. The gene encoding hH1 is located on chromosome 3 while the gene encoding hSkM1 is on chromosome 17 (32). Employing a chromosome 17 hybrid panel, the hSkM1 gene (designated *SCN4A*) was further localized to the region between 17q23.1 and 17q25.3 (32). Using comparable techniques and in situ chromosomal hybridization, the gene encoding the human counterpart of the rat brain II sodium channel was localized to chromosome 2 between 2q21 and 2q24.3 (2, 35, 60). Multiple copies of this gene (*SCN2A*) or several related genes might be present within this region. Mouse brain sodium channel genes may be organized in a similar fashion because homologues of the rat brain I, II, and III genes have been mapped to a contiguous small segment of the mouse chromosome 2 (64). The genes for the mouse homologues of SkM1 and SkM2 have been located on mouse chromosomes 11 and 9, respectively, the latter being isotenic with human chromosome 3 (3, 49).

The structure of the human gene *SCN4A* encoding SkM1 has been analyzed in detail. The coding region for the hSkM1 protein is contained within a 32.5 kb region and consists of 24 exons (54 to 2242 bp in length) and 23 introns (97 to 4850 bp) (30, 66). The locations of the exon-intron junctions bear no apparent relationship to predicted functional domains in the protein; some splice sites even fall in the middle of presumptive transmembrane helices. The positions of the exon-intron boundaries in the human gene are identical to those contained within an 8 kb homologous segment of the rat gene, and 10 of 24 splice junctions in *SCN4A* are positioned in homologous locations in the *para* sodium channel gene in *Drosophila* (30).

SODIUM CHANNELS AND MUSCLE DISEASE

The concept that ion channels might be involved in the pathogenesis of neuromuscular disease is not new. For example, the role of the nicotinic acetylcholine receptor in the pathogenesis of myasthenia gravis has been recognized for 20 years (59). Disorders of muscle excitability involving the sarcolemma have been associated with defects in membrane ionic conductances on the basis of electrophysiological experiments undertaken decades ago; the repetitive myotonic discharges that characterize the hereditary disorder myotonia congenita, and its homologue in the goat, were linked to a pathologic reduction in membrane chloride conductance by the mid 1970s (94). However, only recently has the availability of molecular reagents and techniques made it possible to identify with certainty the channel protein involved in these and other disorders of excitation and the specific amino acid defect that is responsible for abnormal channel function.

Diseases that affect muscle membrane excitability have generally been divided into two groups: those in which the sarcolemma is hyperexcitable, responding to normal depolarizations with long trains of action potentials (myotonic discharges), and those in which the membrane is intermittently

Myotonia   Paralysis

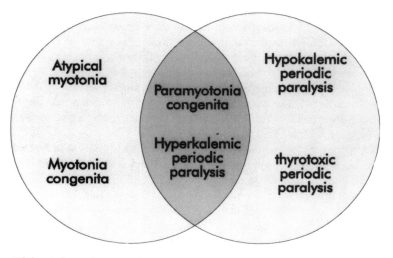

Chloride channels
Sodium channels
Calcium channels

Figure 4 Disorders of muscle membrane excitability range from those in which the sarcolemma is hyperexcitable and fires multiple action potentials in response to a brief activation (myotonia) to those in which the surface membrane becomes intermittently unexcitable, which leads to failure of muscle contraction (periodic paralysis). Several disorders express either myotonia or paralysis depending on physiological and environmental conditions. Many of these disorders of excitability are due to defects in membrane ion channels; sodium channel mutations cause diseases that may exhibit pure myotonia, intermittent paralysis, or a combination of both.

hypoexcitable, leading to muscle weakness or paralysis (9). In the past these extremes were assumed to be associated with different pathophysiological defects; however, it is now clear that either phenotype can result from abnormalities in a single key protein such as the voltage-dependent sodium channel, and that, conversely, similar signs and symptoms may be caused by defects in a number of different channel proteins (Figure 4). To understand fully these disorders and to develop a rational approach to their treatment, a new classification must be established based on the specific molecular defects involved. In order to provide common grounds for discussion, however, the traditional classification of these diseases is first reviewed.

The Periodic Paralyses

The periodic paralyses constitute a group of rare disorders affecting human skeletal muscle that are characterized by intermittent episodes of weakness or paralysis, often with apparently normal neuromuscular function between attacks (for reviews of the clinical aspects, see 8, 55, 89, 96). The severity of these episodes varies from brief periods of muscle stiffness or mild weakness lasting tens of minutes to prolonged periods of flaccid paralysis lasting many hours or even days. Paralytic episodes can be triggered by dietary factors such as a large carbohydrate load, by environmental factors such as cold exposure, or by physiological changes such as rest after vigorous exercise. Although there are some recognized acquired forms, most disorders in this category are inherited in an autosomal-dominant fashion. Episodes of weakness or paralysis are the hallmark of these diseases, but the paralytic phenotype is occasionally associated with signs of membrane hyperexcitability in the form of repetitive electrical discharges and stiffness (myotonia).

Paralytic episodes are often accompanied by shifts in serum potassium concentration that form the basis of the classic diagnostic categories. Characteristic syndromes have been identified in which the serum potassium consistently falls (hypokalemic periodic paralysis) or rises (hyperkalemic periodic paralysis) during an attack, as well as other forms in which no change in serum potassium is observed (Table 1). Although similar in many regards, these forms differ in associated features and each tends to breed true in a given family. Because they share the central characteristic of intermittent muscle weakness, these various forms of periodic paralysis are grouped together in the clinical literature. Underlying this grouping was the implicit assumption that all forms would prove to have a common etiology. Molecular analysis has now shown

Table 1 The hereditary periodic paralyses

	Hypokalemic periodic paralysis	Hyperkalemic periodic paralysis	Paramyotonia congenita
Age of onset	2nd decade	1st decade	Birth
Attack frequency	Infrequent	Frequent	Rare
Attack severity	Severe	Moderate	Variable
Attack duration	Hours to days	Minutes to hours	Hours
Triggering factors	Rest after exercise, carbohydrate load, cold or stress	Rest after exercise, hunger, cold	Cold, exercise
Serum K^+	Low	High	Normal
Myotonia	None	Occasional	Prominent
Inheritance	Dominant	Dominant	Dominant

that different target proteins and mechanisms are involved in spite of the similarity in clinical features.

HYPOKALEMIC PERIODIC PARALYSIS   Hypokalemic periodic paralysis (HOPP), the most common of the inherited disorders in this group, is characterized by a decline in serum [K$^+$] during an attack. Paralytic episodes usually begin during early childhood, and often start during the night. Attacks of weakness can be quite severe and even lead to transient quadriplegia, but the muscles of respiration are usually not affected, perhaps because of their constant activation. Episodes can last for many hours or, in severe cases, for days. Paralytic spells can be precipitated by rest after exercise, cold exposure, excitement, and by high carbohydrate loading. As a provocative diagnostic test, hypokalemia induced by administration of glucose and insulin will often cause paralysis in affected individuals.

Hypokalemic periodic paralysis is inherited as an autosomal-dominant trait but has a lower penetrance in females, with a 3:1 male:female predominance in most studies. The disease is not associated with a known sodium channel gene, but significant linkage has been found to 1q31–32 (28). This locus includes the gene for the dihydropyridine receptor, and a recent report has identified a specific mutation within this Ca^{2+} channel gene that cosegregates with the disease in affected members of 9 out of 25 families, which suggests that HOPP is caused by mutations in the skeletal muscle calcium channel gene (46). Further discussion of this disease lies outside the scope of this review.

HYPERKALEMIC PERIODIC PARALYSIS   In hyperkalemic periodic paralysis (HYPP), episodes of weakness are typically more frequent but milder and shorter than those in HOPP. However, residual weakness may linger after or between attacks. Some patients also develop true myopathic weakness with time that is not reversible. As a hallmark of this disease, the serum potassium concentration rises during an attack. Episodes of weakness or paralysis in HYPP often begin in the first decade of life and may decline in frequency in later years. Paralytic attacks may be precipitated by rest after exercise, immobility, potassium ingestion, irregular diet, cold exposure, or emotional stress.

Some families with HYPP also have myotonia. In some of these kinships, myotonia is present only after cold exposure, while in others it is present at normal ambient temperature. The electrophysiological appearance of the myotonic potentials in HYPP is indistinguishable from those seen in other myotonic disorders such as myotonia congenita. The disorder is inherited as an autosomal-dominant trait with complete penetrance. HYPP is caused by mutations in the SkM1 sodium channel.

PARAMYOTONIA CONGENITA   Paramyotonia congenita (PC) is a rare disorder originally described by Eulenburg (26). Patients with paramyotonia congenita exhibit myotonic symptoms that are made worse by exposure to cold (23). Often there is no myotonia at all in a warm environment, or only mild symptoms. Cooling greatly increases the severity of the myotonic stiffness; in rare cases, continued exposure can lead to weakness and, more rarely, to paralysis of the affected muscles. Both the myotonia and the paralysis are reversible with rewarming although a lag of minutes to hours may ensue. A common complaint of patients with PC is the development of myotonic stiffness of the facial muscles during winter. The disorder is not progressive, and many affected individuals report that symptoms improved with age.

The myotonic symptoms in PC are typically paradoxical; that is, the myotonia is not present or only minimal when movement is begun but increases with further exercise of the involved muscles. This is in direct contrast to the behavior of myotonic symptoms in the more commonly encountered myotonic disorders, including myotonic dystrophy and myotonia congenita, in which abnormal electrical activity typically decreases with exercise. Paramyotonia congenita is inherited as an autosomal-dominant trait. Onset is usually in the first decade. In fact, infants with the disease are often diagnosed by informed family members on the basis of the facial myotonia that these children develop in response to washing the face with cold water. PC is also due to mutations in SkM1.

Sodium Channel Myotonia

Hereditary disorders characterized by diffuse myotonic discharges in skeletal muscle and slowed relaxation after voluntary muscle contraction have been recognized for many years (8). Although myotonia is a clinical feature of myotonic dystrophy, most nondystrophic myotonic syndromes fall under the heading of myotonia congenita. The dominant form of myotonia congenita carries the eponym of Thomsen's disease after the physician who first described it in his extended family (103). The recessively inherited form is also known as the Becker's form (11). In both forms of the disease, myotonia is the predominant feature. This myotonia improves with exercise, in contrast to the paradoxical myotonia in paramyotonia congenita. Neither the dominant nor the recessive form is associated with potassium sensitivity or with paralytic attacks. Both of these diseases are now known to be due to mutations in the skeletal muscle sarcolemmal chloride channel (51).

Several families with symptoms resembling dominantly inherited myotonia congenita have recently been described, in whom the chloride channel is not involved, and linkage to the SCN4A sodium channel gene is present. Some affected individuals have myotonia that fluctuates in intensity from day to day (88), but none have paralytic episodes or weakness. Their myotonic symptoms improve with exercise, which distinguishes them from PC. Other families have been reported in which the myotonia is associated with muscle pain, while in others the myotonia is relieved by treatment with acetazolamide (107), a drug typically used to treat various forms of periodic paralysis associated with sodium channel defects. As a group, these disorders, which resemble the myotonia congenitas in their clinical presentation and electrophysiological features, have been designated the sodium channel myotonias (SCM).

MOLECULAR PATHOLOGY OF SODIUM CHANNEL DISORDERS

Physiological Studies in Periodic Paralysis

Because of the precipitous decline in serum $[K^+]$ seen in hypokalemic periodic paralysis, the most commonly encountered of the periodic paralyses, early investigators hypothesized that paralysis was due to membrane hyperpolarization associated with the lowered extracellular potassium. However, subsequent intracellular recordings showed that depolarization of the muscle sarcolemma accompanies the paralytic episodes seen in all of these unusual disorders (41, 56, 57, 89, 95). Much of the early literature on the periodic paralyses has been reviewed previously (33, 34.) Only the more recent work dealing with the role of sodium channels in these diseases is discussed here.

When the intact intercostal muscle of individuals with periodic paralysis was studied in vitro, the depolarization triggered by change in $[K^+]$ or temperature was found to be caused by an abnormal increase in membrane permeability to sodium ions. In HYPP and PC, the abnormal sodium conductance and the resulting paralysis seen in isolated muscle fibers could be blocked by TTX, which implicated the muscle TTX-sensitive, voltage-dependent sodium channel as the defective protein (56, 57, 87). Voltage-clamp recordings on single isolated intercostal muscle fibers from patients with HYPP demonstrated a small noninactivating sodium current that was present only with elevated extracellular potassium (56).

Single-channel recordings on cultured myotubes derived from a HYPP muscle biopsy (13) support the hypothesis that a primary sodium channel abnormality underlies the pathophysiology of this disease. With normal extracellular potassium, the single-channel kinetics of sodium channels in HYPP appear normal. An increase in $[K^+]_{out}$ to 10 mM had no effect on control channels but caused a small percent of the HYPP sodium channels to exhibit aberrant gating with intermittent loss of inactivation, multiple channel openings during a depolarizing pulse, and bursts of late channel openings.

In prolonged single-channel experiments, recordings showing abnormal inactivation were temporally clustered, suggesting that a defective channel could switch between normal and abnormal kinetic modes on a slow time scale. This alternation between kinetic modes is similar to the modal gating seen in normal cardiac and skeletal muscle sodium channels (70, 75, 76) although the probability of the nonactivating mode is considerably higher (1.5–2%) in the HYPP muscle in culture than in normal muscle. The increased contribution of the noninactivating mode seen in HYPP channels with high potassium would account for the noninactivating sodium current previously reported in voltage-clamp studies on intact muscle fibers.

In vitro measurements have recently been made on resealed fibers and on sarcolemmal blebs from quadriceps muscle biopsies in patients with sodium channel myotonia (58). These measurements showed an abnormal steady-state, inward sodium current that was sensitive to block by TTX. Other membrane conductances, especially chloride conductance, were normal. At the single-channel level, late openings for single sodium channels were increased in the diseased muscle, and the time constant for inactivation was lengthened from a normal value of 1.2 ms to 1.6–2.1 ms in diseased muscle. On prolonged recording, the abnormal inactivation varied in a modal fashion. The single-channel conductance was not affected.

Linkage Analysis

A number of laboratories examined well–characterized families with HYPP for linkage between the *SCN4A* gene encoding the hSkM1 channel on chromosome 17 and expression of the HYPP phenotype (Table 2). In one study, a restriction fragment length polymorphism (RFLP) in the region encoding the sodium channel ID2–3 was employed, and linkage was demonstrated between the *SCN4A* gene locus and a phenotype of HYPP with myotonia (27). A different BglII RFLP was used by a second group to show comparable tight linkage to *SCN4A* in another family expressing HYPP without myotonia (24).

Table 2 Muscle diseases linked to the skeletal muscle sodium channel gene at 17q23.1-25.3

Disorder	Probe	LOD score @ .00	Reference
HYPP with myotonia	hNa2	4.00	27
HYPP with myotonia	Pm8	10.35	85
HYPP with myotonia	hNa2, hGH	3.06	50
HYPP without myotonia	C6b, hNa2	4.09	24
PC	GH1	3.79	24
PC	pM8	4.43	84
MC with pain	pM8	4.19	83

Studies with additional HYPP families subsequently confirmed linkage of this disease to the *SCN4A* sodium channel gene (50, 85). Linkage to *SC4NA* was also established for PC using similar techniques, further confirming that HYPP and PC are allelic disorders at the same gene (24, 84). An atypical form of painful myotonia congenita has been linked to the *SCN4A* gene as well (83), which suggests that some forms of hereditary myotonia congenita may be due to defects in the sodium channel rather than in the sarcolemmal chloride channel.

Identification of Sodium Channel Mutations

Although linkage analysis can implicate a specific candidate gene in the pathogenesis of an hereditary disease, further progress requires identification of the actual mutations that cause abnormal channel function. One approach to the identification of sodium channel mutations at the *SCN4A* locus is to selectively amplify the channel-coding regions with PCR so that they may be compared with known channel sequences (Figure 5). Characterization of the exon-intron structure of hSkM1 (30) allowed suitable PCR primers flanking each exon to be generated; these were first used to screen genomic DNA from seven unrelated individuals with HYPP for mutations (80). Exon DNA was

1. DETERMINE GENOMIC STRUCTURE

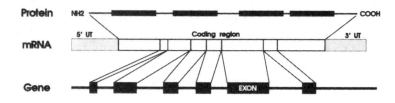

2. AMPLIFY EXONS AND ANALYZE BY SSCP

3. SEQUENCE VARIANTS THAT COSEGREGATE WITH PHENOTYPE

Figure 5   Most mutations in the muscle sodium channel gene have been identified by amplification and screening of genomic DNA containing coding regions for the protein structure. The known mRNA sequence for SkM1 was used to identify the gene on chromosome 17q. After mapping the exon-intron structure of the gene, appropriate pairs of PCR primers were constructed to selectively amplify each exon. Sensitive techniques such as single strand conformational polymorphism (SSCP) electrophoresis allow differences as small as a single base pair to be detected. Abnormal bands can then be removed from the gel and sequenced.

amplified and analyzed for mutations by single strand conformational polymorphism (SSCP). A cytosine to thymidine mutation was identified in three of these individuals that resulted in the substitution of a methionine residue for an absolutely conserved threonine at position 704 in the S5 helix of domain 2 (80). This amino acid substitution segregated with affected members of two families and appeared as a spontaneous mutation in the third. The defect was not found in either parent of the third patient, in unaffected members of the other families, or in any of 109 controls, which suggests that this substitution does not represent a silent polymorphism.

A different approach was employed to identify mutations in two other cases of HYPP (93). In this study, mRNA was prepared from a muscle biopsy of an affected individual. cDNA produced from this mRNA was then sequenced, and an adenine to guanine mutation was found that predicts the substitution of a methionine for a highly conserved valine at position 1592 in S6 of D4 (Table 3). This mutation was also shown to segregate with the expression of the phenotype in the affected members of this family; it appears as a new mutation in another affected family.

Using exon amplification from genomic DNA and SSCP, two separate mutations affecting different positions within the same codon were subsequently identified in three unrelated families with paramyotonia congenita (79). These mutations, which substitute either histidine or cysteine for arginine 1448, affect a conserved positive charge in the S4 helix that is postulated to be involved in channel voltage-dependent activation. One mutation (R1448C) would neutralize this charge, while the second (R1448H) would reduce the

Table 3   Sodium channel mutations producing human muscle disease

Genotype	Substitution	Region	Exon	Phenotype	Reference
C2188T	T704M	D2-S5	13	HYPP	80
C2411T	S804F	D2-S6	14	SCM	66
G3466A	A1156T	D3-S4-5	19	HYPP	66
A3555G	I1160V	D3-S4-5	19	SCM	82a
G3917T	G1306V	D3-D4	22	SCM	58, 67
G3917A	G1306E	D3-D4	22	SCM	58
G3917C	G1306A	D3-D4	22	SCM	58
C3938T	T1313M	D3-D4	22	PC	67
A4078G	M1360V	D4-S1	23	HYPP	57a
T498G	L1433R	D4-S3	24	PC	81
C4342T	R1448C	D4-S4	24	PC	79
C4343A	R1448H	D4-S4	24	PC	79
G4765A	V1589M	D4-S6	24	SCM	37
A4774G	M1592V	D4-S6	24	HYPP	93

net positive charge at this site by substitution of the partially protonated histidine. In a separate PC family, a T to G transversion was identified that substitutes an arginine for a conserved leucine at position 1433 near the extracellular end of the S3 helix in D4 (81). This mutation produces a major change in local charge and sidechain packing at a region of the channel that is predicted to be physically adjacent to the two S4 helix mutations.

Two other mutations (G1306V and T1313M) have been found in families with the PC phenotype that affect conserved amino acids near the N-terminus of the ID3–4 segment, a region that has been implicated in channel inactivation (67). In vitro mutagenesis of residues lying between these two natural mutations markedly reduces or eliminates fast sodium channel inactivation (109).

Additional mutations have been identified in families with symptoms that overlap the traditional diagnostic categories of HYPP, PC, and myotonia congenita (66). One pedigree, with mixed features of PC and HYPP, has an alanine to threonine mutation at position 1566 in the predicted intracellular loop between S4 and S5 in D3. The second pedigree exhibits features of PC and myotonia congenita; this family expresses a serine to phenylalanine mutation at position 804 near the cytoplasmic end of the S6 helix in D2.

Some families with a myotonic disorder of skeletal muscle that resembles myotonia congenita show a linkage to the SCN4A sodium channel gene rather than to the chloride channel gene that is usually mutated in the typical dominant and recessive forms of myotonia congenita (83). Point mutations have now been identified in several of these sodium channel myotonias. Lerche et al (58) reported three dominant point mutations at the same nucleotide in the SNC4A gene. These mutations, in order of the severity of their phenotype, produce substitutions of glutamic acid, valine, or alanine for a highly conserved glycine at position 1306. This glycine is three residues away from the unique IFM triplet that has been shown to be absolutely required for fast channel inactivation (109).

In another family with sodium channel myotonia characterized by responsiveness of affected members to the carbonic anhydrase inhibitor acetazolamide, a point mutation that produces an isoleucine to valine substitution in the short segment joining the S4 and S5 helices in D3 has been identified (78). This region has been postulated to form part of the binding site for the ID3–4 loop during inactivation. A different family expressing myotonia aggravated by cold exposure or increased potassium was analyzed by Heine et al (37). A valine to methionine substitution was found at position 1589, located near the cytoplasmic end of the S6 loop in D4.

Finally, an interesting animal model of human periodic paralysis has recently been described. The American quarterhorse breed has a high incidence of a muscle disease that resembles myotonic hyperkalemic periodic paralysis. This disorder has been linked to the horse homologue of the human SCN4A gene,

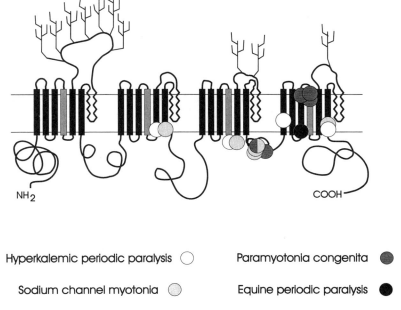

Hyperkalemic periodic paralysis ○   Paramyotonia congenita ●

Sodium channel myotonia ◐   Equine periodic paralysis ●

Figure 6   Location of all published mutations in the SkM1 α-subunit that have been associated with muscle disease.

and a phenylalanine to leucine mutation at a position corresponding to residue 1363 in the human channel D4-S3 has been identified (97). This residue is predicted to lie in the transmembrane domain near the cytoplasmic face of the membrane.

It appears that a variety of point mutations in the sodium channel gene are capable of producing diseases with related phenotypes (Figure 6). Formal analysis of each is needed to determine the mechanisms by which the mutations act, but these experiments of nature will undoubtedly prove valuable in further analyzing channel structure and function.

Expression of Channels Containing Disease Mutations

HYPERKALEMIC PERIODIC PARALYSIS   Although the cosegregation of point mutations with disease expression in affected families and the absence of these mutations from the control population strongly suggest a causal relationship between the *SCN4A* mutations and disease, proof requires expression and analysis of sodium channels containing each mutation. Several of the mutations associated with the HYPP phenotype have been recreated and expressed in

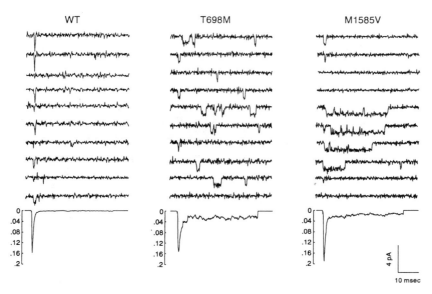

Figure 7 Sodium channel gating in wild-type (WT) and in two HYPP mutations. Single channel currents are shown for cell-attached patches depolarized to −20 mV from a holding potential of −100mV; sweeps are consecutive at 2 Hz. The T698M and M1585V patches contained a single channel each. Below each set of single channel records is the calculated average open channel probability. The modal nature of the inactivation abnormality is most clearly evident in the M1585V single channel data [from Cannon & Strittmatter (17) with permission].

vitro, either in the rat or human SkM1 background. Cannon & Strittmatter (17) introduced the T698M and M1585V mutations described in HYPP into the rat SkM1 wild-type background. The rat and human channels exhibit absolute conservation of sequence in the regions of the D2-S5 and D4-S6 helices in which these mutations occur and have an overall sequence homology of 92%, which leads to the hypothesis that the effects of these mutations should be similar in the rat and human SkM1 homologues. Both mutations seem to disrupt inactivation without affecting the time course of channel activation; this failure of inactivation led to a small but persistent noninactivating sodium current comparable to that previously reported in biopsied muscle fibers from HYPP patients (13).

At the single channel level, the T698M mutation showed prolonged channel open times and multiple reopenings or late first openings during a depolarizing pulse (Figure 7). The M1585V construct showed more normal kinetics in most depolarizations, with occasional complete loss of inactivation and high opening probability throughout the depolarization. Single channel conductance was not affected by either mutation. In this analysis, neither mutant channel showed changes in kinetics when extracellular potassium was increased.

A characteristic feature of these mutants became apparent in prolonged recordings. Episodes of abnormal kinetics clustered temporally, indicating that individual channels could switch on a time scale of seconds to minutes between the normal gating mode and an abnormal mode characterized by delayed inactivation.

A second group reported slightly different results with the same T698M mutation expressed in the rat SkM1 background (22). Although these investigators also found an increased appearance of abnormal inactivation events in their voltage-clamp records, they thought that the increase (3% for the mutant channel vs 1% for the wild-type) was insufficient to explain the phenotype of the disease. In contrast to Cannon & Strittmatter (17), this group reported a significant effect of the mutation on channel activation. They found that the voltage-dependent activation was shifted by 10–15 mV in the depolarizing direction, thus leading to a significant overlap of the activation and inactivation curves. They concluded that this overlap produced the abnormal muscle activity seen in these patients.

Since both of these expression studies utilized the rat rather than the human SkM1 channel, the issue of species-specific effects remained to be addressed. Therefore, Yang et al (112) created the T704M mutation in the normal human SkM1 channel and studied its effects on channel kinetics after expression through transient transfection in tsA201 cells. At the macroscopic level, these sodium channels showed evidence of a small noninactivating current, especially prominent at more positive potentials. They also showed a 9 mV hyperpolarizing shift in the voltage-dependent activation. Although the inactivation rate constant τ_h was not significantly altered, the voltage dependence of steady-state inactivation was shifted ~13 mV in the depolarizing direction.

Cannon et al (14) subsequently carried out a theoretical analysis of the relationship between channel inactivation and the myotonic and paralytic features seen in HYPP. Using a multicompartment computer model that included contributions from an active T tubule network, skeletal muscle action potentials were simulated under conditions of varying steady-state channel open probability. Raising the steady-state open probability (P_o) above 0.075 led to repetitive action potentials in response to prolonged depolarizing current pulses. Depending on the value chosen for P_o, spiking could persist after the termination of the current pulse (myotonia), or the membrane potential could depolarize to a new stable resting level, inactivating normal channels and rendering the membrane nonexcitable. These responses depended in part on T tubule potassium accumulation and were absent if the model lacked an active T tubule system. In a supporting study, P_o was artificially increased in normal rat skeletal muscle by treatment with the anemone toxin ATX II (15); the resulting channel open probability was 0.01–0.02. Under these conditions, repetitive action potentials and myotonic contractions were observed. The myotonic features were eliminated by osmotic detubulation of the muscle fiber. From both studies, the authors conclude that changes in inactivation alone are capable of producing conditions leading to either repetitive action potential generation or paralysis.

PARAMYOTONIA CONGENITA   The two mutations identified in the D4-S4 helix in families with paramyotonia congenita were expressed in the human and the rat SkM1 homologues (20) (Figure 8). Neither one (R1448H and R1448C in the human sequence) affected the activation of whole-cell currents in a human kidney cell line (tsA201) transiently transfected with either rat or human SkM1 mutated constructs. However, both mutations in either construct produced

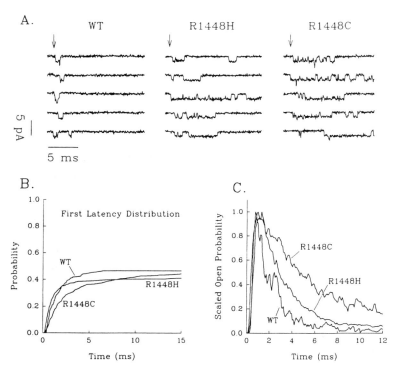

Figure 8   Expression of the R1448C and R1448H mutations in the human SkM1 α-subunit in vitro. (*A*) single-channel currents at – 20 mV from a holding potential of – 120 mV in cell–attached patches containing wild-type (WT) channels, or channels with the R1448H or R1448C mutations. (*B*) First latency distributions for each construct. (*C*) Scaled ensemble averages of the idealized single-channel currents for these three patches.

channels that inactivated more slowly and with less voltage dependence than did the wild-type. For the R1448C mutation, the inactivation rate constant (τ_h) was virtually voltage independent between −100 and −30 mV, wherein the wild-type τ_h showed the steepest dependence. At pH 7.2, τ_h R1448H showed a value and voltage dependence intermediate between the wild-type and the R1448C mutation.

Whereas the R1448C mutation eliminates the positive charge associated with the replaced arginine residue in this S4 helix, the R1448H mutation only reduces it because histidine (pK = 6.8) carries a partial positive charge at physiological pH. To evaluate the contribution of charge to the effects of these mutants, measurements of τ_h as a function of pH between 6.2 and 7.3 were made for wild-type, R1448C, and R1448H. Inactivation rates for wild-type and R1448C showed little change throughout this pH range, but τ_h for R1448H shifted progressively from values near wild-type at pH 6.2 to values comparable to the R1448C mutation at pH 7.8, which indicated that the charge on the substituted residue was critical for its effects on inactivation.

Single-channel analysis of the human mutants shows that the channels inactivate normally from the closed state but poorly or not at all from the open state. This is especially striking in the R1448C mutation, where it appears that an open channel cannot inactivate directly. Maximum likelihood analysis of rates for a model of channel activation and inactivation suggests that both mutations have their principal effect on the rate constants controlling movement between the open and inactivated states, whereas inactivation from the closed state is unaffected. These data suggest a critical role for the D4-S4 helix in the coupling of activation to inactivation. Neither of the mutant constructs in the rat or human background showed potassium sensitivity, and little difference was noted in the temperature dependence of their kinetics of inactivation. The single-channel behavior of these mutations also differed from that reported for the HYPP mutants in that no evidence of modal gating or clustering was observed over time during prolonged recordings.

Yang et al (113) have extended the analysis of mutations causing PC to include a total of five reported mutations associated with this phenotype (Figure 9). In addition to the R1448C and R1448H mutations, the A1156T, T1313M, and L1433R were also expressed in hSkM1 and compared to the S4 mutants. All the PC mutants showed a similar pattern of kinetic abnormalities, with reduced rate of inactivation in the macroscopic currents, accelerated recovery from inactivation, and changes in the voltage dependence of voltage-dependent inactivation. In contrast to the HYPP mutation T704M, none of the mutations had a significant effect on channel activation.

Additional custom mutations have been introduced at L1433 to better define the features of L1433R that affect inactivation (S Ji et al, in preparation). Substitution of alanine for leucine at this position has no effect on either

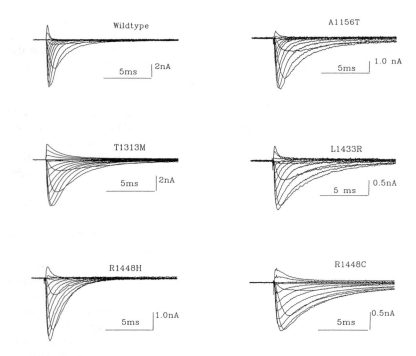

Figure 9 Mutations producing the PC phenotype have a similar effect on channel kinetics when expressed in the human SkM1 α background in vitro. Here, whole-cell, voltage-clamped recordings are shown for five point mutations identified in families with PC. Compared to wild-type, all show slowing of inactivation, increased rate of recovery from inactivation, and abnormal inactivation voltage dependence [from Yang et al (113) with permission].

activation or inactivation. Replacement of L1433 with lysine, glutamic acid, or glutamine slows inactivation and enhances recovery from inactivation in a manner similar to the natural L1433R mutation. Although lysine and arginine both carry a positive charge, the larger arginine has a greater effect on inactivation. Charge alone is not the critical factor because glutamic acid and lysine produce comparable shifts in inactivation kinetics, and because the effect of glutamine substitution is greater than lysine and intermediate between glutamic acid and arginine. None of these mutations alters activation. These observations suggest that the size of the side chain at this location, rather than its charge, is the critical factor determining effects on inactivation. The double mutation L1433R/R1448C is not additive, suggesting that the effect of R1448C on inactivation from the closed state is already maximal.

CONCLUSIONS FROM EXPRESSION STUDIES   Mutations associated with HYPP show abnormalities in modal gating that lead to a biphasic inactivation curve and a residual noninactivating sodium current. This is also true for the mutations with the sodium channel myotonia phenotype. In HYPP, shifts are seen in the steady-state voltage dependence of both activation and inactivation, whereas the rate of recovery from inactivation is not affected. PC mutations, on the other hand, do not affect modal gating. These mutations produce prominent slowing in the inactivation rate and, in some cases, reduce the voltage dependence of τ_h at negative potentials but do not affect the kinetics of channel activation. In addition, all PC mutations increase the rate of recovery from inactivation. These mutations vary, however, in the magnitude and direction of the shift they introduce into the steady-state $H\infty/V$ curve.

In addition to the insight these mutational analyses yield about disease pathophysiology, they also provide information on normal channel structure and function. For example, residues near the extracellular ends of S3 and S4 in D4 must play a critical role in the kinetics of channel inactivation, perhaps by forming part of the receptor surface for the inactivation gate. The pH dependence of the R1448H mutation confirms that this residue in S4 lies on the external surface of the membrane in a position that is accessible to the aqueous environment. In spite of this location, the region, including L1433 and R1448 in D4, is functionally linked to inactivation. The positive charge at 1448 is important in determining the voltage dependence of inactivation, whereas the size of the side chain at 1433 is the critical factor in modifying the rate of channel inactivation. Finally, although the ID3–4 loop has already been implicated in channel inactivation, the cluster of mutations around aa 1306 that produce varying effects on channel inactivation point to this location as particularly important. The absence of a side chain on G1306 might provide a degree of rotational freedom about the peptide backbone that is necessary for bending during the inactivation process and is compromised by the side chain of other residues substituted by these mutations.

No mutation with a periodic paralysis phenotype has yet been identified in D1. Given the number and distribution of the reported mutations, this absence seems unlikely to be due to chance alone. Perhaps D1 plays a role in initiating the activation process that renders a higher percent of spontaneous mutations in this region incompatible with function and therefore lethal. It will be interesting to recreate some of the D4 mutations in comparable locations in D1 to test this hypothesis.

CONCLUSION

In the span of four decades, the sodium channel has been purified, reconstituted, sequenced, functionally expressed, and selectively mutated. The molecular mechanisms responsible for the complex behavior of this large protein are rapidly being explored using a combination of molecular, immunologic, and protein chemical techniques. Amino acid sequences involved in channel activation, inactivation, gating, voltage sensitivity, and toxin binding have been identified. With a mixture of serendipity and insight, this basic information on channel structure has provided an unexpected link to a group of rare and interesting disorders of muscle membrane excitability. A rapid transfer of knowledge from the basic to the clinical side has occurred, creating a new category of clinical disorders caused by mutations in ion channels.

In this wonderful example of the two-way street of science, the advances of basic research have been translated into a detailed understanding of disease pathophysiology that yielded immediate gains in diagnosis and therapy. On the other side of the street, identification of channel mutations associated with specific phenotypes has provided natural transgenic experiments in which new insights into channel function are gained. Clearly, clinical science and basic research have much to gain by maintaining a close-working relationship.

Any *Annual Review* chapter, as well as any article cited in an *Annual Review* chapter, may be purchased from the Annual Reviews Preprints and Reprints service. 1–800–347–8007; 415–259–5017; email: arpr@class.org

---

Literature Cited

1. Adrian RH, Chandler WK, Hodgkin AL. 1970. Voltage clamp experiments in striated muscle fibres. *J. Physiol.* 208:607–44

2. Ahmed CM, Ware DH, Lee SC, Patten CD, Ferrermontiel AV, et al. 1992. Primary structure, chromosomal localization and functional expression of a voltage-gated sodium channel from human brain. *Proc. Natl. Acad. Sci. USA* 89(17):8220–24

3. Ambrose C, Cheng S, Fontaine B, Nadeau JH, MacDonald M, Gusella JF. 1992. The α-subunit of the skeletal muscle sodium channel is encoded proximal to Tk-1 on mouse chromosome 11. *Mamm. Genome* 3:151–55

4. Armstrong CM, Bezanilla F. 1977. Inactivation of the sodium channel. II. Gating current experiments. *J. Gen. Physiol.* 70:567–90

5. Backx PH, Yue DT, Lawrence JH, Marban E, Tomaselli GF. 1992. Molecular localization of an ion-binding site within the pore of mammalian sodium channels. *Science* 257:248–51

6. Bambrick LL, Gordon T. 1988. Neural regulation of [^{3}H]-saxitoxin binding site numbers in rat neonatal muscle. *J. Physiol.* 407:263–74

7. Barchi RL. 1987. Sodium channel diversity: subtle variations on a complex theme. *Trends Neurosci.* 10:221–23

8. Barchi RL. 1992. The nondystrophic myotonic syndromes. In *Handbook of Clinical Neurology,* ed. LP Rowland, S DiMauro, 18:261–86. New York: Elsevier Sci.

9. Barchi RL. 1993. Ion channels and disorders of excitation in skeletal muscle. *Curr. Opin. Neuro. Neurosurg.* 6:40–47

10. Barchi RL, Weigele JB. 1979. Characteristics of saxitoxin binding to the sodium channel of sarcolemma isolated from rat skeletal muscle. *J. Physiol.* 295:383–96

11. Becker PE. 1977. *Myotonia Congenita and Syndromes Associated with Myotonia,* pp. 405–25. Stuttgart: Thieme

12. Bennett PB, Makita N, George AL. 1993. A molecular basis for gating mode transitions in human skeletal muscle sodium channels. *FEBS Lett.* 326(1–3):21–24

13. Cannon SC, Brown RH, Corey DP. 1991. A sodium channel defect in hyperkalemic periodic paralysis: potassium-induced failure of inactivation. *Neuron* 6(4):619–26

14. Cannon SC, Brown RH, Corey DP. 1993. Theoretical reconstruction of myotonia and paralysis caused by incomplete inactivation of sodium channels. *Biophys. J.* 65:270–88

15. Cannon SC, Corey DP. 1993. Loss of Na⁺ channel inactivation by anemone toxin (ATX II) mimics the myotonic state in hyperkalemic periodic paralysis. *J. Physiol.* 466:501–20

16. Cannon SC, McClatchey AI, Gusella JF. 1993. Modification of the Na⁺ current conducted by the rat skeletal muscle α-subunit by coexpression with a human brain β-subunit. *Pflügers Arch.* 423: 155–57

17. Cannon SC, Strittmatter SM. 1993. Functional expression of sodium channel mutations identified in families with periodic paralysis. *Neuron* 10(2):317–26

18. Catterall WA. 1986. Molecular properties of voltage-sensitive sodium channels. *Annu. Rev. Biochem.* 55:953–85

19. Catterall WA. 1988. Structure and function of voltage-sensitive ion channels. *Science* 242:50–61

20. Chahine M, George AL, Zhou M, Ji S, Sun W, et al. 1993. Sodium channel mutations in paramyotonia congenita uncouple inactivation from activation. *Neuron* 12:281–94

21. Chen L-Q, Chahine M, Kallen RG, Barchi RL, Horn R. 1992. Chimeric study of sodium channels from rat skeletal and cardiac muscle. *FEBS Lett.* 309:253–57

22. Cummins TR, Zhou JY, Sigworth FJ, Ukomadu C, Stephan M, et al. 1993. Functional consequences of a Na⁺ channel mutation causing hyperkalemic periodic paralysis. *Neuron* 10:667–78

23. Drager GA, Hammill JF, Shy GM. 1958. Paramyotonia congenita. *Arch. Neurol. Psychiatr.* 80:1–9

24. Ebers GC, George AL, Barchi RL, Ting-Passador SS, Kallen RG, et al. 1991. Paramyotonia congenita and hyperkalemic periodic paralysis are linked to the adult muscle sodium channel gene. *Ann. Neurol.* 30(6):810–16

25. Elmer LW, Obrien BJ, Nutter TJ, Angelides KJ. 1985. Physicochemical characterization of the α-peptide of the sodium channel from rat brain. *Biochemistry* 24(27):8128–37

26. Eulenburg A. 1886. Über eine familiäre,

durch 6 Generationen verfolgbare Form congenitaler Paramyotonie. *Neurol. Centralbl.* 15:265–72

27. Fontaine B, Khurana TS, Hoffman EP, Bruns GAP, Haines JL, et al. 1990. Hyperkalemic periodic paralysis and the adult muscle sodium channel α-subunit gene. *Science* 250:1000–2

28. Fontaine B, Vale-Santos JM, Jurkat-Rott K, Reboul J, Plassart E, et al. 1994. Mapping of hypokalemic periodic paralysis to chromosome 1q31–32 by a genome-wide search in three European families. *Nat. Genet.* 6(3):267–72

29. Gellens ME, George AL, Chen L-Q, Chahine M, Horn R, et al. 1992. Primary structure and functional expression of the human cardiac voltage-sensitive sodium channel. *Proc. Natl. Acad. Sci. USA* 89:554–58

30. George AL, Iyer GS, Kleinfield R, Kallen RG, Barchi RL. 1993. Genomic organization of the human skeletal muscle sodium channel gene. *Genomics* 15: 598–606

31. George AL, Komisarof J, Kallen RG, Barchi RL. 1992. Primary structure of the adult human skeletal muscle voltage-dependent sodium channel. *Ann. Neurol.* 31:131–37

32. George AL, Ledbetter DH, Kallen RG, Barchi RL. 1991. Assignment of a human skeletal muscle sodium channel α-subunit gene (SCN4A) to 17q23.1–25.3. *Genomics* 9:555–56

33. Griggs RC. 1983. Periodic paralysis. *Semin. Neurol.* 3:285–87

34. Griggs RC. 1977. The myotonic disorders and the periodic paralyses. *Adv. Neurol.* 17:143–59

35. Han J, Lu CM, Brown GB, Rado TA. 1991. Direct amplification of a single dissected chromosome polymerase chain reaction: A human brain sodium channel on chromosome 2q22-q23. *Proc. Natl. Acad. Sci. USA* 88:335–39

36. Harris JB, Thesleff S. 1971. Studies on tetrodotoxin resistant action potentials in denervated skeletal muscle. *Acta Physiol. Scand.* 83:382–88

37. Heine R, Pika U, Lehmann-Horn F. 1993. A novel SCN4A mutation causing myotonia aggravated by cold and potassium. *Hum. Mol. Genet.* 2:1349–53

38. Heinemann SH, Terlau H, Stühmer W, Imoto K, Numa S. 1992. Calcium channel characteristics conferred on the sodium channel by single mutations. *Nature* 356:441–43

39. Hodgkin AL, Huxley AF. 1952. The components of membrane conductance in the giant axon of *Loligo*. *J. Physiol.* 116:473–96

40. Hoffman EP, Spier SJ. 1993. Sodium channelopathies: dramatic disease caused by subtle genetic changes. *News Physiol. Sci.* 8:38–41

41. Hofman WW, Smith RA. 1970. Hypokalemic periodic paralysis studied in vitro. *Brain* 93:445–74

42. Hoshi T, Zagotta WN, Aldrich RW. 1990. Biophysical and molecular mechanisms of *Shaker* potassium channel inactivation. *Science* 250:533–38

43. Isom LL, Dejongh KS, Patton DE, Reber BFX, Offord J, et al. 1992. Primary structure and functional expression of the β1-subunit of the rat brain sodium channel. *Science* 256:839–42

44. Ji S, Sun W, George AL, Horn R, Barchi R. 1994. Voltage-dependent regulation of modal gating in the rat SkM1 sodium channel expressed in *Xenopus* oocytes. *J. Gen. Physiol.* 104:625–43

45. Joho RH, Moorman JR, VanDongen AM, Kirsch GE, Silberberg H, et al. 1988. Cloning and expression of the rat brain type III sodium channel gene. *J. Cell Chem.* 13:207–9

46. Jurkat-Rott K, Lehmann-Horn F, Elbaz A, Heine R, Gregg R, et al. 1994. A calcium channel mutation causing hypokalemic periodic paralysis. *Hum. Mol. Genet.* In press

47. Kallen RG, Cohen SA, Barchi RL. 1994 Structure, function, and expression of voltage-dependent sodium channels. *Mol. Neurobiol.* 7:383–428

48. Kallen RG, Sheng ZH, Yang J, Chen L-Q, Rogart RB, Barchi RL. 1990. Primary structure and expression of a sodium channel characteristic of denervated and immature rat skeletal muscle. *Neuron* 4(2):233–42

49. Klocke R, Kaupmann K, George AL, Barchi RL, Jockusch H. 1992. Chromosomal mapping of muscle-expressed sodium channel genes in the mouse. *Mouse Genome* 90:433–39

50. Koch MC, Ricker K, Otto M, Grimm T, Hoffman E, et al. 1991. Confirmation of linkage of hyperkalemic periodic paralysis to chromosome 17. *J. Med. Genet.* 28:583–86

51. Koch MC, Steinmeyer K, Lorenz C, Ricker K, Wolf F, et al. 1992. The skeletal muscle chloride channel in dominant and recessive human myotonia. *Science* 257:797–800

52. Kontis KJ, Goldin AL. 1993. Site-directed mutagenesis of the putative pore region of the rat IIA sodium channel. *Mol Pharmacol.* 43:635–44

53. Krafte DS, Goldin AL, Auld VJ, Dunn RJ, Davidson N, Lester HA. 1990. Inactivation of cloned Na channels expressed in *Xenopus* oocytes. *J. Gen. Physiol.* 96(4):689–706

54. Kraner SD, Tanaka JC, Barchi RL. 1985. Purification and functional reconstitution of the voltage-sensitive sodium channel from rabbit T-tubular membranes. *J. Biol. Chem.* 260:6341–47

55. Lehmann-Horn F, Engel A, Ricker K, Rüdel R. 1994. The periodic paralyses and paramyotonia congenita. In *Myology,* ed. AG Engel, C Franzini-Armstrong, New York: McGraw-Hill. 2nd ed. In press

56. Lehmann-Horn F, Küther G, Ricker K, Grafe P, Ballanyi K, Rüdel R. 1987. Adynamia episodica hereditaria with myotonia: a non–activating sodium current and the effect of extracellular pH. *Muscle Nerve* 10:363–74

57. Lehmann-Horn F, Rüdel R, Ricker K. 1987. Membrane defects in paramyotonia congenita (Eulenburg). *Muscle Nerve* 10:633–41

57a. Lehmann-Horn F, Rüdel R, Ricker K. 1993. Non-dystrophic myotonias and periodic paralysis. *Neuromusc. Disorder* 3:161–68

58. Lerche H, Heine R, Pika U, George AL, Mitrovic N, et al. 1993. Human sodium channel myotonia: slowed channel inactivation due to substitutions for a glycine within the III-IV linker. *J. Physiol.* 470:13–22

59. Lindstrom J, Shelton D, Fujii Y. 1988. Myasthenia gravis. *Adv. Immunol.* 42:233

60. Litt M, Luty J, Kwak M, Allen L, Magenis RE, Mandel G. 1989. Localization of a human brain sodium channel gene SCN2A to chromosome 2. *Genomics* 5(2):204–8

61. Lopez GA, Jan YN, Jan LY. 1991. Hydrophobic substitution mutations in the S4-sequence alter voltage-dependent gating in Shaker K+-channels. *Neuron* 7(2):327–36

62. Makita N, Bennett PB, George AL. 1993. Recombinant human Na+ channel beta-1-subunit functionally associates with skeletal muscle but not cardiac alpha-subunit. *Circulation* 88(4):185

63. Makita N, Bennett PB, George AL. 1994. Voltage-gated Na+ channel β-1 subunit mRNA expressed in adult human skeletal muscle, heart, and brain is encoded by a single gene. *J. Biol. Chem.* 269:7571–78

64. Malo D, Schurr E, Dorfman J, Canfield V, Levenson R, Gros P. 1991. Three brain sodium channel α-subunit genes are clustered on the proximal segment of mouse chromosome-2. *Genomics* 10(3):666–72

65. McClatchey AI, Cannon SC, Slaugenhaupt SA, Gusella JF. 1993. The cloning and expression of a sodium channel β-1-subunit cDNA from human brain. *Hum. Mol. Genet.* 2:745–49

66. McClatchey AI, McKenna-Yasek D, Cros D, Worthen HG, Kuncl RW, et al. 1992. Novel mutations in families with unusual and variable disorders of the skeletal muscle sodium channel. *Nat. Genet.* 2:148–52

67. McClatchey AI, VanDenBergh P, Pericak-Vance, MA, Raskind W, Verellen C, et al. 1992. Temperature-sensitive mutations in the III-IV cytoplasmic loop region of the skeletal muscle sodium channel gene in paramyotonia congenita. *Cell* 68:769–74

68. Messner DJ, Catterall WA. 1985. The sodium channel from rat brain. Separation and characterization of subunits. *J. Biol. Chem.* 260(19):10597–604

69. Moorman JR, Kirsch GE, Brown AM, Joho RH. 1990. Changes in sodium channel gating produced by point mutations in cytoplasmic linker. *Science* 250(4981):688–91

70. Nilius B. 1988. Modal gating behavior of cardiac sodium channels in cell-free membrane patches. *Biophys J.* 53(6):857–62

71. Noda M, Ikeda T, Suzuki H, Takeshima H, Takahashi T, et al. 1986. Expression of functional sodium channels from cloned cDNA. *Nature* 322(6082):826–28

72. Noda M, Suzuki H, Numa S, Stühmer W. 1989. A single point mutation confers tetrodotoxin and saxitoxin insensitivity on the sodium channel II. *FEBS Lett.* 259(1):213–16

73. Papazian DM, Timpe LC, Jan YN, Jan LY. 1991. Alteration of voltage-dependence of Shaker potassium channel by mutations in the S4 sequence. *Nature* 349(6307):305–10

74. Pappone PA. 1980. Voltage-clamp experiments in normal and denervated mammalian skeletal muscle fibres. *J. Physiol.* 306:377–410

75. Patlak JB, Ortiz M. 1989. Kinetic diversity of sodium channel bursts in frog skeletal muscle. *J. Gen. Physiol.* 94(2):279–301

76. Patlak JB, Ortiz M. 1986. Two modes of gating during late Na$^+$ channel currents in frog sartorius muscle. *J. Gen. Physiol.* 87:305–26

77. Patton DE, West JW, Catterall WA, Goldin AL. 1992. Amino acid residues required for fast sodium channel inactivation. Charge neutralizations and dele-tions in the III-IV linker. *Proc. Natl. Acad. Sci. USA* 89(22):10905–9

78. Ptáček LJ, Gouw L, Kwiecinski H, McManis P, Mendell JR, et al. 1994. Sodium channel mutations in acetazolamide-responsive myotonia congenita, paramyotonia congenita and hyperkalemic periodic paralysis. *Ann. Neurol.* 33(3):300–7

79. Ptáček LJ, George AL, Barchi RL, Griggs RC, Riggs JE, et al. 1992. Mutations in an S4 segment of the adult skeletal muscle sodium channel cause paramyotonia congenita. *Neuron* 8(5):891–97

80. Ptáček LJ, George AL, Griggs RC, Tawil R, Kallen RG, et al. 1991. Identification of a mutation in the gene causing hyperkalemic periodic paralysis. *Cell* 67:1021–27

81. Ptáček LJ, Gouw L, Kwiecinski H, McManis P, Mendell JR, et al. 1993. Sodium channel mutations in paramyotonia congenita and hyperkalemic periodic paralysis. *Ann. Neurol.* 33:300–7

82. Ptáček LJ, Johnson KJ, Griggs RC. 1993. Genetics and physiology of the myotonic muscle disorders. *N. Engl. J. Med.* 328:482–89

82a. Ptáček LJ, Tawil R, Griggs RC, Meola G, McManis P, et al. 1994. Sodium channel mutations in acetazolamide-responsive myotonia congenita, paramyotonia congenita, and hyperkalemic periodic paralysis. *Neurology* 44:1500–3

83. Ptáček LJ, Tawil R, Griggs RC, Storvick D, Leppert M. 1992. Linkage of atypical myotonia congenita to a sodium channel locus. *Neurology* 42(2):431–33

84. Ptáček LJ, Trimmer JS, Agnew WS, Roberts JW, Petajan JH, Leppert M. 1991. Paramyotonia congenita and hyperkalemic periodic paralysis map to the same sodium-channel gene locus. *Am. J. Hum. Genet.* 49(4):851–54

85. Ptáček LF, Tyler F, Trimmer JS, Agnew WS, Leppert M. 1991. Analysis in a large hyperkalemic periodic paralysis pedigree supports tight linkage to a sodium channel locus. *Am. J. Hum. Genet.* 49:378–82

86. Redfern P, Thesleff S. 1971. Action potential generation in denervated rat skeletal muscle. II. Action of tetrodotoxin. *Acta Physiol. Scand.* 82(1):70–78

87. Ricker K, Camacho LM, Grafe P, Lehmann-Horn F, Rüdel R. 1989. Adynamia episodica hereditaria: What causes the weakness? *Muscle Nerve* 12:883–91

88. Ricker K, Lehmann-Horn F, Moxley RT. 1990. Myotonia fluctuans. *Arch. Neurol.* 47:268–72

89. Riggs JE. 1988. The periodic paralyses. *Neurol. Clin.* 6(3):485–98

90. Ritchie JM, Rogart R. 1977. The binding of saxitoxin and tetrodotoxin to excitable tissue. *Rev. Physiol. Biochem. Pharmacol.* 79:1–50

91. Roberts RH, Barchi RL. 1987. The voltage-sensitive sodium channel from rabbit skeletal muscle: chemical characterization of subunits. *J. Biol. Chem.* 262(5):2298–303

92. Rogart RB, Regan LF. 1985. Two subtypes of sodium channel with tetrodotoxin sensitivity and insensitivity detected in denervated mammalian skeletal muscle. *Brain Res.* 329(1–2):314–18

93. Rojas CV, Wang JZ, Schwartz LS, Hoffman EP, Powell BR, Brown RH. 1991. A Met to Val mutation in the skeletal muscle Na$^+$ channel α-subunit in hyperkalemic periodic paralysis. *Nature* 354:387–89

94. Rüdel R, Lehmann-Horn F. 1985. Membrane changes in cells from myotonia patients. *Physiol. Rev.* 65(2):310–56

95. Rüdel R, Lehmann-Horn F, Ricker K, Küther G. 1984. Hypokalemic periodic paralysis: in vitro investigation of muscle fiber membrane parameters. *Muscle Nerve* 7(2):110–20

96. Rüdel R, Ricker R, Lehmann-Horn F. 1993. Genotype-phenotype correlations in human skeletal muscle sodium channel diseases. *Arch. Neurol.* 50:1241–48

97. Rudolph JA, Spier SJ, Byrns G, Rojas CV, Bernoco D, Hoffman EP. 1992. Periodic paralysis in Quarter Horses: a sodium channel mutation disseminated by selective breeding. *Nat. Genet.* 2:144–47

98. Satin J, Kyle JW, Chen M, Bell P, Cribbs LL, et al. 1992. A mutant of TTX-resistant cardiac sodium channels with TTX-sensitive properties. *Science* 256:1202–5

99. Stühmer W. 1991. Structure-function studies of voltage-gated ion channels. *Annu. Rev. Biophys. Biophys. Chem.* 20:65–78

100. Stühmer W, Conti F, Suzuki H, Wang XD, Noda M, et al. 1989. Structural parts involved in activation and inactivation of the sodium channel. *Nature* 339:597–603

101. Terlau H, Heinemann SH, Stühmer W, Pusch M, Conti F, et al. 1991. Mapping the site of block by tetrodotoxin and saxitoxin of sodium channel II. *FEBS Lett.* 293(12):93–96

102. Thackeray JR, Ganetzky B. 1994. Developmentally regulated alternative splicing generates a complex array of *Drosophila* para sodium channel isoforms. *J. Neurosci.* 14(5 Pt. 1):2569–78

103. Thomsen J. 1876. Tonische Krämpfe in willkürlich beweglichen Muskeln in Folge congenitaler ererbter psychischer Disposition. *Arch. Psychiatr.* 6:702

104. Thornhill WB, Levinson SR. 1989. *Posttranslational processing of the voltage-regulated sodium channel from eel electroplax.* Presented at Symp. Mol. Biol. Intracellular Protein Sorting Organelle Assembly, 16th Annu. Meet. UCLA Symp. Mol. Cell. Biol. Los Angeles, Calif.

105. Trimmer JS, Agnew WS. 1989. Molecular diversity of voltage-sensitive sodium channels. *Annu. Rev. Physiol.* 51:401–18

106. Trimmer JS, Cooperman SS, Tomiko SA, Zhou JY, Crean SM, et al. 1989. Primary structure and functional expression of a mammalian skeletal muscle sodium channel. *Neuron* 3(1):33–49

107. Trudell RG, Kaiser KK, Griggs RC. 1987. Acetazolamide-responsive myotonia congenita. *Neurology* 37:488–91

108. Weigele J, Barchi RL 1982. Functional reconstitution of the purified sodium channel from rat sarcolemma. *Proc. Natl. Acad. Sci. USA* 79:578–89

109. West JW, Patton DE, Scheuer T, Wang YL, Goldin AL, Catterall WA. 1992. A cluster of hydrophobic amino acid residues required for fast Na$^+$ channel inactivation. *Proc. Natl. Acad. Sci. USA* 89:910–14

110. White MM, Chen L-Q, Kleinfield R, Kallen RG, Barchi RL. 1991. SkM2, a Na$^+$ channel clone from denervated skeletal muscle, encodes a tetrodotoxin-insensitive Na$^+$ channel. *Mol. Pharmacol.* 39:604–8

111. Yang JS, Sladky JT, Kallen RG, Barchi RL. 1991. TTX-sensitive and TTX-insensitive sodium channel mRNA transcripts are independently regulated in adult skeletal-muscle after denervation. *Neuron* 7:421–27

112. Yang JS, Bennett, PB, Makita N, George A, Barchi RL. 1993. Expression of the sodium channel β_1 subunit in rat skeletal muscle is selectively associated with the TTX-sensitive α subunit isoform. *Neuron* 11:915–22

113. Yang N, Ji S, Zhou M, Ptáček LJ, Barchi RL, et al. 1994. Sodium channel muta-

tions in paramyotonia congenita exhibit similar biophysical phenotypes in vitro. *Proc. Natl. Acad. Sci. USA.* In press

114. Yellen G, Jurman ME, Abramson T, MacKinnon R. 1991. Mutations affecting internal TEA blockade identify the probable pore–forming region of a K+ channel. *Science* 251(4996): 939–42

115. Zagotta WN, Hoshi T, Aldrich RW.

1990. Restoration of inactivation in mutants of Shaker potassium channels by a peptide derived from ShB. *Science* 250:568–71

116. Zhou JY, Potts JF, Trimmer JS, Agnew WS, Sigworth FJ. 1991. Multiple gating modes and the effect of modulating factors on the μ1 sodium channel. *Neuron* 7(5):775–85

Annu. Rev. Physiol. 1995. 57:387–416

THE CFTR CHLORIDE CHANNEL OF MAMMALIAN HEART

David C. Gadsby, Georg Nagel[1], and Tzyh-Chang Hwang[2]

Laboratory of Cardiac and Membrane Physiology, The Rockefeller University, New York, NY 10021; [1]Max Planck Institut für Biophysik, Frankfurt, D60596 Germany; [2]Dalton Cardiovascular Research Center, Department of Physiology; University of Missouri, Columbia, Missouri 65211

KEY WORDS: cystic fibrosis, anion channel, gating mechanism, phosphorylation, ATP hydrolysis

INTRODUCTION

Cystic fibrosis (CF), the most prevalent fatal genetic disease among Caucasians, is caused by alterations in the single gene encoding the cystic fibrosis transmembrane conductance regulator (CFTR; 114). The gene alterations result in defective epithelial Cl^- transport and, consequently, a disruption of fluid secretion in respiratory, intestinal, and reproductive epithelia, and of salt reabsorption in sweat glands (109). A single mutation, deletion of the three nucleic acids that code for phenylalanine 508, accounts for two thirds of all diagnosed cases of CF (136), but over 300 other disease-causing mutations have been identified so far.

CFTR is now known to be a Cl^- ion channel, although, as its name implies, this was not at all clear from the deduced amino acid sequence (114). CFTR's predicted topology (Figure 1; 114) of two similar halves, each comprising six putative transmembrane stretches followed by an intracellular nucleotide–binding domain (NBD), linked by a large intracellular regulatory (R) domain containing multiple sites for phosphorylation by protein kinase A (PKA) and protein kinase C (PKC), placed it in the large family of ATP-binding cassette (ABC) transport proteins (71). The ABC family includes numerous bacterial periplasmic transporters as well as eukaryotic members such as the exporter (STE6) of the yeast a-factor mating pheromone, and the mammalian P-glyco-

387

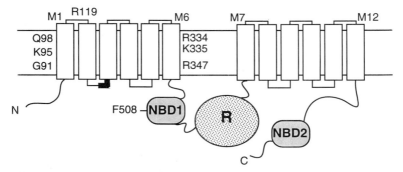

Figure 1 Simplified topological model emphasizing the postulated domain structure of a CFTR Cl⁻ channel including cytoplasmic amino (N) and carboxy (C) termini, two nucleotide-binding domains (NBD1, NBD2), regulatory (R) domain, and the predicted membrane-spanning α-helices (M1-M12). The section (*black*) of the cytoplasmic loop linking M2 and M3 indicates the peptide encoded by exon 5, which is probably deleted in the cardiac isoform of CFTR (74, 75). Eight of the residues identified as sites of mutations in CF patients (including the most common one, F508) are indicated.

protein responsible for multidrug resistance. The two NBDs sported by each member are the presumed sites of the ATP hydrolysis believed to power active transport of the cognate substrate. This evident homology has fueled the persistent notion that CFTR might also function as a transporter that somehow modulates epithelial Cl⁻ channels (85). Regardless of the eventual resolution of this proposal (cf 44; 116, 117), several lines of evidence have removed any lingering doubt that CFTR does indeed function as a small-conductance, ohmic Cl⁻ channel whose gating is regulated by PKA and hydrolyzable nucleoside triphosphates.

First, heterologous expression of CFTR in a wide variety of nonepithelial cells, including HeLa cells (4), Sf9 insect cells (87), Chinese hamster ovary (CHO) cells (127), monkey kidney fibroblast (Vero) cells (36), *Xenopus* oocytes (13, 41), and NIH-3T3 fibroblasts (17), gave rise to high densities of small conductance Cl⁻ channels that were activated via the cAMP signaling pathway and that had linear current-voltage relationships under conditions of high symmetrical Cl⁻ concentrations. Because practically all of these cells normally express negligible levels of CFTR protein and have no endogenous PKA-regulated Cl⁻ channels, the most straightforward conclusion is that CFTR is itself a Cl⁻ channel, rather than a regulator of a covert population of Cl⁻ channels with uniform characteristics, widely expressed in different tissues from several species, but silent until the expression of exogenous CFTR.

Second, point mutations in CFTR cDNA, in proposed transmembrane segments, modify the permeation properties of the resulting expressed channels. For example, expression in 3T3 cells of two CFTR mutants, *K95D* and *K335E*, in which negatively charged amino acids replaced positively charged lysines in the first (M1) and sixth (M6) putative transmembrane α-helices (Figure 1) yielded Cl⁻ channels with altered anion permeability sequences, I⁻ > Br⁻ > Cl⁻ instead of the normal Br⁻ > Cl⁻ > I⁻ (3). Also, three missense mutations associated with relatively mild CF disease, two (*R334W* and *R347P*) neutralizing positively charged arginines in M6 and one (*R119H*) substituting histidine for an arginine near the extracellular end of M2, all diminish open-channel conductance (120). The conclusion that certain residues in M1 and M6 line the anion-selective pore is corroborated by three new pieces of evidence: (*a*) Tabcharani et al (130) found that the charge-switching mutation *R347D* lowered channel conductance and abolished the anomalous mole-fraction effect seen with mixtures of Cl⁻ and SCN⁻ ions, and that channel conductance and anomalous mole-fraction behavior became pH sensitive in the mutant *R347H*. (*b*) McDonough et al (94) showed that mutations at S341 and K335 in M6 (hypothetically separated by two turns of α-helix) altered the affinity and voltage dependence of open-channel block by diphenylamine-2-carboxylate (DPC) (93). (*c*) Finally, Akabas et al (1) substituted a cysteine for each of nine consecutive residues in M1, one at a time, to test their accessibility to water-soluble sulfhydryl-specific reagents and concluded that G91, K95, and Q98 line the pore and hence that M1 is an α-helix.

Probably the most direct evidence that CFTR functions as a Cl⁻ channel comes from the demonstration that recombinant CFTR expressed in Sf9 cells and then extracted with detergent, purified to homogeneity, reconstituted into synthetic liposomes, and finally incorporated into lipid bilayers, produces small ohmic-conductance Cl⁻ channels that are activated by PKA catalytic subunit plus ATP (12).

Before the CF gene was cloned, at a time when defective regulation of outwardly rectifying Cl⁻ channels in epithelia was believed responsible for CF (147), a PKA-regulated Cl⁻ current was found in mammalian cardiac ventricular myocytes (8, 9, 64, 91), with an approximately linear whole-cell current-voltage relationship in symmetrical ~150 mM Cl solutions (9). In cell-attached (47, 48) and excised (48, 96) patches, these cardiac Cl⁻ channels display all the characteristics that identify epithelial CFTR Cl⁻ channels. That is, after the required phosphorylation by PKA catalytic subunit, the cardiac Cl⁻ channels close upon ATP withdrawal but can be reopened by ATP or GTP, but not by ADP or AMP-PNP; their unitary conductance is ohmic and ~12 pS in roughly symmetrical ~150 mM Cl⁻ solutions; their open probability (P_o) is approximately voltage independent; and their rates of opening and closing are low (47, 48, 96). Northern analysis has confirmed the presence of CFTR mRNA in myocytes from regions of the heart and species in which PKA-regulated

Cl⁻ currents can be recorded, but not in tissue from regions with no CFTR-like currents (89, 96). Although their electrocardiological role remains unclear, recent studies of cardiac CFTR channels have provided important insights not only into signaling pathways, regulatory mechanisms of ion channel function, and patterns of channel expression in the heart, but also into the likely gating mechanisms of epithelial CFTR channels. These developments are reviewed below.

SIGNAL TRANSDUCTION PATHWAYS FOR REGULATION OF CARDIAC CFTR

PKA Pathway

In cardiac myocytes, activation of β-adrenoceptors, and subsequently of the adenylyl cyclase-cAMP-PKA phosphorylation pathway, leads to modulation of the activity of a number of ion channels (61) including CFTR Cl⁻ channels. Thus the same Cl⁻ current is elicited in myocytes via β-adrenoceptor activation, by exposure to forskolin (64, 82, 91) or histamine (65, 81), or more directly by intracellular application of cAMP (8, 9, 82, 132, 133) or of the catalytic subunit of PKA (9, 66). Moreover, the Cl⁻ conductance induced by isoproterenol (82), forskolin (81) or cAMP (8) can be completely abolished by introduction of a synthetic inhibitor peptide (PKI) specific for PKA (28). Also, unitary currents characteristic of CFTR Cl⁻ channels are elicited in cell-attached patches by epinephrine or membrane permeant cAMP analogues (47) or in giant excised inside-out patches by direct application of PKA catalytic subunit plus MgATP (96). In myocytes, CFTR Cl⁻ conductance seems to differ qualitatively from other PKA-regulated conductances in that it is not evident before PKA stimulation, whereas substantial basal whole-cell conductances to Ca^{2+} (86, 105) and K^+ (153) are observed (although their magnitudes can be considerably enhanced by phosphorylation). The basis for this apparent difference remains unclear, however, because recent evidence (69, 98, 99) supports the idea (7, 135) that Ca^{2+} channels, like CFTR Cl⁻ channels, require phosphorylation by PKA before they can be opened.

G Protein Involved But not Directly

The GTP-binding protein G_s has been established in biochemical and molecular biological studies to couple the activated β-adrenoceptor to adenylyl cyclase (54). That activation of cardiac CFTR Cl⁻ conductance through β-adrenergic or histaminergic receptors depends on activation of a G protein (likely G_s) is supported by several observations: (a) Withdrawal of GTP from pipette solutions reversibly abolishes activation of the Cl⁻ current by maximally effective concentrations of isoproterenol or histamine, but not its activation by forskolin or pipette cAMP (73). (*b*) Introducing a high concentration of GDPβS prevents Cl⁻ current activation by isoproterenol, but not by forskolin (82). (*c*) With the nonhydrolyzable GTP analogue GTPγS (or GppNHp) in the pipette, a brief exposure to isoproterenol or histamine, but not to forskolin, causes persistent activation of the Cl⁻ current (82). Despite this evidence for G protein involvement, it seems unlikely that the G protein acts directly via a membrane-delimited pathway similar to that established for muscarinic K⁺ channels in atrial myocytes (20, 106) and suggested for cardiac L-type Ca^{2+} and Na⁺ channels (22), both of which are also known to be regulated through phosphorylation by PKA. For CFTR Cl⁻ channels, the direct pathway is made unlikely by the findings (82) that (*a*) pipette application of PKI abolishes Cl⁻ current induced by isoproterenol with either GTP or GTPγS in the pipette, (*b*) isoproterenol does not activate CFTR Cl⁻ current in the presence of PKI, and (*c*) isoproterenol causes no further increase in the Cl⁻ current following maximal stimulation of the PKA pathway with forskolin or intracellular cAMP (although the current could be increased by other maneuvers such as phosphatase inhibition; 81). In epithelia, Cl⁻ secretion can also be elicited through β-adrenoceptor activation (147), and in cells expressing epithelial CFTR, low conductance ohmic Cl⁻ channels can be activated by forskolin (10, cf 68, 129), or by membrane-permeant cAMP analogues (15, 129), or by PKA catalytic subunit plus MgATP applied to excised patches (e.g. 2, 127). The same receptor-G protein–adenylyl cyclase-PKA pathway has therefore been implicated for epithelia (147), although the inferred obligatory role for G proteins has not been established experimentally. However, evidence has been reported for G protein–mediated inhibition of CFTR Cl⁻ channels in airway epithelia although the mechanism is unknown (118).

G Protein Convergence on Cyclase

In myocytes, as in many other cell types, the activity of adenylyl cyclase and the cellular cAMP level are modulated through the inhibitory G protein G_i (54). Accordingly, stimulation of muscarinic receptors by acetylcholine (ACh) or carbachol (CCh) decreases Cl⁻ current induced by isoproterenol or forskolin (63, 64, 82, 132), but not that activated by pipette cAMP (82, 132), which indicates that inhibition is exerted at the level of the adenylyl cyclase and not at that of the β-adrenoceptor, kinase, or phosphatases. The muscarinic inhibitory effect is presumably mediated by G_i because it required pipette GTP (73) and was abolished by pertussis toxin or a high concentration of GDPβS (82). It appears, then, that β-adrenergic and muscarinic pathways converge on adenylyl cyclase, via G_s and G_i proteins, respectively, to regulate CFTR Cl⁻ channels, as previously suggested for regulation of L-type Ca^{2+} current in guinea pig (70) and frog (50, 97, 105) cardiac myocytes.

G Protein-Forskolin Interactions at Cyclase

The ability of G_i to inhibit adenylyl cyclase varies depending on whether the cyclase is stimulated by forskolin or by β-adrenoceptor (i.e. G_s) activation. The concentration-response curve for activation of Cl^- current by forskolin is simply shifted to higher concentrations by exposure to carbachol, with no reduction of the maximal response (79, 132); a qualitatively similar shift results from pipette application of the nonhydrolyzable GTP analogue, GTPγS that, in the absence of receptor agonists, appears to preferentially activate G_i in guinea pig ventricular myocytes (81, 79). However, carbachol does not affect the apparent affinity for isoproterenol, but substantially reduces the maximal Cl^- current it elicits (79). The implication is that G_i interferes noncompetitively with G_s action, but competitively with forskolin action (79). These results are comparable to findings on regulation of Ca^{2+} currents in frog myocytes (51, 105). Surprisingly, in contrast to observations on frog Ca^{2+} currents (20, 105), the maximal Cl^- current response to isoproterenol in guinea pig myocytes dialyzed with GTPγS is the same as when GTP is in the pipette, except that the response persists after washout of isoproterenol and is not diminished by carbachol; this points to kinetic and/or spatial differences between frog and guinea pig in the membrane densities of activated G_i and G_s proteins (79, cf 104), possibly related to differences in temperature. Hescheler et al (70) and Tareen et al (132), measuring Ca^{2+} and Cl^- currents, respectively, also studied muscarinic inhibitory effects in guinea pig myocytes but found that ACh simply shifted the isoproterenol concentration-response curves (as described above for forskolin). These apparent discrepancies might reflect differences in the details of the regulatory pathways for different ion channels in a given cell and/or differences in cycle kinetics of the same G proteins due to small differences in experimental conditions.

Phosphodiesterase Modulation

Because intracellular [cAMP] is determined by the combined activities of adenylyl cyclase and phosphodiesterases (PDEs) that hydrolyze cAMP, the PKA signaling pathway can also be modulated by controlling the activity of the PDEs. Ono et al (100) found in guinea pig myocytes that pipette application of cGMP enhanced the Cl^- conductance induced by submaximal, but not by supramaximal, concentrations of isoproterenol, forskolin, or intracellular cAMP, consistent with cGMP-mediated inhibition of a PDE. Abolition of the cGMP effect by milrinone, a specific inhibitor of cGMP-sensitive PDE, confirmed that conclusion (100). A comparable role for cGMP-sensitive PDE in the regulation of guinea pig myocyte Ca^{2+} current had already been established (101).

REGULATION OF CARDIAC CFTR CHANNELS BY PHOSPHORYLATION AND DEPHOSPHORYLATION

PKA Involved, But PKC Involvement Unclear

Evidence including the direct activation of channels in excised inside-out membrane patches by the catalytic subunit of PKA and MgATP (96) has established the cAMP-PKA signaling system as the major regulatory pathway for cardiac CFTR Cl⁻ channels. The role of PKC remains controversial. Phorbol esters, activators of PKC, elicit a time-independent Cl⁻ conductance in guinea pig (141) or feline ventricular myocytes without (157, 158) or with (145) the inclusion of purified PKC in the pipette. Findings interpreted as suggesting that PKC activates Cl⁻ channels that are identical or similar to CFTR include inhibition of the PKC-activated current by 1 mM anthracene-9-carboxylate (9-AC), and occlusion of the response to forskolin by maximal activation of PKC (145, 157, 158). However, Walsh & Long (145) reported $SCN^-:I^-:Br^-:Cl^-$ permeability ratios of 1.93:1.41:1.00:1.00 for the PKC-activated Cl⁻ conductance, and large outward currents in I⁻, in contrast to the extremely small outward currents carried by I⁻ in cardiac CFTR Cl⁻ channels (40, 102, 145). That the cardiac Cl⁻ channels activated by PKC are CFTR channels is suggested by the recent finding of ~10 pS single Cl⁻ channels elicited by phorbol ester in cell-attached patches on guinea pig ventricular myocytes (33); subsequent application of the PDE isobutylmethylxanthine (IBMX) increased P_o but did not alter channel conductance. The latter observation correlates well with results from epithelial CFTR Cl⁻ channels because serines 686 and 790 in the R domain are phosphorylated by PKC (107), and pre-exposure to PKC greatly potentiates the rate and extent of channel activation by PKA (27, 127). PKC itself can also activate epithelial CFTR Cl⁻ channels, although less effectively than PKA (18). In cell-attached patches on HT-29cl.19A (human colon carcinoma) cells, however, phorbol ester alone failed to activate channels but apparently increased the number of CFTR Cl⁻ channels activated by forskolin without changing their P_o (10). Much remains to be learned about PKC phosphorylation of CFTR.

Dephosphorylation by Phosphatases

Deactivation of PKA-regulated Cl⁻ conductance in myocytes following sudden withdrawal of agonists or introduction of pipette PKI is rapid and complete, which indicates the presence of endogenous protein phosphatases (81). Not surprisingly, therefore, pipette application of okadaic acid or microcystin, both specific inhibitors of phosphatases 1 and 2A (PP1, PP2A), causes an increase in the steady-state level of phosphoprotein and of the activated Cl⁻ conductance, and slows its subsequent deactivation (81). But even after complete inhibition of PP1 and PP2A, some deactivation of the Cl^- current accompanies withdrawal of forskolin, implying that some other phosphatase can also dephosphorylate the Cl^- channel. If that phosphatase were to de-phosphorylate sites essential for Cl^- channel function, then eventually, in the absence of PKA activity, all the Cl^- channels would become dephosphoryl-ated and deactivated. However, in the presence of a maximal concentration of okadaic acid or microcystin, the Cl^- conductance was not fully deactivated after washout of forskolin and/or introduction of PKI; almost half remained for > 20 min (81). These results suggest that two kinds of PKA-phosphory-lated sites control the magnitude of whole-cell Cl^- conductance; one kind can be dephosphorylated only by PP1 and/or PP2A and is required for the Cl^- channels to function, whereas the other kind modulates activity of the Cl^- channels and can be dephosphorylated by some other phosphatase. Whether these modulatory sites can also be dephosphorylated by PP1 and/or PP2A is not known.

Distinct Phosphoforms

Because the R domain of CFTR comprises several consensus sites for PKA phosphorylation (114), and because PKA phosphorylates at least four or five of those serines in vivo and in vitro (29, 107), the simplest interpretation of the above results is that the two kinds of PKA sites exist on each cardiac CFTR Cl^- channel. The two levels of whole-cell Cl^- conductance, residual and fully activated, would then reflect, respectively, partially phosphorylated (at only the essential sites) and fully phosphorylated (at both kinds of sites) Cl^- chan-nels. According to that scheme, because the residual Cl^- conductance is only ~40% of the fully activated Cl^- conductance, the partially phosphorylated Cl^- channels must have a smaller unitary conductance or lower P_o than fully phosphorylated channels (81). Indeed, excised patches containing a single cardiac CFTR channel occasionally show, after addition of PKA, a step in-crease in P_o (from ≤ 0.2 to ≥ 0.6, mainly reflecting an increase in channel open time) that is reduced following PKA removal and may then be restored by readdition of PKA (84). In other words, the P_o of a single-channel molecule can be reversibly modulated by PKA-dependent phosphorylation and dephos-phorylation. Therefore, the persistent, residual whole-cell Cl^- conductance in the presence of okadaic acid (or microcystin) is envisaged as reflecting the low P_o gating mode of partially phosphorylated CFTR Cl^- channels, whereas the larger Cl^- conductance during exposure to forskolin is attributed to the higher P_o of fully phosphorylated CFTR channels. These findings and their interpretation are in keeping with the observations of graded regulation of the P_o of epithelial CFTR channels by incremental PKA phosphorylation of mul-tiple sites in the R domain (27, 113).

Identity of Endogenous Phosphatases

Cardiac CFTR channel current in excised patches generally declines (the rate varies from patch to patch) after removal of PKA, usually with a concomitant reduction of channel open time, sometimes to zero. These changes reflect dephosphorylation because channel activity can be partially (or completely) restored by reapplication of PKA (84), which means that excised patches can contain membrane-bound phosphatases capable of dephosphorylating both kinds of sites discussed above. The okadaic acid- and microcystin-sensitive phosphatase responsible for fully deactivating cardiac CFTR channels is likely to be PP2A because preliminary results indicate that phosphorylated DARPP-32, a specific PP1 inhibitor, fails to affect forskolin-induced whole-cell Cl^- current (83). This result concurs with the finding of Berger et al (18) that, in excised membrane patches, purified PP2A can abolish epithelial CFTR Cl^- channel activity induced by PKA and ATP. The okadaic acid-insensitive phosphatase believed to modulate channel P_o is probably PP2C (81), which is activated by mM levels of Mg^{2+}; PP2B, which is Ca^{2+}/calmodulin dependent, is ruled out because all pipette solutions contained $\geq$ 10 mM EGTA and no added Ca^{2+} (119). Consistent with that conclusion, Ehara & Matsuura (48) did not observe the lower P_o mode of gating of single cardiac CFTR channels when the cytoplasmic free $[Mg^{2+}]$ was kept low (~10 μM); instead, using binomial theory, they determined that upon PKA phosphorylation, each Cl^- channel opened with a high P_o (~0.7), which remained constant for several minutes. Whether phosphatases outside these four major classes could be involved in dephosphorylating CFTR channels remains controversial. Exogenous alkaline phosphatase can dephosphorylate CFTR protein (15a) and can deactivate CFTR channels activated by PKA in excised patches from CHO cells (15a, 127) or from a human pancreatic cell line (14). As noted by Berger et al (18), the reduction of channel activity by alkaline phosphatase is at least partly the result of hydrolysis of ATP by the enzyme, although this could not explain the restoration of channel activity by readdition of PKA in the presence of the alkaline phosphatase (127). The highly variable activity of native, membrane-associated phosphatases in excised patches (e.g. 84) might compromise interpretation of some effects of exogenous phosphatases.

Parcelling Up Multiple Consensus PKA sites

Pin-pointing the multiple sites phosphorylated by PKA and characterizing their influence on CFTR channel function has been difficult. In tryptic phosphopeptide maps of CFTR phosphorylated in vitro or in vivo, Cheng et al (29) identified serines 660, 737, 795 and 813, while Picciotto et al (107) identified serines 660, 700, 737, 813, and 768 and/or 795. Cheng et al (29) initially reported that mutation of serines 660, 737, 795, and 813 to alanine (4SA) abolished cAMP-induced anion secretion in cells transfected with the mutant CFTR, but that sparing any one of the serines allowed a response to cAMP, as if the multiple phosphorylation sites in CFTR were functionally redundant. However, more recent experiments (27, 113) exploiting unitary current measurements as a more sensitive assay of channel function show that 4SA mutant channels are active but with a P_o about half that of wild-type. Indeed, even when all ten PKA consensus sites (nine in the R domain, and one just N-terminal to NBD1) were converted to alanine, PKA could still activate Cl$^-$ channels, albeit with a further ~twofold reduction in P_o, although no phosphorylation of the immunoprecipitated 10SA protein could be detected (27). Similarly, Rich et al (113) mutated four more serines, 686, 700, 712, and 768, in the 4SA channels to yield 8SA mutants, in which the P_o was further reduced. These results suggest that there is a cryptic site (or sites) whose phosphorylation is sufficient for channel activation, but also that at least some of the ten consensus serines play a role in modulating channel P_o and that there may be functionally distinct sites or groups of sites. The possibility that phosphorylation has a simple electrostatic effect was tested by Rich et al (113), who systematically mutated to aspartates the eight serine residues conserved across species. 4SD channels (serines 660, 737, 795, and 813) were not constitutively active, but 6SD channels (with additional serines 686 and 700 mutated) or 8SD channels (with two more serines at positions 712 and 768 mutated), showed phosphorylation-independent, ATP-gated channel activity. Similar results are obtained by changing the same serines to glutamate (X-B Chang, personal communication). However, it seems unlikely that phosphorylation permits gating of CFTR channels merely by adding negative charge to the surface of a relatively rigid R domain and thereby relieving occlusion of the channel mouth because recent evidence suggests that phosphorylation alters the conformation of the R domain (43). On the other hand, without more detailed structural information, or a functional analysis of all possible combinations of mutations of the ten consensus serines, their relationship to the functionally distinct sets of phosphorylation sites identified in native cardiac CFTR Cl$^-$ channels remains speculative.

ROLES OF HYDROLYZABLE AND NONHYDROLYZABLE NUCLEOSIDE TRIPHOSPHATES IN THE GATING OF CARDIAC CFTR Cl$^-$ CHANNELS

Hydrolyzable Nucleoside Triphosphate Required for Channel Opening

A distinctive characteristic of cardiac and epithelial CFTR Cl$^-$ channels is their requirement, following phosphorylation by PKA, for hydrolyzable nucleoside triphosphate before they will open (2, 24, 84, 96), and sudden withdrawal of

MgATP causes cardiac CFTR channels to close within seconds (95). Anderson et al (2) showed that phosphorylated CFTR channels in patches excised from transfected 3T3 and HeLa cells could be opened (provided Mg^{2+} was present) by ATP, GTP, ITP, UTP, or CTP, or by AMP-CPP (an analogue that can donate its γ-phosphate), but not by poorly hydrolyzable analogues like AMP-PNP, AMP-PCP, ATPγS, ADP, or cAMP. The conclusion is that ATP hydrolysis, most likely at NBD1 (because ATP regulates gating of an NBD2 mutant, *K1250M*), is required to open CFTR channels (2). The dependence of cardiac CFTR channel gating on Mg^{2+} has not been investigated (complication from effects on phosphorylation via PP2C are anticipated), but micromolar levels of Ca^{2+} appear to substitute for Mg^{2+} in sustaining a low but significant activity of CFTR channels in patches from transfected mouse cells (115). Recent analyses of the [MgATP] dependence of CFTR channel gating in HeLa and 3T3 cells (152), in mouse L cells (140), or in lipid bilayers (59) have shown an influence on channel closed time but not on open time, which suggests that an ATP-dependent process controls channel opening; ADP was found to compete with ATP in that process.

Inorganic Phosphate Analogues

That the gating transition of CFTR Cl^- channels is driven by the free energy available from ATP hydrolysis is supported by experiments on cardiac CFTR channels using inorganic phosphate (P_i) analogues to interrupt the hydrolytic reaction cycle (Figure 2) and so interfere with channel gating (11). Phosphate analogues like orthovanadate or BeF_3 inhibit ATPases (e.g. 23, 149) by binding so tightly in place of the released P_i following ATP hydrolysis that further hydrolytic cycles are prevented (25). Correspondingly, these analogues are found to markedly stabilize the open conformation of cardiac CFTR channels opened by ATP, prolonging channel open times by some three orders of magnitude (11). In excised patches, this effect was nearly independent of channel P_o and thus, presumably, of the degree of channel phosphorylation (11). Accordingly, in whole-cell current measurements on myocytes treated with okadaic acid or microcystin (77), orthovanadate was found to augment not only the large CFTR Cl^- conductance in the presence of forskolin (attributed to fully phosphorylated channels) but also the smaller residual Cl^- conductance after washout of forskolin (attributed to partially phosphorylated channels). In patches, the kinetics of formation of this stable open-channel state suggest that ATP hydrolysis at one of the NBDs prompts channel opening and that after release of P_i from the open conformation, a relatively slow event (possibly release of ADP; Figure 2) controls the conformational change that closes the channel (11). Biochemical studies should resolve whether the cycle is rate limited by release of the ADP (analogous to GTPases or myosin; 149) or, as in the case of P-type ATPases, by the dephosphorylation of a phosphor-

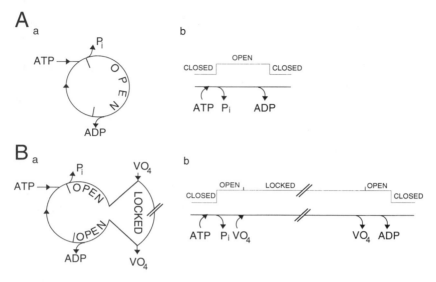

Figure 2   Schematic diagram of coupling of CFTR channel gating to an ATP hydrolysis cycle. (Aa) ATP hydrolysis is required for the conformational change associated with channel opening; release of P_i and eventually of ADP prompt channel closing. (Ab) Linearized version emphasizing timing of channel opening and closing. (Ba) Proposed mechanism for locking of channel in open conformation by orthovanadate, after release of P_i, illustrated in circular (Ba) and linearized (Bb) forms of ATP hydrolysis cycle. The breaks in the VO_4-locked sections reflect the ~400-fold greater dwell time of the VO_4-locked state vs the normal open state (from Reference 11).

ylated intermediate that occurs long after ADP is released. Regardless of the type of hydrolytic cycle involved, the findings suggest that each channel opening (ignoring fast interruptions of open-channel current) is associated with hydrolysis of an ATP and, therefore, that details of individual ATP hydrolysis cycles can be examined in single molecules in situ and in real time (11).

Nonhydrolyzable Analogues

Channel opening by ATP hydrolysis seemed difficult to reconcile with the observation of Quinton & Reddy (110) that in permeabilized, microperfused human sweat ducts, the small apical CFTR Cl⁻ conductance activated in the presence of 0.1 mM ATP (≤2% of that activated with 5 mM ATP) was enhanced by addition of 5 mM AMP-PNP, AMP-CPP, ATPγS, or ATP-MeS (2-methyl-thioadenosine triphosphate). Similar results were obtained in T84 cell monolayers (16), and Hwang et al (84) confirmed that during PKA stimulation with forskolin, introduction of AMP-PNP into guinea pig myocytes dialyzed with ATP enhances activated CFTR Cl⁻ conductance. A solution to

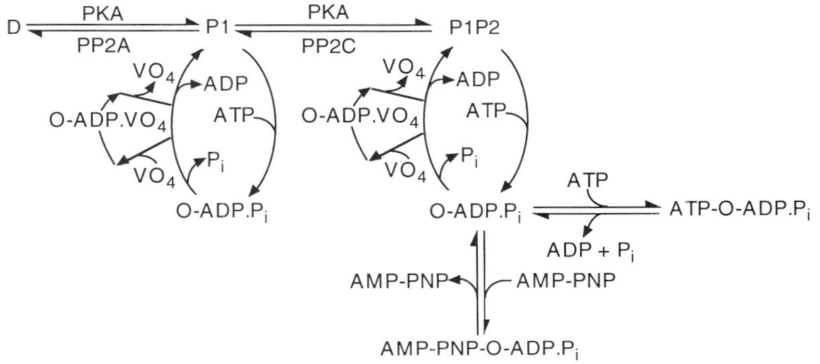

Figure 3 Proposed minimal gating scheme for CFTR Cl⁻ channels based on regulation of the two NBDs by incremental phosphorylation. The upper row shows closed CFTR channel conformations: dephosphorylated (D), partially phosphorylated (P1), and highly phosphorylated (P1P2). Both P1 and P2 sites are phosphorylated by PKA, but P1 sites can be dephosphorylated only by phosphatase (PP) 2A, whereas P2 sites are believed to be dephosphorylated by PP2C. Both P1 and P1P2 phosphoforms permit hydrolysis of ATP (or other hydrolyzable nucleoside triphosphate) at NBD1 to open the channel (state O-ADP.P_i) as indicated by the cycles; the NBD1 hydrolysis cycle can be interrupted for long periods by orthovanadate (VO₄) binding in place of the released product P_i, which results in locking of the channel open conformation. In the case of P1P2 channels, after ATP hydrolysis at NBD1 has opened the channel, NBD2 can then interact with ATP or AMP-PNP to stabilize the open state of the channel (*lower row, right*). Stabilization is lost upon dissociation of AMP-PNP, or of ADP + P_i following hydrolysis of the ATP. The proposed stabilizing action of AMP-PNP (and of ATP) at NBD2 shares analogy with the action of GMP-PNP (and of GTP) to stabilize the activated α-subunit of heterotrimeric G proteins (modified from Reference 84).

this apparent paradox comes from the finding that, although AMP-PNP alone fails to open PKA-phosphorylated CFTR Cl⁻ channels in patches excised from myocytes, AMP-PNP can markedly stabilize the open state of those channels once they have been opened by ATP (84), a finding now confirmed for recombinant epithelial CFTR channels in bilayers (59). The implication is that AMP-PNP can act at only one of CFTR's two NBDs, and then only after ATP has acted at the other. Because AMP-PNP closely resembles ATP in molecular structure (154), yet has a nonhydrolyzable γ-phosphate, the failure of AMP-PNP to open the channels is attributed to the requirement of ATP hydrolysis (at NBD1) for channel opening (Figure 2), and the simplest explanation for its prolongation of the channel open state is that channel closing also normally requires hydrolysis of ATP, but at the other NBD (Figure 3; 84).

Differential Regulation of NBD Function by Incremental Phosphorylation

In contrast to orthovanadate, which stabilized the open states of cardiac CFTR Cl⁻ channels regardless of channel P_o (11), AMP-PNP in the presence of ATP was found to stabilize only the open states of CFTR Cl⁻ channels with high P_o (84). Thus addition of AMP-PNP to pipette ATP had no effect on the partially phosphorylated CFTR channels that underlie the component of whole-cell Cl⁻ conductance persisting after washout of forskolin in myocytes dialyzed with okadaic acid or microcystin. Furthermore, in excised patches, addition of AMP-PNP to ATP was without effect on CFTR channels with low P_o ($\leq$0.2). Because of the link already established between channel P_o and PKA phosphorylation (above), a simple hypothesis is that incremental phosphorylation of CFTR at multiple sites differentially regulates the activity of its two NBDs (84).

Minimal Gating Scheme for CFTR Channels

This hypothesis is summarized in the minimal gating scheme for CFTR Cl⁻ channels illustrated in Figure 3. In this scheme, phosphorylation of the (cryptic?) sites that are dephosphorylated only by the okadaic acid-sensitive phosphatase (likely PP2A) yields a partially phosphorylated channel (Figure 3; P1 phosphoform) in which only NBD1 (at which AMP-PNP cannot act) is functional. The partially phosphorylated channel does not open until ATP is hydrolyzed to ADP+P_i at NBD1, and the channel closes soon after dissociation of these hydrolysis products; this brief channel opening underlies the low P_o ($\leq$0.2 at 0.5 mM ATP) that characterizes partially phosphorylated channels. AMP-PNP has no effect on partially phosphorylated channels, but orthovanadate can bind to the open-channel conformation, following the release of P_i, to form a stable open-channel complex. Additional phosphorylation of the sites that are dephosphorylated by the okadaic acid-insensitive phosphatase (probably PP2C) yields a fully phosphorylated channel (Figure 3; P1P2 phosphoform) and confers function also on NBD2, at which AMP-PNP can act. Opening of fully phosphorylated channels also requires ATP hydrolysis at NBD1. Once the channel has opened, NBD2 becomes available for nucleotide binding, and ATP binding there somewhat stabilizes the open state of the channel (by preventing release of ADP and/or P_i from NBD1), which results in the higher P_o ($\geq$0.6 at 0.5 mM ATP) that is characteristic of fully phosphorylated channels. ATP hydrolysis at NBD2 and dissociation of the resulting products then prompts release of ADP and/or P_i from NBD1, which leads to normal closing of the channel. However, channel closing is greatly delayed (100–1000-fold) when AMP-PNP binds at NBD2 instead of ATP. The implied long residence time of AMP-PNP in NBD2 suggests that AMP-PNP binds there with extremely high affinity so that, because of their close structural similarity, the binding affinity of ATP at NBD2 should be equally high. The much lower apparent affinity of NBD2 for ATP, suggested by the relatively rapid closure of fully phosphorylated channels exposed only to ATP, presumably reflects rapid dissociation from NBD2, not of ATP itself, but of its hydrolysis products ADP and P_i.

This model is broadly consistent with and supported by the large body of data on native and recombinant epithelial CFTR, which implies that CFTR channel gating is unaffected by deletion of exon 5 (cf 59). Anderson & Welsh (5) suggested that the two NBDs are functionally distinct because analogous mutations in NBD1 and NBD2 have different effects on the inhibitory influence of ADP on ATP activation of CFTR channels in mouse mammary epithelial cells. Similarly, Smit et al (122) found that mutations of certain conserved residues in the proposed ATP-binding pockets of NBD1 (K464, D572) and NBD2 (K1250, D1370) have opposite effects on the sensitivity to activation with IBMX of CFTR channels expressed in oocytes; these effects are expected if the mutations interfere with nucleotide hydrolysis, and if ATP hydrolysis at NBD1 opens CFTR channels, but at NBD2 closes them. The failure of Carson & Welsh (24) and Schultz et al (115) to observe an effect of AMP-PNP added in the presence of ATP is also understandable if the channels were studied in the low P_o, partially phosphorylated state; PKA was withdrawn several minutes before testing AMP-PNP in those studies, likely sufficient time for membrane-bound phosphatases to have dephosphorylated the P2 sites and so rendered NBD2 unavailable. Finally, the gating scheme in Figure 3 readily explains the observation (58, 136, cf 122) that mutations that interfere with ATP binding or hydrolysis at NBD1, and hence with channel opening, are associated with more severe channel dysfunction and therefore more severe disease than equivalent mutations at NBD2. However, the proposal illustrated in Figure 3, that NBD function depends on phosphorylation status and that the two NBDs must interact, urges caution in interpreting the behavior of CFTR channels with mutations in the NBDs.

Can Dephosphorylated Open Channels Remain Open?

Deactivation of the whole-cell Cl⁻ conductance after washout of forskolin is complete, but it is severalfold slower in myocytes dialyzed with AMP-PNP plus ATP (half-time ~5 min, similar to the slow closing of channels in excised patches exposed to AMP-PNP and ATP; 84) than in myocytes without AMP-PNP. Because there is no evidence that AMP-PNP inhibits phosphatases, this slow deactivation indicates either that channels locked open by AMP-PNP are insensitive to phosphatases or that the channels remain open long after they have been dephosphorylated. The former suggests that the conformational change accompanying channel opening hinders phosphatase access to the phosphoserines, whereas the latter suggests that PKA phosphorylation is simply permissive for channel gating via ATP hydrolysis at NBD1 but that the R domain per se is less directly involved in channel gating. Experiments with purified phosphatases might help answer this question.

BIOPHYSICAL AND PHARMACOLOGICAL CHARACTERIZATION OF CARDIAC CFTR Cl⁻ CHANNELS

Biophysical and pharmacological properties of an ion channel provide a signature by which that channel may be distinguished from others. Because those characteristics are determined by details of the channel's structure, they form the basis of sensitive functional assays of natural and synthetic channel mutants.

I-V Curves and Rectification

Whole-cell current-voltage (I-V) relationships of the PKA-regulated Cl⁻ conductance in myocytes are nearly linear with approximately symmetrical ~150 mM Cl⁻, but show outward rectification with physiological [Cl⁻] gradients (~150 mM external, and ~20 mM internal, Cl⁻) across the membrane (9, 64, 91). Although this shallow outward rectification is reasonably well described by the Goldman-Hodgkin-Katz constant field equation (81, 82, 102), Overholt et al (102) found no comparable inward rectification after reversing the [Cl⁻] gradient and an outwardly rectifying, rather than linear, I-V with symmetrical low [Cl⁻]. They suggested that the outward rectification reflects channel block by the less permeant anions (e.g. glutamate, aspartate) used to replace Cl⁻ and were able to account for I-V relationships obtained over a range of [Cl⁻] with a one-site, two-barrier model based on Eyring rate theory (102). A comparable range of [Cl⁻] has yet to be tested in excised membrane patches, which should afford improved control of ion concentrations and of channel gating status. Single cardiac CFTR channel I-V relationships published so far show outward rectification with roughly physiological [Cl⁻] (47, 96) and are approximately linear (96), or slightly outwardly rectifying (48), with nearly symmetrical high [Cl⁻].

Single Channel Conductance

Ehara & Ishihara (47) recorded single Cl⁻ channel currents at 35°C in cell-attached patches on guinea pig myocytes stimulated by epinephrine; the limiting slope conductance at positive potentials was ~13 pS. With symmetrical high [Cl⁻] and excised patches, a voltage-independent conductance of ~12 pS was found in inside-out patches at 25°C (96), but a conductance varying between ~9 and ~15 pS was found at extreme negative and positive potentials, respectively, in outside-out patches at 35°C (48). Approximately linear whole-cell I-V relationships under conditions of nearly symmetrical [Cl⁻] have also been reported for PKA-regulated, epithelial CFTR Cl⁻ current in, for example, T84 cells (30), immortalized human airway cells (68), and pancreatic duct cells (55). Expression of epithelial CFTR in a variety of cell types yielded small-conductance (6–10 pS), ohmic Cl⁻ channels (148) in symmetrical [Cl⁻], similar to native CFTR channels in T84 cells (9 pS at 37°C; 129) and in epithelial cells from rat pancreas (4 pS at 22°C; 56), pig thyroid (6 pS at 20°C; 26), human airway (6–7 pS at 20–23°C; 68, 67), and human pancreas (9 pS at 23°C, 12 pS at 37°C; 15), as well as in clathrin-coated vesicles from T84 cells (8 pS at 20°C, 12 pS at 37°C; 19). A comparable limiting slope conductance of 11 pS was found (at 22–25°C, with a 300/50 mM [Cl⁻] gradient) for epithelial CFTR expressed in Sf9 cells, purified, and then reconstituted into lipid bilayers (12).

Ion Selectivity

From shifts of the reversal potential of whole-cell PKA-regulated Cl⁻ current in guinea pig myocytes on replacing most of the extracellular Cl⁻ with test anions, Overholt et al (102) determined the relative permeability sequence of cardiac CFTR channels to be $NO_3^- > Br^- \geq Cl^- \geq I^- >$ isethionate⁻ $\geq$ glutamate⁻. The corresponding conductance sequence, estimated from the slope conductance of the outward (test ion) currents, was $NO_3^- = Cl^- >$ glutamate⁻ $= Br^- \geq$ isethionate⁻ $> I^-$. A low relative permeability of I^- with respect to Cl⁻ has been considered a diagnostic feature of epithelial CFTR Cl⁻ channels (148). Although $P_I/P_{Cl} < 1.0$ (0.4–0.6) was reported in the majority of studies on epithelial CFTR channels (e.g. 3, 6, 30, 31, 55, 68, 117), ratios close to 1.0 [~1.0 (56); 1.1 (87); or even >1.0 (1.7) (128)] have been described. The fewer experiments on CFTR currents in guinea pig myocytes have yielded somewhat less variable P_I/P_{Cl} ratios of 1.3 (40, 141) and 0.9 (102). Factors contributing to the variability of these ratios include: voltage errors due to liquid junction potentials; inapplicability of the bi-ionic assumption due to cytoplasmic accumulation of the test anion; the sidedness of I^- application (cf 128); I^- block of the CFTR channels themselves (reducing both inward and outward channel currents, hence exacerbating effects of changes in other currents including leak currents; possible influence of I^- on the PKA activation pathway (144); and species differences (108) in the amino acid sequence of the putative M1 helix (cf 3).

Multi-Ion Pore

Elegant experiments by Tabcharani et al (130) showed that, unlike the single-site permeation model proposed for cardiac CFTR (102), human epithelial CFTR channels in patches excised from transfected CHO cells are multi-ion, single-file pores. Using symmetrical solutions, Tabacharani et al found the unitary CFTR conductance to be ~7 pS at 154 mM Cl⁻ and ~10 pS at 150 mM SCN⁻, but only 2 pS with 10 mM SCN⁻ plus 144 mM Cl⁻. This anomalous mole-fraction effect revealed interactions between permeating anions. Voltage dependence of the Cl⁻ current inhibition by SCN⁻ implicated a site ~20% into the electric field, which corresponds roughly with the predicted distance of R347 along helix M6 (Figure 1). The charge-reversing mutation *R347D* halved channel conductance (cf 120) and abolished inhibition by SCN⁻ and anomalous mole-fraction behavior. Moreover, by replacing R347 with histidine, channel characteristics such as unitary conductance, block by SCN⁻, and anomalous mole-fraction effect could all be toggled between wild-type and mutant simply by switching the pH between 5.5 and 8.7! Tabcharani et al (130) concluded that the CFTR channel contains at least two binding sites for Cl⁻ ions and that the positive charge on R347 affords one of them and enhances the channel conductance.

Pharmacological Characteristics

The stilbene derivatives DNDS, DIDS, and SITS, inhibitors of the electroneutral anion exchanger (band 3), also block certain Cl⁻ channels including those from *Torpedo* electroplax [DIDS and SITS reversibly; (150)] and epithelial outwardly rectifying Cl⁻ channels [DNDS reversibly, DIDS irreversibly; (21)]. In contrast, epithelial CFTR Cl⁻ channels are not inhibited by DIDS (e.g. 6, 31, 35, 56, 68, 129) or DNDS (68). In cardiac myocytes, on the other hand, Bahinski et al (9) reported that relatively high concentrations of DNDS (91, 131) or SITS irreversibly diminished Cl⁻ current elicited by isoproterenol (or pipette cAMP), but that neither inhibitor was effective on cells dialyzed with higher pipette [EGTA] (50 mM), [Hepes] (40 mM), and [Cl⁻] (20 mM); nor do DIDS or DNDS affect forskolin-induced Cl⁻ conductance in myocytes more vigorously dialyzed via low access resistance (1–4 MΩ) pipettes (80). Harvey (62) similarly saw no effect of DNDS on isoproterenol-elicited Cl⁻ conductance in myocytes but found an enhancement by SITS and DIDS that was not seen when forskolin or 8-Br-cAMP activated the conductance, which suggests an effect on the β-adrenoceptor. Thus DNDS has no direct effect on cardiac CFTR channels but, at high concentration, it may interfere with their regulation via some indirect pathway. Anthracene-9-carboxylate (9-AC), an effective inhibitor of Cl⁻ conductance in skeletal muscle (103), reduces isoproterenol-evoked Cl⁻ conductance in cardiac myocytes in a voltage-independent manner (63) by ~90% at 200 μM (88, cf 142). Reports of effects of arylaminobenzoates such as 5-nitro-2-(3-phenylpropylamino)-benzoate (NPPB) (57) and DPC on CFTR channels are varied. Cardiac PKA-regulated Cl⁻ current was reportedly (142) strongly reduced by 50 μM NPPB, as were single-channel (56) and whole-cell (55) epithelial CFTR Cl⁻ currents by only 10 μM NPPB in pancreatic cells. Haws et al (67) observed a strong, flickery block of CFTR channels by 20–40 μM cytoplasmic, but not extracellular, NPPB in patches excised from Calu-3 (lung adenocarcinoma) cells. However, Haws et al (68) also reported little or no effect of up to 100 μM extracellular or 40 μM cytoplasmic NPPB on CFTR channels in a bronchial cell line over a ≥100 mV voltage range. Cunningham et al (35) reported little effect of either 50 μM NPPB or 3 mM DPC on CFTR Cl⁻ currents in *Xenopus* oocytes at +65 mV. This positive membrane potential might account for the observed weak effect of DPC because McCarty et al (93) and McDonough et al (94) found, in the same expression system, a voltage dependent block of epithelial CFTR Cl⁻ channels by DPC that was half maximal at ~1 mM DPC at 0 mV, but ~300 μM at −100 mV. In preliminary tests on cardiac myocytes, Walsh (142) reported a >80% decrease in PKA-regulated Cl⁻ current by 1 mM DPC, whereas Hwang et al (80) found no noticeable effect on forskolin-induced Cl⁻ conductance of a brief (≤2 min) exposure to 200 μM DPC. Interestingly, sulfonylureas such as the K_{ATP} channel blockers (126) glibenclamide and tolbutamide, and K_{ATP} channel openers such as diazoxide and minoxidil, were found to inhibit PKA-regulated Cl⁻ current in 3T3 cells expressing recombinant epithelial CFTR (121); block appeared voltage independent and was stronger (K_i ~20 μM) and less reversible for glibenclamide than for tolbutamide (K_i ~150 μM). Hongre et al (72) reported much weaker effects of glibenclamide (K_i ~100 μM) and tolbutamide on CFTR current in T84 cells, and Venglarik et al (139) demonstrated by noise analysis that glibenclamide (K_i ~50 μM) and tolbutamide (K_i ~500 μM) are open-channel blockers of CFTR Cl⁻ channels in transfected mouse L cells. In cardiac myocytes, PKA-regulated Cl⁻ current is blocked by glibenclamide (K_i ~30 μM) in a voltage-independent manner (134).

Modulation by Extracellular Na?

When the PKA-regulated Cl⁻ conductance in guinea pig myocytes is elicited by β-adrenoceptor stimulation, it shows a surprising requirement for extracellular Na⁺ (9, 45, 46, 63, 91). Matsuoka et al (91) demonstrated that several inorganic monovalent cations, but not TEA⁺ or Tris⁺, could at least partly replace Na⁺ in supporting isoproterenol activation of Cl⁻ conductance. The apparent requirement for Na⁺ was clarified by Tareen et al (13), who found that it reflected antagonism of β-adrenoceptors by the Na⁺ substitute ions because there was little effect of replacing external Na⁺ by sucrose, and Na⁺ substitutes affected β-adrenoceptor-mediated stimulation of both Cl⁻ and Ca²⁺ currents, but had no effect on Cl⁻ conductance activated by histamine, forskolin, or pipette perfusion with cAMP. The latter finding contrasts with the report of Harvey et al (66) that replacement of Na⁺ by TMA⁺ diminishes Cl⁻ conductance elicited by isoproterenol [choline⁺, Tris⁺, or N-methyl-D-glucamine⁺ (NMG⁺) gave similar results], forskolin, 8-Br-cAMP, IBMX, or inclusion of PKA catalytic subunit in the pipette. However, substitution of TMA⁺ for Na⁺ did not affect Cl⁻ conductance activated by forskolin with ATPγS in the pipette or when 10 mM Na⁺ was added to the usually Na⁺-free pipette solution (66). Some of those results are consistent with the explanation of Tareen et al (133), others can be attributed to activation of muscarinic receptors by TMA⁺

(155), and possibly by choline$^+$, with consequent inhibition of adenylyl cyclase (see above), but some (e.g. with PKA catalytic subunit, or pipette Na$^+$) remain unexplained. However, all authors concur that cardiac CFTR Cl$^-$ channels are not directly influenced by external Na$^+$, a conclusion corroborated by the finding (96) that unitary CFTR current amplitudes in excised membrane patches are unaffected by replacement of extracellular Na$^+$ (by NMG$^+$) and/or cytoplasmic Na$^+$ (by Cs$^+$). Harvey et al (66) interpreted the loss of external Na effects upon including 10 mM Na$^+$ in the pipette to indicate that these effects were indirect, due to secondary changes of intracellular [Na$^+$] which, in turn, reflected incomplete control of the intracellular milieu. However, their hypothesis that intracellular Na$^+$ plays an important role in maintaining the channel in an activated or phosphorylated state (66) is not supported by the finding of Tareen et al (133) that external Na$^+$ replacement (by TEA$^+$) causes the same diminution of isoproterenol-induced Cl$^-$ conductance regardless of pipette [Na] (0, 15, or 115 mM). The discrepant observations may perhaps be attributed to uncontrolled changes (e.g of pH) just beneath the surface membrane of the myocyte (see 78). The influence of extra- and/or intracellular [Na] on regulation of epithelial CFTR Cl$^-$ channels has not been examined.

MOLECULAR BIOLOGICAL CHARACTERIZATION OF CARDIAC CFTR

CFTR mRNA in Heart

The identical biophysical, biochemical, and pharmacological properties of cardiac PKA-activated Cl$^-$ channels and epithelial CFTR Cl$^-$ channels prompted molecular analyses of cardiac mRNA. Nagel et al (96) showed that total RNA purified from guinea pig heart or lung, but not from brain, hybridized with a full-length antisense riboprobe derived from human CFTR cDNA, indicating the presence of a transcript comparable in size to human CFTR. Levesque et al (89) used cDNA prepared from rabbit ventricular mRNA as a template for amplification by the polymerase chain reaction (PCR) with primers flanking both ends of the first nucleotide binding domain (NBD1) of CFTR. The 550 bp PCR product shared about 93% sequence homology with human CFTR (114) and was 98% identical to CFTR on the basis of the deduced amino acid sequence. Northern blot analyses of mRNA from dog pancreas, rabbit and guinea pig ventricle, and human atrium, that used the PCR product as a probe, identified a transcript of about 6.5 kb, demonstrating expression in those tissues of a transcript homologous to CFTR.

Exon 5 Deletion

Further sequencing of amplification products of cardiac CFTR cDNA corresponding to each of the two predicted membrane-spanning domains, M1-M6 and M7-M12, revealed a deletion of 30 amino acids (corresponding to exon 5) at the C-terminal end of the predicted first cytoplasmic loop (Figure 1), which suggests that the cardiac isoform is an alternatively spliced product of CFTR (74). Outside that region, the cardiac CFTR transcript showed >95% identity to that from human epithelia (74). In rabbit and guinea pig, expression of the isoforms seems mutually exclusive because only the cardiac isoform was found in heart, and only the epithelial transcript appeared in epithelia (74). On the other hand, recent data suggest that spliced and unspliced forms are expressed in atria and ventricles of both simian and human hearts (75). The functional significance of this alternative splicing of CFTR remains unclear, although deletion of exon 5 has been reported to interfere with intracellular processing of CFTR expressed in HeLa cells (37), much as deletion of F508 does (58, 37), and a mutation that causes deletion of exon 5 has been detected in CF patients (52, 159). If the CF phenotype associated with deletion of exon 5 is due to defective protein processing (37) with consequent sparse distribution of epithelial CFTR Cl⁻ channels, this could explain the relatively low membrane density of CFTR channels in cardiac myocytes, ≤ 0.1 μm^{-2} (47, 96). Nevertheless, the closely similar gating and other characteristics of the cardiac and epithelial isoforms of the CFTR Cl⁻ channel need not be surprising considering the extensive sequence identity in the nucleotide-binding regions and the regulatory domain (74, 76).

Regional Expression of CFTR in Heart

Takano & Noma (131) mapped the functional distribution of CFTR Cl⁻ channels in rabbit heart and found no isoproterenol-activated Cl⁻ current in cells from the S-A node or atrium, despite evident β-adrenoceptor-mediated modulation of hyperpolarization-activated current in S-A nodal myocytes and L-type Ca^{2+} current in atrial myocytes. They confirmed the presence of the isoproterenol-activated Cl⁻ current in the ventricle and reported an ~twofold greater current density in epicardial than in endocardial myocytes. Hagiwara et al (60) also noted the absence of PKA-regulated Cl⁻ current in rabbit atrium and S-A node, whereas Sorota et al (125) failed to observe it in dog ventricular myocytes, and Matsuura & Ehara (92) found the current in only 10% of guinea pig atrial myocytes. For all these species, these functional measurements correlate well with the regional distribution of expression of the alternatively spliced CFTR transcript (34, 74), further supporting the conclusion that the cardiac isoform of CFTR underlies cardiac PKA-regulated Cl⁻ conductance. There are no molecular data to compare with the reported presence of PKA-regulated Cl⁻ current in cat (157, 158), but not in rat (42) or mouse ventricular myocytes (90). But there are preliminary reports of recordings of PKA-regulated whole-cell Cl⁻ current in simian ventricular myocytes (146) and of whole-cell (76, but cf 124) and single-channel (75) currents in human atrial myocytes, although whether they derive from spliced or unspliced CFTR gene products remains a question (75).

FUNCTIONAL ROLE AND CLINICAL SIGNIFICANCE OF CARDIAC CFTR Cl⁻ CHANNELS

The functional role of CFTR Cl⁻ channels in the heart is unclear but, given the known biochemical and biophysical characteristics of CFTR and its regional pattern of expression, some reasonable predictions can be made. As already mentioned, CFTR Cl⁻ conductance is likely to be significant only following receptor-mediated stimulation of PKA, the major consequences of which in ventricles are increased magnitudes of L-type Ca^{2+} current and delayed rectifier K^+ current. Following the upstroke of the ventricular action potential, Ca^{2+} current activates rapidly, within a few ms, in contrast to the delayed K^+ current, which activates over hundreds of ms. Because CFTR channel gating is approximately voltage independent, and E_{Cl} is normally around -50 to -60 mV (38, 138), a substantial outward, repolarizing Cl⁻ current should flow through CFTR channels instantaneously upon action potential depolarization and should persist throughout the plateau phase. This outward current will partly counter the depolarizing influence of the enhanced Ca^{2+} current with two consequences. First, the action potential plateau will be held away from the Ca^{2+} equilibrium potential and closer to the peak of the Ca^{2+}-channel current-voltage relationship, thus increasing Ca^{2+} entry into the cell. Second, the outward Cl⁻ current will counteract the tendency of the augmented inward Ca^{2+} current to delay repolarization, thus preventing possibly dangerous action potential lengthening [signaled by prolongation of the Q-T interval in the electrocardiogram (EKG)].

Direct tests of these predictions are hampered by the lack of a selective blocker for CFTR Cl⁻ channels, and hopes of exploiting one of the CFTR-knockout mouse models (39, 111, 123) to test them are dashed by preliminary results showing an absence of PKA-activated Cl⁻ current in ventricular myocytes from wild-type mice (90). However, results obtained with incompletely selective blockers on rabbit and guinea pig cardiac myocytes do provide some support for the above predictions. Takano & Noma (131) showed that β-adrenoceptor stimulation in rabbit ventricular myocytes, examined using the nystatin-perforated patch technique at 36°C, caused a small reduction in action potential duration, thus reflecting the net effect of increasing Cl⁻, Ca^{2+}, and K^+ currents. Subsequent exposure to 1 mM DNDS (which can diminish cardiac CFTR Cl⁻ channel current by some indirect mechanism; see above) caused a marked increase in action potential duration. In the same cells, DNDS in the absence of isoproterenol did not influence the action potential, thereby ruling out any major effect on Ca^{2+} or K^+ current. Takano & Noma (131) concluded that DNDS prolongs the action potential in isoproterenol by inhibiting PKA-regulated Cl^- current which, therefore, must normally counter the tendency of the enhanced Ca^{2+} current to lengthen the action potential. That conclusion, derived from ventricular myocytes, is strengthened by their finding that DNDS does not alter the action potential in isoproterenol-stimulated atrial myocytes from the same hearts, because neither PKA-regulated Cl^- current nor expression of CFTR are detectable in rabbit atria (74, 131). To examine the effects on the action potential of modifying PKA-regulated Cl^- current in guinea pig ventricular myocytes, Harvey et al (63) altered intracellular $[Cl^-]$ and Levesque et al (88) applied 200 μM 9-AC; however, they lowered the temperature to prevent the accompanying increase in K^+ current (143). Thus, although a reduction in action potential duration could be demonstrated upon activation of the Cl^- current, the relative contributions of Cl^- and K^+ currents to the shape of the action potential under physiological conditions could not be determined.

Several questions remain concerning CFTR function in human hearts. In contrast to findings in other species, PCR results suggest that CFTR is expressed in atria as well as ventricles from human and simian hearts and, moreover, both spliced and unspliced forms can be detected (75, 89, 146). However, there are no reports yet of PKA-regulated Cl^- currents in human ventricular myocytes, and although preliminary reports of whole-cell (76) and single-channel (75) PKA-regulated Cl^- currents in human atrial myocytes have appeared, Sorota et al (124) failed to elicit Cl^- current in myocytes from human atria with isoproterenol or forskolin despite robust stimulation of Ca^{2+}-channel current.

Assuming that functional CFTR Cl^- channels exist in human ventricle, the consequences of their possible absence in the hearts of CF patients remain unclear. Because it is likely that CFTR channels are largely dephosphorylated and deactivated in normal resting heart and are activated only following PKA stimulation, differences between normal and CF hearts might become apparent only under sympathetic stress. Answers to some of these questions should come from appraisal of EKGs measured with and without sympathetic stress (or administration of isoproterenol) from normal subjects, from CF patients, from CF patients with lung transplants, from CF patients with heart and lung transplants, and from nonCF recipients of transplanted CF hearts. A comprehensive set of such measurements should help clarify the normal physiological role of CFTR Cl^- channels in human heart as well as any electrocardiological dysfunction that might occur in CF patients. Unfortunately, given the present prominent standing of the class III antiarrhythmic drugs that inhibit K^+ channels and prolong cardiac action potentials (32), it is not clear whether the action potential shortenings caused by CFTR Cl^- current should be considered antiarrhythmic and beneficial, or arrhythmogenic and dangerous (78, cf 88).

It remains an intriguing possibility that in addition to its role as a Cl^- channel, cardiac CFTR somehow regulates the activity of another channel (or channels) in cardiac myocytes. A precedent comes from studies of airway epithelial cells in which expression of CFTR (and hence of the small, ohmic conductance Cl^- channels) somehow controls the ability of the distinct, outwardly rectifying Cl^- channels to respond to regulation via PKA (44, 53, 117). A recent suggestion is that CFTR exerts this control indirectly by supplying extracellular ATP, which then acts via purinergic receptors to activate the outwardly rectifying Cl^- channels (116). Also, independent evidence suggests that another ABC transporter, p-glycoprotein, might modulate the activity of a different population of Cl^- channels that are activated by cell swelling (137, but cf 49, 112).

ACKNOWLEDGMENTS

Preparation of this review and our research summarized in it were supported by grants from the National Institutes of Health (HL-36783 and HL-49907) and the American Heart Association, New York City and Missouri Affiliates, and by the assistance of Mari Kuwabara and Peter Hoff.

Literature Cited

1. Akabas MH, Kaufmann C, Cook TA, Archdeacon P. 1994. Amino acid residues lining the chloride channel of the cystic fibrosis transmembrane conductance regulator. *J. Biol. Chem.* 269:14865–68

2. Anderson MP, Berger HA, Rich DR, Gregory RJ, Smith AE, Welsh MJ. 1991. Nucleoside triphosphates are required to open the CFTR chloride channel. *Cell* 67:775–84

3. Anderson MP, Gregory RJ, Thompson S, Souza DW, Paul I, et al. 1991. Demonstration that CFTR is a chloride channel by alteration of its anion selectivity. *Science* 253:202–5

4. Anderson MP, Rich DR, Gregory RJ, Smith AE, Welsh MJ. 1991. Generation of cAMP-activated chloride currents by expression of CFTR. *Science* 251:679–82

5. Anderson MP, Welsh MJ. 1992. Regulation by ATP and ADP of CFTR chloride channels that contain mutant nucleotide–binding domains. *Science* 257:1701–4

6. Anderson MP, Welsh MJ. 1991. Calcium and cAMP activate different chloride channels in the apical membrane of normal and cystic fibrosis epithelia. *Proc. Natl. Acad. Sci. USA* 88:6003–7

7. Armstrong D, Eckert R. 1987. Voltage-activated calcium channels that must be phosphorylated to respond to membrane depolarization. *Proc. Natl. Acad. Sci. USA* 84:2518–22

8. Bahinski A, Gadsby DC, Greengard P, Nairn AC. 1989. Chloride conductance regulated by protein kinase A in isolated guinea-pig ventricular myocytes. *J. Physiol.* 418:32P

9. Bahinski A, Nairn AC, Greengard P, Gadsby DC. 1989. Chloride conductance regulated by cyclic AMP-dependent protein kinase in cardiac myocytes. *Nature* 340:718–21

10. Bajnath RB, Groot JA, De Jonge HR, Kansen M, Bijman J. 1993. Synergistic activation of non-rectifying small conductance chloride channels by forskolin and phorbol esters in cell-attached patches of the human colon carcinoma cell line HT-29cl.19A. *Pflügers Arch.* 425:100–8

11. Baukrowitz T, Hwang T-C, Nairn AC, Gadsby DC. 1994. Coupling of CFTR Cl channel gating to an ATP hydrolysis cycle. *Neuron* 12:473–82

12. Bear CE, Canhui L, Kartner N, Bridges RJ, Jensen TJ. 1992. Purification and functional reconstitution of the cystic fibrosis transmembrane conductance regulator (CFTR). *Cell* 68:809–18

13. Bear CE, Duguay F, Naismith AL, Kartner N, Hanrahan HW, Riordan JR. 1991. Cl⁻ channel activity in *Xenopus* oocytes expressing the cystic fibrosis gene. *J. Biol. Chem.* 266:19142–45

14. Becq F, Fanjul M, Merten M, Figarella C, Hollande E, Gola M. 1993. Possible regulation of CFTR-chloride channels by membrane-bound phosphatases in pancreatic duct cells. *FEBS Lett.* 3:337–42

15. Becq F, Hollande E, Gola M. 1993. Phosphorylation-regulated low-conductance Cl⁻ channels in a human pancreatic duct cell line. *Pflügers Arch.* 425:1–8

15a. Becq F, Jensen TT, Chang X-B, Savoia A, Rommens JM, et al. 1994. Phosphate inhibitors activate normal and defective CFTR chloride channels. *Proc. Natl. Acad. Sci. USA* 91:9160–64

16. Bell CL, Quinton PM. 1993. Regulation of CFTR Cl conductance in secretion by cellular energy levels. *Am. J. Physiol.* 264:C925–31

17. Berger HA, Anderson MP, Gregory RJ, Thompson S, Howard PW, et al. 1991. Identification and regulation of the CFTR-generated chloride channel. *J. Clin. Invest.* 88:1422–31

18. Berger HA, Travis SM, Welsh MJ. 1993. Regulation of the cystic fibrosis transmembrane conductance regulator Cl channels by specific kinases and protein phosphatases. *J. Biol. Chem.* 268:2037–47

19. Bradbury NA, Cohn JA, Venglarik CJ, Bridges RJ. 1994. Biochemical and biophysical identification of cystic fibrosis transmembrane conductance regulator chloride channels as components of endocytic clathrin-coated vesicles. *J. Biol. Chem.* 269:8296–302

20. Breitwieser G, Szabo G. 1985. Uncoupling of cardiac muscarinic and β-adrenergic receptors from ion channels by a guanine nucleotide analogue. *Nature* 317:538–40

21. Bridges RJ, Worrell RT, Frizzell RA, Benos DJ. 1989. Stilbene disulfonate blockade of colonic secretory Cl⁻ channels in planar lipid bilayers. *Am. J. Physiol.* 256:C902–12

22. Brown AM, Birnbaumer L. 1988. Direct G protein gating of ion channels. *Am. J. Physiol.* 254:H401–10

23. Cantley LC Jr, Cantley LG, Josephson L. 1978. A characterization of vanadate interactions with the (Na,K)-ATPase: mechanistic and regulatory implications. *J. Biol. Chem.* 253:7361–68

24. Carson MR, Welsh MJ. 1993. 5′-adenylylimidodiphosphate does not activate CFTR chloride channels in cell-free patches of membrane. *Am. J. Physiol.* 265:L27–32

25. Chabre M. 1990. Aluminofluoride and beryllofluoride complexes: new phosphate analogs in enzymology. *Trends Biochem. Sci.* 15:6–10

26. Champigny G, Verrier B, Gérard C, Mauchamp J, Lazdunski M. 1990. Small conductance chloride channels in the apical membrane of thyroid cells. *FEBS Lett.* 259:263–68

27. Chang X-B, Tabcharani JA, Hou YX, Jensen TJ, Kartner N, et al. 1993. Protein kinase A (PKA) still activates CFTR chloride channel after mutagenesis of all 10 PKA consensus phosphorylation sites. *J. Biol. Chem.* 268:11304–11

28. Cheng HC, Kemp BE, Pearson RB, Smith AJ, Miconi L, et al. 1986. A potent synthetic peptide inhibitor of the cAMP-dependent protein kinase. *J. Biol. Chem.* 261:989–92

29. Cheng SH, Rich DP, Marshall J, Gregory RJ, Welsh MJ, Smith AE. 1991. Phosphorylation of the R domain by cAMP-dependent protein kinase regulates the CFTR chloride channel. *Cell* 66:1027–36

30. Cliff WH, Frizzell RA. 1990. Separate Cl⁻ conductances activated by cAMP and Ca²⁺ in Cl⁻-secreting epithelial cells. *Proc. Natl. Acad. Sci. USA* 87:4956–60

31. Cliff WH, Schoumacher RA, Frizzell RA. 1992. cAMP-activated Cl channels in CFTR-transfected cystic fibrosis pancreatic epithelial cells. *Am. J. Physiol.* 262:C1154–60

32. Colatsky TJ, Argentieri TM. 1994. Potassium channel blockers as antiarrhythmic drugs. *Drug Dev. Res.* 33(3):

33. Collier ML, Hume JR. 1995. Unitary chloride channels activated by protein kinase C in guinea-pig ventricular myocytes. *Circ. Res.* In press

34. Collier ML, Levesque PC, Hart P, Geary Y, Torihashi S, et al. 1994. Diversity of expression of CFTR Cl⁻ channels in heart. *Biophys. J.* 66:A420

35. Cunningham SA, Worrell RT, Benos DJ, Frizzell RA. 1992. cAMP-stimulated ion currents in *Xenopus* oocytes

expressing CFTR cRNA. *Am. J. Physiol.* 31:C783–88

36. Dalemans W, Barbry P, Champigny G, Jallat S, Dott K, et al. 1991. Altered chloride ion channel kinetics associated with DF508 cystic fibrosis mutation. *Nature* 354:526–28

37. Delaney SJ, Rich DP, Thomson SA, Hargrave MR, Lovelock PK, et al. 1993. Cystic fibrosis transmembrane conductance regulator splice variants are not conserved and fail to produce chloride channels. *Nature Genet.* 4:426–31

38. Désilets M, Baumgarten CM. 1986. K^+, Na^+, and Cl^- activities in ventricular myocytes isolated from rabbit heart. *Am. J. Physiol.* 251:C197–208

39. Dorin JR, Dickinson P, Alton EWFW, Smith SN, Geddes DM, et al. 1992. Cystic fibrosis in the mouse by targeted insertional mutagenesis. *Nature* 359:211–15

40. Dousmanis AG, Gadsby DC. 1994. Anion permeability sequence of the open cardiac CFTR Cl channel. *Biophys. J.* 66:A361

41. Drumm ML, Wilkinson DJ, Smit LS, Worrell RT, Strong TV, et al. 1991. Chloride conductance expressed by DF508 and other mutant CFTRs in *Xenopus* oocytes. *Science* 254:1797–99

42. Dukes ID, Cleemann L, Morad M. 1990. Tedisamil blocks the transient and delayed rectifier K^+ currents in mammalian cardiac and glial cells. *J. Pharmacol. Exp. Ther.* 254:560–69

43. Dulhanty AM, Riordan JR. 1994. Phosphorylation by cAMP-dependent protein kinase causes a conformational change in the R domain of the cystic fibrosis transmembrane conductance regulator. *Biochemistry* 33:4072–79

44. Egan M, Flotte T, Afione S, Solow R, Zeitlin PL, et al. 1992. Defective regulation of outwardly rectifying Cl^- channels by protein kinase A corrected by insertion of CFTR. *Nature* 358:581–84

45. Egan TM, Noble D, Noble SJ, Powell T, Twist VW, Yamaoka K. 1988. On the mechanism of isoprenaline- and forskolin-induced depolarization of single guinea-pig ventricular myocytes. *J. Physiol.* 400:299–320

46. Egan TM, Noble D, Noble SJ, Powell T, Twist VW. 1987. An isoprenaline activated sodium-dependent inward current in ventricular myocytes. *Nature* 328:634–37

47. Ehara T, Ishihara K. 1990. Anion channels activated by adrenaline in cardiac muscle. *Nature* 347:284–86

48. Ehara T, Matsuura H. 1993. Single channel study of the cyclic AMP-regulated chloride current in guinea-pig ventricular myocytes. *J. Physiol.* 464:307–20

49. Ehring GR, Osipchuk YV, Cahalan MD. 1994. Swelling-activated chloride channels in multidrug-sensitive and -resistant cells. *J. Gen. Physiol.* 104: In press

50. Fischmeister R, Hartzell HC. 1986. Mechanism of action of acetylcholine on calcium current in single cells from frog ventricle. *J. Physiol.* 376:183–202

51. Fischmeister R, Shrier A. 1989. Interactive effects of isoprenaline, forskolin, and acetylcholine on Ca^{2+} current in frog ventricular myocytes. *J. Physiol.* 417:231–39

52. Fonknechten N, Chomel J-C, Kitzis A, Kahn A, Kaplan J-C. 1992. Skipping of exon 5 as a consequence of the 711 + 1 G → T mutation in the CFTR gene. *Hum. Mol. Genet.* 1:281–82

53. Gabriel SE, Clarke LL, Boucher RC, Stutts MJ. 1993. CFTR and outward rectifying chloride channels are distinct proteins with a regulatory relationship. *Nature* 363:263–66

54. Gilman AG. 1987. G proteins: Transducers of receptor-generated signals. *Annu. Rev. Biochem.* 56:615–49

55. Gray MA, Plant S, Argent BE. 1993. cAMP-regulated whole cell chloride currents in pancreatic duct cells. *Am. J. Physiol.* 264:C591-C602

56. Gray MA, Pollard CE, Harris A, Coleman L, Greenwell JR, Argent BE. 1990. Anion selectivity and block of the small-conductance chloride channel on pancreatic duct cells. *Am. J. Physiol.* 259:C752–61

57. Greger R. 1990. Chloride channel blockers. *Meth. Enzymol.* 191:793–810

58. Gregory RJ, Rich DP, Cheng SH, Souza DW, Paul S, et al. 1991. Maturation and function of cystic fibrosis transmembrane conductance regulator variants bearing mutations in putative nucleotide-binding domains 1 and 2. *Mol. Cell. Biol.* 11:3886–93

59. Gunderson KL, Kopito RR. 1994. Effects of pyrophosphate and nucleotide analogs suggest a role for ATP hydrolysis in cystic fibrosis transmembrane regulator channel gating. *J. Biol. Chem.* 269:19349–53

60. Hagiwara N, Masuda H, Shoda M, Irisawa H 1992. Stretch activated anion channels of rabbit cardiac myocytes. *J. Physiol.* 456:285–302

61. Hartzell HC. 1988. Regulation of cardiac ion channels by catecholamines, acetylcholine and second messenger systems. *Prog. Biophys. Mol. Biol.* 52:165–247

62. Harvey RD. 1993. Effects of stilbene-

disulfonic acid derivatives on the cAMP-regulated chloride current in cardiac myocytes. *Pflügers Arch.* 422:436–42

63. Harvey RD, Clark CD, Hume JR. 1990. Chloride current in mammalian cardiac myocytes. *J. Gen. Physiol.* 95:1077–102

64. Harvey RD, Hume JR. 1989. Autonomic regulation of a chloride current in heart. *Science* 244:983–85

65. Harvey RD, Hume JR. 1990. Histamine activates the chloride current in cardiac ventricular myocytes. *J. Cardiovasc. Electrophysiol.* 1:309–17

66. Harvey RD, Jurevicius JA, Hume JR. 1991. Intracellular Na^+ modulates the cAMP-dependent regulation of ion channels in the heart. *Proc. Natl. Acad. Sci. USA* 88:6946–50

67. Haws C, Finkbeiner WE, Widdicombe JH, Wine JJ. 1994. CFTR in Calu-3 human airway cells: channel properties and role in cAMP-activated Cl conductance. *Am. J. Physiol.* 266:502–12

68. Haws C, Krouse ME, Xia Y, Gruenert DC, Wine JJ. 1992. CFTR channels in immortalized human airway cells. *Am. J. Physiol.* 263:L692–707

69. Herzig S, Patil P, Neumann J, Staschen C-M, Yue DT. 1993. Mechanisms of β-adrenergic stimulation of cardiac Ca^{2+} channels revealed by discrete-time Markov analysis of slow gating. *Biophys. J.* 65:1599–612

70. Hescheler J, Kameyama M, Trautwein W. 1986. On the mechanism of muscarinic inhibition of the cardiac Ca current. *Pflügers Arch.* 407:182–89

71. Higgins CF. 1992. ABC transporters: From microorganisms to man. *Annu. Rev. Cell Biol.* 8:67–113

72. Hongre A-S, Baró I, Berthon B, Escande D. 1994. Effects of sulphonylureas on cAMP-stimulated Cl⁻ transport via the cystic fibrosis gene product in human epithelial cells. *Pflügers Arch.* 426:284–87

73. Horie M, Hwang T-C, Gadsby DC. 1992. Pipette GTP is essential for receptor-mediated regulation of Cl⁻ current in dialyzed myocytes from guinea-pig ventricle. *J. Physiol.* 455:235–46

74. Horowitz B, Tsung SS, Hart P, Levesque PC, Hume JR. 1993. Alternative splicing of CFTR Cl⁻ channels in heart. *Am. Physiol. Soc.* 264:H2214–20

75. Hume JR, Hart P, Geary Y, Levesque PC, Collier ML, et al. 1995. Molecular physiology of cardiac chloride channels. *Heart Vessels Suppl.* 9: In press

76. Hume JR, Hart P, Levesque PC, Collier ML, Geary Y, et al. 1994. Molecular physiology of CFTR Cl⁻ channels in heart. *Jpn. J. Physiol.* 44(Suppl. 1): 5177–82

77. Hwang T-C, Baukrowitz T, Nagel G, Horie M, Nairn AC, Gadsby DC. 1994. Regulation of the gating of cardiac CFTR Cl channels by phosphorylation and ATP hydrolysis. *J. Gen. Physiol.* 104:34a

78. Hwang T-C, Gadsby DC. 1994. Chloride channels in mammalian heart cells. In *Chloride Channels, Current Topics in Membranes*, ed. WB Guggino, 42:317–46. San Diego: Academic

79. Hwang T-C, Horie M, Dousmanis AG, Gadsby DC. 1992. Interactive modulation of PKA-regulated chloride current by forskolin, G_s, and G_i in guinea pig ventricular myocytes. *Biophys. J.* 61: A395

80. Hwang T-C, Horie M, Dousmanis AG, Gadsby DC. 1992. Regulation of PKA-activated Cl conductance in guinea pig ventricular myocytes: whole-cell studies. *J. Gen. Physiol.* 100:69a

81. Hwang T-C, Horie M, Gadsby DC. 1993. Functionally distinct phospho-forms underlie incremental activation of PKA-regulated Cl⁻ conductance in mammalian heart. *J. Gen. Physiol.* 101: 629–50

82. Hwang T-C, Horie M, Nairn AC, Gadsby DC. 1992. Role of GTP-binding proteins in the regulation of mammalian cardiac chloride conductance. *J. Gen. Physiol.* 99:465–89

83. Hwang T-C, Nagel G, Nairn AC, Gadsby DC. 1993. Dephosphorylation of cardiac Cl⁻ channels requires multiple protein phosphatases. *Biophys. J.* 64: A343

84. Hwang T-C, Nagel G, Nairn AC Gadsby DC. 1994. Regulation of the gating of CFTR Cl channels by phosphorylation and ATP hydrolysis. *Proc. Natl. Acad. Sci. USA* 91:4698–702

85. Hyde SC, Emsley P, Hartshorn MJ, Mimmack MM, Gileadi U, et al. 1990. Structural model of ATP-binding proteins associated with cystic fibrosis, multidrug resistance and bacterial transport. *Nature* 346:362–65

86. Kameyama M, Hescheler J, Hofmann F, Trautwein W. 1986. Modulation of Ca current during the phosphorylation cycle in the guinea pig heart. *Pflügers Arch.* 407:123–28

87. Kartner N, Hanrahan JW, Jensen TJ, Naismith AL, Sun S, et al. 1991. Expression of the cystic fibrosis gene in non-epithelial invertebrate cells produces a regulated anion conductance. *Cell* 64:681–91

88. Levesque PC, Clark CD, Zakarov SI,

Rosenshtraukh LV, Hume JR. 1993. Anion and cation modulation of the guinea-pig ventricular action potential during β-adrenoceptor stimulation. *Pflügers Arch.* 424:54–62

89. Levesque PC, Hart PJ, Hume JR, Kenyon JL, Horowitz B. 1992. Expression of cystic fibrosis transmembrane regulator Cl⁻ channels in heart. *Circ. Res.* 71:1002–7

90. Levesque PJ, Hume JR. 1994. ATP_o but not $cAMP_i$ activates a Cl⁻ conductance in mouse ventricular myocytes. *Cardiovasc. Res.* In press

91. Matsuoka S, Ehara T, Noma A. 1990. Chloride-sensitive nature of the adrenaline-induced current in guinea-pig cardiac myocytes. *J. Physiol.* 425:579–98

92. Matsuura H, Ehara T. 1992. Activation of chloride current by purinergic stimulation in guinea pig heart cells. *Circ. Res.* 70:851–55

93. McCarty NA, McDonough S, Cohen BN, Riordan JR, Davidson N, Lester HA. 1993. Voltage-dependent block of the cystic fibrosis transmembrane conductance regulator Cl⁻ channel by two closely related arylaminobenzoates. *J. Gen. Physiol.* 102:1–23

94. McDonough S, Davidson N, Lester HA, McCarty NA. 1994. Novel pore-lining residues in CFTR that govern permeation and open channel block. *Neuron* 13:623–34

95. Nagel GA, Hwang T-C, Nairn AC, Gadsby DC. 1992. Regulation of PKA-activated Cl conductance in guinea pig ventricular myocytes: single-channel studies. *J. Gen. Physiol.* 100:70a

96. Nagel GA, Hwang T-C, Nastiuk KL, Nairn, AC Gadsby DC. 1992. The protein kinase A-regulated Cl channel resembles CFTR (Cystic Fibrosis Transmembrane conductance Regulator). *Nature* 360:81–84

97. Nakajima T, Wu S, Irisawa H, Giles W. 1990. Mechanism of acetylcholine-induced inhibition of Ca current in bullfrog atrial myocytes. *J. Gen. Physiol.* 96:865–85

98. Ono K, Fozzard HA. 1992. Phosphorylation restores activity of L-type Ca^{2+} channels after rundown in inside-out patches from rabbit cardiac cells. *J. Physiol.* 454:673–88

99. Ono K, Fozzard HA. 1993. Two phosphatase sites on the Ca^{2+} channel affecting different kinetic functions. *J. Physiol.* 470:73–84

100. Ono K, Tareen FM, Yoshida A, Noma A. 1992. Synergistic action of cyclic GMP on catecholamine-induced chlor-

101. Ono K, Trautwein W. 1991. Potentiation by cyclic GMP of β-adrenergic effect on Ca^{2+} current in guinea-pig ventricular cells. *J. Physiol.* 443:387–404

102. Overholt JL, Hobert ME, Harvey RD. 1993. On the mechanism of rectification of the isoproterenol-activated chloride current in guinea-pig ventricular myocytes. *J. Gen. Physiol.* 102:871–95

103. Palade PT, Barchi RL. 1977. On the inhibition of muscle membrane chloride conductance by aromatic carboxylic acids. *J. Gen. Physiol.* 69:879–96

104. Parsons TD, Hartzell HC. 1993. Regulation of Ca^{2+} current in frog ventricular cardiomyocytes by guanosine 5'-triphosphate analogues and isoproterenol. *J. Gen. Physiol.* 102:525–49

105. Parsons TD, Lagrutta A, White RE, Hartzell HC. 1991. Regulation of Ca^{2+} current in frog ventricular cardiomyocytes by 5'-guanylylimidodiphosphate and acetylcholine. *J. Physiol.* 432:593–620

106. Pfaffinger PJ, Martin JM, Hunter DD, Nathanson NM, Hille B. 1985. GTP-binding proteins couple cardiac muscarinic receptors to a K channel. *Nature* 317:536–38

107. Picciotto M, Cohn J, Bertuzzi G, Greengard P, Nairn AC. 1992. Phosphorylation of the cystic fibrosis transmembrane conductance regulator. *J. Biol. Chem.* 267:12742–52

108. Price MP, Ishihara H, Sheppard DN, Welsh MJ. 1994. Use of human-*Xenopus* chimeric proteins to analyze the anion permeability of CFTR Cl⁻ currents. *Pediat. Pulmonol.* Suppl. 10:187

109. Quinton PM. 1990. Cystic fibrosis, a disease in electrolyte transport. *FASEB J.* 4:2709–17

110. Quinton PM, Reddy MM. 1992. Control of CFTR chloride conductance by ATP levels through non-hydrolytic binding. *Nature* 360:79–81

111. Ratcliff R, Evans MJ, Cuthbert AW, MacVinish LJ, Foster D, et al. 1993. Production of a severe cystic fibrosis mutation in mice by gene targeting. *Nature Genet.* 4:35–41

112. Reuss L, Altenberg A, Vanoye CG, Han E. 1994. Channel function of the P-glycoprotein (Pgp) of multidrug resistant cancer cells. *Biophys. J.* 66:A3

113. Rich DR, Berger HA, Cheng SH, Travis SM, Saxene M, et al. 1993. Regulation of the cystic fibrosis transmembrane conductance regulator Cl channel by negative charge in the R domain. *J. Biol. Chem.* 268:20259–67

114. Riordan JR, Rommens JM, Kerem BS,

Alon N, Rozmahel R, et al. 1989. Identification of the cystic fibrosis gene: cloning and characterization of complementary DNA. *Science* 245:1066–73

115. Schultz BD, Venglarik CJ, Bridges RJ, Frizzell RA. 1993. Regulation of CFTR Cl⁻ channels by adenine nucleotide phosphates. *FASEB J.* 7:A426

116. Schwiebert EM, Egan ME, Guggino WB. 1994. CFTR- and cyclic AMP-stimulated ATP release from airway epithelial cells is required for stimulation of outwardly rectifying chloride channels. *J. Gen. Physiol.* 104:39a

117. Schwiebert EM, Flotte T, Cutting GR, Guggino WB. 1994. Both CFTR and outwardly rectifying chloride channels contribute to cAMP-stimulated whole cell chloride currents. *Am. J. Physiol.* 266:C1464–77

118. Schwiebert EM, Kizer N, Gruenert DC, Stanton BA. 1992. GTP-binding proteins inhibit cAMP activation of chloride channels in cystic fibrosis airway epithelial cells. *Proc. Natl. Acad. Sci. USA* 89:10623–27

119. Shenolikar S, Nairn AC. 1991. Protein phosphatases: recent progress. In *Advances in Second Messenger Phosphoprotein Research*, ed. P Greengard, GA Robison, 231:1–121. New York: Raven

120. Sheppard DN, Rich DP, Ostedgaard LS, Gregory RJ, Smith AE, Welsh MJ. 1993. Mutations in CFTR associated with mild-disease-form Cl⁻ channels with altered pore properties. *Nature* 362:160–64

121. Sheppard DN, Welsh MJ. 1992. Effect of ATP-sensitive K⁺ channel regulators on cystic fibrosis transmembrane conductance regulator chloride currents. *J. Gen. Physiol.* 100:573–92

122. Smit LS, Wilkinson DJ, Mansoura MK, Collins FS, Dawson DC. 1993. Functional roles of the nucleotide-binding folds in the activation of the cystic fibrosis transmembrane conductance regulator. *Proc. Natl. Acad. Sci. USA* 90:9963–67

123. Snouwaert JN, Brigman KK, Latour NM, Malouf NN, Boucher RC, et al. 1992. An animal model for cystic fibrosis made by gene targeting. *Science* 257:1083–88

124. Sorota S, Rose EA, Oz MC. 1994. Failure to detect a protein kinase A-regulated chloride current in human atrial myocytes. *Biophys. J.* 66:A434

125. Sorota S, Siegel MS, Hoffman BF. 1991. The isoproterenol-induced chloride current and cardiac resting potential. *J. Mol. Cell. Cardiol.* 23:1191–98

126. Sturgess NC, Ashford ML, Cook DL, Hales CN. 1985. The sulphonylurea receptor may be an ATP-sensitive potassium channel. *Lancet* 8453:474–75

127. Tabcharani JA, Chang X-B, Riordan JR, Hanrahan JW. 1991. Phosphorylation-regulated Cl channel in CHO cells stably expressing the cystic fibrosis gene. *Nature* 352:628–31

128. Tabcharani JA, Chang X-B, Riordan JR, Hanrahan JW. 1992. The cystic fibrosis transmembrane conductance regulator chloride channel. Iodide block and permeation. *Biophys. J.* 62:1–4

129. Tabcharani JA, Low W, Elie D, Hanrahan JW, 1990. Low conductance chloride channel activated by cAMP in the epithelial cell line T84. *FEBS Lett.* 270:157–64

130. Tabcharani JA, Rommens JM, Hou Y-X, Chang X-B, Tsui L-C, et al. 1993. Multiion pore behaviour in the CFTR chloride channel. *Nature* 366:79–82

131. Takano M, Noma A. 1992. Distribution of the isoprenaline-induced chloride current in rabbit heart. *Pflügers Arch.* 420: 223–26

132. Tareen FM, Ono K, Noma A, Ehara T. 1991. β-adrenergic and muscarinic regulation of the chloride current in guinea-pig ventricular cells. *J. Physiol.* 440: 225–41

133. Tareen FM, Yoshida A, Ono K. 1992. Modulation of β-adrenergic responses of chloride and calcium currents by external cations in guinea-pig ventricular cells. *J. Physiol.* 457:211–28

134. Tominaga M, Horie M, Okada Y. 1994. Additional similarity of cardiac cAMP-activated Cl⁻ channels to CFTR Cl⁻ channels. Glibenclamide inhibits cardiac cAMP-activated Cl⁻ channels. *Jpn. J. Physiol.* 44(Suppl. 1):S215–18

135. Tsien RW, Bean BP, Hess P, Lansman JB, Nilius B, Nowycky MC. 1986. Mechanism of calcium channel modulation by β-adrenergic agents and dihydropyridine calcium channel agonists. *J. Mol. Cell. Cardiol.* 18:691–710

136. Tsui L-C. 1992. The spectrum of cystic fibrosis mutations. *Trends Genet.* 8:392–98

137. Valverde MA, Hardy SP, Goodfellow H, Higgins CF, Sepúlveda FV. 1994. Protein kinase C-mediated inhibition of volume regulated chloride channel in P-glycoprotein-expressing cells. *Jpn. J. Physiol.* 44(Suppl. 1):S9–15

138. Vaughan-Jones RD. 1982. Chloride activity and its control in skeletal and cardiac muscle. *Phil. Trans. R. Soc. London Ser. B* B299:537–48

139. Venglarik CJ, DeRoos ADG, Singh AK, Schultz BD, Frizzell RA, Bridges RJ.

1994. Sulfonylureas cause open channel blockade of CFTR. *Biophys. J.* 66:A421

140. Venglarik CJ, Schultz BD, Frizzell RA, Bridges RJ. 1994. ATP alters current fluctuations of cystic fibrosis transmembrane conductance regulator: evidence for a three-state activation mechanism. *J. Gen. Physiol.* 104:123–46

141. Walsh KB. 1991. Activation of a heart chloride current during stimulation of protein kinase C. *Mol. Pharmacol.* 40: 342–46

142. Walsh KB. 1994. Agents which block heart Cl⁻ channels also inhibit Ca²⁺ current regulation. *Biophys. J.* 66:A239

143. Walsh KB, Begenisich TB, Kass RS. 1989. β-adrenergic modulation of cardiac ion channels: differential temperature sensitivity of potassium and calcium currents. *J. Gen. Physiol.* 93:841–54

144. Walsh KB, Long KJ. 1992. Inhibition of heart calcium and chloride currents by sodium iodide. Specific attenuation in cAMP-dependent protein kinase-mediated regulation. *J. Gen. Physiol.* 100: 847–65

145. Walsh KB, Long KJ. 1994. Properties of a protein kinase C-activated chloride current in guinea pig ventricular myocytes. *Circ. Res.* 74:121–29

146. Warth JD, Horowitz B, Hume JR. 1994. Identification of CFTR_cardiac in non-human primate ventricular myocytes. *Biophys. J.* 66:A420

147. Welsh MJ. 1987. Electrolyte transport by airway epithelia. *Physiol. Revs.* 67: 1143–84

148. Welsh MJ, Anderson MP, Rich DP, Berger HA, Denning GM, et al. 1992. Cystic fibrosis transmembrane conductance regulator: a chloride channel with novel regulation. *Neuron* 8:821–29

149. Werber M, Peyser YM, Muhlrad A. 1992. Characterization of stable beryl-

lium fluoride, aluminum fluoride, and vanadate containing myosin subfragment 1-nucleotide complexes. *Biochemistry* 31:7190–97

150. White MM, Miller C. 1979. A voltage-gated anion channel from the electric organ of *Torpedo californica*. *J. Biol. Chem.* 254:10161–66

151. Deleted in proof

152. Winter MC, Sheppard DN, Carson MR, Welsh MJ. 1994. Effect of ATP concentration on CFTR Cl⁻ channels: a kinetic analysis of channel regulation. *Biophys. J.* 66:1398–403

153. Yazawa K, Kameyama M. 1990. Mechanisms of receptor-mediated modulation of the delayed outward potassium current in guinea-pig ventricular myocytes. *J. Physiol.* 421:135–50

154. Yount RG. 1975. ATP analogs. *Adv. Enzymol.* 43:1–56

155. Zakharov SI, Overholt JL, Wagner RA, Harvey RD. 1993. Tetramethylammonium activation of muscarinic receptors in cardiac ventricular myocytes. *Am. J. Physiol.* 264:C1625–30

156. Deleted in proof

157. Zhang K, Ten Eick RE. 1993. A single type of chloride current (ICl) induced by activation of protein kinases A and C in feline ventricular myocytes. *Biophys. J.* 64:A239

158. Zhang K, Ten Eick RE. 1994. A single type of chloride current induced by activation of protein kinases A and C in feline ventricular myocytes. *Biophys. J.* 66:A434

159. Zielinski J, Bozon D, Kerem B, Markiewicz D, Durie P, et al. 1991. Identification of mutations in exons 1 through 8 of the cystic fibrosis transmembrane conductance regulator (CFTR). *Genomics* 10:229–35

Annu. Rev. Physiol. 1995. 57:417–45

THE MULTIFUNCTIONAL CALCIUM/CALMODULIN-DEPENDENT PROTEIN KINASE: From Form to Function

Andrew P. Braun and Howard Schulman

Department of Neurobiology, Stanford University School of Medicine, Stanford, California 94305–5401

KEY WORDS: calcium signaling, ion channel regulation, gene expression

INTRODUCTION

The regulation of cellular function by hormones and extracellular molecules, which bind to cell surface receptors, is initiated by signal transduction mechanisms at the plasma membrane that lead to the generation of intracellular signals, or second messengers. These second messengers interact with specific target molecules to initiate a cascade of biochemical events leading to a change in cellular function. A variety of intracellular second messengers, including divalent metals, phospholipid metabolites, and cyclic nucleotides, are known to be generated in response to extracellular stimuli. Calcium acts as an intracellular second messenger in species as diverse as yeast to humans and is involved in cellular processes ranging from contraction to secretion to gene expression. Elevation of cytosolic calcium can occur by influx via regulated ion channels and transporters, or by release from intracellular stores via receptor-generated second messengers (Figure 1). Cells contain a number of intracellular calcium-binding proteins, and in most cell types, the major calcium-binding protein is calmodulin (44, 91), an ~17 kDa, heat-stable protein that binds four calcium ions with an overall high affinity of ~1 μM. This complex of 4(Ca)-calmodulin activates downstream targets. Although the importance of calcium as an intracellular messenger has been long recognized, identifica-

417

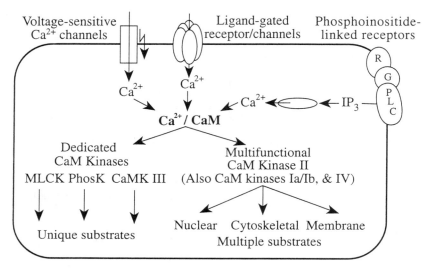

Figure 1 Elevation of intracellular calcium by a variety of extracellular stimuli can lead to the activation of the multifunctional CaM kinase II, along with other multifunctional and dedicated calcium/calmodulin-dependent protein kinases.

tion of the cellular target molecules that effect the signal has been more difficult.

Multifunctional calcium/calmodulin-dependent protein kinase (CaM kinase II or simply CaM kinase) is one such effector of calcium/calmodulin. CaM kinase is a ubiquitous enzyme that is present in all cell types thus far examined. This enzyme is so named because of its requirement for calcium-bound calmodulin for activation and its ability to phosphorylate and alter the function of a variety of substrates (see Table 1 for a list of CaM kinase substrates). In this respect, CaM kinase differs from more dedicated calcium-dependent target effectors, such as myosin light chain kinase (MLCK), whose primary task is to phosphorylate the 20-kDa light chain of myosin, which regulates actin-myosin cross-bridge cycling in smooth muscle, or calcium/calmodulin-dependent protein kinase III, which regulates protein synthesis via phosphorylation of elongation factor-2 (106, 108, 122) (see Figure 1). Two other calcium/calmodulin-dependent protein kinases, referred to as CaM kinase Ia/Ib (27, 107) and CaM kinase IV (or CaM kinase-Gr) (24, 53, 115) also appear to phosphorylate several substrates in vitro and may therefore also function in situ as multifunctional CaM kinases (Figure 1). Much less is known about these two enzymes; however, given several similarities in catalytic properties, it is likely that some functions previously ascribed to multifunctional CaM

Table 1   Substrates for CaM kinase[a]

Protein or complex	Function	Reference[b]
Acetyl-CoA carboxylase	Fatty acid synthesis	—
ATP-citrate lyase	Fatty acid synthesis	—
C protein	Myosin-associated protein	—
Calcineurin	Ca/calmodulin-activated serine/ threonine protein phosphatase	—
Calcium channel, N-type	Presynaptic calcium influx	(58)
Caldesmon	Actin-myosin binding protein	
Calpain	Ca-activated serine protease	(95)
Cardiac Ca^{2+}-ATPase	Calcium reuptake into the SR	(173)
CD20	Integral membrane protein mediating B-lymphocyte activation	(43)
C/EBPβ	Transcriptional regulation	(166)
CRE-binding protein	Transcriptional regulation	
CSF and MPF complexes	Meiotic arrest of unfertilized oocytes	(85)
Cyclic nucleotide phosphodiesterase	Cyclic nucleotide metabolism	
EGF receptor	Stimulation of cell growth	(23)
GABA-modulin	Regulation of GABA receptors	
GABA receptor, type A	Inhibitory synaptic receptor in brain	(96)
AMPA-type glutamate receptor	Na influx/depolarization at postsynaptic nerve terminal	(97, 150)
Glycogen synthase	Carbohydrate metabolism	
HMG-CoA reductase	Cholesterol biosynthesis	
IP$_3$ receptor	IP$_3$-stimulated calcium release	
Intermediate filaments		
Vimentin	Mesenchymal intermediate filament protein	(176)
Desmin	Muscle intermediate filament	
Neurofilaments	Neuronal intermediate filaments	
GFAP	Astroglial intermediate filament	(176)
Keratin, type I, acidic	Epithelial intermediate filament	
Keratin, type II, basic	Epithelial intermediate filament	
Microtubule-associated proteins (MAPs)		
MAP-2	Micotubule assembly	
Tau	Microtubule assembly	
Myelin basic protein	Major myelin sheath protein	
Myosin light chains (smooth muscle)	Myosin subunits, phosphoproteins	—
Myosin light chain kinase (smooth muscle)	Initiates smooth muscle contraction	—
Nitric oxide synthase	NO production in brain	(16)
p56 *lck*	Lymphoid protein tyrosine kinase, involved in T-cell activation	(14)
Lyso-PAF acetyltransferase	Platelet-activating factor synthesis	—
Phenylalanine hydroxylase	Tyrosine synthesis	—
Phosphofructokinase	Glycogen metabolism	—
Phospholamban	Regulation of cardiac SR Ca uptake	—
Phospholipase A$_2$	Receptor-mediated phospholipid hydrolysis	—

Table 1 *(Continued)*

Protein or complex	Function	Reference[b]
Plectin	Intermediate filament-associated protein	—
Pyruvate kinase	Carbohydrate metabolism	—
Ribosomal protein S6	Protein synthesis	—
Ryanodine receptor (cardiac)	SR calcium release	—
Synapsin I	Neurotransmitter release	—
Synaptotagmin	Neurotransmitter release	(118)
Synaptophysin	Neurotransmitter release	(121)
Troponin T and I (skeletal muscle)	Components of tropomyosin complex	—
Troponin I (cardiac muscle)	Component of tropomyosin complex	—
Trypophan hydroxylase	Serotonin biosynthesis	
Tyrosine hydroxylase	Catecholamine biosynthesis	

[a] Abbreviations used: AMPA, α-amino-3-hydroxy-5-methyl-4-isoxazole proprionate; CRE, calcium response element; CSF and MPF, cytostatic factor and M-phase promoting factor, respectively; GFAP, glial fibrillary acidic protein; NMDA, N-methyl-D-aspartate; SR, sarcoplasmic reticulum.

[b] For brevity, references are only provided for recently described substrates; a complete set of references for other listed substrates is given in (56).

kinase are mediated by CaM kinase Ia/Ib and CaM kinase IV. Additional aspects of these and other calcium/calmodulin-dependent protein kinases appear in recent reviews (124, 142, 147).

Most of the work carried out on CaM kinase has focused on understanding its biochemical properties. The strong interest in CaM kinase has been fueled by its fascinating regulatory properties, which are discussed in more detail below, and their consequences for the regulation of cellular functions by this kinase. Our review presents recent information and experimental strategies focusing on CaM kinase as a mediator of calcium mobilizing extracellular stimuli and its functional involvement in calcium-dependent cellular processes.

Structural and Autoregulatory Properties of CaM Kinase

CaM kinase is made up of a multigene family, in which each of the four distinct classes of CaM kinase (α, β, γ, δ) is encoded by a separate gene. The α and β classes are restricted to nervous tissue, whereas γ and δ are found in most tissues including brain (153). Each subunit within the holoenzyme can be divided into three major domains: a N-terminal catalytic domain, a C-terminal association domain, and an autoregulatory domain in the middle (Figure 2). CaM kinase classes share approximately 80–90% identity across these core domains (153). Located past the C-terminus of the autoregulatory domain is a variable region, the site of greatest divergence among the isoforms. Deduced structure of the murine CaM kinase β gene reveals that it is composed of sixteen exons (69), with four exons (vi–ix) encoding the full-length variable region. Insertion/deletion of these exons by alternative splicing of CaM kinase messenger RNA transcripts appears to account for most of the diversity among isoforms, both within a class (e.g. β isoforms) and between classes (e.g. α, β, γ, δ). To date, 2 α, 4 β, 3 γ, and 8 δ isoforms have been identified at the mRNA level (30, 93, 130) (L Brocke et al, unpublished findings). The δ isoforms have a second variable insert at the C-terminus of the protein (see Figure 2). Where examined, the newer isoforms express active kinase with properties similar to the better characterized α and β/β′ isoforms (30) (Brocke et al, unpublished findings). Cells can contain more than a single isoform of the kinase, and it is likely that both homomultimers and heteromultimers of the kinase exist (10, 67, 140). As previously found for multimeric ion channels, the subunit composition of the kinase may modify the properties of the holoenzyme. Although the function of this variable region is not well understood, evidence suggests one function to be the targeting and localization of CaM kinase to specific subcellular compartments or membranes.

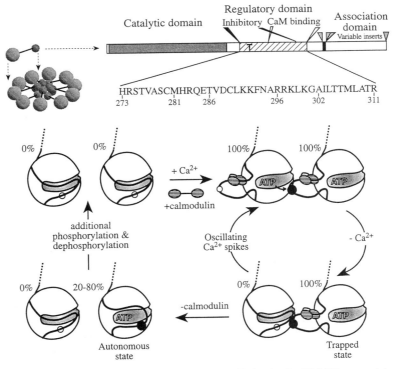

Figure 2 The hub-and-spoke pattern of the holoenzyme. Each subunit of CaM kinase contains an autoregulatory region, whose displacement is critical in maintaining autonomous catalytic activity and calmodulin trapping. It is also the site from which inhibitory peptides have been derived.

Based on electron micrographs of purified rat brain CaM kinase, the holoenzyme is arranged in a hub-and-spoke pattern, with the N-terminal catalytic/regulatory domains of each subunit extending out as spokes from a large central hub region composed of the C-terminal-association domains (67) (Figure 2). CaM kinase constructs made monomeric by truncation of their association domains are calcium-dependent kinases with activity and substrate specificity similar to those of the holoenzyme. Therefore, it is likely that nature has designed the enzyme as a large hub-and-spoke arrangement of subunits (Figure 2) to enable unique autoregulatory functions. We describe a view of CaM kinase (see below) as a molecular device that enables the enzyme to potentiate the action of brief calcium spikes and to decode the frequency by which cellular calcium levels oscillate or spike.

Autophosphorylation provides a critical regulation of CaM kinase (Figure 2). The autoinhibitory domain of the kinase is disrupted by binding of calmodulin at its C-terminal end, which leads to a de-inhibition of the kinase. The autoinhibitory domain can be further disrupted by phosphorylation of a key threonine residue common to all isoforms (Thr^{286} of the α isoform) (reviewed in 56). Phosphorylation of this site is not essential for kinase activity, but it does have two important consequences. First, autophosphorylation increases the affinity of the kinase for calmodulin several hundredfold by reducing the dissociation rate of the kinase-calmodulin complex (100). This novel effect of autophosphorylation essentially traps calmodulin on the autophosphorylated subunit. At high calcium levels, calmodulin off-rate ($1/K_{off}$) is reduced 1000-fold, from a little less than one half to several hundred seconds. Because the on-rate is not markedly affected, the affinity of the kinase for calmodulin increases from 45 nM to 60 pM, one of the highest known. Even when calcium is reduced to physiological levels, calmodulin is trapped on the kinase for several seconds. Importantly, the kinase retains 100% activity as long as calmodulin is trapped, regardless of the calcium level (100) (Figure 2). This dramatic shift in affinity as a result of autophosphorylation should allow the kinase to compete more favorably for a limited amount of free calmodulin. Furthermore, the presence of a phosphate on the autonomy site is itself sufficient to disrupt the autoinhibitory domain, and the kinase retains partial activity (20–80%) even after calmodulin dissociates in this autonomous state.

Autophosphorylation of CaM kinase occurs in situ and is of practical value as it can be used to assess which signaling molecules activate the kinase. Kinase in its basal unphosphorylated state has essentially no activity in the absence of calcium/calmodulin, whereas autophosphorylated kinase has significant calcium/calmodulin-independent or autonomous activity. Hence, assay of autonomous CaM kinase activity in a cell homogenate from control and hormone-stimulated cultures gives a direct measure of the fraction of the kinase that has been activated by stimulation of the cells. For example, depolarization increases autonomous activity of kinase in PC12 cells (86), cerebellar granule cells (40), pituitary cells (13, 25), and hippocampal neurons (42). From 15 to 50% of the kinase can be converted to the calcium-independent form, starting from a basal level of approximately 5%. In PC12 and GH3 cells, this activation is coincident with phosphorylation of the autonomy site, which demonstrates the relevance of this site in situ as well as in vitro.

CaM kinase appears to respond to calcium elevation from a variety of signal transduction mechanisms (Figure 1). For example, bradykinin, which regulates calcium levels in PC12 cells via generation of inositol 1,4,5-trisphosphate (IP_3) and release of intracellular calcium stores, readily activates CaM kinase (86). The autonomous activity appears to outlast the calcium signal, suggesting that autophosphorylation potentiates the effects of calcium. The kinase is also activated by stimulation of the nicotinic receptor and an ATP receptor–operated calcium channel in PC12 cells (87). In hippocampal neurons, glutamate stimulates autophosphorylation of CaM kinase (making it autonomous) and phosphorylation of a glutamate receptor (41, 97, 150). In cultured cortical astrocytes, glutamate activates CaM kinase, which leads to phosphorylation of vimentin and glial fibrillary acidic protein (176). Thus the kinase responds to calcium arising from influx through a variety of channels and receptors, as well as to calcium released from intracellular stores. This places CaM kinase in a central position to orchestrate regulation of numerous physiological processes under hormonal control.

The molecular mechanism of autophosphorylation provides the kinase with particular regulatory properties. Autophosphorylation does not occur by one holoenzyme acting on another. Rather, it is a reaction between two proximate subunits on the same holoenzyme (55, 104). Cotransfection of an active epitope-tagged α-CaM kinase with an untagged catalytically inactive α-CaM kinase produces a heteromultimeric enzyme containing both types of subunits. Addition of calcium/calmodulin to such holoenzymes leads to phosphorylation of the inactive subunit at its autonomy site, demonstrating that autophosphorylation occurs by an inter-subunit reaction (55). Further analysis reveals that this process is cooperative, requiring at least two molecules of calmodulin per holoenzyme. This cooperativity stems from a dual role of calmodulin, which is not only needed for activation of the kinase subunit, but must be bound to the substrate subunit for phosphorylation of the autonomy site to occur (55). The same conformational change that moves the autoinhibitory domain from the active site to activate the kinase may also present it to a neighboring subunit on the same holoenzyme for autophosphorylation (Figure 2). The autonomy site is likely buried in the basal state and not available for inter-subunit autophosphorylation unless calmodulin is bound (137).

There are several important consequences of the dual requirement for calmodulin coupled with the autonomous and calmodulin-trapping states of the kinase. First, it is unlikely that the autonomy site is phosphorylated physiologically under basal conditions, i.e. when calcium concentration is low and calmodulin is not bound to the kinase. Autophosphorylation without bound calmodulin is an important feature of memory models of the kinase that require persistent rephosphorylation of the autonomy site subsequent to a calcium transient (82, 83, 101). Second, the biochemical properties described above may enable CaM kinase to function as a detector of the frequency of calcium spikes under conditions in which individual spikes do not maximally activate CaM kinase (55). Consider the following scenario: Normal stimulation would activate several, but not all, subunits of an average holoenzyme in the cell because of limited free Ca-CaM complex. There is experimental support for the notion that calmodulin, although abundant, is largely bound to a variety of abundant cellular proteins when calcium is elevated (33, 46, 136, 151). Furthermore, not all free calmodulin would be saturated with calcium during rapid transient elevation of calcium. Each calcium spike at low frequency would activate a few subunits of CaM kinase per holoenzyme, and this submaximal activation would be the same regardless of the number of spikes. Occasionally, calmodulin would be bound to two proximate neighbors on a holoenzyme and inter-subunit autophosphorylation and calmodulin trapping would occur, leading to potentiation of the calcium signal. With long inter-spike intervals, calmodulin would dissociate and the kinase would be dephosphorylated before the next spike. At high frequency, however, the inter-spike interval would be too short to allow all trapped calmodulin to dissociate before the next calcium rise and binding of additional calmodulin. The net effect is to increase the number of bound calmodulin molecules per holoenzyme, and thus the probability of proximate neighboring subunits with bound calmodulin, leading to autophosphorylation and trapping. With each successive spike at high frequency, calmodulin would be recruited to the holoenzyme so that it becomes increasingly saturated with calmodulin. The cooperativity of calmodulin trapping may allow the kinase to be a frequency detector with a threshold frequency beyond which it becomes highly active (55). Such a property would allow for greater specificity in calcium signaling, with some enzymes, e.g. calcineurin, being activated at low frequency, and CaM kinase only maximally stimulated at higher frequency.

Experimental Strategies for Studying the Functional Roles of CaM Kinase

A number of criteria (74, 123) can be used to identify in situ substrates or functional roles of a CaM kinase: (a) Stimuli that increase intracellular free calcium leading to phosphorylation of the putative CaM kinase substrate or modification of a putative CaM kinase function should also activate CaM kinase in situ. (*b*) The relevant sites phosphorylated on the substrate in situ should overlap those phosphorylated by the purified kinase on the purified substrate in vitro. (*c*) Inhibition of the kinase should block the phosphorylation or modification of the putative function. (*d*) Activators of the kinase should elicit the phosphorylation or the biological effect. (*e*) Introduction of a calcium-independent form of the kinase into cells should simulate physiological activation of the kinase. (*f*) Reduction in the cellular content of the kinase expression by mutation, antisense, or knockout should reduce activation of the kinase and its consequences on substrate or function.

The first proteins to be implicated as CaM kinase substrates were identified based on overlap in their phosphorylation site in vitro and in situ. These include synapsin I, tyrosine hydroxylase, pyruvate kinase, MLCK, and MAP-2 (reviewed in 56, 123). However, it is difficult to fulfill the phosphorylation site criterion. Best results are obtained when kinase and substrate are available in a purified form, which is not always possible.

An understanding of the structure/function domains of CaM kinase described above led to the development of CaM kinase inhibitors. Cloning and sequencing of the cDNAs for brain CaM kinase suggested the regions of the molecule serving as inhibitor and calmodulin-binding sites (11, 54, 81). These two segments were mapped experimentally using synthetic peptides derived from the predicted amino acid sequence (117, 139) (see Figure 2). For example, synthetic peptides corresponding to sequences 273–302 and 281–302 (based on the autoinhibitory segment of α-CaM kinase) are competitive inhibitors in vitro (K_i 1–2 μM or less) with some selectivity (90). Such peptides lack sequences beyond their C-terminus that are necessary for calmodulin binding and therefore do not block other calmodulin-dependent enzymes. The autoinhibitory domain of all CaM kinase isoforms is nearly identical and such peptides likely inhibit all CaM kinase isoforms. The calmodulin-binding domain comprises residues 296–311; these peptides bind calmodulin with nM affinities and, like calmodulin-binding sequences from other proteins, block all calmodulin-dependent processes. These peptides are membrane impermeant but can be microinjected into cells or used with permeabilized systems (described below). The selectivity of CaM kinase-derived inhibitory peptides for CaM kinase vs protein kinase C has been questioned (61, 138). Selectivity can be affected by assay conditions, including the choice of in vitro substrate, and may appear higher or lower than when applied in situ.

Membrane-permeant organic inhibitors would be preferable, but those currently available are problematic because they also inhibit unrelated targets as well as other kinases. Two interesting inhibitors, KN-62 and KN-93 (144, 154), block activation of the kinase by binding to an unidentified site on CaM kinase and interfering with calmodulin binding. However, KN-62 is also a potent inhibitor of CaM kinase IV (31), and KN-62 has been reported to block the

L-type calcium currents of insulin-secreting HIT cells (78). Similarly, other membrane-permeant calmodulin inhibitors such as W7, trifluoperazine, and calmidazolium have been shown to block L-type calcium currents (73, 109) and cyclic nucleotide-gated channels from rat olfactory neurons (20), in addition to inhibiting calmodulin-dependent processes.

Many of the experimental conclusions implicating functional roles for CaM kinase in situ have been based on the use of synthetic CaM kinase inhibitory peptides. In the majority of cases, experiments have been carried out in single cells using patch-clamp methods, in which peptides (typically 2 kDa or less) are dialyzed via the patch pipette, or microinjected into the cell interior; similar experiments have also been carried out with highly selective anti-CaM kinase antibodies (7). Alternatively, the surface membrane of preparations may be permeabilized, thus allowing entry of externally applied reagents into the cytoplasm (92b). Yet another approach for delivery of the peptide has been the generation of transgenic flies that carry a synthetic mini-gene encoding the inhibitory peptide CaMK 273–302 (Figure 2), derived from the autoinhibitory sequence of CaM kinase (50). In this model, expression of the exogenous inhibitory peptide would produce widespread inhibition of CaM kinase activity because the peptide likely inhibits all isoforms. Such a mini-gene can also be introduced by transient or stable transfection of cell lines. These approaches have proven highly successful experimentally, and many of the studies cited here are based on such strategies.

The recent development of transgenic animal models has widened the scope of studying the functional roles of CaM kinase in vivo. In this approach, a fertilized egg is injected with DNA that is specifically designed to knock out or disrupt a target gene so that the protein product is eliminated. Silva and co-workers (134, 135) used this strategy to study the role of α-CaM kinase, the major isoform in the brain, by breeding homozygous mice lacking the enzyme. This approach leads to the elimination of all isoforms within a given class of CaM kinase, e.g. α- and α_B-CaM kinase would be eliminated in an α-gene knockout, but all isoforms of β-, γ-, and δ-CaM kinase would be retained. If there is redundancy in the function of the kinases, a knockout may produce no effect. Furthermore, because the mutant animal progresses normally through development without α-CaM kinase, there is also the potential for compensatory mechanisms involving the residual kinases or other components to confound interpretation of the data. Unanticipated complications may result from the loss of α-CaM kinase from heteromultimers that also contain β-CaM kinase or other isoforms. The loss of α-CaM kinase may alter subcellular targeting or regulatory function of these residual isoforms. A global strategy of CaM kinase inhibition via a mini-gene inhibitory peptide approach does indeed circumvent difficulties created by the existence of multiple genes for CaM kinase, but it is subject to some of the same compensatory mechanisms and is more likely to produce nonspecific effects. At the same time, however, this approach would preclude accurately defining the functional role of a specific isoform. As described below, the α-CaM kinase knockout produced a clear physiological effect despite the fact that total brain CaM kinase activity was reduced by only half.

Other approaches for the in situ manipulation of CaM kinase that have not been applied include (a) antisense oligonucleotide strategies, in which target mRNA molecules may be acutely knocked out by synthetic oligonucleotide probes (168), and (b) the enzymatic destruction of mRNAs by targeted endoribonuclease molecules, or ribozymes (18, 57), which can be engineered to recognize and cleave a specific nucleotide sequence in the target mRNA molecule.

Rather than eliminate a protein such as CaM kinase, DNA-based strategies could be used to modify or amplify enzyme activity. For example, a CaM kinase with aspartic acid in place of Thr^{286} expresses significant calcium-independent activity by mimicking the negatively charged phosphate group, resulting in an autonomous form of the kinase (36, 159, 162). Generation of transgenic animals carrying such site-directed mutations in CaM kinase or transfection of such a construct could thus allow insightful long-term functional studies of the enzyme. Further strategies to manipulate CaM kinase function could involve dominant negative mutants. For example, transfection and expression of an exogenous CaM kinase construct containing a mutation that inactivates the catalytic domain (Lys^{42} to Met) could simultaneously either displace active endogenous CaM kinase from its binding sites, or co-assemble with newly synthesized endogenous CaM kinase and reroute it to a select compartment (e.g. the nucleus). Such a dominant negative strategy could thus be used to selectively disrupt CaM kinase functions without eliminating the protein itself, which may then be tracked inside the cell, or possibly serve as a marker.

Roles in the Nervous System

CaM kinase was initially found in the CNS as a protein kinase activity stimulated by calcium plus a calcium-binding regulator of cyclic nucleotide phosphodiesterase, now known as calmodulin (125). The enzyme activity was highly concentrated in nerve terminal preparations, or synaptosomes, from brain, but was also found in a variety of tissues including skeletal muscle, heart, lung, kidney, aorta, liver, intestine, uterus, and testis (126, 153). Subsequent studies led to the purification of CaM kinase (10, 75, 98, 175), followed by the molecular cloning of the major brain isoforms, α-, β-, and β'-CaM kinase (11, 54, 81). CaM kinase is thought to be the most abundant protein kinase in the hippocampus, where it accounts for 1–2% of total protein (32). It is generally found in high levels throughout the brain and, on average, comprises 0.25% of total brain protein. It is particularly enriched in the fore-brain where it is concentrated in postsynaptic densities (PSD) (44, 45, 70, 171), although there is evidence that its enrichment in the PSD may be a postmortem effect (146). The isoforms themselves appear to be differentially distributed in the brain. α-CaM kinase is found primarily in the forebrain and cortex, whereas the β isoform tends to have a more uniform distribution across the brain (32, 39, 114). It also appears that these isoforms are developmentally regulated in brain during progression from the late embryo stage to neonate (71, 167). The early rapid rise of β-CaM kinase has recently been attributed to the transient appearance of two new embryonic forms, β_e-CaM kinase and β_e'-CaM kinase (L Brocke et al, unpublished findings). The abundance of CaM kinase in the brain and its cellular distribution gave rise to early speculation that CaM kinase plays an important role(s) in synaptic transmission, as de-scribed below.

One of the first functional roles described for CaM kinase in situ is the activation of tyrosine hydroxylase, the rate-limiting enzyme that catalyzes the hydroxylation of tyrosine to form dopa, which is subsequently converted to the neurotransmitters dopamine, norepinephrine, and epinephrine. Stimulation of PC12 cells, a rat pheochromocytoma-derived cell line with neuronal prop-erties, by agents elevating intracellular calcium leads to the phosphorylation of tyrosine hydroxylase at sites phosphorylated by CaM kinase in vitro and distinct from those recognized by other protein kinases (17, 49, 164). Thus the calcium-dependent activation of CaM kinase may serve to couple the rate of catecholamine synthesis with the degree of neuronal activity and presynaptic neurotransmitter release.

More recently, functional studies of brain CaM kinase have focused on its role in the calcium-dependent regulation of neuronal excitability and synaptic transmission. It is known that calcium influx through voltage-dependent N-type channels at presynaptic terminals triggers vesicle fusion and neurotransmitter release via a complex mechanism that is not completely understood (12, 64). Evidence for the direct involvement of CaM kinase in this process has mainly come from the studies of Greengard and co-workers, who have shown that CaM kinase is tightly associated with synaptic vesicles in the presynaptic terminal. Elevation of intracellular calcium leads to activation of CaM kinase, which then phosphorylates synapsin I, a tightly bound vesicular membrane protein of M_r ~80 kDa, which exists as two alternatively spliced isoforms, denoted Ia and Ib (155). Synapsin I remains attached to synaptic vesicles through binding of its N-terminus to membrane phopholipids (8) and through high affinity interaction of its C-terminal domain with the autoregulatory region of vesicular CaM kinase (9). Phosphorylation of two CaM kinase–spe-cific sites in the C-terminus of synapsin I decreases both its binding to the vesicle and its interaction with actin filaments. This phosphorylation may thus relieve the inhibitory constraint on vesicular movement and allow the vesicles to become available for docking and fusion at the active zone of the presynaptic membrane (48). In the squid giant synapse, microinjection of unphosphorylated synapsin I blocks neurotransmitter release, whereas synapsin I phosphorylated by CaM kinase has no effect (84). Similar inhibitory effects of microinjected synapsin I have also been observed in goldfish Mauthner cell neurons (52). Moreover, introduction of autonomous CaM kinase into rat brain synaptosomes, using freeze-thaw techniques, has been shown to enhance the rates of stimulated catecholamine and glutamate neurotransmitter release, whereas selective peptide inhibitors of CaM kinase reduce this release mediated by the endogenous calcium-dependent mechanism (111).

However, in transgenic mice lacking a functional gene for synapsin I, neuronal development and anatomy appeared normal, and only a modest change in function was observed (120). These mice display selective enhancement of paired-pulse facilitation, a form of synaptic transmission, with no apparent changes in other modes of transmission, such as long-term potentiation (LTP). Thus synapsin I may be critical only in limiting neurotransmitter release elicited by rapid repetitive stimuli. In fact, a related synaptic vesicle protein, synapsin II (155), may be able to functionally compensate in some respects for the loss of synapsin I in these transgenic animals. However, biochemically, synapsin II is not a substrate for CaM kinase in situ, and would thus not substitute for synapsin I in the calcium-dependent regulation of vesicle trafficking. A double knockout of both proteins would be more helpful in defining the exact biological roles of CaM kinase and synapsin isoforms in synaptic vesicle availability and release.

Recent evidence points to an important role for hippocampal CaM kinase in LTP, a model of neuronal plasticity in which the use-dependent strengthening of synaptic connections is thought to contribute to the formation of learning and memory (15, 83). In LTP, mechanisms involving both enhanced neurotransmitter release and greater postsynaptic responsiveness appear to contribute to the observed increase in synaptic efficacy. Following induction of LTP in vivo, enhanced postsynaptic responsiveness lasts for hours to weeks, indicating that long-term cellular processes are invoked (ie. protein phosphorylation, gene expression) to maintain these changes after the brief initial stimulus. Experimentally, this phenomenon has been best studied in brain slices, in which the activity of hippocampal CA1 neurons is recorded in response to stimulatory input via the Schaffer collateral pathway originating in the CA3 region of the hippocampus. Thus changes in the responsiveness of the CA1 neuron to standard stimulation protocols primarily reflect presynaptic and postsynaptic changes in synaptic transmission. Increases in presynaptic release may result, in part, from the calcium-dependent postsynaptic generation of nitric oxide, which is thought to act as a retrograde second messenger to enhance presynaptic neurotransmitter release (99, 127). From early observations, it was known that LTP could be blocked by preventing postsynaptic elevation of intracellular calcium, either by injecting calcium chelators or preventing calcium influx through NMDA-type glutamate receptors.

To elucidate if calcium-dependent protein kinases play a role in LTP, CaM kinase and protein kinase C (PKC) inhibitory peptides were introduced into postsynaptic CA1 neurons. Inhibitory peptides CaMK(273–302) and PKC(19–31) were found to block LTP if introduced prior to tetanic stimulation used to elicit LTP, but had little effect on established LTP, which suggests that these kinases were involved in induction but not in maintenance of LTP (19, 89, 90, 163). Inhibition of all calmodulin-dependent processes by microinjection of CaMK(296–311) (90) or CaMK(281–309) (89) also blocks induction of LTP, although this may result from inhibition of both CaM kinase and nitric oxide synthase. Concern over the specificity of autoinhibitor peptides was raised recently by a study that examined the concentration dependence for LTP block and suggested that the CaM kinase inhibitors blocked induction of LTP via cross-reactivity with PKC (61).

A more direct demonstration of CaM kinase's involvement in LTP came from studies using transgenic mice deficient in α-CaM kinase (134, 135). These mice demonstrate clear impairments in spatial learning tasks previously ascribed to the hippocampus. Furthermore, hippocampal CA1 neurons in slices from homozygous mutant mice do not undergo LTP in established stimulation protocols. Subsequent studies have demonstrated that CA1 neurons from transgenic mice carrying a dysfunctional gene for PKCγ, a calcium-dependent isozyme of PKC, also do not undergo LTP (1, 2). These findings demonstrate important roles for both CaM kinase and PKCγ in the induction of LTP.

A likely pathway by which CaM kinase contributes to the increased postsynaptic responsiveness observed in LTP was recently described by McGlade-McCulloh et al (97). CaM kinase activation in the postsynaptic terminal occurs following calcium influx via NMDA-type glutamate receptors, which are critical to the induction of LTP. These investigators have shown that CaM kinase phosphorylates a recombinant form of the AMPA receptor, GluR1, expressed in Sf9 insect cells, as well as the native AMPA receptor in cultured rat hippocampal neurons (150). Under whole-cell voltage-clamp conditions, intracellular dialysis of autonomous CaM kinase into isolated rat hippocampal neurons enhances kainate-induced inward current through postsynaptic glutamate receptors, presumably via direct phosphorylation of the GluR1 receptor complex. Enhancement of the inward current would result in a larger excitatory postsynaptic potential (EPSP). The phosphorylation-induced changes in GluR1 single-channel kinetics and sensitivity to agonist have yet to be investigated. Taken together, these studies establish a role for CaM kinase in the induction of LTP and further indicate that a possible mechanism involves an increase in postsynaptic macroscopic currents via ionotropic GluR1 glutamate receptors. Additional aspects of glutamate receptor phosphorylation are discussed by Roche et al (119).

At the level of the intact neuron, CaM kinase has also been implicated in the regulation of membrane excitability by neurotransmitters. Two common phenomena in neurons are adaptation, the progressive slowing of action potential discharge during a constant stimulus, and slow after-hyperpolarization (sAHP), which follows trains of action potentials. Calcium-activated potassium channels appear to underlie both adaptation and the sAHP, and in many neurons, these processes are decreased following stimulation by calcium-mobilizing cholinergic agonists. In guinea pig CA1 and CA3 hippocampal neurons, Müller and co-workers (105) have shown that microinjection of CaM kinase inhibitory peptides blocks the cholinergic modulation of adaptation and sAHP, thereby preventing the normal increase in cell excitability produced by cholinergic stimuli. That CaM kinase may act directly on calcium-activated potassium channels to decrease their activity is consistent with the above observations that postsynaptic glutamate receptors are the targets of signaling pathways (i.e. calcium, CaM kinase) that regulate neuronal excitability.

Roles in the Cardiovascular System

In the heart, calcium entry during the plateau of the action potential serves to trigger the release of calcium from the sarcoplasmic reticulum, which leads to calcium binding to the troponin complex, the formation of actin-myosin cross-bridges, and myofibrillar force generation. Thus calcium plays a central role in cardiac excitation-contraction (E-C) coupling, and it is not surprising that a number of regulatory mechanisms exist for calcium in that organ.

The sarcoplasmic reticulum (SR) contains pathways for the release of calcium, which initiates contraction, as well as for its reuptake, which triggers relaxation. Calcium-induced calcium release (CICR) occurs via ryanodine receptors or calcium release channels in the SR, whereas calcium reuptake is mediated principally by the SR Ca^{2+}-ATPase. Recent evidence has shown both pathways are regulated in a calcium-dependent manner via CaM kinase.

The activity of the SR Ca^{2+}-ATPase, or calcium pump, is regulated by another closely associated SR regulatory protein called phospholamban, an amphipathic basic protein of ~6 kDa, with a single transmembrane-spanning domain that exists as a homopentameric complex (148). Phospholamban physically interacts with Ca^{2+}-ATPase (65) and is thought to inhibit pump activity by promoting the aggregation of pump molecules into catalytically unfavorable conformations or interfering with the catalytic site (88, 156). The phosphorylation of phospholamban appears to disrupt the interaction of phospholamban with the pump, thus reversing its inhibitory effect (157, 174). This de-inhibition results in a more rapid rate of calcium reuptake and, hence, a more rapid rate of relaxation following the peak of twitch contraction. Calcium-dependent phosphorylation of phospholamban is known to occur at Thr^{17} of each monomer, by an endogenous SR calcium/calmodulin-dependent protein kinase (165). In vitro, purified CaM kinase also phosphorylates this site, with the same functional consequences on ATPase activity. Therefore, this pathway may represent a feedback mechanism whereby elevated cytoplasmic calcium regulates its own reuptake on the SR and hence contraction. Adjacent to Thr^{17} is Ser^{16}, the phosphorylation site for the cyclic AMP-dependent protein kinase (PKA). The β–adrenergic-induced increase in SR calcium reuptake and in the rate of relaxation is dependent upon PKA-dependent phosphorylation at Ser^{16}. Phosphorylation at this site also appears to be important for the CaM kinase-dependent phosphorylation at Thr^{17} (165). The sequence around the phosphorylation sites ($IRRAS^{16}T^{17}I$) can readily accommodate both kinases because the consensus phosphorylation site of PKA is R-R-X-S/T and that of CaM kinase is R-X-X-S/T. Interestingly, CaM kinase substrates can contain an acidic residue between the Arg and the phosphorylated residue (56), and it is possible that initial phosphorylation of Ser^{16} by PKA introduces an acidic residue that improves phosphorylation of the adjacent Thr^{17} by CaM kinase. Furthermore, CaM kinase also phosphorylates and increases the catalytic activity of the SR Ca^{2+}-ATPase itself (173), which should further enhance calcium reuptake.

In addition to calcium reuptake, CaM kinase may also play a role in CICR, which underlies E-C coupling in the heart (141). Recent evidence has shown that in vitro CaM kinase phosphorylates a distinct site in the cardiac, but not the skeletal, SR calcium release channel, or ryanodine receptor, increasing the open probability (P_o) of the channel following calcium-dependent activation (59, 169). In the intact heart, this would be expected to enhance calcium release from the SR and force generation in response to a contractile stimulus. However, Wang & Best (161) have shown that activation of an endogenous calcium/calmodulin-dependent protein kinase in voltage-clamped skeletal muscle SR membrane leads to a decrease in the P_o of the calcium release channel, which can then be reversed by phosphatase activity.

CaM kinase also appears to be involved in the regulation of calcium entry via the voltage-gated, L-type calcium current (I_{Ca-L}). In cardiac myocytes, and in other excitable cells, elevation of cytoplasmic calcium leads to either inactivation (6, 29, 77, 102) or enhancement (34, 51, 60, 76, 92) of I_{Ca-L} magnitude. In isolated toad smooth muscle cells, McCarron et al (94) recently showed that blockade of endogenous CaM kinase by peptide inhibitors prevents calcium-induced enhancement of I_{Ca-L}, without significantly altering cytoplasmic calcium transients. Similarly, we have recently shown that internal dialysis of CaM kinase inhibitory peptides blocks the calcium-induced enhancement of

I_{Ca-L} in single, voltage-clamped rabbit ventricular myocytes following elevation of cytoplasmic calcium by flash photolysis of the photolabile calcium chelator Nitr-5 (3). Recent studies (172, 177) from other laboratories have provided further evidence that the stimulation- and voltage-dependent enhancement of I_{Ca-L} in cardiac myocytes are also blocked by peptide inhibitors of CaM kinase. These observations confirm the original hypothesis of Marban & Tsien (92) that the observed calcium-induced enhancement of I_{Ca-L} by cardiotonic steroids (digitalis and strophanthidin) was mediated via a calcium-dependent protein kinase. At the single-channel level, CaM kinase-mediated phosphorylation of the calcium channel complex may shift channels from a brief to a long opening mode (5), which should predictably result in a greater macroscopic current. Functionally, enhancement of I_{Ca-L} via CaM kinase would increase calcium entry into the cell during subsequent beats and thereby enhance the filling of SR calcium stores. Greater filling would lead to greater calcium release from the SR with each action potential, a positive inotropic effect.

In vascular smooth muscle, CaM kinase may additionally regulate calcium-dependent force generation through the phosphorylation of the thin filament (actin)-associated regulatory protein caldesmon (63, 131). Caldesmon binds actin and myosin through its C- and N-termini, respectively, and has been proposed to organize or structurally cross-link actin and myosin filaments, thereby decreasing myosin ATPase and preventing cross-bridge cycling. Phosphorylation of caldesmon via CaM kinase decreases its binding to myosin (145), which may relieve its inhibitory effect on myosin ATPase activity and allow cross-bridge cycling following elevation of intracellular calcium. Importantly, the binding of actin and myosin by caldesmon may further serve to maintain the contractile filaments into a three-dimensional meshwork capable of force generation (160).

CaM kinase has also been shown to phosphorylate myosin light chain kinase (MLCK), the rate-limiting enzyme in myofilament contraction. MLCK is also activated via calcium/calmodulin and phosphorylates the 20-kDa light chain on myosin heads, thereby allowing the interaction of myosin with actin and cross-bridge cycling to occur. Phosphorylation of MLCK at a site within the calmodulin-binding region (Ser^{512}) decreases the affinity of MLCK for activator calmodulin (62). Evidence from Stull and co-workers (143, 152) demonstrates that the phosphorylation of MLCK occurs in intact smooth muscle strips in response to contractile stimuli such as carbachol and KCl depolarization. Phosphorylation of MLCK by CaM kinase in situ was found to decrease the calcium sensitivity of the 20-kDa light chain phosphorylation measured by a subsequent in vitro assay. KN-62 was found to specifically block phosphorylation of this site and to block desensitization of MLCK in intact cells in response to ionomycin, without affecting the intracellular calcium level. Phosphorylation of MLCK following a stimulus would thus decrease the sensitivity of the enzyme to activation by calcium/calmodulin, which represents a regulatory mechanism to desensitize smooth muscle to subsequent contractile stimuli.

Roles in Epithelia

Hollow organs of the body that are continuous with the external environment (i.e. the respiratory, urinary, and gastrointestinal tracts) are lined by a surface epithelium that serves as a physical barrier between the underlying tissues of these organs and factors from the external medium. In addition to this protective role, a major function of this surface epithelium is the transcellular secretion and absorption of solutes and water in response to hormonal stimuli.

Recent studies have demonstrated that the epithelial ion channels and transporters, which allow the movement of solutes between the basolateral (serosal) and apical (mucosal) plasma membranes, are regulated by second messenger signaling cascades. For example, cystic fibrosis transmembrane conductance regulator (CFTR), the chloride channel defective in cystic fibrosis, is normally activated by β-adrenergic stimuli via the cAMP/PKA signaling pathway. Similarly, hormonal stimuli causing mobilization of intracellular calcium lead to the activation of a distinct class of epithelial chloride channels via a mechanism involving CaM kinase (103, 158, 170). Chloride currents activated via CaM kinase have also been observed in human neutrophils (128). Although the exact level at which CaM kinase acts in this pathway is not clear, a recent study has shown that CaM kinase directly activates a ~40 pS chloride channel in excised membrane patches from a human T lymphocyte cell line (112). Thus, as in CNS neurons, phosphorylation-dependent regulation may occur directly at the level of the ion channel complex. However, it is unclear whether these chloride channels in lymphocytes are the same as those activated in intact epithelial cells under whole-cell voltage-clamp conditions. Using noise analysis, we have estimated the single-channel conductance of the macroscopic calcium-activated chloride current in T84 epithelial cells to be about 2–3 pS (A Braun & H Schulman, unpublished observations). This estimate is similar to that derived from single-channel recordings of the calcium-activated chloride current in other cell types (72, 149). The functional role of the CaM kinase-activated 40 pS chloride channel in T lymphocytes has not been defined.

Epithelium is known to contain at least the γ and δ isoforms of CaM kinase (35), which have enzymatic and autoregulatory properties similar to the α and β isoforms from brain, which have been most carefully characterized. Because the calcium-dependent chloride channels activated via CaM kinase are distinct from the CFTR chloride channels defective in cystic fibrosis (4), it has been suggested that they may partially compensate for the loss of epithelial chloride secretion normally occurring via CFTR and the cAMP signaling pathways (21, 47).

In addition to chloride channels, CaM kinase also appears to be involved in the activation of a class of amiloride-insensitive, calcium-dependent, nonselective cation channels present in many tissues (116) including epithelium (A Braun & H Schulman, unpublished data). We have observed that elevation of intracellular calcium by A23187 in single, voltage-clamped human T84 epithelial cells transiently activates both a chloride and cation current. Activation of these currents is blocked by intracellular dialysis with CaM kinase inhibitory peptides, as described above, whereas exposure of the cells to the serine/threonine phosphatase inhibitors okadaic acid and microcystin LR leads to persistent activation of these currents following A23187 exposure. Functionally, the calcium-dependent activation of nonselective cation channels would allow a background sodium influx to occur in combination with stimulated chloride secretion across the epithelium. An inward sodium flux across the basolateral epithelial membrane may thus contribute to the maintenance of cellular osmolarity as part of an overall cell volume regulatory mechanism that is invoked during stimulated secretion (37, 38). Alternatively, a calcium-activated cation influx is hypothesized to act as a driving force for chloride movement in the push-pull model of stimulated exocytosis from pancreatic acinar cells (149). Thus, in epithelium, CaM kinase may coordinate the activation of chloride and cation channels such that secretion and cell volume regulation occur in concert.

In the ileal epithelium, sodium chloride absorption across the apical membrane is known to be regulated in a calcium-dependent manner such that absorption is stimulated at low, and inhibited at high, cytosolic free calcium (28). Furthermore, Na^+/H^+ and Cl^-/HCO_3^- exchangers at the apical or brush border membrane have been implicated in mediating the uptake of NaCl (79, 80). To understand the calcium-dependent regulation of this sodium reuptake, Donowitz and co-workers (22) have shown that CaM kinase is present in brush border membranes of ileal epithelium and that the CaM kinase inhibitory peptide CaMK(281–302) produces a modest reduction of sodium uptake in isolated membrane vesicles. These observations implicate CaM kinase in the calcium regulatory pathway; however, it is unclear whether CaM kinase regulates sodium uptake through effects on the primary exchangers themselves.

Roles in Gene Expression

It is now well-established that protein phosphorylation represents a major biochemical mechanism by which hormonal and extracellular stimuli regulate cellular functions. Early studies identified transcription factors as critical phosphoproteins in the signaling cascades. They are a class of proteins that bind to specific regions of genomic DNA and thereby influence the transcription of the associated gene. Perhaps the best understood example of hormonal regulation of gene expression is that of *c-fos*, an immediate early gene that is rapidly upregulated in response to a number of extracellular stimuli. The promoter region of *c-fos* is known to contain specific binding sites for transcription factors that are activated via cAMP and calcium-dependent signaling pathways. The calcium and/or cAMP responsive element (CaRE and/or CRE) is a sequence of 8–10 nucleotides (TGACGTCA) located ~60 base pairs (bp) upstream from the site of transcriptional initiation (132). Elevation of intracellular calcium in PC12 cells, a neuron-like cell line, leads to transcription of *c-fos* through the activation of a CRE-binding protein (CREB) by phosphorylation of this transcription factor specifically at Ser[133] (133). This finding is supported by recent observations that CREB phosphorylated by CaM kinase is able to activate the c-fos promoter in an in vitro transcription assay (26). Another calcium/calmodulin-dependent protein kinase, CaM kinase IV, which has recently been found in the nucleus (66), may also play a role in calcium-dependent activation of transcription factors (31, 92a).

The c-fos promoter contains a second *cis*-acting element that is activated via CaM kinase. This DNA sequence, referred to as the CaM kinase responsive element (CaMRE) (68), is similar (TGACGTTT) to CRE, but does not bind CREB. Rather, CaMRE binds C/EBPβ, another transcription factor belonging to the C/EBP family. Wegner and co-workers (166) have recently shown that transient expression of a truncated, monomeric form of α-CaM kinase (α1– 290) in G/C pituitary cells leads to the in situ phosphorylation of C/EBPβ at Ser[276], resulting in its activation. In some cell types, C/EBPβ appears to be localized predominantly in the nucleus (166), which suggests that it may undergo activation by a kinase already present there. Recent evidence from our laboratory indicates that some isoforms of CaM kinase contain within their variable region a short stretch of amino acids that represents a consensus nuclear localization sequence (NLS) (140). The presence of this NLS in CaM kinase cDNAs encoding the α_B and δ_B isoforms causes the holoenzymes to become localized exclusively to the nucleus when these cDNAs are transiently expressed in either COS-7, rat 291 fibroblasts, or primary cultures of neonatal rat ventricular myocytes (140). Inserting this NLS (Lys-Lys-Arg-Lys) into CaM kinase cDNAs where it is normally absent also leads to the nuclear localization of these holoenzymes following expression in transfected cells. Furthermore, conversion of the first Lys residue to a neutral Asn eliminates nuclear targeting, a characteristic feature of such NLS sequences. These observations verify the CaM kinase KKRK sequence as an authentic NLS. γ_A-CaM kinase also contains this consensus NLS at the same position. Thus at least three classes of CaM kinase contain one alternatively spliced variant with an NLS. These isoforms perhaps represent the CaM kinase that has been detected immunologically in the nucleus (113). The observed nuclear targeting of CaM kinase would thus complement the nuclear localization of transcription factors such as CREB and C/EBPβ. Therefore, phosphorylation and activation of C/EBPβ may represent a mechanism by which CaM kinase plays a role in the regulation of gene expression by certain calcium-mobilizing agents. The relative abundance of CaM kinase, CREB, and C/EBPβ in the nucleus may determine the relative activation or inhibition of *c-fos* by calcium.

In Jurkat T lymphocytes, expression of the interleukin 2 (*IL-2*) gene occurs in response to the mobilization of intracellular calcium by activation of the T cell receptor or hormonal stimuli. Calcium can lead to either induction of *IL-2* or an unresponsive state, depending on the presence of co-stimulation (129). The calcium/calmodulin-dependent protein phosphatase 2B, or calcineurin, is critically involved in the mediation of the calcium signal leading to increased *IL-2* gene expression, and is a major site of action for the immunosuppressive drugs FK-506 and cyclosporin A. Studies from our laboratory suggest that CaM kinase may mediate the negative effect in the stimulation of *IL-2* production seen after a prolonged calcium elevation without a co-stimulatory signal (110). *IL-2* induction was inhibited at at least three regulatory elements that combined to give >90% inhibition. Therefore, as was recently found with CREB (31), CaM kinase may act as a negative rather than a positive regulator of gene transcription, possibly through the phosphorylation-dependent inhibition of specific transcription factors.

Conclusions and Future Directions

CaM kinase is a ubiquitous serine/threonine protein kinase that has been implicated in the regulation of diverse functions ranging from muscle contraction, secretion, and synaptic transmission to gene expression. Its multimeric structure together with the effects of its intrinsic autophosphorylation suggest that CaM kinase may remain activated following the decline of intracellular calcium signals and may function as a type of frequency detector in response to calcium spikes or oscillations. Mapping the functional domains of CaM kinase through biochemical means has led to the development of peptide-based inhibitors of the kinase, as well as to strategies to alter its catalytic and regulatory properties by site-directed mutagenesis. The ability to generate transgenic animal models deficient in specfic CaM kinase isoforms has provided a new dimension in which the functional roles of CaM kinase can be examined.

A number of proteins have now been shown to be substrates in situ for CaM kinase, supporting the notion of CaM kinase as a bona fide multifunctional protein kinase. Additional criteria must be met by all putative substrates to demonstrate their physiological relevance. The development of better inhibitors of CaM kinase and additional experimental strategies for its manipulation in situ will greatly aid the field.

Although numerous isoforms of CaM kinase have been cloned, it is not known, for the most part, which tissues express which isoforms. With the exception of nuclear targeting and modest differences in affinities for calmodulin, we do not know what distinguishes one isoform from another. Based on studies of other protein kinases and phosphatases, it is likely that distinct target proteins anchor the isoforms near substrates at various intracellular sites. The temporal and spatial regulation of receptors and transducers, calcium, calmodulin, CaM kinase, and its substrates likely enable cell stimuli to elicit specific responses. Different calcium-linked signals could regulate different subsets of CaM kinase substrates.

Literature Cited

1. Abeliovich A, Chen C, Goda Y, Silva AJ, Stevens CF, et al. 1993. Modified hippocampal long-term potentiation in PKC-γ-mutant mice. *Cell* 75:1253–62
2. Abeliovich A, Paylor R, Chen C, Kim JJ, Wehner JM, et al. 1993. PKC-γ-mutant mice exhibit mild deficits in spatial and contextual learning. *Cell* 75:1263–71
3. Anderson ME, Braun AP, Schulman H, Premack BA. 1994. The multifunctional calcium/calmodulin-dependent protein kinase mediates calcium-induced enhancement of the L-type calcium current in rabbit ventricular myocytes. *Circ. Res.* In press
4. Anderson MP, Welsh MJ. 1991. Calcium and cAMP activate different chloride channels in the apical membrane of normal and cystic fibrosis epithelia. *Proc. Natl. Acad. Sci. USA* 88:6003–7
5. Armstrong D, Erxleben C, Kalman D, Lai Y, Nairn A, et al. 1988. Intracellular calcium controls the activity of dihydropyridine-sensitive calcium channels through protein phosphorylation and its removal. *J. Gen. Physiol.* 92:10a
6. Armstrong DL. 1989. Calcium channel regulation by calcineurin, a Ca^{2+}-activated phosphatase in mammalian brain. *Trends Neurosci.* 12:117–22
7. Baitinger C, Alderton J, Poenie M, Schulman H, Steinhardt RA. 1990. Multifunctional Ca^{2+}/calmodulin-dependent protein kinase is necessary for nuclear envelope breakdown. *J. Cell Biol.* 111:1763–73
8. Benfenati F, Bahler M, Jahn R, Greengard P. 1989. Interactions of synapsin I with small synaptic vesicles: Distinct sites in synapsin I bind to vesicle phospholipids and vesicle proteins. *J. Cell. Biol.* 108:1863–72
9. Benfenati F, Valtorta F, Rubenstein JL, Gorelick FS, Greengard P, et al. 1992. Synaptic vesicle-associated Ca^{2+}/calmodulin-dependent protein kinase II is a binding protein for synapsin I. *Nature* 359:417–20
10. Bennett MK, Erondu NE, Kennedy MB. 1983. Purification and characterization of a calmodulin-dependent protein kinase that is highly concentrated in brain. *J. Biol. Chem.* 258:12735–44
11. Bennett MK, Kennedy MB. 1987. Deduced primary structure of the β subunit of brain type II Ca^{2+}/calmodulin-dependent protein kinase determined by molecular cloning. *Proc. Natl. Acad. Sci. USA* 84:1794–98
12. Bennett MK, Scheller RH. 1994. A molecular description of synaptic vesicle membrane trafficking. *Annu. Rev. Biochem.* 63:63–100
13. Bennett-Jefferson A, Travis SM, Schulman H. 1991. Activation of multifunctional Ca^{2+}/calmodulin-dependent protein kinase in GH₃ cells. *J. Biol. Chem.* 266:1484–90
14. Bland MM, McDonald OB, Carrera AC. 1994. p56*lck* phosphorylation by Ca^{2+}/calmodulin-dependent protein kinase type II. *Biochem. Biophys. Res. Comm.* 198:67–73
15. Bliss TVP, Collingridge GL. 1993. A synaptic model of memory: long-term potentiation in the hippocampus. *Nature* 361:31–39

16. Bredt DS, Ferris CD, Snyder SH. 1992. Nitric oxide synthase regulatory sites. Phosphorylation by cyclic AMP-dependent protein kinase, protein kinase C, and calcium/calmodulin protein kinase; identification of flavin and calmodulin binding sites. *J. Biol. Chem.* 267:10976–81

17. Campbell DG, Hardie DG, Vulliet PR. 1986. Identification of four phosphorylation sites in the N-terminal region of tyrosine hydroxylase. *J. Biol. Chem.* 261: 10489–92

18. Cech TR, Herschlag D, Piccirilli JA, Pyle AM. 1992. RNA catalysis by a group I ribozyme. Developing a model for transition state stabilization. *J. Biol. Chem.* 267:17479–82

19. Chang G, Rong XW, Feng TP. 1994. Block of induction and maintenance of calcium-induced LTP by inhibition of protein kinase C in postsynaptic neurons in hippocampal CA1 region. *Brain Res.* 646:230–34

20. Chen TY, Yau K-W. 1994. Direct modulation by Ca^{2+}-calmodulin of cyclic nucleotide-activated channel of rat olfactory receptor neurons. *Nature* 368:545–48

21. Clarke LL, Grubb BR, Yandasdas JR, Cotton CU, McKenzie A, et al. 1994. Relationship of a non-cystic fibrosis transmembrane conductance regulator-mediated chloride conductance to organ-level disease in CFTR(-/-) mice. *Proc. Natl. Acad. Sci. USA* 91:479–83

22. Cohen ME, Reinlib L, Watson AJ, Gorelick F, Rys-Sikora K, et al. 1990. Rabbit ileal villus cell brush border Na^+/H^+ exchange is regulated by Ca^{2+}/calmodulin-dependent protein kinase II, a brush border membrane protein. *Proc. Natl. Acad. Sci. USA* 87:8990–94

23. Countaway JL, Nairn AC, Davis RJ. 1992. Mechanism of desensitization of the epidermal growth factor receptor protein-tyrosine kinase. *J. Biol. Chem.* 267:1129–40

24. Cruzalegui FH, Means AR. 1993. Biochemical characterization of the multifunctional Ca^{2+}/calmodulin-dependent protein kinase IV expressed in insect cells. *J. Biol. Chem.* 268:26171–78

25. Cui ZJ, Gorelick FS, Dannies PS. 1994. Calcium/calmodulin-dependent protein kinase II activation in rat pituitary cells in the presence of thyrotropin-releasing hormone and dopamine. *Endocrinology* 134:2245–50

26. Dash PK, Karl KA, Colicos MA, Prywes R, Kandel ER. 1991. cAMP response element–binding protein is activated by Ca^{2+}/calmodulin- as well as cAMP-dependent protein kinase. *Proc. Natl. Acad. Sci. USA* 88:5061–65

27. DeRemer MF, Saeli RJ, Brautigan DL, Edelman AM. 1992. Ca^{2+}-calmodulin-dependent protein kinases Ia and Ib from rat brain. II. Enzymatic characteristics and regulation of activities by phosphorylation and dephosphorylation. *J. Biol. Chem.* 267:13466–71

28. Donowitz M, Welsh MJ. 1986. Ca^{2+} and cyclic AMP in regulation of intestinal Na, K, and Cl transport. *Annu. Rev. Physiol.* 48:135–50

29. Eckert R, Chad JE. 1984. Inactivation of calcium channels. *Prog. Biophys. Mol. Biol.* 44:215–67

30. Edman CF, Schulman H. 1994. Identification and characterization of δ_B-CaM kinase and δ_C-CaM kinase from rat heart, two new multifunctional Ca^{2+}/calmodulin-dependent protein kinase isoforms. *Biochim. Biophys. Acta* 1221:89–101

31. Enslen H, Sun P, Brickey D, Soderling SH, Klamo E, et al. 1994. Characterization of Ca^{2+}/calmodulin-dependent protein kinase IV. Role in transcriptional regulation. *J. Biol. Chem.* 269:15520–27

32. Erondu NE, Kennedy MB. 1985. Regional distribution of type II Ca^{2+}/calmodulin-dependent protein kinase in rat brain. *J. Neurosci.* 5:3270–77

33. Estep RP, Alexander KA, Storm DR. 1989. Regulation of free calmodulin levels in neurons by neuromodulin: relationship to neuronal growth and regeneration. *Curr. Top. Cell. Reg.* 31:161–80

34. Fedida D, Noble D, Spindler AJ. 1988. Use-dependent reduction and facilitation of Ca current in guinea pig myocytes. *J. Physiol.* 405:439–60

35. Fedida D, Noble D, Spindler AJ. 1988. Mechanism of the use dependence of Ca^{2+} current in guinea pig myocytes. *J. Physiol.* 405:461–75

36. Fong Y-L, Taylor WL, Means AR, Soderling TR. 1989. Studies of the regulatory mechanism of Ca^{2+}/calmodulin-dependent protein kinase II. Mutation of threonine 286 to alanine and aspartate. *J. Biol. Chem.* 264:16759–63

37. Foskett JK. 1990. $[Ca^{2+}]_i$ modulation of Cl^- content controls cell volume in single salivary acinar cells during fluid secretion. *Am. J. Physiol.* 259:C998–1004

38. Foskett JK, Melvin JE. 1989. Activation of salivary secretion: Coupling of cell volume and $[Ca^{2+}]_i$ in single cells. *Science* 244:1582–85

39. Fukunaga K, Goto S, Miyamoto E.

1988. Immunohistochemical localization of Ca^{2+}/calmodulin-dependent protein kinase II in rat brain and various tissues. *J. Neurochem.* 51:1070–78

40. Fukunaga K, Rich DP, Soderling TR. 1989. Generation of the Ca^{2+}-independent form of Ca^{2+}/calmodulin-dependent protein kinase II in cerebellar granule cells. *J. Biol. Chem.* 264:21830–36

41. Fukunaga K, Soderling TR, Miyamoto E. 1992. Activation of Ca^{2+}/calmodulin-dependent protein kinase II and protein kinase C by glutamate in cultured rat hippocampal neurons. *J. Biol. Chem.* 267:22527–33

42. Fukunaga K, Stoppini L, Miyamoto E, Müller D. 1993. Long-term potentiation is associated with an increased activity of Ca^{2+}/calmodulin-dependent protein kinase II. *J. Biol. Chem.* 268:7863–67

43. Genot EM, Meier KE, Licciardi KA, Ahn NG, Uittenbogaart CH, et al. 1993. Phosphorylation of CD20 in cells from a hairy cell leukemia cell line. *J. Immunol.* 151:71–82

44. Gnegy ME. 1993. Calmodulin in neurotransmitter and hormone action. *Annu. Rev. Pharmacol. Toxicol.* 32:45–70

45. Goldenring JR, McGuire JS, Delorenzo RJ. 1984. Identification of the major postsynaptic density protein as homologous with the major calmodulin-binding subunit of a calmodulin-dependent protein kinase. *J. Neurochem.* 42:1077–84

46. Gough AH, Taylor DL. 1993. Fluorescence anisotropy imaging microscopy maps calmodulin binding during cellular contraction and locomotion. *J. Cell Biol.* 121:1095–107

47. Gray MA, Winpenny JP, Porteous DJ, Dorin JR, Argent BE. 1994. CFTR and calcium-activated chloride currents in pancreatic duct cells of a transgenic CF mouse. *Am. J. Physiol.* 266:C213–21

48. Greengard P, Valtorta F, Czernik AJ, Benfenati F. 1993. Synaptic vesicle phosphoproteins and regulation of synaptic function. *Science* 259:780–85

49. Griffith LC, Schulman H. 1988. The multifunctional Ca^{2+}/calmodulin-dependent protein kinase mediates Ca^{2+}-dependent phosphorylation of tyrosine hydroxylase. *J. Biol. Chem.* 263:9542–49

50. Griffith LC, Verselis LM, Aitken KM, Kyriacou CP, Danho W, et al. 1993. Inhibition of calcium/calmodulin-dependent protein kinase in *Drosophila* disrupts behavorial plasticity. *Neuron* 10:501–9

51. Gurney AM, Charnet P, Pye JM, Nargeot J. 1989. Augmentation of cardiac calcium current by flash photolysis of intracellular caged-Ca^{2+} molecules. *Nature* 341:65–68

52. Hackett JT, Cochran SL, Greenfield LJ, Brosius DC, Ueda T. 1990. Synapsin I injected presynaptically into goldfish Mauthner axons reduces quantal synaptic transmission. *J. Neurophysiol.* 63:701–6

53. Hanissian SH, Frangakis M, Bland MM, Jawahar S, Chatila TA. 1993. Expression of a Ca^{2+}/calmodulin-dependent protein kinase, CaM kinase-Gr, in human T lymphocytes. Regulation of kinase activity by T cell receptor signaling. *J. Biol. Chem.* 268:20055–63

54. Hanley RM, Means AR, Ono T, Kemp BE, Burgin KE, et al. 1987. Functional analysis of a complementary DNA for the 50-kilodalton subunit of calmodulin kinase II. *Science* 237:293–97

55. Hanson PI, Meyer T, Stryer L, Schulman H. 1994. Dual role of calmodulin in autophosphorylation of multifunctional CaM kinase may underlie decoding of calcium signals. *Neuron* 12:943–56

56. Hanson PI, Schulman H. 1992. Neuronal Ca^{2+}/calmodulin-dependent protein kinases. *Annu. Rev. Biochem.* 61:559–601

57. Haseloff J, Gerlach WL. 1988. Simple RNA enzymes with new and highly specific endoribonuclease activities. *Nature* 334:585–91

58. Hell JW, Appleyard SM, Yokoyama CT, Warner C, Catterall WA. 1994. Differential phosphorylation of two size forms of the N-type calcium channel $\alpha1$ subunit which have different COOH termini. *J. Biol. Chem.* 269:7390–96

59. Hohenegger M, Suko J. 1993. Phosphorylation of the purified cardiac ryanodine receptor by exogenous and endogenous protein kinases. *Biochem. J.* 296:303–8

60. Hryshko LV, Bers DM. 1990. Ca current facilitation during postrest recovery depends on Ca entry. *Am. J. Physiol.* 259:H951–61

61. Hvalby O, Hemmings HC Jr, Paulsen O, Czernik AJ, Nairn AC, et al. 1994. Specificity of protein kinase inhibitor peptides and induction of long-term potentiation. *Proc. Natl. Acad. Sci. USA* 91:4761–65

62. Ikebe M, Reardon S. 1990. Phosphorylation of smooth muscle myosin light chain kinase by smooth muscle Ca^{2+}/calmodulin-dependent multifunctional protein kinase. *J. Biol. Chem.* 265:8975–78

63. Ikebe M, Reardon S, Scott-Woo GC, Zhou Z, Koda Y. 1990. Purification and characterization of calmodulin-depen-

dent multifunctional protein kinase from smooth muscle: Isolation of caldesmon kinase. *Biochemistry* 29:11242–48

64. Jahn R, Sudhof TC. 1994. Synaptic vesicles and exocytosis. *Annu. Rev. Neurosci.* 17:219–46

65. James P, Inui M, Tada M, Chiesi M, Carafoli E. 1989. Nature and site of phospholamban regulation of the Ca^{2+} pump of sarcoplasmic reticulum. *Nature* 342:90–92

66. Jensen KF, Ohmstede C-A, Fisher RS, Sahyoun N. 1991. Nuclear and axonal localization of Ca^{2+}/calmodulin-dependent protein kinase type Gr in rat cerebellar cortex. *Proc. Natl. Acad. Sci. USA* 88:2850–53

67. Kanaseki T, Ikeuchi Y, Sugiura H, Yamauchi T. 1991. Structural features of Ca^{2+}/calmodulin-dependent protein kinase II revealed by electron microscopy. *J. Cell Biol.* 115:1049–60

68. Kapiloff MS, Mathis JM, Nelson CA, Lin CR, Rosenfeld MG. 1991. Calcium/calmodulin-dependent protein kinase mediates a pathway for transcriptional regulation. *Proc. Natl. Acad. Sci. USA* 88:3710–14

69. Karls U, Müller U, Gilbert DJ, Copeland NG, Jenkins NA, et al. 1992. Structure, expression, and chromosome location of the gene for the β subunit of brain-specific Ca^{2+}/calmodulin-dependent protein kinase II identified by transgene integration in an embryonic lethal mouse mutant. *Mol. Cell. Biol.* 12:3644–52

70. Kelly PT, McGuinness TL, Greengard P. 1984. Evidence that the major postsynaptic density protein is a component of a Ca^{2+}/calmodulin-dependent protein kinase. *Proc. Natl. Acad. Sci. USA* 81: 945–49

71. Kelly PT, Shields S, Conway K, Yip R, Burgin K. 1987. Developmental changes in calmodulin-kinase II activity at brain synaptic junctions: Alterations in holoenzyme composition. *J. Neurochem.* 49: 1927–40

72. Klockner U. 1993. Intracellular calcium ions activate a low-conductance chloride channel in smooth-muscle cells isolated from human mesenteric artery. *Pflügers Arch.* 424:231–37

73. Klockner U, Isenberg G. 1987. Calmodulin antagonists depress calcium and potassium currents in ventricular and vascular myocytes. *Am. J. Physiol.* 253:H1601–11

74. Krebs EG. 1973. The mechanism of hormonal regulation by cyclic AMP. In *Endocrinology, Proceedings of the 4th International Congress,* pp.17–29. Amsterdam: Excerpta Medica

75. Kuret J, Schulman H. 1984. Purification and characterization of a Ca^{2+}/calmodulin-dependent protein kinase from rat brain. *Biochemistry* 23:5495–504

76. Lee KS. 1987. Potentiation of the calcium-channel currents in internally perfused mammalian heart cells by repetitive depolarization. *Proc. Natl. Acad. Sci. USA* 84:3941–45

77. Lee KS, Marban E, Tsien RW. 1985. Inactivation of calcium channels in mammalian heart cells: joint dependence on membrane potential and intracellular calcium. *J. Physiol.* 364: 395–411

78. Li G, Hidaka H, Wollheim CB. 1992. Inhibition of voltage-gated Ca^{2+} channels and insulin secretion in HIT cells by the Ca^{2+}/calmodulin-dependent protein kinase II inhibitor KN-62: Comparison with antagonists of calmodulin and L-type Ca^{2+} channels. *Mol. Pharmacol.* 42:489–98

79. Liedtke CM, Hopfer U. 1982. Mechanism of Cl^- translocation across small intestinal brush-border membrane. I. Absence of Na^+-Cl^- cotransport. *Am. J. Physiol.* 242:G263–71

80. Liedtke CM, Hopfer U. 1982. Mechanism of Cl^- translocation across small intestinal brush-border membrane. II. Demonstration of Cl^--OH^- exchange and Cl^- conductance. *Am. J. Physiol.* 242:G272–80

81. Lin CR, Kapiloff MS, Durgerian S, Tatemoto K, Russo AF, et al. 1987. Molecular cloning of a brain-specific calcium/calmodulin-dependent protein kinase. *Proc. Natl. Acad. Sci. USA* 84: 5962–66

82. Lisman JE. 1985. A mechanism for memory storage insensitive to molecular turnover: A bistable autophosphorylating kinase. *Proc. Natl. Acad. Sci. USA* 82:3055–57

83. Lisman JE, Goldring MA. 1988. Feasibility of long-term storage of graded information by the Ca^{2+}/calmodulin-dependent protein kinase molecules of the postsynaptic density. *Proc. Natl. Acad. Sci. USA* 85:5320–24

84. Llinas R, Gruner JA, Sugimori M, McGuinness TL, Greengard P. 1991. Regulation by synapsin I and Ca^{2+}-calmodulin-dependent protein kinase II of transmitter release in squid giant synapse. *J. Physiol.* 436:257–82

85. Lorca T, Cruzalegui FH, Fesquet D, Cavadore JC, Mery J, et al. 1993. Calmodulin-dependent protein kinase II mediates inactivation of MPF and CSF upon fertilization of *Xenopus* eggs. *Nature* 366:270–73

86. MacNicol M, Jefferson AB, Schulman H. 1990. Ca^{2+}/calmodulin kinase is activated by the phosphatidylinositol signaling pathway and becomes Ca^{2+}-independent in PC12 cells. *J. Biol. Chem.* 265:18055–58

87. MacNicol M, Schulman H. 1992. Multiple Ca^{2+} signaling pathways converge on CaM kinase in PC12 cells. *FEBS Lett.* 304:237–40

88. Mahaney JE, Thomas DD. 1991. Effects of melittin on molecular dynamics and Ca-ATPase activity in sarcoplasmic reticulum membranes: Electron paramagnetic resonance. *Biochemistry* 30:7171–80

89. Malenka RC, Kauer JA, Perkel DJ, Mauk MD, Kelly PT, et al. 1989. An essential role for postsynaptic calmodulin and protein kinase activity in long-term potentiation. *Nature* 340:554–57

90. Malinow R, Schulman H, Tsien RW. 1989. Inhibition of postsynaptic PKC or CaMKII blocks induction but not expression of LTP. *Science* 245:862–66

91. Manalan AS, Klee CB. 1984. Calmodulin. *Adv. Cycl. Nucleotide Protein Phosph. Res.* 18:227–78

92. Marban E, Tsien RW. 1982. Enhancement of calcium current during digitalis inotropy in mammalian heart: Positive feed-back regulation by intracellular calcium? *J. Physiol.* 329:589–614

92a. Matthews RP, Guth CR, Wailes LM, Zhao S, Means AR, McKnight GS. 1994. Calcium/calmodulin-dependent protein kinase types II and IV differentially regulate CREB-dependent gene expression. *Mol. Cell. Biol.* 14:6107–16

92b. Mattiazzi A, Hove-Madsen L, Bers DM. 1994. Protein kinase inhibitors reduce SR Ca transport in permeabilized myocytes. *Am. J. Physiol.* 267:H812–20

93. Mayer P, Mohlig M, Schatz H, Pfeiffer A. 1994. Additional isoforms of multifunctional calcium/calmodulin-dependent protein kinase II in rat heart tissue. *Biochem. J.* 298:757–58

94. McCarron JG, McGeown JG, Reardon S, Ikebe M, Fay FS, et al. 1992. Calcium-dependent enhancement of calcium current in smooth muscle by calmodulin-dependent protein kinase II. *Nature* 357:74–77

95. McClelland P, Adam LP, Hathaway DR. 1994. Identification of a latent Ca^{2+}/calmodulin dependent protein kinase II phosphorylation site in vascular calpain II. *J. Biochem.* 115:41–46

96. McDonald BJ, Moss SJ. 1994. Differential phosphorylation of intracellular domains of gamma-aminobutyric acid type A receptor subunits by calcium/calmodulin type 2-dependent protein kinase and cGMP-dependent protein kinase. *J. Biol. Chem.* 269:18111–17

97. McGlade-McCulloh E, Yamamoto H, Tan S-E, Brickey DA, Soderling TR. 1993. Phosphorylation and regulation of glutamate receptors by calcium/calmodulin-dependent protein kinase II. *Nature* 362:640–42

98. McGuiness TL, Lai Y, Greengard P. 1985. Ca^{2+}/calmodulin-dependent protein kinase II. Isozymic forms from rat forebrain and cerebellum. *J. Biol. Chem.* 260:1696–704

99. Meffert MK, Premack BA, Schulman H. 1994. Nitric oxide stimulates Ca^{2+}-independent synaptic vesicle release. *Neuron* 12:1235–44

100. Meyer T, Hanson PI, Stryer L, Schulman H. 1992. Calmodulin trapping by calcium-calmodulin-dependent protein kinase. *Science* 256:1199–202

101. Miller SG, Kennedy MB. 1986. Regulation of brain type II Ca^{2+}/calmodulin-dependent protein kinase by autophosphorylation: A Ca^{2+}-triggered molecular switch. *Cell* 44:861–70

102. Morad M, Davies NW, Kaplan JH, Lux HD. 1988. Inactivation and block of calcium channels by photo-released Ca^{2+} in dorsal root ganglion neurons. *Science* 241:842–44

103. Morris AP, Frizzell RA. 1993. Ca^{2+}-dependent Cl^- channels in undifferentiated human colonic cells (HT-29). II. Regulation and rundown. *Am. J. Physiol.* 264:C977–85

104. Mukherji S, Soderling TR. 1994. Regulation of Ca^{2+}/calmodulin-dependent protein kinase II by inter- and intrasubunit-catalyzed autophosphorylation. *J. Biol. Chem.* 269:13744–47

105. Müller W, Petrozzino JJ, Griffith LC, Danho W, Conner JA. 1992. Specific involvement of Ca^{2+}-calmodulin kinase II in cholinergic modulation of neuronal responsiveness. *J. Neurophysiol.* 68:2264–69

106. Nairn AC, Bhagat B, Palfrey HC. 1985. Identification of calmodulin-dependent protein kinase III and its major M_r 100,000 substrate in mammalian tissues. *Proc. Natl. Acad. Sci. USA* 82:7939–43

107. Nairn AC, Greengard P. 1987. Purification and characterization of Ca^{2+}/calmodulin-dependent protein kinase I from bovine brain. *J. Biol. Chem.* 262:7273–81

108. Nairn AC, Palfrey HC. 1987. Identification of the major M_r 100,000 substrate for calmodulin-dependent protein kinase

III in mammalian cells as elongation factor-2. *J. Biol. Chem.* 262:17299–303

109. Nakazawa K, Higo K, Abe K, Tanaka Y, Saito H, et al. 1993. Blockade by calmodulin inhibitors of Ca^{2+} channels in smooth muscle from rat vas deferens. *Br. J. Pharmacol.* 109:137–41

110. Nghiem P, Ollick T, Gardner P, Schulman H. 1994. Interleukin-2 transcriptional block by multifunctional CaM kinase. *Nature* 371:347–50

111. Nichols RA, Sihra TS, Czernik AJ, Nairn AC, Greengard P. 1990. Calcium/calmodulin-dependent protein kinase II increases glutamate and noradrenaline release from synaptosomes. *Nature* 343:647–51

112. Nishimoto I, Wagner JA, Schulman H, Gardner P. 1991. Regulation of Cl$^-$ channels by multifunctional CaM kinase. *Neuron* 6:547–55

113. Ohta Y, Ohba T, Miyamoto E. 1990. Ca^{2+}/calmodulin-dependent protein kinase II: Localization in the interphase nucleus and the mitotic apparatus of mammalian cells. *Proc. Natl. Acad. Sci. USA* 87:5341–45

114. Oiumet CC, McGuinness TL, Greengard P. 1984. Immunocytochemical localization of calcium/calmodulin-dependent protein kinase II in rat brain. *Proc. Natl. Acad. Sci. USA* 81:5604–8

115. Okuno S, Fujisawa H. 1993. Requirement of brain extract for the activity of brain calmodulin-dependent protein kinase IV expressed in *Escherichia coli*. *J. Biochem.* 114:167–70

116. Partridge LD, Swandulla D. 1988. Calcium-activated non-specific cation channels. *Trends Neurosci.* 11:69–72

117. Payne ME, Fong Y-L, Ono T, Colbran RJ, Kemp BE, et al. 1988. Calcium/calmodulin-dependent protein kinase II. Characterization of distinct calmodulin binding and inhibitory domains. *J. Biol. Chem.* 263:7190–95

118. Popoli M. 1993. Synaptotagmin is endogenously phosphorylated by Ca^{2+}/calmodulin protein kinase II in synaptic vesicles. *FEBS Lett.* 317:85–88

119. Roche KW, Tingley WG, Huganir RL. 1994. Glutamate receptor phosphorylation and synaptic plasticity. *Curr. Opin. Neurobiol.* 4:383–88

120. Rosahl TW, Geppert M, Spillane D, Herz J, Hammer RE, et al. 1993. Short-term synaptic plasticity is altered in mice lacking synapsin I. *Cell* 75:661–70

121. Rubenstein JL, Greengard P, Czernik AJ. 1993. Calcium-dependent serine phosphorylation of synaptophysin. *Synapse* 13:161–72

122. Ryazanov AG, Shestakova EA, Natapov

PG. 1988. Phosphorylation of elongation factor 2 by EF-2 kinase affects rate of translation. *Nature* 334:170–73

123. Schulman H. 1988. The multifunctional Ca^{2+}/calmodulin-dependent protein kinase. *Adv. Second Mess. Phosphoprotein Res.* 22:39–112

124. Schulman H. 1993. The multifunctional Ca^{2+}/calmodulin-dependent protein kinases. *Curr. Opin. Cell Biol.* 5:247–53

125. Schulman H, Greengard P. 1978. Stimulation of brain membrane protein phosphorylation by calcium and endogenous heat-stable protein. *Nature* 271:478–79

126. Schulman H, Greengard P. 1978. Ca^{2+}-dependent protein phosphorylation system in membranes from various tissues, and its activation by 'calcium-dependent regulator'. *Proc. Natl. Acad. Sci. USA* 75:5432–36

127. Schuman EM, Madison DV. 1994. Nitric oxide and synaptic function. *Annu. Rev. Neurosci.* 17:153–83

128. Schumann MA, Gardner P, Raffin TA. 1993. Recombinant human tumor necrosis factor α induces calcium oscillations and calcium-activated chloride current in human neutrophils. The role of calcium/calmodulin-dependent protein kinase. *J. Biol. Chem.* 268:2134–40

129. Schwarz RH. 1990. A cell culture model for T lymphocyte clonal anergy. *Science* 248:1349–56

130. Schworer CM, Rothblum LI, Thekkumkara TJ, Singer HA. 1993. Identification of novel isoforms of the δ subunit of Ca^{2+}/calmodulin-dependent protein kinase II. Differential expression in rat brain and aorta. *J. Biol. Chem.* 268:14443–49

131. Scott-Woo GC, Sutherland C, Walsh MP. 1990. Kinase activity associated with caldesmon is Ca^{2+}/calmodulin-dependent kinase II. *Biochem. J.* 268:367–70

132. Sheng M, Dougan ST, McFadden G, Greenberg ME. 1988. Calcium and growth factor pathways of *c-fos* transcriptional activation require distinct upstream regulatory sequences. *Mol. Cell. Biol.* 8:2787–96

133. Sheng M, Thompson MA, Greenberg ME. 1991. CREB: A Ca^{2+}-regulated transcription factor phosphorylated by calmodulin-dependent kinases. *Science* 252:1427–30

134. Silva AJ, Paylor R, Wehner JM, Tonegawa S. 1992. Impaired spatial learning in α-calcium-calmodulin kinase II mutant mice. *Science* 257:206–11

135. Silva AJ, Stevens CF, Tonegawa S, Wang Y. 1992. Deficient hippocampal

long-term potentiation in α-calcium-calmodulin kinase II mutant mice. *Science* 257:201–6

136. Skene JH. 1990. GAP-43 as a 'calmodulin sponge' and some implications for calcium signalling in axon terminals. *Neurosci. Res. Suppl.* 13: S112–25

137. Smith MK, Colbran RJ, Brickey DA, Soderling TR. 1992. Functional determinants in the autoinhibitory domain of calcium/calmodulin-dependent protein kinase II. Role of His^{282} and multiple basic residues. *J. Biol. Chem.* 267:1761–68

138. Smith MK, Colbran RJ, Soderling TR. 1990. Specificities of autoinhibitory domain peptides for four protein kinases. *J. Biol. Chem.* 265:1837–40

139. Soderling TR. 1990. Protein kinases. Regulation by autoinhibitory domains. *J. Biol. Chem.* 265:1823–26

140. Srinivasan M, Edman CF, Schulman H. 1994. Alternative splicing introduces a nuclear localization signal that targets multifunctional CaM kinase to the nucleus. *J. Cell Biol.* 126:839–52

141. Stern MD, Lakatta EG. 1992. Excitation-contraction coupling in the heart: the state of the question. *FASEB J.* 6: 3092–100

142. Stull JT, Gallagher PJ, Herring BP, Kamm KE. 1991. Vascular smooth muscle contractile elements. Cellular regulation. *Hypertension* 17:723–32

143. Stull JT, Hsu L-C, Tansey MG, Kamm KE. 1990. Myosin light chain kinase phosphorylation in tracheal smooth muscle. *J. Biol. Chem.* 265:16683–90

144. Sumi M, Kiuchi K, Ishikawa T, Ishii A, Hagiwara M, et al. 1991. The newly synthesized selective Ca^{2+}/calmodulin-dependent protein kinase II inhibitor KN-93 reduces dopamine contents in PC12h cells. *Biochem. Biophys. Res. Commun.* 181:968–75

145. Sutherland C, Walsh MP. 1989. Phosphorylation of caldesmon prevents its interaction with smooth muscle myosin. *J. Biol. Chem.* 264:578–83

146. Suzuki T, Okumura-Noji K, Tanaka R, Tada T. 1993. Translocation of cytosolic α-subunit of Ca^{2+}/calmodulin-dependent protein kinase II (CaMKII) to particulate fraction and postsynaptic density (PSD) after decapitation. *Neuroscience* 19:273 (Abstr.)

147. Sweeney HL, Bowman BF, Stull JT. 1993. Myosin light chain phosphorylation in vertebrate striated muscle: Regulation and function. *Am. J. Physiol.* 264:C1085–95

148. Tada M, Kadoma M, Inui M, Fujii J-I.

149. Taleb O, Feltz P, Bossu J-L, Feltz A. 1988. Small-conductance chloride channels activated by calcium on cultured endocrine cells from mammalian pars intermedia. *Pflügers Arch.* 412:641–46

150. Tan S-E, Wenthold RJ, Soderling TR. 1994. Phosphorylation of AMPA-type glutamate receptors by calcium/calmodulin-dependent protein kinase II and protein kinase C in cultured hippocampal neurons. *J. Neurosci.* 14:1123–29

151. Tansey MG, Luby-Phelps K, Kamm KE, Stull JT. 1994. Ca^{2+}-dependent phosphorylation of myosin light chain kinase decreases the Ca^{2+} sensitivity of light chain phosphorylation within smooth muscle cells. *J. Biol. Chem.* 269:9912–20

152. Tansey MG, Word RA, Hidaka H, Singer HA, Schworer CM, et al. 1992. Phosphorylation of myosin light chain kinase by the multifunctional calmodulin-dependent protein kinase II in smooth muscle. *J. Biol. Chem.* 267: 12511–16

153. Tobimatsu T, Fujisawa H. 1989. Tissue-specific expression of four types of rat calmodulin-dependent protein kinase II mRNAs. *J. Biol. Chem.* 264:17907–12

154. Tokumitsu H, Chijiwa T, Hagiwara M, Mizutani A, Terasawa M, et al. 1992. KN-62, 1-[N,O-Bis(5-isoquinolinesulfonyl)-N-methyl-L-tyrosyl]-4-phenylpiperazine, a specific inhibitor of Ca^{2+}/calmodulin-dependent protein kinase II. *J. Biol. Chem.* 265:4315–20

155. Valtorta F, Benfenati F, Greengard P. 1992. Structure and function of the synapsins. *J. Biol. Chem.* 267:7195–98

156. Voss J, Birmachu W, Hussey DM, Thomas DD. 1991. Effects of melittin on molecular dynamics and Ca-ATPase activity in sarcoplasmic reticulum membranes: Time-resolved optical anisotropy. *Biochemistry* 30:7498–506

157. Voss J, Jones LR, Thomas DD. 1994. The physical mechanism of calcium pump regulation in the heart. *Biophys. J.* 67:190–96

158. Wagner JA, Cozens AL, Schulman H, Gruenert DC, Stryer L, et al. 1991. Activation of chloride channels in normal and cystic fibrosis airway epithelial cells by multifunctional calcium/calmodulin-dependent protein kinase. *Nature* 349:793–96

159. Waldmann R, Hanson PI, Schulman H. 1990. Multifunctional Ca^{2+}/calmodulin-

1983. Regulation of Ca^{2+}-pump from cardiac sarcoplasmic reticulum. *Meth. Enzymol.* 157:107–54

dependent protein kinase made Ca^{2+} independent for functional studies. *Biochemistry* 29:1679–84

160. Walsh MP. 1991. Calcium-dependent mechanisms of regulation of smooth muscle contraction. *Biochem. Cell Biol.* 69:771–800

161. Wang J, Best PM. 1992. Inactivation of the sarcoplasmic reticulum calcium channel by protein kinase. *Nature* 359: 739–41

162. Waxham MN, Aronowski J, Westgate SA, Kelly PT. 1990. Mutagenesis of Thr-286 in monomeric Ca^{2+}/calmodulin-dependent protein kinase II elminates Ca^{2+}/calmodulin-independent activity. *Proc. Natl. Acad. Sci. USA* 87:1273–77

163. Waxham MN, Malenka RC, Kelly PT, Mauk MD. 1993. Calcium/calmodulin-dependent protein kinase II regulates hippocampal synaptic transmission. *Brain Res.* 609:1–8

164. Waymire JC, Johnston JP, Hummer-Lickteig K, Lloyd A, Vigny A, et al. 1988. Phosphorylation of bovine adrenal chromaffin cell tyrosine hydroxylase. Temporal correlation of acetylcholine's effect on site phosphorylation, enzyme activation, and catecholamine synthesis. *J. Biol. Chem.* 263:12439–47

165. Wegener AD, Simmerman HK, Lindemann JP, Jones LR. 1989. Phospholamban phosphorylation in intact ventricles. Phosphorylation of serine 16 and threonine 17 in response to β-adrenergic stimulation. *J. Biol. Chem.* 264: 11468–74

166. Wegner M, Cao Z, Rosenfeld MG. 1992. Calcium-regulated phosphorylation within the leucine zipper of C/EBPβ. *Science* 256:370–73

167. Weinberger RP, Rostas JAP. 1986. Subcellular distribution of a calmodulin-dependent protein kinase activity in rat cerebral cortex during development. *Dev. Brain Res.* 29:37–50

168. Weintraub HM. 1990. Antisense RNA and DNA. *Sci. Am.* 262:40–46

169. Witcher DR, Kovacs RJ, Schulman H, Cefali DC, Jones LR. 1991. Unique phosphorylation site on the cardiac ryanodine receptor regulates calcium channel activity. *J. Biol. Chem.* 266: 11144–52

170. Worrell RT, Frizzell RA. 1991. CaMKII mediates stimulation of chloride conductance by calcium in T84 cells. *Am. J. Physiol.* 260:C877–82

171. Wu K, Huang Y, Adler J, Black IB. 1992. On the identity of the major postsynaptic density protein. *Proc. Natl. Acad. Sci. USA* 89:3015–19

172. Xiao R-P, Cheng H, Lederer WJ, Suzuki T, Lakatta EG. 1994. Dual regulation of Ca^{2+}/calmodulin-dependent protein kinase II activity by membrane voltage and by calcium influx. *Proc. Natl. Acad. Sci. USA.* In press

173. Xu A, Hawkins C, Narayanan N. 1993. Phosphorylation and activation of the Ca^{2+}-pumping ATPase of cardiac sarcoplasmic reticulum by Ca^{2+}/calmodulin-dependent protein kinase. *J. Biol. Chem.* 268:8394–97

174. Xu Z-C, Kirchberger MA. 1989. Modulation by polyelectrolytes of canine cardiac microsomal calcium uptake and the possible relationship to phospholamban. *J. Biol. Chem.* 264:16644–51

175. Yamauchi T, Fujisawa H. 1983. Purification and characterization of the brain calmodulin-dependent protein kinase (kinase II), which is involved in the activation of tryptophan 5-mono-oxygenase. *Eur. J. Biochem.* 132:15–21

176. Yano S, Fukunaga K, Ushio Y, Miyamoto E. 1994. Activation of Ca^{2+}/calmodulin-dependent protein kinase II and phosphorylation of intermediate filament proteins by stimulation of glutamate receptors in cultured rat cortical astrocytes. *J. Biol. Chem.* 269: 5428–39

177. Yuan W, Bers DM. 1994. Ca-dependent facilitation of cardiac Ca current is due to Ca-calmodulin-dependent protein kinase. *Am. J. Physiol.* 267:H982–93

Annu. Rev. Physiol. 1995. 57:447–68

THE 5-HT$_3$ RECEPTOR CHANNEL[1]

Meyer B. Jackson

Department of Physiology, University of Wisconsin Medical School, Madison,
Wisconsin 53706–1532

Jerrel L. Yakel

National Institute of Environmental Health Sciences, Research Triangle Park, North
Carolina 27709

KEY WORDS   ligand-gated channels, serotonin receptor, synaptic receptor, desensitization,
            ion permeation, ion channels

INTRODUCTION

The 5-HT$_3$ receptor is a relatively recent addition to the family of receptors with direct coupling to an ion channel. Serotonin, or 5-hydroxytryptamine (5-HT), and catecholamines were more commonly thought to serve as neuromodulators by activating receptors that operate through slow transduction pathways involving G proteins, second messengers, and protein kinases. Within this classical perspective, 5-HT remains a leading candidate for generating use-dependent changes in neural function (28). The recent discovery of 5-HT receptors capable of mediating rapid ionic responses thus adds a new dimension to the physiology of 5-HT rather than replacing an older perspective. With the emergence of both fast and slow receptors for 5-HT, this neurotransmitter conforms to a growing pattern that has taken form as slow receptors have become clearly established for such classical fast neurotransmitters as acetylcholine, glutamate, and GABA. This receptor duality may reflect a widespread need for systems to employ both slow modulation and fast synaptic transmission operating in parallel during the orchestration of complex neural responses.

Some of the earliest physiological studies of 5-HT anticipated the emergence

---

[1]The US Government has the right to retain a nonexclusive, royalty-free license in and to any copyright covering this paper.

of the 5-HT$_3$ receptor. Among the first responses to 5-HT observed in intestinal smooth muscle was a strong neurogenic excitation, referred to as the M response (16). Molluscan neurons exhibited a curare-sensitive depolarization in response to 5-HT (17), as did neurons in the guinea pig submucous plexus (21). 5-HT produced strong and rapid depolarizations in mammalian nodose ganglion neurons (20, 67) as well as in clonal cell lines (6, 39). Although the evidence provided by these studies for direct channel gating was nearly as compelling as the evidence from contemporary studies on receptors for other neurotransmitters, the significance of a 5-HT receptor capable of mediating rapid intercellular communication was largely ignored. Not until the mid-1980s, with the development of highly selective ligands, was the uniqueness of the 5-HT$_3$ receptor firmly established (49, 54, 70). In particular, tropisetron (ICS 205–930; Sandoz); ondansetron (GR38032F; Glaxo); and tropanserin (MDL 72222; Merrell Dow) were found to bind with dissociation constants below 10^{-9} M and to act as potent receptor antagonists. The first agonist specific to the 5-HT$_3$ receptor was 2-methyl-5-HT (69). The higher affinity and selectivity of *meta*-chlorophenyl-biguanide makes it the current agonist of choice (31, 58). All of these compounds have served as powerful experimental tools in identifying the 5-HT$_3$ receptor. Investigators have also employed metaclopramide and curare to block the 5-HT$_3$ receptor, but the actions of these drugs at receptors for other neurotransmitters and the variable effectiveness of these drugs in different preparations compromise their usefulness in receptor identification.

The pharmacological definition of the 5-HT$_3$ receptor–binding site set the stage for the identification of this receptor as a cation-selective ion channel. 5-HT was found to generate depolarizations that peaked within 35 ms of drug application, indicating that signal transduction is probably too rapid for mediation by second messengers and G proteins (71). The subsequent demonstration of single-channel currents activated by 5-HT in cell-free excised patches showed that the response does not depend on the presence of cytoplasmic constituents (9). When the 5-HT$_3$ receptor was cloned, its sequence placed it within the nicotinic/GABA receptor gene superfamily (40). Thus the functional similarities of the 5-HT$_3$ receptor to other ligand-gated channels found a basis in protein structure. Comparisons of molecular and biophysical properties among these receptors promise to expand the scope of our understanding of the diverse forms of rapid chemical synaptic transmission in the nervous system.

DISTRIBUTION AND PHYSIOLOGICAL FUNCTION

The characteristic depolarization resulting from 5-HT$_3$ receptor activation has been observed in a variety of peripheral preparations, including myenteric plexus (41), submucous plexus (9), nodose ganglion (20, 68), superior cervical ganglion (67), vagus nerve (3), and dorsal root ganglion (55). In the central nervous system, rapid responses to 5-HT have been observed only rarely. Between 5 and 10% of the neurons in hippocampal (27, 75) and striatal (75) cell cultures exhibit responses characteristic of the 5-HT$_3$ receptor. The release of dopamine in striatal slices results from activation of 5-HT$_3$ receptors (4). Rapid synaptic currents insensitive to glutamate receptor antagonists, as well as 5-HT responses in the lateral amygdala, are also likely to be mediated by the 5-HT$_3$ receptor (60). 5-HT$_3$ receptor–mediated responses have been identified in hippocampal interneurons (30, 56) and on presynaptic elements in vagal afferents, the area postrema, and the nucleus tractus solitarius (14, 18, 51, 52).

The 5-HT$_3$ receptor is not nearly as abundant as other ligand-gated channels. Thus binding assays require high-affinity ligands. Ligand-binding assays are in general agreement with physiological studies regarding the regional distribution of 5-HT$_3$ receptors and have been especially useful in locating hot spots of high 5-HT$_3$ receptor density in regions such as the entorhinal cortex, amygdala, hippocampus, nucleus accumbens, caudate nucleus, dorsal motor nucleus of the vagus nerve, nucleus tractus solitarius, and area postrema (1, 32, 36, 52). Further analysis of distribution with cDNA probes has confirmed the presence of 5-HT$_3$ receptors in cortical and amygdala locations and identified additional concentrations in several other nuclei (62).

Precise functions of 5-HT$_3$ receptors have been difficult to identify. 5-HT$_3$ receptor ligands have behavioral effects reflecting some role in brain function (7, 19). The clearest functions of 5-HT$_3$ receptors are in emesis and anxiety. 5-HT$_3$ receptor antagonists have found clinical use in controlling nausea associated with cancer chemotherapy. The area postrema 5-HT$_3$ receptors are thought to mediate the emesis reflex (32, 52), although intestinal smooth muscle activation may also be relevant. Evidence also indicates that alcohols enhance 5-HT$_3$ responses in a manner relevant to some of the pharmacological actions of alcohol (19, 37, 57). There is only one report of 5-HT$_3$ receptor–specific antagonists blocking synaptic responses, and this study was carried out in the lateral amygdala (60).

MOLECULAR PROPERTIES

The low abundance of the 5-HT$_3$ receptor presented a serious obstacle to molecular characterization. However, a number of clonal cell lines express 5-HT$_3$ receptors, including the mouse neuroblastoma cell lines N1E-115 (23, 35, 39, 46, 48) and N18 (76), the mouse neuroblastoma X rat glioma hybrid NG108-15 (6, 23, 39, 71), and the mouse neuroblastoma X Chinese hamster embryonic brain cell hybrid NCB-20 (35, 39). These easily maintained cell cultures provide a means of circumventing the problem of low abundance. Using expression cloning techniques, Maricq et al (40) isolated a cDNA encoding a 5-HT$_3$ receptor from an NCB-20 cell cDNA library. Injection into oocytes of mRNA transcribed from this clone induce expression of 5-HT receptors with pharmacological properties characteristic of the 5-HT$_3$ receptor. Presentation of 5-HT to injected oocytes produces the distinctive cation-dependent inward current indicative of 5-HT$_3$ receptor activation (40).

The clone thus isolated by Maricq et al (40) predicts a 487-amino acid polypeptide with a molecular weight of 55,966. The sequence exhibits 27% amino acid identity with the *Torpedo* nicotinic receptor α subunit, 22% identity with the β1 subunit of the bovine GABA$_A$ receptor, and 22% identity with the rat glycine receptor. The most closely related ligand-gated channel is the neuronal nicotinic receptor α7 subunit, with 30% amino acid homology (63). Thus the 5-HT$_3$ receptor gene belongs to the nicotinic/GABA receptor gene superfamily. The closest relative appears to be the nicotinic receptor, but evolutionary distances from other members of this gene superfamily are comparable. The four hydrophobic putative transmembrane segments, found in other ligand-gated channel sequences and traditionally denoted as M1 through M4, are also present in the deduced amino acid sequence of the 5-HT$_3$ receptor (Figure 1A). A characteristic long loop connects segments M3 and M4. As is typical for ligand-gated channels, this loop contains potential sites for phosphorylation by protein kinase A and tyrosine kinase. The NH$_2$-terminal domain contained three potential N-glycosylation sites along with a signature feature of the ligand-gated channel superfamily consisting of a cystine pair separated by 13 amino acids. Another pair of nearest-neighbor cystine residues, shown to form a disulfide bond in the nicotinic receptor α subunit (29), is absent (40). The M2 segment shows particularly strong homology with other ligand-gated channels; the nicotinic receptor α7 subunit is shown for comparison (Figure 1B). In the nicotinic receptor, a variety of studies have indicated that the M2 segment contains residues that line the pore through which ions flow (29). High conservation in this region is consistent with the function of the 5-HT$_3$ receptor as a cation-selective channel.

The initial cloning study showed expression in oocytes that was unusually high considering that the channel was induced from a single gene product (40). Most ligand-gated channels are thought to be hetero-oligomers composed of different subunit types. In support of this view, high expression in oocytes usually requires coinjection of RNA encoding two or more subunits of acetylcholine, GABA, and glutamate receptors. High expression following injection of a single RNA species raises the intriguing possibility that there is a naturally occurring receptor composed entirely from a single subunit of the 5-HT$_3$ receptor gene product. Receptor sensitivity, cooperativity, and single-channel conductance were very similar between the native N1E-115 cell receptor and the cloned subunit expressed in transfected cells, which supports the homo-oligomer hypothesis in this clonal cell line (25). In superior cervical ganglion

A

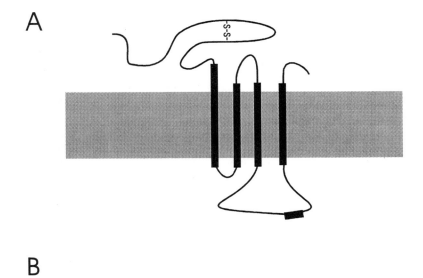

B

M2 Regions

Figure 1 Structural model of the 5-HT₃ receptor. (*A*) Based on hydropathy analysis of the deduced amino acid sequences, four membrane-spanning segments have been proposed (40). A long N-terminal domain contains a characteristic cystine bridge. An alternatively spliced six–amino acid segment is located in the long loop connecting M3 and M4. (*B*) The M2 regions of the 5-HT₃ receptor and other ligand-gated channels show very high homology. The aligned sequence of the nicotinic receptor α7 subunit is shown for comparison (8). Residues either identical or with conservative substitutions are shaded.

neurons, in contrast, different receptor properties indicate the presence of other 5-HT₃ receptor subunits (25).

A 5-HT₃ receptor purified from NCB-20 cells has an apparent molecular weight of 250,000 (42), which could accommodate up to five copies of a gene product with a deduced molecular weight of 56,000 (40). The purified protein contains a polypeptide with a molecular weight of 54,000 (42), which is remarkably similar to that deduced from the gene sequence. However, an additional polypeptide with molecular mass of 38,000 accounted for 30% of the purified protein mass (42). The molecular properties and functional role of this additional polypeptide remain a mystery.

Genomic organization could be of considerable relevance to the issue of the number and variety of subunits because alternative splicing is a major source of diversity in channel proteins. Analysis of genomic DNA of the 5-HT$_3$ receptor showed that the mouse gene contains nine exons distributed over approximately 12 kilobasepairs (kb) of DNA; the organization strongly resembled that of neuronal nicotinic receptor genes (63). These studies uncovered only a single additional splice variant, with six fewer amino acids than the original NCB-20 clone. The alternatively spliced segment resides within the large loop connecting M3 and M4 (Figure 1A). The two splice variants were seen in cDNA libraries prepared from N1E-115 cells (22) and mouse brain (63). The original NCB-20 clone was the longer form (40). Comparisons between the properties of these two variants revealed similar responses to a wide selection of drugs, with one notable exception being a much lower maximal response to the agonist 2-methyl-5-HT (10). Sequence comparisons between the clone obtained from mouse brain cDNA and cell line cDNA indicated that N1E-115 cells and NCB-20 cells express a brain receptor. Northern blot analysis (63) and in situ hybridization have confirmed the expression of this gene in brain. Both splice variants can be detected in the brain, but the variant shorter by six amino acids appears to predominate (22, 63).

Even in the face of limited structural data on receptor variants, functional comparisons of 5-HT$_3$ receptors from differing preparations strongly suggest the existence of multiple molecular forms. Differences in pharmacological profiles were first thought to reflect 5-HT$_3$ receptor subtypes (54), but more recent studies suggest that these distinctions reflect species differences (49). A number of pharmacological studies suggestive of subtypes within a species have also been described (49), but biophysical properties may provide a more convincing basis for distinguishing among molecular variants of the 5-HT$_3$ receptor. These properties, which include channel conductance and permeability as well as desensitization kinetics, are discussed at length in the relevant sections below. Despite the many distinctions that have been made, a clear classification of 5-HT$_3$ receptor subtypes has yet to be formulated. Issues such as species vs regional differences have to be clearly resolved. Correlations between binding-site specificity and ion channel properties have yet to be examined systematically.

Ion Permeation

MONOVALENT CATION SELECTIVITY   As the similarities between the nicotinic receptor and 5-HT$_3$ receptor became apparent, interest grew in the detailed permeation mechanism. The 5-HT$_3$ receptor channel discriminates poorly among inorganic monovalent cations. The permeability ratio for K^+ to Na^+, P_K/P_{Na}, tends to fall either near 0.42 or near 1.1 (49, 70), with the dichotomy suggesting two basic channel varieties. A somewhat higher value of 1.24 was obtained in rat superior cervical ganglion (77), and an intermediate value of 0.89 was obtained in NG108–15 cells (73). In the case of N1E-115 cells, values near 1.1 and 0.4 have been obtained (35, 45). The discrepancy may reflect a difference in the degree of differentiation of this clonal cell line because differentiation was shown to alter many other channel properties in NG108–15 cells (59). In N18 cells (76), PC12 cells (15), and superior cervical ganglion neurons (77), the permeabilities of several monovalent inorganic cations were also investigated and found to be similar.

Organic cations permeate the 5-HT$_3$ receptor channel less effectively than do inorganic cations (73, 76). Guanidinium influx through the 5-HT$_3$ receptor channel has been detected using radio-isotopes (5). As expected for a simple sieving process, larger cations are less permeable than small organic cations. Based on this size dependence Yang proposed a channel diameter of 7.6 Å (76), which is similar to that of the nicotinic receptor channel. Yakel et al (73) found the permeability of three organic cations to be comparable to those of the nicotinic receptor and on that basis proposed a similar diameter.

ANION PERMEABILITY   Although the 5-HT$_3$ receptor channel is predominantly cation selective, anion substitutions were found to shift the reversal potential significantly in N18 cells, indicating that the channel has a small but detectable anion permeability (76). NO_3^- has a permeability ratio relative to Na^+ of 0.08, and Cl^- has a permeability ratio relative to Na^+ of 0.04. The 5-HT$_3$ receptor of NG108–15 cells was different in this respect; complete replacement of intracellular Cl^- by gluconate produced no significant change in the reversal potential, which indicates that the 5-HT$_3$ receptor has a lower Cl^- permeability ratio in NG108–15 cells. Cl^- replacement had a similar negligible effect on reversal potentials in superior cervical ganglion neurons (76) and N1E-115 cells (35). Thus although all these studies concur that anion permeation makes no significant contribution to physiological responses, the specific permeability ratios vary from preparation to preparation. Such differences mirror variations in a number of other channel properties described below.

DIVALENT CATION SELECTIVITY   Interactions with divalent cations were implied by reductions in current in N1E-115 cells following the addition of Ca^{2+} or Mg^{2+} (48). A much stronger blocking action was found for Ca^{2+} in NG108–15 cells (73). In N18 cells the 5-HT$_3$ receptor channel was shown to have significant permeabilities for Ca^{2+}, Ba^{2+}, and Mg^{2+}; P_{Ca}/P_{Na} was 1.12 for 20 mM Ca^{2+} and 0.53 for 100 mM Ca^{2+} (76). In superior cervical ganglion neurons Ca^{2+} permeability ratios were clearly lower, but still detectable. In contrast,

Ca^{2+} permeation through the 5-HT$_3$ receptor channel in NG108–15 cells could not be detected, and an upper bound to the permeability ratio was estimated as 0.09 in 20 mM Ca^{2+} (73). The differences almost certainly reflect different molecular variants of the 5-HT$_3$ receptor in each of these systems. In the comparison of 5-HT$_3$ receptors from N18 cells and NG108–15 cells, large differences were also noted in single-channel conductance (discussed below).

Neuronal nicotinic receptors generally have high Ca^{2+} permeabilities, forming channels in which Ca^{2+} enhances the current induced by acetylcholine (66). In contrast, Ca^{2+} reduces current through channels formed by 5-HT$_3$ receptors (40, 48, 55, 72). This difference was exploited in the characterization of chimeric receptors constructed from the α7 and 5-HT$_3$ receptor clones (12). With approximately 30% homology at the protein level, the neuronal nicotinic receptor α7 subunit has the highest homology with the 5-HT$_3$ receptor among the ligand-gated channels (63). When a chimeric receptor was constructed with the entire putative cytoplasmic domain at the N-terminus coding for the nicotinic receptor and the remainder coding for the 5-HT$_3$ receptor, the expressed channel responded to nicotinic agonists but was blocked by Ca^{2+} in a manner consistent with a 5-HT$_3$ receptor (12). This experiment delineated domains of the protein that determine agonist binding-site specificity and divalent cation sensitivity.

SINGLE-CHANNEL CONDUCTANCE   Measurements of single-channel conductance of the 5-HT$_3$ receptor range from 310 fS to 17 pS (Table 1). The larger

Table 1 Single-channel conductances[a]

Location	Conductance (pS)	Reference
Neurons		
Guinea pig submucous plexus	9.2 and 14.8	9
Guinea pig coelic ganglion	10	61
Rabbit nodose ganglion	16.5	50
Mouse superior cervical ganglion	8.9	25
Rat superior cervical ganglion	11	77
Mouse/rat hippocampus	8.3 (−80 mV)	27
	10.5 (−160 mV)	
Cell lines		
N18	0.59	76
N1E-115	0.31/0.63/5.6	35, 25, 65
NG108–15	9 and 13 (undifferentiated)	59
	4.4 (differentiated)	
Cloned receptor	0.63	25

[a] Single-channel conductances determined as chord conductances. Values <5 pS were from noise analysis. Values >5 pS were from single-channel currents in outside-out patches.

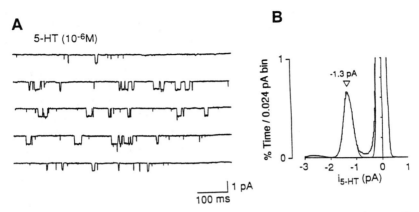

Figure 2 Single-channel currents through 5-HT₃ receptor channels in rabbit nodose ganglion neurons. (*A*) The application of 1 μM 5-HT to excised outside-out patches held at −80 mV activated the single-channel currents shown. (*B*) An amplitude distribution constructed from these single-channel records showed only a single open-channel conductance state (from 50, with permission).

conductance channels are readily detected in single-channel experiments (Figure 2). The smaller conductances reported in many studies require measurement with noise analysis. Although noise analysis is well known to underestimate single-channel conductance for a variety of reasons, these factors cannot account for the wide range of conductance values reported. These disparities more likely reflect differences among receptor variants or subtypes. Some of the single-channel studies hint at the existence of subconductance states of the 5-HT₃ receptor. Although a single open state was observed in rabbit nodose ganglion neurons (50) (Figure 2), levels of 9 and 15 pS were seen in patches from submucous plexus neurons (9). Multiple levels of 9 and 13 pS were also indicated in undifferentiated NG108–15 cells (59).

In addition to subconductance states for a single subtype of 5-HT₃ receptor, single-channel recording may have demonstrated different channel variants in the same species. In patches from differentiated NG108–15 cells, single-channel currents could not be discerned, even though the noise level was low enough to resolve current jumps of the magnitude observed in undifferentiated cells (59). Application of 5-HT to these patches produced noisy currents indicative of channels with a unitary current below the intrinsic noise of the system. Analysis of the noise indicated a conductance of 4.4 pS (59). The channel of differentiated NG108–15 cells may be identical to that in the N1E-115 cells studied by van Hooft et al (65). When special efforts were made, single-channel currents were revealed from which a conductance of 5.6 pS was estimated (65). These channels thus have a much lower conductance than those in undifferentiated NG108–15 cells. The fact that the NG108–15 cell line is a somatic cell hybrid derived from rat and mouse leaves open the possibility that the two conductance variants trace their origins to the two different parent cell lines. However, the neurons of rat superior cervical ganglion are from a single species and show two conductance variants as well. One type had an 11-pS conductance and another had a conductance that was below the noise level and thus much smaller (25, 77). A similar situation was described in cultured hippocampal neurons, in which single-channel currents reflected a conductance on the order of 10 pS, but small noisy currents through much smaller channels were also evident (27). Thus some classes of neurons contain at least two 5-HT$_3$ receptors with different channel properties. This constitutes strong evidence for intraspecific molecular variation.

PORE STRUCTURE   Based on an analysis of ion permeation and single-channel conductance, Yakel et al (73) and Yang (76) evaluated structural models for the 5-HT$_3$ receptor. To accommodate the similar organic cation size cutoffs of the 5-HT$_3$ receptor and the nicotinic receptor, it was proposed that the pore had a diameter at the narrowest region of 7.6 Å (76). To account for the lower single-channel conductance and lower Ca^{2+} permeability relative to the nicotinic receptor, it was proposed that the 5-HT$_3$ receptor pore of NG108–15 cells had either a greater length or less polarizable lining (73). Yang (76) proposed that the pore lining lacked high-field-strength charge, to account for the weak selectivity between cations. Because the 5-HT$_3$ receptor in N18 cells had a markedly higher divalent cation permeability with a strong concentration dependence, Yang (76) proposed that the outer surface of the channel contained a substantial amount of charge. Furthermore, the possibility that divalent cations bind within the channel with different affinities was also suggested. The existence of negatively charged binding sites within the channel is also supported by the observations that Ca^{2+} and Mg^{2+} reduce the current through the 5-HT$_3$ receptor channel (38, 40, 48, 76) and that Ca^{2+} blocks the channel (73).

The nonlinear current voltage plot of the 5-HT$_3$ receptor response may hold additional clues about the pore structure. The slope for inward currents is typically three to four times steeper than for outward current in NG108–15 cells (71, 74), N18 cells (76), N1E-115 and NCB-20 cells (25, 35, 48), superior cervical ganglion neurons (25, 77), hippocampal neurons (27, 71, 75), and in oocytes expressing the 5-HT$_3$ receptor clone (25, 72). The rapid change in conductance during voltage steps suggests that the open channel rectifies (77), and this is borne out by the preservation of rectification in single-channel current voltage plots from nodose (50), superior cervical ganglion (77), and hippocampal (27) neurons. The rectification was greater in 5-HT$_3$ receptors of undifferentiated NG108–15 cells than in differentiated NG108–15 cells (59) but was absent in receptors of guinea pig submucous plexus (9). Rectification is often attributed to a permeation barrier near one side of the membrane, but fixed charge near one surface or the other can also produce this effect. It may be relevant that replacement of intracellular Cl⁻ by gluconate nearly eliminates the rectification in NG108–15 cells (73). Rectification is nearly eliminated by replacement of leucine 286 of the 5-HT$_3$ receptor by either alanine or threonine but not by aromatic amino acids (72). Such replacements may alter the potential energy profile through the pore to shift the barrier to a more central location within the membrane.

Activation

DOSE-RESPONSE BEHAVIOR   Dose-response studies indicate a cooperative activation of the 5-HT$_3$ receptor. Hill coefficients of 1.8 and 2.8 were obtained from NG108–15 cells (74) and N1E-115 cells (45), respectively. The apparent dissociation constants for serotonin were 3.3 and 1.8 µM in the two respective studies. Higashi & Nishi (20) obtained a Hill coefficient of 1.8 in nodose ganglion neurons. Subsequent dose-response studies provided apparent affinities and Hill coefficients in this general range (38, 58). Drug-binding assays also indicate weak but significant cooperativity (23), but the 5-HT dissociation constant below 1 µM probably reflects the complicity of a higher-affinity desensitized conformation. Activation of the cloned receptor expressed in oocytes showed similar cooperativity (Figure 3) (40, 72), with no differences between the two splice variants (10). A careful comparison of 5-HT$_3$ receptor dose-response characteristics from three different mouse preparations indicates a lower cooperativity of activation in the receptor of superior cervical ganglion neurons as compared with the cloned receptor and the N1E-115 cell receptor (25). Because the expressed clone can be presumed to form a homo-oligomer of binding site–containing subunits, it is tempting to speculate that the lower cooperativity of the superior cervical ganglion receptor reflects the presence of additional subunits lacking the agonist-binding site.

The dose-response studies are consistent to the extent that they indicate multiple agonist-binding sites and that occupation of at least two binding sites is required for maximal activation. Multiple agonist-binding sites are consistent with a native receptor containing multiple copies of the subunit cloned by Maricq et al (40). Mutation of leucine 286 within the M2 segment can shift the dose-response curve (Figure 3) (72). According to current views on receptor structure (29), as well as results from chimeric receptors (12), the M2 region of the protein should not contain the agonist-binding sites (Figure 1). Thus the mutation affects receptor activation by an allosteric mechanism, and the shift in apparent affinity illustrates the importance of conformational equilibria in

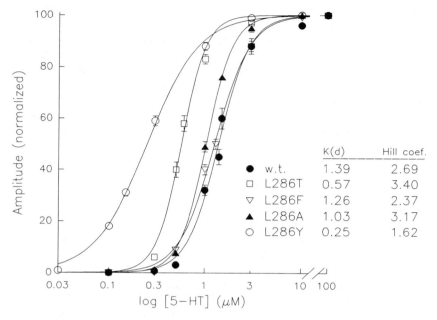

Figure 3 Dose-response behavior of wild-type and mutant 5-HT$_3$ receptors expressed in oocytes. Peak response was plotted vs 5-HT concentration. Filled circles, wild type; open circles, L286Y; squares, L286T; filled triangles, L286A; open triangles, L286F. Each point is a mean ± SEM for 3 to 11 oocytes (from 72, with permission).

receptor activation (26). With more attention to methodological details of physiological preparation and drug application, the comparisons between receptor activation characteristics in native tissue and heterologous expression systems may provide information relevant to the question of whether the native receptor is composed exclusively from one subunit.

KINETICS   The response of the 5-HT$_3$ receptor reaches 90% of its peak within approximately 35 ms of application of saturating 5-HT concentrations to voltage-clamped NG108–15 cells (71), N18 cells (76), and PC12 cells (15). More rapid application of agonist showed exponential activation kinetics in N1E-115 cells; the time constant of 24 ms (43) is consistent with the above-mentioned times for the response to reach 90% of maximum. In excised patches, activation could be obtained within 20 ms in NG108–15 cells (XM Shao & MB Jackson, unpublished data) and 28 ms in superior cervical ganglion neurons (77). The most rapid activation time reported thus far for the 5-HT$_3$ receptor channel is 7 ms in excised patches from mouse and rat hippocampal neurons (27). These measurements may reflect, in part, the time scale for solution change rather than the kinetics of receptor activation. But in the experiments of Mienville (43), it was noted that the ratio of the on and off rates is quite close to published apparent affinities from dose-response studies. However, the linear dependence of activation rate on agonist concentration (43) contradicts the conclusion from dose-response experiments that activation is cooperative. If these measurements do indeed reflect a true activation process, then the rate of binding of this receptor of 1.3×10^6 M^{-1} s^{-1} (43) is slower than that of many other ligand-gated channels, in which the rate of activation approaches the diffusion limit (26). These measurements are important in establishing the intimate association between receptor and channel characteristic of ligand-gated channels and in defining the possibilities for function in rapid forms of synaptic transmission. Since many other types of ligand-gated channels can be activated more than 10 times faster, the 5-HT$_3$ receptor may function in synaptic processes in which speed is less critical.

For receptor variants with large enough channel conductances to observe single-channel currents, records clearly exhibited flickers or brief closed states (Figure 2) (9, 50, 59, 77). In other ligand-gated channels, these flickers were interpreted according to burst analysis as brief sojourns in an intermediate kinetic state of the activation pathway (26). Yang et al (77) described a component of brief closures with a time constant of 0.52 ms that (with a simple theoretical analysis) implies an upper bound to the opening rate of 2 ms^{-1}. With an approximate estimate of two openings per burst, the gating transition would then be estimated as 1 ms^{-1}, and the agonist dissociation rate would be the same. In contrast, the rapid solution exchange studies of Mienville (43) yielded an off rate of 1.7 s^{-1}. Such slow deactivation kinetics would require either longer mean open times or many more openings per burst than have been observed for the 5-HT$_3$ receptor in a different preparation (77). At present the standard models have not reconciled single-channel kinetics with whole-cell response kinetics.

Open-time distributions contained two exponential components (9, 25, 77), as did burst lifetime distributions (77). In nicotinic and GABA receptors, two open-channel states revealed by bi-exponential open-time distributions have proven to be generated by a combination of singly and doubly ligated receptors (26). Thus it is tempting to suggest a similar basis for the multiple open states in the 5-HT$_3$ receptor. This hypothesis lends itself to straightforward testing by examining open-time distributions as a function of agonist concentration.

Desensitization

The comparison of 5-HT$_3$ receptor channels with other members of the ligand-gated channel family has been extended by studies of receptor desensitization. In essentially every preparation tested, the 5-HT$_3$ receptor is desensitized by sustained agonist application. $5\text{-}HT_3$ receptor desensitization has been studied extensively in clonal cell lines, superior cervical ganglion neurons, and heterologous expression systems.

KINETICS   Studies of desensitization reveal mono- and bi-exponential kinetics in different preparations. A single exponential fits the time course of desensitization in N1E-115 cells (44, 45) and N18 cells (76), but fitting clearly requires a sum of two exponentials in superior cervical ganglion cells (77), PC12 cells (15), and NG108–15 cells (Figure 4) (59, 74). In hippocampal and striatal neurons, desensitization also appears to have a biphasic time course, but curve fitting has not been attempted (71, 75). Differences in desensitization kinetics may be another indication of molecular variation, especially because the studies in N18 cells and superior cervical ganglion neurons were conducted in the same laboratory with the same techniques. It should be noted that in two systems showing biphasic desensitization kinetics (undifferentiated NG108–15 cells and superior cervical ganglion neurons), single-channel studies indicate the presence of both low- and high-conductance channels (59, 77). Thus the two kinetic components could reflect the desensitization of two different receptor variants. However, only low-conductance channels (4.4 pS) were observed in differentiated NG108–15 cells (59); therefore the two phases of desensitization are not as easily attributed to mixed populations of receptors. Nevertheless, even in differentiated NG108–15 cells, currently available evidence cannot exclude the possibility that biphasic kinetics reflects the superposition of kinetic processes arising from coexisting receptor variants, each with monophasic desensitization. Indeed, sustained 5-HT application to excised patches from submucous plexus neurons appears to produce selective desensitization of the higher-conductance channel (15 pS), while sparing the lower-conductance channel (9 pS) (9).

The rates of desensitization also vary considerably between and within experimental preparations (Figure 4). Some of this variation relates to Ca^{2+} and voltage (discussed below), but even under similar experimental conditions, the differences remain. Desensitization is slower, with a time constant of 5 s or longer in N1E-115 cells (45) and differentiated NG108–15 cells (59). Desensitization in undifferentiated NG108–15 cells has a time constant of less than 1 s (59), and the fastest component of desensitization in PC12 cells was less than 100 ms (15).

The time course of desensitization varies with agonist concentration; higher concentrations of agonist desensitize the receptor more rapidly (15, 44, 45, 74). In PC12 cells, where two exponentials were observed, the slow component showed an increase in rate at lower concentrations than the fast component (15). In general, the concentration range in which the desensitization rate changes overlaps at least partly with those ranges in which receptor dose-re-

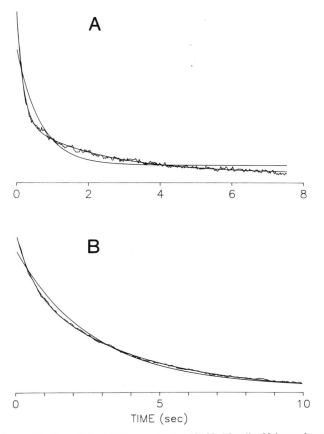

Figure 4 Desensitization of the 5-HT$_3$ receptor in NG108–15 cells. Voltage-clamped cells in culture were presented with 50-mM 5-HT for 10 or more seconds. The decaying portion of the response is shown. A sum of two exponentials fitted the data well, while a single exponential fitted poorly (from 74, with permission). (*A*) A response observed immediately after establishing a whole-cell recording shows rapid desensitization. (*B*) Desensitization became slower as time passed during whole-cell recording, as shown in a response observed 10 min later. This deceleration of desensitization is one of several indications that the kinetics of desensitization can be modulated by cytoplasmic factors (see text).

sponse plots increase most steeply. However, concentrations too low to produce responses still desensitize the receptor slowly (45). Analogy with the nicotinic receptor would suggest that the same receptor-binding sites are engaged for activation and desensitization (26). But given the dependence of EC$_{50}$ on both binding constants and conformational equilibrium constants (26), the comparison of concentration dependence of these two ligand-induced processes sheds no light on this issue. More compelling evidence for an involvement of the same sites in activation and desensitization was provided by Kooyman et al (34), who showed that similar concentrations of tetraethylammonium block both processes.

Additional insight into the desensitization of the 5-HT$_3$ receptor has been provided by an investigation of the 5-HT moiety 5-hydroxyindole (33). This substance binds to the agonist-binding site of the receptor with a low affinity but generates no ion current by itself. When 5-hydroxyindole was present, the peak 5-HT response was 56% larger, and desensitization was 13-fold slower. An allosteric interpretation of these results suggests that 5-hydroxyindole binds to some but not all of the agonist-binding sites and that this ligand binds more tightly to receptors in the open-channel conformations as compared with the desensitized conformation. Regardless of the mechanism of action, 5-hydroxyindole could serve as a useful experimental tool to study the functional role of desensitization in 5-HT$_3$ receptor–mediated synaptic responses, such as those recorded in the amygdala (60).

Mutation of leucine 286 of the cloned 5-HT$_3$ receptor protein profoundly altered desensitization (Figure 5) (72). Replacement of this residue by threonine slowed desensitization relative to wild type. Furthermore, the response of the threonine mutant remained within 19% of the peak after 40 s of agonist exposure (Figure 5). Replacement of leucine 286 by either phenylalanine, tyrosine, or alanine accelerated desensitization. Phenylalanine replacement produced the greatest effect, decreasing the time constant of desensitization by nearly 40-fold. These results indicated that residue 286 lies in a region of the protein that undergoes significant structural change during desensitization to form important physical contacts in the stabilization of different receptor conformations.

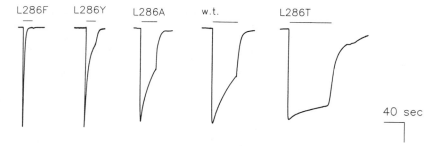

Figure 5 Desensitization kinetics in wild-type and mutant 5-HT$_3$ receptors. Application of 30 μM 5-HT for periods indicated by the bars desensitized receptors expressed in oocytes. Recordings were made in Ca-free bathing solutions. Desensitization was slower in some mutants and faster in others. Current calibration bar was 250 nA for wild type, 500 nA for L286F and L286A, and 100 nA for L286Y and L286T (from 72, with permission).

Striking parallels have been found in two other ligand-gated channels. Mutation of a homologous and highly conserved leucine residue at position 247 in the nicotinic receptor $\alpha 7$ subunit also induces profound alterations in desensitization (53). Similar results were obtained in a mutant GABA receptor resistant to convulsants (78). Insecticide resistance was used to clone the *Drosophila Rdl* gene, a homologue of the vertebrate GABA$_A$ receptor gene (13). The drugs to which the mutant are resistant include cyclodiene insecticides such as dieldrin and convulsants such as picrotoxin. Resistance results from replacement of an alanine residue by serine within the M2 region of the protein, seven amino acids away from leucines 286 and 247 in the aligned sequences of the 5-HT$_3$ receptor and the nicotinic receptor $\alpha 7$ subunit, respectively. Comparison of the response characteristics in *Drosophila* neurons showed that the desensitization of the mutant receptor is nearly tenfold slower (78). These results show a striking conservation of function within a very small domain of the protein and probably reflect a common structural basis underlying the conformational transitions of ligand-gated channels (72).

VOLTAGE AND CALCIUM DEPENDENCE   More positive voltages reduce the rate of desensitization in hippocampal neurons (71), NG108–15 cells (59, 74), superior cervical ganglion neurons (77), and the 5-HT$_3$ receptor expressed in oocytes (72). Desensitization shows no significant dependence on membrane potential in N1E-115 cells (45, 58), where desensitization is much slower. In contrast to the case of differentiated NG108–15 cells, 5-HT responses in undifferentiated NG108–15 cells are similar to those in N1E-115 cells, showing slow desensitization with almost no voltage dependence (59). In preparations showing biphasic desensitization kinetics, results vary with regard to which rate processes are affected. In differentiated NG108–15 cells, depolarization increases the time constants and the relative weight of the slow component (74). In superior cervical ganglion, however, the time constants remain unchanged, while the relative weight of the slow component increases (77).

Ca^{2+} also influences desensitization; Ca^{2+} removal slows desensitization (48, 55, 76). The effect of Ca^{2+} is also observed in the cloned receptor, where Ca^{2+} removal not only slows desensitization, but also eliminates the voltage dependence (72). Injection of the Ca^{2+} chelator BAPTA slows desensitization as well (72). These results suggest that intracellular Ca^{2+} plays a role in desensitization. The more rapid desensitization at more negative voltages may result from the greater Ca^{2+} entry through the 5-HT$_3$ receptor channel. This interpretation is attractive in many respects, but it is difficult to reconcile with the low Ca^{2+} permeability of NG108–15 cell channels (73) and the strong effects of Ca^{2+} in N1E-115 cells (48), in which desensitization is voltage independent (45). Despite these reservations, additional preliminary studies support the role of Ca^{2+} entry by providing a link to the Ca^{2+}-dependent phosphatase calcineurin (2). In NG108–15 cells, the more rapid Ca^{2+} chelator BAPTA reduced desensitization compared to that observed with EGTA. The inhibitors staurosporine and okadaic acid had no effect on desensitization, but the calcineurin inhibitor cyclosporin A-cyclophilin enhanced responses and blocked desensitization. Connecting the voltage dependence of desensitization to calcineurin may also provide a clue about the change in voltage dependence of receptor desensitization during differentiation of NG108–15 cells (59). Both calcium channels (11) and calmodulin-dependent protein kinase (64) show changes during differentiation in this cell line. Thus differentiation may be associated with a general reorganization of Ca^{2+}-regulated proteins.

MODULATION   The parallels with other ligand-gated channels extend even to the realm of receptor modulation. A number of agents that were expected to increase cytoplasmic cAMP accelerate desensitization of the 5-HT_3 receptor in NG108–15 cells (71). Phosphorylation by cAMP-dependent protein kinase accelerates the desensitization of the nicotinic receptor (24). However, the failure of nonhydrolyzable ATP analogues to block 5-HT_3 receptor modulation, as well as the lack of dependence of acceleration on cytoplasmic ATP, suggest that the acceleration of desensitization can occur without the involvement of protein kinase (74). In general, the acceleration of desensitization by various agents is accompanied by changes in fast and slow time constants, as well as by changes in the relative weights of the fast and slow components. The lack of a clear pattern in the kinetic mechanism could mean that multiple signaling pathways enhance desensitization. Acceleration of desensitization was also seen following forskolin treatment in hippocampal neurons (75). However, a cAMP analogue and isobutylmethylxanthine, both of which accelerated desensitization in NG108–15 cells, had no effect on desensitization in superior cervical ganglion neurons (77).

An additional signaling pathway was also implicated by the observation of a deceleration of desensitization during whole-cell voltage clamp in NG108–15 cells (74). In N1E-115 cells, desensitization also became slower following the establishment of a whole-cell voltage clamp (47). This change in desensitization kinetics probably reflects modulation of desensitization by some cytoplasmic factor lost during whole-cell recording. In NG108–15 cells both time constants became slower and the weight of the slow component increased (Figure 4) (74). Nonhydrolyzable ATP analogues prevented this process, suggesting a role for a protein kinase, perhaps through modification at the consensus phosphorylation sites within the loop connecting M3 and M4 (40). Thus the mechanisms for modulation of 5-HT_3 receptors are complex and elusive. Nevertheless, modulation could be important in the regulation of synaptic signals mediated by the 5-HT_3 receptor.

CONCLUSIONS

Receptors for 5-HT with the pharmacological signature of the $5-HT_3$ receptor and biophysical properties of a ligand-gated channel are sparsely distributed in many regions of the central and peripheral nervous systems. Precise physiological functions are still poorly defined. Variations in both functional behavior and pharmacological sensitivity are highly suggestive of molecular variants within this receptor class, but a rigorous classification has yet to be achieved. The most striking general trend in studies of the $5-HT_3$ receptor is the ubiquitous parallel with other ligand-gated channels. Almost every detail of this receptor lends itself to interesting and informative comparisons.

ACKNOWLEDGMENTS

We thank Dr. K Jones for providing preprints and unpublished observations. We thank LO Trussell and T Otis for critical readings of this manuscript. This work was supported by National Institutes of Health grant NS23512.

Literature Cited

1. Abi-Dargham A, Laruelle M, Wong DT, Robertson DW, Weinberger DR, Kleinman JE. 1993. Pharmacological and regional characterization of [³H]LY-278584 binding sites in human brain. *J. Neurochem.* 60:730–37
2. Arbuckle JB, Meigel I, Boddeke HWGM, Docherty RJ. 1993. Inhibition of calcineurin reduces desensitization of 5-HT₃ receptors in NG108–15 neuroblastoma x glioma hybrid cells. *J. Physiol.* 473:267P
3. Azami J, Fozzard JR, Round AA, Wallis DI. 1985. The depolarizing action of 5-hydroxytryptamine on rabbit vagal primary afferents and sympathetic neurones and its selective blockade by MDL72222. *Naunyn-Schmiedebergs Arch. Pharmakol.* 328:423–29
4. Blandina P, Goldfarb J, Green PJ. 1988. Activation of 5-HT₃ receptor releases dopamine from striatal slices. *Eur. J. Pharmacol.* 155:349–50
5. Bönisch H, Barann M, Graupner J, Gothert M. 1993. Characterization of 5-HT₃ receptors of N1E-115 neuroblastoma cells by use of the influx of the organic cation [¹⁴C]-guanidinium. *Br. J. Pharmacol.* 108:436–42
6. Christian CN, Nelson PG, Bullock P, Mullinax D, Nirenberg M. 1978. Pharmacologic responses of cells of a neuroblastoma x glioma hybrid clone and modulation of synapses between hybrid cells and mouse myotubes. *Brain Res.* 147:261–76
7. Costall B, Naylor RJ. 1992. The psychopharmacology of 5-HT₃ receptors. *Pharmacol. Toxicol.* 71:401–15
8. Couturier S, Bertrand D, Matter J-M, Hernandez M-C, Bertrand S, et al. 1990. A neuronal nicotinic acetylcholine receptor subunit (α7) is developmentally regulated and forms a homo-oligomeric channel blocked by α-BTX. *Neuron* 5:847–56
9. Derkach V, Surprenant A, North RA. 1989. 5-HT₃ receptors are membrane ion channels. *Nature* 339:706–9
10. Downie DL, Hope AG, Lambert JJ, Peters JA, Blackburn TP, Jones BJ. 1994. Pharmacological characterization of the apparent splice variants of the murine 5-HT₃ R-A subunit expressed in

Xenopus laevis oocytes. *Neuropharmacology* 33:473–82

11. Eckert R, Hescheler J, Krautwurst D, Schultz D, Trautmann W. 1990. Calcium currents in neuroblastoma x glioma hybrid cells after cultivation with dibutyryl cyclic AMP and Ni^{2+}. *Pflügers Arch.* 417:329–35

12. Eiselé J-L, Bertrand S, Galzi J-L, Devillers-Thiéry A, Changeux J-P, Bertrand D. 1993. Chimaeric nicotinic-serotonergic receptor combines distinct ligand binding and channel specificities. *Nature* 366:479–83

13. ffrench-Constant RH, Rocheleau TA, Steichen JC, Chalmers AE. 1993. A point mutation in a *Drosophila* GABA receptor affecting channel block by picrotoxin and cyclodiene insecticides. *Nature* 363:449–51

14. Fozard JR. 1992. 5-HT_3 receptors in the context of the multiplicity of 5-HT receptors. In *Central and Peripheral 5-HT_3 Receptors,* ed. M Hamon, pp. 1–17. London: Academic

15. Furukawa K, Akaike N, Onodera H, Kyuya K. 1992. Expression of 5-HT_3 receptors in PC12 cells treated with NGF and 8-Br-cAMP. *J. Neurophysiol.* 67:812–19

16. Gaddum JH, Picarelli A. 1957. Two kinds of tryptamine receptors. *Br. J. Pharmacol.* 12:323–28

17. Gerschenfeld HM, Paupardin-Tritsch D. 1974. Ionic mechanisms and receptor properties underlying the responses of molluscan neurones to 5-hydroxytryptamine. *J. Physiol.* 243:427–56

18. Glaum SR, Brooks PA, Spyer KM, Miller RJ. 1992. 5-Hydroxytryptamine-3 receptors modulate synaptic activity in the rat nucleus tractus solitarius in vitro. *Brain Res.* 589:62–8

19. Greenshaw AJ. 1993. Behavioral pharmacology of 5-HT_3 receptor antagonists: a critical update on therapeutic potential. *Trends Pharmacol. Sci.* 14:265–70

20. Higashi H, Nishi S. 1982. 5-Hydroxytryptamine receptors of visceral primary afferent neurones on rabbit nodose ganglia. *J. Physiol.* 323:543–67

21. Hirst GDS, Silinsky EM. 1975. Some effects of 5-hydroxytryptamine, dopamine and noradrenaline on neurones in the submucous plexus of guinea-pig small intestine. *J. Physiol.* 251:817–32

22. Hope AG, Downie DL, Sutherland L, Lambert JJ, Peters JA, Burchell B. 1993. Cloning and functional expression of an apparent splice variant of the murine 5-HT_3 receptor α subunit. *Eur. J. Pharmacol.* 245:187–92

23. Hoyer D, Neijt HC. 1988. Identification of serotonin 5-HT_3 recognition sites in membranes of N1E-115 cells by radioligand binding. *Mol. Pharmacol.* 33:303–9

24. Huganir JL, Delcour AH, Greengard P, Hess GP. 1986. Phosphorylation of the nicotinic acetylcholine receptor regulates its rate of desensitization. *Nature* 321:774–76

25. Hussy N, Lukas W, Jones KA. 1994. Functional properties of the cloned 5-HT_3 receptor: comparison with native mouse receptors. *J. Physiol.* In press

26. Jackson MB. 1993. *Thermodynamics of Membrane Receptors and Channels.* Boca Raton, Fla.: CRC Press

27. Jones K, Surprenant AM. 1994. Single channel properties of 5-HT_3 receptors in primary cultures of rodent hippocampus. *Neurosci. Lett.* 174:133–36

28. Kandel ER, Schwartz JH. 1982. Molecular biology of learning: modulation of transmitter release. *Science* 218:433–43

29. Karlin A. 1993. Structure of nicotinic acetylcholine receptors. *Curr. Opin. Neurobiol.* 3:299–309

30. Kawa K. 1994. Distribution of functional properties of 5-HT_3 receptors in the rat hippocampal dentate gyrus: A patch-clamp study. *J. Neurophysiol.* 71:1935–47

31. Kilpatrick GJ, Butler A, Burridge J, Oxford AW. 1990. 1-(m-chlorophenyl)-biguanide, a potent high affinity 5-HT_3 receptor agonist. *Eur. J. Pharmacol.* 182:193–97

32. Kilpatrick GJ, Jones BJ, Tyers MB. 1987. Identification and distribution of 5-HT_3 receptors in rat brain using radioligand binding. *Nature* 330:746–48

33. Kooyman AR, van Hooft JA, Vijverberg HPM. 1993. 5-Hydroxyindole slows desensitization of the 5-HT_3 receptor–mediated ion current in N1E-115 neuroblastoma cells. *Br. J. Pharmacol.* 108:287–89

34. Kooyman AR, Zwart R, Vijverberg HMP. 1993. Tetraethylammonium ions block 5-HT_3 receptor–mediated ion current at the agonist recognition site and prevent desensitization in cultured mouse neuroblastoma cells. *Eur. J. Pharmacol.* 246:247–54

35. Lambert JJ, Peters JA, Hales TG, Dempster J. 1989. The properties of 5-HT_3 receptors in clonal cell lines studied by patch-clamp techniques. *Br. J. Pharmacol.* 97:27–40

36. Laporte AM, Kidd EM, Verge D, Gozlan H, Hamon M. 1992. Autoradiographic mapping of central 5-HT_3 receptors. See Ref. 14, pp. 157–87

37. Lovinger DM. 1991. Ethanol potentia-

tion of 5-HT$_3$ receptor–mediated ion current in NCB-20 neuroblastoma cells. *Neurosci. Lett.* 122:57–60

38. Lovinger DM. 1991. Inhibition of 5-HT$_3$ receptor–mediated ion current by divalent metal cations in NCB-20 neuroblastoma cells. *J. Neurophysiol.* 66: 1329–37

39. MacDermot J, Higashida H, Wilson SP, Matsuzawa H, Minna J, Nirenberg M. 1979. Adenylate cyclase and acetylcholine release regulated by separate serotonin receptors of somatic cell hybrids. *Proc. Natl. Acad. Sci. USA* 76:1135–39

40. Maricq AV, Peterson AS, Brake AJ, Myers RM, Julius D. 1991. Primary structure and functional expression of the 5-HT$_3$ receptor, a serotonin-gated ion channel. *Science* 254:432–37

41. Mawe GM, Branchek TA, Gershon MD. 1986. Peripheral neural serotonin receptors: identification and characterization with specific antagonists and agonists. *Proc. Natl. Acad. Sci. USA* 83:9799–803

42. McKernan RM, Gillard NP, Quirk K, Kneen CO, Stevenson GI, et al. 1990. Purification of the 5-hydroxytryptamine 5-HT$_3$ receptor from NCB-20 cells. *J. Biol. Chem.* 265:13572–77

43. Mienville J-M. 1991. Comparison of fast responses to serotonin and 2-methyl-serotonin in voltage-clamped N1E-115 neuroblastoma cells. *Neurosci. Lett.* 133: 41–44

44. Neijt HC, Duits IJT, Vijverberg HPM. 1988. Pharmacological characterization of serotonin 5-HT$_3$ receptor–mediated electrical response in cultured mouse neuroblastoma cells. *Neuropharmacology* 27:301–7

45. Neijt HC, Plomp JJ, Vijverberg HPM. 1989. Kinetics of the membrane current mediated by serotonin 5-HT$_3$ receptors in cultured mouse neuroblastoma cells. *J. Physiol.* 411:257–69

46. Neijt HC, Vijverberg HPM, van den Bercken J. 1986. The dopamine response in mouse neuroblastoma cells is mediated by serotonin 5-HT$_3$ receptors. *Eur. J. Pharmacol.* 127:271–74

47. Peters J, Lambert JJ, Malone HM. 1992. Physiological and pharmacological aspects of 5-HT$_3$ receptor function. In *Aspects of Synaptic Transmission: LTP, Galinin, Opioids, Autonomic and 5-HT,* ed. T Stone, pp. 293–313. London: Taylor & Francis

48. Peters JA, Hales TG, Lambert JJ. 1988. Divalent cations modulate 5-HT$_3$ receptor–induced currents in N1E-115 neuroblastoma cells. *Eur. J. Pharmacol.* 151:491–95

49. Peters JA, Malone HM, Lambert JJ.

1992. Recent advances in the electrophysiological characterization of 5-HT$_3$ receptors. *Trends Pharmacol. Sci.* 13: 391–97

50. Peters JA, Malone HM, Lambert JJ. 1993. An electrophysiological investigation of the properties of 5-HT$_3$ receptors of rabbit nodose ganglion neurones in culture. *Br. J. Pharmacol.* 110: 665–76

51. Pratt GD, Bowery NG. 1989. The 5-HT$_3$ receptor ligand, [^{3}H] BRL 43694, binds to presynaptic sites in the nucleus tractus solitarius of the rat. *Neuropharmacology* 28:1367–76

52. Pratt GD, Bowery NG, Kilpatrick GJ, Leslie RA, Barnes NM, et al. 1990. Consensus meeting agrees on distribution of 5-HT$_3$ receptors in mammalian hindbrain. *Trends Pharmacol. Sci.* 11: 135–37

53. Revah F, Bertrand D, Galzi J-L, Devillers-Thiéry A, Mulle C, et al. 1991. Mutations in the channel domain alter desensitization of a neuronal nicotinic receptor. *Nature* 353:846–49

54. Richardson BP, Engel G. 1986. The pharmacology and function of 5-HT$_3$ receptors. *Trends Neurosci.* 9:424–28

55. Robertson B, Bevan S. 1991. Properties of 5-hydroxytryptamine$_3$ receptor–gated currents in adult rat dorsal root ganglion neurones. *Br. J. Pharmacol.* 102:272–76

56. Ropert N, Guy N. 1991. Serotonin facilitates GABAergic transmission in the CA1 region of rat hippocampus in vitro. *J. Physiol.* 441:121–36

57. Sellers EM, Higgins GA, Sobell MB. 1992. 5-HT and alcohol abuse. *Trends Pharmacol. Sci.* 13:69–75

58. Sepuúlveda MI, Lummis SCR, Martin IL. 1991. The agonist properties of m-chlorphenylbiguanide and 2-methyl-5-hydroxytryptamine on 5-HT$_3$ receptors in N1E-115 neuroblastoma cells. *Br. J. Pharmacol.* 104:536–40

59. Shao XM, Yakel JL, Jackson MB. 1991. Differentiation of NG108–15 cells alters channel conductance and desensitization kinetics of the 5-HT$_3$ receptor. *J. Neurophysiol.* 65:630–38

60. Sugita S, Shen KZ, North RA. 1992. 5-hydroxytryptamine is a fast excitatory neurotransmitter at 5-HT$_3$ receptors in rat amygdala. *Neuron* 8:199–203

61. Surprenant A, Matsumoto S, Gerzanich V. 1991. 5-HT$_3$ receptors in guinea-pig coelic neurons. *Soc. Neurosci. Abstr.* 17: 601

62. Tecott LH, Maricq AV, Julius D. 1993. Nervous system distribution of the serotonin 5-HT$_3$ receptor mRNA. *Proc. Natl. Acad. Sci. USA* 90:1430–34

63. Uetz P, Abdelatty F, Villarroel A, Rappold G, Weiss B, Koenen M. 1994. Organisation of the murine 5-HT$_3$ receptor gene and assignment to human chromosome 11. *FEBS Lett.* 339:302–6

64. Vallano ML, Beaman-Hall CM. 1989. Differentiation increases type II calmodulin-dependent protein kinase in the neuroblastoma/glioma cell line 108CG15 (NG108–15). *J. Neurosci.* 9: 539–47

65. van Hooft JA, Kooyman AR, Verkerk A, van Kleef RGDM, Vijverberg HPM. 1994. Single 5-HT$_3$ receptor–gated ion channel events resolved in N1E-115 mouse neuroblastoma cells. *Biochem. Biophys. Res. Commun.* 199:227–33

66. Vernino S, Amador M, Luetje CW, Patrick J, Dani JA. 1992. Calcium modulation and high calcium permeability of neuronal nicotinic acetylcholine receptors. *J. Neurosci.* 8:127–34

67. Wallis DI, North RA. 1978. The action of 5-hydroxytryptamine on single neurones of the rabbit superior cervical ganglion. *Neuropharmacology* 17: 1023–28

68. Wallis DI, Stansfeld CE, Nash HL. 1982. Depolarizing responses recorded from nodose ganglion cells of the rabbit evoked by 5-hydroxytryptamine and other substances. *Neuropharmacology* 21:31–40

69. Watling KJ. 1988. Radioligand binding studies identify 5-HT$_3$ recognition sites in neuroblastoma cell lines and mammalian CNS. *Trends Pharmacol. Sci.* 9:227–29

70. Yakel JL. 1992. 5-HT$_3$ receptors as cation channels. See Ref. 14, pp. 105–28

71. Yakel JL, Jackson MB. 1988. 5-HT$_3$ receptors mediate rapid responses in cultured hippocampus and a clonal cell line. *Neuron* 1:615–21

72. Yakel JL, Lagrutta A, Adelman JP, North RA. 1993. Single amino acid substitution affects desensitization of the 5-hydroxytryptamine type 3 receptor expressed in *Xenopus* oocytes. *Proc. Natl. Acad. Sci. USA* 90:5030–33

73. Yakel JL, Shao XM, Jackson MB. 1990. The selectivity of the channel coupled to the 5-HT$_3$ receptor. *Brain Res.* 533: 46–52

74. Yakel JL, Shao XM, Jackson MB. 1991. Activation and desensitization of the 5-HT$_3$ receptor in a rat glioma x mouse neuroblastoma hybrid cell. *J. Physiol.* 436:293–308

75. Yakel JL, Trussell LO, Jackson MB. 1988. Three serotonin responses in cultured mouse hippocampal and striatal neurons. *J. Neurosci.* 8:1273–85

76. Yang J. 1990. Ion permeation through 5-hydroxytryptamine-gated channels in neuroblastoma N18 cells. *J. Gen. Physiol.* 96:1177–98

77. Yang J, Mathie A, Hille B. 1992. 5-HT$_3$ receptor channels in dissociated rat superior cervical ganglion neurons. *J. Physiol.* 448:237–56

78. Zhang H, ffrench-Constant RH, Jackson MB. 1994. A unique amino acid of the *Drosophila* GABA receptor influences drug sensitivity by two mechanisms. *J. Physiol.* 479:65–75

Annu. Rev. Physiol. 1995. 57:469–93

MECHANISMS OF ACTIVATION OF MUSCLE NICOTINIC ACETYLCHOLINE RECEPTORS AND THE TIME COURSE OF ENDPLATE CURRENTS

B. Edmonds, A. J. Gibb, and D. Colquhoun

Department of Pharmacology and Wellcome Laboratory for Molecular Pharmacology, University College London, Gower Street, London WC1E 6BT, England

KEY WORDS: synaptic currents, central nervous system, ligand-gated ion channels

INTRODUCTION

Fast synaptic currents mediate rapid transmission between neurons in both the peripheral and central nervous systems. These currents are generated by the activation of ligand-gated ion channels. Two classes of channels that have been characterized extensively are the nicotinic acetylcholine receptor (AChR) at the vertebrate neuromuscular junction (nmj) and ionotropic glutamate receptors at central synapses. This review concentrates on the former, and a companion review by B Edmonds et al, this volume, discusses glutamate receptors (see also 102). The aims are to (*a*) summarize recent work concerning the structure of these classes of receptors, (*b*) address current understanding of the mechanisms underlying activation of these receptors, and (*c*) discuss present views of the role of channel gating in determining the time course of synaptic currents. It would be appropriate also to address the relationship between structure and function, but, apart from work on ion permeation, there is little knowledge in this area.

469

We first discuss the principles that underlie the time course of synaptic currents and the methods used to understand it before discussing specific receptors.

PRINCIPLES AND METHODS

Synaptic Currents and Single-Channel Currents

In order to account completely for the time course of a postsynaptic current we need to know (*a*) the amount of transmitter released, (*b*) the time course and geometry of release, (*c*) the shape of the synaptic cleft and the location of the postsynaptic receptors, (*d*) the rates at which diffusion, catabolic enzymes, and uptake mechanisms remove transmitter from the cleft, and (*e*) a complete kinetic description of the activation, desensitization, and block of receptors by the transmitter. The latter is needed not only to describe the response of the receptors to the transmitter but also to describe the binding of the transmitter, which is often a major factor in controlling the rate at which transmitter diffuses from the cleft (62). This is only a start in the process of describing synaptic transmission, which needs, in addition, a knowledge of passive and active electrical characteristics of the postsynaptic structure (matters that are not discussed here). Many uncertainties remain regarding all CNS synapses, and even in the case of the neuromuscular junction substantial gaps in our knowledge exist.

The time course of a synaptic current is the sum of all the individual single-channel currents for each of the receptors on the postsynaptic membrane. The current at time t will be directly proportional to the probability that a channel is open at time t, usually denoted $P_0(t)$ (at least in the case where all open channels have the same conductance). At the single-channel level, we cannot distinguish (arbitrarily) two factors that contribute to the time course of a synaptic current. First there is a shut period (the first latency) before the channel opens (if it opens at all), and then there may be one or more openings. Eventually all the channels will shut again.

Consider what happens after the moment when agonist is applied. The transmitter (agonist) is applied at $t = 0$, and the first opening occurs at time t_0 (the first latency). The first latencies for individual channels will be random variables; the distribution (probability density function, pdf) of the duration t_0 of the latency being denoted $f(t_0)$. We must now consider the probability that the channel, which first opened at t_0, is still open t_1 ms later, i.e. that the channel is open at time $t = t_0 + t_1$ (note that the channel may shut and reopen between t_0 and $t_0 + t_1$). This probability can be written $P(t_1,t_0)$ Thus, we define

$$P(t_1, t_0) = \text{Prob (open at } t_0 + t_1 \mid \text{open at } t_0).$$
$$\text{1.}$$

In general this depends not only on t_1 but also on when the opening first starts, t_0, e.g. when the transmitter concentration is changing with time, the rates of binding transitions change with time.

In the simpler case where the transition probabilities are constant, i.e. when the agonist concentration is constant (e.g. when the concentration is zero throughout most of the synaptic current). This probability is independent of when the first opening begins, thus it can be written as $P(t_1)$, giving

$$P(t_1) = \text{Prob (open at } t_0 + t_1 \mid \text{open at } t_0).$$ 2.

In this case, $P(t_1)$ describes the time course that would be found by averaging single-channel activations (see below) that have been aligned so that the time when the first opening begins is the same for all. In other words, it is the time course that would be observed if the first latencies were negligible.

We now write the synaptic current time course as the convolution of the first latency distribution $f(t_0)$, with $P(t_1,t_0)$, where, as above, $t_1 = t - t_0$. This gives

$$P_0(t) = \int_{t_0 = 0}^{t_0 = t} f(t_0) P(t-t_0,t_0) dt_0$$ 3.

or, when concentration is constant,

$$P_0(t) = \int_{t_0 = 0}^{t_0 = t} f(t_0) P(t-t_0) dt_0.$$ 4.

This result has been used in the context of synaptic currents by Edmonds & Colquhoun (41) (see below). The basis of the relationship is explained in detail and exemplified by Colquhoun & Hawkes (23, 24). The relationship is valid only when there is one open state (not merely one conductance level), and this is not the case for any of the channels discussed here. It can be generalized for any mechanism, as described by Colquhoun & Hawkes (22) (see also 24, 25). Where concentration is constant, the first latency distribution, $P(t_1)$ and $P_0(t)$, can be expressed in terms of sums of exponential terms, which can be evaluated for any specified mechanism as outlined by Colquhoun & Hawkes (25).

When the transmitter concentration is essentially zero throughout most of the synaptic current, the opening(s) that are evoked by transmitter release can be described as a single activation of the channel. In this case, the decay of the synaptic current is controlled by the rate at which channels close spontaneously in the absence of agonist; this closure rate is often referred to as the rate of deactivation of the receptor, or as the offset (as opposed to onset) relaxation rate. The idea of individual channel activations has proven useful in understanding the action of agonists and thus how an activation can be defined.

Definition of Channel Activation

The term activation is generally used to refer to the opening of channels by agonist. It is useful to ask what an individual channel activation looks like. In this context, the term activation refers, roughly speaking, to the events that occur during the time that agonist is bound to the receptor.

First consider how this definition can be more precise in the case where there is only one agonist binding site. After an agonist molecule becomes bound, there may be no channel openings (if the agonist dissociates before an opening occurs), or there may be one or more channel openings before the agonist dissociates. If there are no openings, then the binding is invisible on the experimental record and such events are excluded from consideration. If one or more openings occur during the occupancy, then the channel activation is defined as everything that occurs from the start of the first opening to the end of the last opening (that which precedes agonist dissociation). Such activations may easily be distinguished in single-channel records at equilibrium by making recordings at different agonist concentrations. Clearly the interval between activations will get longer as the agonist concentration is reduced, whereas any shut times that occur within a single activation should have a distribution that does not depend on the agonist concentration. By making measurements at a sufficiently low agonist concentration (e.g the mean length of the shortest shut time component between activations is at least 100 times the mean length of the longest shut time component within activations), it is possible to distinguish individual activations as bursts of openings (24, 32). The definition of an activation for records that are not at equilibrium is discussed below.

Where there are two or more agonist-binding sites, the definition of an activation is more complicated because from the time that the first agonist molecule binds up to the time that the last agonist molecule dissociates, the channel has at least one molecule bound throughout. Given that at least one opening occurs during this time, the activation is defined as everything that occurs from the start of the first opening to the end of the last opening (that which precedes dissociation of the last agonist molecule). Clearly, in records at equilibrium, the mean interval between activations will become longer at lower agonist concentrations. But in this case, the shut times within activations may also depend on concentration, as may the number of openings per activation and the distribution of the length of these openings. This happens because what occurs next to a channel that is only partially occupied will depend on the agonist concentration. For example, the probability that the mono-liganded state becomes occupied by a second agonist molecule (rather than losing its one agonist molecule, or opening) increases at higher agonist concentrations. Thus the number of doubly liganded openings per activation may increase and thereby increase the overall length of the activation, although this effect will be small if the agonist concentration is low enough to give a binding rate that is slow compared with the rate constants for the other routes for leaving the mono-liganded state. This effect has not yet been measured clearly. With rates such as those inferred by Colquhoun & Sakmann (31) for the nicotinic receptor, this is not entirely surprising because, although the length of doubly liganded activations (which contribute the slow component of the burst length) should increase at higher agonist concentrations, the change is predicted to be quite small in the range of agonist concentrations where it is still possible to distinguish clearly the start and end of individual activations on the experimental record. At very low concentrations, when most openings are short (probably mono-liganded, see below), the overall mean activation length will become shorter; noise analysis, however, detects only the slow component of the burst length, which is essentially constant at even the lowest concentrations. The class of rather rare intermediate duration shut times with individual activations (mean length of the order of 1 ms) was attributed tentatively to the mono-liganded shut state by Colquhoun & Sakmann (31) and is therefore counted as being part of the activation (see below).

Individual channel activations may not be the same for measurements that are not made at equilibrium as for measurements that are. If the agonist concentration varies with time, and the activations are concentration dependent, interpretation of nonequilibrium records may be difficult. The simplest case occurs after a very brief application of agonist (such as is thought to occur at many synapses) (see below), when the concentration is zero throughout virtually all of the observation period and the question of concentration dependence does not arise; the activation will end as soon as the first agonist molecule dissociates (neglecting the possibility of mono-liganded openings) because it can never reassociate. The most important consideration in this case is whether the durations of successive openings and shuttings are correlated (23, 22, 49). The existence of such correlations has been demonstrated for ACh receptors (31) and for NMDA receptors (51), as well as for various voltage- and calcium-activated channels. For channels that show no such correlations, the structure of individual activations should be exactly the same as at equilibrium (although the distribution of the latency to the start of the activation will be different from the equilibrium distribution of shut times between activations). However, for channels that do show correlations, the structure of activations will, in principle, differ from those measured at equilibrium, even when equilibrium measurements are made at an agonist concentration that is close to zero. These ideas are explained in greater detail by Colquhoun & Hawkes (24).

Experimental Methods

The classical study of Anderson & Stevens (2) used noise analysis to establish that the endplate current decay was largely controlled by channel closure in the absence of agonist (discussed below). In their analysis, they assumed that agonist binding was much faster than the open-shut reaction, so the time constant inferred from noise could be interpreted as a mean open lifetime. It is now thought that this assumption is generally wrong and that the noise time constant should be interpreted as an approximation to the mean length of a channel activation or burst. This does not invalidate the conclusions about the synaptic current drawn by Anderson & Stevens; the activation length is exactly what would be expected to describe channel closure in the absence of agonist. It does, however, underline the limitations of noise analysis for investigation of underlying receptor mechanisms. This limitation is only important, as pointed out earlier, if it is necessary to know about the binding of agonist as well as channel opening in order to understand the time course of transmitter concentration in the cleft. There is no prospect of being able to measure directly the kinetics of binding on the μs timescale that is necessary, so this must be predicted by attempting to identify an adequate reaction mechanism and to estimate the rate constants in this mechanism.

Single-channel recordings have allowed great advances in identifying reaction mechanisms and their rate constants (reviewed in 24, 32, 73). In the case of the muscle nicotinic receptor, a reasonably complete description has been obtained from steady-state single-channel records (see below). The resulting mechanism allows predictions to be made of what synaptic currents and other relaxations should look like, and these predictions have turned out to be reasonably accurate.

In general, however, it is impossible to predict empirically what a synaptic current (or any sort of macroscopic relaxation) will look like on the basis of steady-state single-channel records; at least, impossible by any method short of identifying the entire mechanism and its rate constants. This is because there is no simple relationship between $f(t_0)$ or $P(t_1)$, defined in Equation 2, and anything that can be measured from the steady-state single-channel recording.

These considerations underscore the value of making nonstationary measurements as well as equilibrium measurements. For agonist-activated channels, this usually means that we want to make concentration jumps, and only recently has it become possible to do this rapidly enough to be useful. These methods now allow concentration pulses as short as 200 μs in duration to be applied to outside-out membrane patches (8, 26, 41, 44, 76). Both macroscopic relaxations and nonstationary single-channel measurements (e.g. first latency distributions) can be measured directly (although there has been concern about whether outside-out patches always behave in the same way as intact cells in relation to desensitization; discussed below). These observations have been useful as empirical measures of relaxation behavior under controlled conditions. They will also be useful for the identification of mechanisms in conjunction with recent developments that allow for missed brief events and the direct maximum likelihood fitting of mechanisms (see, for example, 21, 24, 108).

NICOTINIC ACETYLCHOLINE RECEPTORS (MUSCLE TYPE)

Structure of Muscle Nicotinic Receptors

The results of molecular cloning studies have led to the view that nicotinic AChRs and glutamate receptors are members of two distinct families of ligand-gated ion channels. However, both are thought to be formed by the aggregation of protein subunits around a central pore constituting the ion channel (see 61, 86, 116; B Edmonds et al, Glutamate Receptors, this volume, for reviews). A common feature between families, however, is that each of the identified subunits has four sequences of hydrophobic amino acids, designated M1-M4, that probably span the membrane (but see B Edmonds et al, Glutamate Receptors, this volume).

The only agonist-activated ion channel for which the quaternary structure is known with any certainty is the *Torpedo* electric organ AchR, although there is little doubt that the muscle nicotinic receptors are similarly arranged. Four types of subunits are arranged pseudosymmetrically around the pore as a pentamer ($\alpha_2\beta\gamma\delta$ in embryonic or denervated muscle and $\alpha_2\beta\epsilon\delta$ in adult muscle) (11, 54, 61, 87). The M2 segment of each subunit contains approximately 19 amino acids that contribute to formation of the pore. The results of mutagenesis studies in M2 of AChRs indicate that a ring of residues at position 263 (of mouse muscle α-subunit) is likely to form the narrowest part of the channel and thereby determine the ionic selectivity (14, 59, 119–121). The single-channel conductance is strongly influenced by three rings of negatively charged residues that concentrate positively charged ions near the mouth of the channel (58). Other relevant work on structure is found in references 1, 5, 34, 35, 67, 94, 104, 106, and 117.

There is good evidence from biochemical studies (90) and from electrophysiological work (108) that the two agonist-binding sites of the *Torpedo* receptor are not the same; this is probably also the case for the embryonic mouse receptor (60, 112). However, it appears that the extent to which the two binding sites are nonequivalent may be species dependent. Work on several other species, for example, the human receptor (probably embryonic type) in the TE671 cell line (105), *Electrophorus* receptors (98), and frog endplate receptors (29, 31) suggests a degree of nonequivalence that is considerably lower than that seen in *Torpedo*. Further details are reviewed by Colquhoun (16) and Lingle et al (73).

THE VERACITY OF EXPRESSION SYSTEMS   Heterologous expression of cloned subunit DNAs or RNAs in either *Xenopus* oocytes or in mammalian cell lines (e.g. HEK 293 cells) is now a common procedure. It obviously relies heavily on the assumption that the channels expressed in systems such as oocytes will behave in the same way that they do in their native environment. The ultimate object, after all, is to understand synaptic transmission, so the behavior of a heterologously expressed channel (or a channel in a cell line such as BC3H-1 or PC12) is of interest only insofar as it resembles the receptor behavior in the real synaptic membrane.

The behavior of an individual receptor subtype in an expression system and the homogeneity of expressed proteins are two problems confronting researchers. One of the attractions of heterologous expression was the possibility to work with a known protein of well-defined structure (in contrast to the heterogeneous receptors found on many cells). It now seems that this hope may not be realized.

The first strong quantitative evidence that native channels closely resemble those in oocytes, in some cases at least, came from the study by Mishina et al (87). They showed a close quantitative similarity between the properties of channels formed by coexpression of bovine α-, β-, γ-, and δ-subunit RNAs in oocytes and channels recorded from fetal calf muscle. Likewise, they showed a close quantitative agreement between the properties of channels formed by coexpression of bovine α-, β-, γ-, and ϵ-subunit RNAs in oocytes and channels recorded from adult calf muscle. The agreement was very close, not only for the single-channel conductances, but also for the mean open lifetimes, and for the dependence of the latter on the membrane potential. However, recordings from oocytes may contain some channels unlike those seen in muscle cells, which probably resulted from assembly of incomplete (α, β, δ) receptors. Another example of close quantitative similarity is given by Sine & Claudio (107), who studied a cell line stably transfected with α-, β-, γ-, and δ-subunit cDNAs cloned from BC3H-1 cells (mouse embryonic–type receptor). They show that the conductance, steady-state single-channel kinetics, and binding characteristics are similar to those seen in BC3H-1 cells. It may be that stable transfection yields more faithful reproduction of the receptor than transient transfection. A similar close resemblance between native and expressed receptors has been seen in NMDA-type glutamate receptors (B Edmonds et al, Glutamate Receptors, this volume).

The results of some more recent studies have been less clear. For example, Kullberg et al (66) report a heterogeneous range of single-channel conductances in oocytes injected with mouse α-, β-, δ-, and γ-subunit RNAs, and

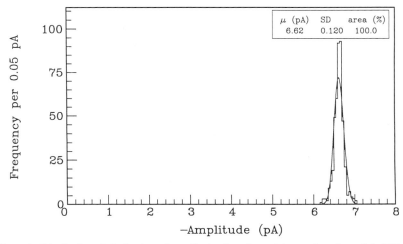

Figure 1 Distribution of single-channel amplitudes from the endplate region of an adult (200 g) rat. Channel openings are elicited by 100 nM acetylcholine in a cell-attached patch. (Unpublished data of DC Ogden & NK Mulrine.) After imposing a resolution of 50 μs for both openings and shuttings, there were 1100 resolved intervals, and the histogram was constructed from 433 amplitudes of openings that were longer than two rise times. The continuous curve is a Gaussian distribution, which was fitted to the data by the method of maximum likelihood; it has a mean of 6.62 pA and a standard deviation of 0.12 pA. The observed distribution has a sharper peak and broader tails than the Gaussian curve, but there is only one narrow peak in the distribution.

only the smallest of these was attributable to bovine α, β, δ channels. However, recordings from mouse embryonic receptors in the BC3H-1 cell line do not show multiple conductance levels (111). Similarly, Camacho et al (11) report that expression of mouse α-, β-, and δ-subunit RNAs, and rat ε-subunit RNA in oocytes produces channels with three distinct conductances. Although Kullberg et al comment on, "the remarkable recapitulation of muscle receptor function by oocytes," the fact is that channels from adult mouse endplates show only one conductance (7). Endplate receptors in 3-week-old rats may show two single-channel conductance levels, which correspond to embryonic and adult forms (88), but adult (>5- or 6-week-old) rat endplates show only one conductance (which is very similar to the largest level seen in oocytes), as illustrated in Figure 1. Thus it seems that the oocyte expression system may be less than ideal, at least for some nicotinic receptors.

There are also contradictions in results from apparently similar experiments. For example, Gibb et al (52) injected oocytes with mouse α-, β-, γ-, and δ-subunit RNAs, but, unlike Kullberg et al (66), they found only one conductance level in most oocytes, and never more than two levels. This apparent homogeneity was bolstered by the fact that Gibb et al also found that the burst lengths of channels were essentially the same from patch to patch. However, the area of one component of the shut-time distribution was found to differ considerably from one recording to another. Consequently, when dose-response curves were constructed by measuring the fraction of time for which the channel was open (P_{open}) as a function of agonist concentration, the curves differed considerably from patch to patch. This led to the conclusion that the expressed receptors were heterogeneous, but that the heterogeneity probably did not arise primarily from expression of receptors with one subunit omitted, because it was not correlated with the single-channel conductance. The reasons for the difference remain unknown. The type of heterogeneity found in this study is a reminder of the fallibility of heterologous expression systems. The discrepancy probably would not have been obvious in most single-channel studies, and it certainly would not have been detected in the far more common sort of experiments in which the whole-cell current is measured.

Investigations of Agonist Mechanisms

ACTIVATION OF RECEPTORS   The idea that channel opening should be considered separately from agonist binding (36, 37) is widely accepted. There is general consensus that the following mechanism can account for the main features of channel activation (excluding desensitization).

$$
\begin{array}{ccc}
\mathbf{R} & & \\
k_{-1} \Big\Updownarrow 2k_{+1} & & \\
\mathbf{AR} \underset{\alpha_1}{\overset{\beta_1}{\rightleftharpoons}} \mathbf{AR}^* & & \\
2k_{-2} \Big\Updownarrow k_{+2} \quad 2k_{-2}^* \Big\Updownarrow k_{+2}^* & & \\
\mathbf{A_2R} \underset{\alpha_2}{\overset{\beta_2}{\rightleftharpoons}} \mathbf{A_2R}^* & &
\end{array}
$$

Colquhoun & Sakmann (31) estimated rate constants for each step in this mechanism (for adult frog endplate receptors at 11°C), and values are shown in Table 1.

The binding and open-shut reactions had comparable rates (as predicted by Colquhoun & Hawkes; 18); thus openings occurred in compact bursts, caused largely by oscillations between the two doubly occupied states A_2R and A_2R^*. A burst consisted, on average, of about 2.9 openings separated by very brief

Table 1

Conditions	Temperature (°C)	k_{+1} $(k_{+2})^a$ $(M^{-1}s^{-1})$	k_{-1} $(k_{-2})^a$ (s^{-1})	β (s^{-1})	α (s^{-1})	$1/(\alpha+\beta)$ (μs)	P_{open}^b
Frog NMJ[c]	11	1.0×10^8	16,300	30,600	714	31.9	0.977
Torpedo[de]							
$-Ca^{2+}$	22	6×10^7 (1×10^8)	500 (70,000)	22,000	15,000	27.0	0.595
$+0.5$ mM Ca^{2+}	22	6×10^7 (1×10^8)	250 (40,000)	45,000	8000	18.9	0.849
$-Ca^{2+}$	12	1×10^6 (3×10^5)	20 (20,000)	5000	1000	167	0.833
BC3H-1[f]							
Fast gaps							
$-Ca^{2+}$	11	—	(7945)	12,783	97	77.6	0.992
$+1.8$ mM Ca^{2+}	11	—	(6500)	13,904	62	71.6	0.996
Intermed. gaps							
$-Ca^{2+}$	11	—	(2136)	412	46.8	2180	0.898
$+1.8$ mM Ca^{2+}	11	—	(860)	321	23.5	2903	0.932

[a] Where only one value given, k_{+1} and k_{+2} (or k_{-1} and k_{-2}) are assumed to be equal.
[b] $\beta/(\alpha + \beta)$.
[c] Colquhoun & Sakmann (30). Low concentrations of ACh on adult frog AChR; -130mV; bandwidth 2–4.5 kHz (-3dB, Bessel).
[d] Sine et al (108). Low and high concentrations of ACh on Torpedo AChR transfected into mouse fibroblasts; -70 or -100mV; bandwidth 10–20 kHz (-3dB, Gaussian).
[e] Ca^{2+}-free solutions included 1 mM Mg^{2+}, and 0.5 mM Ca^{2+} solution containing 0.5 mM Mg^{2+}.
[f] Sine & Steinbach (110). Low concentrations of ACh on BC3H-1 (embryonic mouse) AChR; -100 mV; bandwidth 7–8 kHz (-3dB, Bessel). The results are given for the interpretation that the shortest closed times detected correspond to sojourns in the A_2R state.

shut periods (mean length 21 µs, close to the mean lifetime of A_2R). The mean length of such bursts is predicted to be similar to the time constants for (a) the noise spectrum predicted by this mechanism, and (b) relaxations following a jump to zero acetylcholine concentration. This similarity accounts for the close agreement found by Anderson & Stevens (2) between the time constants for noise and synaptic current decay, despite the fact that neither is likely to be close to the mean open time.

The conclusion that the opening rate constant β is fast is supported by measurements of the rise time of miniature endplate currents (77) and from studies with concentration jumps. The suggestion that the maximum P_o attainable (at high agonist concentration) $\beta/(\alpha + \beta)$ is close to 1 for ACh and for several other agonists has been confirmed from equilibrium concentration-response curves estimated by single-channel measurements of P_o (3, 4, 28, 35, 88, 92; see data in 28, 82). This method for obtaining a concentration-response, although not without its own problems, is usually far more reliable than use of whole-cell currents because corrections for desensitization, and channel block by the agonist itself, are far more reliable for the former method, and because the response is on an absolute scale (from 0 to 1) rather than a relative one.

More recently, concentration jump studies (see above) have been used to investigate nicotinic receptors (38, 45, 46–48). Franke et al (48) give rate constants for activation of the mouse embryonic receptor (at room temperature) that are quite close to those found by Colquhoun & Sakmann (31) for adult frog endplate (at 11°C). Their model also allows for desensitization (although not opening of mono-liganded channels, which contribute little to the macroscopic current). The full potential of the concentration jump method to provide single-channel information (e.g. first latency measurements) has yet to be exploited; the problem of obtaining patches that contain only one channel makes this difficult in practice. It is clear, however, that it provides information (see above) and essential confirmation of inferences about mechanisms and rates that steady-state single-channel records cannot provide.

The use of equilibrium single-channel records to make inferences about mechanisms and rates may be far from unambiguous. For example, Sine & Steinbach (110) suggest that the 'intermediate shut times' (see below) rather than the briefest shut times might represent sojourns in the A_2R state, and this led to a rather low estimate of the opening rate constant β for BC3H-1 cell receptors (see Table 1). It is not obvious which, if any, shut times represent sojourns in the A_2R state. Concentration jumps (74) suggest a value for β of ~15,000 s^{-1}, close to the value predicted by Sine & Steinbach (110) if in fact the fast gaps, and not the intermediate gaps, correspond to occupation of the A_2R state of the receptor. (These estimates are not very different from estimates for other nicotinic receptors.)

In addition to the bursts described above (long bursts), short bursts that are particularly obvious at low agonist concentrations are also observed. These bursts seem to consist largely of single, brief openings. Although the existence of an excess of brief openings was surprising when first observed (30), it is now a commonly observed phenomenon. Colquhoun & Sakmann (31) conclude that at low agonist concentrations many of these brief openings are openings of the singly occupied receptor (AR). However, there are too many brief openings at higher concentrations to be accounted for in this way, as was also concluded by Sine & Steinbach (109) and Auerbach & Lingle (4), although not by Jackson (60).

The mechanism shown above is also deficient in that, although it predicts that intermediate length gaps (of mean length ~1 ms) will occur within an activation (when one agonist molecule dissociates, but then re-associates and produces another opening), the predicted frequency of such gaps is lower than is observed (even when the two binding sites are assumed to be nonequivalent) (31).

COMPLEXITIES OF BEHAVIOR OF ADULT- AND EMBRYONIC-TYPE RECEPTORS Recently, some doubt has been cast on the simple idea that there is one type of embryonic receptor and one type of adult receptor (see reviews 6, 73, 113). Most authors report seeing occasional atypical events, even in adult tissues. For example, Colquhoun & Sakmann (31) saw occasional subconductance levels, and a few atypically long bursts of openings. But in this case and in others, such events have been sufficiently rare that (a) they cannot easily be studied, and (b) they were considered to be of little relevance either to the physiological function of the receptor or to investigation of receptor mechanisms. Perhaps the most striking example of kinetic heterogeneity comes from studies of cultured myotomal muscle cells of *Xenopus* (4) in which three forms of single-channel behavior were found within the embryonic type, and three forms within the adult type. Signs of heterogeneity, albeit more subtle, can be seen in BC3H-1 cell receptors (73, 111); this takes the form of variation in P_o from one cluster of openings to another in recordings at high agonist concentration (also observed when BC3H-1 cell AChR subunits are expressed in oocytes; A Gibb et al, unpublished observations). A similar variability is seen in young (around 3-week-old) rat endplates (88), but is rare in adult rat endplates (NK Mulrine & DC Ogden, personal communication). The reasons for such complexities are, for the most part, not known; however, it appears that most receptors, especially in adult animals, are much less complex than the *Xenopus* myocyte.

CHANNEL MODES   When complex kinetic behavior is observed, it is often not clear whether it is the result of one homogeneous type of channel that can change its behavior from time to time, or whether it results from the presence of several different types of channels. The latter explanation is the more likely in most cases (apart from obvious subconductance levels), but there are cases where changes of behavior have been observed, with tolerable lack of ambiguity, in the middle of clusters of openings recorded at high agonist concentrations, i.e. under conditions where all the openings in a cluster are likely to originate from one individual channel molecule (4, 73, 89). It is difficult to know if and when such changes occur, given the inherently random nature of channel behavior. Such behavior has also been observed in several other channel types (73) including calcium channels (57) and sodium channels (93). A similar phenomenon occurs with NMDA-type glutamate receptors (see B Edmonds et al, Glutamate Receptors, this volume).

When the transition from one sort of behavior to another is relatively infrequent, the different types of behavior are often referred to as modes. There is no reason to think that such transitions are different in kind from any other sort of state transition; thus there is no necessity for the term modes, but it may nevertheless be convenient jargon. Mode switching has been reported to occur when mouse α-, β-, and δ-subunit RNAs and rat ε-subunit RNA, or mouse α-, β-, δ-, and ε-subunit RNAs, are expressed in oocytes (89). It was suggested that each channel type shows three distinct modes, in each of which the channel has a different mean open lifetime, and that these mean lifetimes are much the same for both embryonic and adult receptors. It is also suggested that embryonic and adult receptors differ only in the fraction of time that they spend in each of the modes. Although it is somewhat unexpected that two different proteins should have in common modes with the same lifetimes, it is certainly a possibility. The distinction between modes does, however, depend on some assumptions that need further investigation. First, the analysis (in its use of gamma distributions) assumes that individual open times have a simple exponential distribution (which is not generally true—see below). Second, it is assumed that only two channel proteins are involved, although Kullberg et al (66) showed heterogeneity in this preparation. Third, it is not clear how the inferences would be affected by undetected brief shuttings and openings, nor is it clear that this explanation can account quantitatively for the difference between embryonic and adult receptors. Further work will be needed before this idea gains general acceptance.

DESENSITIZATION OF NICOTINIC RECEPTORS   The phenomenon of desensitization is universal, but knowledge of its mechanism has scarcely advanced since the classical study by Katz & Thesleff (63). Essentially all authors since then have concluded that the sort of cyclic reaction mechanism that was proposed by Katz & Thesleff, with a route from the resting state(s) to the desensitized state(s) that does not go via the open state(s), is necessary to explain the observations. A number of variants of this mechanism have been proposed, e.g. to allow for agonist cooperativity, or a double-exponential time course of desensitization, but the essentials remain intact. There is still no consensus about which states can lead directly to the desensitized state; in particular, it is still not clear to what extent partially or fully liganded receptors can desensitize without opening. On the structural side, the picture is a little better, although Unwin et al (118) showed a distinct difference in the shape of the resting and desensitized receptor (12). In fact, the major advance has probably been the realization that desensitization is a phenomenon of the receptor protein itself. The fact that it occurs with purified receptor protein incorporated into lipid bilayers (68, 97) shows clearly that desensitization does not depend on second messengers or on phosphorylation (see below). An intriguing experiment by Kuhlmann et al (65) showed that physostigmine, which appears to act as an agonist at a site different from that where acetylcholine works, could still open channels (as judged by Cs^+ influx) after desensitization by high acetylcholine concentrations. This result suggests that the change in the receptor molecule that occurs during desensitization does not affect the ability of the channel to open but somehow prevents acetylcholine binding from causing it to open. Many agents have been found to increase the rate at which current declines during agonist application, i.e. they enhance desensitization; however, in most cases no attempt has been made to separate channel blocking effects from direct effects on desensitization (which is not easy given the vague knowledge of desensitization). Clapham & Neher (13) concluded that they could not distinguish channel block and desensitization effects.

A wide variety of time constants for desensitization have been reported (91) that range from tens of milliseconds to tens of minutes, although in individual studies no more than two exponential components have been found. Perhaps the only generalization that can be made about these widely ranging time constants is that rapid application methods always seem to give faster and more profound desensitization. The question of whether this happens only because of the application method is still not resolved. About 75% desensitization was found after a very slow application of 10 μm carbachol (43) over a 10-min duration, as judged by the reduction in the amplitude of focally recorded endplate currents (an ingenious method for making very brief agonist applications). This may be compared with over 99% desensitization found after a few seconds exposure to 1 μM ACh (which is roughly equipotent in outside-out patches from mouse muscle; 48). The desensitization time constants in intact adult endplates were in the second and minute range (two-electrode clamp; 43, 95). Work on adult frog endplates using a Vaseline-gap clamp (10) showed a predominant fast component with 100 μM ACh of about 5 s at 6°C (i.e. about 1.6 s at 22°C with Q10 = 2; 39) and a small component about ten times slower than this. In contrast, measurements that use fast concentration changes (complete in less than 1 ms) on outside-out patches all show much faster desensitization, with a single time constant of about 50 ms for 100 μM ACh (at room temperature) reported for BC3H-1 cells, adult and denervated mouse muscle, and adult frog muscle (38, 45, 46–48). In the intact muscle fiber, diffusion in the unstirred layer means that a peak response cannot be achieved in less than about 250 ms (with 100 μM ACh; 91). Thus the obvious reason for the discrepancy is that this necessarily slow agonist application in intact muscle causes desensitization to appear to be much slower than it really is. The only problem with this argument is that, in outside-out patch experiments, the current has decayed to only 0.1% or so of its peak amplitude after 300 ms (45). An adult frog endplate contains about 10^7 channels (84) with a single-channel conductance of 30 pS (50); thus activation of all channels should produce a current of about 15 μA (at −50 mV), but after 300 ms of desensitization, the current should be only about 0.1% of this, i.e. about 15 nA. However, Cachelin & Colquhoun (10) actually observed peak currents of 10–15 μA at 250 ms after agonist application (despite the fact that the Vaseline gap will not always contain the entire endplate), which suggests that there was not much desensitization during the first 250 ms in their experiments. Franke et al (45) suggest that this paradox can be explained by there being more than 10^7 channels in the endplate; this is certainly a possibility, but the numbers in the literature would have to be wrong by two or three orders of magnitude for this explanation to be satisfactory.

The only obvious alternative explanation is that desensitization may be faster in outside-out patches than in intact cells. This is certainly true for NMDA receptors (see B Edmonds et al, Glutamate Receptors this volume), and a substantial increase in the rate of desensitization after patch formation has been reported for the neuronal nicotinic receptors in medial habenula cells (72). An increase in desensitization rate of up to twofold after patch excision was observed with mouse muscle (48) and for embryonic bovine muscle receptor expressed in oocytes (9). Also, Covarrubias & Steinbach (33) reported a reduction in open time after excision of outside-out patches from BC3H-1 cells. The evidence on the effects of patch excision is still incomplete but suggests that care is needed when interpreting results from isolated patches.

Another approach to the question of the rate of desensitization in intact muscle fibers is to look at clusters of single-channel openings at high agonist concentrations (29, 101, 111). If such clusters are well separated, then the mean cluster length should approximate the macroscopic desensitization time constant (e.g. 23, 49). Franke et al (48) found mean cluster lengths (with 100 μM ACh) of around 50 ms in cell-attached patches as well as in outside-out patches from embryonic mouse muscle. Furthermore, Colquhoun & Ogden (29) found a mean cluster length of 154 ms (at 10–12°C) with 100 μM ACh on cell-attached patches from adult frog muscle, which would probably correspond to no more than 100 ms at 20°C. This suggests a desensitization rate closer to that observed in outside-out patches than to that observed with slow agonist application.

The foregoing examples illustrate the fact that despite all the work that has been done some doubts and discrepancies remain concerning the rate of desensitization in intact muscle fibers.

PHOSPHORYLATION OF NICOTINIC RECEPTORS   The *Torpedo* receptor can be phosphorylated by cyclic AMP-dependent protein kinase, by protein kinase C, and by a protein tyrosine kinase (99). Despite a number of erroneous inferences caused by nonspecific effects of forskolin (122), it is now clear that phosphorylation can cause an acceleration of desensitization (see reviews, 85, 114, 115). The universality of this phenomenon is less certain. For example, Cachelin & Colquhoun (10) found little effect on desensitization of agents aimed at altering phosphorylation in adult frog muscle, and Siara et al (103), using faster agonist application, found no effect on desensitization to result from intracellular application of cAMP, or of a catalytic subunit of cAMP-dependent protein kinase, on the human (embryonic type) nicotinic receptor of the medulloblastoma cell line TE671. Paradoxically, phosphorylation regulated by calcitonin gene–related peptide (CGRP) has been reported to potentiate synaptic responses in 1-day-old *Xenopus* nerve-muscle cultures (75). Effects on receptor aggregation and assembly have also been reported (115).

IS DESENSITIZATION PHYSIOLOGICALLY RELEVANT?   In view of the large amount of work that has been done on desensitization of muscle-type nicotinic receptors and on agents that modify them, it is interesting to ask whether any of it matters for the process of synaptic transmission. Although it is commonplace to read statements such as, "...the nicotinic acetylcholine receptor, whose phosphorylation increases its rate of desensitization, and *thereby modulates synaptic transmission postsynaptically...*" (56; our italics), there is no reason to think that desensitization, or its alteration by phosphorylation or other agents is of the slightest physiological importance, at least as far as normal synaptic transmission in adults is concerned. It appears that these effects are just part of the alarmingly large class of well-documented phenomena in search of a well-defined function. The only paper that has shown convincingly that nerve-released acetylcholine can (at very high stimulation rates) produce a small amount of desensitization is that of Magleby & Pallotta (80); in view of the well-known large safety margin for neuromuscular transmission, it is most unlikely that the function of the synapse could be affected. It is always possible that desensitization could be more important under pathological conditions, or during development, but this has yet to be demonstrated clearly. A physiological role for desensitization at central synapses is much more plausible, although this too has not been clearly demonstrated (see B Edmonds et al, Glutamate Receptors, this volume).

Factors that Control the Time Course of Synaptic Currents

It has been generally supposed since the work of Magleby & Stevens (81) and Anderson & Stevens (2) that the acetylcholine concentration in the synaptic cleft rises very rapidly, and then (as a result of hydrolysis and binding to receptors) falls very rapidly, so that shortly after the peak of a miniature endplate current (mEPC), the acetylcholine concentration has fallen to near zero. In this case, we expect that the time constant for the decay of the mEPC will be controlled by the rate at which channels close spontaneously in the absence of agonist. More precisely, we expect that this time constant will be similar to that of the slow component of the burst length distribution (at least in cases when, as for nicotinic receptors, the gaps within bursts and the first latencies are both short). This, in turn, should be similar to the time constant from noise analysis (21, 23, 24, 31). We also expect that the time constant for the decay of the mEPC should be close to that for the decay of current following a very brief pulse of agonist.

It is surprising, in view of the amount of work that has been done in this field, that nobody appears to have measured both mEPC decay rate and the burst length distribution in the same set of experiments. Therefore, much of the evidence must depend on older noise analysis measurements and on simulations that have been performed with realistic models for receptor activation and binding.

Mishina et al (87) show a close agreement between mEPC decay rate at adult bovine endplates and the mean elementary event duration (the precise definition of the latter is not stated, but short shut periods were neglected so it should be close to the mean burst length). Sakmann (100) shows an example in which individual channel activations (evoked by a low ACh concentration in rat muscle) are aligned on their leading edges; the sum of 1000 such activations showed a peak of 4.7 nA and an exponential decay with a time constant of 2.7 ms. These values are similar to those for mEPCs recorded from rat muscle (27, 53, 55). This alignment procedure is equivalent to assuming that the first latency (see Equation 4) is negligibly short (unlike NMDA receptors; see B Edmonds et al, Glutamate Receptors, this volume). This assumption is not unreasonable. The initial diffusion across the synaptic cleft should take only a few microseconds, and if 10,000 (64) molecules are initially distributed in 0.4 μm^2 of cleft, the concentration would (transiently) be of the order of 1 mM. Thus with an agonist association rate constant of $k_{+1} = 10^8$ $M^{-1} s^{-1}$, the mean latency to the first binding should be about 5 μs. This crude argument is essentially consistent with the results of proper simulation studies.

Experimental work (40) and simulations (15, 78) suggest that both the time course of the diffusion-limited rise in concentration of ACh and the binding of ACh are fast compared with the time course of channel opening; thus the shape of the rising phase of the mEPC is determined primarily by the rate of isomerization of the postsynaptic receptors. Because the receptors directly below the release site (although not the more peripheral receptors) are probably transiently close to being saturated (69–71), this rate constant should be close to $1/(\alpha + \beta)$. With a typical value for β of around 20,000 s^{-1}, this would imply a time constant for the rising phase of 50 µs, i.e. a 20–80% rise time of 69 µs; this is faster than is usually seen experimentally, and it seems likely that diffusion and binding have some effect on the rising phase (69). Detailed simulations, which employ a realistic receptor mechanism to allow for the effect of binding (78, 79), show a predicted decay time constant of 1.53 ms, which is close to the mean burst length of 1.48 ms implied by the rate constants in their mechanism.

It is clear then that although the mEPC decay rate is similar to the mean burst length, evidence for precise agreement is lacking. In fact, several reports suggest that the time course of transmitter concentration may not be entirely negligible, even at room temperature. For example, time constants inferred from noise analysis have been found to be 20–40% shorter than the mEPC decay time constant measured under comparable conditions (27, 53, 96). On frog endplates (at −130 mV, 10°C), a time constant for decay of evoked endplate currents of about 6 ms was found (17), whereas in separate experiments, the time constant for the slow component of the burst length was 4.2 ms (31). These results all support the conclusion that the decay of the endplate current is not solely determined by receptor kinetics (2) but may be prolonged slightly due to repetitive binding of ACh in the synaptic cleft (62).

WHAT HAPPENS AT 37°C?   Head (55) measured the properties of mEPCs in rat diaphragm fibers and found decay time constants of 0.32, 1.73, and 7.27 ms at 37, 22, and 7°C, respectively. The time constant from noise analysis at 37°C was 0.24 ms; thus Head concluded that the time course of transmitter diffusion from the cleft becomes an important factor at 37°C. This would not be entirely surprising because channel open times, in all reported cases, become faster as temperature is increased, whereas it might be expected that the rate of diffusion would not increase as rapidly at higher temperatures. No rules can be made; however, the effect of temperature on diffusion of transmitter from the cleft will depend on the amount of rebinding of transmitter and the temperature dependence of this rebinding (62). Most of the work that is discussed here has been done at room temperature, so the conclusions may not be correct for synaptic transmission at physiological temperature.

CONCLUSION

Much is known about the muscle nicotinic receptor mechanism, and about the factors that control the time course of the synaptic current, but several uncertainties still remain. In particular, the direct quantitative demonstration of the expected relationship between burst length and mEPC decay is largely lacking, and knowledge of the mechanism of desensitization has advanced little in 35 years. Far less is known about neuronal nicotinic receptors and synaptic currents, although present knowledge suggests a qualitative similarity between muscle receptors and those in autonomic ganglia (83). The ultimate goal of relating synaptic events to molecular structures is still a long way away.

Literature Cited

1. Akabas ME, Stauffer DA, Xu M, Karlin A. 1993. Acetylcholine receptor channel structure probed in cysteine-substitution mutants. *Science* 258:307–10
2. Anderson CR, Stevens CF. 1973. Voltage clamp analysis of acetylcholine produced endplate current fluctuations at frog neuromuscular junction. *J. Physiol.* 235:655–91
3. Auerbach A, Lingle CJ. 1987. Activation of the primary kinetic modes of large and small conductance cholinergic ion channels in *Xenopus* myocytes. *J. Physiol.* 393:437–66
4. Auerbach A, Lingle CJ. 1986. Heterogeneous kinetic properties of acetylcholine receptor channels in *Xenopus* myocytes. *J. Physiol.* 378:119–40
5. Blount P, Merlie JP. 1989. Molecular basis of the two non-equivalent ligand binding sites of the nicotinic acetylcholine receptor. *Neuron* 3:349–57
6. Brehm P. 1989. Resolving the structural basis for structural changes in muscle ACh receptor function: it takes nerve. *Trends Neurosci.* 12:174–77
7. Brehm P, Kullberg R. 1987. Acetylcholine receptor channels on adult mouse skeletal muscle are functionally identical in synaptic and nonsynaptic membrane. *Proc. Natl. Acad Sci. USA* 84:2550–54
8. Brett RS, Dilger JP, Adams PR, Lancaster B. 1986. A method for the rapid exchange of solutions bathing excised membrane patches. *Biophys. J.* 50:987–92

9. Butler J, Franke C, Witzemann V, Ruppersberg JP, Merlitze S, et al. 1993. Desensitization of embryonic nicotinic acetylcholine receptors expressed in *Xenopus* oocytes. *Neurosci. Lett.* 152:77–80
10. Cachelin AB, Colquhoun D. 1989. Desensitization of the acetylcholine receptor of frog end-plates measured in a vaseline-gap voltage clamp. *J. Physiol.* 415:159–88
11. Camacho P, Liu Y, Mandel G, Brehm P. 1993. The epsilon subunit confers fast channel gating on multiple classes of acetylcholine receptors. *J. Neurosci.* 13:605–13
12. Changeux J-P, Galzi J-L, Devillers-Thiery A, Bertrand D. 1992. The functional architecture of the acetylcholine nicotinic receptor explored by affinity labelling and site-directed mutagenesis. *Q. Rev. Biophys.* 25:395–432
13. Clapham DE, Neher E. 1984. Substance P reduces acetylcholine-induced currents in isolated bovine chromaffin cells. *J. Physiol.* 347:255–77
14. Cohen BN, Labarca C, Davidson N, Lester HA. 1992. Mutations in M2 alter the selectivity of the mouse nicotinic acetylcholine receptor for organic and alkali metal cations. *J. Gen. Physiol.* 100:373–400
15. Cohen I, van der Kloot W, Attwell D. 1981. The timing of channel opening during miniature endplate currents. *Brain Res.* 223:185–89

16. Colquhoun D. 1986. On the principles of postsynaptic action of neuromuscular blocking agents. In *Handbook of Experimental Pharmacology*, ed. DA Karkevich, 79:59–106. Berlin: Springer-Verlag

17. Colquhoun D, Dreyer F, Sheridan RE. 1979. The actions of tubocurarine at the frog neuromuscular junction. *J. Physiol.* 293:247–84

18. Colquhoun D, Hawkes AG. 1977. Relaxation and fluctuations of membrane currents that flow through drug-operated channels. *Proc. R. Soc. London Ser. B* 199:231–62

19. Colquhoun D, Hawkes AG. 1981. On the stochastic properties of single ion channels. *Proc. R. Soc. London Ser. B* 211:205–35

20. Colquhoun D, Hawkes AG. 1982. On the stochastic properties of bursts of single channel openings, and clusters of bursts. *Philos. Trans. R. Soc. London Ser. B* 230:15–52

21. Colquhoun D, Hawkes AG. 1987. On the stochastic properties of bursts of single ion channel openings, and clusters of bursts. *Philos. Trans. R. Soc. London Ser. B* 300:1–59

22. Colquhoun D, Hawkes AG. 1987. A note on correlations in single ion channel records. *Proc. R. Soc. London Ser. B* 230:15–52

23. Colquhoun D, Hawkes AG. 1994. The interpretation of single channel recordings. In *Microelectrode Techniques: The Plymouth Workshop Handbook*, ed. DC Ogden. Cambridge: Company of Biologists. 2nd ed. In press

24. Colquhoun D, Hawkes AG. 1995. The principles of the stochastic interpretation of ion channel mechanisms. In *Single Channel Recording*, ed. B Sakmann, E Neher. New York: Plenum. 2nd ed. In press

25. Colquhoun D, Hawkes AG. 1995. A Q-matrix cookbook. See Ref. 24, In press

26. Colquhoun D, Jonas P, Sakmann B. 1992. Action of brief pulses of glutamate on AMPA/kainate receptors in patches from different neurones of rat hippocampal slices. *J. Physiol.* 458:261–87

27. Colquhoun D, Large WA, Rang BP. 1977. An analysis of the action of a false transmitter at the neuromuscular junction. *J. Physiol.* 266:361–95

28. Colquhoun D, Mathie A, Mulrine NK, Ogden DC. 1989. Studies on single acetylcholine-receptor channels in muscle endplate and sympathetic neurones. In *Neuromuscular Junction, Fernstrom Symposium*, ed. LC Sellin, R Libelius, S Thesleff, pp. 217–34. Elsevier

29. Colquhoun D, Ogden DC. 1988. Activation of ion channels in the frog endplate by high concentrations of acetylcholine. *J. Physiol.* 395:131–59

30. Colquhoun D, Sakmann B. 1981. Fluctuations in the microsecond time range of the current through single-acetylcholine receptor ion channels. *Nature* 294:464–66

31. Colquhoun D, Sakmann B. 1985. Fast events in single-channel currents activated by acetylcholine and its analogues at the frog muscle end-plate. *J. Physiol.* 369:501–57

32. Colquhoun D, Sigworth FJ. 1995. Fitting and statistical analysis of single channel records. See Ref. 24, In press

33. Covarrubias M, Steinbach JH. 1990. Excision of membrane patches reduces the mean open time of nicotinic acetylcholine receptors. *Pflügers Arch.* 416:385–92

34. Czajkowski C, Karlin A. 1991. Agonist binding site of *Torpedo* electric tissue nicotinic acetylcholine receptor. A negatively charged region of the delta subunit within 0.9 nm of the alpha subunit binding site disulphide. *J. Biol. Chem.* 266:22603–12

35. Czajkowski C, Kaufmann C, Karlin A. 1993. Negatively charged amino acid residues in the nicotinic receptor delta subunit that contribute to the binding of acetylcholine. *Proc. Natl. Acad Sci. USA* 90:6285–89

36. del Castillo J, Katz B. 1957. A comparison of acetylcholine and stable depolarizing agents. *Proc. R. Soc. London Ser. B* 146:362–68

37. del Castillo J, Katz B. 1957. Interaction at end-plate receptors between different choline derivatives. *Proc. R. Soc. London. B.* 146:369–81

38. Dilger JP, Brett RS. 1990. Direct measurement of the concentration- and time-dependent open probability of the nicotinic acetylcholine receptor channel. *Biophys. J.* 57:723–31

39. Dilger JP, Brett RS, Poppers DM, Liu Y. 1991. The temperature dependence of some kinetic and conductance properties of acetylcholine receptor channels. *Biochim. Biophys. Acta* 1063:252–58

40. Dwyer TM. 1981. The rising phase of the miniature endplate current at the frog neuromuscular junction. *Biochim. Biophys. Acta* 646:51–60

41. Edmonds B, Colquhoun D. 1992. Rapid decay of averaged single-channel NMDA receptor activations recorded at

low agonist concentration. *Proc. R. Soc. London Ser. B* 250:279–86

42. Deleted in proof

43. Feltz A, Trautmann A. 1982. Desensitization at the frog neuromuscular junction: a biphasic process. *J. Physiol.* 322:257–72

44. Franke C, Hatt H, Dudel J. 1987. Liquid filament switch for ultra-fast exchanges of solutions at excised patches of synaptic membrane of crayfish muscle. *Neurosci. Lett.* 77:199–204

45. Franke C, Hatt H, Dudel J. 1991. Steep concentration dependence and fast desensitization of nicotinic channel currents elicited by acetylcholine pulses, studied in adult vertebrate muscle. *Pflügers Arch.* 417:509–16

46. Franke C, Hatt H, Parnas H, Dudel J. 1991. Kinetic constants of the acetylcholine (ACh) receptor reaction deduced from the rise in open probability after steps in ACh concentration. *Biophys. J.* 60:1008–16

47. Franke C, Hatt H, Parnas H, Dudel J. 1992. Recovery from the rapid desensitization of nicotinic receptor channels on mouse muscle. *Neurosci. Lett.* 140:169–72

48. Franke C, Parnas H, Hovav G, Dudel J. 1993. A molecular scheme for the reaction between acetylcholine and nicotinic channels. *Biophys. J.* 64:339–56

49. Fredkin DR, Montal MM, Rice J. 1985. Identification of aggregated Markovian models: application to the nicotinic acetylcholine receptor. In *Proceeding of Berkeley Conference in Honor of Jerzy Neuman and Jack Kiefer,* ed. LM Le Cam, RA Olshen, 1:269–89

50. Gardner P, Ogden DC, Colquhoun D. 1984. Conductances of single ion channels opened by nicotinic agonists are indistinguishable. *Nature* 309:160–62

51. Gibb AJ, Colquhoun D. 1992. Activation of NMDA receptors by *L*-glutamate in cells dissociated from adult rat hippocampus. *J. Physiol.* 456:143–79

52. Gibb AJ, Kojima H, Carr JA, Colquhoun D. 1990. Expression of cloned receptor subunits produces multiple receptors. *Proc. R. Soc. London Ser. B* 242:108–12

53. Gibb AJ, Marshall IG. 1984. Pre- and post-synaptic actions of tubocurarine and other nicotinic antagonists during repetitive stimulation at the rat neuromuscular junction. *J. Physiol.* 351:275–97

54. Gu Y, Franco A, Gardner PD, Lapsman JB, Forsayeth JR, et al. 1990. Properties of embryonic and adult muscle acetylcholine receptors transiently expressed in COS cells. *Neuron* 5:147–57

55. Head SD. 1983. Temperature and endplate currents in rat diaphragm. *J. Physiol.* 334:441–59

56. Hemmings HCJ, Nairn AC, McGuinness L, Huganir RL, Greengard P. 1989. Role of protein phosphorylation in neuronal signal transduction. *FASEB J.* 3:1583–92

57. Hess PL, Lansman JB, Tsien RW. 1984. Different modes of Ca channel gating behaviour favoured by dihydropyridine Ca agonists and antagonists. *Nature* 311:538–44

58. Imoto K, Busch C, Sakmann B, Mishina M, Konno T, et al. 1988. Rings of negatively charged amino acids determine the acetylcholine receptor channel conductance. *Nature* 335:645–48

59. Imoto K, Konno T, Nakai J, Wang F, Mishina M, et al. 1991. A ring of uncharged polar amino acids as a component of channel constriction in the nicotinic acetylcholine receptor. *FEBS Lett.* 289:193–200

60. Jackson MB. 1988. Dependence of acetylcholine receptor channel kinetics on agonist concentration in cultured mouse muscle fibres. *J. Physiol.* 397:555–83

61. Karlin A. 1993. Structure of nicotinic acetylcholine receptors. *Curr. Opin. Neurobiol.* 3:299–309

62. Katz B, Miledi R. 1973. The binding of acetylcholine to receptors and its removal from the synaptic cleft. *J. Physiol.* 231:549–74

63. Katz B, Thesleff S. 1957. A study of the 'desensitization' produced by acetylcholine at the motor end-plate. *J. Physiol.* 138:63–80

64. Kuffler SW, Yoshikami D. 1975. The number of transmitter molecules in a quantum: estimate from iontophoretic application of acetylcholine at the neuromuscular synapse. *J. Physiol.* 251(2):465

65. Kuhlmann J, Okonjo KO, Maelicke A. 1991. Desensitization is a property of the cholinergic binding region of the nicotinic acetylcholine receptor, not of the receptor integral channel. *FEBS Lett.* 279:261–68

66. Kullberg R, Owens JL, Camacho P, Mandel G, Brehm P. 1990. Multiple conductance classes of mouse nicotinic acetylcholine receptors expressed in *Xenopus* oocytes. *Proc. Natl. Acad Sci. USA* 87:2067–71

67. Kurosaki T, Fukuda K, Konno T, Mori Y, Tanaka K, et al. 1987. Functional properties of nicotinic acetylcholine receptor subunits expressed in various combinations. *FEBS Lett.* 214:253–58

68. Labarca P, Lindstrom J, Montal M.

1984. Acetylcholine receptor in planar lipid bilayers: characterization of the channel properties of the purified nicotinic acetylcholine receptor from *Torpedo californica* reconstituted in planar lipid bilayers. *J. Gen. Physiol.* 83:473–96

69. Land BR, Harris WV, Salpeter EE, Salpeter MM. 1984. Diffusion and binding constants for acetylcholine derived from the falling phase of miniature endplate currents. *Proc. Natl. Acad. Sci. USA* 81:1594–98

70. Land BR, Salpeter EE, Salpeter MM. 1980. Acetylcholine receptor site density affects the rising phase of miniature endplate currents. *Proc. Natl. Acad Sci. USA* 77:373640

71. Land BR, Salpeter EE, Salpeter MM. 1981. Kinetic parameters for acetylcholine interaction in intact neuromuscular junction. *Proc. Natl. Acad. Sci. USA* 78:7200–4

72. Lester RAJ, Dani JA. 1994. Time-dependent changes in central nicotinic acetylcholine channel kinetics in excised patches. *Neuropharmacology* 33:27–34

73. Lingle CJ, Maconochie D, Steinbach J-H. 1992. Activation of skeletal muscle nicotinic acetylcholine receptors. *J. Membr. Biol.* 126:195–217

74. Liu Y, Dilger JP. 1991. Opening rate of acetylcholine receptor channels. *Biophys. J.* 60:424–32

75. Lu B, Fu W-M, Greengard P, Poo M-M. 1993. Calcitonin gene-related peptide potentiates synaptic responses at developing neuromuscular junction. *Nature* 363:76–79

76. Machonochie DJ, Knight DE. 1989. A method for making solution changes in the sub-millisecond range at the tip of a patch pipette. *Pflügers Arch.* 414:589–96

77. Madsen BW, Edeson RO. 1988. Understanding receptor kinetics has some way to go. Nicotinic receptors and the elusive beta. *Trends Pharmacol. Sci.* 9:315–16

78. Madsen BW, Edeson RO, Lam HS, Milne RK. 1984. Numerical simulation of miniature endplate currents. *Neurosci. Lett.* 48:67–74

79. Madsen BW, Edeson RO, Milne RK. 1987. Neurotransmission parameters estimated from miniature endplate current growth phase. *Brain Res.* 402:387–92

80. Magleby KL, Pallotta BS. 1981. A study of desensitization of acetylcholine receptors using nerve-released transmitter from the frog. *J. Physiol.* 316:225–50

81. Magleby KL, Stevens CF. 1972. A quantitative description of end-plate currents. *J. Physiol.* 223:173–97

82. Marshall CG, Ogden DC, Colquhoun D. 1991. Activation of ion channels in the frog end-plate by several analogues of acetylcholine. *J. Physiol.* 433:73–93

83. Mathie A, Cull-Candy SG, Colquhoun D. 1991. Conductance and kinetic properties of single nicotinic acetylcholine receptor channels in rat sympathetic neurones. *J. Physiol.* 439:717–50

84. Matthews-Bellinger JA, Salpeter MM. 1983. Fine structural distribution of acetylcholine receptors at developing mouse neuromuscular junctions. *J. Neurosci.* 3:644–57

85. Miles K, Huganir RL. 1988. Regulation of nicotinic acetylcholine receptors by protein phosphorylation. *Mol. Neurobiol.* 2:91–124

86. Miller C. 1989. Genetic manipulation of ion channels: a new approach to structure and mechanism. *Neuron* 2:1192–205

87. Mishina M, Takai T, Imoto K, Noda M, Takahashi T, et al. 1986. Molecular distinction between fetal and adult forms of muscle acetylcholine receptor. *Nature* 321:406–11

88. Mulrine NK, Ogden DC. 1988. The equilibrium open probability of nicotinic ion channels at the rat neuromuscular junction. *J. Physiol.* 401:95P

89. Naranjo D, Brehm P. 1993. Modal shifts in acetylcholine receptor channel gating confer subunit-dependent desensitization. *Science* 260:1811–14

90. Neubig R, Cohen JB. 1980. Equilibrium binding of [^{3}-H]-tubocurarine and [^{3}-H]-acetylcholine by *Torpedo* postsynaptic membranes: stoichiometry and ligand interactions. *Biochemistry* 28:5464–75

91. Ochoa ELM, Chattopadhyay A, McNamee MG. 1989. Desensitization of the nicotinic acetylcholine receptor: molecular mechanisms and effect of modulators. *Cell. Mol. Neurobiol.* 9:141–78

92. Ogden DC, Colquhoun D. 1983. The efficacy of agonists at the frog neuromuscular junction studied with single channel recording. *Pflügers Arch.* 399:246–48

93. Patlak J, Ortiz M. 1989. Kinetic diversity of sodium channel bursts in frog skeletal muscle. *J. Gen. Physiol.* 94:279–301

94. Pedersen SE, Cohen JB. 1990. d-Tubocurarine binding sites are located at alpha-gamma and alpha-delta subunit

interfaces of the nicotinic acetylcholine receptor. *Proc. Natl. Acad. Sci. USA* 87:2785–89

95. Pennefather P, Quastel DMJ. 1982. Fast desensitization of the nicotinic receptor at the mouse neuromuscular junction. *Br. J. Pharmacol.* 77:395–404

96. Pennefather P, Quastel DMJ. 1981. Relation between subsynaptic receptor blockade and response to quantal transmitter at the mouse neuromuscular junction. *J. Gen. Physiol.* 78:313–44

97. Popot J-L, Cartaud J, Changeux J-P. 1981. Reconstitution of a functional acetylcholine receptor. Incorporation into artificial lipid vesicles and pharmacology of the agonist-controlled permeability changes. *Eur. J. Biochem.* 118: 203–14

98. Prinz H, Maelicke A. 1983. Interaction of cholinergic ligands with the purified acetylcholine receptor protein. I. Equilibrium binding studies. *J. Biol. Chem.* 258:10263–71

99. Qu Z, Mortiz E, Huganir RL. 1990. Regulation of tyrosine phosphorylation of the nicotinic acetylcholine receptor at the rat neuromuscular junction. *Neuron* 2:367–78

100. Sakmann B. 1992. Elementary steps in synaptic transmission revealed by currents through single ion channels. *Neuron* 8:613–29

101. Sakmann B, Patlak J, Neher E. 1980. Single acetylcholine-activated channels show burst-kinetics in presence of desensitizing concentrations of agonist. *Nature* 286:71–73

102. Schoepfer R, Monyer H, Sommer B, Wisden W, et al. 1994. Molecular biology of glutamate receptors. *Prog. Neurobiol.* 42:353–57

103. Siara J, Ruppersberg JP, Rudel R. 1990. Human nicotinic acetylcholine receptor: the influence of second messengers on activation and desensitization. *Pflügers Arch.* 415:701–6

104. Sine SM. 1993. Molecular dissection of subunit interfaces in the acetylcholine receptor: identification of residues that determine curare selectivity. *Proc. Natl. Acad Sci. USA* 90:9436–40

105. Sine SM. 1988. Functional properties of human skeletal muscle acetylcholine receptors expressed by the TE671 cell line. *J. Biol. Chem.* 263:18052–62

106. Sine SM, Claudio T. 1991. Gamma and delta subunits regulate the affinity and the cooperativity of ligand binding to the acetylcholine receptor. *J. Biol. Chem.* 266:19369–77

107. Sine SM, Claudio T. 1991. Stable expression of the mouse nicotinic acetyl-choline receptor in mouse fibroblasts. Comparison of receptors in native and transfected cells. *J. Biol. Chem.* 266: 13679–89

108. Sine SM, Claudio T, Sigworth FJ. 1990. Activation of *Torpedo* acetylcholine receptors expressed in mouse fibroblasts: single channel current kinetics reveal distinct agonist binding affinities. *J. Gen. Physiol.* 96:395–437

109. Sine SM, Steinbach JH. 1984. Activation of a nicotinic acetylcholine receptor. *Biophys. J.* 45:175–85

110. Sine SM, Steinbach JH. 1986. Activation of acetylcholine receptors on clonal mammalian BC3H-1 cells by low concentrations of agonist. *J. Physiol.* 373: 129–62

111. Sine SM, Steinbach JH. 1987. Activation of acetylcholine receptors on clonal mammalian BC3H-1 cells by high concentrations of agonist. *J. Physiol.* 385: 325–59

112. Sine SM, Taylor P. 1981. Relationship between reversible antagonist occupancy and the functional capacity of the acetylcholine receptor. *J. Biol. Chem.* 256:6692–99

113. Steinbach JH. 1989. Structural and functional diversity in vertebrate skeletal muscle nicotinic acetylcholine receptors. *Annu. Rev. Physiol.* 51:353–65

114. Steinbach JH, Zempel J. 1987. What does phosphorylation do for the nicotinic acetylcholine receptor? *Trends Neurosci.* 10:61–64

115. Swope SL, Moss SJ, Blackstone CD, Huganir RL. 1992. Phosphorylation of ligand-gated ion channels: a possible mode of synaptic plasticity. *FASEB J.* 6:2514–23

116. Unwin N. 1993. Neurotransmitter action: opening of ligand-gated ion channels. *Neuron* 10(Suppl. 1):31–41

117. Unwin N. 1993. Nicotinic acetylcholine receptor at 9A resolution. *J. Mol. Biol.* 229:1101–24

118. Unwin N, Toyoshima C, Kubalek E. 1988. Arrangement of the acetylcholine receptor subunits in the resting and desensitized states, determined by cryo-electron microscopy of crystallized *Torpedo* postsynaptic membranes. *J. Cell Biol.* 107:1123–38

119. Villarroel A, Herlitze S, Koenen M, Sakmann B. 1991. Location of a threonine residue in the α-subunit M2 transmembrane segment that determines the ion flow through the acetylcholine receptor channel. *Proc. R. Soc. London Ser. B* 243:69–74

120. Villarroel A, Herlitze S, Witzemann V, Koenen M, Sakmann B. 1992. Asym-

metry of the rat acetylcholine receptor subunits in the narrow region of the pore. *Proc. R. Soc. London Ser. B* 249: 317–24

121. Villarroel A, Sakmann B. 1992. Threonine in the selectivity filter of the ace-tylcholine receptor channel. *Biophys. J.* 62:196–208

122. Wagoner PK, Pallotta BS. 1988. Modulation of acetylcholine receptor desensitization by forskolin is independent of cAMP. *Science* 240:1655–57

Annu. Rev. Physiol. 1995. 57:495–519

MECHANISMS OF ACTIVATION OF GLUTAMATE RECEPTORS AND THE TIME COURSE OF EXCITATORY SYNAPTIC CURRENTS

B. Edmonds, A. J. Gibb, and D. Colquhoun

Department of Pharmacology and Wellcome Laboratory for Molecular Pharmacology, University College London, Gower Street, London WC1E 6BT, England

KEY WORDS: NMDA receptors, synaptic currents

INTRODUCTION

Excitatory synaptic currents generated by glutamate receptor activation mediate rapid transmission between neurons in the central nervous system. The review on Nicotinic Acetylcholine Receptors (see B Edmonds et al, this volume) deals with muscle-type nicotinic receptors and with some general principles and experimental methods that are germane to the study of synaptic currents. Here we discuss glutamate receptors. The aims are to (*a*) summarize recent work concerning the structure of these classes of receptors, (*b*) address current understanding of the mechanisms underlying activation of glutamate receptors, and (*c*) discuss present views of the role of channel gating in determining the time course of synaptic currents.

At glutamatergic synapses, the situation is more complicated than at the endplate because of at least two factors. First, glutamate usually acts on two distinct classes of receptors (4, 36, 59, 101, 112): a non-N-methyl-D-aspartate (non-NMDA) receptor characterized by insensitivity to the synthetic agonist N-methyl-D-aspartate (NMDA), which produces a synaptic response with a rapid rate of onset and decay, similar in time course to that produced by ACh

495

at the endplate; and an NMDA receptor (sensitive to NMDA) that produces a much slower response (20, 36, 45, 67). Second, NMDA receptors are subject to regulation at a number of distinct sites (see 75, for review).

NMDA RECEPTORS

The structure and function of NMDA receptors have recently been reviewed in detail (47, 75, 97). NMDA receptors present at glutamatergic synapses mediate synaptic currents that rise slowly to a peak (~20 ms) and then decay bi-exponentially with time constants of around 40 and 200 ms that are approximately equal in amplitude (45, 67, 112). This remarkably slow time course is quite different from that for primary fast transmitter receptors like nicotinic and non-NMDA receptors. When the membrane potential is near the resting potential of the cell, current flow through NMDA receptors is rapidly blocked by Mg^{2+} ions entering the pore from the extracellular solution (2, 56, 74, 82). Thus NMDA receptors can be activated, but yield no detectable current. The Mg^{2+} block is voltage dependent, so postsynaptic depolarization resulting from opening of non-NMDA receptors, for example, can relieve the block and allow NMDA receptors to conduct. NMDA receptor channels have a high calcium permeability, around 7% of inward current being carried by Ca^{2+} ions (96) (although muscle and neuronal nicotinic receptors, as well as some non-NMDA receptors, also have substantial Ca^{2+} permeability; 1, 132, and see below). An important consequence of this characteristic is that NMDA receptor activation can lead to the induction of long-lasting changes in synaptic strength, supposedly via an increase in intracellular Ca^{2+} in the postsynaptic neuron, and to cell death (reviewed by 11, 126).

Structure of NMDA Receptors

The molecular structure of NMDA receptors is thought to be similar to that of the nicotinic acetlycholine receptor (AChR) in spite of the lack of homology between the two groups (47). However, unlike the AChR, the identity and precise arrangement of the subunits of the native NMDA receptors are not yet known. The first NMDA receptor subunit to be cloned and sequenced by Nakanishi and co-workers (80) was the NR1 subunit (also referred to as ζ1, in mouse; 131). The amino acid sequence of this subunit indicated that it was similar in size to the non-NMDA receptors, but much larger than other ligand-gated ion channels cloned previously. This led to the cloning of four more NMDA receptor subunits (NR2A-D) (51, 53, 64, 78), also referred to in mouse as ε1-ε4 (76). The NR2 subunits have only about 25% sequence homology with NR1 but have around 50% homology with each other. The NR1 subunit gives only small responses when expressed alone, and none of the NR2 subunits forms functional receptors when expressed alone. Much larger responses are obtained when the NR1 subunit is expressed with one of the NR2 subunits, and it is likely that native NMDA receptors are hetero-oligomers, made from combinations of NR1 with one or more of the NR2 subunits (98).

The properties of recombinant NMDA receptors (kinetics, single-channel conductance, and sensitivity to Mg^{2+} block and to potentiation by glycine) depend on the subunit composition and alternative splicing of NR1 (see 47, 75, 97 for reviews).

Some general conclusions regarding the relationship between the structure and function of NMDA receptors can be drawn. The results of mutagenesis studies on the M2 region show that the asparagine residue in the position analogous to the Q/R site of the non-NMDA receptors has a critical role in determining Ca^{2+} permeability and Mg^{2+} block (93, 133). It has also been shown that receptors formed from NR1/NR2A and from NR1/NR2B subunits have 50 pS conductance channels with a 40 pS subconductance, whereas NR1/NR2C receptors have 38 pS channels with a 19 pS subconductance level (110) (these conductances are for 1 mM external Ca^{2+}; their values are dependent on the Ca^{2+} concentration; 38). There is a close quantitative agreement between the conductance characteristics of these recombinant channels and those of native channels in various cell types (110, 111). The expression of these subunits in cerebellar granule cells changes during development (125), and this correlates well with the conductance of NMDA channels that are observed at different ages in the developing rat cerebellum (33). The kinetic properties, like the conductance properties, are similar for recombinant NR1/NR2A and NR1/NR2B channels, but different from those of NR1/NR2C channels (109; P Béhé et al, in preparation). Unlike the case with nicotinic receptors (see B Edmonds et al, Nicotinic Acetylcholine Receptors, this volume), results so far suggest that expression in both oocytes and HEK293 cells can reproduce the properties of native NMDA channels fairly accurately (111).

NMDA Receptor Single-Channel Currents

Results from studies of excitatory synaptic transmission raise several important questions about the single-channel behavior underlying the component of the synaptic current mediated by NMDA receptors.

In particular it is of interest to know (a) the durations of the openings and closings that make up the activation, (b) the duration of the closed periods that occur between glutamate binding and first opening of the channel (the first latencies), (c) the fraction of channels that are open at the peak of the synaptic current ($P_{o(peak)}$), (d) the fraction of time that the receptor-channel is open during each activation ($P_{o(act)}$), and (e) whether there are any correlations in the data that could result in the grouping of openings or closings at particular places within an activation (e.g. are there always long openings at the beginning of an activation?).

Each of these points is of interest not only for understanding how the synaptic current is produced, but also for understanding how drugs like dizolcipine (MK-801), ketamine, or phencyclidine (which block the NMDA receptor channel; 72) affect the amplitude and time course of NMDA synaptic currents in the brain.

Early single-channel recordings of NMDA receptor currents (82) demonstrated that NMDA receptor activation produced openings of around 4 ms in duration. These were grouped together as bursts of two or three openings separated by short gaps of less than 1 ms duration (27, 48, 55). However, these experiments were performed before the requirement for glycine (57) as a co-agonist (63) on the NMDA receptor was known. Consequently, the glycine concentration was not controlled in these experiments, and relatively high agonist concentrations (often 30–100 M) were needed to generate a measurable amount of channel activity.

Our efforts to identify the structure of NMDA receptor activations at the single-channel level (38, 39) were based on the strategy used at the neuromuscular junction by Colquhoun & Sakmann (26). This strategy employed very low concentrations of agonist (less than 100 nM) to activate the receptor. This would make the frequency of receptor activations so low that it would be immediately obvious where each group of openings (due to a single receptor activation) occurred in the data record because these groups of openings would be separated by very long closed periods.

The results of experiments with low glutamate concentrations indicate that the distribution of channel shut times contains a large number of relatively long closed periods (mean time constant = 7.6 ms). Their duration was not dependent on either the glutamate (39) or the glycine concentrations (40), thus they must represent closed periods within single receptor activations. The presence of these closed periods means that, unlike other ligand-gated channels with similar open times, the NMDA receptor channel is closed for a significant proportion of the time that the agonist is on the receptor. In the terminology of classical pharmacology, glutamate has the characteristics of a partial agonist when activating the NMDA receptor.

NMDA Channel Closed Times

Distributions of NMDA channel closed times were found to be fitted best with five exponential components (29, 38) with mean time constants (and mean relative areas) of $\tau_1 = 68$ μs (38%), $\tau_2 = 0.72$ ms (12%), $\tau_3 = 7.6$ ms (17%), $\tau_4 = 137$ ms (22%), and $\tau_5 = 922$ ms (18%) (38). This suggests that the NMDA receptor can enter a minimum of five different shut states (23). These results were obtained in recordings from dissociated adult rat hippocampal cells (see also 69), and similar results have been obtained from hippocampal CA1 cells in slices (39) and hippocampal granule cells (29, 40).

At present there is little evidence to suggest what physical interpretation can be placed on these proposed shut states. There are clearly at least three shut states (corresponding to τ_1, τ_2, and τ_3 of the shut-time distribution) that represent closed states where the receptor is fully liganded. In addition, it would be expected that there must be shut states corresponding to receptors occupied or unoccupied with either one or two molecules of glutamate or glycine (19), and one or more desensitized states (73, 95).

The fourth component of the shut-time distribution (τ_4) is of interest in relation to possible desensitized states because Lester & Jahr (68) and Clements & Westbrook (19) have proposed that the receptor may enter a short-lived desensitized state (lifetime around 50 ms) during the synaptic current. Clear evidence for a dependence of τ_4 on the glutamate or glycine concentration was not found (39, 40); however, Edmonds & Colquhoun (29) found similar values for τ_4 under conditions where activations were even farther apart (τ_5 up to 10,000 ms) than in the earlier experiments. Therefore it could be that this component of the shut-time distribution represents periods when the channel is closed with glutamate and glycine bound to the receptor. Whether such a state or the receptor is referred to as a desensitized state or just a long-lived shut state is purely a matter of terminology, at least until such time as something is discovered about the physical nature of desensitization.

NMDA Channel Open Times

Distributions of apparent open times were fitted with the sum of three exponential components (38). These had mean time constants (and relative areas) of $\tau_1 = 87$ μs (51%), $\tau_2 = 0.91$ ms (31%), and $\tau_3 = 4.72$ ms (18%). The fastest of these three components represents openings that, despite their high frequency, are so short that they will carry only about 3% of the steady-state NMDA current. In contrast, openings underlying the slow component (τ_3) will carry more than 70% of NMDA current. In recordings where the shortest open time that can be detected is 100 μs or greater, it is often difficult to detect clearly the fastest component of the open times. In these cases, open-time distributions are often adequately fitted with two exponential components.

These results suggest that the NMDA receptor can exist in at least three distinct open states. These are probably all fully liganded because Clements & Westbrook (19) have argued that mono-liganded openings of the NMDA receptor are likely to be very rare, and we also have no compelling evidence from low agonist concentration experiments that mono-liganded openings occur (38). Concentration-response curves for glycine (73) and glutamate (88) and analysis of antagonist action at NMDA receptors (7) also suggest that the receptor has at least two binding sites for both glutamate and for glycine. Therefore it is likely that at least two glutamate and two glycine molecules must be bound to produce efficient activation.

In addition to the three open states predicted from open-time distributions, NMDA channel amplitude distributions show that the receptor channel has at least two different conductance levels, of 50 and 40 pS (in 1 mM external calcium), with about 80% of openings at the 50 pS level. Distributions of 40 and 50pS openings are best fitted with at least two exponential components, which suggests a minimum of four open states for the NMDA receptor.

NMDA Receptor Desensitization

Desensitization of the NMDA receptor is unique in that it was found to be reversed by micromolar concentrations of the co-agonist glycine (6, 73). However, this effect is more complicated than first thought. The initial discovery of the potentiating effect of glycine (57) suggested that glycine caused an increase in the frequency of receptor activations by glutamate (see also 40). With subsequent higher resolution studies in isolated patches or in small cells, no influence of glycine on NMDA receptor desensitization was evident (94), and it became apparent that there was a fundamental difference in the action of glycine at receptors in isolated membrane patches compared with those in relatively undisturbed cells. This question was clearly resolved only by the elegant experiments of Sather et al (94) who demonstrated, by use of their 'nucleated patch' technique, that there is a change in the properties of the NMDA receptor desensitization following patch formation and that the speed of this change was related to the size of the patch or cell under investigation. Following formation of the whole-cell recording configuration, NMDA receptor desensitization in the large nucleated patch gradually becomes glycine-insensitive over a period of a few minutes, and at the same time desensitization becomes faster (the time constant decreasing from over 500 ms to below 100 ms with 300 μM glutamate; 94). In contrast, following formation of an outside-out patch, there is an almost immediate speeding of desensitization and loss of glycine sensitivity (similar speeding of desensitization has also been found for some nicotinic receptors; see B Edmonds, Nicotinic Acetylcholine Receptors, this volume). It is intriguing that following loss of glycine-sensitive desensitization, the receptor response is still potentiated by glycine (as originally demonstrated by Johnson & Ascher; 57), and the EC_{50} for this effect is very close to that for reversal of desensitization (73).

The obvious questions these results raise are: What changes does the receptor undergo following patch formation? Is there a phosphorylation and dephosphorylation mechanism active within the patch that could underlie these effects? Attempts to test these ideas thus far have given negative results. For example, although inclusion of Mg-ATP in the pipette solution can prevent a slow rundown of NMDA responses (71), ATP does not prevent the development of glycine-insensitive desensitization (95). Nor does the inclusion of G protein activators in the pipette solution influence events (95). As for the nicotinic and non-NMDA receptors, unsolved problems concerning desensitization have given rise to much work and some controversy.

Identifying NMDA Receptor Activations

Activations defined as including gaps underlying the first three components of the shut-time distribution were identified at low agonist concentrations, and we refer to these as clusters of channel openings. As mentioned above, the evidence that the first three shut-time components represent gaps within activations is convincing because τ_3 of the shut-time distribution is not dependent on either the glutamate or the glycine concentration (39, 40). Distributions of the length of these clusters of channel openings were fitted with three exponential components (38) with mean time constants (and relative areas) of $\tau_1 = 88$ μs (45%), $\tau_2 = 3.4$ ms (25%), and $\tau_3 = 32$ ms (30%).

Superclusters of channel openings were identified in a way analogous to that used to identify clusters, assuming that the first four shut-time components represent gaps within activations. Distributions of the length of superclusters of channel openings were fitted with three exponential components (38) with mean time constants (and relative areas) of $\tau_1 = 0.16$ ms (34%), $\tau_2 = 4$ ms (16%), and $\tau_3 = 166$ ms (51%). These results can be compared to those of Edmonds & Colquhoun (29) and Lieberman & Mody (69) who found superclusters of similar length and channel open probability (P_{open}). The P_{open} during clusters was 0.62 ± 0.11, whereas the supercluster P_{open} was 0.2 ± 0.05. These values are surprisingly low because the P_{open} during acetylcholine receptor channel activations is about 0.99 (25, 26). The supercluster P_{open} is interesting in relation to the estimate of the channel P_{open} at the peak of the NMDA excitatory postsynaptic current (EPSC) ($P_{o(peak)}$) of 0.28 made by Jahr (54).

Probability of a Channel Being Open

The P_{open} during an activation is easily determined because it can be measured directly from inspection of a single-channel data record (once activations have been defined). However, for channels with a relatively low P_{open} during activation and relatively long first latencies, the $P_{o(peak)}$ (the probability of a channel being open at the peak of the EPSC) may not be the same as the P_{open}. Furthermore, individual activations following a brief agonist pulse may, because of correlations, have a structure different from those recorded under low concentration equilibrium conditions (see B Edmonds et al, Nicotinic Acetlycholine Receptors, this volume; 21). Yet the $P_{o(peak)}$ is the measure most relevant to synaptic transmission because this, along with the number of channels occupied by agonist during synaptic transmission and the single-channel conductance, will determine the peak amplitude of the NMDA EPSC. The $P_{o(peak)}$ clearly depends on the P_{open} during the activation, the length of the activation, and the length of the first latencies, but there is no simple relationship between them (see B Edmonds et al, Nicotinic Acetlycholine Receptors, this volume; 21), so it will not be possible to predict the $P_{o(peak)}$ until the full activation mechanism for the NMDA receptor is known.

An estimate of the $P_{o(peak)}$ for NMDA receptors in cultured hippocampal cells was first made by Jahr (54), who used MK-801 as a tool to estimate $P_{o(peak)}$ from outside-out patch responses to brief applications of glutamate in the presence or absence of the drug. As mentioned above, the estimate is similar to that of the supercluster P_{open} measured by Gibb & Colquhoun (38) and by Lieberman & Mody (69). However, Jahr's estimate of $P_{o(peak)}$ must be regarded as approximate because it was determined indirectly using the assumption that open channel block by MK-801 is rapid enough to block all channels as soon as they open. In addition, it is likely that the P_{open} (and so potentially the $P_{o(peak)}$) of NMDA receptors is higher in outside-out patches than in the undisturbed cell (18). Thus the results of Jahr (54) may not be directly applicable to the NMDA synaptic current, despite the excellent agreement between the time course of the synaptic current and the response of NMDA receptors in outside-out patches to brief applications of glutamate (67).

These results are relevant to considerations of the number of NMDA receptors present at individual synaptic connections. The NMDA component of the miniature excitatory postsynaptic current (mEPSC) is small, resulting from activation of only a few NMDA receptors (4, 101), and yet the density of NMDA receptors is often extremely high in outside-out patches taken from the cell soma. These observations suggest that either NMDA receptors are actively excluded from the sub-synaptic membrane, or that most NMDA receptors at the synapse are inactive. In addition, studies of the proton block of NMDA receptors (118, 119) show that at pH 7.3, 50% of NMDA receptors are blocked by protons. Could it be that during synaptic transmission there is a transient acidification of the synaptic cleft (16) resulting in a substantially greater inhibition of the NMDA response that could account for the surprisingly small size of the NMDA component of the mEPSC?

Correlations in NMDA Channel Gating

Correlations arise in single-channel data because the experimenter can generally only 'see' two states of the channel: open or closed. There may be several closed or open states that are experimentally indistinguishable. Fredkin et al (37) described how this situation generates correlations in the data, and how the presence of these correlations can be used to make inferences about the connections between states of the receptor channel (see e.g. 10). Their work was extended to bursts of openings by Colquhoun & Hawkes (22; see also 21).

Clear correlations are evident in recordings of NMDA channel activity (38). Given the complexity of the open- and shut-time distributions described above, the presence of correlations is not entirely surprising; correlations may occur only if there are at least two shut states and two open states (37). However, compared with endplate AChR data (26), the correlations in the NMDA receptor data are surprisingly strong. A clear positive correlation is observed between the duration of adjacent openings ($r = 0.12 \pm 0.01$) and also adjacent closings ($r = 0.11 \pm 0.01$), whereas there is a clear negative correlation between adjacent openings and closings ($r = -0.056 \pm 0.01$) (38). It is also of interest that there is a correlation between the durations of adjacent clusters ($r = 0.12 \pm 0.017$) (for interpretation, see 22). This latter result supports the evidence that the superclusters, described above, rather than the clusters, may represent single-receptor activations because individual receptor activations should be entirely independent of each other and thus not correlated (if the channel returns to a unique resting state between activations). These correlations are of interest with respect to understanding the generation of the NMDA EPSC (see below, and B Edmonds et al, Nicoty Acetycholine Receptors, this volume).

A Mechanism for the NMDA Receptor Activation

It is clear that if it were possible to define a kinetic mechanism describing most of the known phenomena regarding NMDA receptors (at least to the accuracy achieved by the nicotinic receptor mechanism), it would do much to clarify their behavior. This has not been achieved, but the prospects look promising. The development of exact corrections for missed brief events (41) has allowed maximum likelihood fitting methods to be developed that (a) allow the mechanism itself to be fitted directly (rather than fitting empirical exponentials etc); (b) allow the simultaneous fit of all available data, including non-stationary results (e.g. first latencies) as well as equilibrium single-channel data; and (c) take full account of correlational information (21, 41).

Factors Controlling the Time Course of NMDA Synaptic Currents

In the late 1980s, estimates from noise analysis, or from burst length measurements (2, 27, 48), suggested that the duration of the NMDA receptor activation would be in the range of 10 to 20 ms; much shorter than the synaptic current decay. Two possibilities were advanced to explain the slowness of the decay of the NMDA current.

1. The decay arose from the prolonged presence of a low concentration of glutamate in the synaptic cleft (73). Because of the relatively high apparent (macroscopic) affinity of glutamate for NMDA receptors (85), and its low EC_{50} (e.g. 2–3 μM; 88), it was suggested that a low concentration of

glutamate could produce repeated NMDA receptor activations and thereby generate a slow synaptic current (73).

2. The decay was generated by the kinetic properties of the NMDA receptor itself. This hypothesis was elegantly confirmed by Lester et al (67) who demonstrated that the time course of the synaptic current in hippocampal cell cultures was not altered by rapid application of a competitive antagonist during the NMDA EPSC decay. Thus there is little if any rebinding of glutamate during the synaptic current. Equivalent experiments on synaptic connections in brain slices would be extremely difficult and have not, so far, been reported. However, a conclusion similar to that of Lester et al (67) was reached in experiments on NMDA synaptic currents in hippocampal slices (45). This conclusion no longer seems surprising in view of the evidence that the transmitter concentration may decline rapidly, even relative to the fast non-NMDA receptor–mediated currents (see below).

One possibility is that the length of individual channel activations might be sufficient to explain the slow decay of the NMDA component of the synaptic current. If this were so, NMDA receptor activations aligned on their first opening, to give the waveform of $P(t_1)$ (see Equation 2 in B Edmonds et al, Nicotinic Acetylcholine Receptors, this volume), would decay slowly and reflect the time course of decay of the NMDA component of the synaptic current. However, $P(t_1)$ determined in this way actually shows a decay that is mostly fast (29); the time constant of the decay of the major amplitude component is only about 5 ms, far too brief to account even for the faster (~40 ms) decay time constant reported for the synaptic current. The implication is that the slow phase of synaptic currents mediated by glutamate arises primarily from the long average latency between binding of glutamate to the NMDA receptor and first opening of the channel (29). However, attempts to measure the latencies directly are made difficult by the presence of multiple channels in the patch.

As an alternative to measuring the latencies directly, Jahr (54) determined an approximation to the first latency distribution by looking at the integral of the patch current in the presence of a relatively high concentration of MK-801, using the assumption that every channel would be blocked as soon as it opened. This approximation is really a latency to block by MK-801, but should approach the first latency distribution as the blocker concentration increases. Surprisingly, this approach suggests a mean first latency on the order of 20–30 ms, much shorter than that estimated by Edmonds & Colquhoun (29). Apart from differences in preparations between the two studies, it is possible that the low-concentration activations used by Edmonds & Colquhoun to deconvolve the first latency distributions are different from those that will occur at high concentrations of glutamate and glycine. However, preliminary results suggest that the latencies for NMDA channels from hippocampal granule cells are long (B Edmonds, unpublished data; illustrated in 21).

The Rising Phase of the NMDA Component of the Synaptic Current

The NMDA EPSC rises over a slow time course to reach a peak in 10 to 20 ms (45, 67). Given that NMDA receptors activate slowly, relative to non-NMDA receptors, it is likely that when a postsynaptic potential is generated in a dendritic spine, there will be little if any current flow through NMDA receptors because they do not activate fast enough and will be blocked by Mg^{2+} as soon as the spine repolarizes. However, once activated, if the same synapse is stimulated again while the receptors are still in the activated but blocked state (within the length of the activation), then substantial inward current through the NMDA receptors may result because the time required for Mg^{2+} unblock is very fast. This effect has been demonstrated at the Schaffer collateral-CA1 cell synapse in the hippocampus (20), where the contribution of the NMDA component to the postsynaptic depolarization was seen to increase with successive stimuli in a high frequency train. In addition to this mechanism, back-propagation of action potentials from the cell soma (113) provides additional inward current (and Ca^{2+} influx) through NMDA channels (107).

Phosphorylation of the NMDA Receptor

NMDA receptor subunits have consensus sequences for phosphorylation by protein kinases, and these are regulated by alternative splicing (28, 116). However, until recently, it was not clear whether phosphorylation of these sites could influence NMDA receptor activation. Three recent papers (69, 123, 124) demonstrate that phosphorylation by protein tyrosine kinase (PTK) can increase NMDA receptor activation, whereas protein phosphatases 1 and 2A decrease receptor activation in both whole-cell recordings and in isolated patches, which suggests that the kinase and the Ca-activated phosphatase are membrane bound and close to the receptor. Analysis of single-channel recordings suggests that phosphorylation increases P_{open} within clusters (69, 123) and prolongs receptor activation (69). PTK phosphorylation was suggested (69) not to affect Mg^{2+} block of the NMDA receptor channel. However, attempts to remove residual Mg with EDTA, in the presence of 1.8mM Ca, were not successful probably because Ca displaces Mg from EDTA. In contrast, protein kinase C (PKC) activation has been shown to reduce Mg^{2+} block of NMDA receptors (15), and intriguingly, Sigel et al (99) found that responses of recombinant NR1/NR2A receptors, modified to remove consensus sites for PKC phosphorylation, can still be potentiated by PKC activators. Possibly PKT or PKC phosphorylation underlies the potentiation of NMDA responses produced following long-term potentiation (3) or metabotropic glutamate receptor activation (83), but the physiological role, if any, of phosphorylation remains a matter of (frequent) speculation.

NON-NMDA RECEPTORS

Fast transmission of nerve impulses at most synapses in the CNS occurs by activation of non-NMDA receptors in response to synaptically released glutamate. The non-NMDA component of the synaptic current typically rises in less than 1 ms and decays with a time constant of between 0.2 and 8 ms (35, 36, 45, 70, 81, 101, 112). The non-NMDA-mediated postsynaptic current is fast and functionally similar to current arising from activation of AChRs at the endplate.

Structure of Non-NMDA Receptors

Non-NMDA receptors exist as two distinct subclasses of receptors, referred to as AMPA-preferring receptors and kainate-preferring receptors. The present classification arises from the homology of cloned subunits for the receptor: a group of four subunits, GluR1–4 (or GluRA-D) comprise the AMPA receptor subunits (13, 61), and another group consisting of GluR5–7 (8, 9, 32, 79, 103) in addition to KA-1 and KA-2 (42, 92, 127) comprise the kainate receptor subunits (see 34, 47, 106, 128 for reviews).

Functional Properties of the Cloned Receptors

Before the cloning of non-NMDA receptor subunits, the existence of two distinct classes of non-NMDA receptors was uncertain, largely because there was no known agonist or antagonist that exhibited a high degree of selectivity for these receptors. The initial cloning of AMPA and kainate subunits provided a tentative physical basis for the distinction between the receptor classes; however, the formation of hybrid receptors from both types of subunits would obviously cloud this distinction. The results of recent studies indicate that hybrid receptors are unlikely to form, and therefore support the AMPA-kainate distinction on the receptor level (87).

At present there are two ways (reviewed in 34, 106, 128) in which AMPA and kainate receptors can be distinguished from one another (the commonly used antagonists CNQX and NBQX are not selective). The first is by comparing the size and shape of the response to prolonged applications of varying concentrations of AMPA and kainate. Kainate acts with high potency on kainate receptors and produces a strongly desensitizing response, and at lower potency on AMPA receptors, it produces only modest desensitization, but with rapid onset (89). In contrast, AMPA produces little if any response at kainate receptors and acts with high potency on AMPA receptors to yield a strongly desensitizing response (104). Also, within the AMPA-receptor subgroup, the AMPA variants yield a larger steady-state–to-peak ratio of current in response to prolonged application of glutamate than do the kainate variants (104, 108). Unfortunately, however, the behavior of receptors comprised of both AMPA and kainate subunits in a known combination has not been documented, so a simple examination of the steady-state–to-peak ratio is not a useful diagnostic tool. Secondly, one can use compounds that potentiate responses to agonists and reduce receptor desensitization either at AMPA receptors or kainate receptors. Cyclothiazide acts at AMPA receptors, but not at kainate receptors, whereas the lectin concanavalin A (Con A) acts preferentially at kainate receptors (87). It has also been demonstrated that cyclothiazide, but not Con A, produces substantially greater potentiation of certain AMPA variants of recombinant receptors than do kainate variants (87). These compounds are therefore likely to be useful in identifying tentatively the types of receptors (and possibly subunits) present both in the somatic membrane and at the synapse.

Editing of the messenger RNAs encoding GluR2, GluR5, and GluR6 results in the replacement of a glutamine residue with an arginine in TM2, with a consequent reduction in the Ca^{2+} permeability of the resultant receptor and elimination of the strong inward rectification shown by other subunits (14, 46, 105; reviewed in 34, 47, 128).

Identity of the Native Receptors in the CNS

Progress in identification of the precise subunit composition of native synaptic receptors has so far been modest. Both AMPA and kainate receptor subunits are expressed in abundance in the CNS (34, 47, 77, 128); however, nearly all responses recorded from neurons in the brain have yielded largely nondesensitizing responses to kainate (62), indicating the presence of AMPA receptors, even in regions (hippocampal CA3) where kainate receptor subunit expression is high (60). Moreover, an examination of the properties of what are likely to be GluR2-containing receptors in various regions of the brain also reveals heterogeneity (see below). However, it has not yet been possible to determine with certainty the subunit composition of any native AMPA receptor (60).

Although most native AMPA receptors are largely impermeable to Ca^{2+} and therefore likely to contain the GluR2 subunit, some cultured hippocampal neurons do express Ca^{2+}-permeable receptors (50, 86). Use of the polymerase chain reaction (PCR) to identify the mRNAs present in single cells is a promising method for subunit identification; this method has shown that some cells contain mRNA for only the flop forms of GluR1 and GluR4 (12, 65).

AMPA receptors are by far the most common type of receptor observed in neurons; however, kainate receptors are also sometimes present. Kainate receptor expression (probably GluR6) has been observed in some cultured hippocampal neurons (66). The size of the kainate response was found to decline with process outgrowth, and this may be indicative of migration of kainate receptors to the distal dendrites (66). This would suggest that it may be difficult, using somatic recordings in slices, to eliminate the possibility that kainate receptors are located synaptically. In the periphery, a functional kainate receptor has been identified in some sensory neurons of the dorsal root ganglion (DRG) (49). Kainate receptors in these neurons probably represent a distinct molecular species (containing GluR5; 103); unlike the hippocampal receptors, they are activated by AMPA and do not desensitize completely in the presence of agonist (49, 66). DRG neurons do not receive synaptic input, so the function, if any, of kainate receptors on these cells is not known.

Activation and Desensitization of Non-NMDA Receptors

Most mechanistic studies of non-NMDA receptors have been made either on whole cells or on macroscopic responses recorded in patches. The low single-channel conductance typically found for these receptors has in most instances precluded a detailed analysis of their single-channel properties (however, see 129). Nevertheless, many macroscopic properties of non-NMDA receptors are now well characterized. For example, in comparison to NMDA receptors on which glutamate is a potent agonist (e.g. EC_{50} of 2.3 µM in cultured hippo-campal neurons; 88), the EC_{50} values for non-NMDA receptors are between 500 µM (88, 120) and 1 mM (62) for the peak response (cf 10–20 µM for nicotinic receptors).

The rate of deactivation of non-NMDA receptors is typically fast (0.5–3 ms at room temperature) (24, 31, 43, 44, 90, 100, 115, 120). The reported rates of deactivation of non-NMDA receptors all lie within a fairly narrow range; however, a comparison of the deactivation time course of receptors from, for example, hippocampal neurons (τ ~3 ms; 24, 115) and cerebellar granule cells (τ ~0.6 ms; 31, 100) clearly indicates heterogeneity (see Table 1). Single, non-NMDA channels (from patches giving 10, 20, and 30 pS openings) in cerebellar granule cells have a mean open time of ~0.5 ms and an average burst duration of only 0.6 ms (129). These values are consistent with a rapid deactivation time course in granule cells.

The desensitization rates are more variable than those of deactivation (see Table 2), and there is a suspicion that the desensitization rate may be inversely related to the estimated unitary conductance (43, but see 100). For example, in rat visual cortex, a small 9 pS channel present in pyramidal neurons desensitizes relatively slowly (τ = 12 ms), whereas a large 27 pS channel present in nonpyramidal, aspiny inhibitory neurons desensitizes rapidly (τ = 3.4 ms) (43). The deactivation rates are faster (2–3 ms) but similar for the two cell types (43). Results from single-channel studies on recombinant receptors are clearly necessary and may provide a structural basis for these functional differences.

Table 1 Time course of deactivation of non-NMDA receptors in patches

	Temperature (°C)	Single τ (ms)	Unitary conductance (pS)
Chick spinal cord[a]	22–26	2.5	18
Rat visual cortex[b]	?	—	—
pyramidal	—	2.8	9
aspiny inhibitory	—	1.9	27
Rat cerebellar granule cells[c]	22–24	0.63	29
Rat hippocampus[d]	?	2.9	8 and 35[e]
Rat hippocampus[f,g]	20–24	—	—
CA1	—	2.3	7.9
CA3	—	2.5	7.2
dentate gyrus	—	3.0	?
Chick cochlear nucleus[h]	22	1.2	?

[a] Trussell & Fischbach (120).
[b] Hestrin (43).
[c] Silver et al (100).
[d] Tang et al (115). Temperature is not stated, but slices were maintained at 35 °C.
[e] Duration of application is not stated so the decay time constant could reflect closing of either the high or the low conductance channels, or both.
[f] Colquhoun, et al (24); Jonas & Sakmann (60).
[g] Conductances estimated from fluctuation analysis with 30 μM AMPA.
[h] Raman & Trussel (90). Deactivation was measured at + 60 mV.

Table 2 Time course desensitization of non-NMDA receptors in patches

	Temperature (°C)	Single τ (ms)	Double τ_f (ms)	Double% τ_s (ms)	Unitary conductance (pS)
Chick spinal cord[a]	22–26	4.8	2.2	13.5	18
Rat visual cortex[b]	?	—	—	—	—
pyramidal	—	12.5	—	—	9
aspiny inhibitory	—	3.4	—	—	27
Rat cerebellar granule cells[c]	22–24	4.1	—	—	29
Rat hippocampus[d]	~20–24	3	—	—	35
Rat hippocampus[e,f]	20–24	—	—	—	—
CA1	—	9.3	—	—	7.9
CA3	—	11.3	—	—	7.2
dentate gyrus	—	9.4	—	—	—
Chick cochlear nucleus[g]	22	1.8	1.0	3.50	—
	33	—	0.6	2.6	—

[a] Trussell & Fischbach (120).
[b] Hestrin (43).
[c] Silver et al (100).
[d] Tang et al (114). Desensitization is with 100 mM quisqalate.
[e] Colquhoun et al (24); Jonas & Sakmann (60).
[f] Conductances estimated from fluctuation analysis with 30 μM AMPA.
[g] Raman & Trussell (90); Trussell et al (121).

There is no evidence to suggest that the very fast desensitization rates observed for non-NMDA receptors in outside-out patches are an artifact of patch excision (cf nicotinic receptors; 1; and NMDA receptors, above). Equally there is no good evidence that the rates are the same in intact cells.

Factors that Control the Time Course of Synaptic Currents

The non-NMDA component of synaptic currents is remarkably fast, although it is often the case that large amplitude–evoked EPSCs have a slower time course than the mEPSCs. The reasons for this are unresolved: possible explanations include asynchrony of release at different synaptic sites, and release of multiple packets or vesicles onto a single site (117), both of which could slow the time course of large amplitude–evoked EPSCs. Consequently, most efforts to identify the mechanisms underlying the time course of the non-NMDA synaptic current have focused on mEPSCs or low-amplitude evoked currents.

mEPSCs in nucleus magnocellularis of the chick at high temperature (31–35°C) have a rise time of about 100 μs and decay exponentially with a time constant just over 200 μs (121). Miniature currents recorded at room temperature in a variety of preparations also rise and decay rapidly (43, 100, 101, 120, 121). However, unlike the endplate, for which the decay time constants reported for different preparations are in a relatively narrow range, substantial variability exists in the rates of decay reported for the non-NMDA current in various preparations (see Table 3). It is therefore likely that it will be necessary to investigate each type of synapse for the mechanisms that control the form of the postsynaptic currents.

Recent studies in which both the time course of low-amplitude synaptic currents (either mEPSCs recorded in TTX or spontaneous EPSCs) and the time course of deactivation and desensitization in patches have been investigated in the same preparation suggest that in some cases the synaptic current

Table 3 Time course of the non-NMDA component of mEPSCs

	Temp. (°C)	Single τ (ms)	Double τ_f (ms)	Double τ_s (ms)	% Slow
Chick spinal cord[a]	22–26	2.0	—	—	—
Rat visual cortex[b]	?	—	—	—	—
pyramidal	—	4.6	—	—	—
aspiny inhibitory	—	2.5	—	—	—
Rat cerebellar granule cells[c]	22–24	—	0.61	3.5	18
Chick cochlear nucleus[d]	31–35	0.22	—	—	—

[a] Trussell & Fischbach (120).
[b] Hestrin (43).
[c] Silver et al (100).
[d] Trussell et al (121).

decay is governed largely by the rate of deactivation of the underlying channels (43, 44, 100). In cells of the rat visual cortex, the time course of deactivation of non-NMDA receptors in patches (τ = 2.15 ms), measured with a brief (1 ms) application of glutamate, matches the time course of decay of mEPSCs (44). In addition, the initial decay (τ = 0.61 ms) of the mEPSC in cerebellar granule cells also appears to be shaped primarily by the rate of channel deactivation (100). The fact that non-NMDA receptors from granule cells show bursts (which are open for most of the time) with a mean length close to 0.6 ms (129) suggests that, as for the endplate, the average first latency to channel opening during a synaptic current may be brief relative to the burst length (see Equations 2 and 4 in B Edmonds et al, Nicotinic Acetylcholine Receptors, this volume).

At synapses where differences in the rate of decay of mEPSCs arise from differences in the rate of receptor deactivation, the rate of removal of transmitter from the cleft must be fast relative to the rate of decay of the mEPSC. However, at some synapses, glutamate appears to persist in the cleft for a relatively long period. In this case, the time course of current decay may have a complex dependence on the rate of clearance of glutamate from the cleft, as well as the rates of channel closure and receptor desensitization during the time period over which the glutamate concentration is declining in the cleft. At the mossy fiber to CA3 pyramidal cell synapse, where EPSCs can be recorded with high resolution (58, 59), the value of the decay time constant of the EPSC is between the values found for the time constants of deactivation (τ = 2.5 ms) and desensitization (τ = 11.3 ms) of receptors isolated from the soma of CA3 neurons (24). Thus variations in the time course of synaptic currents between one synapse and another may result either from differences in the rate of deactivation of the underlying non-NMDA receptors, if the rate of transmitter removal is fast relative to the deactivation rate, or when transmitter removal occurs relatively slowly, from a combination of differences in deactivation rates, desensitization rates, and the rate of removal of transmitter. This latter effect is not surprising because, unlike the endplate where the presence of acetylcholinesterase ensures rapid removal of ACh, the rate of removal of glutamate from the synaptic cleft may have a greater dependence on diffusion and therefore may be influenced by the precise geometry of the cleft.

Desensitization and the Time Course of the Non-NMDA mEPSC

In addition to the apparent roles of deactivation and the time course of removal of glutamate from the cleft in shaping the mEPSC time course, there are also reports that show channel desensitization to be an important determinant of synaptic current decay (52, 114, 115, 120–122). This suggestion is usually based on the agreement between the time constant for decay of the synaptic current and the time constant for desensitization as measured by a prolonged application of agonist to an outside-out patch; but when is such agreement expected? Clearly agreement between these two values requires that the transmitter concentration in the cleft remains high (similar to that used for the outside-out patch) and essentially constant throughout the synaptic current. That both the rate of deactivation and the initial rate of desensitization in patches are similar to the rate of decay of the mEPSC was demonstrated in chick spinal neurons (120). It was concluded that desensitization limits the mean burst duration following synaptic activation. The fact that the synaptic current lacks the slow tail, which is present in desensitizing responses, coupled with the fact that the deactivating response to a 1 ms application of glutamate has a time course that matches the mEPSC over its entire duration, suggests that the mEPSC decay is shaped at least partly by the rate of deactivation, although substantial microscopic desensitization can occur in spite of the fact that transmitter is present only briefly (24). Without a complete model for the receptor and knowledge of the time course of glutamate in the cleft, it is not possible to say what proportion of bursts are terminated by entry into the desensitized state (122).

Many reports of a role for desensitization in terminating the synaptic current have relied upon the use of compounds that have been shown to reduce the rate of desensitization of non-NMDA receptors. For example, aniracetam slows the rate of desensitization and has been shown to prolong the time course of both evoked (52) and miniature EPSCs (115) in hippocampal neurons. Because aniracetam also slows the rate of deactivation (from 3 to 6 ms in one report; 115), this drug can not be regarded as a reliable tool to assess the contribution of desensitization to the time course of synaptic currents. Cyclothiazide, which also reduces the rate of AMPA receptor desensitization (130 and see above), gives similar problems (130). At the calyceal synapse of the auditory nucleus of the chick, cyclothiazide was found to slow the decay of large multiquantal EPSCs (121). Although the results suggest that desensitization occurs during the EPSC, the extent to which desensitization actually shapes the decay is not clear.

It is quite possible that some desensitization may occur during a brief agonist application (e.g. as in the double-pulse experiments of 24) without the shape of the current being influenced to any noticeable extent by this desensitization. The extent to which desensitization actually shapes the non-NMDA component of synaptic currents remains uncertain.

Time Course of Transmitter in the Synaptic Cleft of Glutamatergic Synapses

Because little is known of how to simulate the synaptic current (see B Edmonds et al, Nicotinic Acetylcholine Receptors, this volume) for non-

NMDA receptors, knowledge of the time course of the concentration of glutamate in the cleft during synaptic transmission is also uncertain. It is quite likely, however, that the concentration will not decline in a simple exponential manner. For example, if the cleft is treated as a cylinder of radius a, with an instantaneous line source at the center, the fraction of material remaining within the cylinder at time t is $q(t) = 1 - \exp(a^2/4Dt)$ (84), where D is the diffusion coefficient. If the cylinder has an initially uniform concentration then

$$q(t) = 2\pi a^2 \int [J_1 \, (ua)^2/u] \, \exp(-Dtu^2) du,$$

where J_1 is a Bessel function, and the integral is from 0 to ∞ (91) . These functions are similar, and for $a = 0.5$ μm, and D taken as the diffusion coefficient for glutamine at room temperature, both can be approximated roughly (within at most 50% error up to $t = 8$ ms) by two exponentials with time constants of about 150 μs (90% of amplitude) and 3 ms (10%) (R Silver et al, in preparation).

An estimate of the concentration profile of glutamate near the receptors has been obtained for a preparation of hippocampal neurons in culture by measuring the amount of competitive antagonist displaced from NMDA receptors by glutamate during a synaptic event (17). Assuming an instantaneous rise in the concentration of transmitter and a subsequent decline that follows a single exponential time course, a time constant of 1.2 ms was obtained for the decline in glutamate concentration (17). Given that the glutamate concentration at the receptors may not rise in a negligible time (relative to the speed at which it is likely to decay), and the fact that a simple exponential is probably unrealistic (see above), an alternative approach is desirable.

CONCLUSION

It is the case for both types of glutamate receptors, that we still have only the simplest ideas about receptor mechanisms. Although we can say with some confidence that the glutamate concentration in the synaptic cleft falls rapidly relative to the NMDA receptor-mediated synaptic current, the situation is more complex for the non-NMDA receptors, and it is probably not the same at all synapses. The ultimate goal of relating synaptic events in the CNS to molecular structures is still a long way away.

Literature Cited

1. Adams DJ, Dwyer TM, Hille B. 1980. The permeability of endplate channels to monovalent and divalent metal cations. *J. Gen. Physiol.* 75:493–510
2. Ascher P, Nowak L. 1988. The role of divalent cations in the N-methyl-D-aspartate responses of mouse central neurones in culture. *J. Physiol.* 399: 247–66
3. Bashir ZI, Alford S, Davies SN, Randall AD, Collingridge GL. 1991. Long-term potentiation of NMDA receptor–mediated synaptic transmission in the hippocampus. *Nature* 349:156–58
4. Bekkers JM, Stevens CF. 1989. NMDA and non-NMDA receptors are co-localized at individual excitatory synapses in cultured rat hippocampus. *Nature* 341: 230–33
5. Deleted in proof
6. Benveniste MJ, Clements JD, Vyklicky L Jr, Mayer NM. 1990. A kinetic analysis of the modulation of NMDA receptors by glycine in mouse cultured hippocampal neurones. *J. Physiol.* 428: 333–57
7. Benveniste MJ, Mayer ML. 1991. Kinetic analysis of antagonist action at N-methyl-D-aspartatic acid receptors: two binding sites each for glutamate and glycine. *Biophys. J.* 59:560–73
8. Bettler B, Boulter J, Hermans-Borgmeyer I, O'Shea-Greenfield A, Deneris ES, et al. 1990. Cloning of a novel glutamate receptor subunit, GluR5: expression in the nervous system during development. *Neuron* 5: 583–95
9. Bettler B, Egebjerg J, Sharma G, Pecht G, Hermans-Borgmeyer I, et al. 1992. Cloning of a putative glutamate receptor: a low affinity kainate-binding subunit. *Neuron* 8:257–65
10. Blatz AL, Magleby KL. 1989. Adjacent interval analysis distinguishes among gating mechanisms for the fast chloride channel from rat skeletal muscle. *J. Physiol.* 410:561–85
11. Bliss TVP, Collingridge GL. 1993. A synaptic model of memory: long-term potentiation in the hippocampus. *Nature* 361:31–39
12. Bochet P, Audinat E, Lambolez B, Crepel F, Rossier C, et al. 1994. Subunit composition at the single-cell level explains functional properties of a glutamate-gated channel. *Neuron* 12:383–88
13. Boulter J, Hollmann M, O'Shea-Greenfield A, Hartley M, Deneris E, et al. 1990. Molecular cloning and functional expression of glutamate receptor subunit genes. *Science* 249:1033–37
14. Burnashev N, Monyer H, Seeburg PH, Sakmann B. 1992. Divalent ion permeability of AMPA receptor channels is dominated by the edited form of a single subunit. *Neuron* 8:189–98
15. Chen L, Mae-Huang L-Y. 1992. Protein kinase C reduces Mg block of NMDA receptor channels as a mechanism of modulation. *Nature* 356:521–23
16. Chester M, Kaila K. 1992. Modulation of pH by neuronal activity. *Trends Neurosci.* 15:396–402
17. Clements JD, Lester RAJ, Tong G, Jahr CE, Westbrook GL. 1992. Time course of glutamate in the synaptic cleft. *Science* 258:1498–1501
18. Clements JD, Rosenmund C, Westbrook GL. 1993. Synaptic and extrasynaptic NMDA channel gating. *Soc. Neurosci. Abstr.* 19:625
19. Clements JD, Westbrook GL. 1991. Activation kinetics reveal the number of glutamate and glycine binding sites on the NMDA receptor. *Neuron* 7:605–13
20. Collingridge GL, Herron CE, Lester RAJ. 1988. Synaptic activation of N-methyl-D-aspartate receptors in the Schaffer collateral-commissural pathway of rat hippocampus. *J. Physiol.* 399: 283–300
21. Colquhoun D, Hawkes AG. 1994. The principles of the stochastic interpretation of ion channel mechanisms. In *Single Channel Recording*, ed. B Sakmann, E Neher. New York: Plenum. 2nd ed. In press
22. Colquhoun D, Hawkes AG. 1987. A note on correlations in single ion channel records. *Proc. R. Soc. London Ser. B* 230:15–52
23. Colquhoun D, Hawkes AG. 1982. On the stochastic properties of bursts of single channel openings, and clusters of bursts. *Philos. Trans. R. Soc. London Ser. B* 230:15–52
24. Colquhoun D, Jonas P, Sakmann B. 1992. Action of brief pulses of glutamate on AMPA/kainate receptors in patches from different neurones of rat hippocampal slices. *J. Physiol.* 458:261–87
25. Colquhoun D, Ogden DC. 1988. Activation of ion channels in the frog endplate by high concentrations of acetylcholine. *J. Physiol.* 395:131–59
26. Colquhoun D, Sakmann B. 1985. Fast events in single-channel currents activated by acetylcholine and its analogues

at the frog muscle end-plate. *J. Physiol.* 369:501–57

27. Cull-Candy SG, Usowicz MM. 1989. On the multiple-conductance single channels activated by excitatory amino acids in large cerebellar neurones of the rat. *J. Physiol.* 415:555–82

28. Durand GM, Gregor P, Zheng X, Bennett MV, Uhl GR, et al. 1992. Cloning of an apparent splice variant of the rat N-methyl-D-aspartate receptor NMDAR1 with altered sensitivity to polyamines and activators of protein kinase C. *Proc. Natl. Acad. Sci. USA* 89:9359–63

29. Edmonds B, Colquhoun D. 1992. Rapid decay of averaged single-channel NMDA receptor activations recorded at low agonist concentration. *Proc. R. Soc. London Ser. B* 250:279–86

30. Deleted in proof

31. Edmonds B, Silver RA, Colquhoun D, Cull-Candy SG. 1993. Fast deactivation of non-NMDA receptors in outside-out patches. *Soc. Neurosci. Abstr.* 19:1515

32. Egebjerg J, Bettler B, Hermans-Borgmeyer I, Heinemann S. 1991. Cloning of a cDNA for a glutamate receptor subunit activated by kainate but not AMPA. *Nature* 351:745–48

33. Farrant M, Feldmeyer D, Takahashi T, Cull-Candy SG. 1994. NMDA receptor channel diversity in the developing cerebellum. *Nature* 368:335–39

34. Feldmeyer D, Cull-Candy SG. 1994. Elusive glutamate receptors. *Curr. Biol.* 4:82–84

35. Finkel AS, Redman SJ. 1983. The synaptic current evoked in cat spinal motoneurons by impulses in single group 1a axons. *J. Physiol.* 342:615–32

36. Forsythe ID, Westbrook GL. 1988. Slow excitatory postsynaptic currents mediated by N-methyl-D-aspartate receptors on cultured mouse central neurones. *J. Physiol.* 396:515–33

37. Fredkin DR, Montal MM, Rice J. 1985. Identification of aggregated Markovian models: application to the nicotinic acetylcholine receptor. In *Proceedings of the Berkeley Conference in Honor of Jerzy Neuman and Jack Kiefer,* ed. LM Le Cam, RA Olshen, 1:269–89

38. Gibb AJ, Colquhoun D. 1992. Activation of NMDA receptors by L-glutamate in cells dissociated from adult rat hippocampus. *J. Physiol.* 456:143–79

39. Gibb AJ, Colquhoun D. 1991. Glutamate activation of a single NMDA receptor-channel produces a cluster of channel openings. *Proc. R. Soc. London Ser. B* 243:39–45

40. Gibb AJ, Edwards FA. 1991. Glycine does not influence the properties of single clusters of NMDA channel openings in outside-out patches from rat hippocampal granule cells. *J. Physiol.* 437:122P

41. Hawkes AG, Jalali A, Colquhoun D. 1992. Asymptotic distributions of apparent open times and shut times in a single channel record allowing for the omission of brief events. *Philos. Trans. R. Soc. London Ser. B* 337:383–404

42. Herb A, Burnashev N, Werner P, Sakmann B, Wisden W, et al. 1992. The KA-2 subunit of excitatory amino acid receptors shows widespread expression in brain and forms ion channels with distantly related subunits. *Neuron* 8:775–85

43. Hestrin S. 1993. Different glutamate receptor channels mediate fast excitatory synaptic currents in inhibitory and excitatory cortical neurons. *Neuron* 11:1083–91

44. Hestrin S. 1992. Activation and desensitization of glutamate-activated channels mediating fast excitatory synaptic currents in the visual cortex. *Neuron* 9:991–99

45. Hestrin S, Sah P, Nicoll RA. 1990. Mechanisms generating the time course of dual component excitatory synaptic currents recorded in hippocampal slices. *Neuron* 5:247–53

46. Hollmann M, Hartley M, Heinemann S. 1991. Ca^{2+} permeability of KA-AMPA-gated glutamate receptor channels depends on subunit composition. *Science* 252:851–53

47. Hollmann M, Heinemann S. 1994. Cloned glutamate receptors. *Annu. Rev. Neurosci.* 17:31–108

48. Howe JR, Cull-Candy SG, Colquhoun D. 1991. Currents through single glutamate-receptor channels in outside-out patches from rat cerebellar granule cells. *J. Physiol.* 432:143–202

49. Huettner JE. 1990. Glutamate receptor channels in rat DRG neurons: activation by kainate and quisqualate and blockade of desensitization by Con A. *Neuron* 5:255–66

50. Iino M, Ozawa S, Tsuzuki K. 1990. Permeation of calcium through excitatory amino acid receptor channels in cultured rat hippocampal neurones. *J. Physiol.* 424:151–65

51. Ikeda K, Nagasawa M, Mori H, Araki K, Sakimura K, et al. 1992. Cloning and expression of the epsilon 4 subunit of the NMDA receptor channel. *FEBS Lett.* 313:34–38

52. Isaacson JS, Nicoll RA. 1991. Aniracetam reduces glutamate receptor de-

sensitization and slows the decay of fast excitatory synaptic currents in the hippocampus. *Proc. Natl. Acad. Sci. USA* 88:10936–40

53. Ishii T, Moriyoshi K, Sugihara H, Sakurada K, Kadotani H, et al. 1993. Molecular characterization of the family of the N-methyl-D-aspartate receptor subunits. *J. Biol. Chem.* 268:2836–43

54. Jahr CE. 1992. High probability opening of NMDA receptor channels by L-glutamate. *Science* 255:470–72

55. Jahr CE, Stevens CF. 1990. A quantitative description of NMDA receptor-channel kinetic behaviour. *J. Neurosci.* 10: 1830–37

56. Johnson JW, Ascher P. 1990. Voltage-dependent block by intracellular Mg^{2+} of N-methyl-D-aspartate responses in mouse central neurones in culture. *Biophys. J.* 57:1085–90

57. Johnson JW, Ascher P. 1987. Glycine potentiates the NMDA response of mouse central neurones. *Nature* 325: 529–31

58. Johnston D, Brown TH. 1983. Interpretation of voltage-clamp measurements in hippocampal neurons. *J. Neurophysiol.* 50:464–86

59. Jonas P, Major G, Sakmann B. 1993. Quantal components of unitary EPSCs at the mossy fibre synapse on CA3 pyramidal cells of rat hippocampus. *J. Physiol.* 472:615–64

60. Jonas P, Sakmann B. 1991. Properties of AMPA subtype glutamate receptors in pyramidal cells of rat hippocampal slices. *J. Physiol.* 438:321P

61. Keinänen K, Wisden W, Sommer B, Werner P, Herb A, et al. 1990. A family of AMPA-selective glutamate receptors. *Science* 249:556–60

62. Kiskin NI, Krishtal OA, Tsyndrenko AY. 1986. Excitatory amino acid receptors in hippocampus: kainate fails to desensitize them. *Neurosci. Lett.* 63: 225–30

63. Kleckner NW, Dingledine R. 1988. Requirement for glycine in activation of NMDA receptors expressed in *Xenopus* oocytes. *Science* 241:835–37

64. Kutsuwada T, Kashiwabuchi N, Mori H, Sakimura K, Kushiya E, et al. 1992. Molecular diversity of the NDA receptor channel. *Nature* 358:36–41

65. Lambolez B, Audinat E, Bochet P, Crepel F, Rossier J. 1992. AMPA receptor subunits expressed in single Purkinje cells. *Neuron* 9:247–58

66. Lerma J, Paternain AV, Naranjo JR, Mellstrom B. 1993. Functional kainate-selective glutamate receptors in cultured

hippocampal neurons. *Proc. Natl. Acad. Sci. USA* 90:11688–92

67. Lester RAJ, Clements JD, Westbrook GL, Jahr CE. 1990. Channel kinetics determine the time course of NMDA receptor–mediated synaptic currents. *Nature* 346:565–67

68. Lester RAJ, Jahr CE. 1992. NMDA channel behaviour depends on agonist affinity. *J. Neurosci.* 12:635–43

69. Lieberman DN, Mody I. 1994. Regulation of NMDA channel function by endogenous Ca-dependent phosphatase. *Nature* 369:235–39

70. Llano I, Marty A, Armstrong CM, Konnerth A. 1991. Synaptic- and agonist-induced excitatory currents of Purkinje cells in rat cerebellar slices. *J. Physiol.* 434:183–213

71. MacDonald JF, Mody I, Salter MW. 1989. Regulation of N-methyl-D-aspartate receptors revealed by intracellular dialysis of murine neurones in culture. *J. Physiol.* 414:17–34

72. MacDonald JF, Nowak LM. 1990. Mechanisms of blockade of excitatory amino acid receptor channels. *Trends Pharmacol. Sci.* 11:167–72

73. Mayer ML, Vyklicky L, Clements J. 1989. Regulation of NMDA receptor desensitization in mouse hippocampal neurons by glycine. *Nature* 338:425–27

74. Mayer ML, Westbrook GL, Guthrie PB. 1984. Voltage-dependent block by Mg^{2+} of NMDA responses in spinal cord neurones. *Nature* 309:261–63

75. McBain CJ, Mayer MM. 1994. N-methyl-D-aspartic acid receptor structure and function. *Physiol. Rev.* 74: 723–59

76. Meguro H, Mori H, Araki K, Kushiya E, Kutsuwada T, et al. 1992. Functional characterization of a heteromeric NMDA receptor channel expressed from cloned cDNAs. *Nature* 357:70–74

77. Monyer H, Seeburg P, Wisden W. 1991. Glutamate-operated channels: developmentally early and mature forms arise by alternative splicing. *Neuron* 6:799–810

78. Monyer H, Sprengel R, Schoepfer R, Herb A, Higuchi M, et al. 1992. Heteromeric NMDA receptors: molecular and functional distinction of subtypes. *Science* 256:1217–20

79. Morita T, Sakimura K, Kushiya E, Yamazaki M, Meguro H, et al. 1992. Cloning and functional expression of a cDNA encoding the mouse β-2 subunit of the kainate-selective glutamate receptor channel. *Mol. Brain Res.* 14:143–46

80. Moriyoshi K, Masu M, Ishii T, Shigemoto R, Mizuno N, Nakanishi S. 1991.

Molecular cloning and characterization of the rat NMDA receptor. *Nature* 354: 31–37

81. Nelson PG, Pun RYK, Westbrook GL. 1986. Synaptic excitation in cultures of mouse spinal cord neurons: receptor pharmacology and behaviour of synaptic currents. *J. Physiol.* 372:169–90

82. Nowak L, Bregestovski P, Ascher P, Herbet A, Prochiantz A. 1984. Magnesium gates glutamate-activated channels in mouse central neurones. *Nature* 307: 462–65

83. O'Connor JJ, Rowan MJ, Anwyl R. 1994. Long-lasting enhancement of NMDA receptor–mediated synaptic transmission by metabotropic glutamate receptor activation. *Nature* 367: 557–59

84. Ogston AG. 1955. Removal of acetylcholine from a limited volume by diffusion. *J. Physiol.* 128:222–23

85. Olverman HJ, Jones AW, Watkins JC. 1984. L-glutamate has higher affinity than other amino acids for [^{3}H]-D-AP5 binding sites in rat brain membranes. *Nature* 307:460–62

86. Ozawa S, Iino M, Tsuzuki K. 1991. Two types of kainate responses in cultured rat hippocampal neurons. *J. Neurophysiol.* 66:2–11

87. Partin KM, Patneau DK, Winters CA, Mayer ML, Buonanno A. 1993. Selective modulation of desensitization at AMPA versus kainate receptors by cyclothiazide and concanavalin A. *Neuron* 11:1069–82

88. Patneau D, Mayer NE. 1990. Structure-activity relationships for amino acid transmitter candidates acting at NMDA and quisqualate receptors. *J. Neurosci.* 10:2385–99

89. Patneau DK, Vyklicky L, Mayer NE. 1993. Hippocampal neurons exhibit cyclothiazide-sensitive rapidly desensitizing responses to kainate. *J. Neurosci.* 13:3496–509

90. Raman IM, Trussell LO. 1992. The kinetics of the response to glutamate and kainate in neurons of the avian cochlear nucleus. *Neuron* 9:173–86

91. Rideal EK, Tadoyen J. 1954. On overturning and anchoring of monolayers II. Surface diffusion. *Proc. R. Soc. London Ser. A* 258:1498–501

92. Sakimura K, Morita T, Kushiya E, Mishina M. 1992. Primary structure and expression of the γ-2 subunit of the glutamate receptor channel selective for kainate. *Neuron* 8:267–74

93. Sakurada K, Masu M, Nakanishi S. 1993. Alteration of Ca^{2+} permeability and sensitivity to Mg^{2+} and channel

blockers by a single amino acid substitution in the N-methyl-D-aspartate receptor. *J. Biol. Chem.* 268:410–15

94. Sather W, Dieudonne S, MacDonald JF, Ascher P. 1992. Activation and desensitization of NMDA receptors in nucleated outside-out patches of mouse neurones. *J. Physiol.* 450:643–72

95. Sather W, Johnson JW, Henderson G, Ascher P. 1990. Glycine-insensitive desensitization of NMDA responses in cultured mouse embryonic neurons. *Neuron* 4:725–31

96. Schneggenburger R, Zhou Z, Konnerth A, Neher E. 1993. Fractional contribution of calcium to the cation current through glutamate receptor channels. *Neuron* 11:133–43

97. Schoepfer R, Monyer H, Sommer B, Wisden W, Sprengel R, et al. 1994. Molecular biology of glutamate receptors. *Prog. Neurobiol.* 42:353–57

98. Sheng M, Cummings J, Roldan LA, Jan YN, Jan LY. 1994. Changing subunit composition of heteromeric NMDA receptors during development of rat cortex. *Nature* 368:144–47

99. Sigel E, Baur R, Malherbe P. 1994. Protein kinase C transiently activates heteromeric N-methyl-D-aspartate receptor channels independently of the phosphorylatable C-terminal splice domain and of consensus phosphorylation sites. *J. Biol. Chem.* 269:8204–8

100. Silver RA, Colquhoun D, Cull-Candy SG, Edmonds B. 1994. Mechanisms underlying the decay of the fast component of EPSCs in rat cerebellar granule cells. *J. Physiol.* 476P:P67–68

101. Silver RA, Traynelis SF, Cull-Candy SG. 1992. Rapid-time-course miniature and evoked excitatory currents at cerebellar synapses in situ. *Nature* 355:163–66

102. Deleted in proof

103. Sommer B, Burnashev N, Verdoorn TA, Keinänen K, Sakmann B, et al. 1992. A glutamate receptor channel with high affinity for domoate and kainate. *EMBO J.* 11:1651–56

104. Sommer B, Keinänen K, Verdoorn TA, Burnashev N, Wisden W, et al. 1990. Flip and flop, a cell-specific functional switch in glutamate-operated channels of the CNS. *Science* 249:1580–85

105. Sommer B, Köhler M, Sprengel R, Seeburg PH. 1992. RNA editing in brain controls, a determinant of ion flow in glutamate-gated channels. *Cell* 67:11–19

106. Sommer B, Seeburg PH. 1992. Glutamate receptor channels: novel properties

and new clones. *Trends Pharmacol. Sci.* 13:291–96

107. Spruston N, Jonas P, Sakmann B. 1995. Dendritic glutamate receptor channels in rat hippocampal CA3 and CA1 pyramidal neurons. *J. Physiol.* Submitted

108. Stein E, Cox JA, Seeburg PH, Verdoorn TA. 1992. Complex pharmacological properties of recombinant α-amino-3-hydroxy-5-methyl-4-isoxazoleproprionate receptor subtypes. *Mol. Pharmacol.* 42:864–71

109. Stern P, Béhé P, Schoepfer R, Colquhoun D. 1993. Single channel kinetics of recombinant NMDA receptors. *J. Physiol.* 473:P48

110. Stern P, Béhé P, Schoepfer R, Colquhoun D. 1992. Single-channel conductances of NMDA receptors expressed from cloned cDNAs: comparison with native receptors. *Proc. R. Soc. London Ser. B* 250:271–77

111. Stern P, Cik M, Colquhoun D, Stephenson FA. 1994. Single channel properties of cloned NMDA receptors in a human cell line: comparison with results from *Xenopus* oocytes. *J. Physiol.* 476:391–97

112. Stern P, Edwards FA, Sakmann B. 1992. Fast and slow components of unitary EPSCs on stellate cells elicited by focal stimulation in slices of rat visual cortex. *J. Physiol.* 449:247–78

113. Stuart G, Sakmann B. 1994. Active propagation of somatic action potentials into neocortical pyramidal cell dendrites. *Nature* 367:69–72

114. Tang C-M, Dichter M, Morad M. 1989. Quisqualate activates a rapidly inactivating high conductance ionic channel in hippocampal neurons. *Science* 243:1474–77

115. Tang C-M, Shi Q-Y, Katchman A, Lynch G. 1991. Modulation of the time course of fast EPSCs and glutamate channel kinetics by aniracetam. *Science* 254:288–90

116. Tingley WG, Roche KW, Thompson AK, Huganir RL. 1993. Regulation of NMDA receptor phosphorylation by alternative splicing of the C-terminal domain. *Nature* 364:70–73

117. Tong G, Jahr CE. 1994. Multivesicular release from excitatory synapses of cultured hippocampal neurons. *Neuron* 12:51–59

118. Traynelis SF, Cull-Candy SG. 1991. Pharmacological properties and H+ sensitivity of excitatory amino acid receptor channels in rat cerebellar granule neurones. *J. Physiol.* 433:727–63

119. Traynelis SF, Cull-Candy SG. 1990. Proton inhibition of NMDA receptors in cerebellar neurons. *Nature* 345:347–50

120. Trussell LO, Fischbach GD. 1989. Glutamate receptor desensitization and its role in synaptic transmission. *Neuron* 3:209–18

121. Trussell LO, Zhang S, Rahman IM. 1993. Desensitization of AMPA receptors upon multiquantal neurotransmitter release. *Neuron* 10:1185–96

122. Vyklicky L, Patneau DK, Mayer NE. 1991. Modulation of excitatory synaptic transmission by drugs that reduce desensitization at AMPA/kainate receptors. *Neuron* 7:971–84

123. Wang L-Y, Orser BA, Brautigan DL, MacDonald JF. 1994. Regulation of NMDA receptors in cultured hippocampal neurons by protein phosphatases 1 and 2A. *Nature* 369:230–32

124. Wang YT, Salter MW. 1994. Regulation of NMDA receptors by tyrosine kinases and phosphatases. *Nature* 369:233–35

125. Watanabe M, Inoue Y, Sakimura K, Mishina M. 1992. Developmental changes in distribution of NMDA receptor channel subunit mRNAs. *NeuroReport* 3:1138–40

126. Watkins JC, Collingridge GL. 1994. *The NMDA Receptor.* New York: Oxford Univ. Press. 2nd ed.

127. Werner P, Voigt M, Keinänen K, Wisden W, Seeburg PH. 1991. Cloning of a putative high-affinity kainate receptor expressed predominantly in hippocampal CA3 cells. *Nature* 351:742–44

128. Wisden W, Seeburg PH. 1993. A complex mosaic of high-affinity kainate receptors in rat brain. *J. Neurosci.* 13:3582–98

129. Wyllie DJA, Cull-Candy SG. 1994. A comparison of non-NMDA receptor channels in type-2 astrocytes and granule cells from rat cerebellum. *J. Physiol.* 475:95–114

130. Yamada KA, Tang C-M. 1993. Benzothiadiazides inhibit rapid glutamate receptor desensitization and enhance glutamatergic synaptic currents. *J. Neurosci.* 13:3904–15

131. Yamazaki M, Araki K, Shibata A, Mishina M. 1992. Molecular cloning of a cDNA encoding a novel member of the mouse glutamate receptor family. *Biochem. Biophys. Res. Commun.* 183:886–92

132. Zhou Z, Neher E. 1993. Calcium permeability of nicotinic acetylcholine receptor channels in bovine adrenal chromaffin cells. *Pflügers Arch.* 425:511–17

ADDED IN PROOF

133. Burnashev N, Schoepfer R, Monyer H, Ruppersberg JP, Gunther W, et al. 1992. Control by asparagine residues of calcium permeability and magnesium blockade in the NMDA receptor. *Science* 257:1415–19

Annu. Rev. Physiol. 1995. 57:521–46

PHYSIOLOGICAL DIVERSITY OF NICOTINIC ACETYLCHOLINE RECEPTORS EXPRESSED BY VERTEBRATE NEURONS

Daniel S. McGehee and Lorna W. Role

Department of Cell Biology and Anatomy in the Center for Neurobiology and Behavior, Columbia University, College of Physicians and Surgeons, 722 West 168th St., P.I. Annex, New York, NY 10032

KEY WORDS: presynaptic receptor, calcium permeation, heterologous expression, synaptic transmission, receptor modulation

INTRODUCTION

The last decade has revealed an astounding degree of physiological and structural diversity in neurotransmitter-activated receptors. In particular, molecular studies of the acetylcholine-gated receptors in vertebrate muscle cells and *Torpedo* electrocytes gave birth to a new era of research on a related subfamily of nicotinic receptors (nAChRs) expressed by central and peripheral neurons. This review focuses on the nAChR subtypes expressed by neurons, viewed mainly from a physiological perspective. It is intended to complement several excellent recent reviews on muscle-type AChRs (42, 45, 56) and on the anatomical distribution, biochemistry, and molecular biology of neuronal nAChRs (35, 61, 66, 95).

The work summarized in this review has helped answer a long-standing question: How can the well-known behavioral, cognitive, and addictive effects of nicotine be reconciled with the paucity of evidence for CNS synapses where the transmission is mediated by nicotinic receptors? The identification of a large family of neuronal nAChR subunit genes and an array of functionally distinct nAChRs has given a basis for the diverse effects of nicotine. Perhaps

521

most important is emergent evidence for functional roles of pre- as well as postsynaptic CNS nAChRs that contribute to axon extension and modulate transmitter release, and therein effect synapse formation (19, 90, 113).

We first summarize the molecular biology that has catalyzed the transition to the current "status nicotinicus," next discuss the diversity in subunit composition, ionic permeability, localization, and modulation of neuronal nAChRs, and finally consider physiological reasons for the extent of nAChR channel diversity and propose future research directions.

CATALYSTS OF THE TRANSITION TO CURRENT VIEWS OF NEURONAL nAChRs

Pharmacological Studies of Neuronal and Muscle-Type nAChRs Provided Early Evidence for nAChR Diversity

Differences between muscle- and ganglionic-type nAChRs were suggested by early distinctions in antagonist profiles (e.g. 88). Evidence that more than one class of nAChRs must exist came from experiments on the CNS actions of α-bungarotoxin (αBgTx), the classic neuromuscular blocking agent. Although anatomical studies showed widespread, high affinity binding of this toxin in specific CNS regions, these binding sites did not seem equivalent to nicotine-gated receptors. First, with a few striking exceptions (73), neither nicotinic transmission nor nicotine-evoked currents in vertebrate neurons were blocked by αBgTx (22, 95, 98). αBgTx was unable to displace nicotinic agonists from CNS-binding sites, and immunoaffinity purification of CNS nAChRs revealed more than one receptor population with a clear separation of the high affinity nicotine-binding proteins from the αBgTx-binding proteins. Higher resolution autoradiography showed partly overlapping but non-identical patterns of nicotine and αBgTx sites in the CNS (24, 26). Furthermore, study of nAChRs on PNS neuronal somata indicated that the αBgTx-binding sites were not localized to synaptic sites (54, 63) and that αBgTx binding and ACh sensitivity were regulated independently (101).

In fact, if not for crucial studies of the suprachiasmatic nucleus, where light-induced changes in diurnal control of pineal enzyme activity were mimicked by local infusion of ACh and blocked by αBgTx, CNS αBgTx sites would have been doomed to obscurity (116). With considerable debate (22, 27, 66), the overall picture of neuronal nAChRs has settled into two general classes: those activating a nonselective cation conductance, resistant to αBgTx blockade and underlying most transmission, and those with distinct αBgTx-binding sites of uncertain function.

The Neuronal nAChR Subunit Gene Family

With the molecular cloning of a neuronal nAChR subunit–encoding gene (12) (soon followed by others), a new stage in nAChRs research began. The currently known subunits are classified into two subfamilies. The α-type subunits are named on the basis of substantial homology with the α subunit of the muscle nAChR, including the presence of vicinal cysteine residues (Cys 192, Cys 193; α1 numbering), established as a flag for the ACh-binding site of muscle-type AChRs (56). The muscle α subunit is denoted as α1, and α2–8 are distinct neuronal α subunit-encoding genes (34, 35, 50, 83, 93, 95, 97). Most are present in brain cDNA libraries of both rat and chick, but α8 is found only in chick brain, and a new α9 subunit is found only in rat (S Heinemann, personal communication). A second family of β subunits lacking equivalents of cysteines 192 and 193 currently has three members—β2, β3, and β4. Unlike α subunits, the neuronal β subunits do not have strong homology with the muscle β subunit, and are sometimes simply called non-α subunits. In fact, neuronal homologues of β, γ, δ, or ε subunits of the muscle AChR have not been identified, despite considerable effort.

Early physiological studies of heterologous expression of nAChR subunit genes (prior to α7-α9) showed that the combined expression of a neuronal α and a neuronal β subunit in oocytes of *Xenopus laevis* was necessary for formation of ACh-gated channels with properties similar to native neuronal nAChRs. An exception was α4, which when expressed alone yielded a tiny current in response to millimolar concentrations of nicotine. However, it is hard to rule out a contribution of possible endogenous β subunits made by the oocytes, which apparently do make a low level of α-like subunits (17).

In contrast to the situation for α2, α3, and α4 subunits, it was subsequently found that α7, α8, and α9 subunits form ACh-gated channels when expressed as a single subunit. The ability to form homomeric nAChR channels is not all that distinguishes α7, α8, and α9 from their siblings. The mystery of the brain αBgTx sites was finally solved; currents carried by activation of homomeric α7, α8, or α9 nAChR channels, as well as α7/α8 heteromers, are blocked by nanomolar concentrations of αBgTx (33, 47, 99; S Heinemann personal communication).

The nAChR family tree may not yet be complete, despite an extensive search for additional α- and β-like subunit genes. The pattern of subunit expression revealed by in situ hybridization leaves some areas apparently lacking an α or β partner. Also, the array of functional characteristics of native nAChRs is still poorly matched to the channels formed in heterologous expression studies to date (see below). More neuronal nAChR subunit genes may be discovered (39).

Based on the known subunits, more than a thousand distinct neuronal nAChRs are theoretically possible (even disregarding permutations based on stoichiometry or ordering). On the other hand, nAChR diversity may well be constrained by limits on cellular coexpression of particular subunits and by specific structural requirements for subunit association and coassembly. Is diversity in nAChR subunits a cruel joke? Are all of these subunits expressed only to provide thousands of different ways to make the same channel? These fears were quelled by evidence that the diversity of neuronal nAChR subunit genes is actually physiologically significant.

In the following sections we consider evidence for physiological diversity of distinct nAChR subunit combinations, outlining some of their essential features. Finer points of the biophysical properties of both heterologously expressed and native neuronal nAChRs are summarized in Tables 1 and 2. The progress in the last several years can be assessed by comparing these synopses with an earlier review (93).

ANALYSIS OF nAChR PHYSIOLOGY BY STUDY OF SUBUNIT COMBINATIONS IN *XENOPUS* OOCYTES

Early biochemical, anatomical, molecular, and functional studies of the α3 and α4 subunits supported the idea that expressing more than one type of α subunit could provide a range of functional nAChR subtypes (20, 34, 50, 61, 95). An important component of this view derives from detailed analyses of the physiology of particular subunit combinations by heterologous expression.

nAChR Channels Formed by Expression of α/β Subunit Pairs and by α Subunits Alone

The α subunits α2, α3, and α4 form distinct ACh-activated channels when expressed in combination with either β2 or β4 in *Xenopus* oocytes (Table 1; 6, 8, 18, 20, 48, 65, 68, 84, 86, 92). In contrast, the expression of α5 or α6, in combination with any β subunit, or expression of β3 with any of the α sequences, does not produce ACh-activated current (34; M Ballivet, unpublished data). These latter results should be interpreted cautiously because pairwise expression of α and β subunits is not an adequate test for participation in functional nAChR channels.

Unlike the other α subunits, expression of either the α7 (33, 97, 99) or α8 (47) subunit alone supports robust ACh-activated currents that are blocked by nanomolar concentrations of αBgTx. There is no evidence from oocyte expression studies that α7 can combine with other αs or βs because coinjection of other subunits with α7 produces ACh currents pharmacologically indistinguishable from those expressed by injection with α7 alone [β2, β3, β4, and muscle βγδ were tested with chicken α7 (33); α3, α5, β2, and β4 were tested with rat α7 (99)].

Subunit Stoichiometry

Little is known about the regulation of assembly and insertion of neuronal nAChRs into the plasma membrane. By analogy to muscle-type nAChRs, the

Table 1

Subunit combinations	α2β2	α3β2	α3β2	α4β2	α4β2	α4β2α5	α2β4	α3β4	α3β4	α3β4β2	α4β4	α4β4	α7	α7	α8
Species	Rat	Rat	Chick	Rat	Chick	Chick	Rat	Rat	Chick	Rat	Rat	Chick	Rat	Chick	Chick
γ_1 (pS)	34	15	18	13	20	—	—	22	—	—	—	18	—	45	—
τ_1(ms)	0.43, 3	0.2, 4	0.2, 2	6	—	—	—	0.4, 7	—	—	—	—	—	—	—
γ_2(pS)	15	5	—	22	—	—	—	18	—	—	—	—	—	—	—
τ_2(ms)	0.5, 4	0.1, 2	—	8	—	—	—	13	—	—	—	—	—	—	—
other $\gamma_1(\tau)$	—	—	—	34(8)	—	—	—	—	—	—	—	—	~20	—	—
P_{Ca}/P_{Na}	1–1.5	1–1.5	—	1–1.5	—	—	1–1.5	1.1	—	—	1–1.5	—	—	—	—
Agonist profile															
ACh EC_{50} (μM)	—	350	5	—	0.7	100	—	30	160	—	—	5	—	112	1.9
Relative potency	N>D=A>C	D>A>N>C	—	A=N>D>C	A=N=D>Cb	A>>>N	C>N>A>D	C>N=A=D	—	C=A	C>N>A>D	—	N>C>D>A	N>C>A>>D	N=C>A>D
Other agonists (EC_{50} in μM)	—	—	—	—	—	—	—	D (20)	—	—	—	—	—	N (10), TMA (800)	N(1), D(6.5), TMA (10)
Antagonist Profile															
neuronal BgTx	Transient	Prolonged	—	Transient	No block	—	Transient	Transient	—	Partial	Transient	—	—	Block	Block
αBgTx	No block	No block	—	No block	No block	—	—	No block	—	—	—	—	—	Block	Block
Lophotoxin	Partial	Partial	—	Block	—	—	—	No block	—	—	—	—	—	Block	Block
Neosurugotoxin	Partial	Partial	—	Block	—	—	—	—	—	—	—	—	—	—	—
Other Antagonists	—	—	—	—	—	—	—	—	—	—	—	—	—	MLA	MLA
References	11,65,67, 68,84,85, PC(JD)	11,18,65, 68,84,85, 86,87, PC(JD)	34,48 PC(EC)	11,20, 65,68, 84,85, PC(JD)	6,8,30, 48	91	65,68,85, PC(JD)	18,32, 65,68, 85,86,87	20,34	28	65,68,85, PC(JD)	20,34	99	9,10,33, 44,47, 92	47

Notes: γ_1, most prevalent conductance class; γ_2, other conductance seen; τ_1, time constant of the open state of γ_1; τ_2, time constant of the open state of γ_2; A, acetylcholine; C, cytisine; Cb, carbacol; D, DMPP; N, nicotine; TMA, tetramethylammonium; MLA, methyllycaconitine. Data from personal communications indicated by PC with initials of investigators in parentheses. (JD) J Dani, (EC) E Cooper.

Table 2

	PERIPHERAL NERVOUS SYSTEM								CENTRAL NERVOUS SYSTEM				
Location	Chain	Sympathetic Ganglia			PC12	Parasympathetic Ganglia		Sensory	Habenula		IPN	LSN	Hippocampus
		SCG	Chain	Chain		Ciliary	Ciliary	DRG					
Species	Rat (Neonate)	Rat	Chick(E10)	Chick(E17)	Rat cell line	Chick(E8)	Chick(E13)	Rat	Rat	Chick	Rat	Chicken(adult)	Rat
Number of γ classes	>1	2	3	4	3	2–3	2–3	1–(2?)		4	1–2		>2
γ_1 (pS)	37	20	15	38	31	40	40		42	50	35		~30
τ_1 (msec)	0.4, 12	0.2, 1.3	1, 7	2,11	~10	~0.1, 0.5	~0.2, 1.3			ND	ND		2.7
γ_2 (pS)		~50	27	50	22	25	25		26	65	ND		~60
τ_2 (msec)		ND	2, 13	3, 17	~10	0.06, 0.3	0.07, 0.4		ND	ND			<1
Other γ_1,(τ)	26 to 48	25 to 45	50 (3)	23(1.7);65	39(10–20)	~60 (rare)	~60 (rare)			23,40	Others seen		15?
Agonist profile													
ACh EC_{60}	45	60	35	ND		35	133	60	60–80	ND	28		
Relative potency		N>C>D>A	D>N>A>Cb				A>Cb	C>A	N>C>A>D	ND	C>A>N>D	N>>Cb	N>A
Other agonists (EC_{50} μM)													
Antagonist profile													
neuronal BgTx	Block	Block	Block	Block			Block		No block	Block	No block	No block	Block
αBgTx	No block	No block	No block	No block			No block	No block	No block		No block	No block	Block
Other antagonists													MLA
Desensitization													
τ(s),ACht(100 μM)			1, 10			1, 10		PC(EC)	~6		~4		fast
AChR subunits expressed	ND	α3,α5,β2,β4	α3,α4,α5,α7,β2,β4	α3,α4,α5,α7,β2,β3,β4	α3,α5,β2,β3,β4	α3,(α4),β2		α3,α5,β2,β3,β4	α3,α4,β2,β3,β4	α2,α3,α4,α5,α7,α8,β2,β4	α2,α3,α4,α5,β2,β4	α2,α4,β2	α2,α3,α4,α5,α7,β2,β4
Physiology references	74	36, PC(EC)	78,79	78,79	36	71	71	PC(EC)	82	16	82	102	1,4
Expression references		PC(EC)	37,62	37	PC(SR)	13			38,39,110	16,77	38,106	77	1,38,110

Notes: γ_1, most prevalent conductance class; γ_2 other conductance seen; τ_1, time constant of the open state of γ_1; τ_2 time constant of the open state of γ_2; A, acetylcholine; C, cytisine; Cb, carbacol; D, DMPP; N, nicotine; MLA, methyllycaconitine; ND, No data. Data from personal communications indicated by PC with initials of investigators in parentheses. (JD) J Dani, (EC) E Cooper, (SR) S Rogers.

neuronal nAChR channel is assumed to be a pentamer with α subunit stoichiometry of at least two α-type subunits, but there is little direct experimental evidence (see 2, 30). It is not known how many alternative α/β stoichiometries may exist, or if there is flexibility in the ordering of subunits around the ion channel pore (e.g. $\alpha\alpha\beta\beta\beta$ vs $\alpha\beta\alpha\beta\alpha$). Such flexibility could contribute to the number of functionally distinct nAChR channels. In fact, coexpression of a single set of α and β subunits often produces multiple nAChRs distinct in both conductance and opening kinetics (e.g. two to three classes result from injection of either $\alpha2\beta2$, $\alpha3\beta2$, $\alpha4\beta2$, or $\alpha3\beta4$; 84, 86, 20). Multiple subtypes may reflect multiple stoichiometries [i.e. $1(\alpha):4(\beta)$, $2(\alpha):3(\beta)$, $3(\alpha):2(\beta)$, $4(\alpha):1(\beta)$] or different arrangements. Alternatively, the differences may be the result of postranslational modifications. Since multiple conductance subtypes are also evident in a detailed analysis of native nAChRs in rat sympathetic neurons (74; Table 2), it is unlikely that multiple subtypes are an artifact of the expression system.

Biophysical Characteristics of Oocyte-Expressed nAChRs

An overview of the biophysical characteristics of the various α/β combinations expressed in oocytes yields some general insights into the functional contribution of the α- vs β-type nAChR subunits. The single-channel conductances for the α/β pairwise combinations range between 5 and 45 pS, with most between 15 and 20 pS (Table 1). The channel profiles in Figure 1 depict the

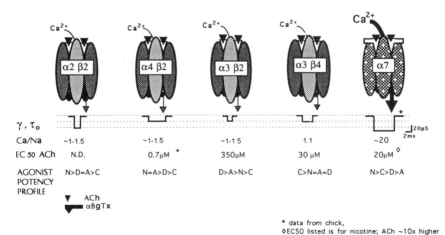

Figure 1 Simplified view of key functional differences among nAChR subunit combinations. Data from expression of rat sequences in *Xenopus* oocytes except where noted. Abbreviations: γ, conductance; τ_o, time constant of the open state; Ca/Na, ratio of the Ca^{2+} vs the Na^+-permeability; N, nicotine; A, acetylcholine; C, cytisine; D, DMPP; ND, no data.

conductance and channel open times for four of the subunit combinations from rat. The conductances are quite similar for the $\alpha4\beta2$, $\alpha3\beta2$, and $\alpha3\beta4$ channels. This could be due, in part, to the high degree of amino acid identity in the TM2 membrane-spanning domain (believed to form the pore) of $\alpha3$, $\alpha4$, $\beta2$, and $\beta4$.

nAChR channel burst duration is influenced by the type of β subunit included in the complex. Expression of $\beta4$ with $\alpha3$ results in receptors with a higher probability of re-opening after closing as compared with $\alpha3\beta2$ receptors (86).

Ca^{2+} PERMEABILITY OF nAChRs EXPRESSED IN OOCYTES Ca^{2+} permeability of a ligand-gated ion channel is of particular physiological importance. Vernino et al (106) first showed that Ca^{2+} permeation through neuronal nAChRs (oocyte-expressed $\alpha3\beta4$ channels) is sufficient to activate Ca^{2+}-dependent cellular processes (endogenous Ca^{2+}-activated Cl^- conductance in the oocyte). This study also showed that neuronal nAChRs were modulated by changes in external [Ca^{2+}], independently of increases in intracellular [Ca^{2+}]). More recently, Dani and colleagues used a new oocyte superfusion system to resolve accurate reversal potentials, and they determined the Ca^{2+}:Na^+ permeability ratio (P_{Ca}/P_{Na}) for muscle $\alpha_2\beta\gamma\delta$ receptors and neuronal $\alpha3\beta4$ receptors as 0.2 and 1.1, respectively (32). The relative Ca^{2+} permeability of other neuronal α/β combinations is also in the range of 1–1.5 (J Dani, personal communication; see Figure 1, Table 1). Although this level of Ca^{2+} permeability is enough for significant increases in intracellular [Ca^{2+}], $\alpha7$ homomeric channels in oocytes are even more permeable to Ca^{2+}, with P_{Ca}/P_{Na} close to 20! This is higher than the P_{Ca}/P_{Na} of ~7 for the NMDA receptor (99). Our understanding of the physiological impact of these ACh-activated Ca^{2+} channels is just beginning.

DESENSITIZATION CHARACTERISTICS OF OOCYTE-EXPRESSED nAChRs   Different subunit combinations in the oocyte also have clear differences in the rate and voltage dependence of nAChR desensitization (18, 48). $\alpha3\beta4$ desensitizes relatively slowly (τ_d of 2 and 20 s; 9, 18, 48, 92) whereas $\alpha3\beta2$, $\alpha7$, $\alpha8$ heteromeric, and $\alpha7$, $\alpha8$ monomeric nAChRs desensitize very rapidly ($\alpha8$: τ_d = 0.1 s with 1 μM nicotine; 47). In view of the differential Ca^{2+} permeability of different nAChRs, apparent differences in desensitization may in part reflect overlap of Ca^{2+}-activated Cl^- conductance with the nAChR currents. The complexity of desensitization confounds comparison of oocyte currents with those in neurons. However, the rapid decay of the $\alpha7$ and $\alpha8$ currents in oocytes appear to be qualitatively similar to the rapidly decaying, αBgTx-sensitive currents in ciliary ganglion neurons (118).

AGONIST/ANTAGONIST SENSITIVITY OF OOCYTE-EXPRESSED nAChRs   Pharmacological profiles of the different α/β subunit combinations expressed in oocytes are shown in Table 1. Although the agonist rank-order potencies vary
markedly among the different subunit combinations, comparison of specific
agonists is informative. For example, cytisine is a potent agonist for all β4-
containing receptors, but it is the least effective agonist for all of the β2-con-
taining receptors. In fact, cytisine can antagonize the interaction of ACh with
β2-containing nAChRs (87). Similarly, α3β4 from rat has a tenfold higher
ACh sensitivity than α3β2 (65, 86). In light of recent studies showing more
extensive β4 expression in the CNS than initially thought (38), further characterization of β4-containing receptors will be useful.

αBgTx is a potent antagonist of α7 and α8 homo-oligomeric channels but
not the other coexpressed α/β combinations. Another component of cobra
venom, originally identified as a blocker of ganglionic nAChRs and known as
neuronal BgTx (nBgTx; 21, 64), differentially inhibits various nAChR subunit
combinations. nBgTx block of rat α3β2, and to a lesser degree α4β2, receptors
is slowly reversible with wash-out, apparently because of high affinity binding
(85). Receptors containing any α in combination with β2, or α2 in combination
with β4, are inhibited by the toxin only if it is co-applied with the agonist at
high nanomolar or micromolar concentrations. This inhibition reverses rapidly
on removal of toxin. Therefore, while sensitivity to nBgTx reflects subunit
composition, the concentration and application protocol are critical. These
studies also show that both α and β subunits contribute to nAChR agonist and
antagonist pharmacology.

Although chick and rat nAChR subunits are similar in some characteristics,
there are surprisingly large differences in conductance, kinetics, and pharmacology of the expressed channels. Rat α3β2 is nearly tenfold less sensitive to
ACh than rat α3β4, whereas the opposite is true for the chick homologues. In
view of these differences, it will be important to characterize in detail the
kinetics of nBgTx inhibition for chick nAChRs. The agonist rank order of α7
homomers is also quite different between rat and chick clones; the latter is
insensitive to DMPP up to 3 mM (47) compared with robust responses of rat
α7 to DMPP at 100 μM (99). Examination of aligned amino acid sequences
from the putative ligand-binding domain of the chick and rat α7 subunits
(Figure 2) reveals several intriguing differences in the primary structures in
this region. For example, Ser 185 in the chick sequence is substituted with a
Lys residue in the rat sequence. This replacement of an uncharged residue with
a charged one near the putative ligand-binding domain (including vicinal Cys
residues and the adjacent Tyr) may be an important determinant of the differences in the agonist binding affinities. The region between the vicinal Cys
residues and TM1, which has been implicated in agonist and antagonist interactions with other neuronal α subunits (67), is also of interest because there

```
L  Q  M  Q  E  A  D  I  S  G  Y  I  S  N  G  E  W  D  L  V   177 chick
L  Q  M  Q  E  A  D  I  S  S  Y  I  P  N  G  E  W  D  L  M   200 rat
                        *        *                 *

G  I  P  G  K  R  T  E  S  F  Y  E  C  C  K  E  P  Y  P  D   197 chick
G  I  P  G  K  R  N  E  K  F  Y  E  C  C  K  E  P  Y  P  D   220 rat
                  *     *

I  T  F  T  V  T  M  R  R  R  T  L  Y  Y  G  L  N  L  L  I   217 chick
V  T  Y  T  V  T  M  R  R  R  T  L  Y  Y  G  L  N  L  L  I   240 rat
*     *                          TM1
```

Figure 2 Partial amino acid sequences of chick and rat α7 nAChR subunits. Asterisks denote differences between the two sequences. Bold letters correspond to the position of vicinal Cys 192, 193, and Tyr 190 of the muscle α1. These amino acids have been shown to be critical for agonist binding. Underlined region corresponds to the beginning of the first membrane-spanning domain (TM1). Chick sequence (33, 97); rat sequence (99).

is a difference at position 199 where a hydrophobic amino acid (Phe) in the chick sequence is a polar residue (Tyr) in the rat sequence.

nAChR Functional Domains Revealed by Mutagenesis Analyses

The nAChR subunits that form homomeric channels provide unique opportunities to examine functional domains involved in determining single-channel conductance, channel open time, ligand binding, Ca^{2+} permeability, and receptor subunit assembly. Changeux et al have examined the effects of a series of mutations of functional domains of homomeric α7 channels. Mutation of a single site (Leu 247 to Thr) in the putative channel domain (TM2) of α7 yields an additional, higher conductance channel (80 pS) that desensitizes slowly and is activated by classical antagonists such as hexamethonium and d-tubocurarine (9, 92). These results suggest that changes in the conductance as well as kinetics of channel opening can occur with mutations in a presumed channel-forming domain. Another possibility is that a desensitized state of the channel is now in an open conformation. Combined substitution and addition of amino acid residues near the cytoplasmic end of TM2 of α7 with residues found in the TM2 region of the anion-selective glycine receptor α1 subunit converted the ion selectivity from cationic to anionic (44). Another mutation near the cytoplasmic end of TM2, in the position referred to as the cytoplasmic ring, (Glu 237 to Ala) abolishes the Ca^{2+} permeability without significantly affecting other characteristics of the ACh responses. In addition, the Ca^{2+} permeability, the apparent affinity for ACh, and the rates of activation and desensitization were also altered by mutations to two adjacent amino acids (Leu 254, Leu 255) close to the extracellular end of TM2 (10).

As mentioned, $\alpha3\beta2$ and $\alpha2\beta2$ receptors expressed in oocytes have dramatically different pharmacology profiles, particularly in their sensitivity to nBgTx and the ratio of responses to nicotine and ACh (Table 1). Luetje et al (67) have exploited these differences to determine that the extracellular domain of $\alpha2$ and $\alpha3$ is critical in ligand-receptor interactions. A series of chimeric α subunits, with portions of $\alpha3$ replaced by corresponding regions of $\alpha2$ (and vice versa), were coexpressed with $\beta2$. Testing for nBgTx sensitivity, as well as the ratio of nicotine/ACh responses, revealed ten amino acids located between the vicinal Cys residues and TM1 that appeared to be essential to both the agonist and antagonist sensitivity. Within that region, site-directed mutagenesis was used to show that Gln 198 in $\alpha3$ (Pro in $\alpha2$) is of critical importance to the pharmacological profile of these nAChRs.

Mutational analyses have also identified β subunit domains involved in the pharmacology of nAChRs. As mentioned above, nBgTx causes a rapid, reversible blockade of $\beta4$-containing receptors and a slower, prolonged inhibition of $\alpha3\beta2$. In chimera experiments, the N-terminal 121 amino acids of the $\beta2$ subunit are sufficient to regulate the kinetics of nBgTx block as well as the partial agonist properties of cytisine on $\alpha3\beta2$ receptors (85). The coupling of agonist binding to channel activation may involve both α and non-α-type subunits due to the location of agonist-binding domains at the interface between an α and a neighboring subunit, as suggested for the muscle nAChR (56).

Coexpression of Three nAChR Subunits Reveals Novel Subtypes Likely to Occur in Vivo

With pairwise injection of nAChR subunits in oocytes, there are few cases where the properties of expressed channels match those measured in neurons. Recent immunoprecipitation studies (29, 105, 112) suggest that native nAChRs may comprise more than one type of α and/or β subunit, so that more than simple α/β pairs would be required to mimic native nAChRs. Two recent studies have addressed such triplex subunit expression with intriguing results (28, 91).

Patrick and colleagues have tested whether nAChRs might include the $\beta2$ and $\beta4$ subunits because their recent in situ data reveal broad and often overlapping expression of these subunits in the CNS (38). Injection of oocytes with RNAs encoding the rat $\alpha3$, $\beta2$, and $\beta4$ subunits produced nAChR-mediated currents with properties intermediate between those produced with either $\alpha3\beta2$ or $\alpha3\beta4$ coexpression (28). Apparently, nAChRs can form with more than one type of β subunit, with each influencing channel properties. Since these α and β subunits are coexpressed in vivo (best studied in PNS neurons), further comparison of native rat nAChR channels with the heterologously expressed α3β2β4 combination should be informative.

Triplex coexpression of subunits has also suggested a role for the α5 subunit, until now a puzzle because α5/β2 or α5/β4 pairs are not expressed despite abundant expression of α5 throughout the CNS. When α5 is coexpressed with other α and β subunits, the properties of the resulting channels are altered. Thus when α5 mRNA is coinjected along with α4 and β2, the channels expressed have a 100-fold lower sensitivity to ACh than those from α4β2 alone. Also, the α5α4β2-containing complex has a conductance more than twice that of the α4β2 complex (91; Table 1). Interestingly, the properties of α5/α4/β2 channels match with native nAChRs expressed in the habenula (16).

THE PHYSIOLOGY AND SUBUNIT COMPOSITION OF NATIVE nAChRs

In situ hybridization, immunohistochemistry, Northern blot analysis, and polymerase chain reaction (PCR) analysis have revealed surprisingly widespread patterns of nAChR subunit gene expression in the CNS (38, 50, 77, 110). Table 2 summarizes the expression of α- and β-type subunits in particular regions of the rat and chick CNS and PNS. The expression of multiple α or β subunit genes is common and is particularly striking in the habenula and hippocampal formation. Even autonomic ganglion neurons, the favored "simple" system for studying neuronal nicotinic transmission, express multiple versions of both α- and β-type subunit genes. Thus recent data indicate a significantly greater variety of both nAChR subunits and nAChR channels in the CNS and PNS than implicated by early biochemical studies that stressed a dominant role of α4 and β2 in the CNS vs α3 and β4 in the periphery (3, 4, 13, 14, 34, 38, 62, 72, 93, 94, 96, 99, 109, 110). Consistent with the diversity in subunit gene expression, a broad spectrum of nAChR subtypes has been characterized in electrophysiological studies of hippocampus (1), habenula (16; but see 80), and autonomic ganglia (74, 79).

Native nAChR Channel Subtypes are Distinguished by Different Biophysical Profiles

Multiple classes of nAChR channels, distinguished on the basis of single-channel conductance and kinetics, have been identified on individual CNS and PNS neurons (93, 95; Table 2). Also, changes in the biophysical and pharmacological properties of nAChRs occur throughout neural development (71, 78, 93).

The conductances of nAChR subtypes in the CNS and PNS range from 15 to 65 pS, with a 30 to 40 pS subtype typically predominant. Subconductance states of nAChR channel classes have been noted in the PNS (74) and the CNS (16). In neurons with more than one type of nAChR channel, often one class of channel dominates the activity (71). Even in CNS regions such as the rat interpeduncular nuclei (IPN) and habenula, with a rich diversity of nAChR subunit genes expressed, a single dominant nAChR channel class is reported. Possibly, other channel subtypes were overlooked because of differential agonist sensitivity (Table 1 and 2) or differential cellular distribution. Comparing native nAChRs with those of heterologously expressed nAChR subunit pairs suggests that (a) native nAChRs have conductances 10–15 pS larger than the typical oocyte-expressed variety, (b) native nAChRs typically reside in the open state longer (two to five times longer on average), and (c) there are few good matches between native and heterologously expressed AChRs.

Native nAChR Subtypes are Distinguished by Different Pharmacological Profiles

AGONIST PHARMACOLOGY   Agonist rank-order profiles of oocyte-expressed nAChR channels and native receptors are revealing of subunit composition of native nAChRs. Different neuronal populations have distinct profiles of activation, e.g. low concentrations of ACh, DMPP, cytisine, and nicotine (Tables 1 and 2). Differences in the potency of ACh are of obvious physiological significance; one purpose of nAChR diversity may be to encode differences in transmitter sensitivity. Meaningful comparison of agonist potency profiles in neurons to those of oocyte-expressed nAChRs is restricted to neurons with one dominant nAChR subtype. Cytisine has a strong subunit dependence, consistent with $\beta4$ being a major component of nAChRs in the rat suprachiasmatic ganglia (SCG), sensory ganglia, habenula, and IPN.

ANTAGONIST PHARMACOLOGY   Antagonist effects are even more subunit dependent. The clearest evidence for contribution of specific subunits to native nAChRs is based on sensitivity to αBgTx, which binds only to $\alpha7$, $\alpha8$, and $\alpha9$ subunits. αBgTx inhibits a rapidly desensitizing ACh-activated current in chick ciliary ganglion neurons (118) and rat hippocampal neurons (1). In contrast, in chick sympathetic neurons αBgTx inhibits a slowly activating and inactivating current that is also blocked by antisense deletion of $\alpha7$ (115). The tenfold lower sensitivity of this current to αBgTx suggests that these $\alpha7$-containing nAChRs may not be homomers.

Neuronal BgTx is another useful antagonist. Many neuronal nAChR-mediated responses are potently blocked by this toxin (e.g. nAChRs in peripheral ganglia, retina, and hippocampus), whereas others are not [rat habenula, IPN, and chick lateral spiriform nucleus (LSN)]. As previously noted, the application paradigm is critical. Individual channel classes may be differentially sensitive to submaximal concentrations of nBgTx, yielding still finer resolution (e.g. 15–25 nM nBgTx has little effect on one channel subtype while largely inhibiting others; 78). The differential sensitivity of $\alpha2\beta2$ vs $\alpha4\beta2$ to both nBgTx and lophotoxin indicates that comparison of the sensitivity to multiple toxins may reveal the subunit compositions of the different channel classes in LSN (which expresses $\alpha 2$, $\alpha 4$, and $\beta 2$).

Insights into Subunit Composition of Native nAChRs

The expression of at least three subunits in chick ciliary ganglia is indicated by studies where nAChRs were immunoprecipitated and the subunit profile probed with specific antibodies ($\alpha 3$, $\beta 4$, and $\alpha 5$; 105). Similar studies of chick brain nAChRs indicate various combinations of $\alpha 3$, $\alpha 4$, $\alpha 5$, and $\beta 2$ in combination with one another, possibly including $\alpha 3 \alpha 5 \beta 2$, $\alpha 4 \alpha 5 \beta 2$, etc (29, 112). Thus immunoprecipitation with subunit-specific antibodies indicates mixing of α-type subunits in a single nAChR complex. Co-immunoprecipitation of nAChRs from chick retina indicates that $\alpha 7/\alpha 8$ heteromers are a major component of several subtypes expressed (3; see below).

Another method of examining subunit composition of native AChRs is to delete individual subunits and assess their functional contribution by biophysical analysis. The participation of several α subunits in nAChR channels in primary neurons has been revealed by deletion using subunit-specific antisense oligonucleotides (16, 62). These studies indicate a prominent role of $\alpha 3$ in the conductance, desensitization, and antagonist profile of all four nAChR channels normally expressed in chicken sympathetic ganglion cells. Similar roles for $\alpha 2$ and $\alpha 4$ are suggested by comparable studies of chicken habenula neurons. The $\alpha 7$ subunit also contributes to the nAChR channels in peripheral autonomic neurons, although the cumulative evidence suggests different types of $\alpha 7$-containing channels in ciliary ganglion vs sympathetic ganglion neurons (115, 118).

Recent studies of $\alpha 5$ in sympathetic neurons have exploited antisense deletion and heterologous expression to show the likely involvement of this subunit in both agonist affinity and single-channel conductance. These experiments use the idea that neurons expressing adequate levels of $\alpha 5$ (relative to other α and β subunits) would produce nAChR channels that are higher-conductance, lower-affinity versions of the comparable α/β subunit combinations. In fact, the levels of $\alpha 5$ are three to ten times higher in mature autonomic neurons than the levels measured in these neurons at earlier stages of embryogenesis. Concurrent with the increase in $\alpha 5$ mRNA expression, large conductance nAChRs predominate over the smaller channels previously expressed (78), and the apparent affinity of mature nAChRs for ACh is three- to fivefold lower than at earlier developmental stages (71). Consistent with this, recent studies using $\alpha 5$-specific antisense oligonucleotides reveal increased apparent affinity for agonists in "$\alpha 5$-minus" autonomic neurons (C Yu & L Role, unpublished data). These results suggest a developmental regulation of nAChRs composed primarily of $\alpha 3 \beta 4$ at early stages of development and of $\alpha 3 \alpha 5 \beta 4$ at later stages (e.g. 59).

A combination of biochemical, molecular, and physiological techniques has been successfully applied to analyzing nAChR composition in chick retina, a prominent site of αBgTx binding. These studies have led to the well-supported proposal for chick retina nAChR subunit composition including α8 homomeric channels and α7/α8 heteromeric channels (3).

Calcium Permeability of Native nAChRs

An important feature of neuronal nAChRs is the ACh-evoked increase in intracellular Ca^{2+} independent of voltage-dependent Ca^{2+} channels (81). Ca^{2+} permeation is more pronounced for some nAChRs than for others, providing a new and physiologically important fingerprint of nAChRs. Utilizing simultaneous whole-cell recording and fura-2 measurement of intracellular Ca^{2+}, two recent studies have shown that Ca^{2+} flux contributes significantly to the total current carried by neuronal nAChRs in adrenal chromaffin cells (107, 120). The nAChRs expressed by these cells are similar to those expressed by peripheral neurons (their crest-derived cousins), which suggests that nAChRs of α3β4 or α3β4α5 subunits conduct Ca^{2+}. In fact, when α3β4 is expressed in oocytes, gating leads to sufficient increases in Ca^{2+} to activate the endogenous Ca^{2+}-activated Cl^- conductances.

Perhaps most exciting is the recent convergence of data indicating that the αBgTx-binding AChRs (i.e. nAChRs including the α7 and/or α8 subunits) are likely to be a significant determinant of neuronal Ca^{2+} permeability. The first hint that native αBgTx nAChRs might play this crucial physiological role emerged from studies of Berg and colleagues showing that the application of nicotine to ciliary ganglion neurons dramatically increased intracellular Ca^{2+} by a mechanism blocked by αBgTx (108). The results were puzzling at the time because the investigators saw no effect of αBgTx on the nicotine-evoked macroscopic currents. Two observations, however, suggested the experiment needed to resolve this puzzle. Examination of the time course of the ACh-evoked currents of heterologously expressed α7 (and α8) homomeric channels, as well as the currents underlying specific nAChR subtypes in hippocampal neurons, revealed that both of these αBgTx-sensitive currents had extremely rapid rates of desensitization (Tables 1 and 2; 1, 47, 99). When Berg and colleagues reexamined the nicotine-activated currents, using rapid agonist application techniques, they found an αBgTx-sensitive current that activated and inactivated in less than 500 ms (118). The relative time course of this rapid αBgTx-sensitive current vs that of the αBgTx-sensitive increase in internal Ca^{2+} can be debated, but ACh can activate significant increases in Ca^{2+} via α7 nAChRs. In fact, α7-containing nAChRs are among the most Ca^{2+}-permeable ligand-gated ion channels identified to date, with α7 homomers characterized by a P_{Ca}/P_{Na} ~20 (99; Table 1). It is important to note that α7-containing channels actively conduct Ca^{2+} at hyperpolarized potentials at which other ligand- or voltage-gated Ca^{2+} permeant channels are inactive. High Ca^{2+} permeability of nAChRs expressed in CNS neurons has also been noted, with the first definitive evidence provided in neurons of the medial habenula nucleus, where the ACh-evoked Ca^{2+} influx can regulate the extent of subsequent GABA receptor activation (81). Ca^{2+} influx through habenula nAChRs at hyperpolarized potentials is approximately twofold greater than that carried by voltage-gated Ca^{2+} channels in the membrane potential range that activates those channels.

Presynaptic nAChRs

In addition to differences in the properties of nAChRs expressed on neuronal somata, several studies have implicated nAChRs in the regulation of transmitter release (111, 113). The observations that nicotine- and αBgTx-binding sites are detected along the axons and within the terminal fields of both CNS and PNS neurons supports axonal transport and synaptic terminal localization of nAChRs. This idea was first put forward in studies of ACh-induced transmitter release from synaptosomes and brain slices pretreated with tetrodotoxin (23, 66, 113). It was further confirmed by focal lesions combined with quantitative radioligand binding, which demonstrated that a significant percent of nicotine- and αBgTx-binding sites are presynaptic in origin (24, 26, reviewed in 103). The anatomical evidence for localization of nAChRs on presynaptic terminals has received increasing support from recent physiological studies. Thus the application of nicotine within specific terminal fields rich in nAChRs can enhance the release of norepinephrine, dopamine, serotonin or GABA (60, 103, 111, 113). Recent studies of identified synapses on CNS and PNS neurons reveal nicotine-induced Ca^{2+} influx as well as facilitation of spontaneous and evoked release of glutamate and ACh. Furthermore, these preliminary pharmacology and antisense deletion studies suggest the involvement of presynaptic α7-containing nAChRs in at least some aspects of this presynaptic facilitation (76).

Admittedly, the existence and physiological significance of presynaptic nAChRs on CNS and PNS neurons has been a subject of controversy for decades (111, 113). At many sites where presynaptic nAChRs are clearly present, evidence for a source of the transmitter is less clear (e.g. sensory nerve terminals; 60, 111, 113). Compelling evidence for the expression and physiological effects of presynaptic nAChRs in the CNS is mounting, however, particularly in the nigrostriatal dopamine system and the medial habenula—IPN projections where cholinergic input and nAChRs are present within the terminal fields, and nicotinic agonists modify the release of dopamine and glutamate respectively (25, 40, 113; D McGehee & L Role, in preparation). The well-known effects of nicotine on cognition and behavior may reflect pre- rather than postsynaptic nAChR activation because prominent presynaptic nAChR expression has been demonstrated in CNS regions implicated in the control of behaviors affected by nicotine (60, 111, 113).

The role of presynaptic nAChRs in the regulation of transmitter release is intriguing, and determination of the mechanism and the subtype(s) of nAChRs involved in the presynaptic effects of nicotine will continue to be an area of active research. The observation that nAChRs can be expressed on both the somata and terminals of neurons supports the idea that specific subtypes of nAChRs may be targeted to presynaptic domains and, hence, uniquely suited to the regulation of transmitter release.

WHY IS THERE SO MUCH DIVERSITY IN NEURONAL nAChRs?

The following discussion of possible reasons for the extent of nAChR diversity begins with ideas well-grounded in experimental support. We also discuss more speculative possibilities.

Role of nAChR Diversity in Synaptic Development and Transmission

A variety of nAChR complexes may be required for developmental changes in nAChR channel properties that accompany synaptic development (71, 79, 78; A Brussard et al, in preparation). nAChRs at various stages of development and with different types of synaptic input show dissimilar channel conductance, kinetics, pharmacology, and subcellular distribution (7, 93, 95). Innervation of autonomic neurons increases ACh sensitivity (46, 53, 71), as well as the number and clustering of surface AChRs in vivo and in vitro (41, 78, 96). Expression of specific nAChR subunits also increases, concurrent with innervation and target contact in autonomic ganglia, and prevention of the presynaptic input inhibits this increase (31, 37, 59). Patch recording at multiple sites on the same cell reveals segregation of nAChR channel subtypes in homogeneous hotspots of a single nAChR subtype at the same time as pre- and postsynaptic innervation (78). Changes in levels of nAChR subunit gene expression during CNS development suggest a similar regulatory role of innervation in the visual system, where increased expression of an nAChR β2 subunit gene occurs in the optic tectum following innervation and is prevented in "eyeless embryos" where the tectum is not innervated (75).

It is controversial whether presynaptic input is required for enhanced nAChR expression in developing ganglion neurons (supporters: 5, 13, 46, 96; detractors: 41, 69). Recent studies suggest that de novo innervation may primarily control the levels of nAChR expression and that target contact collaborates in shaping the precise nAChR profile. Consistent with this, preliminary studies reveal that input and target differentially regulate nAChR subunit expression and the biophysical properties of the nAChRs expressed (37, 59; P Devay et al, unpublished observations; M Jacob, personal communication). Axotomy or denervation of neurons also alters nAChR transcript levels, but with variable effects on ACh-evoked currents, which suggests that a critical period in the regulation of somatic nAChRs may occur early on in neuronal development, prior to either pre- or postsynaptic contact.

Developmental changes in the number of nAChRs expressed clearly influence neuronal excitability. The advantage of expressing multiple nAChR channel subtypes is less obvious unless one views the alterations in nAChR profile as a group. Thus early in development, individual neurons can express several nAChR channel subtypes that are intermingled on the surface of neuronal somata (16, 78). Neuronal maturation results in an up-regulation of larger conductance, longer opening duration channels that are spatially segregated into high density, subtype-homogeneous clusters. In fact, computer modeling of the key physiological properties of one class of neurons for which these changes in the profile of nAChR channel subtypes occur can help evaluate the impact of these changes (A Brussard et al, in preparation). Quantitative comparison of a mixed cluster of pre-innervation nAChRs vs a cluster of typical post-innervation nAChRs in embryonic chick sympathetic neurons reveals that nAChR maturation enhances the probability that a given input will cause cell firing (A Brussard et al, in preparation). Apparently subtle increases in single-channel conductance and opening duration can add up to a significant enhancement of neuronal excitability, reminiscent of the impact of developmental changes in muscle nAChRs (55).

Role of nAChR Diversity in Targeting to Different Cellular Locales

The segregation of nAChRs into subtype-specific patches (see above; 16, 78) requires a mechanism for selective targeting or association of specific nAChR complexes into homogeneous clusters. Spatial segregation has been seen for $GABA_A$ receptor $\alpha 1$ and $\beta 1$ subunits in different membrane regions of polarized epithelial cells (89). However, neither the peptide sequences that might direct segregation nor markers of distinct neuronal somatic microdomains are known.

In contrast, the targeting of specific proteins to axonal vs somatic domains is well described (100), and specific sequence domains have been implicated (57). Both αBgTx and nicotine sites are expressed in specific nerve terminal fields, consistent with a role of nAChR diversity in the targeting of specific nAChR subtypes to axonal terminal rather than somatic locales. Both electrophysiological and receptor-binding studies indicate that nAChRs on the terminals of medial habenula neurons may differ pharmacologically from those expressed on the cell soma (16, 24, 82; D McGehee & L Role, in preparation).

Targeting to a terminal vs soma membrane is essential for presynaptic nAChRs. Differences among the nAChR subunit sequences may have evolved to allow such specific targeting.

Role of nAChR Diversity in Short-Term Changes in nAChR Function

Diversity in nAChR subunit composition may also subserve differences in the susceptibility of specific nAChRs to short-term (modulatory) alterations in nAChR channel function. nAChRs in peripheral neurons can be modulated by protein kinase A (PKA) and protein kinase C (PKC) (93). Peptide neurotransmitters such as VIP and substance P have been implicated as primary messengers for PKA and PKC activation, respectively. The expression of these peptides in afferent projections to sympathetic ganglia is consistent with their role in nAChR modulation (49, 51, 70, 104). Preliminary results suggest that distinct subtypes of nAChR channels in chick sympathetic neurons may differ in their modulation by PKA (S Peng et al, unpublished data).

SUMMARY, CONCLUSIONS, AND FUTURE DIRECTIONS

Our new understanding of the widespread pattern of nAChR expression and the diversity in nAChR properties makes the complex behavioral, cognitive, and addictive effects of nicotine less mysterious. Although there is still little evidence for classical nicotinic synaptic transmission in the CNS, we have a new appreciation for probable presynaptic effects. In future experiments, it will be important to test the hypothesis that CNS nAChRs may function primarily, or even exclusively, as modulators of synaptic transmission, regulating presynaptic excitability and the release of other neurotransmitters. Several studies, since the paper by Brown and colleagues (15), have provided electrophysiological evidence for nicotinic modulation of glutamate-, GABA-, and ACh-mediated transmission (58, 76; D McGehee & L Role, in preparation). These findings add to anatomical and neurochemical evidence for widespread expression of presynaptic nAChRs (23, 24, 25) and the ability of nicotine to regulate the activity of specific dopaminergic, serotinergic, and noradrenergic projections (113). The effects of nicotine on terminals should be further examined with the powerful biophysical techniques now available (e.g. fluorescent imaging of changes in intraterminal Ca^{2+} or membrane potential, vesicle fusion assayed via changes in cell capacitance, and electrochemical detection of amine release). Such studies will help elucidate the role of specific CNS nuclei in the behavioral effects of nicotine. In addition, the combination of molecular genetics and single-channel recording can identify the subunit composition of presynaptic nAChRs, important information for developing treatment strategies for nicotine addiction.

In developing PNS neurons, changes in nAChR subtype expression, as well as in nAChR kinetics, agonist affinity, clustering, and spatial segregation of distinct subtypes, are apparently regulated by both input and target contact. If a given input could induce a synaptic cluster of channels with large conductance, long opening duration, and high affinity, it would guarantee a dominant influence of this input on synaptic integration and transmission. Since nAChR subtypes segregate into homogeneous clusters only on neurons that have received synaptic input, this notion seems reasonable and worth testing directly. The role of various nAChR subtypes during development and synaptogenesis in the CNS requires more investigation.

In particular, the role of Ca^{2+}-permeable nAChRs at developing synapses needs to be explored. If Ca^{2+} permeable nAChRs are expressed in growing cholinergic neurons, the release of ACh from growth cone endings (52, 114) would stimulate Ca^{2+} influx. Increased Ca^{2+} in growth cones is steeply related to neurite extension, neurite retraction, and transmitter release (43). Thus Ca^{2+} permeable nAChRs might stimulate growth cone advancement and release of the transmitter stimulus for this growth. Since high concentrations of ACh (and high internal Ca^{2+}) stop neurite growth (119), growth cone nAChRs may also play a role in neurite arrest upon target contact. Recent studies implicate α7-containing nAChRs in neurite extension (19, 90).

The short-term modulation of distinct nAChR subtypes requires further study because, to date, nAChR modulation by peptides and kinases has largely been confined to macroscopic current analysis, so that the biophysical and molecular details remain unresolved. Most importantly, perhaps, is to ascertain by single-channel analysis whether nAChR modulation by peptides, Ca^{2+}, or kinase activation is subtype specific. In view of the emergent role of presynaptic nAChRs in regulating the release of other neurotransmitters (113), it is also important to test whether presynaptic nAChRs are subject to modulation, providing an even more finely-tuned control of synaptic transmission in the CNS.

Finally, we note the increasingly popular notion that mechanisms underlying synaptic development may contribute to synaptic plasticity. The long-term changes in the number, conductance, and Ca^{2+} permeability of postsynaptic nAChRs seen during development might be recapitulated in their presynaptic cousins and involved in long-term regulation of synaptic function. With the high Ca^{2+} permeability and presynaptic localization of the αBgTx binding, α7-containing nAChRs at specific synapses (24, 76), regulation of these nAChR subtypes would provide an ideal control point for persistent changes in synaptic transmission. As the ligand-activated channel with highest Ca^{2+} permeability (even at hyperpolarized potentials), the once-humble αBgTx-binding site—now the renowned α7/α8 nAChR—may exert substantial control on intracellular Ca^{2+} and thereby control Ca^{2+}-dependent changes in neuronal growth and excitability underlying short- and long-term changes in synaptic transmission.

ACKNOWLEDGMENTS

The authors thank Drs. Paul Clarke, John Dani, Piroska Devay, Michele Jacob, Arthur Karlin, Jose Ramirez-Latorre, and Steve Siegelbaum for their insightful comments on the drafts of this manuscript and for the lively discussions by phone and E-mail. We also thank Drs. Mark Ballivet, Lorna Colquhoun, John Dani, Steve Heinemann, and Jim Patrick, for their willingness to share data prior to publication. Special thanks goes to Bruce Bean, our favorite editor. Work from this laboratory was supported by funds from the National Institutes of Health, Council for Tobacco Research, and the McKnight and Hirschl Foundations.

Any *Annual Review* chapter, as well as any article cited in an *Annual Review* chapter, may be purchased from the Annual Reviews Preprints and Reprints service.
1–800–347–8007; 415–259–5017; email: arpr@class.org

Literature Cited

1. Alkondon M, Albuquerque EX. 1993. Diversity of nicotinic acetylcholine receptors in rat hippocampal neurons. I. Pharmacological and functional evidence for distinct structural subtypes. *J. Pharmacol. Exp. Ther.* 265:1455–73
2. Anand R, Conroy WG, Schoepfer R, Whiting P, Lindstrom J. 1991. Neuronal nicotinic acetylcholine receptors expressed in *Xenopus* oocytes have a pentameric quaternary structure. *J. Biol. Chem.* 266:11192–98
3. Anand R, Peng X, Ballesta JJ, Lindstrom J. 1993. Pharmacological characterization of α-bungarotoxin-sensitive acetylcholine receptors immunoisolated from chick retina: contrasting properties of α7 and α8 subunit-containing subtypes. *Mol. Pharmacol.* 44(5):1046–50
4. Aracava Y, Deshpande SS, Swanson KL, Rapoport H, Wonnacott S, et al. 1987. Nicotinic acetylcholine receptors in cultured neurons from the hippocampus and brain stem of the rat characterized by single channel recording. *FEBS Lett.* 222:63–70
5. Arenella LS, Oliva JM, Jacob MH. 1993. Reduced levels of acetylcholine receptor expression in chick ciliary ganglion neurons developing in the absence of innervation. *J. Neurosci.* 13(10):4525–37
6. Ballivet M, Nef P, Couturier S, Rungger

D, Bader CR, et al. 1988. Electrophysiology of a chick neuronal nicotinic acetylcholine receptor expressed in *Xenopus* oocytes after cDNA injection. *Neuron* 1:847–52
7. Berg DK, Boyd RT, Halvorsen SW, Higgins LS, Jacob MH, Margiotta JF. 1989. Regulating the number and function of neuronal acetylcholine receptors. *Trends Neurosci.* 12:16–21
8. Bertrand D, Ballivet M, Rungger D. 1990. Activation and blocking of neuronal nicotinic acetylcholine receptor reconstituted in *Xenopus* oocytes. *Proc. Natl. Acad. Sci. USA* 87:1993–97
9. Bertrand D, Devillers-Thiery A, Revah F, Galzi JH, Hussy N, et al. 1992. Unconventional pharmacology of a neuronal nicotinic receptor mutated in the channel domain. *Proc. Natl. Acad. Sci.* 89:1261–65
10. Bertrand D, Galzi JH, Devillers-Thiery A, Bertrand S, Changeux JP. 1993. Mutations at two distinct sites within the channel domain M2 alter calcium permeability of neuronal α7 nicotinic receptor. *Proc. Natl. Acad. Sci. USA* 90: 6971–75
11. Boulter J, Connolly J, Deneris E, Goldman S, Heinemann S, Patrick J. 1987. Functional expression of two neuronal nicotinic acetylcholine receptors from

cDNA clones identifies a gene family. *Proc. Natl. Acad. Sci. USA* 84:7763–67

12. Boulter J, Evans K, Goldman D, Martin G, Treco D, et al. 1986. Isolation of a cDNA clone coding for a possible neural nicotinic acetylcholine receptor α-subunit. *Nature* 319:368–74

13. Boyd RT, Jacob MH, Couturier S, Ballivet M, Berg DK. 1988. Expression and regulation of neuronal acetylcholine receptor mRNA in chick ciliary ganglia. *Neuron* 1:495–502

14. Boyd RT, Jacob MH, McEachern AE, Caron S, Berg DK. 1991. Nicotinic acetylcholine receptor mRNA in dorsal root ganglion neurons. *J. Neurobiol.* 22:1–14

15. Brown DA, Docherty RJ, Halliwell JV. 1984. The action of cholinomimetic substances on impulse conduction in the habenulointerpeduncular pathway of the rat in vivo. *J. Physiol.* 353:101–9

16. Brussard AB, Yang X, Doyle JP, Huck S, Role LW. 1994. Developmental regulation of multiple nicotinic AChR channel subtypes in embryonic chick habenula neurons: Contributions of both the α2 and α4 subunit genes. *Pflügers Arch.* In press

17. Buller AL, White MM. 1990. Functional acetylcholine receptors expressed in *Xenopus* oocytes after injection of *Torpedo* β, γ, and δ subunit RNAs are a consequence of endogenous oocyte gene expression. *Mol. Pharmacol.* 37:423–28

18. Cachelin AB, Jaggi R. 1991. β-Subunits determine the time course of desensitization in rat α3 neuronal nicotinic acetylcholine receptors. *Pflügers Arch.* 419:579–82

19. Chan J, Quik M. 1993. A role for the nicotinic alpha-bungarotoxin receptor in neurite outgrowth in PC12 cells. *Neuroscience* 56:441–51

20. Charnet P, Labarca C, Cohen BN, Davidson N, Lester HA, Pilar G. 1992. Pharmacological and kinetic properties of α4β2 neuronal nicotinic acetylcholine receptors expressed in *Xenopus* oocytes. *J. Physiol.* 450:375–94

21. Chiappinelli VA. 1991. κ-Neurotoxins and α-neurotoxins: effects on neuronal nicotinic acetylcholine receptors. In *Snake Toxins,* ed. AL Harvey, pp. 223–58. New York: Pergamon

22. Clarke PBS. 1992. The fall and rise of neuronal alpha-bungarotoxin binding proteins. *Trends Pharmacol. Sci.* 13:407–13

23. Clarke PBS. 1993. Nicotinic receptors in mammalian brain: localization and relation to cholinergic innervation. *Progr. Brain Res.* 98:77–83

24. Clarke PBS, Hamill GS, Nadi NS,

Jacobowitz DM, Pert A. 1986. ³H-nicotine-and ¹²⁵I-alpha-bungarotoxin-labeled nicotinic receptors in the interpeduncular nucleus of rats. II. Effects of habenular deafferentation. *J. Comp. Neurol.* 251:407–13

25. Clarke PBS, Pert A. 1985. Autoradiographic evidence for nicotine receptors on nigratostriatal and mesolimbic dopaminergic neurons. *Brain Res.* 348:355–58

26. Clarke PBS, Schwartz RD, Paul SM, Pert CB, Pert A. 1985. Nicotinic binding in rat brain: autoradiographic comparison of [³H] acetylcholine, [³H] nicotine, and [¹²⁵I]-alpha-bungarotoxin. *J. Neurosci.* 5:1307–15

27. Colquhoun D, Ogden DC, Mathie A. 1987. Nicotinic acetylcholine receptors of nerve and muscle: functional aspects. *Trends Pharmacol. Sci.* 8:465–72

28. Colquhoun L, Dineley K, Patrick J. 1993. A hetero-beta neuronal nicotinic acetylcholine receptor expressed in *Xenopus* oocytes. *Soc. Neurosci. Abstr.* 19:1533

29. Conroy WG, Vernallis AB, Berg DK. 1992. The α5 gene product assembles with multiple acetylcholine receptor subunits to form distinctive receptor subtypes in brain. *Neuron* 9:679–91

30. Cooper E, Couturier S, Ballivet M. 1991. Pentameric structure and subunit stoichiometry of a neuronal actylcholine receptor. *Nature* 350:235–38

31. Corriveau RA, Berg DK. 1993. Coexpression of multiple acetylcholine receptor genes in neurons: quantification of transcripts during development. *J. Neurosci.* 13(6):2662–71

32. Costa ACS, Patrick JW, Dani JA. 1994. Improved technique for studying ion channels expressed in *Xenopus* oocytes, including fast superfusion. *Biophys. J.* 67:1–7

33. Couturier S, Bertrand D, Matter JM, Hernandez MC, Bertrand S, et al. 1990. A neuronal nicotinic acetylcholine receptor subunit (α7) is developmentally regulated and forms a homo-oligomeric channel blocked by α-BgTx. *Neuron* 5:847–56

34. Couturier S, Erkman L, Valera S, Rungger D, Bertrand S, et al. 1990. α5, α3, and non-α3: three clustered avian genes encoding neuronal nicotinic acetylcholine receptor-related subunits. *J. Biol. Chem.* 265:17560–67

35. Deneris ES, Connolly J, Rogers SW, Duviosin R. 1991. Pharmacological and functional diversity of neuronal nicotinic acetylcholine receptors. *Trends Pharmacol. Sci.* 12:34–40

36. Derkach VA, North RA, Selyanko AA, Skok VI. 1987. Single channels activated by acetylcholine in rat superior cervical ganglion. *J. Physiol.* 388:141–51

37. Devay P, Qu X, Role LW. 1994. Regulation of nAChR subunit gene expression relative to the development of pre- and postsynaptic projections of embryonic chick sympathetic neurons. *Dev. Biol.* 162:56–70

38. Dineley-Miller K, Patrick J. 1992. Gene transcripts for the nicotinic receptor subunit, $\beta 4$ are distributed in multiple areas of the rat central nervous system. *Mol. Brain Res.* 16:339–44

39. Duvoisin RM, Deneris ES, Patrick J, Heinemann S. 1989. The functional diversity of the neuronal nicotinic acetylcholine receptors is increased by a novel subunit: $\beta 4$. *Neuron* 3:487–96

40. El-Bizri H, Clarke PBS. 1994. Blockade of nicotinic receptor-mediated release of dopamine from striatal synaptosomes by chlorisondamine administered in vivo. *Br. J. Pharmacol.* 111:414–18

41. Engisch KL, Fischbach GD. 1992. The development of ACH- and GABA-activated currents in embryonic chick ciliary ganglion neurons in the absence of innervation in vivo. *J. Neurosci.* 12:1115–25

42. Froehner SC. 1993. Regulation of ion channel distribution at synapses. *Annu. Rev. Neurosci.* 16:347–68

43. Funte LR, Haydon PG. 1993. Synaptic target contact enhances presynaptic calcium influx by activating cAMP-dependent protein kinase during synaptogenesis. *Neuron* 10:1069–78

44. Galzi J-L, Devillers-Thiery A, Hussy N, Bertrand S, Changeux J-P, Bertrand D. 1992. Mutations in the channel domain of a neuronal nicotinic receptor convert ion selectivity from cationic to anionic. *Nature* 359:500–5

45. Galzi J-L, Revah F, Bessis A, Changeux J-P. 1991. Functional architecture of the nicotinic acetylcholine receptor: from electric organ to brain. *Annu. Rev. Pharmacol.* 31:37–72

46. Gardette R, Listerud MD, Brussaard AB, Role LW. 1991. Developmental changes in transmitter sensitivity and synaptic transmission in embryonic chicken sympathetic neurons innervated in vitro. *Dev. Biol.* 147:83–95

47. Gerzanich V, Anand R, Lindstrom J. 1994. Homomers of $\alpha 8$ and $\alpha 7$ subunits of nicotinic receptors exhibit similar channel but contrasting binding site properties. *Mol. Pharmacol.* 45:212–20

48. Gross A, Ballivet M, Rungger D, Bertrand D. 1991. Neuronal nicotinic acetylcholine receptors expressed in *Xenopus* oocytes: role of the α subunit in agonist sensitivity and desensitization. *Pflügers Arch.* 419:545–51

49. Gurantz D, Harootunian AT, Tsien RY, Dionne VE, Margiotta JF. 1994. VIP modulates neuronal nicotinic acetylcholine receptor function by a cyclic AMP-dependent mechanism. *J. Neurosci.* 14:3540–47

50. Heinemann S, Boulter J, Deneris E, Connolly J, Duvousin R, et al. 1990. The brain nicotinic acetylcholine receptor gene family. *Progr. Brain Res.* 86:195–203

51. Huganir RL, Greengard P. 1990. Regulation of neurotransmitter receptor desensitization by protein phosphorylation. *Neuron* 5:555–67

52. Hume RI, Role LW, Fischbach GD. 1983. Acetylcholine release from growth cones detected with patches of acetylcholine receptor-rich membranes. *Nature* 305:632–34

53. Jacob MH. 1991. Acetylcholine receptor expression in developing chick ciliary ganglion neurons. *J. Neurosci.* 11:1701–12

54. Jacob MH, Berg DK, Lindstrom JM. 1983. The ultrastructural localization of α-bungarotoxin binding sites in relation to synapses on chick ciliary ganglion neurons. *J. Neurosci.* 3:260–71

55. Jaramillo F, Vicini S, Schuetze SM. 1988. Embryonic acetylcholine receptors guarantee spontaneous contractions in rat developing muscle. *Nature* 335:66–68

56. Karlin A. 1993. Structure of nicotinic acetylcholine receptors. *Curr. Opin. Neurobiol.* 3:299–309

57. Kelly RB, Grote E. 1993. Protein targeting in the neuron. *Annu. Rev. Neurosci.* 16:95–127

58. Lena C, Changeux J-P, Mulle C. 1993. Evidence for "preterminal" nicotinic receptors of GABAergic axons in the rat interpeduncular nucleus. *J. Neurosci.* 13:2680–88

59. Levey MS, Brumwell C, Dryer S, Jacob M. 1994. Innervation and target tissue interactions differentially regulate acetylcholine receptor subunit transcript levels in developing neurons in situ. *Neuron.* In press

60. Levin ED. 1992. Nicotinic systems and cognitive function. *Psychopharmacology* 108:417–31

61. Lindstrom J, Schoepfer R, Conroy WG, Whiting P. 1990. Structural and functional heterogeneity of nicotinic receptors. In *The Biology of Nicotine*

Dependence. *Ciba Found. Symp.* ed. G. Bock, J Marsh, 152:23–52. New York: Wiley

62. Listerud M, Brussard AB, Devay P, Colman DR, Role LW. 1991. Functional contribution of neuronal AChR subunits by antisense oligonucleotides. *Science* 254:1518–21

63. Loring RH, Dahm LM, Zigmond RE. 1985. Localization of α-bungarotoxin binding sites in ciliary ganglion of the embryonic chick: an autoradiographic study at the light and electron microscopic level. *Neuroscience* 14:645–60

64. Loring RH, Zigmond RE. 1988. Characterization of neuronal nicotinic receptors by snake venom neurotoxins. *Trends Neurosci.* 11:73–78

65. Luetje CW, Patrick J. 1991. Both α- and β-subunits contribute to the agonist sensitivity of neuronal nicotinic acetylcholine receptors. *J. Neurosci.* 11:837–45

66. Luetje CW, Patrick J, Seguela P. 1990. Nicotine receptors in the mammalian brain. *FASEB J.* 4:2753–60

67. Luetje CW, Piattoni M, Patrick J. 1993. Mapping of ligand binding sites of neuronal nicotinic acetylcholine receptors using chimeric alpha subunits. *Mol. Pharmacol.* 44(3):657–66

68. Luetje CW, Wada K, Rogers S, Abramson SN, Tsuji K, et al. 1990. Neurotoxins distinguish between different neuronal nicotinic acetylcholine receptor subunit combinations. *J. Neurochem.* 55:632–40

69. Mandelzys A, Pie B, Deneris ES, Cooper E. 1994. The developmental increase in ACh current densities on rat sympathetic neurons correlates with changes in nicotinic ACh receptor α-subunit gene expression and occurs independent of innervation. *J. Neurosci.* 15:2357–64

70. Margiotta JF, Berg DK, Dionne VE. 1987. Cyclic AMP regulates the proportion of functional acetylcholine receptors on chicken ciliary ganglion neurons. *Proc. Natl. Acad. Sci. USA* 84:8155–59

71. Margiotta JF, Gurantz D. 1989. Changes in the number, function, and regulation of nicotinic acetylcholine receptors during neuronal development. *Dev. Biol.* 135:326–39

72. Margiotta JF, Howard M. 1994. Eye-extract factors promote the expression of acetylcholine sensitivity in chick dorsal root ganglion neurons. *Dev. Biol.* 163: In press

73. Marshall LM. 1981. Synaptic localization of α-bungarotoxin binding which blocks synaptic transmission at frog sympathetic ganglion neurons. *Proc. Natl. Acad. Sci. USA* 78:1948–52

74. Mathie A, Cull-Candy SG, Colquhoun D. 1991. Conductance and kinetic properties of single nicotinic acetylcholine receptor channels in rat sympathetic neurones. *J. Physiol.* 439:717–50

75. Matter JM, Matter-Sadzinski L, Ballivet M. 1990. Expression of neuronal nicotinic acetylcholine receptor genes in the developing chick visual system. *EMBO J.* 9:1021–26

76. McGehee DS, Yang X, Devay P, Heath MJS, Role LW. 1993. Nicotine potentiates synaptic transmission through presynaptic, αBgTx-sensitive acetylcholine receptors. *Soc. Neurosci. Abstr.* 19:463

77. Morris BJ, Hicks AA, Wisden W, Darlison MG, Hunt SP, Barnard EA. 1990. Distinct regional expression of nicotinic acetylcholine receptor genes in chick brain. *Mol. Brain Res.* 7:305–15

78. Moss BL, Role LW. 1993. Enhanced ACh sensitivity is accompanied by changes in ACh receptor channel properties and segregation of ACh receptor subtypes on sympathetic neurons during innervation in vivo. *J. Neurosci.* 13:13–28

79. Moss BL, Schuetze SM, Role LW. 1989. Functional properties and developmental regulation of nicotinic acetylcholine receptors on embryonic chicken sympathetic neurons. *Neuron* 3:597–607

80. Mulle C, Changeux J-P. 1990. A novel type of nicotinic receptor in the rat central nervous system characterized by patch-clamp techniques. *J. Neurosci.* 10:169–75

81. Mulle C, Choquet D, Korn H, Changeux J-P. 1992. Calcium influx through nicotinic receptor in rat central neurons: its relevance to cellular regulation. *Neuron* 8:135–43

82. Mulle C, Vidal C, Benoit P, Changeux J-P. 1991. Existence of different subtypes of nicotinic acetylcholine receptors in the rat habenulo-interpeduncular system. *J. Neurosci.* 11:2588–97

83. Nef P, Oneyser C, Alliod C, Couturier S, Ballivet M. 1988. Genes expressed in the brain define three distinct neuronal nicotinic acetylcholine receptors. *EMBO J.* 7:595–601

84. Papke RL, Boulter J, Patrick J, Heinemann S. 1989. Single-channel currents of rat neuronal nicotinic acetylcholine receptors expressed in *Xenopus* oocytes. *Neuron* 3:589–96

85. Papke RL, Duvoisin RM, Heinemann SF. 1993. The amino terminal half of the nicotinic β-subunit extracellular domain regulates the kinetics of inhibition by neuronal bungarotoxin. *Proc. R. Soc. London Ser. B* 252(1334):141–48

86. Papke RL, Heinemann SF. 1991. The role of the β4-subunit in determining the kinetic properties of rat neuronal nicotinic acetylcholine α3-receptors. *J. Physiol.* 440:95–112

87. Papke RL, Heinemann SF. 1993. Partial agonist properties of cytisine on neuronal nicotinic receptors containing the β2 subunit. *Mol. Pharmacol.* 45:142–49

88. Paton WDM, Zaimis EJ. 1951. Paralysis of autonomic ganglia with methonium salts. *Br. J. Pharmacol.* 6:155–68

89. Perez-Velazquez JL, Angelides KJ. 1993. Assembly of GABA$_A$ receptor subunits determines sorting and localization in polarized cells. *Nature* 361: 457–60

90. Pugh PC, Berg DK. 1993. Neuronal ACh receptors that bind α-BGT mediate neurite retraction in a calcium-dependent manner. *Soc. Neurosci. Abstr.* 19:463

91. Ramirez-Latorre JA, Qu X, Role LW. 1993. Participation of α5 in neuronal nicotinic AChR channels. *Soc. Neurosci. Abstr.* 19:1533

92. Revah F, Bertrand D, Gaizi JL, Devillers-Thiery A, Mulle C, et al. 1991. Mutations in the channel domain alter desensitization of a neuronal nicotinic receptor. *Nature* 353:846–49

93. Role LW. 1992. Diversity in primary structure and function of neuronal nicotinic acetylcholine receptor channels. *Curr. Opin. Neurobiol.* 2:254–62

94. Rust G, Burgunder J-M, Lauterburg TE, Cachlin AB. 1994. Expression of neuronal nicotinic acetylcholine receptor subunit genes in the rat autonomic nervous system. *Eur. J. Neurosci.* 6:478–85

95. Sargent PB. 1993. The diversity of neuronal nicotinic acetylcholine receptors. *Annu. Rev. Neurosci.* 16:403–33

96. Sargent PB, Pang DZ. 1989. Acetylcholine receptor-like molecules are found in both synaptic and extrasynaptic clusters on the surface of neurons in the frog cardiac ganglion. *J. Neurosci.* 9: 1062–72

97. Schoepfer R, Conroy WG, Whiting P, Gore M, Lindstrom J. 1990. Brain α-bungarotoxin binding protein cDNAs and MAbs reveal subtypes of this branch of the ligand-gated ion channel gene superfamily. *Neuron* 5:35–48

98. Schuetze SM, Role LW. 1987. Developmental regulation of nicotinic acetylcholine receptors. *Annu. Rev. Neurosci.* 10:403–57

99. Seguela P, Wadiche J, Dineley-Miller K, Dani JA, Patrick JW. 1993. Molecular cloning, functional properties and distribution of rat brain α7: a nicotinic

100. Sheng M, Tsaur M-L, Jan YN, Jan LY. 1992. Subcellular segregation of two A-type K$^+$ channel proteins in rat central neurons. *Neuron* 9:271–84

101. Smith MA, Margiotta JF, Berg DK. 1983. Differential regulation of acetylcholine sensitivity and α-bungarotoxin-binding sites on ciliary ganglion neurons in cell culture. *J. Neurosci.* 7:149–70

102. Sorenson EM, Chiappinelli VA. 1990. Intracellular recording in avian brain of a nicotinic response that is insensitive to kappa-bungarotoxin. *Neuron* 5:307–15

103. Stolerman IP. 1990. In *Nicotine Psychopharmacology: Molecular, Cellular, and Behavioural Aspects*, ed. S Wonnacott, MAH Russell, IP Stolerman, pp. 278–306. New York: Oxford Univ. Press

104. Valenta DCC, Downing JE, Role LW. 1993. Peptide modulation of acetylcholine receptor desensitization controlling transmitter release from sympathetic neurons in vitro. *J. Neurophysiol.* 69: 928–42

105. Vernallis AB, Conroy WG, Berg DK. 1993. Neurons assemble acetylcholine receptors with as many as three kinds of subunits while maintaining subunit segregation among receptor subtypes. *Neuron* 10:451–64

106. Vernino S, Amador M, Luetje CW, Patrick J, Dani JA. 1992. Calcium modulation and high calcium permeability of neuronal nicotinic acetylcholine receptors. *Neuron* 8:127–34

107. Vernino S, Rogers M, Radcliff KA, Dani JA. 1994. Quantitative measurement of calcium flux through muscle and neuronal nicotinic acetylcholine receptors. *J. Neurosci.* In press

108. Vijayaraghavan S, Pugh PC, Zhang ZW, Rathouz MM, Berg DK. 1992. Nicotinic receptors that bind α-bungarotoxin on neurons raise intracellular free Ca^{2+}. *Neuron* 8:1–20

109. Wada E, McKinnon D, Heinemann S, Patrick J, Swanson LW. 1990. The distribution of mRNA encoded by a new member of the neuronal nicotinic acetylcholine receptor gene family (α5) in the rat central nervous system. *Brain Res.* 526:46–53

110. Wada E, Wada K, Boulter J, Deneris E, Heinemann S, et al. 1989. Distribution of α2, α3, α4, and β2 neuronal nicotinic receptor subunit mRNAs in the central nervous system: a hybridization histochemical study in the rat. *J. Comp. Neurol.* 284:314–35

111. Wessler I. 1992. Acetylcholine at motor

nerves: storage release, and presynaptic modulation by autoreceptors and adrenoreceptors. *Int. Rev. Neurobiol.* 34: 283–384

112. Whiting PJ, Schoepfer R, Conroy WG, Gore MJ, Keyser KT, et al. 1991. Expression of nicotinic acetylcholine receptor subtypes in brain and retina. *Mol. Brain Res.* 10:61–70

113. Wonnacott S, Drasdo A, Sanderson E, Rowell P. 1990. Presynaptic nicotinic receptors and the modulation of transmitter release. *Ciba Found. Symp.* 152: 87–101

114. Young SH, Poo MM. 1983. Spontaneous release of transmitter from growth cones of embryonic neurones. *Nature* 305: 634–37

115. Yu C, Role LW. 1993. Participation of the $\alpha 7/\alpha$-bungarotoxin binding subunit in neuronal nAChR channel currents. *Soc. Neurosci. Abstr.* 19:463

116. Zatz M, Brownstein MJ. 1981. Injection of α-bungarotoxin near the superchiasmatic nucleus blocks the effects of light on nocturnal pineal enzyme activity. *Brain Res.* 213:438–42

117. Zhang M, Wang YT, Vyas DM, Neuman RS, Bieger D. 1993. Nicotinic cholinoceptor-mediated excitatory postsynaptic potentials in rat nucleus ambiguus. *Exp. Brain Res.* 96:83–88

118. Zhang ZW, Vijayaraghavan S, Berg DK. 1994. Neuronal acetylcholine receptors that bind α-bungarotoxin with high affinity function as ligand-gated ion channels. *Neuron* 12:167–77

119. Zheng JQ, Felder M, Conner JA, Poo M. 1994. Turning of nerve growth cones induced by neurotransmitters. *Nature* 368:140–44

120. Zhou Z, Neher E. 1993. Calcium permeability of nicotinic acetylcholine receptor channels in bovine chromaffin cells. *Pflügers Arch.* 425:511–17

Annu. Rev. Physiol. 1995. 57:547–64

IN DEFENSE OF THE ORAL CAVITY: Structure, Biosynthesis, and Function of Salivary Mucins

Lawrence A. Tabak

Departments of Dental Research and Biochemistry, School of Medicine and Dentistry, University of Rochester, Rochester, New York 14642–8611

KEY WORDS: GalNAc transferase, glycoprotein, mucin biosynthesis, O-glycosylation, saliva

INTRODUCTION

The oral environment, like other mucosal surfaces of the body, is coated by a slimy, viscoelastic coat termed mucus. This adherent layer, consisting predominately of salivary glycoproteins, proteins, and lipids, forms a jelly–like blanket that represents the perimeter defense of the tissue/environmental interface (77). The unique physicochemical and rheological properties of the mucus coat are contributed largely by the heavily O-glycosylated mucin-glycoproteins (mucins).

Salivary mucins are synthesized by the mucus acinar cells of the paired submandibular (SMG) and sublingual (SLG) glands, as well as minor salivary glands distributed throughout the palatal and buccal mucosa. Serous acinar cells, such as those found in the human or rat parotid glands, do not contribute to the production of salivary mucins.

Much of our current understanding of salivary mucin function has been derived by inference. Various subjective and objective functional losses have been catalogued in persons who lack the ability to produce adequate levels of saliva (4). Relevant findings include (*a*) the sensation of oral dryness, particularly among those subjects with compromised mucus gland function (26); (*b*) difficulty with swallowing; and (*c*) an increased susceptibility to dental cavity (caries) formation and the appearance of opportunistic yeast infections (thrush mouth). These findings have led to a generalized view that saliva functions to (*a*) hydrate and lubricate the oral structures; (*b*) facilitate the oral phase of

547

0066–4278/95/0315–0547$05.00

swallowing by enhancing the formation of a slippery food bolus; (c) prevent demineralization of tooth mineral; and (d) regulate the oral microbial flora.

Based upon the general physicochemical properties of mucins and in vitro demonstrations of related activities, a number of these general salivary functions have been attributed specifically to mucins (77). Some corroboration has been obtained by the apparent restoration of specific functions through the use of mucin-based saliva substitutes (8, 21) in subjects who lack endogenous secretion. To date, however, no individuals who specifically fail to express salivary mucins have been examined, and thus direct evidence for specific in vivo functions is lacking.

It is the purpose of this review to consider the structural features of salivary mucin that underlie its proposed functions. Approaches to the direct evaluation of mucin function are detailed. A consideration of mucin biosynthesis and structure/function relationships of these glycoproteins may suggest future strategies for the development of artificial mucins for use in salivary substitutes.

STRUCTURE OF SALIVARY MUCINS

Like other secreted mucins, salivary mucins are high molecular weight glycoproteins composed of a degenerate protein backbone (apomucin) enriched in hydroxyamino acids (threonine and/or serine) and proline. In addition, hundreds of carbohydrate side chains (oligosaccharides) are linked O-glycosidically to many, but not necessarily all, of the hydroxyamino acids.

Several unique structural features underlie the physicochemical properties of salivary mucins and their various biological functions. These include repeating sequences of amino acids, termed tandem repeats, a clustered arrangement of O-glycans, stabilization of suprastructure by noncovalent and covalent forces, and a diverse array of oligosaccharide side chains.

Apomucins

The very properties that endow mucins with their protective qualities have rendered them highly refractory to conventional biochemical characterization. Only recently have recombinant DNA methods made it possible to deduce the complete amino acid sequence of human salivary mucin MG2 (9) and a rat submandibular gland (RSMG) mucin (3), as well as a large portion of the porcine submandibular gland (PSMG) mucin (23).

These salivary apomucins vary greatly in size (Figure 1); the protein cores of MG2 and RSMG mucin are relatively small with calculated masses of 39 and 32.5 kDa, respectively (3, 9). In contrast, PSMG apomucin contains at least 2,800 amino acids (23). The protein backbone of each of these salivary mucins is modular in design, consisting of discrete domains (Figure 1). The N-terminal domain of both the MG2 and RSMG apomucins contains putative signal sequences. There are relatively few potential O-glycosylation sites, and they are arranged in a nonrepeating fashion. Two nonconserved cysteine residues are found within this region in both the MG2 and RSMG mucins; biochemical evidence indicates that they do not participate in interchain disulfide linkages (25, 78). In MG2, there are four potential N-glycosylation sites in the N-terminal domain and sequence analysis indicates that at least the first site (Asn [97]) is occupied (62). The function of this N-terminal domain is not known, but there is evidence to suggest that it is removed in the RSMG prior to secretion (3).

The central region of these salivary apomucins is dominated by the presence of a variable number of tandem repeats ranging from 13 to 81 amino acids in length (3, 9, 23, 80). Although there is no sequence homology among these repeating elements, all are highly enriched in hydroxyamino acids and proline, and thus the majority of potential O-glycosylation sites are localized within these regions (Figure 1). Both structural predictions (22, 23) and circular dichroism studies (22, 67) indicate that PSMG and ovine submandibular gland (OSMG) apomucins lack appreciable secondary structure. Sequence analysis of salivary mucin tandem repeats indicates that they are distinct from those found in the membrane–bound mucin, MUC-1, which is the only tandem repeat thus far observed to have an intrinsic secondary structure (polyproline β-turn helix) independent of carbohydrate (25).

The C-terminal domain of the MG2 and RSMG mucins is serine– and threonine–enriched but is relatively low in proline level. No obvious repeat motif is observed, although in the RSMG apomucin there is a stretch of 16 amino acids in which 14 are serine or threonine, and a similar domain is found in the MG2 apomucin where 10–12 residues are serine or threonine.

In PSMG apomucin, there is an additional C-terminal domain. The region is highly enriched in cysteine residues and is homologous to sequences found in a bovine SMG mucin–like protein (6). Functionally, this domain is the attachment site of disulfide–bonded subunits and accounts for the extraordinarily high molecular weight of PSMG mucin (68). Thus there are at least two distinct forms of salivary apomucins: those that lack a cysteine–enriched domain and therefore lack subunit structure, and those that are composed of multiple, covalently bound subunits. The cysteine–enriched domain is globular in nature and is highly sensitive to proteolytic cleavage (23, 68). Since PSMG mucin has been purified only from glandular extracts, it is not known if this cleavage occurs physiologically or as a result of some glandular protease that is active during the extraction of the glandular material.

Clustering of O-Glycans

The O-glycosidic linkage between N-acetylgalactosamine (GalNAc) and the hydroxyl group of threonine or serine represents a key structural determinant

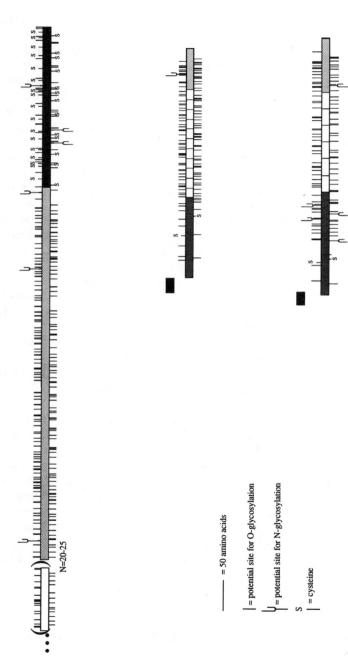

Figure 1 A schematic representation of PSMG (*top*), RSMG (*middle*), and MG2 (*bottom*) apomucins drawn to scale. Homologous domains are shaded in this same manner. Potential N- and O-glycosylation sites are indicated, as are the locations of all cysteine residues.

of mucin function. Steric interactions between O–linked GalNAc residues and the peptide backbone result in a significant stiffening and expansion of the protein core (38, 67), and this effect is potentiated by the presence of regularly repeating clusters of sugar side chains afforded by the underlying tandem repeat design of the protein backbone. Surprisingly, the overall length and structure of O-glycans have little effect on mucin shape; rather, maximum expansion occurs with disaccharide structures, and little enhancement is observed with larger oligosaccharides (68, 72). This suggests that all mucins should exhibit similar rheological properties, but they do not. The structural basis for dissimilar gel–forming properties is not clearly understood but likely relates to differences in the stabilization of the mucin-suprastructure.

Stabilization of Mucin Suprastructure

The marked expansion of mucin shape, which occurs as a result of the addition of O-glycans, results in a significant macromolecular overlap and interweaving. The ensuing suprastructure is stabilized largely by noncovalent interactions among oligosaccharide side chains (66, 72). Thus mucins with longer side chains tend to be more viscous (66, 72) and appear to have higher elasticity and adhesiveness, and lower solubility. In the higher molecular weight salivary mucins, suprastructure is further secured by the disulfide bonding of multiple subunits (23, 31).

The sticky, highly charged character of mucins has made it challenging to isolate these glycoproteins from other molecules. These physical associations have provided indirect evidence for "heterotypic complexing" in which salivary mucins are thought to selectively bind nonmucinous proteins such as secretory IgA, lysozyme, link proteins, and lipids as a means of concentrating protective molecules in the mucus coat (77). However, it has proven difficult to distinguish between true protein-protein interactions and artifactual associations due to sample handling (e.g. coprecipitation during dialysis and lyophilization, disulfide bond exchange). Clearly, independent quantitative evaluation of such interactions is needed (30). Nevertheless, the physicochemical properties of salivary mucins could be altered by complex formation, and several examples of functional change have been reported (e.g. 7). Thus the structural elements that underlie complexation of mucin with nonmucin molecules may represent yet another significant determinant of mucin function.

Diversity of Salivary Mucin Oligosaccharides

Structural studies of salivary mucin oligosaccharides have pointed to the considerable variation in the type and relative amounts of O-glycans present, a phenomenon termed microheterogeneity. For example, it has been determined that the distribution of blood group A+ tetrasaccharide among PSMG mucins isolated from different animals ranged from 0 to 59%, whereas the H blood group trisaccharide comprised between 4 and 58% of the total glycan (28). However, analysis of single gland preparations of mucin indicated that the distribution of O-glycan types was highly conserved between the left and right glands of an individual animal. This suggests that the glycosylation apparatus is much more tightly controlled than previously thought, although interanimal variation is substantial. A second significant point to emerge from this analysis is that only about 75% of the hydroxyamino acids were glycosylated. This points to an important void in our current understanding of mucin structure. We do not have an unambiguous and complete map of the specific sites of O-glycosylation for any mucin-glycoprotein. Obviously, this would be prerequisite for any definitive analysis of the conformation of the molecule.

Salivary mucin oligosaccharides range in complexity from simple mono- and disaccharides to highly branched structures. From the physicochemical standpoint, only a disaccharide is needed to achieve maximal expansion of three–dimensional mucin structure (68). Therefore, it is important to determine if the function of the remaining carbohydrate is to provide bulk packing, i.e. a means by which mucin suprastructure is stabilized noncovalently as described above, or if, in fact, these sugars encode specific forms of information such as recognition sites in microbial adhesion in vivo (see below) (14).

REGULATION OF SALIVARY MUCIN BIOSYNTHESIS

In contrast to proteins or nucleic acids whose synthesis is directed by a template–based mechanism, much of the genetic information required to express a salivary mucin is transferred indirectly (74 and references therein). Thus it has been argued that mucin heterogeneity reflects, in part, the lack of overall coordination among the various co- and posttranslational modifications that are required. A number of experimental tools are becoming available that will allow the analysis of biosynthetic coordination. In particular, it will be important to determine the extent to which salivary apomucin expression is coordinated with the repertoire of transcripts encoding the various glycosyltransferases that attach the O-glycans of the protein backbone.

Expression of Salivary Apomucin

We know relatively little about the mechanisms that regulate the expression of salivary apomucins. Southern blot analysis of human and rat DNA suggests a low gene copy number for the salivary mucins studied to date and the presence of genetic polymorphism (3, 9). RSMG mucin displays allelic variation in the length of tandem repeat domain, although the variation does not contribute to as high a degree of polymorphism as is observed in the human MUC1 gene (3, 48).

In contrast to other Muc gene products that appear to be expressed in multiple tissue types (48), the expression of salivary apomucins appears to be restricted principally to SMG and SLGs (3, 9). It is not known if salivary apomucins are expressed in a tumor–specific manner, as has been demonstrated for several other Muc gene products (48).

The experimental manipulation of apomucin expression offers an attractive strategy to examine mucin function in vivo. Targeted knock out experiments in which the expression of an apomucin was ablated or temporarily shut down (e.g. via the expression of an antisense construct) could provide some insight. Given the potential functional redundancy observed in nature, however, it is possible that no altered phenotype would be detected. An alternative approach would be to overexpress apomucin to determine if increased mucin levels afford enhanced resistance to specific environmental insults.

N–Linked Glycosylation

Addition of N–linked oligosaccharide side chains is initiated as a cotranslational event with the en bloc transfer of a $(N\text{-acetylglucosamine})_2 \text{mannose}_9 \text{glucose}_3$ precursor oligosaccharide from a dolichol lipid carrier to an asparagine residue on the nascent polypeptide chain. The precursor oligosaccharide undergoes subsequent remodeling, which involves removal of all glucose and some mannose residues. Additional sugars such as N-acetylglucosamine, galactose, fucose, and sialic acids may be added to yield the final structures (65).

Several salivary mucins have been definitively shown to contain N–linked oligosaccharides (e.g. 16), and others contain potential N-glycosylation sites. The function of such units is thought to be related to intracellular processing. Proper covalent oligomerization of rat gastric mucin subunits appears to be dependent upon the presence of N-glycans (15). Additionally, because the acquisition of N–linked sugars precedes O-glycosylation, it is plausible that O-glycosylation is influenced by the presence of N-glycans. Direct analysis of these possibilities should be testable through the use of site–directed mutagenesis methods.

O–Linked Glycosylation

UDP-GalNAc: Polypeptide N-acetylgalactosaminyltransferase (polypeptide GalNAc transferase), catalyzes the initial step in mucin type O-glycosylation, i.e. the covalent attachment of GalNAc to a hydroxyamino acid. Since O-glycosylation proceeds in a stepwise manner, the addition of GalNAc to threonine or serine represents the first committed step in O-glycan biosynthesis and is thus an important control point in the process. Control may be exerted in at least three discrete levels: (*a*) expression and availability of glycosyltransferases, (*b*) expression and availability of substrate, and (*c*) availability of the sugar nucleotide donor. It is not known whether these levels of control function independently of one another, or if there are elements of coordination among them.

Studies of polypeptide GalNAc transferase substrate specificity have tended to emphasize either the effects of local secondary structure (accessibility) or the role played by flanking amino acids (signal motifs), although, clearly, these two elements must be considered in concert. Salivary apomucins do not assume ordered secondary structure (22, 23, 67) and may therefore function as a passive scaffold for sugar attachment (22, 38).

Pattern analysis of sequences flanking (24, 55, 86) known glycosylation sites as well as in vitro studies with synthetic substrates (24, 54, 55, 56, 83) have indicated that the binding sites of the polypeptide GalNAc transferase are large (24) and tolerate a broad range of amino acids (24, 54, 56). However, highly charged or bulky groups seem to inhibit glycosylation of specific sites (24, 56), and it has not been determined if these relationships hold in vivo.

Several key questions relative to initiation remain. The failure to uncover a definitive signal motif may simply reflect an experimental averaging of multiple polypeptide GalNAc transferase specificities (e.g. compare references 24, 32, 54, 82, 83). An attractive means for resolving this issue would be to genetically ablate expression of the cloned transferase (32, 33) and determine if any activity remains. Experimental ambiguity also remains with regard to the occupancy of a given site (i.e. the degree to which a specific site is glycosylated), although there are now analytical methods that should help resolve this question (e.g. 59). Finally, it remains unclear whether O-glycosylation of multiple hydroxyamino acids proceeds simultaneously (e.g. 58) or in a hierarchical manner, that is, either through preferential glycosylation of specific sites (54, 82, 83) or a recycling of precursor mucin through a polypeptide GalNAc transferase–containing compartment (36).

O-glycans continue to mature as the mucin courses through the Golgi apparatus. Elongation is regulated largely by substrate specificity; i.e. the product of the first glycosyltransferase reaction becomes the substrate for the second (5, 84). Additionally, the peptide context of a glycosylation site may also influence the elongation of O-glycans (11). Thus a key question for future inquiry relates to whether salivary mucin glycoforms (e.g. 61) arise from differential glycosylation of unique apomucins in the same cell, or from the restricted expression of apomucin in subsets of cells that have different repertoires of glycosyltransferases.

Superimposed over the substrate specificities of the individual glycosyltransferases are the mechanisms that regulate the expression and localization of the enzymes within the Golgi apparatus. While the ubiquitous nature of glycosyltransferase expression is suggestive of "housekeeping" genes, the broad range of expression observed among different organs argues for some degree of tissue specificity. Although there is some indirect evidence that hormones can modulate levels of salivary gland glycosylation (reviewed in 74) and mucin content (17, 46), there is surprisingly little direct evidence for hormonal regulation of O-glycosylation (12). Thus the extent to which hormones influence O-glycosylation remains to be determined.

SALIVARY MUCIN FUNCTION

Structurally there are two distinct forms of salivary mucins, those that are composed of multiple, covalently bonded subunits and are thus very large, and those that consist of single polypeptide chains and are therefore relatively small. Both mucin forms are found in human saliva—the large molecular weight form is termed MG1 (45), and the smaller mucin is termed MG2 (60). Available evidence suggests that these structurally distinct mucins play somewhat different roles within the oral cavity. The enhanced rheological properties of the larger mucins lend themselves to coating functions, whereas the smaller mucins tend to exert their effects more in solution via interaction with microorganisms.

Alimentation

Gustatory and masticatory stimulation markedly increase salivary flow rates as well as the output of acinar cell products such as mucins, which aid in the initial phase of swallowing (35). Saliva likely serves as a masticatory lubricant; it facilitates the slide and glide of tooth surfaces during chewing and aids in the formation and swallowing of a food bolus. Attempts have been made to quantify some of these properties. For example, mucin–containing human SMG/SLG saliva is 50–100% more viscous than human parotid saliva (27, 40). As a quantitative approximation of salivary lubrication, the frictional coefficient of a tooth (in point contact) being dragged across a glass surface has been measured in the presence of saliva, MG1 and MG2, and various mucin– and nonmucin–containing artificial salivas. Mucin–containing artificial saliva most closely approximates the lubricity of human SMG/SLG saliva (40). On a molar basis, MG1 is a better lubricant than MG2 (42). However, the structural basis for this property is not yet defined. Other relevant properties that must be quantitated include mucin elasticity and adhesiveness, each of which is likely to contribute to mucin function.

Tissue Coating

The unique rheological properties of the salivary mucins contribute to the formation of a salivary thin film (estimated to be 0.07–0.1 mm in thickness), which covers all intra–oral surfaces (13). Thus in common with other mucins, a primary function of salivary mucins is tissue coating; that is, the resultant demulcent coat is thought to hydrate and lubricate the soft tissues of the mouth (77).

Subjects lacking all major salivary gland function rarely have normal oral mucosa, which indicates that the salivary secretions help maintain oral mucosal integrity (87). Indeed, patients provided with a mucin-containing artificial saliva show improvement in the health of their soft tissues (8). However, few studies have attempted to quantify the contribution of the salivary mucins to the formation of the mucus coat. In rodents, surgical removal of the SMG/SLGs results in a 36% decrease in the thickness of the oral mucus coat and an estimated 43% reduction in adherent mucin content (64). However, the quality of the salivary coat in situ has not been characterized sufficiently to allow for comparison to mucosal status.

There is some evidence to suggest that there is a selective interaction between specific salivary components and the soft tissues of the mouth. Both MG1 and MG2 have been identified within the mucus coat formed in vivo (10, 70), and each undergoes limited proteolytic cleavage (10). Mucins isolated from the mucus coat are associated with noncovalently bound lipids (70). There is evidence for covalent cross–linking of specific mucosal components via transglutaminase; however, mucins do not appear to participate in this process (10). Thus it is not known if mucins passively coat the soft tissues of the mouth, or if there are specific mucin-tissue interactions. It would be of great practical value to understand the forces that are responsible for the formation and maintenance of the mucus coat because this integument is the primary barrier to the delivery of pharmaceuticals transmucosally.

In contrast to other mucosal surfaces of the body, the oral cavity contains nonshedding, mineralized surface structures (teeth) that are highly vulnerable to microbial insult (29). The selective adsorption of salivary mucins to the tooth surface contributes to the formation of the acquired enamel pellicle, which may serve as a permeability barrier and thus help to protect the under-lying hard tissue from demineralization by acids formed by the tooth-borne flora. The acquired enamel pellicle also serves as the initial attachment point for the microorganisms that colonize the tooth surface.

MG1 has a higher affinity for tooth mineral (hydroxyapatite) than MG2, and only MG2 is competitively displaced from hydroxyapatite by salivary cystatins (76). MG1 and salivary cystatin have been localized in 2 h pellicle formed in situ (2). These results suggest that MG1 and MG2 interact differently with hydroxyapatite. MG2 fails to adsorb in appreciable quantities to the tooth, thus rendering it available to interact with oral microorganisms in solution, whereas MG1 participates in the formation of the protective integument on the tooth surface. Mucins have historically been classified on the basis of their affinity for hydroxyapatite chromatography matrices (e.g. major and minor mucins; see 77 for review), although the functional importance of this observation has not been widely appreciated.

Salivary pellicles formed in vitro are able to protect tooth enamel from demineralization in the face of an acid challenge. Pellicle formed from mucin–depleted human SMG/SLG saliva provides only 30% of the original protection observed with the intact secretion, thus indicating that mucins contribute markedly to the protective effect against acid demineralization in vitro (53). There is some evidence that complex formation occurs during the maturation of the acquired enamel pellicle (see 75, 77 for review). An important challenge for the future will be to define the topographical relationships among the pellicular components.

Modulation of the Oral Flora

The mouth also serves as a major portal of entry and passage for infectious microorganisms. Upon entering the oral environment, microorganisms are rapidly enveloped with a salivary coat. There is evidence for selective interactions between specific salivary macromolecules such as mucin and specific microorganisms. Thus salivary mucins, in concert with other factors in saliva, help to modulate both the number and type of microorganism that colonize the mouth by favoring attachment and subsequent proliferation of certain organisms while promoting the clearance of others (29, 75, 77).

Although there have been numerous descriptive studies of microbial-salivary mucin interaction (see 29, 75, 77 and references therein), relatively little progress has been made in defining the specific nature of the binding sites. Such data are essential for an evaluation of the feasibility of creating anti–adhesion therapeutics. Perhaps the best–characterized example relates to the interactions between specific strains of oral streptococci and MG1 and MG2. Human SMG/SLG saliva aggregates several streptococcal strains in a sialic acid–dependent manner (47). Several laboratories have demonstrated that MG2 interacts with streptococci either in solution, which results in agglutination (41, 44, 71), or when adsorbed onto a solid phase, which leads to adherence (44, 51, 69). In contrast, MG1 does not appear to interact with the streptococci surveyed (44, 51, 71). When human SMG/SLG saliva is immunochemically depleted of MG2, the ability to agglutinate streptococci is lost. When MG1 is removed, however, the streptococci are still agglutinated (43). Inhibition studies with complex oligosaccharides indicate that μM quantities of the predominate acidic trisaccharide of MG2, sialic acid $\alpha 2,3$ galactose $\beta 1,3$ GalNAc, inhibits MG2-streptococcal interaction (50). Interestingly, this specificity is identical to that of an *Escherichia coli* adhesin, which localizes to the tips of fimbriae (49).

All microbial-salivary mucin interaction cannot be explained on the basis of the recognition of this trisaccharide structure alone. For example, several strains of microorganisms are agglutinated by PSMG, OSMG, and BSMG mucins, which have very different O-glycans (39). This suggests that some common physicochemical property of these mucins may be responsible for the observed interactions. Cooperative binding between BSMG or OSMG mucin and rotaviruses has been described. Although the viruses can recognize sialic acid–containing trisaccharides, this preference is superseded when binding to higher valency ligands such as bovine or ovine salivary mucins (85). Such phenomena may underlie the generalized agglutinability of microorganisms with mucins of varying carbohydrate structure. There is also recent evidence to suggest that MG2-*Pseudomonas aeruginosa* interaction is mediated, in part, via protein-protein interactions between the bacterial pili and a trypsin–labile domain of the mucin (62), as well as by MG2-sIgA complexes (7).

Salivary mucins are degraded in vivo, presumably by enzymes that are elaborated by the oral flora (10). Exposure of penultimate sugar residues through the action of exoglycosidase activities could result in the loss of specific binding sites or the expression of new binding sites within the dental pellicle, an event we have termed structural modulation (77). For example, removal of terminal sialic acid residues results in decreased interaction of mucin with several streptococcal strains but has no effect on others (41, 51, 69).

It is also likely that mucins can serve as metabolic substrates for specific organisms thereby affording them a selective advantage. For example, mico-organisms in the gut have been shown to adapt to produce blood group degrading enzymes (34). The synergistic degradation of mucin by *Streptococcus oralis* and *Streptococcus sanguis* in mixed chemostat cultures has been documented (81).

PROSPECTS FOR MUCINS AS ORAL THERAPEUTICS

The sensation of oral dryness (xerostomia) is a prevalent problem, particularly among the elderly, with estimates ranging from 12–29% in different populations (26, 52, and references therein). Individuals who experience a complete loss of salivary function are clearly at risk for xerostomia and other untoward sequelae (4, 26). However, more subtle forms of salivary dysfunction may exist, i.e. a situation where the level of an essential salivary component is reduced below a critical threshold level. For example, the sensation of oral dryness is not directly related to decreased salivary output because this subjective complaint has been described among individuals with normal flow rates (26, 52). A wide range of human salivary mucin concentration is observed (1, 19). There are significant reductions in the concentrations of MG1 and MG2 in both stimulated and unstimulated SM/SL saliva collected from individuals aged 65–83 years compared with a group of subjects with ages ranging from

18–35 years of age (19). Similar decreases are observed in mice (18). An obvious next step would be to quantitate levels of salivary mucins in xerostomic subjects who have normal salivary output to determine if there is a measurable threshold of mucin concentration.

Several approaches are being explored to deliver adequate mucin levels to the oral cavity of compromised individuals. In situations where some salivary gland tissue remains, salivary mucin levels may be enhanced via selective stimulation of the signal transduction pathways (17). For example, chronic systemic exposure to the β-adrenergic agonist isoproterenol significantly elevated mucin levels in mouse SMGs (20) and MSMG saliva (17).

For individuals who have a total lack of salivary function, replacement represents the most immediate therapeutic option. Several clinical trials have demonstrated that mucin–based salivary substitutes are more readily accepted and provide greater relief from xerostomia than their nonmucin–based counterparts (8, 21). However, not all patients respond to these preparations (8, 21), and their cost and lack of substantiveness diminish their attractiveness. The cost involved in expressing and purifying recombinant proteins from mammalian host cells make the feasibility of such an approach unlikely. The successful over–expression of the polypeptide GalNAc transferase in Sf9 cells (33) suggests that these insect cells may be re-engineered to produce cell factories capable of producing desired recombinant glycoproteins at a lower cost (33, 79). Yeast such as *Saccharomyces cerevisiae* produce O-glycans in the form of mannosyl residues attached to serine or threonine (73). It would be interesting to determine if such structures would impart mucin-like properties to a heterologously expressed apomucin. However, because there are no mammalian counterparts to these oligosaccharide structures, it is likely that these would prove to be highly antigenic in humans and therefore not usable.

Several synthetic approaches to mucin engineering have been reported. The challenge will be to adequately model the physicochemical properties of hydroxyamino acid-GalNAc bond clusters and then determine the smallest number of units required to achieve the desired biological effect. Difficulties with stereospecificity and the requirement for multiple protection/de–protection cycles make chemical synthesis expensive and labor intensive. The alternative of chemoenzymatic synthesis avoids the need for multiple protection/de–protection steps because no unwanted side products are formed and reactions proceed in a highly stereo– and regional–selective fashion (37). For example, enzymatic coupling of N– and O–linked glycopeptides has been accomplished via subtilisin catalysis (88). The recent cloning of the polypeptide GalNAc transferase (32, 33) should facilitate progress towards chemoenzymatic synthesis of mammalian forms of mucin O-glycans.

Ultimately, the most cost–efficient approach to creating an artificial mucin would be to design a peptide mimetic. Two strategies are currently being explored to mimic carbohydrate structure/function with peptides. In the first, large libraries of randomly generated peptides are screened for their ability to mimic some carbohydrate–specific function (e.g. 57). Once a peptide is identified, it can then be subjected to mutagenesis to determine the most complementary structure. The second approach, which has met with some success, is the creation of antiidiotypic antibodies to monoclonal antibodies directed against known carbohydrate structures. For example, immunization of a rabbit with a mouse monoclonal antibody to human anti-A blood group substance resulted in an anti–Id that mimics the shape of the blood group-A oligosaccharide (63).

While the complete synthesis of a "designer" mucin is not likely to occur in the immediate future, the work required to reach this goal will undoubtedly provide additional insight into the structure, function, and synthesis of this important class of macromolecule.

ACKNOWLEDGMENTS

I thank the members of my laboratory group, past and present, for their many contributions. The efforts of Earl Albone in creating Figure 1 are appreciated. Thanks are extended to Pat Noonan for her help in preparing the chapter. Work from our laboratory has been supported by the National Institute of Dental Research, and I am most grateful for this support.

Literature Cited

1. Aguirre A, Testa-Weintraub LA, Banderas JA, Haraszthy GG, Reddy MS, Levine MJ. 1993. Sialochemistry: A diagnostic tool? *Crit. Rev. Oral Biol. Med.* 4(3/4):343–50
2. Al-Hashimi I, Levine MJ. 1989. Characterization of in vivo salivary–derived enamel pellicle. *Arch. Oral Biol.* 34(4):289–95
3. Albone EF, Hagen FK, VanWuyckhuyse BC, Tabak LA. 1994. Molecular cloning of a rat submandibular gland apomucin. *J. Biol. Chem.* 269:16845–52
4. Bertram U. 1967. Xerostomia: Clinical aspects, pathology and pathogenesis. *Acta Odontol. Scand.* 25(Suppl. 49):11–126
5. Beyer TA, Rearick JI, Paulson JC, Prieels J-P, Sadler JE, Hill RL. 1979. Biosynthesis of mammalian glycoproteins. *J. Biol. Chem.* 254(24):12531–41

6. Bhargava AK, Woitach JT, Davidson EA, Bhavanandan VP. 1990. Cloning and cDNA sequence of a bovine submaxillary gland mucin-like protein containing two distinct domains. *Proc. Natl. Acad. Sci. USA* 87:6798–802
7. Biesbrock AR, Reddy MS, Levine MJ. 1991. Interaction of a salivary mucin–secretory immunoglobulin A complex with mucosal pathogens. *Infect. Immunol.* 59:3492–97
8. Blixt-Johansen G, Ek A-C, Ganowiak W, Granérus A-K, von Schenck H, et al. 1992. Improvement of oral mucosa with mucin containing artificial saliva in geriatric patients. *Arch. Gerontol. Geriatr.* 14:193–201
9. Bobek LA, Tsai H, Biesbrock AR, Levine MJ. 1993. Molecular cloning, sequence, and specificity of expression of the gene encoding the low molecular

weight human salivary mucin (MUC7). *J. Biol. Chem.* 268(27):20563–69

10. Bradway SD, Bergey EJ, Scannapieco FA, Ramasubbu N, Zawacki S, Levine MJ. 1992. Formation of salivary-mucosal pellicle: The role of transglutaminase. *Biochem. J.* 284:557–64

11. Brockhausen I, Möller G, Merz G, Adermann K, Paulsen H. 1990. Control of mucin synthesis: The peptide portion of synthetic O-glycopeptide substrates influences the activity of O-glycan core 1 UDPgalactose:N-acetyl-α-galactosaminyl-R β3-galactosyltransferase. *Biochemistry* 29:10206–12

12. Chilton BS, Kaplan HA, Lennarz WJ. 1988. Estrogen regulation of the central enzymes involved in O– and N–linked glycoprotein assembly in the developing and the adult rabbit endocervix. *Endocrinology* 123(3):1237–44

13. Collins LMC, Dawes C. 1987. The surface area of the adult human mouth and thickness of the salivary film covering the teeth and oral mucosa. *J. Dent. Res.* 66(8):1300–2

14. Corfield T. 1992. Mucus glycoproteins, super glycoforms: How to solve a sticky problem? *Glycoconj. J.* 9:217–21

15. Dekker J, Strous GJ. 1990. Covalent oligomerization of rat gastric mucin occurs in the rough endoplasmic reticulum, is N-glycosylation–dependent, and precedes initial O-glycosylation. *J. Biol. Chem.* 265(30):18116–22

16. Denny PA, Denny PC. 1982. A mouse submandibular sialomucin containing both N– and O–glycosylic linkages. *Carbohydr. Res.* 110:305–14

17. Denny PA, Hong SH, Klauser DK, Denny PC. 1992. Increased mucin levels in submandibular saliva from mice following repeated isoproterenol treatment. *Arch. Oral Biol.* 37(1):73–75

18. Denny PA, Klauser DK, Villa BJ, Hong SH, Denny PC. 1991. The effect of ageing on mucin contents in mouse submandibular glands. *Arch. Oral Biol.* 36(7):477–81

19. Denny PC, Denny PA, Klauser DK, Hong SH, Navazesh M, Tabak LA. 1991. Age–related changes in mucins from human whole saliva. *J. Dent. Res.* 70(10):1320–27

20. Denny PC, Denny PA, Villa BJ, Klauser DK. 1991. Increased mucin levels in submandibular glands of aged male mice after chronic isoproterenol treatment. *Arch. Oral Biol.* 36(7):483–89

21. Duxbury AJ, Thakker NS, Wastell DG. 1989. A double–blind cross–over trial of a mucin–containing artificial saliva. *Br. Dent. J.* 166:115–20

22. Eckhardt AE, Timpte CS, Abernethy JL, Toumadje A, Johnson WC, Hill RL. 1987. Structural properties of porcine submaxillary gland apomucin. *J. Biol. Chem.* 262(23):11339–44

23. Eckhardt AE, Timpte CS, Abernethy JL, Zhao Y, Hill RL. 1991. Porcine submaxillary mucin contains a cystine–rich, carboxylterminal domain in addition to a highly repetitive, glycosylated domain. *J. Biol. Chem.* 266(15):9678–86

24. Elhammer AP, Poorman RA, Brown E, Magiora LL, Hoogerheide JG, Kézky FJ. 1993. The specificity of UDP-GalNAc:polypeptide N-Acetylgalactosaminyltransferase as inferred from a database of in vivo substrates and from the in vitro glycosylation of proteins and peptides. *J. Biol. Chem.* 268(14):10029–38

25. Fontenot JD, Tjandra N, Bu D, Ho C, Montelaro RC, Finn OJ. 1993. Biophysical characterization of one–, two– and three–tandem repeats of human mucin (muc-1) protein core. *Cancer Res.* 53:5386–94

26. Fox PC, Busch KA, Baum BJ. 1987. Subjective reports of xerostomia and objective measures of salivary gland performance. *J. Am. Dent. Assoc.* 115:581–84

27. Gans RF, Watson GE, Tabak LA. 1990. A new assessment in vitro of human salivary lubrication using a compliant substrate. *Arch. Oral Biol.* 35(7):487–92

28. Gerken TA, Jentoft N. 1987. Structure and dynamics of porcine submaxillary mucin as determined by natural abundance carbon-[13] NMR spectroscopy. *Biochemistry* 26:4689–99

29. Gibbons RJ, van Houte J. 1975. Bacterial adherence in oral microbial ecology. *Annu. Rev. Microbiol.* 29:19–44

30. Guarente L. 1993. Strategies for the identification of interacting proteins. *Proc. Natl. Acad. Sci. USA* 90:1639–41

31. Gupta R, Jentoft N. 1989. Subunit structure of porcine submaxillary mucin. *Biochemistry* 28:6114–21

32. Hagen FK, VanWuychhuyse B, Tabak LA. 1993. Purification, cloning, and expression of a bovine UDP-GalNAc:polypeptide N-acetyl-galactosaminyltransferase. *J. Biol. Chem.* 268(25):18960–65

33. Homa FL, Hollander T, Lehman DJ, Thomsen DR, Elhammer AP. 1993. Isolation and expression of a cDNA clone encoding a bovine UDP-GalNAc: polypeptide N-acetylgalactosaminyltransferase. *J. Biol. Chem.* 268(17):12609–16

34. Hoskins LC, Agustines M, McKee WB, Boulding ET, Kriaris M, Niedermeyer G. 1985. Mucin degradation in human

colon ecosystems. Isolation and properties of fecal strains that degrade ABH blood group antigens and oligosaccharides from mucin glycoproteins. *J. Clin. Invest.* 75:944–53

35. Hughes CV, Baum BJ, Fox PC, Marmary Y, Yeh CK, Sonies BC. 1987. Oralpharyngeal dysphagia: a common sequela of salivary gland dysfunction. *Dysphagia* 1:173–77

36. Hull SR, Sugarman ED, Spielman J, Carraway KL. 1991. Biosynthetic maturation of an ascites tumor cell surface sialomucin. *J. Biol. Chem.* 266(21): 13580–86

37. Ichikawa Y, Look GC, Wong C-H. 1992. Enzyme–catalyzed oligosaccharide synthesis. *Anal. Biochem.* 202:215–38

38. Jentoft N. 1990. Why are proteins O–glycosylated? *Trends Biochem. Sci.* 15: 291–94

39. Koop HM, Valentijn-Benz M, Nieuw Amerongen AV, Roukema PA, de Graaff J. 1990. Aggregation of oral bacteria by human salivary mucins in comparison to salivary and gastric mucins of animal origin. *Antonie van Leeuwenhoek J. Microbiol. Serol.* 58:255–63

40. Levine MJ, Aguirre A, Hatton MN, Tabak LA. 1987. Artificial salivas: present and future. *J. Dent. Res.* 66(Spec. Issue):693–98

41. Levine MJ, Herzberg MC, Levine MS, Ellison SA, Stinson MW, et al. 1978. Specificity of salivary-bacterial interactions: Role of terminal sialic acid residues in the interaction of salivary glycoproteins with *Streptococcus sanguis* and *Streptococcus mutans*. *Infect. Immunol.* 19(1):107–15

42. Levine MJ, Jones PC, Loomis RE, Reddy MS, Al-Hashimi I, et al. 1987. Functions of human saliva and salivary mucins: An overview. In *Oral Mucosal Disease: Biology, Etiology, Therapy. Proc. Second Dows Symp.*, ed. IC Mackenzie, CA Squier, E Dablesteen, pp. 24–27. Copenhagen: Laegeforeningens Forlag

43. Levine MJ, Reddy MS, Tabak LA, Loomis RE, Bergey EJ, et al. 1987. Structural aspects of salivary glycoproteins. *J. Dent. Res.* 66:436–41

44. Ligtenberg AJM, Walgreen-Weterings E, Veerman ECI, de Soet JJ, de Graaff J, Nieuw Amerongen AV. 1992. Influence of saliva on aggregation and adherence of *Streptococcus gordonii* HG 222. *Infect. Immunol.* 60(9):3878–84

45. Loomis RE, Prakobphol A, Levine MJ, Reddy MS, Jones PC. 1987. Biochemical and biophysical comparison of two mucins from human submandibular-sublingual saliva. *Arch. Biochem. Biophys.* 258(2):452–64

46. Matsuura S, Hand AR. 1991. Quantitative immunocytochemistry of rat submandibular secretory proteins during chronic isoproterenol administration and recovery. *J. Histochem. Cytochem.* 39(7):945–54

47. McBride BC, Gisslow MT. 1977. Role of sialic acid in saliva-induced aggregation of *Streptococcus sanguis. Infect. Immunol.* 18:35–40

48. Metzgar RS, Hollingsworth MA, Kaufman B. 1993. Pancreatic mucins. In *The Pancreas: Biology, Pathobiology and Disease*, ed. VLW Go, EP DiMagno, JD Gardner, E Lebenthal, HA Reber, GA Scheele, 17:351–67. New York: Raven. 2nd ed.

49. Moch T, Hoschützky H, Hacker J, Kröncke K-D, Jann K. 1987. Isolation and characterization of the α-sialyl-β-2,3-galactosyl-specific adhesin from fimbriated *Escherichia coli. Proc. Natl. Acad. Sci. USA* 84:3462–66

50. Murray PA, Levine MJ, Tabak LA, Reddy MS. 1982. Specificity of salivary-bacterial interactions: II. Evidence for a lectin on *Streptococcus sanguis* with specificity for a NeuAcα2,3-Galβ1,3GalNAc sequence. *Biochem. Biophys. Res. Comm.* 106(2):390–96

51. Murray PA, Prakobphol A, Lee T, Hoover CI, Fischer SJ. 1992. Adherence of oral streptococci to salivary glycoproteins. *Infect. Immunol.* 60(1):31–38

52. Närhi TO. 1994. Prevalence of subjective feelings of dry mouth in the elderly. *J. Dent. Res.* 73(1):20–25

53. Nieuw Amerongen AV, Oderkerk CH, Driessen AA. 1987. Role of mucins from human whole saliva in the protection of tooth enamel against demineralization in vitro. *Caries Res.* 21:297–309

54. O'Connell B, Hagen FK, Tabak LA. 1992. The influence of flanking sequence on the O-glycosylation of threonine in vitro. *J. Biol. Chem.* 267(35): 25010–18

55. O'Connell B, Tabak LA, Ramasubbu N. 1991. The influence of flanking sequences on O-glycosylation. *Biochem. Biophys. Res. Comm.* 180(2):1024–30

56. O'Connell BC, Tabak LA. 1993. A comparison of serine and threonine O-glycosylation by UDP-GalNAc: polypeptide N-acetylgalactosaminyltransferase. *J. Dent. Res.* 72(12):1554–58

57. Oldenburg KR, Loganathan D, Goldstein IJ, Schultz PG, Gallop MA. 1992. Peptide ligands for a sugar–binding protein isolated from a random peptide li-

brary. *Proc. Natl. Acad. Sci. USA* 89: 5393–97

58. Piller V, Piller F, Fukuda M. 1990. Biosynthesis of truncated O-glycans in the T cell line Jurkat. *J. Biol. Chem.* 265(16):9264–71

59. Pisano A, Redmond JW, Williams KL, Gooley AA, 1993. Glycosylation sites identified by solid–phase Edman degradation: O–linked glycosylation motifs on human glycophorin A. *Glycobiology* 3(5):429–35

60. Prakobphol A, Levine MJ, Tabak LA, Reddy MS. 1982. Purification of a low–molecular weight, mucin–type glycoprotein from human submandibular-sublingual saliva. *Carbohydr. Res.* 108: 111–22

61. Reddy MS, Bobek LA, Haraszthy GG, Biesbrock AR, Levine MJ. 1992. Structural features of the low–molecular-mass human salivary mucin. *Biochem. J.* 287: 639–43

62. Reddy MS, Levine MJ. 1993. Low–molecular-mass human salivary mucin, MG2: Structure and binding of *Pseudomonas aeruginosa*. *Crit. Rev. Oral Biol. Med.* 4(3/4):315–23

63. Rochu D, Crespeau H, Fine A, Gane P, Rouger P, et al. 1988. ABO-blood-group–related idiotypic network: Mimicry of oligosaccharide epitope by rabbit antiidiotypic antibodies to murine monoclonal anti–A antibody. *Res. Immunol.* 141:373–87

64. Sarosiek J, Bilski J, Murty VLN, Slomiany A, Slomiany BL. 1988. Role of salivary epidermal growth factor in the maintenance of physicochemical characteristics of oral and gastric mucosal mucus coat. *Biochem. Biophys. Res. Comm.* 152(3):1421–27

65. Schachter H. 1986. Biosynthetic controls that determine the branching and microheterogeneity of protein–bound oligosaccharides. *Biochem. Cell Biol.* 64: 163–81

66. Sellers LA, Allen A, Morris ER, Ross-Murphy SB. 1988. Submaxillary mucins: Intermolecular interactions and gel–forming potential of concentrated solutions. *Biochem. J.* 256:599–607

67. Shogren R, Gerken TA, Jentoft N. 1989. Role of glycosylation on the conformation and chain dimensions of O–linked glycoproteins: Light–scattering studies of ovine submaxillary mucin. *Biochemistry* 28:5525–36

68. Shogren RL, Jamieson AM, Blackwell J, Jentoft N. 1986. Conformation of mucous glycoproteins in aqueous solvents. *Biopolymers* 25:1505–17

69. Stinson MW, Levine MJ, Cavese JM,

Prakobphol A, Murray PA, et al. 1982. Adherence of *Streptococcus sanguis* to salivary mucin bound to glass. *J. Dent. Res.* 61(12):1390–93

70. Slomiany BL, Murty VLN, Mandel ID, Zalesna G, Slomiany A. 1989. Physicochemical characteristics of mucus glycoproteins and lipids of the human oral mucosal mucus coat in relation to caries susceptibility. *Arch. Oral Biol.* 34(4): 229–37

71. Slomiany BL, Piotrowski J, Czajkowski A, Shovlin FE, Slomiany A. 1993. Differential expression of salivary mucin bacterial aggregating activity with caries status. *Int. J. Biochem.* 25(6):935–40

72. Soby L, Jamieson AM, Blackwell J, Jentoft N. 1990. Viscoelastic properties of solutions of ovine submaxillary mucin. *Biopolymers* 29:1359–66

73. Strahl-Bolsinger S, Immervoll T, Deutzmann R, Tanner W. 1993. *PMT1*, the gene for a key enzyme of protein O-glycosylation in *Saccharomyces cerevisiae*. *Proc. Natl. Acad. Sci. USA* 90: 8164–68

74. Tabak LA. 1991. Genetic control of salivary mucin formation. *Mol. Genet. Mouth; Front. Oral Physiol.* 8:77–94

75. Tabak LA, Bowen WH. 1989 Roles of saliva (pellicle), diet, and nutrition on plaque formation. *J. Dent. Res.* 68(Spec. Issue):1560–66

76. Tabak LA, Levine MJ, Jain NK, Bryan AR, Cohen RE, et al. 1985. Adsorption of human salivary mucins to hydroxyapatite. *Arch. Oral Biol.* 30(5): 423–27

77. Tabak LA, Levine MJ, Mandel ID, Ellison SA. 1982. Role of salivary mucins in the protection of the oral cavity. *J. Oral Pathol.* 11:1–17

78. Tabak LA, Mirels L, Monte LD, Ridall AL, Levine MJ, et al. 1985. Isolation and characterization of a mucin-glycoprotein from rat submandibular glands. *Arch. Biochem. Biophys.* 242(2):383–92

79. Thomsen DR, Post LE, Elhammer AP. 1990. Structure of O-glycosidically linked oligosaccharides synthesized by the insect cell line Sf9. *J. Cell. Biochem.* 43:67–79

80. Timpte CS, Eckhardt AE, Abernethy JL, Hill RL. 1988. Porcine submaxillary gland apomucin contains tandemly repeated identical sequences of 81 residues. *J. Biol. Chem.* 263:1081–88

81. van der Hoeven JS, Camp PJM. 1991. Synergistic degradation of mucin by *Streptococcus oralis* and *Streptococcus sanguis* in mixed chemostat cultures. *J. Dent. Res.* 70(7):1041–44

82. Wang Y, Abernethy JL, Eckhardt AE,

Hill RL. 1992. Purification and characterization of a UDP-GalNAc:polypeptide N-acetylgalactosaminyltransferase specific for glycosylation of threonine residues. *J. Biol. Chem.* 267(18):12709–16

83. Wang Y, Agrwal N, Eckhardt AE, Stevens RD, Hill RL. 1993. The acceptor substrate specificity of porcine submaxillary UDP-GalNAc:polypeptide N-acetylgalactosaminyltransferase is dependent on the amino acid sequences adjacent to serine and threonine residues. *J. Biol. Chem.* 268(31):22979–83

84. Williams D, Longmore G, Matta KL, Schachter H. 1980. Mucin synthesis. *J. Biol. Chem.* 255(23):11253–61

85. Willoughby RE. 1993. Rotaviruses preferentially bind O–linked sialylglycoconjugates and sialomucins. *Glycobiology* 3(5):437–45

86. Wilson IBH, Gavel Y, von Heijne G. 1991. Amino acid distributions around O–linked glycosylation sites. *Biochem. J.* 275:529–34

87. Wolff A, Fox PC, Ship JA, Atkinson JC, Macynski AA, Baum BJ. 1990. Oral mucosal status and major salivary gland function. *Oral Surg. Med. Oral Pathol.* 70:49–54

88. Wong C-H, Schuster M, Wang P, Sears P. 1993. Enzymatic synthesis of N– and O–linked glycopeptides. *J. Am. Chem. Soc.* 115(14):5893–5901

Annu. Rev. Physiol. 1995. 57:565–583

THE HYDROPHOBIC BARRIER PROPERTIES OF GASTROINTESTINAL MUCUS

L. M. Lichtenberger

Department of Physiology and Cell Biology, The University of Texas at Houston Medical School, Houston, Texas 77030

KEY WORDS: stomach, surfactants, phospholipid, peptic ulcer, prostaglandins, *Helicobacter pylori*

INTRODUCTION

Ever since the demonstration by Spallanzani in the eighteenth century that human gastric juice had the capacity to digest meat, gastrointestinal investigators have been trying to elucidate the mechanism by which our gastric lining resists autodigestion (103). The concept of the "gastric mucosal barrier" to acid, introduced by Davenport in the mid-1960s, demonstrated that the mammalian stomach was as impermeable to luminal acid as it was to other electrolytes, whereas lipid-soluble damaging agents had ready access to the epithelium (8–12). This work, which demonstrated the resistance of the epithelium to luminal acid, has subsequently been confirmed by many investigators, most recently in isolated gastric glands, employing acid-sensitive fluorescent probes to provide an estimate of intracellular pH (96). Because of these efforts, we now understand that the acid-resistant barrier properties of the stomach can be attributed to a multiplicity of factors that encompass extracellular and plasmalemmal diffusion barriers to protons; ion exchange pumps that serve to regulate intracellular acidification arising from proton influx; the ability of the surface epithelium to secrete bicarbonate into the interstitial and luminal space to buffer protons; the maintenance of local blood flow to the gastrointestinal (GI) epithelium; and the process of reconstitution in which undifferentiated mucus cells rapidly migrate to cover a denuded surface. The general subject of gastric barrier function has been the subject of numerous, excellent reviews (3, 89); thus it is our purpose to present evidence that the initial line of defense

565

present within or on the surface of the mucus gel layer is the long-overlooked lipidic elements of mucus that provide the extracellular gel layer with hydrophobic, nonwettable, acid-resistant properties.

Most if not all epithelia that are exposed to a potentially noxious extracellular environment possess a prominent mucus lining, and the stomach is no exception. Indeed, this layer, which is visible to the naked eye and increases in thickness in response to the presence of intraluminal irritants, led to the suggestion by Beaumont 150 years ago that the acid-resistant properties of the stomach can be attributed to its mucus coat (70). We now know that the gastric mucus gel layer, which can range in thickness from 50–300 μm, is a hydrated, polymeric gel consisting of < 10% protein, carbohydrate, and lipid (2, 3, 88, 89). Its potential physiological importance is also underscored by the fact that the majority of epithelial cells that line the surface and glandular luminal lining of the stomach are mucous cells whose histochemical staining characteristics, which are reflective of the charge state of their respective oligosaccharide groups, vary in accordance to their localization within the mucosa (2). Because glycoproteins represent > 80% of the organic constituents of mucus, much effort has been directed toward characterizing these constituents and evaluating their contribution to the barrier properties of the stomach. As a consequence we now know that mucus glycoprotein is a polymer with a M_r between 2–6 $\times 10^6$ and a strongly negative charge density due to the presence of sialic acid and sulfated oligosaccharides. The subunits, M_r between 0.4–0.6 $\times$ 10^6, are associated by disulfide bonds present in nonglycosylated regions of the protein that are susceptible to proteolytic cleavage (2, 3). It is also clear that the contribution of mucus glycoprotein to the barrier properties of the stomach is limited and resides primarily in the polymeric gel–forming properties of the glycoprotein and its ability to entrap HCO_3^- and generate a pH gradient across the width of the mucus gel layer (3, 31, 42, 74, 102). Conversely, it is clear that mucus glycoproteins serve as weak diffusion barriers to luminal acid and that the mucus/HCO_3^- pH gradient is rapidly dissipated when the pH of the bulk solution falls to values below 2.5, which is a rather common occurrence in the interprandial state. Thus it is conceivable that the lipidic elements of the mucus gel layer play a prominent role as a barrier to luminal acid, similar to their function as surface barriers in many cells and tissues such as the skin (101).

BASIS IN SCIENCE AND INDUSTRY FOR A HYDROPHOBIC LIPIDIC BARRIER TO ACID

The physical sciences, and specifically the field of surface wettability analysis, have elucidated the fact that materials that are intrinsically hydrophobic, or whose surfaces are transformed to that state, are nonwettable and resistant to environmental acid (1, 75). The examples as noted by Hills are numerous

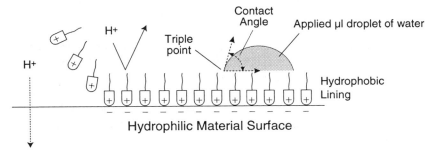

Figure 1   Deposition of cationic surfactants on a negatively charged surface to form a compact monolayer. The aliphatic hydrocarbon chains extend into the lumen to form a hydrophobic lining, which can be assessed by contact angle analysis.

and include plastic containers to hold acid such as the encasing of the car battery; the use of paraffin and other waxes to prevent acid from etching lithography plates, except in areas carved by the artist; the addition of surfactants to cosmetic materials and fabrics to provide them with water-repellent properties; and the injection-application of cationic surfactants along the surfaces of metallic pipelines carrying oil/gas and water to prevent environmental corrosion (33, 34, 36, 37). It is the latter example, cationic surfactants as corrosion inhibitors, that may prove to be particularly pertinent in providing an understanding of how the mucus gel lining of the stomach resists luminal acid. These specific cationic surfactants, which are schematically depicted in Figure 1, contain a long, straight (saturated) aliphatic group of 16–20 carbons attached to a positively charged hydrophilic end, which frequently is a tertiary ammonium group. The amphipathic molecules in turn bond electrostatically to negatively charged surface groups such as would be present on metallic surfaces and form a compact monolayer with the hydrocarbon chains extending outward. As a result, the surface wettability of the underlying material undergoes a marked transition from a hydrophilic/wettable to a hydrophobic/nonwettable state. This change in surface wettability can be assessed by contact angle analysis, also depicted in Figure 1. This standard test is based on the balance of surface forces acting at the air/liquid/solid triple point of a µl droplet of water and a solid surface, as originally expressed in Young's equation (36). It can be performed simply by either optical measurement of the angle formed between the tangential line running along the surface of the droplet and the test surface (using an instrument called a goniometer) (34), or by the computation of surface forces acting at the triple point by axiosymmetric contact angle analysis, a process that has recently been automated (72).

THE HYDROPHOBIC CHARACTERISTICS OF THE GI MUCOSAL SURFACE

In 1983, Hills, Butler, and I employed contact angle analysis to demonstrate that the canine gastric mucosal surface was exceedingly hydrophobic, with readings that ranged between 75–90° (40). In order to make the measurement, we needed to institute a method to remove bulk fluid from the mucosal surface of the biopsy tissue, which was accomplished by a combination of light filter paper blotting and limited air-drying of 15–30 min prior to contact angle analysis. Concern about the effects of tissue autolysis was subsequently reduced by a morphological examination of the tested tissue at the light and electron microscopic level and the fact that, in a series of tissues identically prepared, manipulations in experimental conditions or biopsy location resulted in marked and consistent alterations in the wettability of the mucosal surface (23–25, 44). We demonstrated that in sharp contrast to the stomach, the canine and rodent duodenal and jejunal mucosa were hydrophilic in nature, presenting contact angles of < 10°, and it was clear that the hydrophobic properties of the mucosae progressively increased caudally in the distal ileum and colon (18, 40, 94). Since the initial report, our laboratory and others have demonstrated that the gastric mucosal surface of a number of mammalian species including humans is hydrophobic in nature (18, 46, 62, 91, 92). Studies pioneered by Northfield et al used a technique that permitted contact angle analysis of antral endoscopic biopsy samples and reported a mean contact angle reading of ~70° (27, 92). In contrast to the consistency of gastric contact angles across species lines, the reduction in hydrophobic properties in the proximal duodenum varies considerably among species, with values only modestly lower than gastric values being recorded in the duodenal bulb region of human, opossum, and rabbit (46, 62, 92). The reason for this species difference is unknown, but a case can be made that may relate to the presence of the submucosal Brunner's glands that are present throughout most of the duodenum in the human, opossum, and rabbit and occupy only a limited peri-pyloric area of the duodenal bulb region in rodents and dogs. It also should be noted that a similar pattern was encountered for the distal esophagus, with most species having a wettable surface except those possessing submucosal glands (46). It is also clear that the distal gut of rabbits and rats have notable hydrophobic surface characteristics, with contact angles of the distal colonic mucosa comparable to that recorded in the animal's stomach (62, 94).

The ontogenic development of the gastric mucosal hydrophobic lining has been studied by Dial et al (16, 18, 19), who demonstated that this biophysical property, which is low at birth, increases to adult values from 2–4 weeks of age postnatally. Further, they demonstrated that the ability of "gastroprotective" prostaglandins to enhance gastric surface hydrophobicity (discussed in more detail below) and gastric barrier properties was seen only in rat pups 14 days of age and older.

An early misconception regarding contact angle readings of mucosal biopsies was that they reflected the hydrophobic property of the GI epithelial surface and not that of its overlying mucus gel layer. This was concluded because the luminal surface of the tissue was blotted prior to contact angle analysis and because the filter paper employed contained adherent mucus that was clearly lifted from the tissue. However, both light and electron microscopic analysis subsequently revealed that the tissue has a prominent mucus gel layer at the time of contact angle analysis that is as thick or thicker than the unblotted mucosa (24, 44). Thus it appears that the mechanical act of surface blotting stimulated mucus release to rapidly replace that lifted off the tissue and that this process occurred even after biopsy excision. The contribution of the mucus gel layer to the surface hydrophobicity of GI tissue was further confused by a report from Hills (35), which provided evidence that under certain in vitro conditions mucus can act as a wetting agent. However, convincing morphometric evidence (24) showed that the hydrophobic properties of the mucus gel layer were clearly dependent upon the presence of an intact mucus gel layer. Recent experiments from our laboratory demonstrated that the normal hydrophilic surface properties of a glass fiber filter (contact angles < 10°) could be transformed to a hydrophobic state (contact angles > 80°) after porcine mucin (containing 5% lipid) is applied to its surface (59). The findings outlined in the above section led us to the conclusion that the hydrophobic properties of the GI mucosa, as determined by contact angle analysis, were directly related to the surface property of the mucus gel layer and not the tissue itself, although the latter may also be endowed with nonwettable properties.

Lastly, it should be noted that the hydrophobic property of the mucus gel layer can be demonstrated with the use of fluorescent probes that partition within and/or enter an excited state when associated with a hydrophobic microenvironment. Using these fluorescent probes, Slomiany et al and our laboratory confirmed the hydrophobic nature of gastric mucus and showed how the fluorescent signal can be employed as a sensitive index of alterations in hydrophobicity under a variety of experimental conditions affecting barrier integrity (30, 56).

CONTRIBUTIONS OF SURFACE-ACTIVE LIPIDS TO MUCUS HYDROPHOBICITY

In 1979, Waseff et al (98) reported that the gastric mucosa possessed unusually large concentrations of the highly surface-active phospholipid dipalmitoylphosphatidylcholine (DPPC) in proportions comparable to levels found in pulmonary surfactant. This group also noted that the gastric mucosa contained a family of phospholipid remodeling enzymes that are similar to those present in alveolar type II cells and suggested that the presence of surfactant and their processing enzymes in the lung and stomach may be reflective of their common embryological origin (97). Our laboratory and those of other investigators (7, 57) confirmed the earlier finding, with Slomiany et al providing strong biochemical evidence that the gastric mucus contained a significant lipidic fraction approaching 20% of the organic material (85, 87). In addition to a phospholipid fraction, they reported the presence of high concentrations of glyceroglucolipids, ceramides of varying oligosaccharide composition, as well as lipidic species covalently associated with the glycoprotein backbone (85–90). Most of these same lipidic constituents have been biochemically characterized in the mucus gel layer of a number of species including humans. However, some controversy exists as to whether DPPC and other saturated forms of the surface-active phospholipid present in gastric mucus are found in comparable concentrations to that measured in pulmonary surfactant. Schmitz & Renooij (83) indicate that gastric mucosal DPPC represents < 10% of the phosphatidylcholine fraction, far less than the 30–40% reported by Waseff et al (98). The reasons for the discrepancies are unclear but may relate to the problems of collecting pure gastric mucus not contaminated with gastric membranes or exfoliated cells. However, it should be pointed out that a number of laboratories including ours have reported that the gastric mucosa, studied in vivo and in vitro, has a dynamic ability to rapidly incorporate luminally and systemically administered precursors into phospholipids and neutral lipids (14, 83). Moreover, both the biosynthesis and secretion of phospholipids appear to be tightly regulated by gastric secretagogues (81, 84) and agents that either protect or damage the epithelium (4, 6, 14, 66, 68).

The evidence is substantial that in addition to its glycoprotein constituents, mucus contains significant amounts of polar/neutral lipids and a family of glycolipids, some of which are covalently associated with the mucin backbone. In addition to affecting surface hydrophobicity, which is the focus of this review, compelling evidence suggests that these covalently and noncovalently bound lipids play an important role in conferring both viscous and lubricant properties to mucus as well as serving as scavengers against free radical attack (7, 28, 88). It is presently uncertain which of these lipidic elements contributes to the surface hydrophobicity of the mucus gel layer, but a case can be made for the pivotal role of phospholipids based on their amphipathic nature, their established surface activity, and their close chemical resemblance to cationic surfactants employed industrially. It is also a fact that the transference of a monolayer of DPPC to a hydrophilic, negatively charged surface results in a transformation of the test surface to a more hydrophobic state, similar to the previously stated action of cationic surfactants (79). Lastly, evidence indicates that of all the lipidic constituents of mucus, phospholipids appear to undergo the largest changes in concentration, being increased by gastroprotective agents, and reduced by agents/conditions, which lead to gastritis and the development of peptic ulceration (4, 6, 68) (discussed in more detail below).

MORPHOLOGICAL LOCALIZATION OF LIPIDS IN THE GI MUCOSA AND MUCUS GEL LAYER

Morphological techniques offer a powerful alternative approach in the investigation of whether the GI epithelium has the capacity to synthesize, store, and secrete surface-active lipids into its immediate extracellular environment. Some of the same fluorescent probes that were used to elucidate the hydrophobic properties of gastric mucus can also be employed to assess where these domains are localized. Treatment of frozen sections with two of these fluorescent hydrophobic probes, Nile Red and anilinonaphthaline-sulfonic acid (ANS), revealed strong staining of the adherent mucus gel layer and hot spots within the surface mucous cells (48, 56). At higher power it appeared that the apical secretory package was stained by the fluorescent probes together with a larger organelle localized below the nucleus.

Ultrastructural examination can also provide important information on the specific localization and arrangement of these lipids within the mucus gel layer that provide the tissue with a possible barrier to luminal acid. Efforts to determine these specifics have been greatly facilitated by the work of anatomists, who developed preservation and staining techniques to visualize pulmonary surfactant. This was not a trivial task because of the ready solubility of surfactant lipids in organic solvents employed in conventional processing techniques and the weak staining characteristics of saturated lipids with osmium tetroxide. The problem was further compounded because it was also imperative to preserve the adherent mucus gel layer, which is easily removed as the tissue undergoes lengthy processing steps required for electron microscopy. In an attempt to resolve these difficulties, our laboratory tested a number of procedures and ultimately decided upon a modification of the iodoplatinate (IP) technique originally developed by Dierichs et al (20, 45, 47). Accordingly, paraformaldehyde/glutaraldehyde-fixed tissue was initially embedded in agarose to stabilize the mucus gel layer and then sectioned into 200 μm slices. These sections were subjected to cytochemical staining with IP (to react with the zwitterionic phospholipids) and dehydration steps with acetone, prior to infiltration and embedding with Epon and thin sectioning (45, 47). It should be noted that acetone was substituted for ethanol in the dehydration step in order to preserve phospholipids, which have significant solubility in the latter solvent, and that no counterstain was used prior to electronmicroscopy because the reaction products to uranyl acetate/lead citrate tended to obscure the ultrastructural image.

Employing the above technique, together with another stain for choline-based phospholipids (ferric-hematoxylin), we demonstrated the presence of a gradient of reactivity along the oxyntic mucosa, with the surface mucous cells being most heavily stained (45). At the electron microscopic level, IP reaction products appear to be associated with the endoplasmic reticulum (ER), the mucus secretory granules, and an organelle not previously described that localized in the infranuclear region of the cell and could be seen budding off the ER (48). Because of its size and localization, we call this organelle a Large Infranuclear Inclusion Body (LIIB) and suggest that it is the same structure that appeared as fluorescent hot spots beneath the nucleus in ANS- and Nile Red–treated frozen sections. Subsequent ultrastructural studies revealed that the cellular volume and density of LIIBs are prostaglandin-dependent and that these organelles appear to undergo maturation to a multivesicular structure (LIIB-II) that traffics to the basolateral and luminal membranes where it is discharged into the extracellular space (49). (See Figure 2 a-d for electron micrographic plates that depict these LIIB properties). In addition to this multivesicular structure, the mucus gel layer contains IP-reactive lamellar, vesicular, and filamentous structures (Figure 2 e,f). Most notable is the presence of a filamentous band (see arrowhead in Figure 2e) of IP-reactive material that appears to coat the luminal surface of the mucus gel layer and is associated with the hydrophobicity of the mucosa as assessed by contact angle analysis (4, 47). Similar filamentous structures have recently been observed within and on the surface of the human gastric mucus gel layer, prepared and stained in accordance with the IP procedure. It has been suggested that the density of these structures is reduced in *H. pylori*–infected tissue (63).

Tannic acid fixation followed by osmium tetroxide is another ultrastructural technique that was originally developed to preserve and stain pulmonary surfactant (43). This technique has also been applied to the GI mucosa by a number of investigators to demonstrate the presence of surfactant-like particles (13, 37, 38, 53). Employing a modification of this technique, Hills demonstrated the presence of an oligolamellar lining closely apposed to the rodent gastric mucosal surface, together with the presence of lamellar bodies that are coming off adjacent surface mucous cells in a process suggestive of secretion (37,38). Similar lamellar-like structures have been observed within and on the surface of human esophageal mucosa, using the tannic acid technique (53). De-Schryver-Kecskemeti et al (13) also employed this method to visualize lamellar structures occupying the intercellular and luminal space surrounding the rodent enterocyte. This group provided convincing evidence that these lamellar structures, which constitute >50% DPPC, were covalently associated with one or more apoproteins identified as SP-B and the brush border enzyme alkaline phosphatase (22, 95). The significance of this association with alkaline phosphatase is uncertain, but in a subsequent paper, it was reported that the gen-

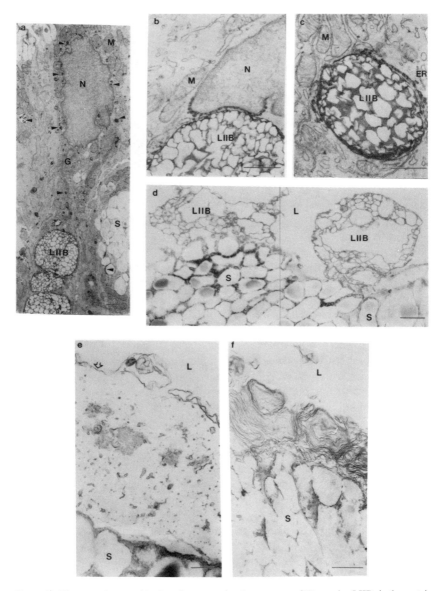

Figure 2   Electron micrographic plate demonstrating the presence of IP-reactive LIIBs in the gastric surface mucous cell. These organelles are localized beneath the nucleus (*a*) and are frequently associated with the nuclear and ER membranes (*b,c*) where they appear to traffic to the luminal (*d*) and intercellular space (not shown). Additionally, lamellar, myelinated, and filamentous structures can be seen within the mucus gel layer (*e*, *f*), occasionally forming an filamentous band over the luminal interface (*e, arrowhead*).

eration of surfactant particles by human Caco-2 cells could be consistently stimulated if the cultured cells were transfected with cDNA encoding rat intestinal alkaline phosphatase (95). Lastly, morphological evidence with fluorescent hydrophobic and phospholipid-selective cytochemical stains indicates that the submucosal glands present in the distal esophagus and proximal duodenum (Brunner's glands) are able to store and secrete surfactant-like particles, the role of which is described below (46, 48).

EFFECT OF ULCEROGENIC AGENTS AND/OR CONDITIONS ON GI MUCOSAL HYDROPHOBICITY AND LIPID METABOLISM

Over the past 12 years, a series of in vitro and in vivo experiments have been performed on laboratory animals to establish that mucosal phospholipid metabolism and hydrophobicity are attenuated by many damaging agents/conditions including aspirin, salicylic acid, ethanol, bile salts, phospholipase enzymes, and cold-restraint stress. These findings, which are consistent with the thesis that surface hydrophobicity is an important barrier property, must be interpreted cautiously, because it is just as likely that hydrophobicity is affected as a consequence not a cause of barrier disruption. Insight into the causal relationship of these two properties comes from the studies of Goddard et al (23, 25), who demonstrated in a canine gastric mucosal Ussing Chamber system that aspirin and salicylic acid induce rapid reductions in mucosal hydrophobicity within minutes of exposure and that the ability of both agents to affect mucosal hydrophobicity and barrier integrity (as assessed by monitoring transmural potential difference) is dependent on the molecules being in the undissociated lipid-soluble state (pH < pKa) (see 8). In an attempt to understand the molecular mechanism by which aspirin, salicyclic acid and other nonsteroidal antiinflammatory drugs (NSAIDS) affect mucosal hydrophobicity, we have recently performed a series of in vitro experiments. These studies revealed that after an initial hydrophobic intermolecular interaction, the free carboxyl group present in all NSAIDs forms a strong electrostatic bond with the positively charged head group of zwitterionic phospholipids (i.e. DPPC) and, in doing so, increases the phospholipid's solubility (in water) and neutralizes its surface activity (60). Thus it is conceivable that among other actions (inhibition of cyclo-oxygenase activity) NSAIDs topically act on the tissue to disrupt the hydrophobic protective lining of the mucus gel layer.

It is now well-established that infection with the bacteria *H. pylori* is tightly associated with the development of chronic active gastritis and ultimately with duodenal ulcer disease (5). The evidence is also convincing that eradication of the infection with Triple Therapy, which includes bismuth salts and two antibiotics, can lead to ulcer healing and most importantly an extremely low rate of ulcer recurrence (5, 32). This latter result is in sharp contrast to the experience with potent antisecretory drugs, which induce rapid ulcer healing during treatment but result in high recurrence rates once treatment is terminated (5, 32). Thus a strong case can be made that *H. pylori,* which colonizes within the mucus gel layer, elaborates one or more products that lead to a defect in gastric barrier properties, with luminal acid playing a necessary but permissive role in tissue injury. However, the mechanism by which the bacteria attenuates barrier integrity has yet to be elucidated.

Insight into a potential mechanism came from a series of studies demonstrating that both symptomatic and asymptomatic subjects who were infected with *H. pylori* had a consistent and highly significant reduction in antral mucosal hydrophobicity as determined by contact angle analysis of collected endoscopic biopsy tissue (26, 27, 91, 92). Further, if these same subjects entered a 2–4 week treatment protocol with either H_2-blockers or Triple Therapy to induce ulcer healing, mucosal hydrophobicity remained abnormally low in the former group but rapidly recovered if the bacterial infection was eradicated in the latter group (26). These findings are particularly interesting because they provide strong evidence that the surface hydrophobic properties of the stomach are not merely a reflection of mucosal integrity, since this biophysical property remains attenuated in "healed" gastric mucosa in the infected group treated with H_2 receptor–antagonists. Consistent with the above findings based on contact angle analysis, two recent morphological studies have reported either an absence or a diminution of lamellar and filamentous surfactant-like structures in the gastric mucus gel layer of *H. pylori*–infected subjects (63, 80). Further, several groups have recently demonstrated that the antral mucosal concentration of phospholipids are significantly reduced in biopsy specimens collected from *H. pylori*–infected subjects in comparison to subjects with comparable gastric pathology that was not infected with the bacteria (65, 66). These authors also provided evidence that the reduction in phospholipid concentration was primarily attributed to a loss in the zwitterionic species phosphatidylcholine and phosphatidylethanolamine, which possess the greatest surface activity.

The mechanism by which *H. pylori* reduces surface hydrophobicity is presently being studied. Slomiany et al initially demonstrated that the bacteria possesses low levels of phospholipase A_2 and nonspecific lipase activity that can be inhibited by bismuth salts. This work was confirmed and extended by a number of laboratories (54, 71, 100). As a result we now have evidence that *H. pylori* contains phospholipase A_1, A_2, and C activity, all of which can be inhibited by bismuth salts used in Triple Therapy. We recently reported that *H. pylori* lysates and filtrates can remove a phospholipid monolayer from a glass substrate, as demonstrated by contact angle analysis (71). Furthermore, this transition to a wettable state can be blocked in the presence of bismuth salts. Hills reported that *H. pylori* within the mucus gel layer was coated by an oligolamellar lining of phospholipid-like material and appeared to have similar phospholipid-like material within its cytoplasm (39). Based on these morphological observations, he speculated that one of the mechanisms by which the bacteria survives within its acidic niche is by coating its own surface with phospholipids that have been selectively extracted from the host's mucus gel layer, thereby simultaneously attenuating the stomach's barrier to luminal acid.

Another potential mechanism by which *H. pylori* can disrupt a phospholipid monolayer is by secreting a factor that competes with zwitterionic phospholipids for binding sites on the mucus gel layer. One such factor that is avidly generated by the urease activity of the bacteria (*H. pylori* has the highest urease activity of any bacteria on record) is ammonia, which is present in the gastric juice of infected patients in concentrations of 4–10 mM (5, 64). At acidic pH normally found in the gastric juice, ammonia will be converted to ammonium ion. Moreover, we recently demonstrated that ammonium has the capacity to disrupt the packing of DPPC monolayers and to transform the stomach of rats to a wettable state if co-administered with a mucolytic agent (the mucolytic agent, acetylcysteine, has no effect by itself) (59). These results suggest that *H. pylori*, which colonizes within the gastric mucus gel layer, can attenuate the hydrophobic barrier property in at least two ways: by phospholipase-catalyzed hydrolysis of surfactant-like phospholipids, and by generating high concentrations of ammonium within the mucus gel layer, which by virtue of their similar charge density compete with zwitterionic phospholipids for negative-binding sites on the surface of the mucus gel layer (see Figure 3 for a schematic representation of this model).

EFFECT OF GASTROPROTECTIVE AGENTS ON GI MUCOSAL HYDROPHOBICITY AND LIPID METABOLISM

The concept of "cytoprotection" was born in the mid-1970s when Robért and associates demonstrated that a class of specific prostaglandin analogues had the capacity to protect the mucosa from a series of ulcerogenic conditions at doses below their efficacy to inhibit gastric acid secretion (77). The protective mechanisms activated by these cytoprotective drugs include an increase in mucus secretion; an increase in mucosal HCO_3^- output; a reduction in vascular permeability; and a maintenance of gastric blood flow (3). Morphological studies further indicated that although the macroscopic appearance of gastric tissue of prostaglandin-treated rats, which were subsequently challenged with

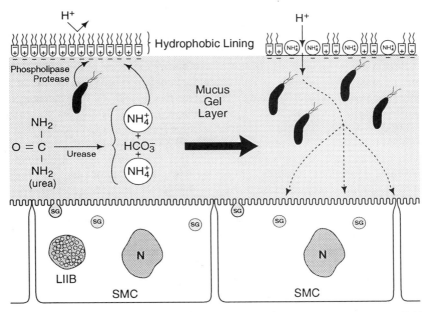

Figure 3 Schematic representation of the presence of a monolayer of surface-active phospholipids at the luminal interface of the mucus gel layer. Also shown are two mechanisms by which *H. pylori* can compromise this hydrophobic phospholipid barrier: by phospholipase-catalyzed hydrolysis, and generating high concentrations of ammonium ion within the mucus gel to compete with zwitterionic phospholipids for negatively charged glycoprotein binding sites. SG = secretory granule; LIIB = Large Infranuclear Inclusion Body; SMC = surface mucous cell; N = nucleus.

an ulcerogenic agent, appeared normal, the surface epithelium was, in fact, necrotic, whereas glandular tissue did appear to be protected from injury (3). Accordingly, it was suggested that the term cytoprotection be replaced by the less provocative and more precise term gastroprotection.

In addition to the changes in barrier properties outlined above, our laboratory demonstrated that gastroprotective prostaglandins had the capacity to increase the surface hydrophobicity of canine gastric mucosa, mounted in an Ussing Chamber preparation, when administered to the nutrient compartment in the absence of an injurious agent (23, 24, 44, 53, 58). Furthermore, prostaglandin treatment (to the nutrient compartment) clearly prevented the reduction in gastric mucosal hydrophobicity in response to luminal exposure to either aspirin or salicylic acid. The molecular basis for this prostanoid effect on surface hydrophobicity is less clear, but in vivo and in vitro studies indicate that prostaglandins have the capacity to stimulate phospholipid and neutral lipid biosynthesis and/or accumulation, respectively (57, 61, 66, 82). Moreover, Kao et al have reported that prostaglandins acutely increase the cellular density and volume of LIIB-II organelles in the rodent gastric surface mucous cell and appear to increase the density of surfactant-like particles within the mucus gel layer overlying the epithelium (49).

Robért and associates also observed that a brief exposure of the stomach to one of a number of mild irritants could elicit a protective response to a subsequent ulcerogenic challenge (76). The mechanism of this increase in intrinsic barrier function, which is called adaptive cytoprotection, is presently being elucidated and, again, evidence has come forth that surfactant-like lipids may be involved. This evidence is based on the recent studies of Lugea et al, who demonstrated that the addition of a low concentration of HCl to the proximal duodenal mucosa can protect the tissue from a subsequent challenge with a supraphysiological dose of HCl, as does prostaglandin E_2, and that this protective effect is not seen if a non-ionic detergent is perfused into the bowel to solubilize luminal phospholipid (61). They also performed biochemical analysis of the mucosa to demonstrate that the low dose of HCl effectively increased the concentration of the zwitterionic phospholipid phosphatidylcholine on the surface of the duodenal mucosa.

Lastly, phospholipids and surface hydrophobicity have been implicated in the protective mechanisms elicited by other gastroprotective agents including geranylgeranylacetone(6, 67), terprenone (4), aluminum-based antacids (99), sucralfate (38), and bismuth salts (78). The effects of heavy metals such as aluminum, bismuth, and gold on mucosal hydrophobicity are presently being studied, with preliminary evidence (L Lichtenberger, unpublished) indicating that the major effect may be in the recruitment and stabilization of a phospholipid monolayer at the luminal interface of the mucus gel layer.

EFFICACY OF EXOGENOUS PHOSPHOLIPIDS TO FORTIFY THE GASTRIC MUCOSAL BARRIER AND THEIR THERAPEUTIC POTENTIAL

In 1983 we reported that pylorus-ligated rats were protected from a necrotizing dose of HCl if pretreated with a liposomal suspension of exogenous phospholipids, with DPPC being most prominent (57). The protective action of exogenous phospholipids has been confirmed in a variety of species and ulcer models including studies in rat, *Necturus*, dog and human (21, 29, 50, 73, 93). It was also noted that certain phospholipid-containing foods (i.e. bananas and milk/cream) can elicit significant protection of laboratory animals to variety of ulcer challenges (15, 17, 41). In a series of studies, Dial demonstrated the efficacious protective activity of human milk and dairy products against acid, ethanol, and stress-induced ulcerogenesis (15, 17). The fact that comparable protection can be elicited by an aqueous suspension of an extract of milk lipids strongly suggests a role of dietary lipids in mucosal protection (15, 17, 51). Our studies with mixtures of phospholipids and neutral lipids, as occur in milk products, indicate that neutral lipid is required for full activity, perhaps by forming a less stable microemulsion that facilitates the rapid deposition of the phospholipid monolayer to the mucosal surface (79).

Perhaps the greatest therapeutic potential of exogenous phospholipids may be in the reduction of NSAID-induced mucosal inflammation and GI bleeding. Laboratory experiments indicate the protective efficacy of various synthetic and natural phospholipid preparations in this regard, and pilot clinical studies with purified fractions of phospholipids from dairy products and soy bean (*Essential*) are encouraging (29, 52, 55, 73). It is also likely that the protective activity of exogenous phospholipids can be optimized as we increase our understanding of the molecular association between zwitterionic phospholipids and NSAIDs. Our laboratory has recently extended these observations and demonstrated that the association of NSAIDs (aspirin, indomethacin, and diclofenac) with DPPC prior to administration optimizes drug delivery and prevents the NSAID from complexing with intrinsic GI mucosal zwitterionic phospholipids to attenuate the hydrophobic barrier properties of the tissue (60, 73). As a consequence, the GI side effects of NSAIDs (as assessed by quantifying mucosal lesions and intraluminal bleeding) are markedly reduced 80–90% if the molecule is administered as a complex with DPPC, although their antiinflammatory and antipyretic activities are unaffected. Thus future studies are warranted to determine the full potential of surfactant therapy to fortify the mucosal barrier in the treatment and prevention of erosive diseases of the GI tract.

SUMMARY

Impressive evidence has accumulated over the past 12 years indicating that one of the potentially important biophysical characteristics of mucus relates to its hydrophobic character. This surface property is region specific and reaches high values in the stomach and colon, where barrier properties against noxious agents in the lumen are most important. The hydrophobic properties of mucus appear to be related to its lipidic constituents and specifically to the presence of phospholipid surfactants that are synthesized, stored, and secreted by GI mucus cells in a regulated fashion.

Literature Cited

1. Adamson AW. 1967. *The Physical Chemistry of Surfaces.* pp. 476–78. New York: Intersciences. 2nd ed.
2. Allen A. 1989. Gastrointestinal mucus. In *The Gastrointestinal System,* ed. SG Schultz, JG Forte, BB Rauner, 3:309–82. Bethesda: Am. Physiol. Soc.
3. Allen A, Flemström G, Garner A, Kivilaakso E. 1993. Gastroduodenal mucosal protection. *Physiol. Rev.* 73:823–57
4. Aono M, Moriga M, Mizata K, Uchino H. 1986. Effect of terprenone on the content of phospholipids in gastric secretions in man. *Gastroenterol. Jpn.* 21:454–58
5. Berstad K, Berstad A. 1993. *Helicobacter pylori* infection in peptic ulcer disease. *Scand. J. Gastroenterol.* 28:561–67
6. Bilski J, Sarosiek J, Murty VLN, Aono M, Moriga M, et al. 1987. Enhancement of the lipid content and physical properties of gastric mucus by geranylgeranylacetone. *Biochem. Pharmacol.* 36:4059–65
7. Butler BD, Lichtenberger LM, Hills BA. 1983. Distribution of surfactants in the canine GI tract and their ability to lubricate. *Am. J. Physiol.* 7:G645–51
8. Davenport HW. 1964. Gastric mucosal injury by fatty and acetyl salicylic acids. *Gastroenterology* 46:245–53
9. Davenport HW. 1967. Ethanol damage to the oxyntic glandular mucosa. *Proc. Soc. Exp. Biol. Med.* 126:657–62
10. Davenport HW. 1970. Effect of lysolecithin, digitonin, and phospholipase A upon the dog's gastric mucosal barrier. *Gastroenterology* 59:505–9
11. Davenport HW. 1972. Why the stomach does not digest itself. *Sci. Am.* 226:86–93
12. Davenport HW, Warner HA, Code CF. 1964. Functional significance of gastric mucosal barrier to sodium. *Gastroenterology* 47:142–52
13. DeSchryver-Kecskemet K, Eliakim R, Carroll S, Stenson WF, Moxley MA, Alpers DH. 1989. Intestinal surfactant-like material. *J. Clin. Invest.* 84:1355–61
14. Dial EJ, Kao Y-CJ, Lichtenberger LM. 1991. Effects of 16, 16 dimethyl prostaglandin E_2 on glycoprotein and lipid synthesis of gastric epithelial cells grown in primary culture. *In Vitro Cell Dev. Biol.* 27A:39–46
15. Dial EJ, Lichtenberger LM. 1984. A role for milk phospholipids in protection against gastric acid: studies in adult and suckling rats. *Gastroenterology* 87:379–85
16. Dial EJ, Lichtenberger LM. 1986. Development of gastric mucosal protection against acid in the rat: role of corticosteroids and prostaglandins *Gastroenterology* 91:318–25
17. Dial EJ, Lichtenberger LM. 1987. Milk protection against experimental ulcerogenesis in rats. *Dig. Dis. Sci.* 32:1145–50
18. Dial EJ, Lichtenberger LM. 1988. Surface hydrophobicity of the gastric mucosa in the developing rat. Effects of corticosteroids, thyroxine and prostageandin E_2. *Gastroenterology* 94:57–67
19. Dial EJ, Lichtenberger LM. 1989. Development of the gastric barrier to acid. In *Human Gastrointestinal Development,* ed. E Lebenthal, pp. 353–63. New York: Raven
20. Dierichs R, Inczedy-Marcsek K. 1976. Iodoplatinate as a marker of quarternary ammonium compounds in electron microscopy. *J. Histochem. Cytochem.* 24:962–70
21. Dunjic BS, Axelson J, AriRajab A, Larsson K, Bengmark S. 1993. Gastroprotective capability of exogenous phosphatidylcholine in experimentally induced chronic gastric ulcers in rats. *Scand. J. Gastroenterol.* 28:89–94
22. Eliakim R, DeSchryver-Kecskemeti, Nogee L, Stenson WF, Alpers DH. 1989. Isolation and characterization of small intestinal surfactant-like particle containing alkaline phosphatase and other digestive enzymes. *J. Biol. Chem.* 264:20614–19
23. Goddard PJ. 1990. *Relation between acid back–diffusion and luminal surface hydrophobicity in canine gastric mucosa: effects of salicylate and prostaglandin.* PhD thesis. Univ. Texas at Houston 147 pp.
24. Goddard PJ, Kao Y-CJ, Lichtenberger LM. 1990. Luminal surface hydrophobicity of canine gastric mucosa is dependent on a surface mucous gel. *Gastroenterology* 98:361–70
25. Goddard PJ, Lichtenberger LM. 1987. Does aspirin damage the canine gastric mucosa by reducing its surface hydrophobicity? *Am. J. Physiol.* 15:G421–30
26. Goggin PM, Marrero JM, Spychal RI, Jackson PA, Corbishley CM, Northfield TC. 1992. Surface hydrophobicity of gastric mucosa in *Helicobacter pylori*

infection: effect of clearance and eradication. *Gastroenterology* 103:1486–90

27. Goggin PM, Northfield TC, Spychal RI. 1991. Factors affecting gastric mucosal hydrophobicity in man. *Scand. J. Gastroenterol.* 26(Suppl. 181):65–73

28. Gong D, Turner B, Bhaskar KR, Lamont JT. 1990. Lipid binding to gastric mucin: protective effect against oxygen radicals. *Am. J. Physiol.* 22:G681–86

29. Gundermann K-J, ed. 1993. *The "Essential" Phospholipids as a Membrane Therapeutic.* pp. 100–6, 167–74. Szcecin, Poland: Pol. Sect. Eur. Soc. Biochem. Pharmacol.

30. Gwpzdzinski K, Slomiany A, Nishikawa H. 1988. Gastric mucin hydrophobicity: effects of associated and covalently bound lipids, proteolysis, and reduction. *Biochem. Int.* 17:907–17

31. Heatley NG. 1959. Mucosubstances as a barrier to diffusion. *Gastroenterology* 37:313–17

32. Hentschel E, Brandstätter G, Dragosics B, Hirschl AM, Nemec H, et al. 1993. Effect of ranitidine and amoxicillin plus metronidazole on the eradication of *Helicobacter pylori* and the recurrence of duodenal ulcer. *N. Engl. J. Med.* 328:308–12

33. Hills BA. 1981. What is the true role of surfactant in the lung. *Thorax* 36:1–4

34. Hills BA. 1983. Water repellency induced by pulmonary surfactants. *J. Physiol.* 325:175–86

35. Hills BA. 1985. Gastric mucosal barrier: stabilization of hydrophobic lining to the stomach by mucus. *Am. J. Physiol.* 249:G342–49

36. Hills BA. 1988. Surfaces and surfactants. In *The Biology of Surfactant.* pp. 1–27. Cambridge: Cambridge Univ. Press.

37. Hills BA. 1990. A physical identity for the gastric mucosal barrier. *Med. J. Aust.* 153:76–81

38. Hills BA. 1991. A common physical basis for gastric mucosal barrier and the action of sucralfate. *Am. J. Med.* 91:43S–51S

39. Hills BA. 1993. Gastric mucosal barrier: evidence for *Helicobacter pylori* ingesting gastric surfactant and deriving protection from it. *Gut* 34:588–93

40. Hills BA, Butler BD, Lichtenberger LM. 1983. Gastric mucosal barrier: the hydrophobic lining to the lumen of the stomach. *Am. J. Physiol.* 7:G561–68

41. Hills BA, Kirkwood CA. 1989. Surfactant approach to the gastric mucosal barrier: protection of rats by banana even when acidified. *Gastroenterology* 97:294–303

42. Hollander F. 1954. The two component mucus barrier. *Arch. Int. Med.* 93:107–20

43. Kalina M, Pease DC. 1977. The preservation of ultra-structure in saturated phosphatidylcholines by tannic acid in model systems and Type II pneumocytes. *J. Cell Biol.* 74:726–41

44. Kao Y-CJ, Goddard PJ, Lichtenberger LM. 1990. Morphological effects of aspirin and prostaglandin on the canine gastric mucosal surface: analysis with a phospholipid cytochemical stain. *Gastroenterology* 98:592–606

45. Kao Y-CJ, Lichtenberger LM. 1987. Localization of phospholipid-rich zones in rat gastric mucosa: possible origin of a protective hydrophobic lining. *J. Histochem. Cytochem.* 35:1285–98

46. Kao Y-CJ, Lichtenberger LM. 1990. Hydrophobic properties of the mucus cells of the stomach and submucosal glands. *Gastroenterology* 98:A67 (Abst.)

47. Kao Y-CJ, Lichtenberger LM. 1990. A method to preserve extracellular surfactant-like phospholipids on the luminal surface of the rodent gastric mucosa. *J. Histochem. Cytochem.* 38:427–31

48. Kao Y-CJ, Lichtenberger LM. 1991. Phospholipid- and neutral-lipid-containing organelles of rat gastroduodenal mucous cells. *Gastroenterology* 101:7–21

49. Kao Y-CJ, Lichtenberger LM. 1993. Effect of 16,16 dimethyl prostaglandin E_2 on the lipidic organelles of rat gastric surface mucous cells. *Gastroenterology* 104:103–13

50. Kiviluto T, Paimela H, Mustonen H, Kivilaakso E. 1991. Effect of exogenous surface-active phospholipid on intracellular pH and membrane resistances in isolated *Necturus* antral mucosa exposed to luminal acid and barrier breaking agents. *Gastroenterology* 100:38–46

51. Kivinen A, Salminen S, Homer D, Vapaatalo H. 1992. Gastroprotective effect of milk phospholipids, butter serum lipids and butter serum on ethanol and acetylsalicylic acid induced ulcers in rats. *Michwissenschaft* 47:573–75

52. Kivinen A, Tarpila S, Salminen S, Vapaatalo H. 1992. Gastroprotection with milk phospholipids: a first human study. *Michwissenschaft* 47:694–96

53. Kwun SY, Spychal RT. 1992. Ultrastructural identification of surfactant-like material in human esophageal mucosa. *Gastroenterology* 102:A104 (Abstr.)

54. Langston SR, Cesareo SD. 1992. *Helicobacter pylori* associated phospholipase A_2 activity: a factor in peptic

ulcer production? *J. Clin. Pathol.* 45: 221–24

55. Leyck S, Dereu N, Etschenberg E, Ghyczy M, Graf E, et al. 1985. Improvement of gastric tolerance of non-steroidal anti-inflammatory drugs by polyene phosphatidylcholine (Phospholipon R100). *Eur. J. Pharmacol.* 117:35–42

56. Lichtenberger LM, Ahmed TN, Barreto JC, Kao Y-CJ, Dial EJ. 1992. Use of fluorescent hydrophobic dyes in establishing the presence of lipids in the gastric mucus gel layer. *J. Clin. Gastroenterol.* 14(Suppl. 1):S82–87

57. Lichtenberger LM, Graziani LA, Dial EJ, Butler BD, Hills BA. 1983. Role of surface-active phospholipids in gastric cytoprotection. *Science* 219:1327–29

58. Lichtenberger LM, Richard JE, Hills BA. 1985. Effect of 16,16 dimethyl-prostaglandin E_2 on the surface hydrophobicity of aspirin-treated canine gastric mucosa. *Gastroenterology* 88: 308–14

59. Lichtenberger LM, Romero JJ. 1994. Effect of ammonium ion on the hydrophobic and barrier properties of the gastric mucus gel layer. *J. Gastroenterol. Hepatol.* In press

60. Lichtenberger LM, Wang ZM, Romero JJ, Barreto JC. 1994. Certain NSAIDs chemically associate with surface phospholipids: insight into mechanism and reversal of NSAID-induced gastric injury. *Gastroenterology* 106(4):A125 (Abst.)

61. Lugea A, Mourelle M, Guarner F, Domingo A, Salas A, Malagelada J-R. 1994. Mucosal secretion of phosphatidylcholines as mediators of adaptive cytoprotection of the rat duodenum. *Gastroenterology.* 107:720–27

62. Mack DR, Neumann AW, Policova Z, Sherman PM. 1992. Surface hydrophobicity of the intestinal tract. *Am. J. Physiol.* 262:G171–77

63. Mauch F, Bode G, Ditschuneit H, Malfertheiner P. 1993. Demonstration of a phospholipid-rich zone in the human gastric epithelium damaged by *Helicobacter pylori. Gastroenterology* 105:1698–704

64. Mobley HL, Cortesia M, Rosenthal LE, Jones BD. 1988. Characterization of urease from *Campylobacter pylori. J. Clin. Microbiol.* 26:831–36

65. Nardone G, D'Armieto F, Corso G, Civiletti C, Coscione P, et al. 1994. Lipids of human gastric mucosa: effect of inflammatory infiltrates. *Helicobacter pylori* infection and non-alcoholic cirrhosis. *Gastroenterology.* 107:362–68

66. Nishisaki H, Sakamoto C, Konda Y,

Nakano O, Matozaki T, et al. 1992. Effects of antiulcer drags on phosphatidylcholine synthesis in isolated guinea pig gastric glands. *Dig. Dis. Sci.* 37:1593–99

67. Nishizawa Y, Sakurai H, Oketani K, Horie T, Yamato C, Moriga M. 1987. Effects of taurocholic acid/HCl alone or after pretreatment with geranylgeranylacetone on phospholipid metabolism in rat gastric mucosa. *Biochem. Pharmacol.* 36:4111–17

68. Nishizawa Y, Sakurai H, Yamato C, Moriga M. 1987. Effects of ethanol alone or after pretreatment with 20% ethanol on phospholipid metabolism in rat gastric mucosa. *Biochem. Biophys. Acta* 917:372–80

69. Orchard JL, Bickerstaff CA. 1986. Gastric mucosal phospholipid concentrations in human patients with gastritis, gastric ulcer, and normals. *Gastroenterology* 90:A1573

70. Osler W. 1929. *Beaumont's Experiments and Observations on the Gastric Juice and the Physiology of Digestion.* Boston: Int. Physiol. Cong.

71. Ottletz A, Romero JJ, Hazell SL, Graham DY, Lichtenberger LM. 1993. Phospholipase activity of *Helicobacter pylori* and its inhibition by bismuth salts: Biochemical and biophysical studies. *Dig. Dis. Sci.* 38:2071–80

72. Padmanabham S, Bose A. 1988. Importance of direct measurement of dynamic contact angles during wetting of solids. *J. Colloid Interface Sci.* 126:164–70

73. Parnham MJ, Leyck S. 1988. Phospholipon 100. *Drugs Future* 13:324–25

74. Pfeiffer CJ. 1981. Experimental analysis of hydrogen ion diffusion in gastro-intestinal mucus glycoprotein. *Am. J. Physiol.* 3:G176–82

75. Ridel E. 1967. Wetting. *Soc. Chem. Ind. monogragraph 25.* London: Soc. Chem. Ind.

76. Robért A, Nezamis JE, Lancaster C, Daries JP, Field SO, Hanchar AJ. 1983. Mild irritants prevent gastric necrosis through "adaptive cytoprotection" mediated by prostaglandins. *Am. J. Physiol.* 245:G113–21

77. Robért A, Nezamis JE, Lancaster C, Hanchar AJ. 1979. Cytoprotection by prostaglandins in rats: Prevention of gastric necrosis produced by alcohol, HCl, NaOH, hypertonic NaCl and thermal injury. *Gastroenterology* 70:359–70

78. Romero JJ, Carryl O, Lichtenberger LM. 1994. Spice rapidly attenuates the hydrophobic lining of the rat stomach. *Gastroenterology* 106(4):A167 (Abst.)

79. Romero JJ, Kao Y-CJ, Lichtenberger

LM. 1990. Gastric protective activity of mixtures of polar and neutral lipids in rats. *Gastroenterology* 99:311–26

80. Sbarbati A, Deganello A, Tamassia G, Bertini M, Gaburro D, Osculati F. 1992. Surfactant-like material in the antral mucosa of children. *J. Pediatr. Gastroenterol.* 13:279–84

81. Scheiman JM, Kraus ER, Boland CR. 1992. Regulation of canine gastric mucin synthesis and phospholipid secretion by acid secretagogues. *Gastroenterology* 103:1842–50

82. Scheiman JM, Kraus ER, Bonnville LA, Weinhold PA,BolandCR. 1991. Synthesis and prostaglandin E_2–induced secretion of surfactant phospholipid by isolated gastric mucous cells. *Gastroenterology* 100:1232–40

83. Schmitz MGJ, Renooij W. 1990. Phospholipids from rat, human, and canine gastric mucosa. *Gastroenterology* 99: 1292–96

84. Sengupta S, Piotrowski E, Slomiany A, Slomiany BL. 1991. Role of adrenergic and cholinergic mediators in gastric mucus phospholipid secretion. *Biochem. Int.* 24:1145–53

85. Slomiany A, Galicki NI, Kojima K, Baras-Grnszka Z, Slomiany BL. 1981. Glyceroglucolipids of the mucous barrier of dog stomach. *Biochim. Biophys. Acta* 665:88–91

86. Slomiany A, Jozwiak Z, Takagi A, Slomiany BL. 1984. The role of covalently bound fatty acids in the degradation of human gastric mucus glycoprotein. *Arch. Biochem.* 229:560–67

87. Slomiany BL, Kasinathan C, Slomiany A. 1989. Lipolytic activity of *Campylobacter pylori:* effect of colloidal bismuth subcitrate (De-Nol). *Am. J. Gastroenterol.* 84:1273–77

88. Slomiany BL, Sarosiek J, Slomiany A. 1987. Gastric mucus and the mucosal barrier. *Dig. Dis. Sci.* 5:125–45

89. Slomiany BL, Slomiany A. 1991. Role of mucus in gastric mucosal protection. *J. Physiol. Pharmacol.* 42:141–61

90. Slomiany A, Yano S, Slomiany BL, Glass GBJ. 1978. Lipid composition of the gastric mucous barrier in the rat. *J. Biol. Chem.* 253:3785–91

91. Spychal RT, Goggin PM, Marrero JM, Saverymuttu SH, Yu CW, et al. 1990. Surface hydrophobicity of gastric mucosa in peptic ulcer disease: relationship to gastritis and *Campylobacter pylori* infection. *Gastroenterology* 98:1250–54

92. Spychal RT, Marrero JM, Saverymuttu SH, Northfield TC, 1989. Measurement of the surface hydrophobicity of human gastrointestinal mucosa. *Gastroenterology* 97:104–11

93. Swarm RA, Ashley SW, Soybel DI, Ordway FS, Cheung LY. 1987. Protective effect of exogenous phospholipid on aspirin-induced gastric mucosal injury. *Am. J. Surg.* 153:48–53

94. Tatsumi Y, Lichtenberger LM. 1994. Trinitrobenzensulfonic acid (TNBS) reduces colonic mucosal hydrophobicity by formation of a complex with zwitterionic phospholipids. *Gastroenterology.* 106:A781 (Abstr.)

95. Tietze CC, Becich MJ, Engle M, Stenson WF, Eliakim R, Alpers DH. 1992. Surfactant-like particle production by Caco-2 cells is stimulated by tranfection with rat intestinal alkaline phosphatase cDNA. *Am. J. Physiol.* 263:G756–66

96. Walsbren SJ, Gelbel JP, Modlin IM, Boron WF. 1994. Unusual permeability properties of gastric gland cells. *Nature* 368:332–34

97. Wassef MK, Lin YN, Horowitz MI. 1978. Phospholipid-deacylating enzymes of rat stomach mucosa. *Biochim. Biophys. Acta* 528:318–30

98. Wassef MK, Lin YN, Horowitz MJ. 1979. Molecular species of phosphatidylcholine from rat gastric mucosa. *Biochim. Biophys. Acta* 573:222–26

99. Weberg R, Berstad K, Berstad A. 1990. Acute effects of antacids on gastric juice components in duodenal ulcer patients. *Eur. J. Clin. Invest.* 20:511–15

100. Weit Kamp J-H, Perez-Perez GI, Bode G, Blaser MJ. 1992. Characteristics of *Helicobacter pylori* phospholipase C activity. *Gastroenterology* 102:A946 (Abst.)

101. Wertz PW, Downing DT. 1982. Glycolipids in mammalian epidermis: structure and function in the water barrier. *Science* 217:1261–62

102. Williams SE, Turnburg LA. 1980. Retardation of acid diffusion by pig gastric mucus: a potential role in mucosal protection. *Gastroenterology* 79:299–304

103. Wolfe S. 1965. Gastric secretions. In *The Stomach.* pp. 53–79. New York: Oxford Univ. Press

Annu. Rev. Physiol. 1995. 57:585–605

SIGNAL TRANSDUCTION, PACKAGING AND SECRETION OF MUCINS

Gordon Forstner

Division of Gastroenterology, Department of Pediatrics, University of Toronto, Research Institute, Hospital for Sick Children, Toronto, Canada M5G 1X8

KEY WORDS: exocytosis, receptor activation, intracellular transport, microtubules

INTRODUCTION

Recent advances in gene identification have revealed a degree of heterogeneity in secreted mucins that was barely imaginable a few years ago. Although mucin gene expression tends to be organ and cell specific (40), epithelia from the respiratory, intestinal, and reproductive tracts independently express at least three different gene products (1). Gene expression may be altered, as well, by malignant transformation, metabolic, and regulatory factors (40, 54). Although specific mRNAs can be identified relatively easily, the separation and assay of individual mucins by biochemical or immunological means continues to be difficult. With few exceptions, therefore, our understanding of the factors that control intracellular transport and secretion of these mucus glycoproteins is based on composite rather than specific data. Thus it is likely that significant modifications will emerge as more specific analyses become available. Nevertheless, during the past five years, considerable progress has been made towards clarifying the general features of packaging and exocytosis of secreted mucins, particularly in the gastrointestinal tract. The latter is emphasized in this review, but an effort has been made to include contributions from other systems wherever possible.

INTRACELLULAR PROCESSING

Endoplasmic Reticulum and Golgi

Like other packaged secretory glycoproteins, mucins are synthesized as nascent peptides on membrane-bound ribosomes and cotranslationally trans-

585

0066–4278/95/0315–0585$05.00

ported into the cysternae of the rough endoplasmic reticulum. The mucin peptides destined for secretion differ from membrane-bound mucins such as MUC1 because they have cysteine-rich domains at N and C termini. Pulse-chase analyses of assembly, processing, and transport of rat gastric mucin (98) and human MUC2 in LS180 cells (60) have been performed. Mucins are oligomerized in the endoplasmic reticulum (ER) by disulfide bonding (20, 60), an event that follows N-glycosylation and perhaps limited O-glycosylation (60). Oligomerization occurs independently of vectorial transport because it is not blocked by treatment with the proton ionophore CCCP or incubation at 15°C (18). Nevertheless, oligomerization is essential for escape from the ER because monomers do not enter the Golgi. In general, movement of proteins from the ER to the cis-Golgi is energy dependent and often modulated by molecular chaperones (25). Mucin-specific chaperones may exist but have not been identified. The membrane-bound mammary gland sialomucins episialin (MUC1) (56) and ASPG (90) undergo proteolytic cleavage in the ER. The purpose of this is unclear because the cleaved segments remain noncovalently bound through subsequent processing steps. Mutant proteins lacking the epis-ialin cleavage site are also processed normally (56). An analogous cleavage takes place in MUC2 (38) and its homologue in rat intestine, MLP (106), thereby liberating a C terminal "link" peptide that remains covalently bound by disulfide bonds to the glycosylated core mucin. In ASPG, MUC2, and MLP, a single asp-pro bond is broken, which suggests that the event is specific and possibly of functional significance. However, the site of the link peptide cleavage in secreted mucins has not been localized to a particular organelle and may not be in the ER.

Glycosylation may play a role in facilitating ER processing and transport. Most mucin oligosaccharide is O-glycosidically linked to serine and threonine residues in central tandem repeat-rich regions. Cotranslational initiation of O-glycosylation by addition of N-acetylgalactosamine (GalNAc) residues has been claimed (99) but not firmly established. Most GalNAc is probably added later in the ER or in the cis-cisternae of the Golgi complex (69). Nevertheless, in LS180 cells, we found that a small fraction, 13%, of nascent, monomeric mucin bound specifically to a GalNAc-specific lectin, compared with 5% to a mature control mucin (60), which suggests that some GalNAc was added to MUC2 before oligomerization and therefore at an early phase of ER transport. If early O-glycosylation does take place, its significance is uncertain. In ma-lignantly transformed cells O-glycosylation could represent aberrant expression of core glycosyl transferases in the ER, as described in HT29 cells (24). Addition of GalNAc residues to the core peptide of porcine submaxillary mucin has a major conformational effect (91), however, that could influence folding of nascent peptide chains. Using rat intestinal mRNA in an in vitro translation system, we observed that the addition of GalNAc and microsomal vesicles augments mucin synthesis (43), which suggests that O-glycosylation could assist the efficient transfer of nascent mucins to the ER. MUC2 (38) and MLP (106) possess a number of N-glycosylation sites. Carbohydrate analyses of the link peptide have consistently demonstrated a significant amount of mannose (26), which indicates that the N-glycosylation sites are probably expressed. This is important in the present context because N-glycosylation occurs co-translationally. Inhibition of N-glycosylation by tunicamycin impaired disulfide dependent oligomerization of gastric mucin and subsequent transport through the cell (18), which suggests that N-asparagine-linked high-mannose oligosaccharide chains may facilitate early folding. Tunicamycin also increased the monomer-oligomer ratio in MUC2 at early chase periods (60), as one might expect if oligomerization were impeded.

Brefeldin A and monensin, both of which inhibit Golgi transport at an early stage, prevented the appearance of mature sulfated mucin in gastric mucus-secreting cells and limited synthesis to a truncated molecule rich in naked (unextended) core GalNAC residues (18). In colonic LS180 adenocarcinoma cells, monensin prevented incorporation of radioactive glucosamine into MUC2 and also inhibited sialylation (60). Therefore, core GalNAc residues are added in the *cis*-Golgi, or earlier, while elongation of 0-oligosaccharide chains takes place in the mid- and *trans*-Golgi. Precursor labeling suggests that gastric mucin oligosaccharide chains, like those of other glycoproteins, are completed within Golgi cisternae (83). Recycling of membrane-bound mucin through the *trans*-Golgi appears to facilitate increased sialylation (57), but recycling of secretory mucins from storage granules to Golgi has not been reported. At present, however, it is not wise to exclude the possibility that secretory mucin undergoes further processing after entering condensing or storage granules.

Condensation and Granule Formation

As Golgi processing reaches completion, mucins collect at nodular dilatations that appear at random along the tubular components of the *trans*-Golgi stack (80). The dilatations subsequently bud from the Golgi tubules to form condensing granules. During the transition from condensing granules to mature storage granules, an increase in electron density occurs (86), which suggests that the mucins become more concentrated. The directional signal that targets mucins to secretory granules has not been elucidated, but in other secretory systems the signal is present in the primary amino acid sequence (15, 65); thus the existence of directional signals in secreted mucins seems likely. It may even be possible that mutations or splicing variants exist that cause most of the product to be secreted without storage. The oft-cited absence of goblet cells in the acutely inflamed colonic mucosa of patients with ulcerative colitis is one possible example of a pathological situation in which misdirection of mucins could play a role.

The Ca^{2+} content of mature granules is high (100, 103, 105). Ca^{2+} probably aids condensation by charge shielding, which enhances apolar interactions and favors collapsed, compact, quaternary molecular structures (103). Additional factors within the granule may be necessary to stabilize mucin condensation by increasing polymer-polymer affinity (103). A high intragranular Ca^{2+} content suggests that the granule membrane must contain Ca^{2+} channels coupled to a high energy source. We do not know whether intragranular pH is low as in many other secretory granules, but H^+-Ca^{2+} exchange may be a requirement (67). The development of methods for isolating mucin granules and mucin granule membranes would provide a basis for addressing these questions.

MUCIN SECRETION

Mucus-secreting cells vary in the complexity of their substructural architecture. In the stomach and gall bladder, mature granules are concentrated at the apical pole of the cell beneath the plasma membrane but are not clearly separated from other cytoplasmic constituents (101). Goblet cells lining the small intestine and colon begin their lives in this form in the lower crypt (79), but as they migrate upward, acquire a highly organized array of vertically oriented microtubules and circular or oblique intermediate filaments known as the theca (96). The theca defines the outer limit of the storage granular zone, separating granules from most of the remaining cytoplasm and, incidentally, giving the goblet cell its distinctive shape. In all mucin-secreting cells, apical granules extrude their contents by exocytosis after fusion of granule and plasma membranes and formation of a fusion pore.

Exocytosis of mucins cannot simply rely on the opening of a fusion pore and the release of granule contents by diffusion. The material concentrated in storage granules is likely to be so viscous that an expulsionary force is necessary. One possibility is that the force is provided by the rapid expansion of mucin molecules that takes place on exposure to extracellular fluid (103). The energy would be provided by charge repulsion of polyanionic chains once the charge-shielding effect of intragranule Ca^{2+} was removed. It is also possible that mucins are flushed out of the granule by active secretion of fluid at the granule base. Secretary granules in other cells possess membranes with chloride (21, 36) and potassium (35) channels, chloride-bicarbonate exchangers, and ATP-dependent proton pumps (71), ostensibly to maintain low intragranular pH, but also able to support washout secretion.

Apocrine cells such as intestinal goblet cells accelerate exocytosis by opening fusion pores in a sequential manner between previously fused and adjacent granules. The process, known as compound exocytosis, results in a generalized emptying of stored mucin and cavitation of the central storage area. As contents are evacuated, a considerable loss of cytoplasm and sloughing of excess granule membranes take place (94). Compound exocytosis is therefore a rather extreme process, reserved in all probability for emergencies. Most cells seem to recover quickly, however. Complete refilling of the intestinal goblet has been estimated to take 60–120 min (96).

Unregulated Secretion

STORAGE VS NONSTORAGE PATHWAYS   Cells generally secrete proteins via one or a combination of two pathways: (a) a steady vesicular constitutive pathway in which no storage occurs, and in which no receptor-mediated secretory regulation takes place; and (b) a pathway that involves intermediate packaging and storage of secretory products in a retaining area, thus necessitating regulated release in response to specific stimuli (12). Proteins are extruded by exocytosis in either case; the essential difference is that vesicles in constitutive pathways are transported directly to the plasma membrane and undergo immediate exocytosis without requiring a signal other than contact with the membrane, whereas in regulated pathways, storage vesicles gather in clusters beneath the plasma membrane awaiting a signal to release their contents. If mucin in storage granules was not released until cells were stimulated, one would expect to find evidence of feed-back inhibition of synthesis and transport when the granule compartment was full. Instead, it is clear from autoradiographic and pulse-chase studies that the resting unstimulated goblet cell continues to synthesize and incorporate new mucin into storage granules. Mucin storage granules must therefore participate in unregulated, as well as regulated, secretory processes.

There is, in fact, no clear evidence that a constitutive secretory pathway of the classical type plays a significant role in mucin secretion, although it is possible that mucus cells retain this option. The cell line SW1116, derived from a colonic adenocarcinoma, may be an example of a mutant line that has adopted the classical constitutive pathway. SW1116 cells have a relatively sparse population of intracellular vesicles that contain mucin, yet continually secrete mucin in large amounts (107). Few of the vesicles are distended with material in the manner of true storage granules. The cell line is generally refractory to secretagogues although it does respond minimally to Ca^{2+} ionophores. Thus constitutive secretion is prominent, and regulated secretion is comparatively minor. Electron micrographs of immunolocalized mucin suggest that some storage granules are formed, presumably accounting for the small regulated response. Baseline secretion is also partially inhibited by arachidonic acid, so that some of the constitutive secretion may be regulated (107).

The architectural rigidity of goblet cells makes it possible to chart the course of separate streams of secretory granules through the storage compartment, and it is clear that continual, single-granule exocytosis accounts for baseline or unstimulated secretion from intestinal goblet cells in the resting state (93). The granules that are involved in this baseline secretion are located at the periphery of the granule mass (Figure 1) next to the theca but are not otherwise different from other secretory granules. When radioactive monosaccharide precursors are incorporated into colonic goblet cell mucins and followed by pulse-chase autoradiography, labeling is confined to the peripheral granules in the resting state (93), and the elapsed time between labeling in the Golgi and extrusion at the cell apex is 6 h (96). This timing fits well with minimum transit times of 4–6 h from ER to bathing media recorded when labeling of immunoprecipitable mucins was followed in rat gastric segments (19). It takes approximately 4 h for labeled mucin to travel from the Golgi region to apical granules in goblet cells (96). By contrast, in columnar cells, the transport of labeled glycoprotein from Golgi vesicles to plasma membrane by a vesicular, nonstorage constitutive route takes 30 min (5). Pulse-chase immunoprecipitation experiments do not distinguish between storage and nonstorage pathways. However, the prolonged time required for secretion of immunoprecipitable

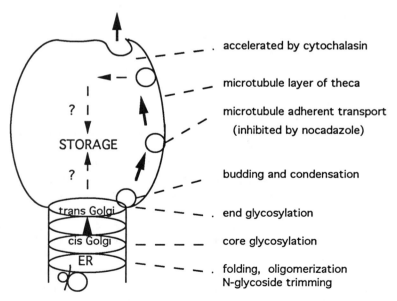

Figure 1   Baseline mucin secretion in the goblet cell. After processing in the Golgi, mucin granules are guided to the surface by microtubules. The scheme emphasizes the fact that the route of entry into the storage compartment is unknown.

mucins suggests that virtually all the mucin is delivered to the exterior via storage granules.

Although unregulated in the sense of not requiring a known stimulus, the baseline lateral movement of granules is, like the movement of vesicles in other cells (12), controlled by interactions with microtubules and actin. Granule interaction with the vertical assembly of microtubules is essential for their orderly translocation to the cell apex. Depolymerization of microtubules by nocadazole inhibits and disorients this baseline secretion, which causes the migration of some condensing vacuoles to the cell base (69). Taxol, an agent that prevents depolymerization of microtubules, impedes migration of the basally placed granules out of the supranuclear zone (70). When goblet cells were treated with cytochalasin D and dihydrocytochalasin B to depolymerize apical actin filaments, granular secretion was accelerated (69), which suggests that filaments that underlie the apical membrane are a barrier to secretion.

It is not obvious why mucin must be collected in storage granules before escaping from the cell in an unregulated manner. The process may be necessary to concentrate mucins to an optimal physical state. The storage mechanism could also be used to delay a targeting choice between retention in the granule mass or secretion. Some of the lateral granules, for example, do seem to move toward the middle of the plasma membrane above the main granule mass as if entering the storage pool (69). It is also possible that the granules that are involved in baseline secretion also participate in regulated secretion when the cell is stimulated. Thus the goblet cell could ensure the continuous replenishment of its surface coat with a concentrated product in a nonstimulatory environment and still be able to call upon all of its stored mucin when stimulated.

Regulated Secretion

SINGLE GRANULE VS COMPOUND EXOCYTOSIS Whereas single granules are released steadily from the peripheral zone of the mucin granule mass in goblet cells, central granules appear to be much more inert and are released principally by compound exocytosis. This conclusion is supported by precursor labeling studies that demonstrate rapid labeling of mucins in peripheral granules, but almost no labeling of central granules over the 6 h time span required to transfer the peripheral granules to the cell surface. The mucin stored in central granules is released by compound exocytosis, a regulated event that requires secretagogue stimulation (95). Single granules are therefore released without stimulation from the periphery of the granule mass, whereas central granules require a regulatory stimulus for release. In contrast, release of peripheral granules is stimulated by disruption of actin filaments (69), whereas compound exocytosis is not.

Although it is useful conceptually to distinguish between unregulated single granule and regulated compound exocytosis, a sharp distinction is not always possible. It is frequently difficult, particularly when cells are stimulated submaximally, to identify compound exocytosis even when secretion of immunologically or radioactively identified mucin is measurable. Recent evidence, compiled by computer-assisted morphometric analysis, suggests that carbachol induces secretion in the villus cells of the ileum without triggering compound exocytosis, presumably by accelerating single-granule exocytosis (73). It is not clear whether lateral or central granules, or both, participate in this form of regulated secretion. There is no reason a priori to think that lateral granules should be excluded. On the basis of a mucin epitope designated 5H7, which is recognized only in mature goblet cells, Chambraud et al (14) estimated that all granules, including those in the central core, are replaced twice during the migration of rat jejunal goblet cells through the middle one half of the villus without evidence of compound exocytosis. Central granules may turn over via ongoing single-granule exocytosis to a greater extent than is currently appreciated.

MEASURING REGULATED SECRETION   The large variety of assays in use to measure secreted mucin greatly complicates the interpretation of results. The reason for the lack of uniformity is partly historical. Nonspecific methods were introduced first and have been hard to supplant. Specific methods are more demanding; mucins are difficult to purify and the specificity of sensitive tools, such as antibodies, hard to verify.

Chemical and radioactive precursor labeling techniques measure a single attribute such as a monosaccharide, which is not restricted to mucins, nor necessarily evenly distributed among them. A purification step, limiting the measurement to high molecular weight or high density molecules, is a minimum requirement. Augeron et al (3), for example, used SDS/PAGE on 3% gels to isolate the large molecular weight mucin molecules. Precursor labeling depends upon the implicit assumption that there will be uniform labeling of the material in the granules. This is not easily achieved because of the inertness of central granules. The best remedy is to expose cells to an isotopically labeled precursor for a short pulse period and to examine them post-chase when it is determined that the label has entered mucins in storage granules and disappeared from more rapidly turned over glycoproteins (42, 74, 89). Kim et al (46) and Augeron et al (3) describe an acceptable alternative. Cells were incubated with radioactive precursor for a prolonged period (24 h) in an attempt to establish uniform labeling, then washed and chased for a short period in the presence of secretagogues. Optimum time periods should be determined for each set of experimental conditions.

It seems evident that compositional methods will give way to immunological approaches if only because the latter have the capacity to identify individual mucin molecules. Mucins are strong antigens. High titre polyclonal antibodies against purified mucin preparations can be raised easily, and polyclonal and monoclonal antibodies against specific peptide or carbohydrate epitopes can also be made (60, 107). Immunoassays with a high sensitivity and specificity for secreted mucins have been developed by a number of laboratories (28, 61, 84, 85, 107), and specific antibodies have made it possible to study the synthesis and secretion of a single mucin, MUC2, in the LS180 cell line (60). Secreted mucins can be measured relatively easily by an enzyme-linked immunosorbent assay (ELISA) or radioimmunoassay in media from tissue culture cells containing 10^5 cells (61), as well as in washings from gut sacs and intestinal perfusates (33). An enzyme-linked lectin assay (ELLA) that relies on the affinity of soybean agglutinin for GalNAc has also been described (16). Although resembling an ELISA in technique, an ELLA is really an assay for a specific sugar determinant. In mouse small intestinal washings, the lectin bound several glycoproteins, which were probably not mucins, as well as more typical high molecular weight glycoproteins (16).

A special case can be made for microscopic assays because they focus directly on the exocytotic event and are potentially capable of exquisite sensitivity. Considerable experience has been obtained using histological assessment of compound exocytosis as the assay end point. When thin sections of well-oriented tissue are examined by light microscopy, compound exocytosis is clearly visible as cavitation, which correlates well with autoradiography and electron microscopic assessments (95). The method possesses the virtue of visual certainty but does not give a quantitative estimate of secretion. Computer-assisted morphometric analysis suggests that there may be a loss of mucin granule mass during secretagogue stimulation under circumstances where there is no evidence of compound exocytosis (73). This method correlates reasonably well with an ELISA using three different secretagogues (77). Recent advances in computer-assisted video enhanced microscopy suggest that it will be possible to count single-granule exocytotic events quantitatively within seconds of stimulation (17).

Many of the recent studies of mucin secretion in the stomach, trachea, and submandibular gland have been carried out using mucosal explants (87, 89) or on isolated cell preparations (8, 23, 28, 42, 45, 88), maintained for a short time in culture media. Immortalized mucin-secreting cell lines have been derived principally from colonic adenocarcinomas. In some of the cell lines (all subcloned from HT29 colonic adenocarcinoma cells) (2, 41, 49), a majority of the cells produce mucins, resemble goblet cells, and grow in monolayers. Unfortunately, none of these clones is readily available, and they grow rather slowly. Other established adenocarcinoma cell lines such as T84 (61), LS174T (68), LS180T (60), and SW1116 (107) are available through the American Type Culture collection and can be studied with comparative ease. The number of stimuli to which most lines respond and the apparent similarity of response patterns to that of the parent tissue (22) suggest that few receptors have been lost during transformation. The SW1116 adenocarcinoma cell line is an interesting exception, as noted above.

Specific Agonists and Receptors

Mucin-secreting cells respond to multiple stimuli and possess a variety of receptors coupled to an assortment of intracellular transduction pathways. Multiple receptor-mediated stimulatory pathways obviously create an opportunity for cross talk and graded response patterns. Typically, stimuli induce rather than inhibit secretion, and where more than one stimulus is involved, positive enhancement of responses appears to be the rule. There is evidence that the receptors on particular cells may vary from site to site and between species, thus offering an opportunity for qualitatively different responses to particular stimuli.

PHOSPHOLIPASE C ACTIVATORS   Cholinergic agonists stimulate mucin secretion in submandibular gland (28), stomach (42, 88, 89), small intestine (16, 73, 75, 94, 95), trachea (34), and in T84 (61) and HT29 (74, 84) adenocarcinoma cells. Intestinal villus and colonic surface goblet cells were initially thought to be refractory to cholinergic stimulation because no response was demonstrable by the cavitation assay (94, 95), but these cells do respond by accelerating single-granule exocytosis (73). Muscarinic receptors have been identified by ^{3}H QNB (quinuclidinyl benzilate) binding to isolated villus and crypt cells of the rat small intestine, as well as to colon (81, 104) and to HT29 cells (48), but these receptors have not yet been identified specifically in mucin-secreting cells. Muscarinic receptors generally activate phospholipase C, which, by releasing inositol 1,4,5-trisphosphate (IP_3) and diacylglycerol (DAG), causes an increase in intracellular Ca^{2+} and activates protein kinase C (PKC). Coupling in this manner has been demonstrated explicitly in gastric mucus cells (88) and submandibular gland mucus cells (28).

Luminal ATP releases mucins from primary cultures of tracheal epithelial cells via P2 receptors (45). Luminal ATP/UTP, but not ADP, stimulates goblet cell degranulation from dog tracheal goblet cells (17). Serosal purine nucleotides also stimulate degranulation in dog trachea (17), but in this case, ADP and ATP are equally active, which indicates that apical and basal receptors are distinct. In airway goblet cells, P2 receptors appear to be coupled to a calcium-generating system via IP_3 (47). ATP increases mucin release and IP_3 in parallel, and both responses are blocked by pretreatment with pertussis toxin, in keeping with the probable involvement of a pertussis toxin-sensitive GTP-binding protein.

In enzymatically dispersed submandibular gland acinar cells, methoxamine, an α_1-adrenergic agonist, and substance P stimulate mucin secretion and increase intracellular IP_3. Exogenous IP_3 elicits mucin secretion in a dose dependent manner (28). Mucin secretion is also stimulated in a dose dependent manner in Cl.16E cells (3) by two neuropeptides, neurotensin and neuromedin N. Small peptides containing the carboxyl terminus of neurotensin are also effective stimulants, whereas peptides lacking the C terminus are not. The rank order of potency among the peptides is identical for the inhibition of ^{125}I-neurotensin binding to cell membranes and stimulation of mucin secretion. Neurotensin and neuromedin N, therefore, likely stimulate mucin secretion via the same receptor. The neurotensin receptor is coupled to phospholipase C via a pertussis toxin-insensitive G protein in the parent HT29 cell line (7). In Cl.16E cells, neurotensin elicited a rise in intracellular calcium without an increase in cAMP (3), which suggests that mucin secretion is probably stimulated in a similar manner in the derivative line.

ADENYLATE CYCLASE ACTIVATORS   Mucin secretion is stimulated by a number of agents that elevate intracellular cAMP concentration. Vasoactive intestinal polypeptide (VIP) stimulated mucin secretion in submandibular gland (102) and T84 cells (59, 61) but not in rat small intestine (82). In Cl.16E cells, an initial report indicated that VIP was not effective alone (50) but a small stimulatory response was subsequently found (3). ^{125}I-VIP binding studies revealed a single class of receptors with a specificity VIP > rat growth hormone-releasing factor (GRF) > PHI = human GRF > secretin that is typical of human colonic cells (50). A VIP receptor protein with a M_r of 63,000 was identified. Carbachol-induced secretion was strongly potentiated by addition of VIP, thus proving that these receptors were functionally active. VIP and neurotensin also stimulated mucin secretion additively (3) when added in maximally effective doses, which suggests that Ca^{2+} and cAMP pathways stimulate exocytosis independently in Cl.16E cells.

Cholera toxin stimulated mucin secretion from rat small intestine (33) and colon (13), mouse duodenum (16), and HT29 (Cl.16E) cells (85). T84 cells were not responsive (61). Mucin secretion was stimulated by prostaglandin E_1 in T84 cells (61), by prostaglandin E_2 in HT29 cells (76) and rabbit gastric mucin-secreting cells (87, 89), and by prostaglandin $F2_\beta$ (9) in rat submandibular acini and rat stomach cells (52). Prostacyclin stimulated mucin secretion from prairie dog gall bladder mucosa (51). In addition, mucin release was stimulated by secretin in rat stomach cells (42), and by adrenergic analogues in submandibular gland cells (8), cat tracheal cells (55), and rat gastric cells (42). The effect of some of these agonists is likely to vary from one cell type to the next. For instance, secretin and prostaglandin $F2_\beta$ stimulate gastric mucus secretion (42) but have no effect on T84 cells (G Forstner, unpublished results).

In submandibular acini, isoproterenol-induced mucin secretion was stimulated independently of cAMP even though a rise in cAMP was elicited (8). Cholera toxin stimulated mucin secretion in the rat small intestine, but the response could not be duplicated by a number of agents that elevate intracellular cAMP (82). Moore et al (64) recently showed that the cholera toxin response in intact tissue may involve signal transduction through more than one cell type. Cholera toxin-induced secretion by goblet cells in the rat small intestine was reduced approximately 40% by atropine and was almost completely inhibited when primary afferent nerves were destroyed by exposing neonatal animals to capsaicin. Therefore, much of the response in intact mucosa seems to involve a neurogenic loop in which the goblet cell functions as the cholinergically activated effector. Mucin-secreting cells are also stimulated by VIP, catecholamines, substance P, purine nucleotides, neurotensin, and neuromedin N, so that the list of neurogenic agonists that are capable of stimulating mucin secretion as part of similar loops is large. Direct investigation of neurogenic stimulation has been limited. Electrical stimulation of the cut ends of the vagus stimulated release of mucin from the feline trachea. However, more than one agonist might have been released because secretion was incompletely inhibited by pretreatment with atropine, phentolamine, and propanolol (34).

GUANYLATE CYCLASE–SELECTIVE SECRETION   The possibility that nitric oxide stimulates mucin secretion was initially suggested by the observation that nitric oxide synthase activity was highest in elutriated gastric cell fractions enriched in mucin-secreting cells (11). The nitric oxide donors, nitroprusside, S-nitroso-N-acetylpenicillamine, and isosorbide dinitrate (ISDN) were subsequently shown to stimulate mucin release from isolated rat gastric mucosal cells (10). The secretory response was not blocked by atropine or indomethacin. Nitric oxide often acts by activating guanylate cyclase (63). In rat gastric mucosa, ISDN increased intracellular cGMP in proportion to its effect on mucin secretion. Furthermore, dibutyryl cGMP and a cGMP phosphodiesterase inhibitor, MB 22948, also stimulated mucin secretion, implicating cGMP as a likely second messenger (10).

INFLAMMATORY MEDIATORS   Because of the importance of mucin in the protection of epithelial surfaces, one might expect that secretion of mucin would be accelerated during inflammatory-immune responses. Parasite rejection models have shown that there is a great increase in the number of goblet cells, mast cells, and mononuclear cells near intestinal parasites such as *Nippostrongylus brasiliensis* just before expulsion of the parasite (62). The goblet cell hyperplasia is T cell dependent. Expulsion is accompanied by mast cell degranulation and an outpouring of mucus, which suggests that one might stimulate the other. However, in a less ambiguous mast cell degranulation model produced by inducing IgE-mediated hypersensitivity to intraluminal food antigens in rats, specific secretion of mucin was not detected by immunoassay during intestinal anaphylaxis, even though histamine was released and widespread loss of epithelium occurred (72). Histamine does not stimulate mucin secretion in T84 cells (61). Other potential mucin secretagogues that might be released by mast cells have not been examined rigorously. Mast cell protease I failed to stimulate mucin secretion in T84 cells, however (G Forstner, unpublished data).

Macrophages and lymphocytes are possible sources of mucus secretagogues. Inflammatory cells as well as endothelial cells are potential sources of nitric oxide (63). Mucus secretion by explants from mouse duodenum was stimulated by exposure to culture supernatants of peritoneal exudate cells that had been treated with *Escherichia coli* lipopolysaccharide to induce interleukin-1. Partially purified rabbit alveolar macrophage-derived IL-1α and human recombinant IL-1β were also effective (16). Interleukin-1, therefore, appears to be capable of stimulating secretion of mucin in the intestine. Whether it does so directly or through production of another agent such as a prostaglandin requires further study. The mouse mucosal explants were also stimulated to secrete mucin by cholera toxin and acetylcholine but did not respond to a number of potential lymphocyte mediators, e.g PGE$_2$, PGD$_2$, 5-HTEE, 15-HETE, LTB$_4$, LTC$_4$, as well as IL-2, IL-3, and substance P (16). Therefore, IL-1 appears to be a relatively specific mucin secretagogue. Macrophages also produce a 68-kDa protein, MMS-68, that appears to be a novel cytokine capable of stimulating mucin release from respiratory and colonic epithelial cells (97). MMS-68 is expressed by lamina propia cells in normal colonic mucosa and in colonic mucosa from patients with Crohn's disease but rather poorly in colonic mucosa from patients with ulcerative colitis.

OTHER STIMULI   Mustard oil (66), two proteases (elastase and chymotrypsin) (46), and oxygen free radicals (39) stimulate mucin secretion in gastric, intestinal, and respiratory cells. Cultured hamster airway goblet cells, although not responsive to many of the secretagogues that stimulate other cells, are nevertheless stimulated by a number of physical stimuli such as high and low pH, hypoosmolarity, and physical strain induced by contraction of the supporting gel (44). The signal transduction mechanisms used by these agents have not been explored.

Intracellular Signal Transduction Pathways

Thus far there appear to be no exceptions to the general rule that a rise in intracellular Ca^{2+} triggers mucin secretion. This has been demonstrated by stimulation with Ca^{2+} ionophores in Ca^{2+}-containing media in cells isolated from rabbit stomach (89), from submandibular gland (78), and in the colonic adenocarcinoma cell lines T84 (59, 61), SW1116 (107), and HT29–18N$_2$ (53). Removal of extracellular Ca^{2+} completely abolishes the response to acetylcholine and A23187, a calcium ionophore, in explant cultures of gastric fundic cells (89), which suggests that calcium entry into the cytosol accounts for most of the secretory signal. Highly purified gastric mucus cells generated IP$_3$ in response to acetylcholine. An initial peak in intracellular Ca^{2+}, ostensibly released from stores, was independent of extracellular Ca^{2+} (88) and was followed by a sustained Ca^{2+} elevation. Removal of extracellular Ca^{2+} abolished the sustained rise, thus indicating that it depended on calcium entry. Mucin secretion was closely correlated with the rise in intracellular IP$_3$ and the initial intracellular Ca^{2+} peak. Preincubation with the membrane-permeable ester form of the calcium chelator BAPTA (BAPTA/AM) abolished both the secretory response to acetylcholine and the rise in intracellular Ca^{2+} without affecting formation of IP$_3$. These studies suggest that acetylcholine-induced mucin secretion in gastric mucus-producing cells depends exclusively on a rise in intracellular Ca^{2+}.

PKC appears to function in mucin secretion almost as constantly as Ca^{2+}. DAG and the phorbol ester PMA stimulate secretion from mucus-producing cells isolated from submandibular gland (28), gastric mucus explants (89), T84 (61) and HT29–18N$_2$ (53) adenocarcinoma cells, but not, curiously, primary cultures of hamster tracheal epithelium (46). When T84 cells are stimulated by maximally effective concentrations of Ca^{2+} ionophore, increased mucin secretion occurs when PMA is added, which suggests that Ca^{2+} and PKC activate complementary but separate portions of the exocytotic response (61). PKC can apparently mediate secretion independently of Ca^{2+} in these cells. Stimulation by PMA was not affected by removing Ca^{2+} from the medium or by chelating intracellular Ca^{2+} with BAPTA (32). PMA and DAG both stimulate mucin secretion in submandibular gland (27,) and the effects of phorbol ester and exogenous IP$_3$ were additive (28). Thus Ca^{2+} and PKC may stimulate mucin secretion independently in some cells.

Forskolin stimulated mucin secretion in gastric mucus cells (89), T84 cells (31), and HT29–18N$_2$ cells (53). Removal of extracellular Ca^{2+} and depletion of intracellular Ca^{2+} did not prevent forskolin from stimulating mucin secretion in gastric mucus cells (89), which suggests that protein kinase A (PKA) and Ca^{2+} mediate secretion independently, at least in the stomach. We obtained similar results in T84 cells (31). Forskolin stimulated mucin secretion at an extracellular Ca^{2+} concentration of 47 nM, and at the time when intracellular Ca^{2+} was chelated by BAPTA. Some interdependency of Ca^{2+} and cAMP-dependent pathways was apparent, however, because maximal stimulation by A23187 could not be augmented by addition of forskolin. The likeliest explanation is that Ca^{2+} and PKA are co-activators of a crucial step in exocytosis, but this remains to be explored. The effects of forskolin and PMA on T84 cell mucin secretion, in contrast to those of forskolin and Ca^{2+}, are additive in the presence and the absence of Ca^{2+}, suggesting that the two pathways are independent. In submandibular gland, the relationship is more complex. Forskolin alone stimulates mucin secretion, but phorbol ester produces an additive effect on cAMP production and mucin secretion (29). When adenylate cyclase was activated via the β-adrenergic receptor, PKC inhibited cAMP production and phosphorylated a 55-kDa protein, which suggests that PKC can desensitize adenylate cyclase by direct phosphorylation of the β receptor, as in other systems (92).

As a more detailed characterization of secretory pathways in specific mucin-secreting cells becomes available, conventional interpretations will no doubt come into question. The control of mucin secretion in the rat submandibular gland may already have provided such an example. Secretion is stimulated most strongly by β-adrenergic agents (8) and is followed by a rise in cAMP. However, β-adrenergic stimulation of mucin secretion was not affected when the cAMP rise was abolished by incorporating excess cAMP phosphodiesterase into intact cells (8). Furthermore, intracellular BAPTA inhibited the β-adrenergic response without affecting the rise in cAMP (58), which suggests that exocytosis is triggered by intracellular Ca^{2+} rather than cAMP. Paradoxically, β-adrenergic agents do not elevate IP_3 levels (23) and therefore do not use IP_3 to access intracellular Ca^{2+} pools. Additional stimulatory mediators undoubtedly exist. In T84 cells, Ca^{2+} ionophores continue to stimulate mucin secretion in the absence of both medium and intracellular Ca^{2+} through a mechanism that is inhibited by the protein kinase inhibitors staurosporine and H7 (32). A portion of the stimulatory response to Ca^{2+} ionophores in the presence of Ca^{2+} is also inhibited by staurosporine and H7. The pattern of inhibition is unlike that seen with forskolin or phorbol ester-induced secretion, which indicates that a unique kinase may be involved (32).

Compelling evidence thus indicates that multiple intracellular signals can stimulate mucin secretion. The interaction of these signals (illustrated in Figure 2) will remain a fruitful area of study for some time. The central portion of the scheme (Figure 2) includes events intimately connected to exocytosis that are unexplored in mucin-secreting cells. Studies in other systems suggest that proteins of the rab family, their regulators (6), and G proteins (37) are likely to be important.

Co-Secretion of Fluid and Electrolytes

Mucins are high molecular weight, gel-forming glycoproteins, thus one might expect that secretion would be particularly dependent upon the co-secretion

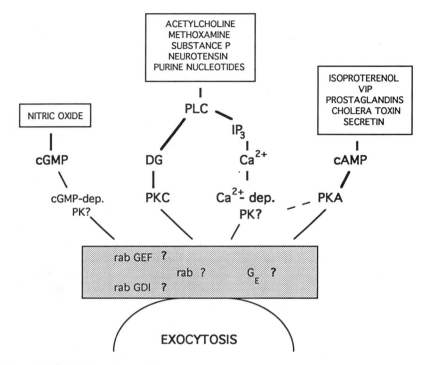

Figure 2   Regulated mucin secretion.

of fluid and electrolyte, either through the base of newly opened secretory granules, or through apical secretion via plasma membrane channels of mucus or neighboring epithelial cells. Kreusel et al (49) took advantage of the highly enriched (80%) goblet cell content of the HT29/B6 clone and its ability to grow in closed monolayers on filter membranes to examine ionic secretion in Ussing chambers. The short-circuit current of unstimulated monolayers was 0.1 ± 0.01 μmol $\cdot$ h^{-1} $\cdot$ cm^{-2} and rose to $1.9 \pm 0.1$$\mu$mol $\cdot$ h^{-1} $\cdot$ cm^{-2} when 10^{-5} M forskolin was added serosally, and a sharp rise in cAMP was seen. The increase in short-circuit current was a measure of the Cl$^-$ secretion. A rise in short-circuit current (Cl$^-$ secretion) could also be triggered by VIP, PGE$_1$, and dibutryl cAMP, which indicates that mucin-secreting cells actively secrete Cl$^-$. Cl$^-$ secretion was inhibited by disulfonic stilbenes (apical) and Ba^{2+} (serosal), both of which inhibit Ca^{2+} ionophore-induced mucin secretion in T84 cells (59). Mucus cells may therefore depend on the close integration of Cl$^-$ secretion and granule exocytosis to maximize their secretory responses.

CONCLUDING THOUGHTS

Mucus cells are set to respond to a large number of stimuli from nerves, endothelium, inflammatory, and probably even adjacent cells. Several signal transduction pathways can converge on the exocytotic event, stimulating secretion or enhancing output when more than one pathway is activated. The convergence provides the basis for graded responses based on the number of stimuli provided to the cell. Large gaps in our knowledge still remain. We have little idea of how or if signals generated by exocytosis are fed back to control transcription, translation, or intracellular transport. We do not know how or why mucins appear to be targeted, almost exclusively, to condensing granules when a nonstorage baseline secretory route would seem to be simpler and probably less costly to the cell. We do not know how signals are supplied to the plasma membrane and secretory granule to elicit exocytosis, single or compound. We also do not know whether prolonging or increasing the secretory stimulus alters mucin gene expression in a way that could be of physiological or pathological significance. Questions such as these will provide the stimulus and direction for future investigation.

Literature Cited

1. Audie JP, Porchet IN, Copin MC, Gosselin B, Aubert JP. 1993. Expression of human mucin genes in respiratory, digestive, and reproductive tracts ascertained by in situ hybridization. *J. Hist. Cytochem.* 41:1479–85

2. Augeron C, Laboisse CL. 1984. Emergence of permanently differentiated cell clones in a human colonic cancer cell line in culture after treatment with sodium butyrate. *Cancer Res.* 44:3961–69

3. Augeron C, Voisin T, Maoret JJ, Berthan B, Laburthe M, Laboisse CL. 1992. Neurotensin and neuromedin N stimulate mucin output from human goblet cells (Cl.16E) via neurotensin receptors. *Am. J. Physiol.* 262:G470–76

4. Deleted in proof

5. Bennett G, Leblond CP. 1970. Formation of cell coat material for the whole surface of columnar cells in the rat small intestine as visualized by autoradiography with L-fucos-^{3}H. *J. Cell Biol.* 46:409–16

6. Boguski MS, McCormick F. 1993. Proteins regulating Ras and its relatives. *Nature* 366:643–54

7. Bozou JC, Rochet N, Magnaldo I, Vincent JP, Kitabgi P. 1989. Neurotensin stimulates inositol triphosphate-mediated calcium mobilization but not protein kinase C activation in HT29 cells. Involvement of a G protein. *Biochem. J.* 264:871–78

8. Bradbury NA, Dormer RL, McPherson MA. 1989. Introduction of cyclic AMP phosphodiesterase into rat submandibular acini prevents isoproterenol-stimulated cyclic AMP rise without affecting mucin secretion. *Biochem. Biophys. Res. Commun.* 161:661–71

9. Bradbury NA, McPherson MA. 1987. Actions of prostaglandins E_2 and $F_{2\alpha}$ on release of ^{14}C-labelled mucins from rat submandibular salivary acini in vitro. *Arch. Oral Biol.* 32:719–22

10. Brown JF, Keates AC, Hanson PJ, Whittle BJR. 1993. Nitric oxide generators and cGMP stimulate mucus secretion by rat gastric mucosal cells. *Am. J. Physiol.* 265:G418–22

11. Brown JF, Tepperman BL, Hanson PJ, Whittle BJR, Moncada S. 1992. Differential distribution of nitric oxide synthase between cell fractions isolated from the rat gastric mucosa. *Biochem. Biophys. Res. Commun.* 184:680–85

12. Burgess TL, Kelly RB. 1987. Constitutive and regulated secretion of proteins. *Annu. Rev. Cell Biol.* 3:243–93

13. Chadee K, Keller K, Forstner J, Innes DJ, Ravdin JI. 1991. Mucin and nonmucin secretagogue activity of *Entamoeba histolytica* and cholera toxin in rat colon. *Gastroenterology* 100:986–87

14. Chambraud W, Bernadac A, Gowel JP, Maroux S. 1989. Renewal of goblet cell mucus granules during the cell migration along the crypt-villus axis in rabbit jejunum: an immunolabelling study. *Biol. Cell* 65:151–62

15. Chu WN, Baxter JD, Reudelhuber TL. 1990. A targetting sequence for dense secretary granules resides in the active renin protein moiety of human preprorenin. *Mol. Endocrinol.* 90:1905–13

16. Cohan N, Scott AL, Dinarello CA, Prendergast RA. 1991. Interleukin-1 is a mucus secretagogue. *Cell. Immunol.* 136:425–34

17. Davis CW, Dowell ML, Lethem M, Van Scott M. 1992. Goblet cell degranulation in isolated canine tracheal epithelium: response to exogenous ATP, ADP, and adenosine. *Am. J. Physiol.* 262:C1313–23

18. Dekker J, Strous GJ. 1990. Covalent oligomerization of rat gastric mucin occurs in the rough endoplasmic reticulum, is N-glycosylation-dependent, and precedes initial O-glycosylation. *J. Biol. Chem.* 265:18116–22

19. Dekker J, van Beurden-Lamers WMO, Strous GJ. 1989. Biosynthesis of gastric mucus glycoprotein of the rat. *J. Biol. Chem.* 264:10431–37

20. Dekker J, van der Ende A, Aelmans PH, Strous GJ. 1991. Rat gastric mucin is synthesized and secreted exclusively as filamentous oligomers. *Biochem. J.* 279:251–56

21. DeLisle R, DiDomenico J, Hopfer U. 1986. Electrolyte permeabilities of pancreatic zymogen granules: implications for pancreatic secretion. *Am. J. Physiol.* 250:G489–96

22. Dharmsathaphorn K, Pandol SJ. 1986. Mechanism of chloride secretion induced by carbachol in a colonic epithelial cell line. *J. Clin. Invest.* 77:348–54

23. Doughney C, Dormer RL, McPherson MA. 1987. Adrenergic regulation of formation of inositol phosphates in rat submandibular acini. *Biochem. J.* 241:705–9

24. Egea G, Franci C, Gambus G, Lesuffleur T, Zweibaum A, Real FX. 1993. cis-Golgi resident proteins and O-glycans are abnormally compartmentalized in the RER of colon cancer cells. *J. Cell Sci.* 105:819–30

25. Ellis RJ, van der Vies SM. 1991. Molecular chaperones. *Annu. Rev. Biochem.* 60:321–47

26. Fahim REF, Specian RD, Forstner G, Forstner JF. 1987. Characterization and localization of the putative 'link' component in rat small-intestinal mucin. *Biochem. J.* 243:631–40

27. Fleming N, Bilan PT, Sliwinska-Lis E. 1986. Effects of phorbol ester and diacylglycerols on secretion of mucin and arginine esterase by rat submandibular gland cells. *Eur. J. Physiol.* 406:6–11

28. Fleming N, Bilan PT, Sliwinski-Lis E, Carvalho V. 1987. Muscarinic, α_1-adrenergic and peptidergic agonists stimulate phosphoinositide hydrolysis and regulate mucin secretion in rat submandibular gland cells. *Eur. J. Physiol.* 409:416–21

29. Fleming N, Maellow L, Bhullar D. 1992. Regulation of the cAMP signal transduction pathway by protein kinase C in rat submandibular cells. *Eur. J. Physiol.* 421:82–90

30. Fleming N, Sliwinski-Lis E, Burke DN. 1989. G regulatory proteins and muscarinic receptor signal transduction in mucous acini of rat submandibular gland. *Life Sci.* 44:1027–35

31. Forstner G, Zhang Y, McCool D, Forstner J. 1994. Regulation of mucin secretion in T84 adenocarcinoma cells by forskolin: relationship to Ca^{2+} and PKC. *Am. J. Physiol.* 266:G606–12

32. Forstner GG, Zhang Y, McCool D, Forstner J. 1993. Mucin secretion by T84 cells: stimulation by PKC, Ca^{2+}, and a protein kinase activated by Ca^{2+} ionophore. *Am. J. Physiol.* 264:G1096–102

33. Forstner JF, Roomi NW, Fahim REF, Forstner GG. 1981. Cholera toxin stimulates secretion of immunoreactive intestinal mucin. *Am. J. Physiol.* 240:G10–16

34. Fung DCK, Beacock DJ, Richardson PS. 1992. Vagal control of mucus glycoconjugate secretion into the feline trachea. *J. Physiol.* 453:435–47

35. Gasser KW, DiDomenico J, Hopfer U. 1988. Potassium transport by pancreatic and parotid zymogen granule membranes. *Am. J. Physiol.* 255:C705–11

36. Gasser KW, DiDomenico J, Hopfer U. 1988. Secretagogues activate chloride transport pathways in pancreatic zymo-

gen granules. *Am. J. Physiol.* 254:G93–99

37. Gomperts BD. 1990. GE: a GTP-binding protein mediating exocytosis. *Annu. Rev. Physiol.* 52:591–606

38. Gum JR, Hicks JW, Toribara NW, Rothe EM, Lagace RE, Kim YS. 1992. The human MUC2 intestinal mucin has cysteine-rich domains located both upstream and downstream of its central repetitive region. *J. Biol. Chem.* 267: 21375–83

39. Hiraishi H, Terano A, Ota S, Mutoh H, Sugimoto T, et al. 1991. Oxygen metabolites stimulate mucous glycoprotein secretion from cultured rat gastric mucous cells. *Am. J. Physiol.* 261:G662–68

40. Ho SB, Niehans KJ, Lyftogt C, Yan PS, Cherwitz DL, et al. 1993. Heterogeneity of mucin gene expression in normal and neoplastic tissues. *Cancer Res.* 53:641–51

41. Huet C, Sahuquillo-Merino C, Coudrier E, Louvard D. 1987. Absorptive and mucus-secreting subclones isolated from a multipotent intestinal cell line (HT-29) provide new models for cell polarity and terminal differentiation. *J. Cell Biol.* 105:345–57

42. Keates AC, Hanson PJ. 1990. Regulation of mucus secretion by cells isolated from the rat gastric mucosa. *J. Physiol.* 423:397–409

43. Khatri I, Huan LJ, Forstner G, Forstner JF. 1991. Evidence for in vitro microsomal glycosylation of mucin peptide. *Glycocon. J.* 8:209

44. Kim KC. 1991. Biochemistry and pharmacology of mucin-like glycoproteins produced by cultured airway epithelial cells. *Exp. Lung Res.* 17:533–45

45. Kim KC, Lee BC. 1991. P2 purinoceptor regulation of mucin release by airway goblet cells in primary culture. *Br. J. Pharmacol.* 103:1053–56

46. Kim KC, Nassiri J, Brody JS. 1989. Mechanisms of airway goblet cell mucin release: studies with cultured tracheal surface epithelial cells. *Am. J. Resp. Cell Mol. Biol.* 1:137–43

47. Kim KC, Zheng Q, Van-Seuningen I. 1993. Involvement of a signal transduction mechanism in ATP-induced mucin release from cultured airway goblet cells. *Am. J. Resp. Cell Mol. Biol.* 8:121–25

48. Kopp R, Lambrecht G, Mutschler E, Moser U, Tacke R, Pfeiffer A. 1989. HT-29 colon carcinoma cells contain muscarinic M3 receptors coupled to phosphoinositide metabolism. *Eur. J. Pharmacol.* 172:397–405

49. Kreusel K-M, Fromm M, Schultzke J, Hegel U. 1991. Cl⁻ secretion in epithelial monolayers of mucus-forming human colon cells (HT-29/B6). *Am. J. Physiol.* 261:C574–82

50. Laburthe M, Augeron C, Rouyer-Fessard C, Roumagnac I, Maoret J, et al. 1989. Functional VIP receptors in the human mucus–secreting colonic epithelial cell line Cl.16E. *Am. J. Physiol.* 256:G443–50

51. LaMont JT, Turner BS, DiBenedetto D, Handin R, Schafer Al. 1983. Arachidonic acid stimulates mucin secretion in prairie dog gallbladder. *Am. J. Physiol.* 245:G92–98

52. LaMont TT, Ventola AS, Maull EA, Szabo S. 1983. Cysteamine and prostaglandin $F_{2\beta}$ stimulate rat gastric mucin release. *Gastroenterolgy* 84:306–13

53. Lencer WI, Reenhart FD, Neutra MR. 1990. Interaction of cholera toxin with cloned human goblet cells in monolayer culture. *Am. J. Physiol.* 258:G96–102

54. Lesuffleur T, Porchet N, Aubert J-P, Swallow D, Gum JR, et al. 1993. Differential expression of the human mucin genes *MUC1* to *MUC5* in relation to growth and differentiation of different mucus-secreting HT-29 cell populations. *J. Cell Sci.* 106:771–83

55. Liedtke CM, Rudolph SA, Boat TF. 1983. Beta-adrenergic modulation of mucin secretion in cat trachea. *Am. J. Physiol.* 244:C391–98

56. Ligtenberg MJL, Kruijshaar L, Buijs F, van Meijer M, Litvinov SV, Hilkens J. 1992. Cell-associated episialin is a complex containing two proteins derived from a common precursor. *J. Biol. Chem.* 267:6171–77

57. Litvinov SV, Hilkens J. 1993. The epithelial sialomucin, episialin, is sialylated during recycling. *J. Biol. Chem.* 268:21364–71

58. Lloyd Mills C, Dormer RL, McPherson MA. 1991. Introduction of BAPTA into intact rat submandibular acini inhibits mucin secretion in response to cholinergic and beta-adrenergic agonists. *FEBS Lett.* 289:141–44

59. Marcon MA, McCool DJ, Forstner JF, Forstner GG. 1990. Inhibition of mucin secretion in a colonic adenocarcinoma cell line by DIDS and potassium channel blockers. *Biochim. Biophys. Acta* 1052: 17–23

60. McCool DJ, Forstner JF, Forstner GG. 1994. Synthesis and secretion of mucin by the human colonic tumour cell line LSI80. *Biochem. J.* 302:111–18

61. McCool DJ, Marcon MA, Forstner JF, Forstner GG. 1990. The T84 human colonic adenocarcinoma cell line produces mucin in culture and releases it

in response to various secretagogues. *Biochem, J.* 267:491–500

62. Miller HRP, Narva Y, Parishm CR. 1979. Intestinal goblet cell differentiation in *Nippostrongylus*-infected rats after transfer of fractionated thoracic duct lymphocytes. *Int. Arch. Allergy Appl. Immunol.* 59:281–85

63. Moncada S, Palmer RMJ, Higgs EA. 1991. Nitric oxide: physiology, pathophysiology and pharmacology. *Pharm. Rev.* 43:109–42

64. Moore BA, Sharkey KA, Mantle M. 1993. Neural mediation of cholera toxin–induced mucin secretion in the rat small intestine. *Am. J. Physiol.* 265: G1050–56

65. Moore HPH, Kelly RB. 1986. Re-routing of a secretary protein by fusion with human growth hormone sequences. *Nature* 321:443–46

66. Neutra MR, O'Malley LJ, Specian RD. 1982. Regulation of intestinal goblet cell secretion. II. A survey of potential secretagogues. *Am. J. Physiol.* 242:G380–87

67. Nicaise G, Maggio K, Thirion S, Horoyon M, Keicher E. 1992. The calcium loading of secretary granules. A possible key event in stimulus-secretion coupling. *Biol. Cell* 75:89–99

68. Niv Y, Byrd JC, Ho SB, Kim YS. 1992. Mucin synthesis and secretion in relation to spontaneous differentiation of colon cancer cells in vitro. *Int. J. Cancer* 50: 147–52

69. Oliver MG, Specian RD. 1990. Cytoskeleton of intestinal goblet cells: role of actin filaments in baseline secretion. *Am. J. Physiol.* 259:G991–97

70. Oliver MG, Specian RD. 1991. Cytoskeleton of intestinal goblet cells: role of microtubules in baseline secretion. *Am. J. Physiol.* 260:G850–57

71. Pazoles CJ, Pollard HJ. 1978. Evidence for stimulation of anion transport in ATP-evoked transmitter release from isolated secretary vesicles. *J. Biol. Chem.* 253:3962–69

72. Perdue MH, Forstner JF, Roomi NW, Gall DG. 1984. Epithelial response to intestinal anaphylaxis in the rat: goblet cell secretion and enterocyte damage. *Am. J. Physiol.* 247:G632–37

73. Phillips TE. 1992. Both crypt and villus intestinal goblet cells secrete mucin in response to cholinergic stimulation. *Am. J. Physiol.* 262:G327–31

74. Phillips TE, Huet C, Bilbo PR, Podolsky DK, Louvard D, Neutra MR. 1988. Human intestinal goblet cells in monolayer culture: characterization of a mucus-secreting subclone derived from the HT29 colon adenocarcinoma cell line. *Gastroenterology* 94:1390–403

75. Phillips TE, Phillips TH, Neutra MR. 1984. Regulation of intestinal goblet cell secretion III. Isolated intestinal epithelium. *Am. J. Physiol.* 247:G674–81

76. Phillips TE, Stanley CM, Wilson J. 1993. The effect of 16,16-dimethyl prostaglandin E_2 on proliferation of an intestinal goblet cell line and its synthesis and secretion of mucin glycoproteins. *Pros. Leuk. Essent. Fatty Acids* 48:423–28

77. Phillips TE, Wilson J. 1993. Signal transduction pathways mediating mucin secretion from intestinal goblet cells. *Dig. Dis. Sci.* 38:1046–54

78. Qissel DO, Terano A, Ota S, Mutoh H, Sugimoto T, et al. 1981. Role of calcium and cAMP in the regulation of rat submandibular mucin secretion. *Am. J. Physiol.* 241:C76–86

79. Radwan KA, Oliver MG, Specian RD. 1990. Cytoarchitectural reorganization of rabbit colonic goblet cells during baseline secretion. *Am. J. Anat.* 189: 365–76

80. Rambourg A, Clermont Y, Hermo W, Segretain D. 1987. Tridimensional architecture of the Golgi apparatus and its components in mucous cells of Brunner's gland of the mouse. *Am. J. Anat.* 179:95–107

81. Rimele TJ, O'Dorisio MS, Gaginella T. 1981. Evidence of muscarinic receptors on rat colonic epithelial cells: binding of ^{3}H-quinuclidinyl benzilate. *J. Pharm. Exp. Ther.* 218:426–34

82. Roomi N, Laburthe J, Fleming N, Crowther R, Forstner J. 1984. Cholera-induced mucin secretion from rat intestine. Lack of effect of cyclic AMP, cyclo- heximide, VIP and colchicine. *Am. J. Physiol.* 247:G140–48

83. Roth J. 1984. Cytochemical localization of terminal N-acetyl-D-galactosamine residues in cellular compartments of intestinal goblet cells: implications for the topology of 0-glycosylation. *J. Cell Biol.* 98:399–406

84. Roumagnac I, Laboisse C. 1987. A mucus-secreting human epithelial cell line responsive to cholinergic stimulation. *Biol. Cell* 61:65–68

85. Roumagnac I, Laboisse CL. 1989. A simple immunofiltration assay for mucins secreted by a human colonic epithelial cell line. *J. Immunol. Meth.* 122: 265–71

86. Sandoz D, Nicolas G, Laine M. 1985. Two mucous cell types revisited after quick-freezing and cryosubstitution. *Biol. Cell* 54:79–88

87. Seidler U, Knafla K, Kownatzki R, Sewing K. 1988. Effects of endogenous and exogenous prostaglandins on glycoprotein synthesis and secretion in isolated rabbit gastric mucosa. *Gastroenterology* 95:945–51

88. Seidler U, Pfeiffer A. 1991. Inositol phosphate formation and $[Ca^{2+}]_i$ in secretagogue-stimulated rabbit gastric mucous cells. *Am. J. Physiol.* 260:G133–41

89. Seidler U, Sewing K. 1989. Ca^{2+}-dependent and -independent secretagogue action on gastric mucus secretion in rabbit mucosal explants. *Am. J. Physiol.* 256: G739–46

90. Sheng Z, Hull SR, Carraway KL. 1990. Biosynthesis of the cell surface salomucin complex of ascites 13762 rat mammary adenocarcinoma cells from a high molecular weight precursor. *J. Biol. Chem.* 265:8505–10

91. Shogren RL, Jamieson AM, Blackwell J, Jentoft N. 1986. Conformation of mucous glycoproteins in aqueous solvents. *Biopolymers* 25:1505–17

92. Sibley DR, Nambi P, Peters J, Lefkowitz RJ. 1984. Phorbol diesters promote receptor phosphorylation and adenylate cyclase desensitization in duck erythrocytes. *Biochem. Biophys. Res. Commun.* 121:973–79

93. Specian RD, Neutra MR. 1984. Cytoskeleton of intestinal goblet cells in rabbit and monkey. *Gastroenterology* 87:1313–25

94. Specian RD, Neutra MR. 1980. Mechanism of rapid mucus secretion in goblet cells stimulated by acetylcholine. *J. Cell Biol.* 85:626–40

95. Specian RD, Neutra MR. 1982. Regulation of intestinal goblet cell secretion. I. Role of parasympathetic stimulation. *Am. J. Physiol.* 242:G370–79

96. Specian RD, Oliver MG. 1991. Functional biology of intestinal goblet cells. *Am. J. Physiol.* 260:C183–93

97. Sperber K, Ogata S, Sylvester C, Aisenberg J, Chen A, et al. 1993. A novel human macrophage-derived intestinal mucin secretagogue: implications for the pathogenesis of inflammatory bowel disease. *Gastroenterology* 104: 1302–9

98. Strous GJ, Dekker J. 1992. Mucin-type glycoproteins. *Crit. Rev. Biochem. Mol. Biol.* 27:57–92

99. Strous GJAM. 1979. Initial glycosylation of proteins with acetylgalactosaminylserine linkages. *Proc. Natl. Acad. Sci. USA* 76:2694–98

100. Takano Y, Asai M. 1988. Histochemical, ultrastructural and X-ray microprobe analytical studies of localization of calcium in the mucous lining of the rat duodenum. *Histochemistry* 89:429–36

101. Tamura S, Fujita H. 1983. Fine structural aspects on the renewal and development of surface mucous cells and glandular cells of the gastric body of the adult golden hamster. *Arch. Hist. Jpn.* 46:501–21

102. Turner JT, Camden JM. 1990. The influence of vasoactive intestinal peptide receptors in dispersed acini from rat submandibular gland on cyclic AMP production and mucin release. *Arch. Oral Biol.* 35:103–8

103. Verdugo P. 1990. Goblet cell secretion and mucogenesis. *Annu. Rev. Physiol.* 52:157–76

104. Wahawisan R, Wallace LJ, Gaginella TS. 1983. Muscarinic receptors exist on ileal crypt and villus cells of the rat. *Fed. Proc.* 12:761

105. Werner RR, Coleman JR. 1975. Electron probe analysis of calcium transport by small intestine. *J. Cell Biol.* 64:54–74

106. Xu G, Huan L-J, Khatri IA, Wang D, Bennick A, et al. 1992. cDNA for the carboxyl-terminal region of a rat intestinal mucin-like peptide. *J. Biol. Chem.* 267:5401–7

107. Yedgar S, Eidelman O, Malden E, Roberts D, Etchebenigaray R, et al. 1992. Cyclic AMP-independent secretion of mucin by SW1116 human colon carcinoma cells. *Biochem. J.* 283:421–26

Annu. Rev. Physiol. 1995. 57:607–34

EPITHELIAL MUCIN GENES

Sandra J. Gendler and Andrew P. Spicer

Department of Biochemistry and Molecular Biology, Samuel C. Johnson Medical Research Building, Mayo Clinic Scottsdale, 13400 East Shea Boulevard, Scottsdale, Arizona 85259

KEY WORDS: MUC, mucus, O-glycosylation, tandem repeat, glycoprotein

INTRODUCTION

Mucins make up a large part of the mucus covering of the lumenal surfaces of epithelial organs that serve as selective physical barriers between the extracellular milieu and the plasma membrane and cell interior. Mucins are subdivided into secretory and membrane-associated forms. Secretory mucins constitute the viscous mucus of the tracheobronchial, gastrointestinal, and reproductive tracts and typically form extremely large oligomers through linkage of protein monomers via disulfide bonds. These proteins are secreted from the cell and remain at the apical surface of the epithelial cells in the form of a mucus gel. The membrane-associated mucins, however, have a hydrophobic membrane-spanning domain and have not been observed to form oligomeric complexes. Mucin-like glycoproteins have also been found in nonepithelial tissues that are not barrier tissues. They serve as ligands for selectins and are involved in lymphocyte trafficking (130). These molecules fall under the broad definition of mucin, a protein containing, as greater than 50% of its mass, O-linked oligosaccharides. Ultimately, it may be necessary to refine the definition of a mucin or to expand the proposed functions, mainly protection and lubrication, to cover a much wider range of possibilities. The nonepithelial mucins are not discussed in any detail in this review.

Although the membrane-associated and secreted mucins differ greatly in their structures and possibly in their functions, the genes and consequently the proteins have a common feature. A major portion of each of the genes consists of tandem repeats of a defined number of nucleotides (Table 1). These tandem repeats are precisely maintained, which results in a polymorphism at the DNA

607

Table 1   Sequences of tandem repeats of the mucin genes cloned

MUC1	**GST**APPAHG**VTS**APD**TR**PAP (20 aa)
Muc-1	D**STSS**PVH**S**G**TSS**PA**TS**APE (20–21 aa) (mouse)
MUC2	P**TTTP**I**TTTTT**V**TP**T**PTP**TG**T**Q**T** (23 AA)
Muc-2	P**ST**P**ST**PPP**ST** (11–12 aa) (rat MLP)
MUC3	H**ST**P**S**F**TSS**I**TTTETTS** (17 aa)
rMUC176	**TTT**PDV (6 aa) (also rat M2)
MUC4	**TSS**A**ST**GHA**T**PLPV**TD** (16 aa)
MUC5AC	**TTSTTS**AP (8 aa)
MUC5B	**SST**PG**T**AH**TLT**VL**TTTATT**P**T**A**T**G**ST**A**T**P (29 aa)
RAM 7S	**TTTT**II**T**I (8 aa) (rat)
MUC6	**S**PF**SST**GPM**T**A**TS**FQ**TTTT**YP**T**P**S**HPQ**TTL**P**TH**VPPF**ST**SLV-**T**P**ST**G**T**VI**T**P**TH**AQM**AT**S**AS**IH**ST**P**T**G**T**IPPP**TTL**K**AT**G**STH**-**T**APPM**T**P**TTS**G**TS**QAH**SS**F**ST**AK**TST**SH**S**H**TSS**THHPEV**T**P**TSTTT**I**T**P-NP**TST**G**TST**PVAH**TTS**A**TSS**RLP**T**PF**TT**H**S**PP**T**G**S** (169 aa)
MUC7	**TT**AAPP**T**P**S**A**TT**PAPP**SSS**APPE (23 aa)
PSM	GAGPG**TT**A**SS**VGV**TET**ARP**S**VAG**S**G**TT**G**T**V**S**GA**S**G**STGSSS**G**S**PGA**T**GA-**S**IGQPE**TS**R**IS**VAG**SS**GAPAV**SS**GA**S**QAAG**TS** (81 aa) (porcine)
FIM-B.1	GE**ST**PAP**S**E**TT** (11 aa) *(Xenopus)*
FIM-A.1	VP**TT**PE**TTT** (9 aa) and E**TTT** (4 aa) *(Xenopus)*
FIM-C.1	**TTT**KA**TTT** (8 aa motif) *(Xenopus)*
ASGP-1	I**TTL**PQ**S**QH**T**G**S**MK**TT**RNPQ**TT**G**TT**EV**TTTL**SA**SSS**DQVQVE-**TTS**Q**TTL**SPD**TTTTT**SHAPRE**SSS**PP**STS**VIL**TTT**A**ST**EG**T**SGD-**T**GH**T**MA**TT**QG**ST**PA**TT**EI**S**V**T**P**ST**QKM**S**PV**ST**F**STST**QE (124 aa) (rat)

The possible sites of O-glycosylation are shown in bold type. The sequences are human unless otherwise noted.

level that is also exhibited by the proteins (40, 139). The repeat units of the different mucins exhibit no similarity to each other either in sequence or number of amino acids (aa) in the repeat. However, in each case threonines (Thr) and/or serines (Ser) make up a high percent of the amino acids, which gives the molecules the potential to be highly O-glycosylated. Due to the presence of tandem repeats, there is great variability in the sizes of the mucin molecules. The size variations suggest that absolute length is not crucial to mucin function but rather that the core protein exists in an extended form as a scaffold for O-linked carbohydrate.

The sugars linked to the core protein are probably significant to the function of the membrane-associated and secreted mucins. Hundreds of oligosaccharide chains are attached to a single core protein. These chains vary in length from one to twenty sugars and are neutral, sialylated, or sulfated. The core protein bears different oligosaccharide structures in different tissues, and the oligosaccharide structures are altered in disease (see below). The reason for this structural diversity is unknown, but it presumably is of functional importance. The structures of the sugar polymers offer tremendous versatility, in that there are far more ways to link together monosaccharides than there are to link amino acids (38). The heterogeneity of the oligosaccharide structures had previously suggested a lack of specific function. However, more recent studies have shown that biological activity of recombinant molecules can be highly dependent upon glycosylation (38). The identification of the molecular partners for the selectin family of carbohydrate-binding proteins as mucin-like glycoproteins has also served to renew interest in the carbohydrate structures on mucins (130).

Until recently, mucins were analyzed by purifying the molecules from tissues or cell lines and then analyzing the amino acid and carbohydrate composition, in addition to performing structural analyses. Some sequence data were obtained, but results were often difficult to interpret because of molecular heterogeneity. A breakthrough was the derivation of antibodies directed to the deglycosylated core proteins of mucins (18, 40, 90). These reagents allowed the isolation of cDNA clones (in most cases, partial cDNAs) for eight human mucin genes and five rodent genes. Cloning studies are now yielding information about the structure and gel-forming capacity of the mucin monomer, as well as laying the groundwork for analysis of the regulation of mucin biosynthesis. Knowledge of control of synthesis and posttranslational modifications is necessary to understand alterations in secretion, expression, and processing that occur in disease. In this review, we focus on our current knowledge of epithelial mucin gene structures and the deduced protein structures obtained from molecular cloning techniques. There are a number of excellent, recent review articles on the biology, biochemistry, biosynthesis, structure, and possible functions of mucins (11, 25, 26, 42, 47, 65, 78, 99, 107, 121, 123, 138, 142).

MEMBRANE-ASSOCIATED MUCINS

MUC1

Attention has recently focused on an integral membrane mucin glycoprotein (variously called MUC1, PEM, or episialin) that is developmentally regulated and aberrantly expressed by carcinomas, which makes it an important marker in malignancy (15, 18, 44, 141, 165). Antibodies raised against carcinomas originating from many tissues react with epitopes present on this mucin. Because many antibodies that recognize epithelial mucins were derived independently, the MUC1 mucin has been variously designated HMFG antigen

(141), epithelial membrane antigen (EMA) (109), PAS-0 (129), DUPAN-2 (101), peanut-lectin binding urinary mucin (PUM) (81), Ca1 (16), nonpenetrating glycoprotein (NPGP) (27), NCRC11 antigen (35), epitectin (57), MAM-6 (63), DF3 antigen (87), sebaceous gland antigen (SGA) (32), H23 antigen (82), polymorphic epithelial mucin (PEM) (39), and episialin (95). This variety of names has led to confusion as to the identities of the various molecules. According to Human Genome Mapping conventions, the mucin gene loci should be designated with the letters MUC, followed by a number reflecting the order in which the genes were cloned. The transmembrane mucin has been, therefore, designated MUC1. By convention, the mouse homologue is referred to as Muc- followed by the number of its homologue. We refer to the protein as MUC1 until a function has been defined and a sensible name can be employed.

MUC1 GENE AND DEDUCED PROTEIN STRUCTURE   *MUC1* was the first mucin core to be cloned and is the only mucin for which full-length cDNA and genomic clones for both human and mouse have been published (39–41, 90, 91, 95, 132, 134, 152, 158). The full-length cDNA sequence of the human *MUC1* gene encodes a protein with distinct domains: an amino terminal signal peptide domain consisting of a signal peptide and degenerate repeats, a large domain made up of variable numbers of a 20 amino acid repeat, and the carboxy terminus consisting of degenerate repeats, mucin–like unique sequence, a hydrophobic membrane-spanning domain of 31 amino acids, and a cytoplasmic domain of 69 amino acids (Figure 1). The cytoplasmic tail appears to interact with the actin cytoskeleton (110). Two splice variants of unknown significance have been described that resulted from the use of two alternative splice acceptor sites for exon 2 (95, 158). These variants differed by 27 base pairs (bp), which resulted in an altered signal sequence and, hence, a different

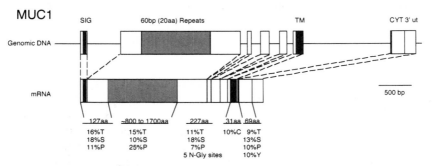

Figure 1   Diagrammatic representation of the human *MUC1* gene and mRNA drawn approximately to scale. Boxes represent the seven exons. The gene shown contains 18 consensus repeat units and spans approximately 6 kb. SIG = signal sequence; TM = transmembrane domain; CYT = cytoplasmic tail; 3′ ut = 3′ untranslated region.

amino terminus. The splice recognition site is allele dependent and is based on a single adenine/guanine (A/G) nucleotide difference in exon 2, eight nucleotides downstream of the second splice acceptor site (93).

There is a large variation in the number of repeats per allele (from 25 to > 125 repeats) (41). Common sizes of the tandem repeat portion of the molecule in an unrelated Northern European population are 820 and 1700 aa (41 and 85 repeats); the remainder of the core consists of 480 aa, some of which are actually degenerate repeats occurring at the ends of the repeat domain. The calculated molecular mass of the core is about 120 to 225 kDa. The repeat unit sequence is rich in Ser (10%), Thr (15%) and Pro (25%) residues. This region of the protein is extensively O-glycosylated. The deduced aa sequence also contains five potential N-glycosylation sites. MUC1 has been shown to undergo N-glycosylation (62, 96).

MUC1 is a transmembrane protein (113), although a soluble form exists in tissue culture supernatants and bodily fluids (13, 21). A secreted form of the MUC1 mucin, presumed to be produced by alternative splicing, has also been described (157). Other investigators, however, have failed to confirm the presence of this variant mRNA (41, 90, 95). We have recently shown that the soluble form can arise without the mechanism of alternate splicing. This soluble form lacks the cytoplasmic tail, which suggests that the mucin is released from the membrane by the action of a protease (13). Recycling of MUC1 from the membrane to the *trans*-Golgi network followed by further sialylation and a cleavage event that would remove the transmembrane and cytoplasmic tail portions of the molecule has been reported (94, 97). This recycling mechanism could provide an alternate method for the core protein to be secreted from the cell.

MUC1 cDNA clones have been obtained from mammary gland, pancreas, and ovary mRNA (40, 41, 90, 95, 137, 158). Although the core protein expressed by the different tissues is identical, the mature glycosylated forms appear distinct. MUC1 expressed by the mammary gland has a M_r in the range of 250 to 500 kDa and exhibits about 50% carbohydrate by weight (129), whereas MUC1 from the pancreas has a M_r that exceeds 1000 kDa and is about 80% carbohydrate (89). MUC1 from colon carcinoma cells is 80 to 90% carbohydrate by weight and has a M_r of 600 to 800 kDa (6). Clearly, the core protein can be glycosylated in distinct ways by normal tissues and tumors of the mammary gland, colon, and pancreas (6, 19, 20, 53–55, 73, 84). The primary sequence presumably does not dictate the glycosylation patterns; they may be dependent upon glycosyltransferase and glycosidase expression or availability of substrates.

REGULATION OF THE *MUC1* GENE   The complete *MUC1* coding sequence is contained in seven exons spanning between 4 and 7 kilobase pairs (kb) of

DNA, depending on the number of repeat units present (Figure 1) (91). The regulatory sequences appear to be contained within a 10 kb SacII fragment that contains the *MUC1* gene, 1.6 kb of 5′ sequence, and 1.9 kb of 3′ flanking sequences. This fragment confers tissue-specific expression of human *MUC1* in transgenic mice (112). *MUC1* is located on chromosome 1q21 (103, 140) in a region of closely packed genes. About 2600 bp upstream of the *MUC1* transcription start site is the polyadenylation sequence for the thrombospondin-3 gene (151), and within about 1 kb of the *MUC1* polyA site an unidentified gene has been located (S Gendler & T Duhig, unpublished data). Both genes exhibit patterns of expression distinct from that of *MUC1*, and thus the promoters are presumed to be independent.

Promoter analyses ongoing in a number of laboratories will provide better understanding of the regulation of *MUC1* in carcinomas. Several regions within 550 bp of the transcription start site of the gene appear to be involved in the control of expression of the *MUC1* gene. A sequence called E-MUC1, located at −84/−72 bp, appears to determine the tissue-specific expression of the *MUC1* gene (86). A second regulatory region, located at −505/−485 bp, has been identified that appears to bind to a 45-kDa protein (1). This region overlaps with a sequence that is similar to a motif common to milk protein promoters that bind the milk protein–binding factor (154). Just upstream of E-MUC1, at −133/−102, a region of nonrandom purine/pyrimidine strand asymmetry exists, and perfect homopurine mirror repeats (PMR) have been identified (71). One PMR is sensitive to S1 nuclease digestion, and a 27-kDa protein binds to the purine-rich strand. Although the function of this region is unknown, the PMR motif appears to be associated with the formation of H-DNA conformations (intramolecular triplexes), which may be involved in regulation of transcription of some genes. In addition, a soluble factor from normal human colonic connective tissues that is capable of stimulating the production of MUC1 by human colon carcinoma cells has recently been described (75). The region important in this regulation is called responsive mucin element (RME) and is located at −531/−520 (131). Hormonal modulation of *MUC1* has been observed in the endometrium, with highest expression observed in the secretory phase in the human (61, 124) and during estrus and proestrus in the mouse (14). The specific promoter elements responsible for this regulation have not been identified.

MOUSE *Muc-1* GENE   The mouse *Muc-1* gene was cloned utilizing a 3′ human cDNA. The deduced mouse Muc-1 protein is similar to the human MUC1 protein, although the protein is smaller because the gene contains a fixed number (16) of repeats of 20–21 aa (134, 152). Homology with the human protein is only 34% in the tandem repeat domain, which exhibits conservation mainly of Ser and Thr, presumed sites of O-glycosylation. Homology rises to

87% in the transmembrane and cytoplasmic domains, which suggests that these regions may be functionally important. Similar levels of homology in these regions were found in gibbon, bovine, rabbit, hamster, and guinea pig (A Spicer & S Gendler, unpublished data). The genomic structure of the mouse homologue is similar to that of its human counterpart, with all exon/intron boundaries conserved. Introns 1–5 showed from 50 to 62% homology; the promoter region was 72% homologous, which is not surprising because the human and mouse genes show similar patterns of expression (113, 134). The mouse gene is located on chromosome 3 within a region that is syntenic with an area on human chromosome 1 (85, 104, 105, 133).

DEVELOPMENTAL EXPRESSION OF *Muc-1*   The development of an antiserum to the MUC1 cytoplasmic tail that was cross-reactive with other species enabled us to examine the expression of mouse *Muc-1* in adult and embryo (15, 113, 134). By immunohistochemistry, the Muc-1 protein was first detected in mouse embryonic stomach, pancreas, and lung at gestational day 12 (vaginal plug = day 1). In each case, the protein was expressed on the apical surface of the lumenal epithelial cells. Muc-1 protein expression correlated well with the epithelial differentiation status of the stomach, pancreas, lung, trachea, kidney, salivary and mammary glands (15, 113, 134). Expression in the mammary gland is stimulated by insulin, prolactin, and hydrocortisone (111).

FUNCTIONS OF MUC1   Numerous functions are proposed for MUC1. Its high level of expression in carcinomas and metastatic lesions suggests that it has a role in tumor progression and metastasis. It is thought to be an anti-adhesive protein due to its large, extended conformation (17, 36, 78). It may block cell-cell interactions by destabilizing cell-cell and/or cell-matrix interactions (92, 156) and thus aid in epithelial morphogenesis (15, 65). Alternatively, MUC1 may act as an adhesive by presenting carbohydrates as ligands for selectin-like molecules and thus aid metastatic dissemination (3, 98, 120). This is particularly relevant because MUC1 was recently shown to express sialyl Lewis[x] and sialyl Lewis[a], ligands for P- and E-selectins (6, 55). Cells expressing MUC1 may modulate immune functions. Mucin-expressing cells are resistant to natural killer (NK) and cytotoxic T cell killing (128, 148) and metastasize more readily (136). Carcinoma-associated MUC1 expresses an epitope that tumor-reactive cytotoxic T cells (CTL) recognize in a non-major histocompatability complex (MHC)-restricted manner (8, 74, 79). In this respect, it appears that a high level of expression of MUC1 by tumors is disadvantageous to the tumor cells (88), but this is not necessarily so. In patients with breast and pancreatic carcinomas, the MUC1 protein can be detected in the circulation (21, 60, 64, 102), and free MUC1 protein produced by tumors appears to inhibit the CTL lysis of target cells (8) and may be immunosuppressive (37). High levels of circulating MUC1 might, therefore, block the specific T cell activity and thus aid the cells in escaping from T cell–mediated lysis.

Rat Ascites Sialomucin Glycoproteins, ASGP-1 and ASGP-2

Mucin molecules called ASGP-1 and ASGP-2, with possible bifunctional capabilities, were described on the cell surface of 13762 rat mammary adeno-carcinoma cells. It is hypothesized that they protect against immune recognition and NK cell killing (128) and correlate with metastatic potential (135). The sialomucin is synthesized as a large precursor that is cleaved during passage through the endoplasmic reticulum (ER) into ASGP-1, the sialomucin portion, and ASGP-2, the membrane-associated N-glycosylated glycoprotein (126). The cDNA hybridizes to a large 9 kb mRNA (127). ASGP-2 deduced sequence consists of a large extracellular domain of 684 aa with 24 potential N-glycosylation sites, a transmembrane domain of 25 aa, and a cytoplasmic tail of 20 aa. The extracellular domain contains two EGF-like repeats that can modulate EGF receptor phosphorylation activity (127). ASGP-2 can activate the protooncogene receptor kinase p185[neu] and is found complexed with it in 13762 cells. The EGF-like repeats contain six Cys residues located at constant positions and are thought to be involved in protein-protein interactions. Extension of the ASGP-2 sequence by 5' rapid amplification of cDNA ends (RACE) yielded the full-length sequence (159). The ASGP-1 portion of the 9 kb transcript has a short unique amino terminal region of 50 aa, including a putative signal sequence, a tandem repeat domain containing 11 repeats of 117 to 124 aa, and a 3' unique sequence of 609 aa (Table 1). Nine of the repeats are in tandem and are 70 to 90% identical to a consensus repeat of 124 aa; the two end repeats are separated from the others by short unique sequences. Two percent of the carboxy terminal residues are Cys. ASGP-1 has a calculated molecular mass of 224 kDa. There are similarities between ASGP-1 and ASGP-2 and MUC1. These include (a) the presence of three Cys residues in or near the transmembrane domain that may be a site for palmitylation, (b) a cleavage event that occurs during passage to the cell surface, and (c) endocytosis with further sialylation. It will be interesting to analyze the role of ASGP-1 and ASGP-2 in cell behavior. The dual functionality of this protein complex raises the possibility that other mucins may also be multifunctional.

SECRETED MUCINS

The primary structures of secreted mucins are now becoming available through the use of molecular cloning techniques. In most cases, full-length sequences have not been obtained. The genes and proteins are much larger than the transmembrane mucin, MUC1, with genomic sequences of up to 100 kb or possibly larger. These mucins also contain tandem repeats (Table 1). The human mucin gene tandem repeats show low levels of homology with their corresponding rodent homologues, although high levels of homology (up to 90%) have been observed between the unique portions of the gene sequences. The secreted mucins also have Cys-rich domains that are homologous to each other and to von Willebrand factor (vWF) (see below). This domain may be responsible for self-dimerization of the mucin molecules. Homology has been detected between nearly all of the secreted mucins (except MUC7) for which 3' carboxy terminal domains have been reported, including MUC2, rMuc-2, MUC5, porcine and bovine submaxillary mucins, *Xenopus laevis* FIM-B.1, and vWF.

Intestinal Mucins

MUC2   Much effort has been expended cloning the gene for MUC2, a mucin found in small intestine, colon, and airways (Table 2) (43, 48, 51, 52, 77, 144). Using antiserum made to the stripped mucin core protein purified from LS174T human colon carcinoma cells (22), a λgt11 expression library made from human small intestine was screened, and partial cDNA clones for MUC2 were selected, purified, and sequenced (48, 51, 52, 144). Subsequent cloning steps utilizing conventional cDNA library screening, polymerase chain reaction (PCR), RACE, anchored PCR, and genomic clones, yielded the complete sequence of 15,563 bp for the polypeptide core (52). The gene appears to code for a large (>5100 aa) secreted protein. Purified intestinal and colonic mucins have been separated into at least two fractions, acidic and neutral, with different amino acid compositions (45, 155). The MUC2 repeat units are more similar to the acidic fraction of intestinal mucin. The gene has been mapped to chromosome 11p15 (46).

MUC2 is a highly repetitive gene, comprised of two tandem repeat domains, one with about 100 fairly precise 23 aa repeats in the most common allele (different alleles show from 50 to 100 repeats) and a second with a 347 aa irregular Thr/Ser/Pro-rich repeat (51, 144). It also contains four D-domains (regions of homology found in vWF) that are Cys-rich regions with a high degree of sequence similarity to four D-domains of prepro vWF (52) (Figure 2). The tandem repeat and the Thr/Ser/Pro-rich N-terminal domains contain most of the sites for O-glycosylation. Approximately 78% of the Thr are glycosylated, thus the 100 repeats could possess up to 1000 O-linked oligosaccharide chains (23). The structure of this upstream repeat region differs from the structures of MUC1 and from the large repeat domain of MUC2 because the repeat units are often discontinuous. The repeats are mainly 48 bp in length with several repeats containing additional 21–24 bp segments (51, 144).

Three D-domains are located in the amino terminal portion and one at the

Table 2   Cellular location of MUC1 through MUC7 in normal epithelial tissues

				Mucin genes				
	1	2	3	4	5B	5AC	6	7
Bronchus								
Ciliated epithelium	+	—	—	+	—	+	NT[a]	NT
Serous glands	+	—	—	—	+	—	—	NT
Mucous glands	—	—	—	+	+	+	—	NT
Lung alveoli	—	—	—	NT	NT	NT	NT	NT
Breast								
Secretory tubule, acini, duct	+	—	—	+	NT	NT	—	NT
Endometrium	+	—	—	NT	NT	NT	NT	NT
Prostate glandular epithelium	+	—	—	NT	NT	NT	—	NT
Ovary	—	NT	NT	NT	NT	NT	NT	—
Cervix	+	NT	—	+	+	+	NT	NT
Kidney								
Proximal tubules	—	NT	NT	NT	NT	NT	NT	NT
Distal tubules	+	NT	NT	NT	NT	NT	NT	NT
Collecting ducts	+	NT	NT	NT	NT	NT	NT	NT
Glomeruli	—	NT	NT	NT	NT	NT	NT	NT
Salivary gland								
Serous acini	—	—	—	NT	NT	NT	NT	—
Mucous acini	—	—	—	NT	NT	NT	NT	+
Intercalated duct	+	+	+	NT	NT	NT	NT	NT
Striated duct	+	+	+	NT	NT	NT	NT	NT
Esophagus squamous epithelium	+	—	—	NT	NT	NT	NT	NT
Stomach								
Surface epithelium	+	—	—	+	NT	+	+	—
Mucous neck cells	+	—	—	NT	NT	—	+	—
Gastric glands	+	—	—	—	NT	—	NT	—
Gallbladder epithelium	+	—	+	NT	NT	NT	+	NT
Pancreas								
Ducts, ductules	+	—	—	NT	NT	NT	NT	NT
Centroacinar cells	+	—	—	NT	NT	NT	NT	NT
Acini	—	—	—	NT·	NT	NT	NT	NT
Islets of Langerhans	—	—	—	NT	NT	NT	NT	NT
Small intestine								
Columnar enterocytes	—	—	+	+	—	—	NT	NT
Goblet cells	—	+	-	+	—	—	+	NT
Colon								
Columnar cells	—	—	+	+	—	—	+	NT
Goblet cells	—	+	—	+	—	+	NT	NT

[a] NT, not tested.

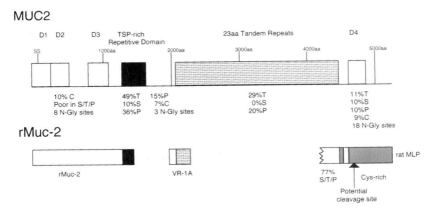

Figure 2 Linear representation of the human MUC2 protein and respective alignments of three independent rat Muc-2 (rMuc-2) cDNA clones. SS = signal sequence.

carboxy terminal region, an orientation that is similar to that in prepro vWF. The D-domains are likely involved in oligomer formation via disulfide linkages. The D-domains in prepro vWF are required for oligomerization of vWF and involved in packing vWF into specific storage granules. vWF dimerization occurs in the endoplasmic reticulum; trimers and larger multimers form in the Golgi (summarized in 52). Similarly, rat gastric mucin forms dimers and larger multimers in the ER shortly after synthesis (30). Details on the packaging and oligomerization of MUC2 are not yet known. Gum (52) speculates that MUC2 may be able to catalyze its own dimerization, based on conservation of sequences Cys-X-X-Cys that appear to be involved in the disulfide isomerase activity. The D-domains show sequence similarity to rat MUC2, frog integumentary mucin FIM-B.1, porcine and bovine submaxillary mucins, and vWF (51).

The large, secreted gel-forming mucins are probably involved in lubrication and protection of the epithelial tissues they line. Gum and colleagues suggest additional functions for these mucins based on their similarity to properties of vWF (52). Like vWF, MUC2 may bind collagen or other connective tissue components when tissue architecture is disrupted by cancer or inflammatory bowel disease. This may lead to increased dysplasia and inflammation, an interaction with cells involved in inflammation or immune responses, or metastasis. Further studies are necessary to clarify the functions of MUC2.

rMUC-2 (MLP) Several groups appear to be cloning different portions of the rat homologue of *MUC2*. The Forstner group (162) has purified the putative "link" 118-kDa protein released from rat intestinal mucin by thiol reduction, obtained peptide sequence, and using PCR and cDNA cloning, isolated clones that code for 1121 aa of the mucin-like peptide (MLP) (72, 161, 163). The first 258 aa code for a Ser/Thr/Pro-rich (77%) region followed by 42 aa of a Cys-rich sequence, 54 aa that contain 4.5 tandem repeats of 11–12 aa (Table 1), followed by 767 aa of a Cys-rich domain (Figure 2). Within this last domain is the cleavage point that would generate the link protein. The cleavage point is between an Asp and a Pro, and it is unclear whether this cleavage occurs in vivo or during in vitro purification procedures. A similar situation exists for the porcine submaxillary mucin, which, when purified in the presence of large amounts of proteinase inhibitors, retains the carboxy terminal link protein as part of the apomucin (34). Both the link protein, which is the carboxy terminal portion of the clone, and the amino terminal sequences hybridized to a >9 kb mRNA from the intestine. The human and rat link portion of the cDNAs cross-hybridized to rat and human intestinal RNAs (161).

A second group cloning another part of rat Muc-2 (rMuc-2) used the strategy of purifying small intestine mucins, deglycosylating a peptide, generating antiserum, and utilizing expression cloning (24, 56). The isolated clone, designated VR-1A, has an open reading frame of 235 aa, consisting of 53 aa with 13% Cys and 2% Ser, followed by 182 aa with 64% Ser/Thr and 14% Pro. There are no tandem repeats in this region. Both this clone and a clone for MLP hybridized to the same size mRNA species. Pulsed-field analysis of genomic DNA revealed that rMuc-2 (MLP) and VR-1A probes hybridized to identically sized bands, whereas no bands in common were found in Southern hybridizations with a variety of enzymes (56). These data suggest that clone VR-1A and rMuc-2 are part of the same gene but correspond to different regions of the gene (Figure 2). Both VR-1A and rMuc-2 (MLP) are localized to rat chromosome 1 (56).

The amino terminus of rMuc-2 has been obtained using an N-terminal probe for human MUC2 (108). The amino terminus (1391 aa) is Cys-rich and lacks tandem repeats; downstream is a 122 aa Thr/Ser/Pro-rich (92%) region with irregular repeats. Identity between the human and rat nonrepeat regions is about 80%, whereas the irregular repeat domain shows about 38% identity with the human homologue. Homology with human MUC2 found both at the C- and N-termini suggest that the rat gene is organized similarly to the human gene and that the various groups are sequencing the same gene (Figure 2). Northern blots and in situ hybridization using probes for rMuc-2 show expression in the small intestine and colon, with the normal lung, liver, stomach, submandibular gland, and spleen being negative (108, 163). MUC2 is expressed in the lungs of humans with chronic bronchitis (77) and cystic fibrosis, (43) and in rats' lungs with SO_2 damage (9, 76, 108).

MUC3   Sequences from the tandem repeat domain of a second human intestinal mucin gene called *MUC3* have been obtained by screening a small intestine library with antibodies to deglycosylated mucin (50). The tandem repeat of 51 bp codes for a 17 aa repeat unit (Table 1) that contains 71% Thr/Ser and 6% Pro and appears to represent the major neutral fraction of intestinal mucin (155). RNA analysis of MUC3 shows expression in small intestine, colon, and colonic tumors. *MUC3* maps to chromosome 7q22 (50).

rMUC176(M2)   The rat, like the human, appears to express at least two intestinal mucin genes. Two groups (49, 83) have isolated clones with extensive Thr-rich tandem repeat domains of TTTPDV (Table 1). Clones for M2 encode 30 tandem repeats, followed by 82 aa of unique hydrophobic sequence that may serve as a transmembrane domain and/or form hydrophobic interactions with other molecules (83). rMUC176 contains 92 aa of a unique sequence 3′ to the tandem repeat domain, consisting of 16% Ser/Thr and 9% Cys (49). Thus, M2 and rMUC176 probably represent different regions of the same mucin gene. Probes for both clones hybridized to RNA of about 9 kb from small intestine and colon.

Tracheobronchial Mucins

MUC4   Tandem repeat sequences only are available for MUC4. The clone was selected from a human tracheobronchial mucosa library (115). The published sequence is comprised of 48 bp tandem repeats coding for 16 aa repeats that occur at least 39 times and contain about 50% Ser/Thr (Table 1). Antibodies have only recently been raised against this sequence; consequently, expression patterns have been determined using in situ hybridization. Expression is observed in a variety of tissues including lung, mammary gland, cervix, stomach, and small and large intestine (Table 2).

MUC5A   A variety of clones and sequences have been reported for MUC5 (5, 28, 114, 147). These clones map to chromosome 11p15, and all were isolated using an antiserum made to deglycosylated tracheobronchial mucins. Recent cloning and mapping experiments have shown that MUC5A and MUC5C are from the same gene now called *MUC5AC* (52a). Confirmation of identity was provided by pulsed-field gel electrophoresis analysis of genomic DNA digested with rare-cutting restriction enzymes. The DNA bands hybridizing to JER 47 (MUC5A) and JER 58 (MUC5C) were identical in each case and differed from bands detected by the JER 57 (MUC5B) probe (52a). In this gene, the tandem repeat domain is interrupted several times with a subdomain encoding a 130 aa Cys-rich peptide, which contains the TR-3A and TR-3B peptides previously isolated from human tracheobronchial mucin by Rose et al (122). A clone,

NP3a, containing these peptides was recently described and called MUC5 (100). Thus MUC5 and MUC5AC appear to be part of the same gene. The MUC5AC portion of the gene exhibits tandemly repeated domains with a consensus repeat of TTSTTSAP (Table 1) alternating with a Cys-rich domain. This structure is evident in the largest clone (1.4 kb) sequenced, JER 47. This clone consists of two 8 aa tandem repeats followed by a 130 aa Cys-rich domain containing the peptide sequences TR-3A and TR-3B. This is followed by 21 additional 8 aa repeats similar to the consensus repeat, a second 130 aa Cys-rich domain (with the TR-3A and TR-3B peptides), and four additional 8 aa repeats. Another clone sequenced, JER 58, consists entirely of repeats of 8 aa. A third clone, JUL 32, contains five consensus repeats flanked on both sides by a small amount of Cys-rich sequence. Thus sequences from several clones suggest tandem repeat domains alternating with Cys-rich domains. The Cys-rich domains of 130 aa contain 10 conserved Cys residues. Two similar Cys-rich domains were found in the MUC2 sequence, one located between D3 and the Thr/Ser/Pro-rich repetitive region, and the second between the Thr/Ser/Pro-rich region and the 23 aa tandem repeat domain (Figure 2).

MUC5, which is likely part of the same gene, encodes the same peptide sequences as are found in the 130 aa Cys-rich domains of MUC5AC (100). Airway mucin from a patient with asthma was purified and sequences of tryptic peptides obtained. A nasal polyp cDNA library was screened with unique oligonucleotide probes and a carboxy terminal clone (NP3a) of 3.6 kb was selected. Deduced aa sequence confirmed that clone NP3a is indeed coding for the tracheobronchial mucin glycoprotein. Ser, Thr (18%), and Cys (8%) are distributed fairly evenly throughout the 1056 aa sequence. Although five unique tandem repeats of TTVGP/S were identified in MUC5 (aa 496–520), the clone NP3a does not contain the eight aa consensus repeats found in MUC5AC. Homology was observed to the Cys-rich domains of MUC2, rMuc-2 (MLP), bovine submaxillary mucin, and vWF. In particular, high percents of the cysteines are conserved. The region of vWF that shows homology is required for tail-to-tail dimerization of vWF in the ER, and thus the conserved Cys residues may be involved in the polymerization of tracheobronchial mucin (100).

MUC5 transcripts of varying sizes (from 2 to 10 kb) were detected in nasal polyp and tracheal RNA and in some colonic and pancreatic cancer cell lines (153). MUC5 is localized to chromosome 11, as are MUC2 and MUC6 (145). The complete sequence of MUC2 and the 3′ carboxy terminal sequence of MUC5 indicate that they are unique genes. However, it is possible that MUC6 and several airway mucin sequences that have been mapped to chromosome 11p15 are part of the same gene; completion of full-length cDNA sequences will clarify this issue. Alternatively, chromosome 11p15 may be a locus that contains a cluster of genes for secreted mucins, and this clustering could indicate a common evolutionary origin for these genes. Clusters of similar genes have been observed on other chromosomes: e.g. genes coding for complement regulatory proteins are clustered on chromosome 1q32 (85); hemoglobin genes are in close proximity to each other on chromosome 11; and genes of the MHC are on chromosome 6.

MUC5B   The MUC5B group of clones (JUL 7, JUL 10, JER 57, JER 28) have been more fully characterized and found to contain 87 bp tandem repeats encoding peptides that are nonrepetitive because of numerous deletions or insertions (33). Out of 55 possible complete tandem repeat sequences, only 22 units have the perfect 87 bp repeat (Table 1). In contrast to the other mucins characterized, these repeats are not in tandem. Even though the frequent insertions and deletions upset the repeat unit, the sequence remains highly mucin-like. The deduced aa sequences of these clones (a total of 1671 aa) contain about 1–2% Cys dispersed throughout, and high levels of Thr (21–27%), Ser (10–14%), and Pro (12–18%). Southern blot analysis of human genomic DNA suggests that all four clones are part of the same gene because they hybridize to the same restriction fragments in five enzyme digests. Northern analysis shows expression in tracheal, bronchial, gastric, and colonic mucosae (33).

RAM 7S   Partial sequence for a rat airway mucin (RAM) has been obtained by screening a library with SMUC41, a cDNA clone for MUC2 (146). An open reading frame of 276 bp codes for seven variable 7–12 aa tandem repeats and five nontandem copies of the consensus sequence TTTTIITI (Table 1). Sequence homology with SMUC41 is 60%. RAM 7S hybridized to mRNA from the small and large intestine and from the trachea following SO_2 treatment.

CANINE TRACHEOBRONCHIAL MUCIN   A canine tracheal mucin cDNA has been selected using antisera to deglycosylated mucin (149). The complete cDNA of 3.7 kb codes for a deduced protein of 1118 aa, with a molecular mass of ~126 kDa. The sequence is mucin-like, rich in Thr, Pro, Ser, Gly, and Ala. Although no precise repeats have been found, motifs of TPTPTP and TTTTPV occur throughout the sequence. The carboxy terminus contains 16 of the 29 Cys present; however, this region shows no homology with other secreted mucins. The remaining Cys are scattered throughout the sequence, although the region between 790–1660 nucleotides that is richest in Thr/Pro/Ser lacks any Cys. Regions rich in Thr and Pro exhibit homology with MUC2 (149).

Gastric Mucin

MUC6   Clones for a gastric mucin, MUC6, have been identified using antiserum to deglycosylated human gastric mucin (145). The sequence is noteworthy for coding for tandem repeats of 169 aa in length, the longest repeat unit reported thus far (Table 1). The repeats have an aa composition typical of that for a mucin, with Thr (30%), Ser (18%) and Pro (15%) accounting for 63% of the aa. No unique sequence has been reported. The mRNA is large and polydisperse, which is not surprising because the gastric apomucin peptide is 900 kDa (138). MUC6 has highest expression in the stomach and gall bladder, with weaker expression in the terminal ileum and right colon (Table 2). However, the specific cell types expressing MUC6 have not been identified. Chromosomal localization places MUC6 on chromosome 11p15.4–15.5, in the same general area as the MUC2 and MUC5 genes. mRNA expression patterns suggest that the genes are distinct, although final proof will have to await full-length sequences for the various MUC5 and MUC6 genes. It is likely that another distinct gastric mucin will be found because, as previously reported, gastric epithelial mucous cells produce a neutral mucin and the gastric gland mucous neck cells produce an acidic mucin (31, 107). With so little sequence available, it is difficult to assign the MUC6 protein to either category.

A gastric mucin from the mouse has recently been isolated using antisera prepared to deglycosylated gastric mucin (125). Clones contained 48 bp repeats that code for 16 aa repeats with a consensus sequence of QTSSPNTGKTSTISTT. The antisera stained the cytoplasm of surface and neck mucous cells; chief and parietal cells were negative.

Salivary Gland Mucin

MUC7   The second full-length sequence for a mucin has recently been published (12). In contrast to the MUC2 gene, which codes for a large secreted protein, the MUC7 gene encodes a small secreted mucin that appears to be free of disulfide bonds. Human saliva contains both high and low M_r mucin glycoproteins, MG1 and MG2 (116). Biochemical analysis of MG2 identified a protein of 120–150 kDa that is composed of about 30% protein and 68% carbohydrate. Expression cloning using antiserum to deglycosylated MG2 followed by PCR amplification from a cDNA library to obtain the 5′ end yielded a sequence of 2350 bp, now called MUC7. The deduced sequence contains an MG2-derived tryptic peptide, thus confirming its identity (119). The translated region encodes a protein of 377 aa and contains a region of six almost perfect tandem repeats of 23 aa consisting largely of Ser (17%), Thr (22%), and Pro (35%) (Table 1). The amino terminal unique sequence of 164 aa contains a strongly hydrophobic region of 20 aa that is likely to be a signal sequence. The two Cys residues that are present within the protein are likely to be involved in intramolecular rather than intermolecular disulfide bonds because MUC7 exists as a monomer. The carboxy terminal unique sequence of 75 aa is mucin-like, with 33% Thr/Ser (3:1 ratio) and 9% Pro. Possible N-glycosylation sites (five in number) are found in both the 5' unique and 3' unique sequences. MUC7 mRNA of 2.4 kb is expressed by submandibular and sublingual glands, with parotid gland, tonsils, stomach, uterus, placenta, and ovaries negative. The gene for MUC7 is located on chromosome 7 (12).

PSM   Partial sequence has been reported for porcine submaxillary gland mucin (PSM) following screening of libraries with immunoglobulins to the deglycosylated core protein (34, 67, 143). The deduced sequence was identical to 44 residues from the amino terminus of a tryptic peptide isolated from the apomucin (143). PSM is devoid of secondary structure except for the carboxy terminal domain and exists as a long, extended structure that is highly glycosylated (67, 143). The sequence is dominated by a large tandem repeat domain that consists of 81 aa repeated from 130 to 200 times. Accordingly, the tandem repeat domain may vary from 10,530 to 16,200 aa in length. A probe to the repeat region hybridized to mRNA that is polydisperse and ranges from 5 to 20 kb in size (34). A unique, mucin-like sequence is found on either side of the repeat domain. The amino terminus consists of 120 aa, and the sequence carboxy terminal to the repeat is 450 aa in length. Thr, Ser, Gly, and Ala account for ~75% of the sequences of the tandem repeat and unique mucin-like region, and it is likely that most of the glycosylation is found in these portions of the molecule. There are also several sites for N-glycosylation, and it is not known whether N-linked sugars occur in this protein (34). The carboxy terminal portion of the molecule (230 aa) is the only globular portion and contains the Cys residues (34) that are found in the secreted mucins. There is striking sequence similarity between the carboxy terminal residues of PSM and bovine mucin-like protein (10), with 82% of the aa identical, including the 30 Cys residues, with no gaps in either sequence. There is also homology in the unique, mucin-like sequence that is 5' to the Cys-rich domain. Sixty-two percent of the residues are identical, although gaps must be introduced to achieve the best fit (34). It is likely, given the homologies cited above, that the bovine mucin-like protein is actually bovine submaxillary mucin and the cDNA is not full length. The Cys-rich region also shows 31% homology to the Cys-rich carboxy terminal domain of the *Xenopus* integumentary mucin FIM-B.1 (34). Thus this domain may have evolved prior to the separation of mammals and amphibia (34). The gene was localized to chromosome 5q2.3 (80).

BOVINE SUBMAXILLARY MUCIN-LIKE PROTEIN (BSM)   Sequence for BSM has been reported (10). The deduced sequence of 563 aa consists of 339 aa of mucin-like sequence (composition of Ser/Thr 39%, Pro 4%) followed by a

Cys-rich domain (11%) of 244 aa with homology to PSM (see above). Pro (5%) remains fairly constant throughout the sequence, and Ser/Thr drops to 12% of the Cys-rich region. Although reported to be the link protein of bovine submaxillary mucin, it is also possible that this clone is not full length, and a 5' sequence, including a tandem repeat domain, remains to be isolated. This is supported by the fact that the ATG start sequence does not match the Kozak consensus sequence (10). In addition, cDNA cloning of the bovine mucin-like protein has not been accompanied by any biochemical analysis that would substantiate the great differences in structure of the bovine and porcine submaxillary mucin molecules (34).

Frog Integumentary Mucins (FIMs)

FIM-B.1   Three frog integumentary mucins (*X. laevis*) produced by the merocrine mucous glands have been described. FIM-B.1 contains a Cys-rich carboxy terminal domain that is homologous with vWF, MUC2, rMuc-2, MUC5, PSM, and BSM (see above), and procollagen and thrombospondin (117, 118). Because this domain is responsible for vWF dimerization (150), it is likely that it serves a similar function in mucins. Most of the molecule consists of acidic type-B repeats of 11 aa that share similarity with the repeats in FIM-A.1 (Table 1) and contain many sites for O-linked glycosylation (Figure 3). Interrupting the repeats is a region similar to the short consensus repeat (SCR) (64 aa) typical of many proteins from the complement receptor family, which contains four Cys, Phe, Tyr, Gly, Trp, and Pro that are conserved. The FIM-B.1 message is extremely polydisperse; this polydispersity may be the result of alternative splicing of a huge array of cassettes. The gene is also polymorphic. This gene differs from other mucin genes in that the repeat sequences are separated by introns (118). The function of FIM-B.1 is not known, although it could serve to protect against microbial infection. Probst hypothesized that the SCR sequence may disturb the adhesion of potential pathogenic bacteria to the host by competitive inhibition as many bacteria adhere to host cells via SCR (118).

FIM-A.1   FIM-A.1 is present in frog skin in much larger amounts than FIM-B.1 and was originally called spasmolysin (69). This 43-kDa mucin is a mosaic protein, consisting of an amino terminal signal sequence, 13 acidic Thr-rich type-A repeats of 9 aa length, 7 repeats of the sequence ETTT (Table 1), and four P-domains with high homology to porcine pancreatic spasmolytic polypeptide (Figure 3). The mature protein has a molecular mass of about 130 kDa and consists of 70% carbohydrate (58). It is expressed exclusively in mature mucous glands of *X. laevis* skin (58). The P-domain is a characteristic shuffled module (~50 aa in length) containing six invariant Cys residues that form three

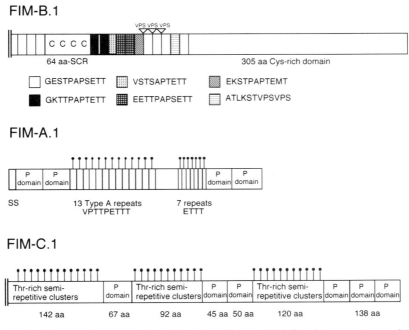

Figure 3 Diagrammatic representation of the three *X. laevis* FIM (frog integumentary mucin) genes. SCR = short consensus repeat.

intramolecular disulfide bridges (or trefoil motif). It is a potential modulator of cell growth, by analogy to EGF-like repeats. In mucins, P-domains are thought to have a role in protein-protein or lectin-like interactions (70). Other proteins with P-domains are pS2, human and rat intestinal trefoil factor; human, porcine, and mouse spasmolytic peptide; xP2 and xP4 (*X. laevis*) (70). Preferred sites of expression of P-domains are mucin-secreting epithelia and tissues with various pathological conditions (70). Spasmolysins inhibit gastrointestinal motility, induce gastric acid secretion, and show growth-stimulatory effects on colon and breast tumor cells (69).

FIM-C.1   Partial sequence for a third polymorphic frog integumentary mucin (FIM-C.1) has been described (59). FIM-C.1 contains three semi-repetitive Thr-rich (up to 80%) clusters (predominant motif is TTTKATTT, Table 1) and six P-domains (Figure 3). The polymorphism observed among different animals appears to be due to the variable lengths of the Thr-rich domains. The polydispersity is probably similar to that observed for FIM-B.1, where cassettes of repetitive sequences represent single exons, and alternative splicing generates a polydisperse message and protein (59, 118). FIM-C.1 appears to be present in the cone cells in mucous glands, the only place that FIM-A.1 is not expressed (59).

MUCIN EXPRESSION

Although the study of mucins is expanding rapidly, the patterns of expression of many of the mucin genes have not been extensively investigated. The exceptions are *MUC1, MUC2,* and *MUC3* for which the expression patterns are fairly well established using antibodies to core proteins and mRNA analyses (4, 44, 68, 165). *MUC1* is expressed on the apical cell surface of nearly all the simple epithelial tissues that line ducts and glands (Table 2) (165). The exception appears to be colon, in which expression is either not detected in normal colon (using antibodies) or found at very low levels, although strong expression is found in adenomas (stage III) and carcinomas (2, 68, 106, 165). Surprisingly, the level of mRNA appears to be about the same in both normal and malignant colon (2, 68, 106). In mouse, normal colon was negative for *Muc-1* mRNA using a sensitive RT-PCR assay (15), although expression has been occasionally detected. Expression of *MUC1* is greatly increased in carcinomas and metastatic lesions (66, 164), and the glycosylation is altered. The aberrant glycosylation was intially detected using the SM-3 monoclonal antibody (18). Subsequent analyses of oligosaccharide side chains revealed that they were shorter in breast tumor cells than on the normally processed mucin (19, 20, 53, 73). Other mucins exhibit altered glycosylation (7, 23, 29), which suggests that underglycosylation of mucins is a widespread phenomenon in carcinomas. However, the secreted mucins do not, in general, exhibit increased expression in carcinomas, although good quantitative studies have not been performed. *MUC2* appears to be specifically expressed by the goblet cells of the small intestine and colon, although expression may be detected in diseased lungs of humans and rats (9, 68, 76, 77, 160). *MUC3* expression is stronger in the small intestine than in the lung, and *MUC4* is broadly expressed in the small intestine, colon, stomach, cervix, and lung. *MUC5* is not only highly expressed in airway epithelium but also in some human colon and pancreatic adenocarcinoma cell lines (153). *MUC6* is most highly expressed in stomach and gall bladder, but the specific cells expressing it have not been identified. *MUC7* is expressed by the mucous acini in the salivary gland, although it was not tested on tracheobronchial, small intestine, colon, or prostate tissues (12). The recent availability of antibodies and cDNA probes for many mucins should enable good analyses of mucin expression and regulation, thus providing insight into the altered expression of mucins in diseases such as cancer, cystic fibrosis, asthma, and chronic obstructive pulmonary disease.

SUMMARY

The last seven years have been exciting in the world of mucin biology. Molecular analyses of mucin genes and deduced protein structures have provided insight into structural features of mucins and tools with which to examine expression, secretion, and glycosylation, thereby enabling a better understanding of the role of mucins in normal physiological processes and in disease. Functional studies are in progress both in vitro using cDNAs and cell lines and in vivo utilizing mutant mice in which a particular mucin gene has been inactivated or overexpressed. These studies should help determine whether the functions of mucins are restricted to protection and lubrication, or if they are involved in the adhesion of tumor cells to other cells or tissue components or in modulation of the immune system.

ACKNOWLEDGMENTS

We thank Drs. J Gum, YS Kim, MA Hollingsworth, M Rose, C Basbaum, JA Voynow, K Carraway, and V Guyonnet Duperat for sharing their manuscripts in preparation or in press.

Literature Cited

1. Abe M, Kufe D. 1993. Characterization of *cis*-acting elements regulating transcription of the human DF3 breast carcinoma–associated antigen (*MUC1*) gene. *Proc. Natl. Acad. Sci. USA* 90: 282–86

2. Andrews CW Jr, Jessup JM, Goldman H, Fayes DF, Kufe DW, et al. 1993. Localization of tumor-associated glycoprotein DF3 in normal, inflammatory, and neoplastic lesions of the colon. *Cancer* 72:3185–90

3. Aruffo A, Dietsch MT, Wan H, Hellström KE, Hellström I. 1992. Granule membrane protein 140 (GMP140) binds to carcinomas and carcinoma-derived cell lines. *Proc. Natl. Acad. Sci. USA* 89:2292–96

4. Audie JP, Porchet JN, Copin MC, Gosselin B, Aubert JP. 1993. Expression of human mucin genes in respiratory, digestive, and reproductive tracts ascertained by in situ hybridization. *J. Histochem. Cytochem.* 41(10): 1479–85

5. Aubert JP, Porchet N, Crepin M, Duterque-Coquillaud M, Vergnes G, et al. 1991. Evidence for different human tracheobronchial mucin peptides deduced from nucleotide cDNA sequences. *Am. J. Respir. Cell. Mol. Biol.* 5:178–85

6. Baeckstrom D, Hansson GC, Nilsson O, Johansson C, Gendler SJ, Lindholm L. 1991. Purification and characterization of a membrane-bound and a secreted mucin-type glycoprotein carrying the carcinoma-associated sialyl-Lewis[a] epitope on distinct core proteins. *J. Biol. Chem.* 266:21537–47

7. Bara J, Mollicone R, Herrera-Zabaleta E, Gautier R, Daher N, Oriol R. 1988. Ectopic expression of the Y (Ley) antigen defined by monoclonal antibody 12-4LE in distal colonic adenocarcinomas. *Int. J. Cancer* 41:683–89

8. Barnd DL, Lan MS, Metzgar RS, Finn OJ. 1989. Specific, major histocompatibility complex-unrestricted recognition of tumor-associated mucins by human cytotoxic T cells. *Proc. Natl. Acad. Sci. USA* 86:7159–63

9. Basbaum C, Gallup M, Gum J, Kim Y, Jany B. 1990. Modification of mucin gene expression in the airways of rats exposed to sulfur dioxide. *Biorheology* 27(3–4):485–89

10. Bhargava AK, Woitach JT, Davidson EA, Bhavanandan VP. 1990. Cloning and cDNA sequence of a bovine sub-

maxillary gland mucin-like protein containing 2 distinct domains. *Proc. Natl. Acad. Sci. USA* 87:6798–6802

11. Bhavanandan VP. 1991. Cancer-associated mucins and mucin-type glycoproteins. *Glycobiology* 1(5):493–503

12. Bobek LA, Tsai H, Biesbrock AR, Levine MJ. 1993. Molecular cloning, sequence, and specificity of expression of the gene encoding the low molecular weight human salivary mucin (*MUC7*). *J. Biol. Chem.* 268(27):20563–69

13. Boshell M, Lalani E-N, Pemberton L, Burchell J, Gendler S, Taylor-Papadimitriou J. 1992. The product of the human *MUC1* gene when secreted by mouse cells transfected with the full-length cDNA lacks the cytoplasmic tail. *Biochem. Biophys. Res. Commun.* 185:1–8

14. Braga VMM, Gendler SJ. 1993. Modulation of Muc-1 mucin expression in the mouse uterus during estrus cycle, early pregnancy and placentation. *J. Cell Sci.* 105:397–405

15. Braga VMM, Pemberton LF, Duhig T, Gendler SJ. 1992. Spatial and temporal expression of an epithelial mucin, Muc-1, during mouse development. *Development* 115:427–37

16. Bramwell ME, Bhavanandan VP, Wiseman G, Harris H. 1983. Structure and function of the CA antigen. *Br. J. Cancer* 48:177–83

17. Bramwell ME, Wiseman G, Shotton DM. 1986. Electron-microscopic studies of the CA antigen, epitectin. *J. Cell Sci.* 86:249–61

18. Burchell J, Gendler S, Taylor-Papadimitriou Girling A, Lewis A, et al. 1987. Development and characterization of breast cancer reactive monoclonal antibodies directed to the core protein of the human milk mucin. *Int. J. Cancer* 47:5476–82

19. Burchell J, Taylor-Papadimitriou J. 1993. Effect of modification of carbohydrate side chains on the reactivity of antibodies with core-protein epitopes of the MUC1 gene product. *Epith. Cell Biol.* 2:155–62

20. Burchell J, Taylor-Papadimitriou J, Boshell M, Gendler S, Duhig T. 1989. A short sequence, within the amino acid tandem repeat of a cancer-associated mucin, contains immunodominant epitopes. *Int. J. Cancer* 44:691–96

21. Burchell J, Wang D, Taylor-Papadimitriou J. 1984. Detection of the tumour associated antigens recognised by the monoclonal antibodies HMFG-1 and 2 in serum from patients with breast cancer. *Int. J. Cancer* 34:763–68

22. Byrd JC, Lamport DTA, Siddiqui B, Kuan S-F, Erikson R, et al. 1989. Deglycosylation of mucin from LS174T colon cancer cells by hydrogen fluoride treatment. *Biochem. J.* 261:617–25

23. Byrd JC, Nardelli J, Siddiqui B, Kim YS. 1988. Isolation and characterization of colon cancer mucin from xenografts of LS174T cells. *Cancer Res.* 48(23):6678–85

24. Carlstedt I, Herrmann A, Karlsson H, Sheehan J, Fransson L-A, Hansson GC. 1993. Characterization of two different glycosylated domains from the insoluble mucin complex of rat small intestine. *J. Biol. Chem.* 268(25):18771–81

25. Carraway KL, Fregien N, Carraway KL III, Carraway CAC. 1992. Tumor sialomucin complexes as tumor antigens and modulators of cellular interactions and proliferation. *J. Cell Sci.* 103:299–307

26. Carraway KL, Hull SR. 1991. Cell surface mucin–type glycoproteins and mucin-like domains. *Glycobiology* 1(2):131–38

27. Ceriani RL, Peterson JA, Lee JY, Moncada R, Blank EW. 1983. Characterization of cell surface antigens of human mammary epithelial cells with monoclonal antibodies prepared against human milk fat globule. *Somat. Cell Mol. Genet.* 9:415–27

28. Crepin M, Porchet N, Aubert JP, Degand P. 1990. Diversity of the peptide moiety of human airway mucins. *Biorheology* 27:471–84

29. Dahiya R, Kwak K-S, Byrd JC, Ho S, Yoon W-H, Kim YS. 1993. Mucin synthesis and secretion in various human epithelial cancer cell lines that express the *MUC1* mucin gene. *Cancer Res.* 53:1437–43

30. Decker J, Strous GJ. 1990. Covalent oligomerization of rat gastric mucin occurs in the rough endoplasmic reticulum, is N-glycosylation dependent, and precedes initial O-glycosylation. *J. Biol. Chem.* 265:18116

31. Dekker J, Van Beurden-Lamers WMO, Strous GJ. 1989. Biosynthesis of gastric mucus glycoprotein of the rat. *J. Biol. Chem.* 264:10431–37

32. de Kretser TA, Thorne HJ, Jacobs DJ, Jose DG. 1985. The sebaceous gland antigen defined by the OM-1 monoclonal antibody is expressed at high density on the surface of ovarian carcinoma cells. *Eur. J. Cancer Clin. Oncol.* 9:1019–35

33. Dufosse J, Porchet N, Audie J-P, Guyonnet Duperat V, Laine A, et al. 1993. Degenerate 87-base-pair tandem

repeats create hydrophilic/hydrophobic alternating domains in human mucin peptides mapped to 11p15. *Biochem. J.* 293:329–37

34. Eckhardt AE, Timpte CS, Abernethy JL, Zhao Y, Hill RL. 1991. Porcine submaxillary mucin contains a cystine-rich, carboxyl-terminal domain in addition to a highly repetitive, glycosylated domain. *J. Biol. Chem.* 266(15):9678–86

35. Ellis IO, Robins RA, Elstron CW, Blamey RW, Ferry B, Baldwin RW. 1984. A monoclonal antibody, NCRC-11, raised to human breast carcinoma 1. Production and immunohistological characterization. *Histopathology* 3:510–16

36. Fontenot J, Tjandra N, Bu D, Ho C, Montelarao RC, Finn OJ. 1993. Biophysical characterization of one-, two-, and three-tandem repeats of human mucin (muc-1) protein core. *Cancer Res.* 53:5386–94

37. Fung PYS, Longenecker BM. 1991. Specific immunosuppressive activity of epiglycanin, a mucin-like glycoprotein secreted by a murine mammary adenocarcinoma (TA3-HA). *Cancer Res.* 51: 1170–76

38. Geisow MJ. 1991. The coming age of glycobiology. *Tibtech* 9:221–25

39. Gendler S, Taylor-Papadimitriou J, Duhig T, Rothbard J, Burchell J. 1988. A highly immunogenic region of a human polymorphic epithelial mucin expressed by carcinomas is made of tandem repeats. *J. Biol. Chem.* 263:12820–23

40. Gendler SJ, Burchell JM, Duhig T, Lamport D, White R, et al. 1987. Cloning of partial cDNA encoding differentiation and tumor–associated mucin glycoproteins expressed by human mammary epithelium. *Proc. Natl. Acad. Sci. USA* 84:6060–64

41. Gendler SJ, Lancaster CA, Taylor-Papadimitriou J, Duhig J, Peat T, Burchell J. 1990. Molecular cloning and expression of a human tumor–associated polymorphic epithelial mucin. *J. Biol. Chem.* 265:15286–93

42. Gendler SJ, Spicer AP, Lalani E-N, Duhig T, Peat N, et al. 1991. Structure and biology of a carcinoma-associated mucin, MUC1. *Am. Rev. Respir. Dis.* 144:S42–47

43. Gerard C, Eddy RL Jr, Shows TB. 1990. The core polypeptide of cystic fibrosis tracheal mucin contains a tandem repeat structure. *J. Clin. Invest.* 86:1921–27

44. Girling A, Bartkova J, Burchell J, Gendler SJ, Gillett C, Taylor-Papadimitriou J. 1989. A core protein epitope of the PEM mucin detected by the monoclonal antibody SM-3 is selectively exposed in a range of primary carcinomas. *Int. J. Cancer* 43:1072–76

45. Gold DV, Shochat D, Miller F. 1981. Protease digestion of colonic mucin. Evidence for the existence of two immunochemically distinct mucins. *J. Biol. Chem.* 256(12):6354–58

46. Griffiths B, Matthews DJ, West L, Attwood J, Povey S, et al. 1990. Assignment of the polymorphic intestinal mucin gene (*MUC2*) to chromosome 11p15. *Ann. Hum. Genet.* 54:277–85

47. Gum JR Jr. 1992. Mucin genes and the proteins they encode: structure, diversity, and regulation. *Am. J. Respir. Cell Mol. Biol.* 7:557–64

48. Gum JR, Byrd JC, Hicks JW, Toribara NW, Lamport DTA, Kim YS. 1989. Molecular cloning of human intestinal mucin cDNAs. Sequence analysis and evidence for genetic polymorphism. *J. Biol. Chem.* 264:6480–87

49. Gum JR, Hicks JW, Lagace RE, Byrd JC, Toribara NW, et al. 1991. Molecular cloning of rat intestinal mucin. *J. Biol. Chem.* 266:22733–38

50. Gum JR, Hicks JW, Swallow DM, Lagace RL, Byrd JC, et al. 1990. Molecular cloning of a novel human intestinal mucin gene. *Biochem. Biophys. Res. Commun.* 171:407–15

51. Gum JR, Hicks JW, Toribara NW, Rothe E-M, Lagace RE, Kim YS. 1992. The human MUC2 intestinal mucin has cysteine-rich subdomains located both upstream and downstream of its central repetitive region. *J. Biol. Chem.* 267: 21375–83

52. Gum JR Jr, Hicks JW, Toribara NW, Siddiki B, Kim YS. 1994. Molecular cloning of human intestinal mucin (*MUC2*) cDNA. *J. Biol. Chem.* 269(4): 2440–46

52a. Guyonnet Duperat V, Audie J-P, Debauilleul V, Laine A, Buisine M-P, et al. 1994. Characterization of human mucin gene *MUC5AC*: a consensus cysteine-rich domain for 11p15 mucin genes? *Biochem. J.* In press

53. Hanisch F-G, Uhlenbruck G, Peter-Katalinic J, Egge H, Dabrowski J, Dabrowski U. 1989. Structures of neutral O-linked polylactosaminoglycans on human skim milk mucins. *J. Biol. Chem.* 264:872–73

54. Hanisch F-G, Uhlenbruck G, Peter-Katalinic J, Egge H, Dabrowski U, Dabrowski J. 1989. Unbranched polylactosamino-O-glycans on human skim milk mucins exhibit GalB(1–4)Glc-

NAcB(1–6) repeating units. *Soc. Exp. Biol.* 43:155–62

55. Hanski C, Drechsler K, Hanisch F-G, Sheehan J, Manske M, et al. 1993. Altered glycosylation of the MUC-1 protein core contributes to the colon carcinoma–associated increase of mucin-bound sialyl-Lewis[x] expression. *Cancer Res.* 53:4082–88

56. Hansson GC, Baeckström D, Carlstedt I, Klinga-Levan K. 1994. Molecular cloning of a cDNA coding for a region of an apoprotein from the 'insoluble' mucin complex of rat small intestine. *Biochem. Biophys. Res. Commun.* 198: 181–90

57. Harris H. 1984. The carapace of the cancer cell. *J. R. Coll. Physicians London* 18:161–65

58. Hauser F, Gertzen E-M, Hoffmann W. 1990. Expression of spasmolysin (FIM-A.1): an integumentary mucin from *Xenopus laevis*. *Exp. Cell Res.* 189:157–62

59. Hauser F, Hoffmann W. 1992. P-domains as shuffled cysteine-rich modules in integumentary mucin C.1 (FIM-C.1) from *Xenopus laevis*. Polydispersity and genetic polymorphism. *J. Biol. Chem.* 267(34):24620–24

60. Hayes DF, Sekine H, Ohno T, Kufe D. 1985. Detection of circulating plasma DF3 antigen levels in breast cancer patients. *J. Clin. Invest.* 75:1671–78

61. Hey NA, Graham RA, Seif MW, Aplin JD. 1994. The polymorphic epithelial mucin MUC1 in human endometrium is regulated with maximal expression in the implantation phase. *J. Clin. Endocrinol. Metab.* 78(2):337–42

62. Hilkens J, Buijs F. 1988. Biosynthesis of MAM-6, an epithelial sialomucin. *J. Biol. Chem.* 263(9):4215–22

63. Hilkens J, Buijs F, Hilgers J, Hageman P, Calafat J, et al. 1984. Monoclonal antibodies against human milk-fat globule membranes detecting differentiation antigens of the mammary gland and its tumors. *Int. J. Cancer* 34:197–206

64. Hilkens J, Kroezen V, Bonfrer JM, De J, Bakker M, Bruning PF. 1986. MAM-6 antigen, a new serum marker for breast cancer monitoring. *Cancer Res.* 46: 2586–87

65. Hilkens J, Ligtenberg MJL, Vos HL, Litvinov SY. 1992. Cell membrane–associated mucins and their adhesion-modulating property. *Trends Biochem. Sci.* 17:359–63

66. Hilkens J, Wesseling J, Vos HL, Ligtenberg MJL, Buijs F, Calafat J. 1992. *High levels of episialin modulate*

cell-cell and cell-extracellular matrix adhesion and inhibits cytolysis by specific and non-specific cytotoxic effector cells. 2nd Intl. Workshop on Carcinoma-Associated Mucins, p. 20. Cambridge, England

67. Hill RL, Eckhardt AE, Wang Y, Abernethy JE, Swamy N. 1992. Structure and glycosylation of porcine submaxillary mucin. See Ref. 66, p. 18

68. Ho SB, Niehans GA, Lyftogt C, Yan PS, Cherwitz DL, et al. 1993. Heterogeneity of mucin gene expression in normal and neoplastic tissues. *Cancer Res.* 53:641–51

69. Hoffmann W. 1988. A new repetitive protein from *Xenopus laevis* skin highly homologous to pancreatic spasmolytic polypeptide. *J. Biol. Chem.* 263(16): 7686–90

70. Hoffmann W, Hauser F. 1993. The P-domain or trefoil motif: a role in renewal and pathology of mucous epithelia? *Trends Biochem. Sci.* 18:239–43

71. Hollingsworth MA, Closken C, Harris A, McDonald CD, Pahwa GS, Maher JI. 1994. A nuclear factor that binds purine-rich, single–stranded oligonucleotides derived from S1-sensitive elements upstream of the *CFTR* gene and the *MUC1* gene. *Nucleic Acids Res.* 22(7):1138–46

72. Huan LJ, Xu G, Forstner G, Forstner J. 1992. A serine, threonine and proline-rich region near the carboxyl-terminus of a rat intestinal mucin peptide. *Biochim. Biophys. Acta* 1132:79–82

73. Hull S, Bright A, Carraway K, Abe M, Hayes D, Kufe D. 1989. Oligosaccharide differences in the DF3 sialomucin antigen from normal human milk and the BT20 human breast carcinoma cell line. *Cancer Commun.* 1:261–67

74. Ioannides CG, Fisk B, Jerome KR, Irimura T, Wharton JT, Finn OJ. 1993. Cytotoxic T cells from ovarian malignant tumors can recognize polymorphic epithelial mucin core peptides. *J. Immunol.* 151:3693–703

75. Irimura T, McIsaac AM, Carlson DA, Yagita M, Grimm EA, et al. 1990. Soluble factor in normal tissues that stimulates high-molecular weight sialoglycoprotein production by human colon carcinoma cells. *Cancer Res.* 50:3331–38

76. Jany B, Gallup M, Tsuda T, Basbaum C. 1991. Mucin gene expression in rat airways following infection and irritation. *Biochem. Biophys. Res. Commun.* 181(1):1–8

77. Jany BH, Gallup MW, Yan P-S, Gum JR, Kim YS, Basbaum CB. 1991. Hu-

man bronchus and intestine express the same mucin gene. *J. Clin. Invest.* 87:77–82

78. Jentoft N. 1990. Why are proteins O-glycosylated? *Trends Biochem. Sci.* 15:291–94

79. Jerome KR, Domenech N, Finn OJ. 1993. Tumor-specific cytotoxic T cell clones from patients with breast and pancreatic adenocarcinoma recognize EBV-immortalized B cells transfected with polymorphic epithelial mucin complementary DNA. *J. Immunol.* 151(3):1654–62

80. Johansson M, Chowdhary B, Gu F, Ellegren H, Gustavsson I, Andersson L. 1993. Genetic analysis of the gene for porcine submaxillary gland mucin: physical assignment of the MUC and interferon gamma genes to chromosome 5. *J. Hered.* 84:259–62

81. Karlsson S, Swallow DM, Griffiths B, Corney G, Kopkinson DA, et al. 1983. A genetic polymorphism of a human urinary mucin. *Ann. Hum. Genet.* 47:263–69

82. Keydar I, Chou CS, Hareuveni M, Tsarfaty I, Sahar E, et al. 1989. Production and characterization of monoclonal antibodies identifying breast tumor–associated antigens. *Proc. Natl. Acad. Sci. USA* 86:1362–66

83. Khatri IA, Forstner GG, Forstner JF. 1993. Suggestive evidence for two different mucin genes in rat intestine. *Biochem. J.* 294:391–99

84. Khorrami A, Lan MS, Metzgar RS, Kaufman B. 1989. Characteristics of a sulphated human pancreatic adenocarcinoma mucin glycoprotein. *Glycoconj. J.* 6:428

85. Kingsmore SF, Moseley WS, Watson ML, Sabina RL, Holmes EW, Seldin MF. 1990. Long-range restriction site mapping of a syntenic segment conserved between human chromosome 1 and mouse chromosome 3. *Genomics* 7:75–83

86. Kovarik A, Peat N, Wilson D, Gendler SJ, Taylor-Papadimitriou J. 1993. Analysis of the tissue-specific promoter of the *MUC1* gene. *J. Biol. Chem.* 268:9917–26

87. Kufe D, Inghirami G, Abe M, Hayes D, Justi-Wheeler H, Schlom J. 1984. Differential activity of a novel monoclonal antibody (DF3) with human malignant versus benign breast tumours. *Hybridoma* 3:223–32

88. Lalani E-N, Berdichevsky F, Boshell M, Shearer M, Wilson D, et al. 1991. Expression of the gene coding for a human mucin in mouse mammary tumor cells can affect their tumorigenicity. *J. Biol. Chem.* 266:15420–26

89. Lan MS, Bast RC Jr, Colnaghi MI, Knapp RC, Colcher D, et al. 1987. Co-expression of human cancer–associated epitopes on mucin molecules. *Int. J. Cancer* 39:68–72

90. Lan MS, Batra SK, Qi W-N, Metzgar RS, Hollingsworth MA. 1990. Cloning and sequencing of a human pancreatic tumor mucin cDNA. *J. Biol. Chem.* 265:15294–99

91. Lancaster CA, Peat NG, Duhig T, Wilson D, Taylor-Papaditriou J, Gendler SJ. 1990. Structure and expression of the human polymorphic epithelial mucin gene: an expressed VNTR unit. *Biochem. Biophys. Res. Commun.* 173:1019–29

92. Ligtenberg MJ, Buijs F, Vos HL, Hilkens J. 1992. Suppression of cellular aggregation by high levels of episialin. *Cancer Res.* 52:2318–24

93. Ligtenberg MJL, Gennissen AMC, Vos HL, Hilkens J. 1991. A single nucleotide polymorphism in an exon dictates allele dependent differential splicing of episialin mRNA. *Nucleic Acids Res.* 19:297–301

94. Ligtenberg MJL, Kruijshaar L, Buijs F, van Meijer M, Litvinov SV, Hilkens J. 1992. Cell-associated episialin is a complex containing two proteins derived from a common precursor. *J. Biol. Chem.* 267:6171–77

95. Ligtenberg MJL, Vos HL, Gennissen AMC, Hilkens J. 1990. Episialin, a carcinoma-associated mucin, is generated by a polymorphic gene encoding splice variants with alternative amino termini. *J. Biol. Chem.* 265:5573–78

96. Linsley PS, Kallestad JC, Horn D. 1988. Biosynthesis of high molecular weight breast carcinoma associated mucin glycoproteins. *J. Biol. Chem.* 263(17):8390–97

97. Litvinov SV, Hilkens J. 1993. The epithelial sialomucin, episialin, is sialylated during recycling. *J. Biol. Chem.* 268(28):21364–71

98. Majuri ML, Mattila P, Renkonen R. 1992. Recombinant E-selectin-protein mediates tumor cell adhesion via sialyl-Le(a) and sialyl-Le(x). *Biochem. Biophys. Res. Commun.* 182(3):1376–82

99. McKenzie IFC, Xing P-X. 1990. Mucins in breast cancer: recent immunological advances. *Cancer Cells* 2(3):75–78

100. Meerzaman D, Charles P, Daskal E, Polymeropoulos MH, Martin BM, Rose MC. 1994. Cloning and analysis of cDNA encoding a major airway glyco-

protein, human tracheobronchial mucin (MUC5). *J. Biol. Chem.* 269:12932–39

101. Metzgar RS, Gaillard MT, Levine SJ, Tuck FL, Bossen EH, Borowitz MJ. 1982. Antigens of human pancreatic adenocarcinoma cells defined by murine monoclonal antibodies. *Cancer Res.* 42: 601–8

102. Metzgar RS, Rodriguez N, Finn OJ, Lan MS, Daasch VN, et al. 1984. Detection of a pancreatic cancer–associated antigen (DU-PAN-2 antigen) in serum and ascites of patients with adenocarcinoma. *Proc. Natl. Acad. Sci. USA* 81:5242–46

103. Middleton-Price H, Gendler S, Malcolm S. 1988. Close linkage of PUM and SPTA within chromosome band 1q21. *Ann. Hum. Genet.* 52:273–78

104. Moseley WS, Seldin MF. 1989. Definition of mouse chromosome 1 and 3 gene linkage groups that are conserved on human chromosome 1: evidence that a conserved linkage group spans the centromere of human chromosome 1. *Genomics* 5(4):899–905

105. Moseley WS, Watson ML, Kingsmore SF, Seldin MF. 1989. CD1 defines conserved linkage group border between human chromosomes 1 and mouse chromosomes 1 and 3. *Immunogenetics* 30 (5):378–82

106. Nakamori S, Ota DM, Cleary KR, Shirotani K, Irimura T. 1994. MUC1 mucin expression as a marker of progression and metastasis of human colorectal carcinoma. *Gastroenterology* 106:353–61

107. Neutra MR, Forstner JF. 1987. Gastrointestinal mucus: synthesis, secretion, and function. In *Proceedings of the Gastrointestinal Tract,* ed. LR Johnson, pp. 975–1009. New York: Raven

108. Ohmori H, Dohrman AF, Gallup M, Tsuda T, Kai H, et al. 1994. Molecular cloning of amino terminal region of a rat *MUC2* mucin gene homologue: evidence for expression in both intestine and airway. *J. Biol. Chem.* 269:17833–40

109. Ormerod MG, Monaghan P, Easty D, Easty GC. 1981. Asymmetrical distribution of epithelial membrane antigen on the plasma membranes of human breast cell lines in culture. *Diag. Histopath.* 4:89–93

110. Parry G, Beck JC, Moss L, Bartley J, Ojakian GK. 1990. Determination of apical membrane polarity in mammary epithelial cell cultures: the role of cell-cell, cell-substratum, and membrane-cytoskeleton interactions. *Exp. Cell Res.* 188:302–11

111. Parry G, Li J, Stubbs J, Bissell MJ, Schmidhauser C, et al. 1992. Studies of Muc-1 mucin expression and polarity in the mouse mammary gland demonstrate developmental regulation of Muc-1 glycosylation and establish the hormonal basis for mRNA expression. *J. Cell Sci.* 101:191–99

112. Peat N, Gendler SJ, Lalani E-N, Duhig T, Taylor-Papadimitriou J. 1992. Tissue-specific expression of a human polymorphic epithelial mucin (MUC1) in transgenic mice. *Cancer Res.* 52:1954–60

113. Pemberton L, Taylor-Papadimitriou J, Gendler SJ. 1992. Antibodies to the cytoplasmic domain of the MUC1 mucin show conservation throughout mammals. *Biochem. Biophys. Res. Commun.* 185:167–75

114. Perini J-M, Vandamme-Cubadda N, Aubert J-P, Porchet N, Mazzuca M, et al. 1991. Multiple apomucin translation products from human respiratory mucosa mRNA. *Eur. J. Biochem.* 196:321–28

115. Porchet N, Van Cong N, Dufosse J, Audie JP, Guyonnet-Duperat V, et al. 1991. Molecular cloning and chromosomal localization of a novel human tracheo-bronchial mucin cDNA containing tandemly repeated sequences of 48 base pairs. *Biochem. Biophys. Res. Commun.* 175:414–22

116. Prakobphol A, Levine MJ, Tabak LA, Reddy MS. 1982. Purification of a low-molecular weight, mucin-type glycoprotein from human submandibular- sublingual saliva. *Carbohydr. Res.* 108(1): 111–22

117. Probst JC, Gertzen EM, Hoffmann W. 1990. An integumentary mucin (FIM-B.1) from *Xenopus laevis* homologous with von Willebrand factor. *Biochemistry* 29:6240–44

118. Probst JC, Hauser F, Joba W, Hoffmann W. 1992. The polymorphic integumentary mucin B.1 from *Xenopus laevis* contains the short consensus repeat. *J. Biol. Chem.* 267(9):6310–16

119. Reddy MS, Bobek LA, Haraszthy GG, Biesbrock AR, Levine MJ. 1992. Structural features of the low-molecular mass human salivary mucin. *Biochem. J.* 287: 639–43

120. Rice GE, Bevilacqua MP. 1989. An inducible endothelial cell surface glycoprotein mediates melanoma adhesion. *Science* 246:1303–6

121. Rose MC. 1992. Mucins: structure, function, and role in pulmonary diseases. *Am. Physiol. Soc.* 263:L413–29

122. Rose MC, Kaufman B, Martin BM. 1989. Proteolytic fragmentation and

peptide mapping of human carboxyamidomethylated tracheobronchial mucin. *J. Biol. Chem.* 264:8193–99

123. Roussel P, Lamblin G, Lhermitte M, Houdret N, Lafitte J-J, et al. 1988. The complexity of mucins. *Biochimie* 70:1471–82

124. Rye PD, Bell SC, Walker RA. 1993. Immunohistochemical expression of tumour-associated glycoprotein and polymorphic epithelial mucin in the human endometrium during the menstrual cycle. *J. Reprod. Fertil.* 97:551–56

125. Shekels LL, Lyftogt CT, Kieliszewski M, Ho SB. 1994. Murine gastric mucin: purification characterization and cloning. *Gastroenterology* 106:A178

126. Sheng Z, Hull SR, Carraway KL. 1990. Biosynthesis of the cell surface sialomucin complex of ascites 13762 rat mammary adenocarcinoma cells from a high M_r precursor. *J. Biol. Chem.* 265:8505–10

127. Sheng Z, Wu K, Carraway KL, Fregien N. 1992. Molecular cloning of the transmembrane component of the 13762 mammary adenocarcinoma sialomucin complex. *J. Biol. Chem.* 267(23):16341–46

128. Sherblom AP, Moody CE. 1986. Cell surface sialomucin and resistance to natural cell-mediated cytotoxicity of rat mammary tumor ascites cells. *Cancer Res.* 9:4543–46

129. Shimizu M, Yamauchi K. 1982. Isolation and characterization of mucin-like glycoproteins in human milk fat globule membranes. *J. Biochem.* 91:515–24

130. Shimizu Y, Shaw S. 1993. Mucins in the mainstream. *Nature* 366:630–31

131. Shirotani K, Taylor-Papadimitriou J, Gendler SJ. 1994. Transcriptional regulation of *MUC1* gene in colon carcinoma cells by a soluble factor: identification of a regulatory element. *J. Biol. Chem.* 269:15030–35

132. Siddiqui J, Abe M, Hayes D, Shani E, Yunis E, Kufe D. 1988. Isolation and sequencing of a cDNA coding for the human DF3 breast carcinoma-associated antigen. *Proc. Natl. Acad. Sci. USA* 85:2320–23

133. Spicer AP. 1993. *Functional and evolutionary analysis of the mouse Muc-1 gene.* PhD thesis. Univ. London, England. 332 pp.

134. Spicer AP, Parry G, Patton S, Gendler SJ. 1991. Molecular cloning and analysis of the mouse homologue of the tumor-associated mucin, MUC1, reveals conservation of potential O-glycosylation sites, transmembrane, and cytoplasmic domains and a loss of minisatellite-like

polymorphism. *J. Biol. Chem.* 266:15099–109

135. Steck PA, Nicolson GL. 1983. Cell surface glycoprotein of 13762NF mammary adenocarcinoma clones of differing metastasis potentials. *Exp. Cell. Res.* 147:255–67

136. Steck PA, North SM, Nicolson GL. 1987. Purification and partial characterization of a tumor-metastasis-associated high M_r glycoprotein from rat 13762NF mammary adenocarcinoma cells. *Biochem. J.* 242:779–87

137. Stern L, Palatsides M, De KT, Ford M. 1992. Expression of the tumor-associated mucin MUC1 in an ovarian tumor cell line. *Int. J. Cancer* 50(5):783–90

138. Strous GJ, Dekker J. 1992. Mucin-type glycoproteins. *Crit. Rev. Biochem. Mol. Biol.* 27:57–92

139. Swallow DM, Gendler S, Griffiths B, Taylor-Papadimitriou J, Bramwell ME. 1987. The human tumour-associated epithelial mucins are coded by an expressed hypervariable gene locus *PUM*. *Nature* 328:82–84

140. Swallow DM, Gendler SJ, Griffiths B, Kearney A, Povey S, et al. 1987. The hypervariable gene locus *PUM*, which codes for tumour-associated epithelial mucins is located on chromosome 1, within the region 1q21–24. *Ann. Hum. Genet.* 51:289–95

141. Taylor-Papadimitriou J, Peterson JA, Arklie J, Burchell J, Ceriani RL, Bodmer WF. 1981. Monoclonal antibodies to epithelium-specific components of the human milk fat globule membrane: production and reaction with cells in culture. *Int. J. Cancer* 28:17–21

142. Taylor-Papadimitriou J, Stewart L, Burchell J, Beverley P. 1993. The polymorphic epithelial mucin as a target for immunotherapy. *Ann. NY Acad. Sci.* 690:69–79

143. Timpte CS, Eckhardt AE, Abernethy JL, Hill RL. 1988. Porcine submaxillary gland apomucin contains tandemly repeated, identical sequences of 81 residues. *J. Biol. Chem.* 263:7686–90

144. Toribara NW, Gum JR, Culhane PJ, Lagace RE, Hicks JW, et al. 1991. *MUC-2* human small intestinal mucin gene structure: repeated arrays and polymorphism. *J. Clin. Invest.* 88:1005–13

145. Toribara NW, Roberton AM, Ho SB, Kuo W-L, Gum E, et al. 1993. Human gastric mucin: identification of a unique species by expression cloning. *J. Biol. Chem.* 268:5879–85

146. Tsuda T, Gallup M, Jany B, Gum J, Kim Y, Basbaum C. 1993. Characterization of a rat airway cDNA encoding

a mucin–like protein. *Biochem. Biophys. Res. Commun.* 195:363–73

147. Van Cong N, Aubert JP, Gross MS, Porchet N, Degand P, Frezal J. 1990. Assignment of human tracheobronchial mucin gene(s) to 11p15 and a tracheobronchial mucin–related sequence to chromosome 13. *Hum. Genet.* 86:167–72

148. van de Wiel-van Kemenade E, Ligtenberg MJL, de Boer AJ, Buijs F, Vos HL, et al. 1993. Episialin (MUC1) inhibits cytotoxic lymphocyte-target cell interaction. *J. Immunol.* 151(2):767–76

149. Verma M, Davidson EA. 1993. Molecular cloning and sequencing of a canine tracheobronchial mucin cDNA containing a cysteine-rich domain. *Proc. Natl. Acad. Sci. USA* 90:7144–48

150. Voorberg J, Fontijn R, Calafat J, Janssen H, van Mourik JA, Pannekoek H. 1991. Assembly and routing of von Willebrand factor variants: the requirements for disulfide-linked dimerization reside within the carboxy-terminal 151 amino acids. *J. Cell Biol.* 113:195–205

151. Vos HL, Devarayalu S, de Vries Y, Bornstein P. 1992. Thrombospondin 3 (Thbs3), a new member of the thrombospondin gene family. *J. Biol. Chem.* 267:12192–96

152. Vos HL, Devries Y, Hilkens J. 1991. The mouse episialin (*Muc-1*) gene and its promoter-rapid evolution of the repetitive domain in the protein. *Biochem. Biophys. Res. Commun.* 181:121–30

153. Voynow J, Rose MC. 1994. Quantitation of mucin mRNA in respiratory and intestinal epithelial cells. *Am. J. Respir. Cell Mol. Biol.* In press

154. Watson CJ, Gordon KE, Robertson M, Clark AJ. 1991. Interaction of DNA-binding proteins with a milk protein gene promoter in vitro: identification of a mammary gland–specific factor. *Nucleic Acids Res.* 19(23):6603–10

155. Wesley A, Mantle M, Man D, Qureshi R, Forstner G, Forstner J. 1985. Neutral and acidic species of human intestinal mucin. *J. Biol. Chem.* 260(13):7955–59

156. Wesseling J, Ligtenberg M, Vos H, van der Valk S, Buijs F, Hilkens J. 1992. The mucin-like glycoprotein episilian modulates cell-cell and cell-matrix adhesion. See Ref. 66, p. 70

157. Williams CJ, Wreschner DH, Tanaka A,

Tsarfaty I, Keydar I, Dion AS. 1990. Multiple protein forms of the human breast tumor–associated epithelial membrane antigen (EMA) are generated by alternative splicing and induced by hormonal stimulation. *Biochem. Biophys. Res. Commun.* 170:1331–38

158. Wreschner DH, Hareuveni M, Tsarfaty I, Smorodinsky N, Horev J, et al. 1990. Human epithelial tumor antigen cDNA sequences: differential splicing may generate multiple protein forms. *Eur. J. Biochem.* 189:463–73

159. Wu K, Fregien N, Carraway KL. 1994. Molecular cloning and sequencing of the mucin subunit of a heterodimeric, bifunctional cell surface glycoprotein complex of ascites rat mammary adenocarcinoma cells. *J. Biol. Chem.* 269: 11950–55

160. Xing PX, Prenzoska J, Layton GT, Devine PL, McKenzie IF. 1992. Second-generation monoclonal antibodies to intestinal MUC2 peptide reactive with colon cancer. *J. Natl. Cancer Inst.* 84(9): 699–703

161. Xu G, Huan L, Khatri I, Sajjan US, McCool D, et al. 1992. Human intestinal mucin-like protein (MLP) is homologous with rat MLP in the C-terminal region, and is encoded by a gene on chromosome 11p15.5. *Biochem. Biophys. Res. Commun.* 183(2):821–28

162. Xu G, Huan L-J, Khatri IA, Wang D, Bennick A, et al. 1992. cDNA for the carboxyl-terminal region of a rat intestinal mucin–like peptide. *J. Biol. Chem.* 267:5401–7

163. Xu G, Wang D, Huan LJ, Cutz C, Forstner GG, Forstner JF. 1992. Tissue-specific expression of a rat intestinal mucin–like peptide. *Biochem. J.* 286: 335–38

164. Zaretsky JZ, Weiss M, Tsarfaty I, Hareuveni M, Wreschner DH, Keydar I. 1990. Expression of genes coding for pS2, c-erbB2, estrogen receptor and the H23 breast tumor–associated antigen. A comparative analysis in breast cancer. *FEBS Lett.* 265:46–50

165. Zotter S, Hageman PC, Lossnitzer A, Mooi WJ, Hilgers J. 1988. Tissue and tumor distribution of human polymorphic epithelial mucin. *Cancer Rev.* 11–12:55–101

Annu. Rev. Physiol. 1995. 57:635–57

MUCIN BIOPHYSICS

Rama Bansil[1], *Eugene Stanley*[1], *and J. Thomas LaMont*[2]

[1]Center for Polymer Studies and Department of Physics, Boston University, Boston, Massachusetts 02215; [2]Section of Gastroenterology, Evans Department of Clinical Research, Boston University School of Medicine, Boston, Massachusetts 02118

KEY WORDS: gelation, viscoelasticity, light scattering, viscous fingering, diffusion in mucus

INTRODUCTION

Mucus, the slimy, viscous secretion that covers epithelial surfaces throughout the body, contains water, salts, immunoglobulins, secreted proteins, and mucin. Mucus secretions are thought to have important protective and lubricative properties, primarily owing to their ability to form a gel layer adherent to the underlying epithelium. Specialized epithelial cells called mucus or goblet cells secrete mucus, which adheres to the epithelial surface and forms a protective diffusion barrier between the lumen and the cell surface. The most abundant macromolecule in mucus is mucin, the general term for members of a closely related family of glycoproteins found in mucus secretions. Mucins can be defined structurally as large (M_r 10^6–10^7), viscous glycoproteins composed of approximately 75% carbohydrate and 25% amino acids linked via O-glycosidic bonds between N-acetylgalactosamine and serine or threonine residues. The purpose of our review is to describe the physical-chemical properties of epithelial mucins, particularly those that relate to aggregation or polymerization, sol-gel transition, and viscosity, because these properties appear to underlie physiological function. Where possible, we assign specific biophysical functions (e.g. molecular shape, aggregation properties, behavior at low pH) to known structural domains on the mucus molecule.

Molecular Architecture of Epithelial Mucins

The basic architecture of a typical epithelial mucin is shown in Figure 1 (84); a mucin monomer represents the entire secreted peptide encoded by mucin mRNA and synthesized by a mucus cell. Mucins are elongated rod-shaped molecules

635

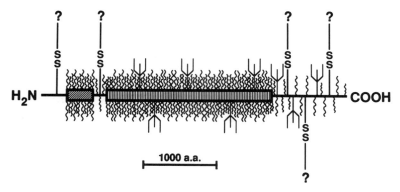

Figure 1 Schematic of intestinal mucin. The amino terminus is on the left, carboxyl on right. A cysteine-rich region occupies the last of the carboxyl end of the molecule. The glycosylated portion is boxed and contains mostly *O*-linked oligosaccharides (*wavy vertical lines*), as well as a few *N*-linked oligosaccharides (*tridents*). Whether the SS bridges are intra- or intermolecular is still open to question. (from *J. Clin. Invest.* 1991. 88:1012. Copyright permission Am. Soc. Clin. Invest.).

whose central core is a linear polypeptide (100 to 250 kDa) called apomucin (81). The unglycosylated peptide or apomucin does not exist as such in mucus or goblet cells because native mucins isolated from body secretions or tissues are always heavily glycosylated. Oligosaccharide side chains are attached by *O*-glycosidic linkage to serine and threonine residues that account for up to one-third of the amino acids in the glycosylated region. Mucin oligosaccharides of 2 to 12 monosaccharide residues may be linear or branched and project ra- dially from the peptide core. Glycosylated regions of apomucin are generally encoded by tandem repeats of DNA that encode from 6 to 169 amino acids (37). Tandem repeats are linked together in arrays up to 100 repeating units to give long glycosylated regions with total M_r of 10^6 kDa.

The nonglycosylated regions of apomucin do not contain tandem repeats, have fewer serines and threonines, and are enriched in cysteine. These regions are often at the amino or carboxyl terminals of apomucin (Figure 1) and resemble typical globular proteins as regards amino acid composition and folding. The large size of mucin genes (up to 30 kb) and the presence of glycosylated tandem repeats have slowed progress in cloning mucin DNA. At present only partially cloned sequences are available. However, full-length sequences of *MUC2* and possibly other mucin genes, including up-stream regulatory sequences, will be published within a year or two.

Function of Mucin Domains

What functions are subserved by the glycosylated and nonglycosylated domains of mucin? Early biochemical analysis (50) suggested that a separate peptide (link peptide) cross-linked monomers in rat intestinal mucin, but recent DNA sequence data indicate that the link peptide is an integral part of apomucin, not a separate protein (91). The importance of the cysteine-rich regions in polymerization has been deduced by loss of viscous- and gel-forming properties after treatment of mucins with proteolytic enzymes that attack only the cysteine-rich regions, or by exposure to reducing agents such as dithiothreitol that disrupt disulfide bonds (81). The protease-sensitive portion of rat intestinal mucin contains a repetitive element of approximately 350 amino acids with considerable sequence homology to von Willebrand factor, a serum protein important in blood coagulation (92). These cysteine-rich motifs in von Willebrand factor are involved in oligomerization, and the presence of similar cysteine-rich motifs in human intestinal mucin (38) and human tracheobroncheal mucin (52) suggests a similar function in mucin aggregation. However, as discussed below, the disulfide bonds in mucin may be primarily intramolecular, and their function may be to provide a suitable conformation that allows cross-linking of monomers by noncovalent bonds.

The function of the glycosylated tandem repeats has been studied extensively in ovine submaxillary mucin, a salivary glycoprotein with simple disaccharides of sialic acid GalNAc. Light scattering and circular dichroism studies of native and glycosidase-treated salivary mucin revealed that GalNAc residues attached to threonine on the peptide core are essential in maintaining a highly extended random coil configuration (33, 69). Removal of all disaccharides led to collapse or denaturation of the molecule. Sialic acid residues played only a minor role in maintaining the extended configuration of the molecule. Since deglycosylated mucin (or apomucin) is insoluble in water, the oligosaccharides allow hydration of the molecule and contribute to gel formation by binding water.

The function of the more complex oligosaccharides on typical epithelial mucins has not been carefully studied. General properties of mucin-bound carbohydrates include protease resistance, large water–holding capacity and high charge density from sialic acid and sulfate residues, which are charged at neutral pH. The remarkable complexity of mucin oligosaccharides has hindered detailed assessment of their properties. For example, the major human colonic mucin species contains 21 separate oligosaccharide groups ranging in size from 2 to 12 sugar residues (60, 61); many of these oligosaccharides represent minor variations of a basic biantennary structure.

Models of Mucin Polymerization and Gelation

The interactions of mucin are responsible for structural organization at several length scales, ranging from intramolecular interactions at the level of isolated apomucin molecules, to intermolecular interactions that give rise to supramolecular aggregates and eventually the visco-elastic characteristics of the mucus gel. Mucin monomers (Figure 1) form large aggregates in solution that take the form of extended rods or threads. For example, electron microscopy of purified pig gastric mucin reveals linear structures 5 nm in diameter and ranging in length from 100 to 5000 nm (68). Similar size ranges were observed for human cervical and tracheobronchial mucins (68), which indicates that mucins from different organs and species have a similar general structure. Considerable flexibility of mucin threads was suggested by the appearance of loops, kinks, and turns. Although the preparation of mucin for electron microscopy involved denaturing solvents, no globular or folded structures have been described, although indirect evidence suggests that the cysteine-rich, nonglycosylated portions of mucin are folded as globular polypeptides. Human cervical mucin ($M_r \sim 10^7$) can be dissociated in reducing agents to form monomers or subunits ($M_r \sim 2 \times 10^6$). Exhaustive trypsin digestion of subunits produces T domains ($M_r \sim 4 \times 10^5$), large glycopeptides that consist mostly of tandem repeats with little or no naked peptide. Monomers of cervical mucin have an average length of about 390–460 nm, and T domains of 90–100 nm by electron microscopy (67), which suggests that monomers are assembled from subunits joined end-to-end by thiol-dependent associations.

Mucin molecules in solution can cross-link to form aggregates via H-bonds, and electrostatic and hydrophobic interactions, as well as via weak Van der Waals forces. Increasing the number of cross-links leads to the formation of a gel, wherein a sufficient number of the polymers are connected to form a network that extends over the sample. At the sol-gel transition, the solution of linear or branched polymeric molecules exhibits a transition from a fluid with a finite viscosity and zero elasticity to a gel with infinite viscosity and finite elasticity (21, 28). The concentration at which the sol-gel transition occurs depends on the molecular weight of the polymer, the fraction of cross-linkable groups per polymer, and external variables such as temperature, pH, or ionic strength, which affect cross-link formation. If the cross-links are covalent, aggregation and gelation are irreversible, whereas if the cross-links are noncovalent, they will break and reform (i.e. exist in chemical equilibrium), in which case aggregation/gelation is reversible. Which interactions are involved in the aggregation/gelation of mucin and whether the gel is reversible or irreversible are still open questions.

Silberberg has proposed one hypothesis for polymerization with covalent cross-link formation that involves lectin-like binding between terminal cysteine-rich regions of one monomer with a specific sugar sequence on an adjacent monomer (72). In this model, intramolecular disulfide bonds fold the apomucin in such a way that it possesses specific lectin activity; reducing agents allow this region to unfold with loss of lectin activity and the ability to polymerize. The carbohydrate recognition site for the lectin must not occur too frequently in the tandem repeat section of mucin because too many lectin-binding sites would allow condensation of molecules into highly aggregated clumps. The lectin polymer model is consistent with certain features of mucin solution behavior and requires that only one end of the mucin subunit contains the cysteine-rich globular sequence required for lectin activity. However, the primary structure of human intestinal mucin, as recently deduced from cDNAs (38), suggests that both amino and carboxyl terminals of mucin contain cysteine residues that participate in forming intramolecular disulfide bridges. These bifunctional mucin subunits could theoretically form disulfide bonds at either the amino or carboxyl terminus, thereby leading to formation of extended chains or threads. However, we favor the hypothesis that noncovalent bonds are involved in gelation and that intramolecular disulfide bridges provide the necessary configuration for the formation of extended head-to-tail linear polymers (13).

There are several mechanisms by which noncovalent bonds lead to reversible gelation, also called physical gelation (10). These include (a) gelation by the formation of secondary bonds in entangled polymer solutions, (b) gelation by the formation of locally ordered junction zones as in polysaccharide gels (62), and (c) gelation caused by differing solvent affinities of the different blocks of a multiblock copolymer (34, 35).

The idea that gelation of mucin can arise from its entanglement properties has been discussed by several authors (13, 86). High molecular weight polymer solutions are considered dilute if the individual chains do not overlap and semi-dilute beyond a concentration called the overlap concentration c^*, at which the chains just begin to overlap (21). At concentrations $c > c^*$ the solution also exhibits viscoelastic behavior due to the presence of transient entanglements. However, these polymers will eventually flow when subjected to external forces. If the polymer can form noncovalent interactions, then semi-dilute and concentrated solutions will also display rheological behavior characteristic of aggregates and eventually of reversible gelation (10). Because mucin has a very high molecular weight, its overlap concentration is very low, and mucin solutions at concentrations 2–4 mg/ml (approx 1 μm) are already in the semi-dilute regime where polymer chains are overlapped. At the much higher concentrations typically found in vivo (>20 mg/ml) (1), the extensively entangled monomers will behave like a transient gel. Such close contact between neighboring molecules greatly increases the formation of noncovalent interactions that stabilize the entangled network and gives it the rheological characteristics of a weak, reversible gel.

The cross-linking of many biological gels is due to the formation of locally ordered regions involving the cooperative interactions of several weak bonds in a localized region, called the junction zone (10, 62). Although each individual bond may have an energy comparable to kT, the energy due to thermal fluctuations and cooperative interactions of multiple bonds in these junction zones can provide the energy to stabilize the gel network. For example, gelatin and polysaccharide gels (62) are stabilized by helical junction zones, whereas physical gels of synthetic, atactic polystyrene involve the formation of microcrystalline regions (36). Whether mucin gelation involves the formation of junction zones remains a question because neither thermodynamic studies of mucin gelation nor X-ray or neutron diffraction studies of local order have been reported.

The possibility that mucin gels involve solvent-mediated interactions arises because the glycosylated regions are hydrophilic, whereas nonglycosylated sections are rich in hydrophobic amino acids (76). The differing affinities of these two domains for water can lead to physical gelation by a mechanism similar to that seen in synthetic multiblock copolymers (34); these are linear polymers made of two different polymeric blocks A and B linked covalently to form a tri-block polymer (ABA) or a multiblock polymer $(AB)_n$ with $n > 2$. In a solvent that is poor for the A block but good for the B block, the A blocks of neighboring polymers tend to associate by excluding the solvent. The B blocks act as bridges to link the domains formed by A blocks, which leads eventually to the formation of a physical gel. Such gels have been seen in several synthetic multiblock copolymers (34, 35). If this mechanism plays a role in mucin gelation, then gel formation would require intact nonglycosylated regions; this is consistent with the observation that mucin does not gel when the nonglycosylated regions are disrupted either by disulfide bond reduction or by peptide bond–breaking enzymes (1, 9, 13).

Techniques to Study Biophysical Properties of Mucin

The structure and dynamics of mucin in solutions and gels have been investigated by light scattering (3, 11, 12, 15, 39 40, 66, 69, 70, 85), sedimentation equilibrium (40), and gel chromatography (1, 13, 40) to determine the molecular weight and size; by electron microscopy to study the shape, size, and morphology (55, 67, 68); and by viscosity measurements and dynamical mechanical measurements (rheological techniques) to determine the viscoelastic properties of mucin and mucus gels (1, 64, 73, 74). Several studies of the secondary and tertiary structure by NMR have also been reported (33, 79, 80). At present there are no reports of infrared, Raman spectroscopy, X-ray, and neutron scattering studies of mucin.

In comparing these measurements, it is important to recognize that the results depend strongly on how the material was purified. Most biophysical studies of mucin involve preparations obtained in the void volume of large-pore, gel-filtration columns, further purified by density gradient centrifugation in CsCl solutions to remove nonmucin proteins, lipids, and DNA. This yields a polydisperse sample (40) with broad distribution of high molecular weight glycoproteins (M_r of 10^6 to 10^7). A few studies have been performed on mucins that were further fractionated into narrower M_r fractions (66, 69).

Because mucin is such a complex polymer with numerous functional groups capable of interacting via several noncovalent mechanisms, detailed quantitative interpretations of these data are extremely difficult. Models based on simpler polymers should serve only as a guide in the interpretation of these data. The best strategy to unravel the structure of mucin would be to use many different biophysical techniques on mucins subjected to a variety of biochemical treatments. In the following sections we briefly review the advantages and shortcomings of applying these techniques to mucin.

Static Light Scattering Studies of Mucin

Light scattering techniques allow estimation of M_r, size, and shape of mucin macromolecules in solution. The basic quantity measured in a static light scattering experiment is the excess intensity (I) of light scattered by a solution relative to the pure solvent at different scattering angles (θ) and concentrations (c) (16, 59). The data are plotted on the so-called Zimm plot of I^{-1} vs $q^2 + jc$, where $q = (4\pi n \sin \theta/2)/\lambda$ is the scattering vector, n the refractive index of the solvent, λ the wavelength of light, and j any conveniently chosen integer to make the magnitudes of q^2 and c comparable. By extrapolating to zero angle and zero concentration, one can determine the weight-average molecular weight of the polymer, M_r, the particle scattering function, $P(\theta)$, which depends on the shape and size of the scattering particle, and the second virial coefficient reflecting polymer-solvent interactions. Assuming a random coil conformation for mucin, it is possible to determine its radius of gyration R_g from the particle-scattering function (59).

Light scattering experiments require the preparation of dust-free solutions whose concentrations and change in refractive index of the solvent per unit concentration of the added polymer are accurately known. For mucin, values of the refractive index increment have been reported to range from 0.101 ml/g for cervical mucin (12), 0.125 ml/g for ovine submaxillary mucin (69), to 0.14 ml/g for respiratory mucin (15). Because the calculation of M_r depends on $(dn/dc)^2$, a 10% error in this quantity produces a 20% error in M_r; thus it is best to measure dn/dc with a differential refractometer for the sample being studied. Polydispersity in the mucin preparation will strongly affect the determination of molecular weight because light scattering measures the average $\Sigma N_i m_i^2 / \Sigma N_i m_i$ where N_i and m_i denote the number and mass of the ith species in the mixture, e.g. a 1:9 mixture of 10^7 and 2×10^6 K molecules will lead to an effective M_r of 4.9×10^6. Thus measurements on very dilute solutions (<1 mg/ml) of mucin separated into narrow molecular weight fractions are the most reliable. Several light scattering studies of mucins have been reported including submaxillary mucin (69, 70, 85), respiratory mucins (15, 39, 66), human cervical mucin (12), intestinal mucin (11), and gastric mucin (3). These studies give M_r ranging from 1–15 million and R_g from 50–200 nm.

A scaling relation $R_g = R_0 M_r^\alpha$ provides an overall characterization of the shape of a polymeric molecule; $\alpha = 0.33$ for a sphere, 0.5–0.6 for a random coil, and 1 for a rigid rod (24, 72). Several authors have studied this scaling relationship for mucin (12, 15, 39, 45, 69) and find that the exponent $\alpha \approx 0.55$ is characteristic of a somewhat stiff random coil; in contrast to $\alpha \sim 0.33$ for globular proteins (45, 51). Proteins denatured in guanidine HCl show $\alpha \sim 0.5$, but the constant that is a measure of the size of the statistical segment is about seven times larger in mucin than in denatured random coil proteins (45), which indicates that on a short-length scale, mucin is much stiffer. Most likely this stiffness is related to the clustering of oligosaccharide side chains in heavily glycosylated regions. This conclusion is also supported by measurements of $1/P(\theta)$ vs q^2, which show that the data for mucin fall between the expected values for monodisperse random coils and rigid rods (12, 15). Shogren et al (69) used the worm-like chain model to determine the dimensions of mucin from light scattering measurements. They obtained relatively high values for the persistence length (12–14 nm for submaxillary mucin). Because the persistence length is the average distance that a polymer chain traverses before a significant change in direction occurs, such high values indicate a rather stiff chain. Light scattering measurements of the second virial coefficient in mucin are not accurate because A_2 is very close to zero, and even negative values indicative of poor-solvent conditions leading to polymer aggregation have been reported (66).

Dynamic Light Scattering

The diffusion constant of polymers in solutions can be determined using the technique of quasielastic light scattering, also known as dynamic light scattering (DLS), which probes the fluctuations in the scattered intensity (16, 59). These fluctuations are caused by random movement of particles in and out of the scattering volume and can be determined by measuring the intensity autocorrelation function. For a fixed scattering angle, the characteristic time of correlation function decay is proportional to the diffusion constant of particles undergoing Brownian motion in suspension. The diffusion constant is significantly reduced if the polymer aggregates because it is proportional to the inverse of the hydrodynamic radius of the particle. Currently available digital correlators allow the measurement of diffusion constants over six or more decades, covering the range from low molecular weight proteins to sub-micron size aggregates.

Verdugo and co-workers (46) observed two diffusional modes in DLS studies of cervical mucus that suggest the existence of an entangled network, the faster mode representing the fluctuations of the average entanglement spacing, and the slower mode representing the slow diffusion of mucin aggregates held together by weak noncovalent bonds. Shogren et al (70) interpreted their DLS data on salivary mucin in terms of a slow diffusive mode and a faster mode that combine the rotational diffusion with the translational diffusion. Varma et al (85) used a similar interpretation in their study of the effect of Ca on the structure of porcine submaxillary mucin. The rotational diffusion constant is best measured in a depolarized dynamic light–scattering experiment, and until such data become available with mucin, the interpretation of the fast mode as a rotation of mucin molecules remains tentative. However, the translational diffusion measurements are well established and show that in dilute solution (<2 mg/ml), mucin has a hydrodynamic size of ~65 nm for gallbladder mucin (77) and ~50–100 nm for several fractions of ovine salivary mucins (70). Steiner et al (78) showed that R_h for tracheal mucin decreased upon the addition of Ca^{2+}.

Aggregation of most mucin solutions can be observed by DLS at concentrations above 4 mg/ml. DLS studies of pig gastric mucin (9) show that diffusion constants characteristic of the native mucin ($D_t \sim 10^{-8}$ cm^2/s), and small aggregates ($D_t \sim 10^{-9}$ cm^2/s) were identified even in dilute solutions of pig gastric mucin (1 mg/ml). Very large aggregates, with D_t in the range of 10^{-10}–10^{-11} cm^2/s, were seen at pH <4 in mucin solutions of higher concentration (10 mg/ml). Such aggregation was not observed when mucin was reduced, after pronase digestion, or in high ionic strength. The diffusion constant of the units obtained after S-S bond breakage was four times faster than that of native (unreduced) mucin. The absence of large aggregates after reduction of S-S bonds implies that intramolecular S-S bonds provide the appropriate conformation that allows noncovalent interactions responsible for aggregation. The appearance of aggregates below pH 4 suggests that amino acids with pK ~4 are involved in maintaining this conformation. The nonglycosylated region of pig gastric mucin is rich in aspartate and glutamate, with pKs of 3.9 and 4.1, respectively. Perhaps the protonation of these groups decreases electrostatic repulsion of the nonglycosylated regions. By combining different biophysical techniques with specific biochemical alterations of mucin, one should be able to determine the molecular interactions responsible for aggregation.

Sedimentation Velocity and Sedimentation Equilibrium

Sedimentation velocity and equilibrium methods have proven valuable for study of biological macromolecules including mucins (40). Low-speed sedimentation equilibrium using Rayleigh interference optics is a reliable method for determination of molecular weight. Sedimentation velocity can be determined using Schlieren optics, in which macromolecular concentrations are measured in terms of refractive index increments. Sedimentation equilibrium measurements in ultra-short columns provide the second virial coefficient, a measure of solute-solvent interactions.

Sedimentation velocity and equilibrium studies show that reduction of disulfide bonds results in marked reduction in size of purified lung mucin (17). These methods have also been used to show the heterogeneity and polydispersity in purified mucin solutions. Broad distributions of the molecular weight for pig gastric mucin were reported using the sedimentation equilibrium (18) as well as sedimentation velocity method (56). Harding (40) provides a detailed review of these methods applied to mucin.

The combined results of sedimentation equilibrium and static and dynamic light scattering indicate that mucin in solution is a loosely coiled, extended molecule consisting of glycosylated and nonglycosylated regions linked linearly. Log-log plots of R_g, D_t, sedimentation coefficient s, and intrinsic viscosity vs molecular weight are all in reasonable agreement with the scaling predictions for a stiff, random coil polymer. Such a structure promotes entanglement at lower concentrations than is possible with a globular structure.

Nuclear Magnetic Resonance and Other Spectroscopic Techniques

The techniques described above are sensitive to overall molecular size and shape, but the secondary structure of the peptide backbone, the effects of glycosylation on conformation and detection of H-bonds, salt bridges, and other bonds involving specific chemical groups can only be obtained from spectroscopic techniques such as NMR, infrared and Raman spectroscopy, and circular dichroism. At present, mucin has not been examined by X-ray and neutron diffraction techniques, which are traditionally used to obtain high-resolution structural information in proteins.

^{13}C NMR studies on salivary mucins (33) and gastric mucin (80), and ^{1}H NMR on gastric mucin (79) as well as on the synthetic peptide analogue of the peptide core of the human epithelial mucin coded by the *muc*-1 gene have been reported recently (29). Earlier work (4, 9) using ^{13}C NMR spectra of pig gastric mucin showed resonances attributable to the predominant carbohydrate moieties of mucin. Sterk et al (80) used two-dimensional NMR techniques to give a more precise assignment to contributions from the peptide core as well as from the oligosaccharides. Gerken et al (33) also assigned resonances to the peptide core. In both studies, dynamics of the sugar moieties and amino acid side chains were determined from ^{13}C relaxation times (T_1 and T_2) and nuclear Overhauser effect (NOE). The dynamics in solution can be described by fast motions of glycosidic side chains and of aliphatic amino acid residues as well as by slow motion of the entire molecule (79, 80). Solid-state magic angle spinning (MAS) data (80) showed that motions of the CH_2OH groups are significantly slowed in gastric mucin gels and aggregates, which suggests that H-bonds may be responsible for the increased viscosity of mucin gels. It should be noted that the measurements (80) were performed on a very low

molecular weight fragment (M_r 18,000) obtained by reducing native mucin in mercaptoethanol; clearly results on the high molecular weight mucin are needed to understand the role of H-bonds in gastric mucin aggregation. Gerken et al (33) showed that the mobility of carbon depends on the amino acid and its glycosylation state, being less mobile in the glycosylated case. The length of the carbohydrate side chain was shown to have a lesser effect; however, this may reflect the presence of only mono- and disaccharides.

^{1}H NMR data on the low molecular weight fragment studied by Sterk (79) and a 60-amino acid synthetic polypeptide analogous to the human epithelial mucin (29) show that these fragments retain a stable ordered structure and that the protons are protected from exchange with the solvent. These data lend further support to a mucin model with a linear assembly of relatively stiff glycopeptide segments linked via flexible, naked peptide regions. Thus on a short-length scale, comparable to the size of the peptide that is coded by the tandem repeat sequences observed in most mucin genes, the mucin molecule appears ordered or stiff, whereas on a large length scale, comparable to the size of the entire molecule, it appears as a random coil polymer.

Viscoelastic Properties of Mucus Gels and Mucin Solutions

The rheological properties of a polymer solution or gel are characterized by the parameters of viscosity and elasticity (27, 71). At the sol-gel transition, the viscosity becomes infinite and the network in the gel provides resistance to elastic deformations. A force applied at any point on the surface of the gel sample will be transmitted through the network and will deform it until the applied stresses are balanced by the stress induced in the network strands. The rheological characteristics of mucus and reconstituted mucins can range from those of a highly viscous solution to a true gel, depending on the source of mucus, and experimental and physiological variables such as pH, ionic strength, and the presence of other molecules (73).

The viscosity of mucin solutions is related to its functional properties and changes with variation of mucin molecular weight as well as its state of aggregation. For example, oral mucus of caries-resistant individuals has lower viscosity than that of caries-susceptible individuals owing to variation in the mucin molecular size and the bound lipid content of mucus secretions (75). Aggregation of pig gastric mucus at low pH and low ionic strength is reflected by at least 100-fold increases of viscosity measured by the falling ball technique (9). Intrinsic viscosity measurements in gastric mucin using capillary viscometers also show a nonlinear, asymptotic rise as a function of mucin concentration at low pH, indicative of eventual gelation at some concentration (1). Because mucin is a non-Newtonian fluid, its viscosity is strongly dependent on the shear rate (5), as revealed by several authors using cone and plate and other viscosity measurements at well-defined shear rates. Apparent viscosity of frog epithelial mucus increases by one order of magnitude as the shear rate decreases from 1–0.1 s⁻¹ (74), a characteristic of a weak visco-elastic material close to the sol-gel transition.

The mechanical properties of a weak viscoelastic gel (32) are characterized by two parameters, G' and G''; the degree of solid-like behavior reflected by the storage or elastic modulus (G') and the liquid-like properties by the loss or viscous modulus (G''). A viscoelastic material is more viscous below the sol-gel transition ($G'' > G'$), whereas above the transition, it is more elastic ($G' > G''$). Thus the incipient gel can be identified as just forming at the sol-gel transition by the condition that $G' = G''$. The quantity $\tan \delta = G''/G'$ is a measure of the gel strength. The response of these two moduli to shear frequency provides a measure of how the gel responds to shear forces generated by fluid flow. This property is of obvious relevance to the ability of intestinal mucus to withstand the large shear forces found in the digestive tract and to the movement of particles over the epithelial surface. The gel acts as a mechanical coupler.

Under certain conditions, native mucus and purified mucin exhibit several of the gel-like properties mentioned above (64, 73). Native bovine cervical mucus at midcycle has rheological characteristics that are similar to an incipient gel at the threshold of the sol-gel transition with $G' = G''$ (32). Scanning electron microscopic studies of cervical mucus reveal a filamentous three-dimensional network with pores or channels (55). The size of channels and filaments appears to depend on the estrus cycle, with the average spacing being smaller in the progestational state and larger in midcycle. The mechanical spectra of native mucus gels and purified mucin at physiological concentrations (20–50 mg/ml, depending on the source of the mucin) are similar. At these concentrations, the materials are clearly gels with the storage modulus $G' > G''$, and $\tan \delta \sim 0.4$–0.2 (6, 65). In contrast, S-S reduced mucin or proteolytically digested mucin have $\tan \delta \sim 2$–4, which indicates an inability to form a gel (1, 6). Respiratory mucus and mucin also show similar mechanical properties characteristic of weak viscoelastic gels. Whereas mucus and reconstituted mucin gels are usually weak with low values of G', considerable strengthening of gels occurs, as reflected by an increase in G', when mucoadhesive polymers such as polyacrylic acid are added to mucin (53).

Swelling Behavior of Mucus Gels

Mucus is 80 to 90% hydrated, thus the swelling behavior of mucin gels is highly relevant to their physiological function. A covalently cross-linked gel will swell to an equilibrium limit, depending on the elasticity of the network, rather than dissolve upon the addition of more solvent (28). Gels whose molecules are capable of electrostatic interactions can swell as much as a thousandfold (47). A reversible gel will not swell on addition of further solvent because the sol-gel transition in these gels depends on polymer concentration. Such a gel will eventually dissolve upon dilution, although the dissolution process may be very slow. Swelling behavior ranges from no further swelling to swelling enormously depending on the source of mucus, its freshness, and the method of preparation of mucin (73). Because mucins are polyanions, their swelling is governed by a Donnan equilibrium arising from the competing effects of electrostatic repulsions of negative charges on the polyanion and attractive interactions of free cations with fixed negative charges (83). This phenomenon explains the dependence of the degree and rate of swelling on pH and ionic strength. Donnan effects also provide a mechanism for the storage in goblet cells of a condensed network of mucin that swells extensively upon secretion, as evidenced by video microscopy (86).

Diffusion of Macromolecules Through Mucus and Mucin Gels

The presence of a mesh or compartments in a gel significantly retards the diffusional movement of other macromolecules through it (21, 24, 57). The diffusion constant depends on the relative size of diffusant and the mesh size of the gel. Macromolecules larger than the correlation length of the gel lose their lateral mobility and diffuse very slowly by a process called reptation (21, 24), whereas smaller molecules can diffuse laterally as well. Molecules and particles that are much larger than the mesh size of the gel may be immobilized in the gel. The diffusion coefficients of several macromolecules of varying molecular weight through native porcine mucus are reduced by a factor ranging from 10 to 30 as compared with the diffusion constant in aqueous solution (23). Macromolecules with M_r >30,000 were retarded more, perhaps because reptation occurs above this molecular weight. The role of mucus as a diffusional barrier to the movement of large particles depends crucially on the size of the pores in the gel. Saltzman et al (63) used electron microscopy to show that cervical mucus at midcycle has 100 nm pores, which allows antibodies and other large molecules to diffuse through the mucus, although the process is greatly slowed. Adhesive interactions between mucus and particles may be responsible for immobilization of large particles.

Hydrodynamic Properties of Mucin Gels

Among the biophysical properties of mucin that have recently received considerable attention are those related to its hydrodynamic properties when interacting with other fluids. Generically, these properties are termed viscous fingering and refer explicitly to what happens when one fluid displaces another under pressure. When the displacing fluid is more viscous than the fluid being displaced, the interface is simple; the less viscous fluid is completely displaced in a symmetric fashion. However, when the displacing fluid is less viscous, the interface between the two fluids can be complex; some of the displaced fluid remains behind the interface in lacunae, or "fjords," as the less viscous fluid penetrates in a hierarchy of branching structures or channels, termed viscous fingers.

Exactly such viscous fingers form when HCl is injected into solutions of gastric mucin (8), raising the possibility that these channels may be relevant to the resolution of the age-old paradox concerning how acid can pass into the lumen of the stomach without simultaneously digesting the stomach itself. Indeed, physiologists have been puzzled as to why the stomach does not "digest itself" (19) ever since the 18th century scientist Ferchault de Reaumur showed that gastric juice could digest meat. The concentration of HCl in the mammalian stomach after each meal is sufficient to digest the stomach; yet, for reasons not fully understood, the gastric epithelium remains undamaged in this harsh environment.

A number of mammalian tissues (e.g. lung, stomach, intestinal, cervical) secrete mucus that forms a gel layer some 200–500 μm thick between the epithelium and the environment. Whether gastric mucus provides an effective barrier against the harsh acid environment (pH 1–2) of the stomach has been the subject of investigation for many years (2, 41, 42, 89). Early studies appeared to indicate that mucus does not have the ability to impede diffusion of hydrogen ions. The role of mucus as a barrier was considered to be more due to the presence of bicarbonate ions providing an unstirred layer trapping hydrogen ions (41). Davenport (19) suggested that the tight junctions between the epithelial cells prevented the hydrogen ions from invading the deeper mucosa, but later studies have shown that acid-induced injury to cells can occur even when the tight junctions alone are still intact, which implies that such junctions are not effective barriers to hydrogen ion diffusion.

Recent investigations indicate that solutions of gastric mucin can significantly retard diffusion of hydrogen ions (48, 58, 87, 88). Even more significantly, both in vitro and in vivo studies have demonstrated the existence of a gradient from pH 1–2 at the luminal surface to pH 6–7 at the cell surface (82, 88). It would appear that the pH gradient is maintained because hydrochloric acid, secreted by parietal cells deep in the gastric glands, somehow manages to traverse the mucus layer without gross acidification and is inhibited from diffusing back from the lumen.

How does gastric mucus support this pH gradient between lumen and mucosa and why it is not lost during active acid secretion? Until recently, little was known about how HCl secreted by parietal cells reaches the lumen. Although it is commonly accepted that mucus is a diffusion barrier for luminal acid, there is no explanation of how the acid traverses the mucus layer in the first place. Recently, Holm & Flemstrom studied HCl secretion in vivo in the rat stomach using a pH-sensitive dye (43). During active HCl secretion, they observed discrete blue spots directly above the crypts. The authors suggest that HCl travels in channels through the mucus layer. Since mucus is considerably more viscous than HCl, Fabry (25) suggests that the hydrodynamic phenomenon of viscous fingering may be involved.

As mentioned above, the phenomenon of viscous fingering (44) explains the ability of a low viscosity fluid to pass through a fluid of higher viscosity without mixing (7, 31, 54). Depending upon the narrowness of the fingers and the size of the fjords, the driving fluid may penetrate the stationary fluid without grossly displacing it. Recently, Bhaskar et al (8) presented evidence supporting the possibility that migration of HCl through mucus may involve viscous fingering. Specifically, they demonstrated that injection of HCl into solutions of pig gastric mucin produces fingering patterns that are strongly dependent on pH and mucin concentration (Figure 2a–d). Above pH 4, discrete fingers were observed, while below pH 4, HCl neither penetrated the mucin solution nor formed fingers. These results suggest that HCl secreted under pressure by the gastric gland can penetrate the mucus gel layer (pH 5–7) through narrow fingers, whereas HCl in the lumen (pH 2) is prevented from either diffusive or convective return to the epithelium by the high viscosity of gastric mucus gel on the luminal side. Accordingly, when mucin was injected into acid, the interface was shown to be stable against perturbations and developed symmetrically (see Figure 2e). To extend the relevance of the two-dimensional viscous fingering experiments to the in vivo situation where the acid jet originates in the gastric gland and travels toward the lumen through a layer of mucus, Bhaskar et al (8) also studied acid migration through a column of mucin solution. When acid was injected into water, it diffused irregularly into the water. When HCl was injected at the same flow rate into a solution of gastric mucin, the acid traveled in a discrete plume to the top. It then layered across the top of the mucus layer and did not diffuse downward into the solution. When simultaneously injected with a pair of syringes at two ports, the acid traveled in two discrete plumes that did not intermix.

Bhaskar et al (8) hypothesized that such channels or fingers would be likely in view of the profound increase in gastric mucin viscosity at low pH. The size and shape of the fingers were found to be sensitive to concentration and pH of the mucin solution, temperature, and acid velocity. More precise characterization of the fingering patterns as a function of these physiological parameters is critical to the hypothesis that viscous fingering provides channels for secreted acid to reach the lumen without disrupting the mucus layer. If the fingering pattern consists of multiple branches with many fine "twigs" (22), a major displacement of the mucus layer would occur. By contrast, if under normal physiological conditions a single finger forms to provide a narrow channel, as suggested (8), this would not disrupt the mucus gel layer.

In summary, hydrodynamic theory implies that a low viscosity fluid (HCl, in the present case) secreted under pressure into a high viscosity fluid (gastric

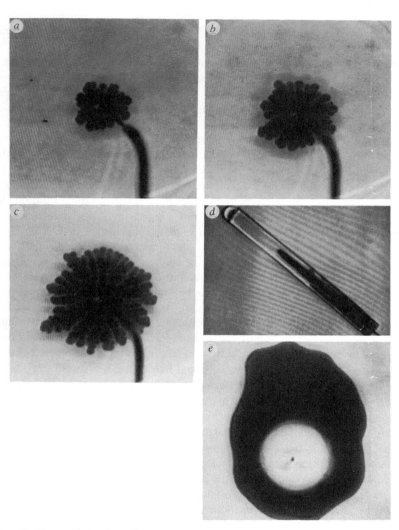

Figure 2 Viscous fingers formed by HCl (*dark*) injected into solutions of gastric mucin (*light*). The patterns were recorded with a video CCD camera. Several frames are shown: (*a-c*) fingering pattern for HCl into mucin (10 mg/ml, pH 7) at successive time intervals. For tip-splitting fingers, constant injection rate results in a decrease in interfacial velocity with time. The increase in finger packing may be due to this variation. (*d*) Single finger produced by injection of HCl (*dark*) into mucin (*light*) in the channel geometry. (*e*) Mucin (*light*) injected into HCl (*dark*) does not produce viscous fingers but rather results in complete symmetric displacement.

mucus) must display the phenomenon of viscous fingering. Viscous fingering offers a mechanism by which HCl can traverse ~500 μm of mucus between the crypt opening and the gastric lumen [and whereby a volume of 250 ml/hr of HCl (49) can pass through a much smaller protective volume of 30–50 ml of mucus] without the mucus layer suffering major disruption.

Viscous fingers are interpreted theoretically with the prototype model of diffusion limited aggregation (DLA) (90). Recently, several phenomena of biological interest including the growth of bacterial colonies (30), the retinal vasculature (26), and neuronal outgrowth (14) have attracted the attention of DLA aficionados. Like many models in statistical mechanics, the rule defining DLA is simple. At time 1, we place in the center of a computer screen a white pixel and release a random walk from a large circle surrounding the white pixel (Figure 3a). The four perimeter sites have an equal a priori probability p_i to be stepped on by the random walk; accordingly we write

$$p_i = 0.25 \ (i = 1,...,4). \hspace{3cm} 1.$$

The DLA rule is that the random walker sticks irreversibly——thereby forming a cluster of mass $M = 2$. There are $N_p = 6$ possible sites, henceforth called growth sites (Figure 3b), but now the probabilities are not all identical; each of the potential growth sites of the two tips has growth probability $p_{max} \approx 0.22$, whereas each of the four growth sites on the sides has growth probability $p_{min} \approx 0.14$. Because a side on the tip is 50% more likely to grow than a site on the sides, the next site is more likely to be added to the tip. One of the main features of modern approaches to DLA is that instead of focusing on the tips that are getting richer, the focus is on the fjords, which are getting poorer——a

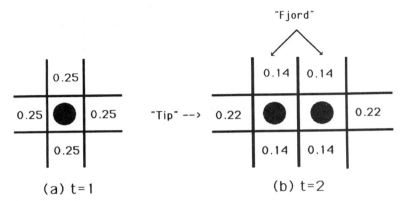

Figure 3 (a) Square lattice DLA at time t = 1, showing the four growth sites, each with growth probability $p_i = 0.25$. (b) DLA at time t = 2, with six growth sites, and their corresponding growth probabilities p_i.

A

B

Figure 4 (a) Large DLA cluster on a square lattice. (b) Results of viscous fingering experiments of Bhaskar et al (8). In the experiment, HCl without added trypan blue was injected into mucin solution containing the acid indicator dye bromophenol blue, which turns yellow at acidic pH (color not shown in figure). The absence of changes in the color of the acid indicator dye indicates that during the passage of HCl, hydrogen ions are confined to the boundary of the fingers and do not diffuse into the mucin solution.

situation perhaps more familiar to scientists who all know the feeling that "once you get behind you stay behind!"

Although the third particle is more likely to stick at the tip, this does not mean that the next particle will stick on the tip. Indeed, the most that one can say about the cluster is to specify the growth site probability distribution, i.e. the set of numbers,

$$\{p_i\} \ i = 1...N_p, \qquad\qquad 2.$$

where p_i is the probability that perimeter site (growth site) is the next to grow, and N_p is the total number of perimeter sites ($N_p = 4,6$ for the cases $M = 1,2$ shown in Figure 1a,b, respectively). The recognition that the set of $\{p_i\}$ provides essentially the maximum amount of information about the system is connected to the fact that tremendous attention has been paid to these p_i and to the analogues of the p_i in various closely related systems.

If the DLA growth rule is simply iterated, we obtain a large cluster, from the tips to the fjords, characterized by a range of growth probabilities that spans several orders of magnitude. Figure 4a shows such a large cluster, where each pixel is colored according to the time it was added to the aggregate. From the fact that the last to arrive particles (green pixels) are never found to be adjacent to the first to arrive particles (white pixels), we conclude that the p_i for the growth sites on the tips must be vastly larger than the p_i for the growth sites in the fjords. Based on these studies, it is quite possible that DLA models what occurs when acid is forced under pressure into mucin.

ACKNOWLEDGMENT

This work was partially supported by the National Science Foundation and the National Institutes of Health. RB thanks the Bunting Institute of Radcliffe College for fellowship support.

Literature Cited

1. Allen A. 1981. Structure and function of gastrointestinal mucus. In *Physiology of the Gastrointestinal Tract,* ed. LR Johnson, 1:617–39. New York: Raven
2. Allen A, Garner A. 1980. Gastric mucus and bicarbonate secretion and their possible role in mucosal protection. *Gut* 21:249–62
3. Allen A, Mantle M, Pearson JP. 1980. The polymeric structure and properties of mucus glycoproteins. In *Perspectives in Cystic Fibrosis,* ed. J Sturgess, pp. 102–12. Toronto: Can. Cystic Fibrosis Found.
4. Barrett-Bee K, Bedford G, Loftus P. 1982. The use of natural-abundance high

resolution carbon-[13]NMR in the study of mucus glycoproteins. *Biosci. Rep.* 2:257–63

5. Bell AE, Allen A, Morris E, Ross-Murphy S. 1984. Functional interactions of gastric mucus glycoprotein. *Int. J. Biol. Macromol.* 6:309–15

6. Bell AE, Sellers LA, Allen A, Cunliffe WJ, Morris ER, Ross-Murphy SB. 1985. Properties of gastric acid duodenal mucus; effect of proteolysis, disulfide reduction, bile, acid, ethanol and hypertonicity on mucus gel structure. *Gastroenterology* 88:269–80

7. Ben-Jacob E, Garik P. 1990. The formation of patterns in nonequilibrium growth. *Nature* 343:523–30

8. Bhaskar KR, Garik P, Turner BS, Bradley JD, Bansil R, et al. 1992. Viscous fingering of HCl through gastric mucin. *Nature* 360:458–61

9. Bhaskar KR, Gong D, Bansil R, Pajevic S, Hamilton JA, et al. 1991. Profound increase in viscosity and aggregation of pig gastric mucin at low pH. *Am. J. Physiol.* 261:G827–32

10. Burchard W, Stadler R, Freitas LL, Moller M, Omeis J, Muhleisen E. 1988. Covalent, thermoreversible and entangled network: an attempt at comparison. In *Biological and Synthetic Polymer Network,* ed. O Kramer. New York: Elsevier Appl. Sci.

11. Carlstedt I, Herrmann A, Karlsson H, Sheehan J, Fransson L-Å, Hansson GC. 1993. Characterization of two different glycosylated domains from the insoluble mucin complex of rat small intestine. *J. Biol. Chem.* 268:18771–79

12. Carlstedt I, Lindgren H, Sheehan JK. 1983. The macromolecular strucure of human cervical–mucus glycoproteins. *Biochem. J.* 213:427–35

13. Carlstedt I, Sheehan JK, Corfield AP, Gallagher JT. 1985. Mucus glycoproteins: a gel of a problem. *Essays Biochem.* 20:40–76

14. Caserta F, Stanley HE, Eldred W, Daccord G, Hausmann R, Nittmann J. 1990. Physical mechanisms underlying neurite outgrowth: a quantitative analysis of neuronal shape. *Phys. Rev. Lett.* 64:95–98

15. Chace KV, Naziruddin B, Desai VC, Flux M, Sachdev GP. 1989. Physical properties of purified human respiratory mucus glycoproteins: effects of sodium chloride concentration on the aggregation properties and shape. *Exp. Lung Res.* 15:721–37

16. Chu B. 1974. *Laser Light Scattering.* New York: Academic

17. Creeth JM, Bhaskar KR, Horton J, Das I, Lopez-Vidriero MT, Reid L. 1977. The separation and characterization of bronchial glycoproteins by density gradient methods. *Biochem. J.* 167:557–69

18. Creeth JM, Coupe B. 1984. Studies on the molecular weight distributions of two mucins. *Biochem. Soc. Trans.* 12: 618–21

19. Davenport HW. 1967. Salicylate damage to the mucosal barrier. *N. Engl. J. Med.* 23:1307–12

20. Davenport HW. 1972. Why the stomach does not digest itself. *Sci. Am.* 226:86–94

21. deGennes PG. 1979. *Scaling Concepts in Polymer Physics.* Ithaca: Cornell Univ. Press

22. deGennes PG. 1987. Time effects in viscoelastic fingering. *Europhys. Lett.* 3:195–97

23. Desai MA, Mutlu M, Vadgama P. 1992. A study of macromolecular diffusion through native porcine mucus. *Experientia* 48:22–26

24. Doi M, Edwards SF. 1986. *The Theory of Polymer Dynamics.* Oxford: Clarendon

25. Fabry TL. 1990. How the parietal secretion crosses the gastric mucus without being neutralized. *Gastroenterology* 98:A42

26. Family F, Masters BR, Platt DE. 1989. Fractal pattern formation in human retinal vessels. *Physica D* 38:98–103

27. Ferry JD. 1970. *Viscoelastic Properties of Polymers.* New York: Wiley. 2nd ed.

28. Flory PJ. 1953. *Principles of Polymer Chemistry.* Ithaca: Cornell Univ. Press

29. Fontenot JD, Tjandra N, Bu D, Ho C, Montelaro RC, Finn OJ. 1993. Biophysical characterization of one-, two-, and three-tandem repeats of human mucin (muc-1) protein core. *Cancer Res.* 53: 5386–94

30. Fujikawa H, Matsushita M. 1989. Fractal growth of *Bacillus subtilis* on agar plates. *J. Phys. Soc. Jpn.* 58: 3875–78

31. Garik P, Hetrick J, Orr B, Barkey D, Ben-Jacob E. 1991. Interfacial cellular mixing and the determination of global deposit morphology. *Phys. Rev. Lett.* 66: 1606–9

32. Gelman RA, Meyer FA. 1979. Mucociliary transference rate and mucus viscoelasticity: dependence on dynamics storage and loss modulus. *Am. Rev. Resp. Dis.* 120:553–57

33. Gerken TA, Butenhof KJ, Shogren R. 1989. Effects of glycosylation on the conformation and dynamics of O-linked glycoproteins: carbon-[13] NMR studies

of ovine submaxillary mucin. *Biochemistry* 28:5536–43

34. Glotzer SC, Bansil R, Gallagher PD, Gyure MF, Sciortino F, Stanley HE. 1993. Physical gels and microphase separation in multiblock copolymers. *Physica A* 201:482–95

35. Guenet JM. 1992. *Thermoreversible Gelation of Polymers and Biopolymers.* New York: Academic

36. Guenet JM, Klein M, Menelle A. 1989. Evidence by neutron diffraction of ordered structures in atactic polystyrene/carbon disulfide physical gels. *Macromolecules* 22:493–94

37. Gum JR. 1992. Mucin genes and the proteins they encode: structure, diversity and regulation. *Am. J. Respir. Cell. Mol. Biol.* 7:557–64

38. Gum JR, Hicks JWQ, Torbara NW, Rothe E-M, Legace RE, et al. 1992. The human MUC-2 intestinal mucin has cysteine-rich subdomains located both upstream and downstream of its central repetitive region. *J. Biol. Chem.* 267: 21375–83

39. Gupta R, Jentoft N, Jamieson AM, Blackwell J. 1990. Structural analysis of purified human tracheobronchial mucins. *Biopolymers* 29:347–55

40. Harding SE. 1989. The macrostructure of mucus glycoproteins in solution. *Adv. Carbohydr. Chem. Biochem.* 47: 345–81

41. Heatley NG. 1959. Mucosubstance as a barrier to diffusion. *Gastroenterology* 37:313–17

42. Hollander F. 1954. Two-component mucous barrier: its activity in protecting gastroduodenal mucosa against peptic ulceration. *Arch. Int. Med.* 93:107–29

43. Holm L, Flemstrom G. 1990. Microscopy of acid transport at the gastric surface in vivo. *J. Int. Med.* 228 (Suppl.):91–95

44. Homsy GM. 1987. Viscous fingering in porous media. *Annu. Rev. Fluid Mech.* 19:271–311

45. Jentoft N. 1990. Why are proteins O-glycosylated? *Trends Biochem. Sci.* 15: 291–94

46. Lee WI, Verdugo P, Blandau RJ, Gaddum-Rosse P. 1977. Molecular arrangement of cervical mucus: a reevaluation based on laser light-scattering spectroscopy. *Gynecol. Invest.* 8:254–66

47. Li Y, Tanaka T. 1990. Swelling of gels and diffusion of molecules. In *Springer Proceedings in Physics: Dynamics and Patterns in Complex Fluids,* ed. A Onuki, K Kawasaki, 52:44–54. Berlin/Heidelberg: Springer-Verlag

48. Lucas M. 1982. Restriction of hydrogen and sodium ion diffusion in porcine gastric mucin: a concentration dependent phenomenon. *Adv. Exp. Med. Biol.* 144:193

49. Makhlouf GM. 1981. See Ref. 1, pp. 551–66

50. Mantle M, Allen A. 1981. Isolation and characterization of the native glycoprotein from pig small intestine mucus. *Biochem. J.* 195:267–73

51. McDonnell ME, Jamieson AM. 1976. *Biopolymers* 15:1283–99

52. Meerzaman D, Charles P, Daskal E, Polymeropoulos MH, Martin BM, et al. 1994. Cloning and analysis of cDNA encoding a major airway glycoprotein, human tracheobronchial mucin (MUC-5). *J. Biol. Chem.* 269:12932–39

53. Mortazavi SA, Carpenter BG, Smart JD. 1993. A comparative study on the role played by mucus glycoproteins in the rheological behaviour of the mucoadhesive/mucosal interface. *Int. J. Pharm.* 94: 195–201

54. Nittmann J, Daccord G, Stanley HE. 1985. Fractal growth of viscous fingers: quantitative characterization of a fluid instability phenomenon. *Nature* 314: 141–44

55. Odeblad E. 1977. Physical properties of cervical mucus. In *Advances in Experimental Medicine and Biology. Mucus in Health and Disease,* ed. M Elstein, DV Parke, 89:217–25. New York: Plenum

56. Pain RH. 1980. *Symp. Soc. Exp. Biol.* 34:359–76

57. Pajevic S, Bansil R, Konak C. 1993. Diffusion of linear polymer chains in methyl methacrylate gels. *Macromolecules* 26:305–12

58. Pfeiffer CJ. 1981. Experimental analysis of hydrogen ion diffusion in gastrointestinal mucus glycoprotein. *Am. J. Physiol.* 240:G176–82

59. Phillies GD, Billmeyer FW. 1986. Elastic and quasielastic light scattering by solutions and suspensions. In *Optical Methods of Analysis,* pp. 1–87. New York: Wiley

60. Podolsky DK. 1985. Oligosaccharide structures of human colonic mucin. *J. Biol. Chem.* 260:8262–71

61. Podolsky DK. 1985. Oligosaccharide structures of human colonic mucin species. *J. Biol. Chem.* 260:15510–15

62. Rees DA. 1969. Structure, conformation, and mechanism in the formation of polysaccharide gels and networks. *Adv. Carbohydr. Chem. Biochem.* 24: 267–329

63. Saltzman WM, Radomsky ML, Whaley

656   BANSIL, STANLEY & LaMONT

KJ, Cone RA. 1994. Antibody diffusion in human cervical mucus. *Biophys. J.* 66:508–15

64. Sellers LA, Allen A. 1989. Gastrointestinal mucus gel rheology. In *Symposia of the Society for Experimental Biology XLIII: Mucus and Related Topics,* ed. E Chantler, NA Ratcliffe, pp. 65–71. Cambridge, UK: Company of Biologists

65. Sellers LA, Allen A, Morris ER, Ross-Murphy SB. 1987. Mechanical characterization and properties of gastro- intestinal mucus gel. *Biorheology* 24: 615–23

66. Shankar V, Virmani AK, Naziruddin B, Sachdev GP. 1991. Macromolecular properties and polymeric structure of canine tracheal mucins. *Biochem. J.* 276: 525–32

67. Sheehan JK, Carlstedt I. 1990. Electron microscopy of cervical-mucus glycoproteins and fragments therefrom. *Biochem. J.* 265:169–78

68. Sheehan JK, Oates K, Carlstedt I. 1986. Electron microscopy of cervical, gastric and bronchial mucus glycoproteins. *Biochem. J.* 239:147–53

69. Shogren R, Gerken TA, Jentoft N. 1989. Role of glycosylation on the conformation and chain dimensions of O-linked glycoproteins: light-scattering studies of ovine submaxillary mucin. *Biochemistry* 28:5525–35

70. Shogren R, Jamieson AM, Blackwell J, Cheng PW, Dearborn DG, Boat TF. 1983. Solution properties of porcine submaxillary mucin. *Biopolymers* 22:1657–75

71. Silberberg A. 1977. Basic rheological concepts. In *Mucus in Health and Disease,* ed. M Elstein, DV Podke, pp. 181–90. New York: Plenum

72. Silberberg A. 1987. A model for mucus glycoprotein structure. *Biorheology* 24: 605–14

73. Silberberg A. 1989. Mucus glycoprotein, its biophysical and gel-forming properties. See Ref. 64, pp. 43–63

74. Silberberg A, Meyer FA, Gilboa A, Gelman RA. 1977. Function and properties of epithelial mucus. See Ref. 55, pp. 171–80

75. Slomiany BL, Murty VLN, Mandel ID, Zalesna G, Slomiany A. 1989. Physicochemical characteristics of mucus glycoproteins and lipids of the human oral mucosal mucus coat in relation to caries susceptibility. *Arch. Oral Biol.* 34:229–37

76. Smith BF, LaMont JT. 1984. Hydrophobic binding properties of bovine gallbladder mucin. *J. Biol. Chem.* 259: 12170–77

77. Smith BF, Peetermans JA, Tanaka T,

LaMont JT. 1989. Subunit interactions and physical properties of bovine gallbladder mucin. *Gastroenterology* 97: 179–87

78. Steiner CA, Litt M, Nossal R. 1984. Effect of Ca on the structure and rheology of canine tracheal mucin. *Biorheology* 21:235–52

79. Sterk H. 1988. On the structure of mucus glycoproteins: ^1H NMR nuclear Overhauser enhancement study. *Int. J. Biol. Macromol.* 10:213–16

80. Sterk H, Fabian W, Hayn E. 1987. Dynamic behavior of mucus glycoproteins: a ^{13}C NMR relaxation study. *Int. J. Biol. Macromol.* 9:58–62

81. Strous GJ, Dekker J. 1992. Mucin-type glycoproteins. *Crit. Rev. Biochem. Mol. Biol.* 27:57–92

82. Takeuchi K, Magee D, Critchlow J, Matthews J, Silen W. 1983. Studies of the pH gradient and thickness of frog gastric mucus gel. *Gastroenterology* 84: 331–40

83. Tam PY, Verdugo P. 1981. Control of mucus hydration as a Donnan equilibrium process. *Nature* 292:340–42

84. Toribara NW, Gum JR, Culhane PJ, Legace RE, Hicks JW, et al. 1991. *MUC-2* human small intestinal mucin gene structure, repeated arrays and polymorphism. *J. Clin. Invest.* 88:1005–13

85. Varma BK, Demers A, Jamieson AM, Blackwell J, Jentoft N. 1990. Light scattering studies of the effect of Ca on the structure of porcine submaxillary mucin. *Biopolymers* 29:441–48

86. Verdugo P. 1993. Polymer gel phase transition in condensation-decondensation of secretory products. In *Responsive Gels: Volume Transitions II,* ed. K Dusek, pp. 145–56. Berlin: Springer-Verlag

87. Williams SE, Turnberg LA. 1980. Retardation of acid diffusion by pig gastric mucus: a potential role in mucosal protection. *Gastroenterology* 79:299–304

88. Williams SE, Turnberg LA. 1981. Demonstration of a pH gradient across mucus adherent to rabbit gastric mucosa: evidence for a mucus-bicarbonate barrier. *Gut* 22:94–96

89. Williams SE, Turnberg LA. 1982. Studies of the protective properties of gastric mucus. *Adv. Exp. Med. Biol.* 144:187–88

90. Witten TA, Sander LM. 1981. Diffusion-limited aggregation, a kinetic critical phenomenon. *Phys. Rev. Lett.* 47: 1400–3

91. Xu G, Huan L-J, Khatri I, Sajjan US, McCool D, et al. 1992. Human intestinal mucin-like protein (MLP) is homologous with rat MLP in the C-terminal

region, and is encoded by a gene on chromosome 11 p 15.5. *Biochem. Biophys. Res. Commun.* 183:821–28

92. Xu G, Huan L-J, Khatri IA, Wang D, Bennick A, et al. 1992. cDNA for the carboxyl-terminal region of a rat intestinal mucin-like peptide. *J. Biol. Chem.* 267:5401–7

Annu. Rev. Physiol. 1995. 57:659–82

NITRIC OXIDE AS A NEUROTRANSMITTER IN PERIPHERAL NERVES: Nature of Transmitter and Mechanism of Transmission

M. J. Rand and C. G. Li

Pharmacology Research Laboratory, Department of Medical Laboratory Science, Royal Melbourne Institute of Technology, Melbourne 3001, Australia

KEY WORDS: L-arginine, guanylate cyclase, nitrergic nerves, nitric oxide synthase, nonadrenergic noncholinergic nerves

PREFATORY NOTE

We coined the adjectival term nitrergic to describe the mode of transmission that involves nitric oxide (NO) and, by extension, the transmitter and the nerves from which it originates (100, 135, 136). This term is noncommittal about the exact nature of the transmitter, as was the case when Dale coined the terms cholinergic and adrenergic (42). It is advisable at the outset to alert the reader to our opinion that NO as such is not likely to be the substance that mediates transmission, that is, conveys a message from nerve terminals across the neuroeffector junction to the responding smooth muscle cells. Instead, the mediator appears to be a NO donor that acts as a carrier for NO from its site of formation to its site of action.

The evidence for this assertion is presented below. We have used the term nitrergic when our appraisal of the balance of the evidence indicates that it is justified.

EVIDENCE FOR NITRERGIC TRANSMISSION

First Demonstration

The involvement of NO in neuroeffector transmission was first demonstrated in 1989, in anococcygeus muscles of the rat (60, 100, 134) and mouse (55).

659

The definitive evidence was blockade of the nonadrenergic noncholinergic (NANC) stimulation-induced relaxation of the muscle by N^G-substituted analogues of L-arginine that were known to inhibit the enzyme nitric oxide synthase (NOS), which converts molecular oxygen (O_2) and L-arginine to NO and L-citrulline (see 124). Furthermore, the blockade could be overcome or prevented by L-arginine but not D-arginine, thereby indicating the specificity of the effect. We have suggested elsewhere that these stereospecific effects provide the gold standard for identification of nitrergic transmission (143).

Before the possibility of nitrergic transmission was envisaged, many similarities were noted between the endothelium-derived relaxing factor (EDRF) and the NANC relaxant transmitter of the anococcygeus muscle and the related retractor penis muscle (51, 58), and when it was subsequently shown that EDRF was NO (124), or a closely related substance (see below), it became clear that many of the pharmacological tools that had provided clues about the nature of EDRF were also applicable in studies of the nitrergic NANC relaxant transmitter (61, 113, 135, 136, 143). These studies are considered below in the section headed Blockade of Nitrergic Transmission.

Subsequent Evidence for Nitrergic Transmission

Since the first demonstration of nitrergic transmission, hundreds of papers have shown its wide distribution in the autonomic and enteric nervous systems. Numerous reviews have covered the matter generally (135, 136, 143, 149, 153), or focused on specific regions or organs including the anococcygeus and retractor penis muscles (113), the cerebral vasculature (163), the respiratory tract (13), esophageal function (168), gastric function (95), the ileocolonic junction (25), the gastrointestinal tract (157), the urinary tract (7), the genital system (61), and the penis (152).

Histological Localization of Nitrergic Nerve Terminals

The first studies on the immunohistochemical localization of neuronal NOS revealed the presence of peripheral as well as central immunoreactive neurons (32). The finding that neuronal NOS possesses NADPH diaphorase activity (44, 78) provided a simpler method for histochemical detection of NOS using the reduction of nitro blue tetrazolium (NBT) to formazan as the marker. In several studies in which both methods were used, NOS immunoreactivity and NADPH diaphorase activity were colocalized (for review, see 143). The histochemical localization of NOS in peripheral neurons provided the morphological basis for nitrergic neuroeffector transmission in rat and mouse anococcygeus muscles; the respiratory tract of guinea pigs, rats, ferrets, and humans; the urinary tract of rats, pigs, and sheep; the rat uterus; rat and guinea pig hearts; blood vessels; the gall bladder of mice and guinea pigs; and the gastrointestinal tract of rats, mice, guinea pigs, dogs, pigs, and humans (143).

Physiological Role of Nitrergic Transmission

In most studies of nitrergic neuroeffector transmission, field stimulation of intrinsic nerves in tissues has been used, and, although responses to other likely transmitters and mediators have been blocked by appropriate means, an element of doubt about the physiological significance of the findings remains. Better evidence for physiological function of nitrergic neurons is provided by reflex activation of specific neural pathways. Reflex-induced effects mediated by nitrergic nerves in the gastrointestinal tract have been reviewed recently (143), as have distension-induced peristalsis in the ileum (85, 160) and swallow-induced peristalsis in the esophagus (4).

NITROMIMETICS

We use this term for substances that mimic responses to nitrergic nerve stimulation, analogous to the term cholinomimetics for substances mimicking responses to cholinergic nerve stimulation. All of the substances regarded as nitrovasodilators, in reference to their main therapeutic use, are nitromimetics and are potent relaxants of smooth muscle in organs other than blood vessels. Thus a term with more general applicability that still retains the nitro- is appropriate. An essential component of the evidence for any particular mediator is that exogenous administration should produce effects closely resembling those of the transmitter. Therefore, it is worth considering those nitromimetics that could be potential candidates as the nitrergic transmitter.

Nitric Oxide

Responses to nitrergic nerve stimulation are mimicked by aqueous solutions of NO gas; however, there are three forms of the nitrogen monoxide loosely termed NO: the nitrosium ion (NO^+), the neutral free radical ($NO\cdot$), and the nitroxyl ion (NO^-), and these have different properties and biological reactivities (154). The form produced by NOS has not been established, but it is generally assumed to be the free radical. It is probable that the particular form depends on the prevailing redox state and may differ between NOS isozymes and perhaps between tissues. In neutral aqueous solutions, NO is likely to be predominantly in the free radical form. However, the main form in acidified solutions of sodium nitrite is the nitrosium ion (154). The nitroxyl ion can probably be eliminated as a messenger form of NO because sodium nitroxyl had only one-thousandth of the relaxant activity of aqueous NO on endothelium-denuded strips of rabbit aorta (50).

Nitroso-Alcohols

The simplest nitrovasodilators, and the first to be used therapeutically, are the organic nitrites (e.g. amyl nitrite), which are NO-donating nitroso-alcohols.

The reverse reaction of alcohols with NO to form nitroso-alcohols proceeds readily (121). It was shown some years ago that the nerve stimulation-induced relaxations of the rat and rabbit anococcygeus and the bovine retractor penis muscles, which are now known to be nitrergically mediated, were selectively inhibited by ethanol (59), and more recently we found that a range of alcohols inhibited relaxations elicited by nitrergic nerve stimulation, NO and the NO donor sodium nitroprusside (SNP) in rat anococcygeus muscles and gastric fundus strips (141). Their effect was attributed to sequestration of NO to form nitroso-alcohols when the alcohol is in excess, but it was postulated that NO is released when the nitroso-alcohol is in excess. It follows that the affinity of the alcohols for NO is greater than that of the adducting agent, which we consider to be a component of the nitrergic transmitter.

Nitrosothiols

Thiols, like alcohols, readily react with acidified sodium nitrite to form nitrosothiols (94), which decompose to yield NO and the corresponding disulfide (176). However, they differ from aliphatic alcohols in that they do not block the nitrergic transmitter, and they potentiate the action of NO (see below).

The nitrosothiols that may be physiologically relevant are derivatives of endogenously occurring thiols: of these, S-nitrosocysteine (NOCys), S-nitrosoglutathione (NOGS), and S-nitrosocoenzyme A (NOCoA) have been commonly used in pharmacological studies. NOCys and other nitrosothiols mimic nitrergic nerve stimulation-induced relaxant responses of the mouse (54) and rat (103, 140) anococcygeus and bovine retractor penis (107) muscle, and NOCys mimics nitrergic nerve stimulation-induced relaxations (A McLaren et al, unpublished observations) and hyperpolarization (93) in the rat gastric fundus and stimulation-induced hyperpolarization in the dog colon (162).

The potency of aqueous NO in relaxing rat anococcygeus muscles was greatly enhanced when it was mixed with a solution of cysteine, although the cysteine solution alone had no effect (JS Gillespie et al, personal communication), and similar results were obtained with the bovine retractor penis muscle (107). Likewise, we showed that the relaxant action of NO on the rat anococcygeus muscle was much greater and more prolonged in the presence of cysteine than in its absence (138, 143). The simplest explanation of these findings is that NO forms NOCys, and this is more stable than free NO but readily donates NO to soluble guanylate cyclase. In accord with this, NOCys, S-nitrosocysteamine, and NOGS were three to ten times more potent than NO as relaxants of endothelium-denuded strips of rabbit aorta (50). However, the interaction with cysteine is more complex because the half-life of NOCys was prolonged by cysteine (10 μM–1 mM) in a concentration-dependent manner (50).

A mixture of L-cysteine (10 mM) with NO (50 μM) resulted in the appearance of a third compound that was responsible for the greater relaxant action than that produced by NO alone (107). An enhanced relaxation was also produced when NO was mixed with L-cysteamine, L-cysteine methyl ester, N-acetyl-L-cysteine, or glutathione, all of which have a free sulfhydryl group and probably form nitrosothiols; however, this effect was not obtained by mixing with related substances that do not have a free sulfhydryl group (107). The new relaxant produced by mixing NO with a cysteine solution required acid conditions and traces of O_2 (107); however, an acid condition was not apparently necessary for the enhancement observed when NO was added directly to the tissue in the presence of cysteine (138, 143).

Although solutions of nitrosothiols release NO spontaneously into headspace gas, the rates of release of NO do not correspond to the potencies of the nitrosothiols as relaxants of rabbit aortic smooth muscle (94, 116), nor do these rates of release correspond to their potencies as relaxants of the mouse anococcygeus muscle (54). Nitrosothiols are highly polar with partition coefficients of 0.02–0.05 in a two-phase system of octanol and aqueous buffer at pH 7.4; therefore, it is unlikely that they would diffuse passively through cell membranes (94). These findings suggest either release of the NO moiety at the membrane surface followed by diffusion to cytosolic guanylate cyclase, or transfer of the NO moiety to a carrier substance of effector cells, or to a membrane transport mechanism for nitrosothiols. A stereoselective cell surface receptor for L-NOCys has been suggested (98), but the L- and D-isomers are equipotent as relaxants of the rabbit aorta (50).

BLOCKADE OF NITRERGIC TRANSMISSION

Neuroeffector transmission can be blocked in a number of ways: Those applicable to nitrergic transmission are inhibition of synthesis of the transmitter, inhibition of release, inactivation of the released transmitter, blockade of the effector site of action, and disruption of second messenger systems mediating the effector response.

Inhibition of Synthesis

Failure of nitrergic transmission without a corresponding reduction in the responses to nitromimetics occurs in most tissues with inhibitors of neuronal NOS. In numerous studies on nitrergic neuroeffector transmission, those used are N^G-monomethyl-L-arginine (L-NMMA), N^G-nitro-L-arginine (L-NNA), and its methyl ester (L-NAME).

Mono- and di-N-methylated L-arginines (L-NMMA and L-NDMA) occur naturally, and their content in various tissues (about 3–20% that of free L-arginine) may be sufficient for inhibitory modulation of NOS (92, 170). N-methylated L-arginines are hydrolyzed by a specific enzyme to citrulline and the corresponding methylamine (92). The metabolism of L-NMMA may partly explain its relatively low potency as a NOS inhibitor. In the bovine retractor penis muscle, stimulation-induced relaxations were blocked by L-NNA but not by L-NMMA (106, 114). Furthermore, the inhibitory effect of L-NNA required a 30-fold excess of L-arginine to overcome it, whereas in the rat anococcygeus muscle a threefold excess of L-arginine was sufficient to overcome the inhibitory effect of L-NMMA. The inhibitory effect of L-NNA in the mouse anococcygeus muscle was overcome by precursors for the biosynthesis of L-arginine including L-citrulline (54). Conversion of the citrulline formed from L-NMMA to L-arginine, via argininosuccinic acid, would counteract its inhibitory effect. In the bovine retractor penis and rat anococcygeus muscles, L-NMMA was more potent than L-arginine in overcoming the blockade of stimulation-induced relaxations produced by L-NNA and L-NAME (114).

The intermediate metabolite in the biosynthesis of L-arginine from L-citrulline, argininosuccinic acid, is also a N^G-substituted derivative of L-arginine and appears to inhibit endothelial and neuronal NOS because it reduces endothelium-dependent relaxations (66, 137) and nitrergic transmission in the rat anococcygeus muscle (137), although its effect is transient, probably because of rapid metabolism to L-arginine by argininosuccinase. However, in the congenital disorder of argininosuccinic aciduria, the level of argininosuccinic acid is raised substantially, and it has been suggested that the severe mental retardation and other neurological signs in this disorder could be due to impaired NO production (53).

NOS can be inhibited by agents other than N^G-substituted L-arginines and analogous compounds. One such is diphenylene iodonium (DPI), which inhibits macrophage NOS (158) and presumably also endothelial and neuronal NOS because it blocks vasorelaxant responses to EDRF (139, 158, 172) and nitrergic nerve stimulation-induced relaxations in the rat anococcygeus muscle (139). Its blocking activity is not affected by L-arginine apparently because of interference with NADPH and perhaps other nucleotide cofactors (158). Pretreatment with NADPH is reported to prevent DPI blockade of EDRF (172); we are unable to confirm this. However, pretreatment with NADPH does prevent the blocking action of DPI on nitrergic relaxations of the rat anococcygeus muscle (A Najbar et al, unpublished observations).

The substrate used for detecting NADPH-diaphorase reactivity, NBT, inhibits NOS (78), possibly by competing for the NADPH-binding site, but other mechanisms have been suggested (150). Our attempt to determine whether NBT affected nitrergic nerve stimulation-induced relaxations in the rat anococcygeus muscle were frustrated because it produced a long-lasting complete loss of tone. The mechanism of this effect has not been explored (CG Li & MJ Rand, unpublished observations).

The similarity between NOS (and NADPH diaphorase) and cytochrome P_{450} reductase (31, 89) led us to test the effects of the P_{450} substrate and competitive inhibitor 7-ethoxyresorufin (7-ER). It inhibits NOS activity in rat brain homogenates and human placental tissue (47, 104) and blocks nitrergic nerve stimulation-induced relaxations of rat anococcygeus muscles; however, it is also a superoxide generator, which is largely responsible for its blocking activity because it is overcome by superoxide dismutase (SOD) (142). The seleno-organic compound ebselen, which breaks a cysteine thiolate/Fe^{3+} bond of some P_{450} enzymes, is a relatively selective inhibitor of the endothelial isoform of NOS (178). Its effects on nitrergic transmission have yet to be determined.

NO biosynthesis requires the presence of O_2 and is impaired by hypoxia (145). Functionally, anoxia impairs the production of EDRF (see 46a) and the nitrergic transmitter in the bovine retractor penis and rat anococcygeus muscles (30).

Inhibition of Release

In all other modes of transmission so far investigated, transmitter release can be modulated by agonists acting on specific prejunctional receptors (for review, see 175). The receptors involved in modulation of transmitter release are coupled to second messenger systems (41). There is evidence that nitrergic nerve terminals in various tissues are endowed with muscarinic cholinoceptors (19, 101, 165), α_2-adrenoceptors (22, 96, 109), and opioid receptors (15, 17), and their activation inhibits transmission.

Automodulation, whereby the transmitter acts on receptors associated with the sites of release to exert negative feedback control of transmission, occurs at the terminals of most types of neurons. In nitrergic terminals, automodulation is not likely to involve an increase in the cGMP level (119) but might occur by combination of NO with the heme group associated with NOS, which inhibits the enzyme (10, 145, 146).

Inactivation

Endothelium-dependent relaxations and relaxations elicited by NO and NO donors are blocked by oxyhemoglobin (61, 108, 113, 124). Its effect is due to high affinity binding of NO (57), which is irreversible because the complex is rapidly (< 0.1 s) converted to methemoglobin and NO^{3+} (88). Oxyhemoglobin was known to block selectively NANC inhibitory transmission in the bovine retractor penis and rat anococcygeus before it was found to be nitrergic (28, 29, 37, 56). It has proven to be a valuable tool for providing supporting evidence for nitrergic transmission.

Endothelium-dependent relaxations and relaxations elicited by NO are also blocked by intact erythrocytes, but nitrergic nerve stimulation-induced relaxations of the bovine retractor penis muscle are not affected (62, 63), which indicates that the nitrergic transmitter does not readily cross the erythrocyte membrane.

Hydroxocobalamin reacts with NO to form nitrosocobalamin. This reaction apparently inactivates NO because hydroxocobalamin blocks relaxations induced by EDRF, NO, and the nitrosothiols NOCys, NOGS and nitroso-N-acetylpenicillamine (SNAP) in rat aortic rings, as does oxyhemoglobin (103, 133, 140). However, hydroxocobalamin does not block responses to nitrergic nerve stimulation in rat anococcygeus muscles, although it inhibits relaxations induced by NO and SNP and has little or no effect on responses to glyceryl trinitrate, NOCys, or SNAP, whereas oxyhemoglobin blocks relaxations elicited by all these agents (103, 140).

Superoxide-generating substances rapidly inactivate NO and block responses to EDRF, and removal of superoxide with SOD negates the blocking activity of superoxide generators and prolongs the half-life of NO (72, 148). The superoxide generators hydroquinone and pyrogallol were reported to reduce relaxations elicited by nitrergic nerve stimulation in the rat anococcygeus muscle (64), and hydroquinone reduced nitrergic relaxation in the opossum internal anal sphincter (38). However, nitrergic nerve stimulation-induced relaxations were not affected by hydroquinone or pyrogallol in the bovine retractor penis (64) or by hydroquinone in the mouse anococcygeus muscle or guinea pig trachea (77); thus, at least in these tissues, either the transmitter is resistant to inactivation by superoxide, or it is protected by SOD.

A certain amount of superoxide is normally generated in tissues and may affect nitrergic transmission, as suggested by the findings that SOD increased responses to nitrergic nerve stimulation in the rat colon and ileum (75, 84). However, SOD does not enhance relaxant responses to nitrergic nerve stimulation in the opossum internal anal sphincter (38), the rat anococcygeus muscle (139), or circular muscle of the dog jejunum (156), whereas relaxant responses to NO are enhanced. Therefore, the nitrergic transmitter must be selectively protected by SOD. The presence of SOD was required for detection by a cascade superfusion technique of a NO-like factor released from the canine ileocolonic junction and rat gastric fundus by nitrergic nerve stimulation (20, 23, 26, 36); however, in a cascade system the transmitter is acting at a site remote from the point of release and would be inactivated by endogenous superoxide to a greater extent than a transmitter within the neuroeffector junction.

The role of SOD in protecting the transmitter has been explored recently by W Martin (personal communication), who showed that after inhibition of SOD by treatment of the bovine retractor penis muscle with diethyldithiocarbamate, the transmitter-induced relaxations were almost completely blocked by superoxide generators and were then restored by SOD, whereas in the untreated muscle the superoxide generators had no effect.

Blockade of Action on Effector Tissues

The signal transduction system for the smooth muscle relaxing actions of the nitrergic transmitter, EDRF, NO, and NO donors involves activation of soluble guanylate cyclase and the production of the second messenger cGMP (150). The system can be bypassed by using 8-bromo cGMP, a cell-permeable analogue of cGMP, and was useful for helping to determine the site of blockade of nitrergic transmission in the opossum esophagus (49), dog pyloric sphincter (18), rat gastric fundus (11) and ileum (84), and the guinea pig ileum (129). A number of mechanisms for the mediation of relaxation of smooth muscle by the rise in the intracellular cGMP level have been proposed, but the precise details have not yet been fully elucidated (67, 105) and may differ between tissues.

Increases in the level of cyclic GMP produced by nitrergic nerve stimulation have been observed in the bovine retractor penis and rat anococcygeus muscles (27, 122); rat gastric fundus (83), ileum (84), and proximal colon (159); opossum internal anal sphincter (40); dog proximal colon (173) and internal anal sphincter (71); the lower esophageal sphincter of the opossum (126, 167) and human (14); and the rabbit urethra (48).

Specific inhibition of cGMP phosphodiesterase would be expected to enhance or prolong the actions of the nitrergic transmitter. In fact, zaprinast (M&B 22948) enhanced relaxations of the rat anococcygeus muscle elicited by nitrergic nerve stimulation (122) and prolonged the inhibitory junction potential in the dog pyloric sphincter, ileocolonic sphincter, and proximal colon elicited by nitrergic nerve stimulation (18, 173, 174). However, zaprinast did not affect relaxations of the rat gastric fundus induced by the nitrergic transmitter or NO, although it potentiated SNP-induced relaxations (11).

Inhibition of soluble guanylate cyclase by methylene blue (81) is part of the battery of tests that can be used to demonstrate nitrergic transmission. However, interpretation of the findings should be weighed against the reports that methylene blue inhibits NOS (118) and generates superoxide (73, 111, 112, 177). Lack of an effect of methylene blue should also be treated with caution because it did not block relaxant responses to some agents that activate guanylate cyclase (73, 112, 117). As concerns nitrergic transmission, methylene blue was reported to be without effect on electrical and mechanical responses of smooth muscle from the dog proximal colon evoked by nitrergic nerve stimulation (173), but this was disputed (80). In smooth muscle of the rat gastric fundus, methylene blue was reported to be without effect on the hyperpolarizations produced by nitrergic nerve stimulation, NOCys, or SNP (93).

LY-83583 (6-analino-5,8-quinolinedione) (125), another putative inhibitor of soluble guanylate cyclase, also generates superoxide (52). LY-83583 blocked responses to NO in the rat gastric fundus, and this effect was reduced by SOD, but LY-83583 did not affect responses to nitrergic nerve stimulation (12).

Other putative inhibitors of soluble guanylate cyclase that have been used in studies on nitrergic neuroeffector transmission include N-methylhydroxylamine, which reduced NO-induced but not nitrosothiol-induced relaxations of mouse anococcygeus muscle (54), and cystamine (144), which blocked the electrical responses to nitrergic nerve stimulation of smooth muscle in the opossum esophagus (49).

Although activation of soluble guanylate cyclase by the nitrergic transmitter and generation of second messenger cGMP is sufficient to account for the relaxation of smooth muscle in effector tissues, this does not preclude the possibility of other actions. Potential targets include: heme groups associated with enzymes other than guanylate cyclase; free sulfhydryl groups of enzymes, receptors, or other functional proteins (76, 91, 150, 154); alcoholic hydroxy groups; and formation of nitrosamines with secondary amines. Nitrosylation of sulfhydryl groups blocks the NMDA receptor-channel complex (97), and nitrosylation of coenzyme A, a cofactor for choline acetyltransferase, inhibits the activity of the enzyme (169) and may result in a slowly developing impairment of cholinergic transmission. A further possibility is the action of NO on contractile proteins that reduces their sensitivity to Ca^{2+} (130). The activity of a cytosolic ADP-ribosyltransferase is increased by NO donors (34, 179). Whether any of these effects are produced by the nitrergic transmitter or are involved in nitrergic transmission has not been established.

COMPOSITION OF THE NITRERGIC TRANSMITTER

Detection of Release

Methods for measuring NO in biological systems have been reviewed recently (8, 91), and some have been applied to the measurement of NO released from various tissues by nitrergic nerve stimulation. The release of NO into headspace gas during nitrergic nerve stimulation of the opossum internal anal sphincter has been detected by chemiluminescence assay (39). However, this method does not discriminate between free NO and NO derived from NO donors. The stimulation-induced release of NO (or a NO-like substance) from isolated preparations has been detected by the cascade superfusion technique (20, 23, 26, 36); however, agents that discriminate between free NO and the nitrergic transmitter were not used in these experiments, which leaves the exact identity of the substance in question. In a recent study, the nitrergic transmitter behaves pharmacologically like NO (181). NOS activation resulting from stimulation of isolated myenteric ganglia (70) and strips of rat colon circular muscle (69) has been detected by the production of [³H]-citrulline after loading the tissues with L-[^{3}H]-arginine, which indicates that equivalent amounts of NO were generated by the enzyme, but again this does not identify the nature of the transmitter actually released.

Nature of EDRF

Because EDRF and the nitrergic transmitter are similar in many respects (51, 58), and because both subserve messenger roles, it is worthwhile considering the nature of EDRF, bearing in mind that comparison of EDRF with putative messengers is complicated by the release of substances other than NO (35). The original postulate that EDRF was NO was supported by the findings that the amount of NO detected by chemiluminescence (131) or by formation of methemoglobin (87) accounted for the vasorelaxant action. This postulate has been questioned on a number of grounds that were critically reviewed by Moncada and his colleagues (50, 124), who concluded that the original postulate, that EDRF is in fact NO, was correct.

EDRF was proposed to be a nitrosothiol (81, 16, 127, 147). However, evidence against this is that a low concentration of cysteine (5 μM) abolishes responses to NO and EDRF, but responses to NOCys and nitrosocysteamine are not reduced (50). In contrast, a high concentration of cysteine (1 mM) potentiates the vasorelaxant actions on rat isolated aortic rings of acidified sodium nitrite and linsidomine (9), and aqueous NO (50; CG Li & MJ Rand, unpublished observations) but EDRF-mediated relaxations are not affected (9; CG Li & MJ Rand, unpublished observations).

The free radical NO• reacts stoichiometrically with stable free radical derivatives of imidazolineoxyl N-oxide to form NO_2• (which then reacts with water to form nitrite, nitrate, and hydrogen ions) and the corresponding imidazolineoxyl (1). EDRF-mediated relaxations of rabbit aortic rings elicited by acetylcholine or ATP were blocked by these substances, and the imidazolineoxyl product of the reaction was identified in the aortic tissue in the absence but not in the presence of L-NMMA (1). These findings support the view that EDRF is NO•.

It has also been suggested that EDRF is a dinitrosyl iron cysteine complex (DINC) (171); however, the relaxant action of DNIC was much more prolonged than that of EDRF, NO, or nitrosothiols and was only weakly inhibited by oxyhemoglobin (50).

Nature of the Nitrergic Transmitter

Although EDRF is likely to be NO, there is evidence that the nitrergic transmitter is not NO. Therefore, EDRF and the nitrergic transmitter may not be identical.

Despite the fact that neuronal NOS is essential for generating the nitrergic transmitter and that aqueous NO mimics responses to the nitrergic transmitter, NO does not meet one of the essential criteria for acceptance as the transmitter;

that is, responses to the putative transmitter (NO) and those produced by nerve stimulation should be affected in comparable ways by various interacting agents. As concerns blocking agents: Hydroquinone blocked relaxant responses to NO but not those to nitrergic nerve stimulation in the bovine retractor penis muscle (64) and mouse anococcygeus muscle (77); hydroxocobalamin blocked responses of the rat anococcygeus muscle to NO but did not affect stimulation-induced relaxations (103, 140); LY-83583 blocked NO- but not stimulation-induced relaxations of the rat gastric fundus (12); and low concentrations of 7-ER blocked NO- but not stimulation-induced relaxations of the rat anococcygeus muscle (142). Furthermore, responses of the rat anococcygeus muscle to NO, but not those to nitrergic nerve stimulation, were potentiated by cysteine (138, 143). Another difference is that NO is inactivated by hemoglobin within intact erythrocytes, whereas the nitrergic transmitter of the bovine retractor penis muscle is not affected, although it is blocked by free hemoglobin (63), which suggests that the nitrergic transmitter does not readily cross the erythrocyte membrane.

A number of workers have suggested that the transmitter is a nitrosothiol, possibly nitrosocysteine (54, 93, 103, 141, 162). However, NOCys does not meet the above-mentioned criterion in the mouse anococcygeus muscle (54) or in the rat gastric fundus (93) because hydroquinone greatly reduces responses to NOCys in these tissues but does not affect nitrergic transmission. Furthermore, neither NOCys nor NOGS meet the criterion in the bovine retractor penis muscle because hydroquinone and pyrogallol block their relaxant actions but do not affect nitrergic relaxations (107). It is possible that the nitrergic transmitter is not identical in all tissues, and its nature may depend on the local availability of thiols or other compounds that can form NO adducts: we expressed this view previously (143) and JS Gillespie (personal communication) also considers it a possibility.

The role of endogenously formed nitrosothiols as putative nitrergic transmitters has been investigated by using sulfhydryl inhibitors. We (99) used ethacrynic acid, which was specifically developed as a sulfhydryl-binding diuretic to replace the more toxic mercurial diuretics. After exposure of rat anococcygeus muscles to ethacrynic acid (0.1 mM), relaxant responses to nitrergic nerve stimulation and also to NO and the NO donors SNP and GTN were virtually abolished, but the relaxant action of papaverine was only slightly reduced. The inhibitory effects of ethacrynic acid were blocked by the presence of cysteine during the period of exposure, which indicates that the inhibition was due to interaction with thiol groups. If cysteine was added after the effects of ethacrynic acid were established, the response to nitrergic nerve stimulation was slightly but significantly restored, but responses to the NO donors remained blocked. Liu and colleagues (107) used diamide (1 mM) and N-ethylmaleimide (0.3 mM) and studied their effects on relaxations of strips of bovine retractor penis muscles. These agents did not appear to reduce the tone appreciably (unlike ethacrynic acid which reversibly abolished tone in the rat anococcygeus muscle; 99). Diamide and N-ethylmaleimide reduced relaxations elicited by nitrergic nerve stimulation, NO, and GTN, but the relaxant action of isoprenaline was also reduced. The inhibitory effect of diamide against stimulation-induced relaxations, but not that of N-ethylmaleimide, was partly overcome by addition of the thiols cysteine, glutathione, or dithiothreitol. However, the inhibitory effects of both agents were completely prevented by the simultaneous presence of the thiols. The outcome of these and other investigations is that sulfhydryl inhibitors may disrupt nitrergic transmission and the NO/guanylate cyclase signal system at several points. Free sulfhydryl groups protect the inactivation of NOS in purification procedures (128), and the NADPH-diaphorase activity of rat brain is inhibited by a number of thiol-binding compounds (89, 79). Thus sulfhydryl inhibitors could impair the activity of NOS, but this does not explain the blockade of responses to NO and NO donors. The key to action may be at a regulatory point after the formation of cGMP because ethacrynic acid blocked the relaxant activity of SNP on the rat aorta but did not affect the production of cGMP (144).

An important conclusion arising from the evidence that the nitrergic transmitter is not free NO but is more likely to be a nitroso-adduct (such as a nitrosothiol) concerns the source of the adducting substances. In all the cases mentioned above, isolated tissues in physiological salt solutions were used; therefore, the adducting substance must have been derived from the tissue, and formation of the adduct may possibly have been within the nitrergic nerve terminals. Since the neurotransmitter NO adduct does not diffuse through erythrocyte membranes (63), it probably does not diffuse through axonal membranes. This conclusion raises the question of the mechanism of release of the transmitter, which is further considered below.

MECHANISM OF NITRERGIC TRANSMISSION

Absence of Preformed Store of Transmitter

NO is a readily diffusible, highly reactive, labile substance; therefore, it is highly unlikely that it could be stored as such in a biological compartment. However, it is conceivable that a NO-yielding substance could be contained in, for example, a transmitter storage vesicle (82). Gillespie and his colleagues (58, 61, 113) made many attempts to isolate the inhibitory transmitter, which was subsequently shown to be nitrergic (106, 114), from the retractor penis muscle. Their approach was based on the original finding of Ambache et al (3) that an acid extract of the bovine retractor penis mimicked stimulation-induced relaxations. This extract, termed inhibitory factor (IF), lacked biological activity unless exposed to acid and the actions of an acid-activated extract were attributed to nitric oxide (115). More recently, it was suggested that activated IF is actually a nitrosothiol (90). A major hindrance to regarding IF as the inhibitory transmitter is that it can be extracted from many tissues that lack a nitrergic innervation. Moreover, NOS inhibitors have a rapid action in blocking nitrergic transmission, and this blocking action does not depend on repeated stimulation (100, 143, 156). In contrast, inhibitors of the biosynthesis of acetylcholine or noradrenaline only gradually reduce stimulation-induced responses after long-lasting repetitive stimulation has almost exhausted the preformed stores in cholinergic and noradrenergic nerve terminals, respectively. These findings suggest that the nitrergic transmitter is formed on demand and a preformed store is sparse or absent.

Ultrastructure of Nitrergic Nerve Terminals

Studies on the morphology of nerve terminals in three tissues that are now known to receive a nitrergic innervation have been reviewed by Gillespie and his colleagues (61, 113). In rat anococcygeus muscles, about 60% of the varicose fibers are noradrenergic; the remainder, which must include nitrergic nerve fibers, contain small clear vesicles resembling those in cholinergic nerves and small granular vesicles in varying proportions. In the bovine retractor penis, varicosities of NANC fibers contain numerous large and small granular vesicles, and fractionation of homogenates reveals that the activity of a smooth muscle relaxant factor is greatest in a fraction containing mainly vesicle-like structures. In the penile artery of the bull, the varicosities contain predominantly either granular or small clear vesicles, and, although many of these may correspond to noradrenergic and cholinergic fibers, respectively, they probably also include nitrergic fibers. Thus the ultrastructure of nitrergic nerve terminals resembles that of other autonomic nerve terminals in containing vesicles within varicosities, and Gillespie and his colleagues (61, 113) conclude that the vesicles are likely to be the source of the transmitter that was released by exocytosis, as are other transmitters. However, since the evidence from functional studies indicates that there is no preformed store of transmitter, it is possible that the vesicles may contain a transmitter-generating system that is activated after exocytosis. In homogenates of bovine retractor penis and anococcygeus muscles, NOS activity is present in both soluble and particulate fractions (123, 151), and the latter may correspond to a vesicular fraction. It is often stated that NOS isolated from brain homogenates is cytosolic, but unless the procedures are specifically designed to avoid disruption of subcellular organelles, it can not be claimed that neuronal NOS is a cytosolic enzyme. Ultrastructural studies on NOS localization in peripheral nerves have not been conducted under conditions that would allow determination of whether NOS is in subcellular organelles that might correspond to transmitter storage vesicles.

Calcium Is Essential for Transmitter Release

Activation of NOS requires the presence of Ca^{2+}, and there is good evidence that release of the nitrergic transmitter follows from the influx of Ca^{2+} triggered by the action potential. Nitrergic transmission, but not responses to NO or NO donors, was reduced when Ca^{2+} influx was inhibited by ω-conotoxin (2, 21, 43, 45, 180) or by using a high Mg^{2+}, low Ca^{2+} medium (156). Furthermore, enhancement of Ca^{2+} influx by tetraethylammonium chloride enhanced nitrergic transmission (46, 65). These findings indicate that excitation-secretion coupling in nitrergic transmission requires a rise in the cytosolic Ca^{2+} concentration. In other modes of transmission, a rise in the cytosolic Ca^{2+} concentration results in translocation of vesicles, fusion with the plasma membrane, and exocytotic release of their contents (86), and this may occur in nitrergic neurons. An alternative view is that a rise in cytosolic Ca^{2+} activates NOS intraneuronally and that changes in the amount of Ca^{2+} influx are reflected in different degrees of activation of NOS.

Spontaneous Release of Transmitter

Agents that impair nitrergic transmission have been reported to raise the basal tone in a number of smooth muscle preparations with a nitrergic innervation. This occurred with NOS inhibitors in rat (60, 100, 106) and rabbit anococcygeus muscles (68); rat gastric fundus (23, 102) and distal colon (120); dog gastric antrum (130), ileocolonic junction (24, 174), and urethra (74); bovine retractor penis (106); human ileum (110) and taenia coli (161); and guinea pig colon (33); with oxyhemoglobin in dog ileocolonic junction (24), guinea pig colon (33), and rat anococcygeus (103); and with methylene blue in guinea pig colon (33). The simplest hypothesis to explain these findings is spontaneous release of the nitrergic transmitter, which raises the question of the mechanism of spontaneous release. On the assumption that NOS is activated intraneuronally, it is necessary to postulate a sufficient concentration of Ca^{2+} to produce enough NO to hold down basal tone. However, if there is exocytosis of a NO-generating system, spontaneous release could be attributed to the random exocytosis of vesicles, like that which accounts for miniature end-plate potentials in other modes of transmission.

Is NOS Released?

One expectation of exocytotic release of a NO-generating system is that it would remain active only until the cofactors were used up because the regeneration of NADPH, FAD, and FMN would require intracellular mechanisms. However, while the active system was still present, NO could be formed from extracellular L-arginine. In fact, it has been reported that L-arginine slightly decreased tone in the rat anococcygeus muscle (60) and gastric fundus (23, 102), and increased nitrergic relaxations of rat (100) and mouse (55) anococcygeus muscles, the pig trigone (132), and the rabbit urethra (5, 6), and increased the release of NO, measured by bioassay, from the dog ileocolonic junction (26). However, it has also been reported that L-arginine did not enhance stimulation-induced relaxations of rat anococcygeus or bovine retractor penis muscles (60, 106, 114, 134); dog duodenal longitudinal muscle (164, 166), jejunum (155), or urethra (74); or human ileal smooth muscle (110). Whether L-arginine has an effect could depend either on the availability of endogenous substrate or on the previous history of nitrergic nerve stimulation. Previous stimulation could either determine the amount of NOS released by exocytosis or affect the residual level of Ca^{2+} in association with NOS and hence the activity of the enzyme.

CONCLUDING REMARKS

In this review we have concentrated on the pharmacological tools for investigating various aspects of nitrergic neuroeffector transmission, potential candidates for the transmitter, and possible mechanisms of release. It is clear that more and sharper tools are required, that further candidate transmitters must be explored, and that the mechanism of release should be elucidated. Much attention has been paid to the differences between nitrergic and other modes of transmission, but our approach has been to seek as much common ground as possible. Generalizations about neurotransmission that accommodate nitrergic transmission must be developed, and these findings in turn may have to be modified if further unusual transmitters are discovered.

   Limitation of space does not allow a more comprehensive account of nitrergic transmission, which calls for consideration of cotransmitters, interaction with other transmitter systems, and the activation of nitrergic nerves by other agents; these matters have been considered to some extent elsewhere (143). A broad view of the physiological and pathophysiological roles of nitrergic transmission will have to be elaborated as a prelude to the development of therapeutic agents that interact with it.

ACKNOWLEDGMENTS

The writing of this chapter and work from the authors' laboratory reported in it were supported by program grants from the National Health and Medical Research Council and the Australian Tobacco Research Foundation. We are grateful to our colleagues Drs. George Harris, Julianne Reid, Margot Story, and Professor David Story for their critical appraisal of drafts.

Literature Cited

1. Akaike T, Yoshida M, Miyamoto Y, Sato K, Kohno M, et al. 1993. Antagonistic action of imidazolineoxyl N-oxides against endothelium-derived relaxing factor/•NO through a radical reaction. *Biochemistry* 32:827–32

2. Altiere RJ, Diamond L, Thompson DC. 1992. Omega-conotoxin-sensitive calcium channels modulate autonomic neurotransmission in guinea-pig airways. *J. Pharmacol. Exp. Ther.* 260:98–103

3. Ambache N, Killick SW, Zar MA. 1975. Extraction from ox retractor penis of an inhibitory substance which mimics its atropine-resistant neurogenic relaxation. *Br. J. Pharmacol.* 54:409–10

4. Anand N, Paterson WG. 1994. Role of nitric oxide in esophageal peristalsis. *Am. J. Physiol.* 266:G123–31

5. Andersson KE, Garcia Pascual A, Forman A, Tøttrup A. 1991. Non-adrenergic, non-cholinergic nerve-mediated relaxation of rabbit urethra is caused by nitric oxide. *Acta Physiol. Scand.* 141:133–34

6. Andersson KE, Garcia-Pascual A, Persson K, Forman A, Tøttrup A. 1992. Electrically-induced, nerve-mediated relaxation of rabbit urethra involves nitric oxide. *J. Urol.* 147:253–59

7. Andersson KE, Persson K. 1993. The L-arginine/nitric oxide pathway and non-adrenergic, non-cholinergic relaxation of the lower urinary tract. *Gen. Pharmacol.* 24:833–39

8. Archer S. 1993 Measurement of nitric oxide in biological models. *FASEB J.* 7:349–60

9. Arvola P, Pörsti I, Vuorinen P, Huhtala H, Metsä-Ketalä T, Vaapatalo H. 1992. L-cysteine augments the vasorelaxation induced by sodium nitrite and SIN-1 but not that due to acetylcholine. *Eur. J. Pharmacol.* 214:289–92

10. Assreuy J, Cunha FQ, Liew FY, Moncada S. 1993. Feedback inhibition of nitric oxide synthase activity by nitric oxide. *Br. J. Pharmacol.* 108:833–37

11. Barbier AJ, Lefebvre RA. 1992. Effect of 3-isobutyl-1-methylxanthine and zaprinast on non-adrenergic non-cholinergic relaxation in the rat gastric fundus. *Eur. J. Pharmacol.* 210:315–23

12. Barbier AJ, Lefebvre RA. 1992. Effect of LY 83583 on relaxation induced by non-adrenergic non-cholinergic nerve stimulation and exogenous nitric oxide in the rat gastric fundus. *Eur. J. Pharmacol.* 219:331–34

13. Barnes PJ, Belvisi MG. 1993. Nitric oxide and lung disease. *Thorax* 48:1034–43

14. Barnette MS, Barone FC, Fowler PJ, Grous M, Price WJ, Ormsbee HS. 1991. Human lower oesophageal relaxation is associated with raised cyclic nucleotide content. *Gut* 32:4–9

15. Barnette MS, Grous M, Manning CD, Callahan JF, Barone FC. 1990. Inhibition of neuronally induced relaxation of canine lower esophageal sphincter by opioid peptides. *Eur. J. Pharmacol.* 182:363–68

16. Bates JN, Harrison DG, Myers PR, Minor RL. 1991. EDRF: nitrosylated compound or authentic nitric oxide. *Basic Res. Cardiol.* 86(Suppl. 2):17–26

17. Bayguinov O, Sanders KM. 1993. Regulation of neural responses in the canine pyloric sphincter by opioids. *Br. J. Pharmacol.* 108:1024–30

18. Bayguinov O, Sanders KM. 1993. Role of nitric oxide as an inhibitory neurotransmitter in the canine pyloric sphincter. *Am. J. Physiol.* 264:G975–83

19. Blanquet F, Abysique A, Gonella J. 1994. In vivo study of the role of muscarinic receptors in the parasympathetic control of rabbit colonic motility. *J. Auton. Nerv. Syst.* 46:217–27

20. Boeckxstaens GE, Bult H, Pelckmans PA. 1991. Nitric oxide release in response to stimulation of nonadrenergic, noncholinergic nerves. *J. Cardiovasc. Pharmacol.* 17(Suppl. 3):S238–42

21. Boeckxstaens GE, De Man JG, Pelckmans PA, Cromheeke KM, Herman AG, Van Maercke YM. 1993. Ca^{2+} dependency of the release of nitric oxide from non-adrenergic non-cholinergic nerves. *Br. J. Pharmacol.* 110:1329–34

22. Boeckxstaens GE, De Man JG, Pelckmans PA, Herman AG, Van Maercke YM. 1993. α_2-adrenoceptor-mediated modulation of the nitrergic innervation of the canine isolated ileocolonic junction. *Br. J. Pharmacol.* 109:1079–84

23. Boeckxstaens GE, Pelckmans PA,

Bogers JJ, Bult H, De Man JG, et al. 1991. Release of nitric oxide upon stimulation of non-adrenergic, non-cholinergic nerves in the rat gastric fundus. *J. Pharmacol. Exp. Ther.* 256: 441–47

24. Boeckxstaens GE, Pelckmans PA, Bult H, De Man JG, Herman AG, Van Maercke YM. 1990. Non-adrenergic non-cholinergic relaxation mediated by nitric oxide in the canine ileocolonic junction. *Eur. J. Pharmacol.* 190:239–46

25. Boeckxstaens GE, Pelckmans PA, Rampart M, Verbeuren TJ, Herman AG, Van Maercke YM. 1991. Non-adrenergic non-cholinergic mechanisms in the ileocolonic junction. *Arch. Int. Pharmacodyn. Ther.* 303:270–81

26. Boeckxstaens GE, Pelckmans PA, Ruytjens IF, Bult H, De Man JG, et al. 1991. Bioassay of nitric oxide released upon stimulation of non-adrenergic noncholinergic nerves in the canine ileocolonic junction. *Br. J. Pharmacol.* 103: 1085–91

27. Bowman A, Drummond AH. 1984. Cyclic GMP mediates neurogenic relaxation in the bovine retractor penis muscle. *Br. J. Pharmacol.* 81:665–74

28. Bowman A, Gillespie JS. 1982. Block of some non-adrenergic inhibitory responses of smooth muscle by a substance from haemolysed erythrocytes. *J. Physiol.* 328:11–26

29. Bowman A, Gillespie JJ, Pollock D. 1982. Oxyhaemoglobin blocks non-adrenergic inhibition in the bovine retractor penis muscle. *Eur. J. Pharmacol.* 85:221–24

30. Bowman A, McGrath JC. 1985. The effect of hypoxia on neuroeffector transmission in the bovine retractor penis and rat anococcygeus muscles. *Br. J. Pharmacol.* 85:869–75

31. Bredt DS, Hwang PM, Glatt CE, Lowenstein C, Reed RR, Snyder SH. 1991. Cloned and expressed nitric oxide synthase structurally resembles cytochrome P-450 reductase. *Nature* 351: 714–18

32. Bredt DS, Hwang PM, Snyder SH. 1990. Localization of nitric oxide synthase indicating a neural role for nitric oxide. *Nature* 347:768–70

33. Briejer MR, Akkermans LMA, Meulemans AL, Lefebvre RA, Schuurkes JA. 1992. Nitric oxide is involved in 5-HT-induced relaxations of the guinea-pig colon ascendens in vitro. *Br. J. Pharmacol.* 107:756–61

34. Brüne B, Dimmeler S, Molina y Vedia L, Lapetina EG. 1993. Nitric oxide: a signal for ADP-ribosylation of proteins. *Life Sci.* 279:286–90

35. Buga GM, Gold ME, Wood KS, Chaudhuri G, Ignarro LJ. 1989. Endothelium-derived nitric oxide relaxes nonvascular smooth muscle. *Eur. J. Pharmacol.* 161: 61–72

36. Bult H, Boeckxstaens GE, Pelckmans PA, Jordaens FH, Van Maercke YM, Herman AG. 1990. Nitric oxide as an inhibitory non-adrenergic non-cholinergic neurotransmitter. *Nature* 345:346–47

37. Byrne NG, Muir TC. 1984. Electrical and mechanical responses of the bovine retractor penis to nerve stimulation and to drugs. *J. Auton. Pharmacol.* 4:261–71

38. Chakder S, Rattan S. 1992. Neurally mediated relaxation of opossum internal anal sphincter: influence of superoxide anion generator and the scavenger. *J. Pharmacol. Exp. Ther.* 260:1113–18

39. Chakder S, Rattan S. 1993. Release of nitric oxide by activation of nonadrenergic noncholinergic neurons of internal anal sphincter. *Am. J. Physiol.* 264: G7–12

40. Chakder S, Rattan S. 1993. Involvement of cAMP and cGMP in relaxation of internal anal sphincter by neural stimulation, VIP, and NO. *Am. J. Physiol.* 264:G702–7

41. Cooper JR. 1991. Biochemical mechanisms involved in regulating transmitter release. In *Presynaptic Regulation of Neurotransmitter Release: A Handbook,* ed. J Feigenbaum, M Hanani, pp. 251–64. Freund: Tel Aviv

42. Dale HH. 1933. Nomenclature of fibres in the autonomic system and their effects. *J. Physiol.* 80:P10–11

43. Daniel EE, Haugh C, Woskowska Z, Cipris S, Jury J, Fox-Threlkeld JET. 1994. Role of nitric oxide-related inhibition in intestinal function: relation to vasoactive intestinal polypeptide. *Am. J. Physiol.* 266:G31–39

44. Dawson TM, Bredt DS, Fotuhi M, Hwang PM, Snyder SH. 1991. Nitric oxide synthase and neuronal NADPH diaphorase are identical in brain and peripheral tissues. *Proc. Natl. Acad. Sci. USA* 88:7797–801

45. De Luca A, Li CG, Rand MJ, Reid JJ, Thaina P, Wong-Dusting HK. 1990. Effects of ω-conotoxin GVIA on peripheral neuroeffector transmission in various tissues. *Br. J. Pharmacol.* 101:437–47

46. De Man JG, Boeckxstaens GE, Pelckmans PA, De Winter BY, Herman AG, Van Maercke YM. 1991. Prejunctional modulation of the nitrergic

innervation of the canine ileocolonic junction via potassium channels. *Br. J. Pharmacol.* 110:559–64

46a. De May JG, Vanhoutte PM. 1983. Anoxia and endothelium-dependent reactivity in canine femoral artery. *J. Physiol.* 335:65–74

47. Di Iulio JL, Gude NM, Li CG, Rand MJ, King RG. 1993. Cytochrome P450 inhibitor 7-ethoxyresorufin inhibits human placental nitric oxide synthase. *Clin. Exp. Pharmacol. Physiol. Suppl.* 1:20

48. Dokita S, Morgan WR, Wheeler MA, Yoshida M, Latifpour J, Weiss RM. 1991. N^G-nitro-L-arginine inhibits nonadrenergic, non-cholinergic relaxation in rabbit urethral smooth muscle. *Life Sci.* 48:2429–36

49. Du C, Murray J, Bates JN, Conklin JN. 1991. Nitric oxide: mediator of NANC hyperpolarization of opossum oesophageal smooth muscle. *Am. J. Physiol.* 261:G1012–16

50. Feelisch M, te Poel M, Zamora R, Deussen A, Moncada S. 1994. Understanding the controversy over the identity of EDRF. *Nature* 368:62–65

51. Furchgott RF. 1988. Studies on relaxation of rabbit aorta by sodium nitrite: the basis for the proposal that the acid-activatable inhibitory factor from bovine retractor penis is inorganic nitrite and the endothelium-derived relaxing factor is nitric oxide. In *Vasodilatation: Vascular Smooth Muscle, Peptides, Autonomic Nerves, and Endothelium*, ed. PM Vanhoutte, pp. 401–14. New York: Raven

52. Furchgott RF, Jothianandan D. 1991. Endothelium-dependent and -independent vasodilation involving cyclic GMP: relaxation induced by nitric oxide, carbon monoxide and light. *Blood Vessels* 28:52–61

53. Garthwaite J. 1991. Glutamate, nitric oxide and cell-cell signalling in the nervous system. *Trends Neurosci.* 14:60–67

54. Gibson A, Babbedge R, Brave SR, Hart SL, Hobbs AJ, et al. 1992. An investigation of some S-nitrosothiols, and of hydroxy-arginine, on the mouse anococcygeus. *Br. J. Pharmacol.* 107:715–21

55. Gibson A, Mirzazadeh S, Hobbs AJ, Moore PK. 1990. L-N^G-monomethyl-arginine and L-N^G-nitro-arginine inhibit non-adrenergic, non-cholinergic relaxation of the mouse anococcygeus. *Br. J. Pharmacol.* 99:602–6

56. Gibson A, Tucker JF. 1982. The effects of vasoactive intestinal polypeptide and

of adenosine 5′ triphosphate on the isolated anococcygeus muscle of the mouse. *Br. J. Pharmacol.* 77:97–103

57. Gibson QH, Roughton FJW. 1957. The kinetics and equilibria of the reactions of nitric oxide with sheep haemoglobin. *J. Physiol.* 136:507–26

58. Gillespie JS. 1987. Searching for the non-adrenergic, non-cholinergic autonomic transmitter. In *Pharmacology*, ed. MJ Rand, C Raper, pp. 161–70. Amsterdam: Exerpta Medica

59. Gillespie JS, Hunter JC, McKnight AT. 1982. The effect of ethanol on inhibitory and motor responses in the rat and rabbit anococcygeus and the bovine retractor penis muscle. *Br. J. Pharmacol.* 75:189–98

60. Gillespie JS, Liu XR, Martin W. 1989. The effects of L-arginine and N^G-monomethyl-L-arginine on the response of the rat anococcygeus muscle to NANC nerve stimulation. *Br. J. Pharmacol.* 98:1080–82

61. Gillespie JS, Liu X, Martin W. 1990. The neurotransmitter of the non-adrenergic non-cholinergic inhibitory nerves to smooth muscle of the genital system. In *Nitric Oxide from L-Arginine. A Bioregulatory System*, ed. S Moncada, pp. 147–64. Amsterdam: Elsevier

62. Gillespie JS, Sheng H. 1988. Influence of haemoglobin and erythrocytes on the effects of EDRF, a smooth muscle inhibitory factor, and nitric oxide on vascular and non-vascular smooth muscle. *Br. J. Pharmacol.* 95:1151–56

63. Gillespie JS, Sheng H. 1989. A comparison of haemoglobin and erythrocytes as inhibitors of smooth muscle relaxation by the NANC transmitter in the BRP and rat anococcygeus and by EDRF in the rabbit aortic strip. *Br. J. Pharmacol.* 98:445–50

64. Gillespie JS, Sheng H. 1990. The effects of pyrogallol and hydroquinone on the response to NANC nerve stimulation in the rat anococcygeus and the bovine retractor penis muscles. *Br. J. Pharmacol.* 99:194–96

65. Gillespie JS, Tilmisany AK. 1976. The action of tetraethylammonium chloride on the response of the rat anococcygeus muscle to motor and inhibitory nerve stimulation and to some drugs. *Br. J. Pharmacol.* 58:47–55

66. Gold ME, Wood KS, Buga GM, Byrns RE, Ignarro LJ. 1989. L-Arginine causes whereas L-argininosuccinic acid inhibits endothelium-dependent vascular smooth muscle relaxation. *Biochem. Biophys. Res. Commun.* 161:536–43

67. Goy MF. 1991. cGMP: The wayward

child of the cyclic nucleotide family. *Trends Neurosci.* 14:293–99

68. Graham AM, Sneddon P. 1993. Evidence for nitric oxide as an inhibitory neurotransmitter in rabbit isolated anococcygeus. *Eur. J. Pharmacol.* 237:93–99

69. Grider JR. 1993. Interplay of VIP and nitric oxide in regulation of the descending relaxation phase of peristalsis. *Am. J. Physiol.* 264:G334–40

70. Grider JR, Jin JG. 1993. VIP release and L-citrulline production from isolated ganglia of the myenteric plexus: evidence for regulation of vasoactive intestinal peptide release by nitric oxide. *Neuroscience* 54:521–26

71. Grous M, Joslyn AF, Tompson W, Barnette MS. 1991. Changes in intracellular cyclic nucleotide content accompanies relaxation of the isolated canine internal anal sphincter. *J. Gastrointest. Motil.* 3:46–52

72. Gryglewski RJ, Palmer RMJ, Moncada S. 1986. Superoxide anion is involved in the breakdown of endothelium-derived relaxing factor. *Nature* 320:454–56

73. Gryglewski RJ, Zembowicz A, Salvemini D, Taylor GW, Vane JR. 1992. Modulation of the pharmacological actions of nitrovasodilators by methylene blue and pyocyanin. *Br. J. Pharmacol.* 106:838–45

74. Hashimoto S, Kigoshi S, Muramatsu I. 1993. Nitric oxide-dependent and -independent neurogenic relaxation of isolated dog urethra. *Eur. J. Pharmacol.* 231:209–14

75. Hata F, Ishii T, Kanada A, Yamano N, Kataoka T, et al. 1990. Essential role of nitric oxide in descending inhibition in the rat proximal colon. *Biochem. Biophys. Res. Commun.* 172:1400–6

76. Henry Y, Lepoivre M, Drapier JC, Ducrocq C, Boucher JL, Guissani A. 1993. EPR characterization of molecular targets for NO in mammalian cells and organelles. *FASEB J.* 7:1124–34

77. Hobbs AJ, Tucker JF, Gibson A. 1991. Differentiation by hydroquinone of relaxations induced by exogenous and endogenous nitrates in non-vascular smooth muscle: role of superoxide anions. *Br. J. Pharmacol.* 104:645–50

78. Hope GT, Michael GJ, Knigge KM, Vincent SR. 1991. Neuronal NADPH diaphorase is a nitric oxide synthase. *Proc. Natl. Acad. Sci. USA* 88:2811–14

79. Hope GT, Vincent SR. 1989. Histochemical characterization of neuronal NADPH-diaphorase. *J. Histochem. Cytochem.* 37:653–61

80. Huizinga JD, Tomlinson J, Pintin-Quezada J. 1992. Involvement of nitric oxide in nerve-mediated inhibition and action of vasoactive intestinal peptide in colonic smooth muscle. *J. Pharmacol. Exp. Ther.* 260:803–8

81. Ignarro LJ. 1989. Endothelium-derived nitric oxide: pharmacology and relationship to the actions of organic nitrate esters. *Pharmacol. Res.* 6:651–59

82. Ignarro LJ. 1990. Nitric oxide: a novel signal transduction mechanism for transcellular communication. *Hypertension* 16:477–83

83. Ito S, Kurokawa A, Ohga A, Sawabe K. 1990. Mechanical, electrical, and cyclic nucleotide responses to peptide VIP and inhibitory nerve stimulation in rat stomach. *J. Physiol.* 430:337–53

84. Kanada A, Hata F, Suthamnatpong N, Maehara T, Ishii T, et al. 1992. Key roles of nitric oxide and cyclic GMP in nonadrenergic and noncholinergic inhibition in rat ileum. *Eur. J. Pharmacol.* 216:287–92

85. Kanada A, Hosokawa M, Suthamnatpong N, Maehara T, Takeuchi T, Hata F. 1993. Neuronal pathway involved in nitric oxide-mediated descending relaxation in rat ileum. *Eur. J. Pharmacol.* 250:59–66

86. Kandel ER. 1991. Transmitter release. In *Principles of Neural Science,* ed. ER Kandel, JH Schwartz, TM Jessell, pp. 194–212. New York: Elsevier

87. Kelm M, Schrader J. 1988. Nitric oxide from the isolated guinea-pig heart. *Eur. J Pharmacol.* 155:317–21

88. Kelm M, Schrader J. 1990. Control of coronary vascular tone by nitric oxide. *Circ. Res.* 66:1561–75

89. Kemp MC, Kuonen DR, Sutton A, Roberts PJ. 1988. Rat brain NADPH-dependent diaphorase: a possible relationship to cytochrome P450 reductase. *Biochem. Pharmacol.* 37:3063–70

90. Kerr SW, Buchanan LV, Bunting S, Mathews WR. 1992. Evidence that S-nitrosothiols are responsible for the smooth muscle relaxing activity of the bovine retractor penis inhibitory factor. *J. Pharmacol. Exp. Ther.* 263:285–92

91. Kiechle FL, Malinski T. 1993. Nitric oxide. Biochemistry, pathophysiology, and detection. *Am. J. Clin. Pathol.* 100:567–75

92. Kimoto M, Tsuji H, Ogawa T, Sasaoka K. 1993. Detection of N^G,N^G-dimethylarginine dimethylaminohydrolase in the nitric oxide-generating systems of rats using monoclonal antibody. *Arch. Biochem. Biophys.* 300:657–62

93. Kitamura K, Lian Q, Carl A, Kuriyama

H. 1993. S-Nitrosocysteine, but not sodium nitroprusside, produces apaminsensitive hyperpolarization in rat gastric fundus. *Br. J. Pharmacol.* 109:415–23

94. Kowaluk EA, Fung HL. 1990. Spontaneous liberation of nitric oxide cannot account for in vitro vascular relaxation by S-nitrosothiols. *J. Pharmacol. Exp. Ther.* 255:1256–64

95. Lefebvre RA. 1993. Non-adrenergic non-cholinergic neurotransmission in the proximal stomach. *Gen. Pharmacol.* 24:257–66

96. Lefebvre RA, Smits GJM. 1992. Modulation of non-adrenergic non-cholinergic inhibitory neurotransmission in rat gastric fundus by the α_2-adrenoceptor agonist, UK-14,304. *Br. J. Pharmacol.* 107:256–61

97. Lei SZ, Pan ZH, Aggarwal SK, Chen HSV, Hartman J, et al. 1992. Effect of nitric oxide production on the redox modulatory site of the NMDA receptor-channel complex. *Neuron* 8:1087–99

98. Lewis SJ, Davisson RL, Bates JN, Johnson AK, Ohta H, Talman WT. 1994. Stereoselective cardiovascular actions of centrally-injected S-nitrosocysteine in conscious rats. *Abstr. 15th Sci. Meet. Int. Soc. Hypertens., Melbourne*, p. 176, S31

99. Li CG, Brosch SF, Rand MJ. 1994. Inhibition by ethacrynic acid of NO-mediated relaxations of the rat anococcygeus muscle. *Clin. Exp. Pharmacol. Physiol.* 21:293–99

100. Li CG, Rand MJ. 1989. Evidence for a role of nitric oxide in the neurotransmitter system mediating relaxation of the rat anococcygeus muscle. *Clin. Exp. Pharmacol. Physiol.* 16:933–38

101. Li CG, Rand MJ. 1989. Prejunctional inhibition of non-adrenergic non-cholinergic transmission in the rat anococcygeus muscle. *Eur. J. Pharmacol.* 168:107–10

102. Li CG, Rand MJ. 1990. Nitric oxide and vasoactive intestinal polypeptide mediate non-adrenergic, non-cholinergic inhibitory transmission to smooth muscle of the rat gastric fundus. *Eur. J. Pharmacol.* 191:303–9

103. Li CG, Rand MJ. 1993. Effects of hydroxocobalamin and haemoglobin on NO-mediated relaxations in the rat anococcygeus muscle. *Clin. Exp. Pharmacol. Physiol.* 20:633–40

104. Li CG, Rand MJ. 1993. Inhibition of NO-mediated vasodilatation by the cytochrome P450 inhibitor 7-ER. *Clin. Exp. Pharmacol. Physiol.* Suppl. 1:43 (Abstr.)

105. Lincoln TM, Cornwell TL. 1993. Intracellular cyclic GMP receptor proteins. *FASEB J.* 7:328–38

106. Liu X, Gillespie JS, Gibson IF, Martin W. 1991. Effects of N^G-substituted analogues of L-arginine on NANC relaxation of the rat anococcygeus and bovine retractor penis muscles and the bovine penile artery. *Br. J. Pharmacol.* 104:53–58

107. Liu X, Gillespie JS, Martin W. 1994. Non-adrenergic, non-cholinergic relaxation of the bovine retractor penis muscle: role of S-nitrosothiols. *Br. J. Pharmacol.* 111:1287–95

108. Lüscher T, Vanhoutte PM. 1990. *The Endothelium: Modulator of Cardiovascular Function.* p. 9. Boca Raton, Fla.: CRC

109. MacDonald A, Kelly J, Dettmar PW. 1990. Pre- and post-junctional α-adrenoceptor-mediated responses in the rat gastric fundus in vitro. *J. Pharm. Pharmacol.* 42:752–57

110. Maggi CA, Barbanti G, Turini D, Giuliani S. 1991. Effect of N^G-monomethyl L-arginine (L-NMMA) and N^G-nitro L-arginine (L-NOARG) on non-adrenergic non-cholinergic relaxation in the circular muscle of the human ileum. *Br. J. Pharmacol.* 103:1970–72

111. Marczin N, Ryan US, Catravas JD. 1992. Methylene blue inhibits nitrovasodilator- and endothelium-derived relaxing factor-induced cyclic GMP accumulation in cultured pulmonary arterial smooth muscle cells via generation of superoxide anion. *J. Pharmacol. Exp. Ther.* 263:170–79

112. Marshall JJ, Wei EP, Kontos HA. 1988. Independent blockade of cerebral vasodilation from acetylcholine and nitric oxide. *Am. J. Physiol.* 255:H847–54

113. Martin W, Gillespie JS. 1991. L-arginine derived nitric oxide: the basis of inhibitory transmission in the anococcygeus and retractor penis muscle. In *Novel Peripheral Neurotransmitters*, ed. C Bell, pp. 65–79. New York: Pergamon

114. Martin W, Gillespie JS, Gibson IF. 1993. Actions and interactions of N^G-substituted analogues of L-arginine on NANC neurotransmission in the bovine retractor penis and rat anococcygeus muscles. *Br. J. Pharmacol.* 108:242–47

115. Martin W, Smith JA, Lewis MJ, Henderson AH. 1988. Evidence that inhibitory factor extracted from bovine retractor penis is nitrite, whose acid activated derivative is stabilized nitric oxide. *Br. J. Pharmacol.* 93:579–86

116. Mathews WR, Kerr SW. 1993. Biological activity of S-nitrosothiols: the role

of nitric oxide. *J. Pharmacol. Exp. Ther.* 267:1529–37

117. Matsumoto T, Okamura T, Kinoshita M, Toda N. 1993. Interactions of nitrovasodilators and atrial natriuretic peptide in isolated dog coronary arteries. *Eur. J. Pharmacol.* 237:31–37

118. Mayer B, Brunner F, Schmidt K. 1993. Inhibition of nitric oxide synthesis by methylene blue. *Biochem. Pharmacol.* 45:367–74

119. Mayer B, Klatt P, Bohme E, Schmidt K. 1992. Regulation of neuronal nitric oxide and cyclic GMP formation by Ca^{2+}. *J. Neurochem.* 59:2024–29

120. Middleton SJ, Cuthbert AW, Shorthouse M, Hunter JO. 1993. Nitric oxide affects mammalian distal colonic smooth muscle by tonic neural inhibition. *Br. J. Pharmacol.* 108:974–79

121. Millar IT, Springall HD. 1966. *The Organic Chemistry of Nitrogen, Third Edition,* pp. 84–87. Oxford: Clarendon

122. Mirzazadeh S, Hobbs AJ, Tucker JF, Gibson A. 1991. Cyclic nucleotide content of the rat anococcygeus during relaxations induced by drugs or by non-adrenergic, non-cholinergic field stimulation. *J. Pharm. Pharmacol.* 43:247–57

123. Mitchell JA, Sheng H, Förstermann U, Murad F. 1991. Characterization of nitric oxide synthases in non-adrenergic, non-cholinergic nerve containing tissue from the rat anococcygeus muscle. *Br. J. Pharmacol.* 104:289–91

124. Moncada S, Palmer MJ, Higgs EA. 1991. Nitric oxide: physiology, pathophysiology and pharmacology. *Pharmacol. Rev.* 43:109–42

125. Mülsch A, Busse R, Liebau S, Förstermann U. 1988. LY 83583 interferes with the release of endothelium derived relaxing factor and inhibits soluble guanylate cyclase. *J. Pharmacol. Exp. Ther.* 247:283–88

126. Murray LA, Du C, Ledlow A, Mantemach PL, Conklin JL. 1992. Guanylate cyclase inhibitors: effect on tone, relaxation, and cGMP content of lower esophageal sphincter. *Am. J. Physiol.* 263:G97–101

127. Myers PR, Minor RL, Guerra R, Bates JN, Harrison DG. 1990. Vasorelaxant properties of the endothelium-derived relaxing factor more closely resemble S-nitrosocysteine than nitric oxide. *Nature* 345:161–63

128. Nathan CF. 1992. Nitric oxide as a secretory product of mammalian cells. *FASEB J.* 6:3051–64

129. Osthaus LE, Galligan JJ. 1992. Antagonists of nitric oxide synthesis inhibit nerve-mediated relaxations of longitudi-

nal muscle in guinea pig ileum. *J. Pharmacol. Exp. Ther.* 260:140–45

130. Ozaki H, Blondfield DP, Hori M, Publicover NG, Kato I, Sanders KM. 1992 Spontaneous release of nitric oxide inhibits electrical, Ca^{2+} and mechanical transients in canine gastric smooth muscle. *J. Physiol.* 445:231–47

131. Palmer RMJ, Ferrige AG, Moncada S. 1987. Nitric oxide release accounts for the biological activity of endothelium-derived relaxing factor. *Nature* 227:524–26

132. Persson K, Andersson KE. 1992. Nitric oxide and relaxation of pig lower urinary tract. *Br. J. Pharmacol.* 106:416–22

133. Rajanayagam MAS, Li CG, Rand MJ. 1993. Differential effects of hydroxocobalamin on NO-mediated relaxations in rat aorta and anococcygeus muscle. *Br. J. Pharmacol.* 108:3–5

134. Ramagopal MV, Leighton HJ. 1989. Effect of N^G-monomethyl-L-arginine on field stimulation-induced decreases in cytosolic Ca^{2+} levels and relaxation in the rat anococcygeus muscle. *Eur. J. Pharmacol.* 174:297–99

135. Rand MJ. 1992. New perspectives in neurotransmission: nitric oxide, the mediator of nitrergic transmission. *Proc. Aust. Physiol. Pharmacol. Soc.* 23:1–16

136. Rand MJ. 1992. Nitrergic transmission: nitric oxide as a mediator of non-adrenergic, non-cholinergic neuro-effector transmission. *Clin. Exp. Pharmacol. Physiol.* 19:147–69

137. Rand MJ, Li CG. 1992. Effects of argininosuccinic acid on nitric oxide-mediated relaxations in rat aorta and anococcygeus muscle. *Clin. Exp. Pharmacol. Physiol.* 19:331–34

138. Rand MJ, Li CG. 1992. Differential effects of cysteine and glutathione on NO- and stimulation-induced relaxations of the rat anococcygeus muscle. *Proc. Aust. Physiol. Pharmacol. Soc.* 23:175P (Abstr.)

139. Rand MJ, Li CG. 1993. The inhibition of nitric oxide-mediated relaxations in rat aorta and anococcygeus muscle by diphenylene iodonium. *Clin. Exp. Pharmacol. Physiol.* 20:141–48

140. Rand MJ, Li CG. 1993. Differential effects of hydroxocobalamin on relaxations induced by nitrosothiols in rat aorta and anococcygeus muscle. *Eur. J. Pharmacol.* 241:249–54

141. Rand MJ, Li CG. 1993. Effects of ethanol and other aliphatic alcohols on NO-mediated relaxations in rat anococcygeus muscles and gastric fundus strips. *Br. J. Pharmacol.* 111:1089–94

142. Rand MJ, Li CG. 1993. Effects of the

cytochrome P450 inhibitor 7-ER on relaxations to nitrergic nerve stimulation and exogenous nitric oxide. *Clin. Exp. Pharmacol. Physiol.* Suppl. 1:59 (Abstr.)

143. Rand MJ, Li CG. 1994. Nitric oxide in the autonomic and enteric nervous systems. In *Nitric Oxide in the Nervous System,* ed. SR Vincent. London: Academic. In press

144. Rapoport RM, Murad F. 1983. Effects of ethacrynic acid and cystamine on sodium nitroprusside-induced relaxation, cyclic GMP levels and guanylate cyclase activity in rat aorta. *Gen. Pharmacol.* 19:61–65

145. Rengasamy A, Johns RA. 1993. Regulation of nitric oxide synthase by nitric oxide. *Mol. Pharmacol.* 44:124–28

146. Rogers NE, Ignarro LJ. 1992. Constitutive nitric oxide synthase from cerebellum is reversibly inhibited by nitric oxide formed from L-arginine. *Biochem. Biophys. Res. Commun.* 189:242–49

147. Rubanyi GM, Johns A, Wilcox D, Bates FN, Harrison DG. 1991. Evidence that S-nitrosothiol, but not nitric oxide, may be identical with endothelium-derived relaxing factor. *J. Cardiovasc. Pharmacol.* 17(Suppl. 3):S41–45

148. Rubanyi GM, Vanhoutte PM. 1986. Superoxide anion and hyperoxia inactivate endothelium-derived relaxing factor. *Am. J. Physiol.* 250:H822–27

149. Sanders KM, Ward SM. 1992. Nitric oxide as a mediator of nonadrenergic noncholinergic neurotransmission. *Am. J. Physiol.* 262:G379–92

150. Schmidt HHHW, Lohmann SM, Walter U. 1993. The nitric oxide and cGMP signal transduction system—regulation and mechanism of action. *Biochim. Biophys. Acta* 1178:153–75

151. Sheng H, Schmidt HHHW, Nakane M, Mitchell JA, Pollock JS, et al. 1992. Characterization and localization of nitric oxide synthase in non-adrenergic, non-cholinergic nerves from bovine retractor penis muscle. *Br. J. Pharmacol.* 106:768–73

152. Sjöstrand NO. 1994. Nitric oxide and neural regulation of the penis. See Ref. 143. In press

153. Sneddon P, Graham A. 1992. Role of nitric oxide in the autonomic innervation of smooth muscle. *J. Auton. Pharmacol.* 12:445–56

154. Stamler JS, Singel DJ, Loscalzo J. 1992. Biochemistry of nitric oxide and its redox-activated forms. *Science* 258:1898–902

155. Stark ME, Bauer AJ, Sarr MG, Szurzewski JH. 1993. Nitric oxide mediates inhibitory nerve input in human and canine jejunum. *Gastroenterology* 104:398–409

156. Stark ME, Bauer AJ, Szurszewski JH. 1991. Effect of nitric oxide on circular muscle of the canine small intestine. *J. Physiol.* 444:743–61

157. Stark ME, Szurszewski JH. 1992. Role of nitric oxide in gastrointestinal and hepatic function and disease. *Gastroenterology* 103:1928–49

158. Stuehr D, Fasehun OA, Kwon NS, Gross SS, Gonzalez JA, et al. 1991. Inhibition of macrophage and endothelial cell nitric oxide synthase by diphenyleneiodonium and its analogs. *FASEB J.* 5:98–103

159. Suthamnatpong N, Hata F, Kanada A, Takeuchi T, Yagasaki O. 1993. Mediators of nonadrenergic, noncholinergic inhibition in the proximal, middle and distal regions of rat colon. *Br. J. Pharmacol.* 108:348–55

160. Suzuki N, Mizuno K, Gomi Y. 1994. Role of nitric oxide in the peristalsis of isolated guinea-pig ileum. *Eur. J. Pharmacol.* 251:221–27

161. Tam SF, Hillier K. 1992. The role of nitric oxide in mediating non-adrenergic non-cholinergic relaxation in longitudinal muscle of human taenia coli. *Life Sci.* 51:1277–84

162. Thornbury KD, Ward SM, Dalziel HH, Carl A, Westfall DP, Sanders KM. 1991. Nitric oxide and nitrosocysteine mimic nonadrenergic noncholinergic hyperpolarization in canine proximal colon. *Am. J. Physiol.* 261:G553–57

163. Toda N. 1994. Nitric oxide and the regulation of cerebral blood flow. See Ref. 143. In press

164. Toda N, Baba H, Okamura T. 1990. Role of nitric oxide in non-adrenergic, non-cholinergic nerve-mediated relaxation in dog duodenal longitudinal muscle strips. *Jpn. J. Pharmacol.* 53:281–84

165. Toda N, Inoue S, Okunishi H, Okamura T. 1990. Intra- and extraluminally-applied acetylcholine on the vascular tone or the response to transmural stimulation in dog isolated mesenteric arteries. *Naunyn-Schmiedeberg's Arch. Pharmacol.* 341:30–36

166. Toda N, Tanobe Y, Baba H. 1991. Suppression by N^G-nitro-L-arginine of relaxations induced by non-adrenergic, non-cholinergic nerve stimulation in dog duodenal longitudinal muscle. *Jpn. J. Pharmacol.* 57:527–34

167. Torphy TJ, Fine CF, Burman M, Barnette MS, Ormsbee HS. 1986. Lower esophageal sphincter relaxation is associated with increased cyclic nucleotide content. *Am. J. Physiol.* 251:G786–93

168. Tøttrup A. 1993. The role of nitric oxide in oesophageal motor function. *Dis. Esophagus* 6:2–10

169. Tu SI, Byler DM, Cavanaugh JR. 1984. Nitrite inhibition of acyl transferase by coenzyme A via the formation of an S-nitrosothiol derivative. *J. Agric. Food Chem.* 32:1057–60

170. Vallance P, Leone A, Calver A, Collier J, Moncada S. 1992. Endogenous dimethylarginine as an inhibitor of nitric oxide synthesis. *J. Cardiovasc. Pharmacol.* 20(Suppl. 12):S60–62

171. Vedernikov YP, Mordvintcev PI, Malenkova IV, Vanin AF. 1992. Similarity between the vasorelaxing activity of dinitrosyl iron cysteine complexes and endothelium-derived relaxing factor. *Eur. J. Pharmacol.* 211:313–37

172. Wang YX, Poon CI, Poon KS, Pang CCY. 1993. Inhibitory actions of diphenyleneiodonium on endothelium-dependent vasodilatations in vitro and in vivo. *Br. J. Pharmacol.* 110:1232–38

173. Ward SM, Dalziel HH, Bradley ME, Buxton IL, Keef K, et al. 1992. Involvement of cyclic GMP in non-adrenergic, non-cholinergic inhibitory neurotransmission in dog proximal colon. *Br. J. Pharmacol.* 107:1075–82

174. Ward SM, McKeen ES, Sanders KM. 1992. Role of nitric oxide in non-adrenergic, non-cholinergic inhibitory junction potentials in canine ileocolonic sphincter. *Br. J. Pharmacol.* 105:776–82

175. Westfall TC, Martin JR. 1991. Presynaptic receptors in the peripheral and central nervous system. See Ref. 41, pp. 311–70

176. Williams DLH. 1985. S-nitrosation and the reactions of S-nitroso compounds. *Chem. Soc. Rev.* 14:171–96

177. Wolin MS, Cherry PD, Rodenburg JM, Messina EJ, Kaley G. 1990. Methylene blue inhibits vasodilation of skeletal muscle arterioles to acetylcholine and nitric oxide via the extracellular generation of superoxide anions. *J. Pharmacol. Exp. Ther.* 254:872–76

178. Zembowicz A, Hatchett RJ, Radziszewski W, Gryglewski J. 1993. Inhibition of endothelial nitric oxide synthase by ebselen. Prevention by thiols suggests the inactivation by ebselen of a critical thiol essential for the catalytic activity of nitric oxide synthase. *J. Pharmacol. Exp. Ther.* 267: 1112–18

179. Zhang J, Snyder SH. 1992. Nitric oxide stimulates auto–ADP-ribosylation of glyceraldehyde-3-phosphate dehydrogenase. *Proc. Natl. Acad. Sci. USA* 89: 9382–85

180. Zigmunt PM, Zigmunt PKE, Högestätt ED, Andersson KE. 1993. Effects of ω-conotoxin on adrenergic, cholinergic and NANC neurotransmission in the rabbit urethra and detrusor. *Br. J. Pharmacol.* 110:1285–90

ADDED IN PROOF

181. Boeckxstaens GE, De Man JF, De Winter BY, Herman AG, Pelckmans PA. 1994. Pharmacological similarity between nitric oxide and the nitrergic neurotransmitter in the canine ileocolonic junction. *Eur. J. Pharmacol.* 264:85–89

Annu. Rev. Physiol. 1995. 57:683–706

NITRIC OXIDE SIGNALING IN THE CENTRAL NERVOUS SYSTEM

J. Garthwaite and C. L. Boulton

Wellcome Research Laboratories, Langley Court, South Eden Park Road, Beckenham BR3 3BS, England

KEY WORDS: cyclic GMP, synaptic plasticity, ion channels, neurotransmitter release, cerebral blood flow

INTRODUCTION

Nitric oxide (NO) was first recognized as a messenger molecule in the central nervous system (CNS) in 1988 (52), when it was identified as the unstable intercellular factor that had been hypothesized, a year earlier (53), to mediate the increased cyclic GMP (cGMP) levels that occur on activation of glutamate receptors, particularly those of the NMDA (*N*-methyl-D-aspartate) subtype. The presence of an NO-forming enzyme (NO synthase, or NOS) in the brain was later confirmed (74), and this enzyme was subsequently purified (14) and its cDNA cloned and sequenced (12).

The discovery that NO functions as a signaling molecule in the brain opened a new dimension in our concept of neural communication, one overlaying the classical picture of chemical neurotransmission, where information is passed between neuronal elements at discrete loci (synapses), and in one direction, with a diffusive type of signal that disregards the spatial constraints on neurotransmitter activity normally imposed by membranes, transporters, and inactivating enzymes. In principle, NO could spread out from its site of production to influence many different tissue elements (neuronal, glial, and vascular) that are not necessarily in close anatomical juxtaposition.

During the past few years, much information on the enzymology and molecular characteristics of NO synthesis has accrued, as reviewed in other articles in this volume. Furthermore, data from immunocytochemistry, in situ hybridization, and NADPH diaphorase histochemistry have combined to give

683

0066–4278/95/0315–0683$05.00

a reasonably coherent picture of the anatomical locations of NO-generating cells and their processes throughout the CNS (134). The brain contains by far the highest activity of NOS of any tissue so far examined (108), and the widespread distribution of the enzyme therein indicates that NO could be involved in practically all aspects of CNS function. We do not attempt here to review all of the putative roles of NO in the CNS that have accumulated in recent years but instead focus on the cellular and molecular mechanisms of neural NO signaling and signal transduction.

REGULATION OF NO FORMATION

Neurons

Under normal conditions, NOS in the CNS apparently occurs exclusively in neurons (13). The production of NO by intact neurons in response to excitatory stimuli requires Ca^{2+} (52), which reflects the dependence of the activity of neuronal NOS (nNOS) on Ca^{2+} and calmodulin (14, 74). Depending on the location of the enzyme, NOS activation is coupled to one of two main types of physiological stimuli: postsynaptic neurotransmitter receptor stimulation leading to Ca^{2+} influx or mobilization, and action potentials in presynaptic nerves eliciting Ca^{2+} influx through voltage–sensitive Ca^{2+} channels.

Postsynaptically, a major stimulus for NO formation is the activation of receptors for the principal excitatory neurotransmitter glutamate. Of special importance are NMDA receptors whose associated ion channel has a high effective permeability to Ca^{2+}. Other ion channel–coupled glutamate receptors of both the AMPA (α-amino-3-hydroxy-5-methyl-4-isoxazolepropionate) and kainate subtypes have also been implicated, as have G protein-coupled, or metabotropic, glutamate receptors (94, 123). Evidence also indicates that the action of several other neurotransmitters or neuromodulators may be linked to NO formation; these include 5HT, bradykinin, endothelin, acetylcholine, and noradrenaline (33, 101, 102).

NOS PLASTICITY   Although frequently considered constitutive, the NOS may be subject to dramatic up- or down-regulation. Up-regulation was first suggested by in situ hybridization studies of dorsal root ganglia. In normal rats, few neurons in lumbar ganglia express detectable NOS mRNA, but 2 days after transection of the sciatic nerve, mRNA was found in about a third of the neurons. This increase lasted for at least 2 months (133). NADPH diaphorase histochemistry and NOS immunohistochemistry have confirmed expression of the enzyme protein under similar conditions (40, 126). Results obtained using the histochemical technique have further indicated that neurons in the spinal cord (120, 135, 140) and several brain areas (62, 68, 73, 100, 110, 141, 144) react to injury in a similar fashion. Other factors may also regulate NOS expression; increases in mRNA have been detected in the paraventricular nucleus of the hypothalamus in response to stress (18) and lactation (19), in the pituitary in response to gonadectomy (20), and in the hippocampus as a result of treatment with a combination of lithium and the anticholinesterase drug tacrine (5).

The pineal gland exhibits an example of NOS down-regulation by a physiological stimulus. In this gland, constant light exposure markedly reduced NOS enzymatic activity (by 80% after 8 days). Normal activity was restored when the experimental animals were returned to a light-dark cycle for 2 days, and it appears that noradrenaline (which is released in the gland during darkness) is responsible for the photoneural regulation of NOS in the pineal (111).

Glial Cells

When maintained in tissue culture, astrocytes have been observed to generate NO in a Ca^{2+}-dependent manner in response to bradykinin, noradrenaline, or a metabotropic glutamate receptor agonist (2, 90). Whether they have this neuron-like property in vivo is not clear. Astrocytes and microglial cells in primary culture express a Ca^{2+}-independent, inducible type of NO synthase (iNOS) when exposed to bacterial lipopolysaccharide and/or cytokines (9, 44, 118). This expression is reminiscent of several peripheral cell types, including macrophages, neutrophils, vascular smooth muscle cells, and hepatocytes, in which NO generated by this isoform is believed to participate in immunological defense against invading pathogens (see S Gross & M Wolin, this volume). Molecular cloning shows the sequence of the astroglial iNOS to be similar (>90% homology) to the enzyme in peripheral cells, which suggests that it is the product of the same gene (45). Information on the in vivo regulation and expression of iNOS in the CNS is still sparse, although viral infection (30, 75) and neural injury (136) have been associated with central iNOS expression.

SPREAD OF NO BY DIFFUSION

A key property of NO that sets it apart from other CNS signaling molecules is its extreme diffusibility in both aqueous and lipid environments, which allows a rapid three-dimensional spread of the signal irrespective of the presence of membranes. The important question arises as to how far NO travels before its concentration becomes too low to matter. NO is an unstable free radical species with a half-life that is often said to be as short as a few seconds. Although in vivo the half-life of NO may be much longer (86), we should consider how a fast rate of inactivation would affect the distribution of NO.

In the absence of direct experimental evidence, some insight can be gained by examining a theoretical model based on established diffusion equations (25,

139a). The concentration of NO (C) in an infinite medium at any distance (r) from a point source after time = t can be represented by the following equation:

$$C = \frac{S}{4\pi Dr} erfc \; \frac{r}{2\sqrt{Dt}},$$

where S is the source strength and D is the diffusion coefficient, which has been measured as 3.3×10^{-5} cm^2/s (81). Taking $S = 21 \times 10^{-18}$ mol/s at the center of a spherical structure of diameter 1 μm (i.e. approximating the dimensions of a dendritic spine or nerve terminal), the NO concentration at the surface will be 1 μM, which corresponds to the concentration measured directly at the surface of a stimulated endothelial cell (81). At steady state, when t in the equation is large, $erfc[r/2\sqrt{(Dt)}] = 1$, and the concentration of NO is inversely proportional to the distance from the source. If we assume that the biologically relevant threshold concentration of NO is 1 nM, a value based on the relaxing effect of NO on aortic smooth muscle (42), the tissue volume in which NO can exert physiological effects becomes equal to a sphere of diameter 1000 μm. Such a volume would enclose about a billion synapses.

This model so far ignores inactivation of NO. If the half-life is short, say 5 s, NO concentrations near to the source would be scarcely affected because diffusion is so fast. Even 20 μm away, the steady-state concentration would be reduced by only 10%. Farther away, significant reductions would be expected such that the distance at which the concentration falls to 1 nM decreases to 170 μm instead of 500 μm. Thus, even with a half-life of a few seconds, NO generated at a single point source should be able to influence function within a sphere with a diameter of approximately 0.3 mm, which is still very large compared with the dimensions of a synapse (the distance from the center of a dendritic spine to the center of an attached presynaptic terminal is approximately 1 μm, and the width of the synaptic cleft is approximately 20 nm).

Given such a large sphere of influence relative to the small size and high packing density of synapses and other neural elements in the CNS, this analysis raises important questions about how any specificity of action can be incorporated into a signaling mechanism that employs NO, a topic discussed below.

NO SIGNAL TRANSDUCTION

Soluble Guanylyl Cyclase and cGMP

Neuronal excitation leads to elevations in cGMP levels in numerous different brain areas including the cerebellum, cerebral cortex, striatum, and hippocampus through Ca^{2+}-dependent NO formation and the subsequent activation of the soluble form of guanylyl cyclase (sGC). This response implies that sGC is a major target for NO in the CNS, just as it is in smooth muscle cells of blood vessels and other peripheral tissues (e.g. gut, airways) where the resultant rise in cGMP, in these cases, mediates muscle relaxation.

In support of this possibility, the distributions of NOS and NO–stimulated cGMP formation closely correspond to each other in vivo (125). At the cellular level, however, the distributions are usually complementary rather than identical; that is, in a given brain area, the population of cells (mainly neurons) that accumulate cGMP in response to NO are frequently, but not always, distinct from the population of neurons that synthesize NO. This observation reinforces the notion that NO primarily operates as an intercellular messenger. The results also support the hypothesis (50) that, so far as interneuronal signaling is concerned, NO represents a potential line of communication from post- to presynaptic elements, and vice versa, as well as between presynaptic fibers or postsynaptic structures.

sGC exists as a heterodimer made up of α and β subunits of approximately 80 and 70 kDa, respectively. Both subunits are required for enzyme activity. The NO recognition site is an associated heme moiety to which NO binds with high affinity. Enzyme activation may be the result of subsequent conformational change in the enzyme protein (130).

Each subunit can have several isoforms (49). Of the β variety, however, only the β_1 subunit has been identified in rat brain. The widespread distribution of the mRNA for this subunit compared with α_1 has led to the suggestion (43) that β_1 may be a universal component that combines with different α subunits depending on the brain region. In some areas, β_1 and α_1 are both expressed at high levels, which suggests that they are functional partners, but in other areas, α_1 is low relative to β_1, thus indicating the presence of one or more other subunits yet to be identified. The implication that sGC heterogeneity exists is interesting, and a full characterization of this family of proteins, including their anatomical distributions, will be important.

cGMP SIGNAL TRANSDUCTION   Unlike in smooth muscle and platelets where NO-stimulated cGMP accumulation is translated into an easily measured endpoint (respectively, relaxation and inhibition of aggregation), the function of cGMP in the CNS is still unclear, although some recent findings are beginning to shed new light on this old problem.

Direct channel gating   cGMP-operated channels are well known in retinal photoreceptor cells, where they are responsible for the dark (inward) current carried by Na^+ and Ca^{2+} ions. In the light, phosphodiesterases that hydrolyze cGMP are activated, resulting in channel closure and membrane hyperpolarization. A similar channel is present in olfactory cells but, in this instance, cAMP is thought to be the principal physiological ligand, even though it is less potent than cGMP (143a).

Outside of photoreceptors, two groups independently found evidence for cGMP-operated channels in retinal bipolar cells (92, 117). These channels function much like those in rods, although in this case, receptors for the rod neurotransmitter (glutamate) couple (through a G protein) to cGMP hydrolysis. Shiells & Falk (116) have also suggested that NO may be the stimulator of cGMP synthesis in these cells because the NO donor nitroprusside, but not activators of particulate guanylyl cyclases, could reproduce the effects of cGMP.

Recently, investigators using polymerase chain reaction (PCR) amplification techniques have detected DNA sequences specific for cyclic nucleotide-gated channels in several peripheral tissues including aorta, heart, and kidney. The same study also found a strong signal from the cerebellum (in rabbit), the only brain area apparently examined (6). The aortic cDNA encodes a channel that is highly homologous (94%) to the bovine olfactory channel, less so to the rod channel (57%), and that is gated by cGMP 40-fold more potently than by cAMP. The implication is that an analogous channel exists in the cerebellum.

A similar PCR-based approach has revealed that ganglion cells in the retina express transcripts for a channel more like the one in rods (3). Furthermore, patch-clamp recordings from isolated ganglion cells showed the presence of a functional nonspecific cation channel that was activated by cGMP much more effectively than by cAMP and that could also be activated by NO donors. Thus NO generated in nearby cells (putatively the amacrine cells) may result in depolarization of ganglion cells by activating soluble guanylyl cyclase. The authors (3) of this paper cite unpublished work showing that (unspecified) regions of the CNS also express cGMP-gated channels.

In summary, direct gating of neuronal cation channels by cGMP may be a much more widespread mechanism of NO signal transduction than was originally anticipated.

Protein kinases   In smooth muscle, the multiple effects of cGMP (ultimately leading to relaxation) have mostly been ascribed to activation of cGMP-dependent protein kinase (cG-PK) (41). Until recently, cG-PK was believed to have only a limited role in the CNS because it is found in only one type of neuron, the cerebellar Purkinje cell (80). It is now recognized that there are at least two broad classes of this enzyme, cG-PK1 and cG-PKII. Type I, a soluble enzyme composed of two identical subunits (each about 78 kDa), is widely distributed and exists in two alternatively spliced versions, Iα and Iβ. cG-PKIα corresponds to the enzyme in Purkinje cells, where it directs the phosphorylation of a putative phosphatase inhibitor known as the G-substrate. The type II kinase is a monomer (86 kDa) and a particulate enzyme that was originally thought to be present only in intestinal brush border epithelial cells where it regulates Cl^- secretion.

Surprisingly, a cG-PKII has now been cloned and expressed from mouse brain. The protein has a predicted molecular mass of 87 kDa and shows significant homology (about 50% identity overall) to cG-PKI. In transfected COS-1 cells, the kinase was potently activated by cGMP (apparent K_a value, 300 nM) but not by cAMP. Of the tissues examined, cG-PKII is expressed most abundantly in brain and lung, with lesser amounts in kidney and testis (132). Whether it corresponds to the intestinal kinase is unclear at present.

These results clearly bring cG-PK back into focus as a possible transduction mechanism for the NO-cGMP pathway in the CNS, although numerous questions remain regarding the anatomical distribution of this isoform in brain and spinal cord and the identity of its target proteins. One candidate target is DARPP-32, a dopamine- and cAMP-regulated phosphoprotein that, in substantia nigra at least, can also be phosphorylated by cG-PK in response to NO (131). In its phosphorylated form, DARPP-32 is a potent inhibitor of protein phosphatase 1; hence, through this mechanism, NO could maintain enzyme or receptor proteins in their phosphorylated states.

Phosphodiesterases   cGMP can either activate or inhibit specific subtypes of cyclic nucleotide phosphodiesterases (PDEs) and thereby effect changes either in its own levels or those of cAMP. Three PDEs are generally considered relevant: a cGMP-inhibited PDE (cGI-PDE) that selectively hydrolyzes cAMP; a cGMP-stimulated PDE (cGS-PDE) that hydrolyzes both cAMP and cGMP; and a cGMP-binding, cGMP-specific PDE (cG-BPDE). Of these, only cGS-PDE appears to be abundant in the brain. Particularly high levels are present in the cerebral cortex, hippocampus, and basal ganglia, whereas low levels are found in cerebellum (121). In hippocampal pyramidal neurons, cGMP suppresses a Ca^{2+} current, apparently through cGS-PDE-induced reduction in cAMP levels (32). Because these neurons also contain soluble guanylyl cyclase (43), NO may produce the same effect, although this remains to be investigated. Roles of the cGS-PDE in other brain regions have not been described.

ADP ribosyl cyclase   Cyclic ADP ribose, which is formed enzymatically from NAD^+ by ADP ribosyl cyclase, mobilizes Ca^{2+} from internal stores that are distinct from those sensitive to inositol trisphosphate. The stores sensitive to cyclic ADP ribose are thought to be the ryanodine- and caffeine-sensitive stores that participate in Ca^{2+}-induced Ca^{2+} release (46). Cyclic ADP ribose-induced Ca^{2+} release has been observed in many different tissues, including brain microsomes, but the stimulus for cyclic ADP ribose formation remained unknown until recently. Unexpectedly, studies on sea urchin eggs found that cGMP can evoke intracellular Ca^{2+} release and a rise in cytosolic Ca^{2+}, apparently by stimulating the formation of cyclic ADP ribose (47). These are important findings, with immediate potential relevance for NO/cGMP signal transduction in the CNS, but whether the mechanism applies to neurons (and other cell types) remains to be seen.

Cyclooxygenases

NO may be important in the regulation of the activity of another type of enzyme, cyclooxygenase (COX). COXs are rate limiting in the synthesis of prostaglandins, thromboxane A2, and prostacyclin from arachidonic acid. COXs comprise two types, inducible and constitutive, known as COX-1 and COX-2 respectively. Like sGC, COXs are heme–containing enzymes that can directly bind NO. The result may be an increase in enzyme activity. McCann and colleagues (103) reported that in hypothalamic fragments, NO mediates the release of PGE_2 that is induced by noradrenaline (acting on α_1 receptors). PGE_2 then stimulates (via cAMP) the release of leuteinizing hormone–releasing hormone. Analogous effects of NO on prostaglandin release occur in various peripheral tissues, including a macrophage cell line in which NO from endogenous or exogenous sources stimulates PGE_2 production via COX-1 and COX-2 in a cGMP-independent manner (109).

Although these results are interesting, they all come from experiments on intact cells, and conclusive evidence for a direct stimulation of COX by NO is lacking. An alternative explanation could be that NO somehow prevents the auto-inactivation of COX (119). The possible relevance of these results to the CNS is that the brain is unique in its expression of inducible COX-2, rather than COX-1, as the predominant isoform of the enzyme under normal conditions (39). In situ hybridization and immunocytochemistry show that COX-2 is present in the forebrain and in discrete populations of neurons elsewhere, with the highest levels being in the granule and pyramidal cells of the hippocampus and in pyramidal cells in the cerebral cortex. Moreover, a rapid but transient (peak after 1–2 h) increase in expression was observed following seizures or synaptic activation of NMDA receptors (143). Future studies must determine if NO regulates COX-2 activity (directly or indirectly) at these locations and, if so, the physiological significance of the resulting production of prostanoids that, like NO, could function as diffusive intercellular messengers.

Other Enzymes

NO can bind to iron-sulfur centers of various enzymes, causing loss of activity (91). These enzymes include cis-aconitase (citric acid cycle), NADH-ubiquinone oxidoreductase (mitochondrial complex I), and succinate-ubiquinone oxidoreductase (mitochondrial complex II). NO can also inhibit ribonucleotide reductase, an iron-containing enzyme that is rate limiting for DNA synthesis.

Glycolysis may also be affected as a result of the covalent, NO–stimulated, ADP ribosylation of glyceraldehyde-3-phosphate dehydrogenase. The mechanism appears to involve NO-mediated nitrosylation of a thiol (cysteine) at the active site, cleavage of bound NAD^+, and then transfer of the resulting ADP-ribose moiety onto the nitrosylated residue. The last step inhibits the enzyme activity (15).

Loss of activity of these enzymes is long lasting and, to produce it, NO needs to be at high levels for prolonged periods of time. Thus these targets should be most relevant to immunological defense, or toxicity, as mediated by the inducible NO synthase.

ACUTE REGULATION OF NEURONAL AND NEUROENDOCRINE FUNCTION BY NO

Neuronal Firing and Ion Channel Modulation

Unlike neurotransmitters, NO or NOS inhibitors applied to individual neurons in vitro frequently do not produce obvious alterations in membrane potential or firing behavior. This result suggests that the actions of NO do not translate directly into acute effects on excitability. Nevertheless, whole-animal studies have provided evidence that the manipulation of central NO levels can markedly affect the sympathetic outflow and, hence, systemic blood pressure (114, 128), alter respiratory rhythm (79), and influence pain thresholds in the spinal cord (84), which suggests that NO is capable of modifying the electrical activity of neurons. We consider some of the possible mechanisms below.

NEURONAL FIRING   Two of the clearest examples of the effects of NO on neuronal firing activity have come from studies on invertebrates (molluscs). In one study, the NO donor S-nitrosocysteine was perfused onto the buccal ganglion, which is involved in feeding behavior. Increased or decreased firing in different buccal motoneurons occurred, along with associated changes in buccal feeding movements. Inhibitors of NOS had the opposite effects, indicating that NO in this ganglion regulates feeding behavior (89). The other study examined the molluscan equivalent of the olfactory bulb, the procerebral lobe, in which the characteristic electrical activity is an oscillation arising from the interactions between neurons that fire in bursts and nonbursting cells that receive inhibitory signals from the bursting ones (54). Field oscillation frequency was increased by NO donors and decreased by NOS inhibitors. At the single-cell level, NO increased the burst frequency of the bursting cells, thereby increasing the frequency of inhibitory postsynaptic potentials in the non-bursters and eliminating their firing. These results indicate that NO plays an obligatory role in the oscillatory dynamics of neurons in the procerebral lobe and suggest that it participates in odor detection and, possibly, odor learning in this animal.

Modifications in neuronal firing induced by NO have also been observed in mammals. For example, in corticothalamic neurons, NO dampens oscillatory firing behavior (95). In vagal motoneurons, NO donor drugs increase firing rate, and NOS inhibition reduces the excitatory effect of NMDA (129), whereas in the carotid body, NOS inhibitors increase chemoreceptor firing (98, 137). In locus coeruleus neurons, NOS inhibitors augment the amplitude of glutamatergic excitatory postsynaptic potentials (142).

Thus, in different neurons, the net effect of NO on neuronal activity may be either to modulate the firing pattern or to increase or decrease tonic firing rate. However, in most cases whether NO is acting pre- or postsynaptically remains unclear.

ION CHANNEL MODULATION   Apart from a direct action mediated through cGMP-gated channels (see above), the NO/cGMP pathway may modulate other ionic conductances, for example, by promoting phosphorylation or dephosphorylation or by modifying cAMP levels. In thalamic neurons, NO donors or 8-bromo-cGMP evoked a small depolarization associated with a fall in input resistance when the membrane potential was maintained at -60 to -90 mV. This change in polarization resulted from a positive shift in the voltage dependence of the hyperpolarization-activated cation conductance, I_h, the net effect being that oscillatory activity was dampened, but tonic firing was unaffected (95). Through this mechanism, NO could play an important role in the regulation of thalamocortical activity.

Ca^{2+} currents can also be influenced, although the effect may differ among neurons. cGMP depresses Ca^{2+} currents in hippocampal neurons (32); NO has a similar action in avian ciliary ganglion neurons (72) and reduces depolarization-induced Ca^{2+} entry into PC12 cells (28). Elsewhere, Ca^{2+} currents may be enhanced, as was first observed in molluscan neurons (96); in rat superior cervical ganglia, for example, intracellularly applied NO donors increase the amplitude of Ca^{2+} currents and also reduce the inhibitory effect of noradrenaline on these same currents (22). In considerations of these different effects on neuronal Ca^{2+} currents, a pertinent observation is that in frog cardiac myocytes, NO donors can increase and decrease the Ca^{2+} current (L-type) depending on their concentration (85).

In smooth muscle, the NO/cGMP pathway activates large Ca^{2+}-dependent K^+ channels ($I_{K(Ca)}$), which leads to membrane hyperpolarization and closure of voltage-sensitive Ca^{2+} channels (105a). In avian ciliary ganglia, however, an NO donor (and L-arginine) inhibited a poorly defined $I_{K(Ca)}$ independently of its action on Ca^{2+} channels (21). Suppression of $I_{K(Ca)}$ postsynaptically will promote repetitive firing, but should it occur presynaptically, increased neurotransmitter release may result.

Neurotransmitter Release and Uptake

The proposal that NO acts presynaptically to modify the release of neurotransmitters (52) has prompted several mainly neurochemical investigations. The effects of NO donors have led investigators to suggest that the release of various transmitters, including excitatory and inhibitory amino acids, catecholamines, and acetylcholine, may be influenced by NO, predominantly in the positive direction. However, crucial controls for the effects of the NO carrier molecules (57) were not usually performed.

More convincing are experiments showing that authentic NO (57), endogenous NO present in unstimulated tissue (16, 99), or NO generated by NMDA receptor activation (29, 60, 88, 122) influences transmitter release.

Indiscriminate stimulation of transmitter release would not, however, be a sensible physiological function for a diffusible molecule such as NO and, unfortunately, relevant physiological investigations are scarce. In cultured hippocampal neurons, one study found that brief exposure to low concentrations of authentic NO (5–10 nM) led to an enduring increase in the frequency of miniature excitatory postsynaptic currents (93)—a result suggesting a presynaptic action on glutamatergic nerve terminals. In contrast, in hippocampal slices, perfusion of 100 nM NO on its own did not affect baseline synaptic transmission (presynaptic fibers stimulated at 0.02 Hz) but, when paired with weak tetanic stimulation (50 Hz for 0.5 s), it induced a long-lasting potentiation of synaptic efficacy, possibly by a presynaptic mechanism (147). On the other hand, perfusion of NO donor drugs, or an inhibitor of cGMP breakdown, reversibly depressed hippocampal synaptic transmission [monitored using low-frequency stimulation (0.033 Hz)], apparently also by a presynaptic mechanism (11). Thus NO may be able to modulate vesicular release of neurotransmitter in either direction, or not at all, depending on the coincident level of presynaptic activity and NO concentration.

A recent study has indicated that NO might affect neurotransmitter uptake (97) because NO donors inhibited the transport of radiolabeled dopamine, serotonin, and glutamate, but not that of noradrenaline, into synaptosome preparations from the striatum. The inhibition had an unexpectedly slow time course and its physiological relevance requires further evaluation.

Neurotransmitter Receptors

Manzoni et al (83) suggested that NO blocked NMDA receptors based on the effects of NO donor drugs on NMDA receptor-mediated currents and proposed that such an action served as a negative feedback mechanism. These effects were not observed in experiments on cerebellar slices (35), but analogous results were obtained from cortical neurons, and Lei et al (76) proposed that the effect was brought about by nitrosation of thiol groups associated with the receptor. An important criticism of these investigations is the heavy reliance placed on the effects of NO donor drugs that have reactivities not shared by authentic NO and that generate unknown NO concentrations. Many NO donors react with thiols to release NO, and nitrosothiols, for example, can directly transfer NO onto other thiol groups; NO itself, however, cannot directly nitrosate these groups.

Therefore, an essential direction to explore is whether endogenously generated NO inhibits NMDA receptors. Two studies support this possibility, one showing that L-arginine inhibits NMDA-induced increases in intracellular Ca^{2+} levels in cultured striatal neurons, and that this inhibition can be blocked by NOS inhibition or hemoglobin (82), and the other showing that NOS inhibition increases the amplitude of synaptically activated NMDA receptor currents (70). Neither of these studies provide direct evidence for modulation of the receptors by NO, however, and further experiments specifically designed to address the issue are needed.

Neuroendocrine Functions

Several recent reports have indicated that NO regulates hormone release in the hypothalamo-pituitary axis. In explants of the hypothalamus, inhibition of NOS augments release of corticotropin-releasing hormone provoked by elevated K^+ or interleukin-1β, whereas L-arginine and NO donors are inhibitory (24). NOS inhibitors also augment the increased plasma adrenocorticotrophic hormone levels induced by administration of interleukin-1β, vasopressin, and oxytocin in vivo (105), increase plasma oxytocin (but not vasopressin) levels in dehydrated rats (127), augment luteinizing hormone release from dispersed pituitary cells stimulated by gonadotrophin-releasing hormone (20), and potentiate growth hormone release stimulated by growth hormone-releasing hormone in the pituitary (71). In all of these cases, therefore, NO inhibits hormone secretion. Conversely, in other in vitro experiments, NO was proposed to mediate hypothalamic hormone release, including the release of corticotropin-releasing factor induced by interleukin-2 and carbachol, but not by noradrenaline (69); the release of luteinizing hormone-releasing hormone induced by noradrenaline (103) or glutamate (104); and the release of somatostatin induced by growth hormone-releasing factor (1).

NO AND SYNAPTIC PLASTICITY

Synaptic plasticity refers to the capacity of synaptic connections to become selectively and persistently strengthened, or weakened, in response to external stimuli. The phenomenon has long excited neuroscientists attempting to identify a cellular correlate of learning and memory. Long-lasting, activity-dependent changes in synaptic efficacy occur in several brain structures, including the hippocampus, cortex, and cerebellum, areas that have attracted considerable interest as possible sites for the formation and storage of memory.

The best-studied form of plasticity in the brain is the long-term potentiation (LTP) of synaptic transmission, which is observed at all excitatory synapses in the hippocampal formation. It can be measured as a sustained increase in the magnitude of excitatory postsynaptic potentials (EPSPs) after the delivery of brief trains of high-frequency electrical stimuli to afferent fibers innervating the neurons. LTP recorded at synapses of CA1 pyramidal neurons after the activation of the presynaptic Schaffer collateral-commissural pathway is the most frequently used model for the study of synaptic plasticity, and the type of plasticity in which NO has been most strongly implicated.

Long-Term Potentiation

The molecular and cellular mechanisms that underlie the persistent changes in synaptic strength characterizing LTP must still be resolved. One of the most hotly debated questions concerning LTP, and one that is crucial to understanding the process, concerns the locus (pre- or postsynaptic) at which the modification of synaptic efficacy occurs. For the CA1 region of the hippocampus, a partial answer to this question came from the discovery that the induction of LTP requires postsynaptic NMDA receptor activation and the associated influx of Ca^{2+} (7). However, increasing evidence suggests that at least part of the sustained increase in synaptic strength results from an increased release of the neurotransmitter glutamate from the presynaptic terminal. If induction of LTP is postsynaptic but expression of LTP has at least a component that is presynaptic, then a retrograde trans-synaptic messenger becomes necessary.

NO, being freely diffusible and generated as a result of Ca^{2+} influx associated with NMDA receptor activation, is an attractive candidate for a retrograde messenger (48, 52), but its role in LTP remains controversial.

A first requirement would be that NOS is present in the appropriate postsynaptic neurons and is activated by NMDA receptor stimulation. Until recently, convincing evidence that CA1 pyramidal neurons contained NOS was lacking, although they do stain when the NADPH diaphorase histochemical technique is used (125). A recent immunocytochemical study has shown that CA1 neuronal cell bodies and dendrites in hippocampal sections can be labeled by selective neuronal NOS antibodies provided that unusually gentle fixation techniques are used (138). Surprisingly, immunocytochemistry using antibodies against endothelial NOS has also produced dense staining of the same cells (31). Thus, CA1 neurons probably do contain Ca^{2+}-stimulated NOS. Furthermore, exposure of hippocampal slices to NMDA, or tetanic stimulation of Schaffer collateral fibers, leads to NO formation, as judged by measurements of cGMP accumulation (23, 36).

The second prediction is that NOS inhibitors should block LTP. A number of LTP studies carried out in the CA1 region of hippocampal slices in vitro have demonstrated this to be so (8, 10, 56, 59, 93, 112). LTP has also been prevented by perfusion of the slices with the NO scavenger hemoglobin (10, 59, 93, 112), which supports a transcellular messenger role for NO because hemoglobin only accesses the extracellular space. However, these studies contain several inconsistencies. One is in the concentration of inhibitor required to block LTP. Whereas Bohme et al (8) reported a complete block of potentiation using a relatively short preincubation of slices with 100 nM L-nitro-arginine, others have required long incubations at 1000- or even 10,000-fold greater concentrations (59, 112). The effects of NOS inhibitors and of hemoglobin may also be the result of inhibition of the depolarization that occurs during the high-frequency stimulus, rather than an effect upon LTP per se (90a). Moreover, the time course of the block of LTP by NOS inhibitors also varies greatly between experiments. Potentiation of synaptic transmission in the CA1 region has been reported to consist of several time-dependent, and possibly mechanistically distinct, phases, of which LTP is a form that persists for over 1 hour. Short-term potentiation (<30 min) and posttetanic potentiation (<5 min) are also observed. It has been reported that NOS inhibitors block all phases of potentiation (8, 93) or, in contrast, leave short-term potentiation intact (59, 112).

A more serious problem is that several groups have been unable to obtain any block of LTP with NOS inhibitors, and a number of confounding variables have come to light. This dilemma has led to the suggestion that NO only participates when a relatively weak stimulus is used for LTP induction (23, 58; but see 56). Possibly the most detailed analysis of experimental differences has been conducted by Williams et al (139), who reported that an effect of NOS inhibitors upon LTP was apparent only in slices from young (5- to 7-week-old) rats and when experiments were performed at a temperature of 24°C. NOS inhibition did not affect LTP when experiments were performed at 30°C in slices from young animals and produced no effects at either temperature in tissue from adult rats. Although some groups reporting positive effects of NOS inhibitors carried out their experiments at low temperatures (59, 112), others used temperatures of 30–32°C (8, 10, 93), which suggests factors other than temperature are also important.

Schuman & Madison (113) used a different experimental protocol to test for the involvement of a diffusible messenger in LTP. They made intracellular recordings from two electrically independent neurons (however, supplied by a common set of afferent fibers) and observed that, in one cell, induction of LTP by means of combined postsynaptic depolarization and low-frequency (1 Hz) stimulation of presynaptic fibers resulted in potentiation at synapses of the second cell, but only if the second cell was nearby, specifically a distance of approximately 150 µm or less, measured at the level of the cell somata.

Potentiation of the second neuron did not occur if LTP was prevented in the first neuron by the inclusion of a NOS inhibitor in the microelectrode. Furthermore, induction of LTP in a population of neurons could overcome the inhibition of LTP imposed on one individual neuron by intracellular application of a NOS inhibitor, suggesting that NO released from noninhibited neurons could compensate for the absence of NO production in the inhibited neuron and result in potentiation. These results provide convincing evidence that NO participates in LTP, at least under certain experimental conditions, and that its diffusible nature allows a previously unsuspected distributed potentiation of synaptic transmission to take place.

Another expectation of the NO hypothesis is that delivery of exogenous NO should, under appropriate circumstances, elicit LTP. One study reported that perfusion of the NO donor sodium nitroprusside caused a depression of synaptic transmission that reverted to a sustained potentiation upon washout (8). In another study, perfusion of a solution containing NO (0.1 μM) had no effect on its own but, when paired with an electrical presynaptic fiber stimulation at a frequency below the threshold for inducing LTP, a potentiation of synaptic responses ensued (147). In contrast, application of several different NO donors during low-frequency stimulation reversibly depressed synaptic transmission in the CA1 region (11).

These apparently disparate findings probably also relate to different experimental conditions and are potentially reconcilable. Because the NO spreads from its source (see above) over a potentially large area, possibly encompassing millions of synapses, it is very unlikely that it acts indiscriminately, especially if one of its roles is to strengthen synapses. A more plausible mechanism would be for NO to modify the behavior of target elements in a manner that depends on their activity, as hypothesized by Gally et al (48). In accordance with this theory, it was found that when presynaptic fibers are stimulated at high frequency (50 Hz) in the presence of NO, synapses become potentiated, but when presynaptic activity is low (0.25 Hz), NO causes synaptic depression (146). Other variables, such as the NO concentration and the duration of exposure to NO, are also likely to be important in determining the outcome.

Taken together, the data support a role for NO in LTP although, given the variable results from in vitro experiments, its precise significance must await in vivo studies. As far as the signal transduction pathway is concerned, high-frequency stimulation results in an accumulation of cGMP in the CA1 region of the hippocampus that is blocked by NOS inhibitors (23). Furthermore, the cGMP analogue 8-Br-cGMP potentiates synaptic responses when paired with a tetanus to the afferent fibers, too weak in itself to induce LTP, and hippocampal slices perfused with selective inhibitors of cG-PK fail to show LTP after a high-frequency stimulus (145). These findings suggest that cGMP mediates NO–dependent LTP.

Long-Term Depression

Implicit in the idea that synapses can be strengthened is a recognition that they may also be depressed. The phenomenon of long-term depression (LTD) can be observed in the hippocampus upon repetitive low-frequency stimulation (1–2 Hz) of presynaptic axons (34), and the induction of LTD reportedly can be blocked by NOS inhibitors and hemoglobin (67), although these results need to be confirmed.

A more widely studied example of LTD is in the cerebellum, where it is thought to be a correlate of cerebellar motor learning (65). It is manifest as a persistent depression of EPSPs recorded at the synapse between parallel fibers and Purkinje cells, the only output neurons of the cerebellar cortex. Purkinje cells have two glutamatergic excitatory inputs via the parallel fibers and climbing fibers; LTD occurs when the two are stimulated simultaneously, and this process requires activation of both AMPA and metabotropic glutamate receptors (78). The expression of LTD appears to be postsynaptic, because quantal analysis has failed to demonstrate any change in presynaptic transmitter release (63), and a decreased sensitivity of postsynaptic AMPA receptors has been reported.

In the absence of climbing-fiber activation, parallel-fiber stimulation results in LTP rather than LTD (106); thus a signal produced by the climbing fibers is needed for the development of LTD. Climbing-fiber activation generates Ca^{2+}-mediated action potentials in Purkinje cell dendrites. The production of these potentials is associated with a large influx of calcium ions, and LTD can be abolished if this process is disrupted (107). The actual mechanism by which the parallel fibers and climbing fibers interact to bring about a reduced sensitivity of postsynaptic AMPA receptors is far from understood, although NO appears to participate under at least some conditions.

Two experimental strategies have been employed to induce LTD in vitro. In one, AMPA receptors and metabotropic receptors are simultaneously activated by exogenous agonists and in the other, parallel fiber-mediated EPSPs are paired with calcium spike firing elicited by depolarization of the postsynaptic cell. Using both these approaches, LTD could be blocked by perfusing the preparations with inhibitors of NOS (26, 27, 66) and also with hemoglobin (66). Shibuki & Okada (115) found further evidence implicating NO in cerebellar LTD. Using an electrochemical NO probe, they demonstrated endogenous NO release following climbing-fiber stimulation. Moreover, exogenous NO or cGMP could substitute for climbing-fiber activation so that, when paired with parallel fiber activity, LTD ensued.

The source of the NO in cerebellar LTD remains uncertain because Purkinje cells do not appear to contain NOS. Since climbing-fiber lesions result in a reduced release of NO, as measured either electrochemically or by biochemical assessment of cGMP accumulation (115, 124), NO is probably released from climbing fibers themselves or from other cells onto which these fibers synapse. Purkinje cells appear to be the target for NO because dialysis of Purkinje cells with NO donors or in conjunction with parallel fiber stimulation, depresses the parallel fiber-mediated EPSP (27, 61). Hence, the decreased responsiveness of the postsynaptic AMPA receptors may depend upon an increased concentration of cGMP in Purkinje cells and, putatively, a subsequent activation of protein kinase G (61, 66).

In spite of these apparently compelling results implicating NO in LTD, studies using cultured Purkinje cells have shown that LTD obtained by pairing depolarization of the cell with iontophoretic glutamate pulses is unaffected by NOS inhibitors or hemoglobin and that it could not be replicated by the NO donor nitroprusside (55, 77). As with hippocampal LTP, NO-dependent and -independent forms of cerebellar LTD appear to exist.

NEURAL NO AND LOCAL CEREBRAL BLOOD FLOW

Although the role of endothelial-derived NO in the regulation of blood vessel tone is well established (87), the identification of neurons as a source of NO led to the hypothesis that NO may represent the long-sought factor that couples increased local blood flow to neural activity (48). Considerable data suggest that NO participates in the maintenance of resting cerebrovascular tone and, more controversially, that it mediates certain vasodilator responses (38, 64), but the role of NO derived from central neurons, as opposed to endothelial cells or parasympathetic NOS-containing fibers, is still unclear. One finding shows that topical application of NMDA to the rabbit brain in vivo results in a vasodilatation of arterioles on the pial surface that was blocked by NOS inhibitors and reproduced by nitroprusside (37). However, the response to NMDA was also blocked by tetrodotoxin, which inhibits neuronal firing, thereby indicating that the NO signal was not a direct consequence of NMDA receptor activity but may be the result of stimulation of neuronal circuits.

The question was recently explored using a different technique. Akgoren et al (4) electrically stimulated the parallel fibers in the rat cerebellum, which led to a frequency dependent increase in blood flow at the cerebellar surface. This response was reduced by a NOS inhibitor, by an elevated Mg^{2+} concentration (which inhibits synaptic transmission), and most revealingly, by an inhibitor of the AMPA and kainate types of non-NMDA glutamate receptors. These results, together with those showing that activation of AMPA and kainate receptors is associated with NO production in the cerebellum (123) and that parallel fiber-mediated synaptic transmission is blocked by AMPA and kainate antagonists (51) make the first convincing case for the idea that

NO derived from central neurons as a result of synaptic activation of glutamate receptors can influence local blood flow.

CONCLUDING COMMENTS

Recent years have seen an explosion of interest in NO in the CNS, resulting in the implication of this unexpected and atypical messenger molecule in a wide range of neural functions. Because of space limitations, we have focused mainly on the cellular and molecular mechanisms of NO signaling rather than on its broader proposed roles, such as in learning, cognition, and the regulation of sensory, motor, and sexual behavior. We have also left aside discussion of the possible pathological roles of NO, when generated either by excessive glutamate receptor stimulation or as a result of iNOS expression, in CNS disease states.

At the cellular and synaptic level, it is probably unrealistic to define a function of the NO-cGMP signaling pathway in the CNS in the same way that one does with conventional neurotransmitter systems because the NO-cGMP pathway is so different. For a spatially diffuse signal such as NO to have biological meaning, a different set of rules must govern specificity of action. In synapses, for example, the effect of NO appears to depend on the coincident functional state of the participating cellular elements, to the extent that the net result can be an increase, a decrease, or no change in synaptic efficacy. An important task is to understand NO-cGMP signal transduction mechanisms more precisely. However, little is known about the actions of cGMP in the CNS compared with other tissues such as smooth muscle and platelets, although, as discussed above, several promising avenues are opening up. The identification of a potent and selective inhibitor of the NO-stimulated guanylyl cyclase enzyme (J Garthwaite et al, submitted) should greatly assist progress.

Literature Cited

1. Aguila MC. 1994. Growth hormone–releasing factor increases somatostatin release and mRNA levels in the rat periventricular nucleus via nitric oxide by activation of guanylate cyclase. *Proc. Natl. Acad. Sci. USA* 91:782–86
2. Agullo L, Garcia A. 1992. Characterization of noradrenaline-stimulated cyclic GMP formation in brain astrocytes in culture. *Biochem. J.* 288:619–24
3. Ahmad I, Leinders-Zufall T, Kocsis JD, Shepherd GM, Zufall F, Barnstable CJ. 1994. Retinal ganglion cells express a cGMP-gated cation conductance activatable by nitric oxide donors. *Neuron* 12: 155–65

4. Akgoren N, Fabricius M, Lauritzen M. 1994. Importance of nitric oxide for local increases of blood flow in rat cerebellar cortex during electrical stimulation. *Proc. Natl. Acad. Sci. USA* 91: 5903–7

5. Bagetta G, Corasaniti MT, Melino G, Paoletti AM, Finazzi-Agro A, Nistico G. 1993. Lithium and tacrine increase the expression of nitric oxide synthase mRNA in the hippocampus of rat. *Biochem. Biophys. Res. Commun.* 197: 1132–39

6. Biel M, Altenhofen W, Hullin R, Ludwig J, Freichel M, et al. 1993. Primary structure and functional expression of a cyclic nucleotide–gated channel from rabbit aorta. *FEBS Lett.* 329:134–38

7. Bliss TVP, Collingridge GL. 1993. A synaptic model of memory: long-term potentiation in the hippocampus. *Nature* 361:31–39

8. Bohme GA, Bon C, Stutzmann J-M, Doble A, Blanchard J-C. 1991. Possible involvement of nitric oxide in long-term potentiation. *Eur. J. Pharmacol.* 199: 379–81

9. Boje KM, Arora PK. 1992. Microglial-produced nitric oxide and reactive nitrogen oxides mediates neuronal cell death. *Brain Res.* 587:250–56

10. Bon C, Bohme GA, Doble A, Stutzmann J-M, Blanchard J-C. 1992. A role for nitric oxide in long-term potentiation. *Eur. J. Neurosci.* 4:420–24

11. Boulton CL, Irving AJ, Southam E, Potier B, Garthwaite J, Collingridge G. 1994. The nitric oxide-cyclic GMP pathway and synaptic depression in rat hippocampal slices. *Eur. J. Neurosci.* 6: 1528–35

12. Bredt DS, Hwang PM, Glatt CE, Lowenstein C, Reed RR, Snyder SH. 1991. Cloned and expressed nitric oxide synthase structurally resembles cytochrome P-450 reductase. *Nature* 351: 714–18

13. Bredt DS, Hwang PM, Snyder SH. 1990. Localization of nitric oxide synthase indicating a neural role for nitric oxide. *Nature* 347:768–70

14. Bredt DS, Snyder SH. 1990. Isolation of nitric oxide synthetase, a calmodulin requiring enzyme. *Proc. Natl. Acad. Sci. USA* 87:682–85

15. Brune B, Dimmeler S, Vedia LMY, Lapetina EG. 1994. Nitric oxide: a signal for ADP-ribosylation of proteins. *Life Sci.* 54:61–70

16. Bugnon O, Schaad NC, Schorderet M. 1994. Nitric oxide modulates endogenous dopamine release in bovine retina. *NeuroReport* 5:401–4

17. Deleted in proof

18. Calzal L, Giardino L, Ceccatelli S. 1993. NOS mRNA in the paraventricular nucleus of young and old rats after immobilization stress. *NeuroReport* 4: 627–30

19. Ceccatelli S, Eriksson M. 1993. The effect of lactation on nitric oxide synthase gene expression. *Brain Res.* 625: 177–79

20. Ceccatelli S, Hulting A-L, Zhang X, Gustafsson L, Villar M. 1993. Nitric oxide synthase in the rat anterior pituitary gland and the role of nitric oxide in regulation of luteinizing hormone secretion. *Proc. Natl. Acad. Sci. USA* 90: 11292–96

21. Cetiner M, Bennett MR. 1993. Nitric oxide modulation of calcium–activated potassium channels in postganglionic neurones of avian cultured ciliary ganglia. *Br. J. Pharmacol.* 110:995–1002

22. Chen C, Schofield G. 1993. Nitric oxide modulates Ca^{2+} channel currents in rat sympathetic neurons. *Eur. J. Pharmacol.* 243:83–86

23. Chetkovich DM, Klann E, Sweatt JD. 1993. Nitric oxide synthase-independent long-term potentiation in area CA1 of hippocampus. *NeuroReport* 4:919–22

24. Costa A, Trainer P, Besser M, Grossman A. 1993. Nitric oxide modulates the release of corticotropin-releasing hormone from the rat hypothalamus in vitro. *Brain Res.* 605:187–92

25. Crank J. 1979. *The Mathematics of Diffusion.* Oxford: Clarendon

26. Crepel F, Jaillard D. 1990. Protein kinases, nitric oxide and long-term depression of synapses in the cerebellum. *NeuroReport* 1:133–36

27. Daniel H, Hemart N, Jaillard D, Crepel F. 1993. Long–term depression requires nitric oxide and guanosine 3′:5′ cyclic monophosphate production in rat cerebellar Purkinje cells. *Eur. J. Neurosci.* 5:1079–82

28. Desole MS, Kim W-K, Rabin RA, Laychock SG. 1994. Nitric oxide reduces depolarization-induced calcium influx in PC12 cells by a cyclic GMP-mediated mechanism. *Neuropharmacology* 33:193–98

29. Dickie BGM, Lewis MJ, Davies JA. 1992. NMDA–induced release of nitric oxide potentiates aspartate overflow from cerebellar slices. *Neurosci. Lett.* 138:145–48

30. Dighiero P, Reux I, Hauw J-J, Fillet AM, Courtois Y, Goureau O. 1994. Expression of inducible nitric oxide synthase in cytomegalovirus-infected glial

cells of retinas from AIDS patients. *Neurosci. Lett.* 166:31–34

31. Dinerman JL, Dawson TM, Schell MJ, Snowman A, Snyder SH. 1994. Endothelial nitric oxide synthase localized to hippocampal pyramidal cells: implications for synaptic plasticity. *Proc. Natl. Acad. Sci. USA* 91:4214–18

32. Doerner D, Alger BE. 1988. Cyclic GMP depresses hippocampal Ca^{2+} current through a mechanism independent of cGMP-dependent protein kinase. *Neuron* 1:693–99

33. Drummond GI. 1983. Cyclic nucleotides in the nervous system. *Adv. Cyclic Nucleotide Res.* 15:373–494

34. Dudek SM, Bear MF. 1993. Bidirectional long-term modification of synaptic effectiveness in the adult and immature hippocampus. *J. Neurosci.* 13:2910–18

35. East SJ, Batchelor AM, Garthwaite J. 1991. Selective blockade of NMDA receptor function by the nitric oxide donor nitroprusside. *Eur. J. Pharmacol.* 209:119–21

36. East SJ, Garthwaite J. 1991. NMDA receptor activation in rat hippocampus induces cyclic GMP formation through the L-arginine-nitric oxide pathway. *Neurosci. Lett.* 123:17–19

37. Faraci FM, Breese KR. 1993. Nitric oxide mediates vasodilatation in response to activation of N-methyl-D-aspartate receptors in brain. *Circ. Res.* 72:476–80

38. Faraci FM, Brian JE. 1994. Nitric oxide and the cerebral circulation. *Stroke* 25:692–703

39. Feng L, Sun W, Xia Y, Tang WW, Chanmugam P, et al. 1993. Cloning two isoforms of rat cyclooxygenase: differential regulation of their expression. *Arch. Biochem. Biophys.* 307:361–68

40. Fiallos-Estrada CE, Kummer W, Mayer B, Bravo R, Zimmermann M, Herdegen T. 1993. Long-lasting increase of nitric oxide synthase immunoreactivity NADPH-diaphorase reaction and c-JUN co-expression in rat dorsal root ganglion neurons following sciatic nerve transection. *Neurosci. Lett.* 150:169–73

41. Francis SH, Corbin JD. 1994. Structure and function of cyclic nucleotide-dependent protein kinases. *Annu. Rev. Physiol.* 56:237–72

42. Furchgott RF, Jothianandan D. 1991. Endothelium-dependent and -independent vasodilation involving cyclic GMP: relaxation induced by nitric oxide carbon monoxide and light. *Blood Vessels* 28:52–61

43. Furuyama T, Inagaki S, Takagi H. 1993.

44. Galea E, Feinstein DL, Reis DJ. 1992. Induction of calcium-independent nitric oxide synthase activity in primary rat glial cultures. *Proc. Natl. Acad. Sci. USA* 89:10945–49

45. Galea E, Reis DJ, Feinstein DL. 1994. Cloning and expression of inducible nitric oxide synthase from rat astrocytes. *J. Neurosci. Res.* 37:406–14

46. Galione A. 1992. Ca^{2+}-induced Ca^{2+} release and its modulation by cyclic ADP-ribose. *Trends Pharmacol. Sci.* 13:304–6

47. Galione A, White A, Willmott N, Turner M, Potter BVL, Watson SP. 1993. cGMP mobilizes intracellular Ca^{2+} in sea urchin eggs by stimulating cyclic ADP-ribose synthesis. *Nature* 365:456–59

48. Gally JA, Montague PR, Reeke GN Jr, Edelman GM. 1990. The NO hypothesis: possible effects of a short-lived rapidly diffusible signal in the development and function of the nervous system. *Proc. Natl. Acad. Sci. USA* 87:3547–51

49. Garbers DL. 1992. Guanylyl cyclase receptors and their endocrine paracrine and autocrine ligands. *Cell* 71:1–4

50. Garthwaite J. 1991. Glutamate nitric oxide and cell-cell signalling in the nervous system. *Trends Neurosci.* 14:60–67

51. Garthwaite J, Beaumont PS. 1989. Excitatory amino acid receptors in the parallel fibre pathway in rat cerebellar slices. *Neurosci. Lett.* 107:151–56

52. Garthwaite J, Charles SL, Chess-Williams R. 1988. Endothelium-derived relaxing factor release on activation of NMDA receptors suggests role as intercellular messenger in the brain. *Nature* 336:385–88

53. Garthwaite J, Garthwaite G. 1987. Cellular origins of cyclic GMP responses to excitatory amino acid receptor agonists in rat cerebellum in vitro. *J. Neurochem.* 48:29–39

54. Gelperin A. 1994. Nitric oxide mediates network oscillations of olfactory interneurons in a terrestrial mollusc. *Nature* 369:61–63

55. Glaum SR, Slater NT, Rossi DJ, Miller RJ. 1992. Role of metabotropic glutamate (ACPD) receptors at the parallel fibre-Purkinje cell synapse. *J. Neurophysiol.* 68:1453–62

56. Gribkoff VK, Lum-Ragan JT. 1992. Evidence for nitric oxide synthase inhibitor-sensitive and insensitive hippocampal synaptic potentiation. *J. Neuro-physiol.* 68:639–42

43. Localizations of α-1 and β-1 subunits of soluble guanylate cyclase in the rat brain. *Mol. Brain Res.* 20:335–44

57. Guevara-Guzman R, Emson PC, Kendrick KM. 1994. Modulation of in vivo striatal transmitter release by nitric oxide and cyclic GMP. *J. Neurochem.* 62:807–10

58. Haley JE, Malen PL, Chapman PF. 1993. Nitric oxide synthase inhibitors block long-term potentiation induced by weak but not strong tetanic stimulation at physiological brain temperatures in rat hippocampal slices. *Neurosci. Lett.* 160:85–88

59. Haley JE, Wilcox GL, Chapman PF. 1992. The role of nitric oxide in hippocampal long-term potentiation. *Neuron* 8:211–16

60. Hanbauer I, Wink D, Osawa Y, Edelman GM, Gally JA. 1992. Role of nitric oxide in NMDA-evoked release of [³H]-dopamine from striatal slices. *NeuroReport* 3:409–12

61. Hartell NA. 1994. cGMP acts within cerebellar Purkinje cells to produce long term depression via mechanisms involving PKC and PKG. *NeuroReport* 5:833–36

62. Herdegen T, Brecht S, Mayer B, Leah J, Kummer W, et al. 1993. Long-lasting expression of JUN and KROX transcription factors and nitric oxide synthase in intrinsic neurons of the rat brain following axotomy. *J. Neurosci.* 13:4130–45

63. Hirano T. 1991. Differential pre- and postsynaptic mechanisms for synaptic potentiation and depression between a granule cell and a Purkinje cell in rat cerebellar culture. *Synapse* 7:321–23

64. Iadecola C, Pelligrino DA, Moskowitz MA, Lassen NA. 1994. Nitric oxide synthase inhibition and cerebrovascular regulation. *J. Cereb. Blood Flow Metab.* 14:175–92

65. Ito M. 1989. Long-term depression. *Annu. Rev. Neurosci.* 12:85–102

66. Ito M, Karachot L. 1990. Messengers mediating long-term desensitization in cerebellar Purkinje cells. *NeuroReport* 1:129–32

67. Izumi Y, Zorumski CF. 1993. Nitric oxide and long-term synaptic depression in the rat hippocampus. *NeuroReport* 4:1131–34

68. Jia Y-S, Wang X-A, Ju G. 1994. Nitric oxide synthase expression in vagal complex following vagotomy in the rat. *NeuroReport* 5:793–96

69. Karanth S, Lyson K, McCann SM. 1993. Role of nitric oxide in interleukin 2-induced corticotropin-releasing factor release from incubated hypothalami. *Proc. Natl. Acad. Sci. USA* 90:3383–87

70. Kato K, Zorumski CF. 1993. Nitric oxide inhibitors facilitate the induction of hippocampal long-term potentiation by modulating NMDA responses. *J. Neurophysiol.* 70:1260–63

71. Kato M. 1992. Involvement of nitric oxide in growth hormone (GH)–releasing hormone–induced GH secretion in rat pituitary cells. *Endocrinology* 131:2133–38

72. Khurana G, Bennett MR. 1993. Nitric oxide and arachidonic acid modulation of calcium currents in postganglionic neurones of cultured avian ciliary ganglia. *Br. J. Pharmacol.* 109:480–85

73. Kitchener PD, Van der Zee CEEM, Diamond J. 1993. Lesion-induced NADPH-diaphorase reactivity in neocortical pyramidal neurones. *NeuroReport* 4:487–90

74. Knowles RG, Palacios M, Palmer RMJ, Moncada S. 1989. Formation of nitric oxide from L-arginine in the central nervous system: a transduction mechanism for stimulation of the soluble guanylate cyclase. *Proc. Natl. Acad. Sci. USA* 89:5159–62

75. Koprowski H, Zheng YM, Heber-Katz E, Fraser N, Rorke L, et al. 1993. In vivo expression of inducible nitric oxide synthase in experimentally induced neurologic diseases. *Proc. Natl. Acad. Sci. USA* 90:3024–27

76. Lei SZ, Pan Z-H, Aggarwal SK, Chen H-SV, Hartman J, et al. 1992. Effect of nitric oxide production on the redox modulatory site of the NMDA receptor-channel complex. *Neuron* 8:1087–99

77. Linden DJ, Connor JA. 1992. Long-term depression of glutamate currents in cultured cerebellar Purkinje neurons does not require nitric oxide signaling. *Eur. J. Neurosci.* 4:10–15

78. Linden DJ, Dickinson MH, Smeyne M, Connor JA. 1991. A long-term depression of AMPA currents in cultured cerebellar Purkinje neurons. *Neuron* 7:81–89

79. Ling L, Karius DR, Fiscus RR, Speck DF. 1992. Endogenous nitric oxide required for an integrative respiratory function in the cat brain. *J. Neurophysiol.* 68:1910–12

80. Lohmann SM, Walter U, Miller PE, Greengard P, De Camilli P. 1981. Immunohistochemical localization of cyclic GMP-dependent protein kinase in mammalian brain. *Proc. Natl. Acad. Sci. USA* 78:653–57

81. Malinsky T, Taha Z, Grunfeld S, Patton S, Kapturczak M, Tombouliant P. 1993. Diffusion of nitric oxide in the aorta wall monitored in situ by porphyrinic microsensors. *Biochem. Biophys. Res. Commun.* 193:1076–82

82. Manzoni O, Bockaert J. 1993. Nitric oxide synthase activity endogenously modulates NMDA receptors. *J. Neurochem.* 61:368–70

83. Manzoni O, Prezeau L, Marin P, Deshager S, Bockaert J, Fagni L. 1992. Nitric oxide-induced blockade of NMDA receptors. *Neuron* 8:653–62

84. Meller ST, Gebhart GF. 1993. Nitric oxide (NO) and nociceptive processing in the spinal cord. *Pain* 52:127–36

85. Mery P-F, Pavoine C, Belhassen L, Pecker F, Fischmeister R. 1993. Nitric oxide regulates cardiac Ca^{2+} current. *J. Biol. Chem.* 268:26286–95

86. Meulemans A. 1994. Diffusion coefficients and half-lives of nitric oxide and N-nitroso-L-arginine in rat cortex. *Neurosci. Lett.* 171:89–93

87. Moncada S, Palmer RMJ, Higgs EA. 1991. Nitric oxide: physiology pathophysiology and pharmacology. *Pharmacol. Rev.* 43:109–42

88. Montague PR, Gancayco CD, Winn MJ, Marchase RB, Friedlander MJ. 1994. Role of NO production in NMDA receptor-mediated neurotransmitter release in cerebral cortex. *Science* 263:973–77

89. Moroz LL, Park J-H, Winlow W. 1993. Nitric oxide activates buccal motor patterns in *Lymnaea stagnalis*. *NeuroReport* 4:643–46

90. Murphy S, Minor RL Jr, Welk G, Harrison DG. 1990. Evidence for an astrocyte-derived vasorelaxing factor with properties similar to nitric oxide. *J. Neurochem.* 55:349–51

90a. Musleh WY, Shaki K, Baudry M. 1993. Further studies concerning the role of nitric oxide in LTP induction and maintenance. *Synapse* 13:370–75

91. Nathan C. 1992. Nitric oxide as a secretory product of mammalian cells. *FASEB J.* 6:3051–64

92. Nawy S, Jahr CE. 1990. Suppression by glutamate of cGMP–activated conductance in retinal bipolar cells. *Nature* 346:269–71

93. O'Dell TJ, Hawkins RD, Kandel E, Arancio O. 1991. Tests of the roles of two diffusible substances in long-term potentiation: evidence for nitric oxide as a possible early retrograde messenger. *Proc. Natl. Acad. Sci. USA* 88:11285–89

94. Okada D. 1992. Two pathways of cyclic GMP production through glutamate receptor-mediated nitric oxide synthesis. *J. Neurochem.* 59:1203–10

95. Pape H-C, Mager R. 1992. Nitric oxide controls oscillatory activity in thalamocortical neurons. *Neuron* 9:441–48

96. Paupardin-Tritsch D, Hammond C,

Gerschenfeld HM, Nairn AC, Greengard P. 1986. cGMP-dependent protein kinase enhances Ca^{2+} current and potentiates the serotonin-induced Ca^{2+} current increase in snail neurones. *Nature* 323:812–14

97. Pogun SK, Baumann MH, Kuhar MJ. 1994. Nitric oxide inhibits [^{3}H] dopamine uptake. *Brain Res.* 641:83–91

98. Prabhakar NR, Kumar GK, Chang C-H, Agani FH, Haxhiu MA. 1993. Nitric oxide in the sensory function of the carotid body. *Brain Res.* 625:16–22

99. Prast H, Philippu A. 1992. Nitric oxide releases acetylcholine in the basal forebrain. *Eur. J. Pharmacol.* 216:139–40

100. Regidor J, Montesdeoca J, Ramirez-Gonzalez JA, Hernandez-Urquia CM, Divac I. 1993. Bilateral induction of NADPH-diaphorase activity in neocortical and hippocampal neurons by unilateral injury. *Brain Res.* 631:171–74

101. Reiser G. 1990. Mechanisms of stimulation of cyclic-GMP level in a neuronal cell line mediated by serotonin (5-HT3) receptors. Involvement of nitric oxide arachidonic acid metabolism and cytosolic Ca^{2+}. *Eur. J. Biochem.* 189:547–52

102. Reiser G. 1990. Endothelin and a Ca^{2+} ionophore raise cyclic GMP levels in a neuronal cell line via formation of nitric oxide. *Br. J. Pharmacol* 101:722–26

103. Rettori V, Belova N, Dees WL, Nyberg CL, Gimeno M, McCann SM. 1993. Role of nitric oxide in the control of luteinizing hormone-releasing hormone release in vivo and in vitro. *Proc. Natl. Acad. Sci. USA* 90:10130–34

104. Rettori V, Kamat A, McCann SM. 1994. Nitric oxide mediates the stimulation of luteinizing-hormone releasing hormone release induced by glutamic acid in vitro. *Brain Res. Bull.* 33:501–3

105. Rivier C, Shen GH. 1994. In the rat, endogenous nitric oxide modulates the response of the hypothalamic-pituitary-adrenal axis to interleukin-1β vasopressin and oxytocin. *J. Neurosci.* 14:1985–93

105a. Robertson BE, Schubert R, Hescheler J, Nelson MT. 1993. cGMP-dependent protein kinase activates Ca-activated K^+ channels in cerebral artery smooth muscle cells. *Am. J. Physiol.* 265:C299–303

106. Sakurai M. 1987. Synaptic modification of parallel fibre-Purkinje cell transmission in in vitro guinea-pig cerebellar slices. *J. Physiol.* 394:463–80

107. Sakurai M. 1990. Calcium is an intracellular mediator of the climbing fiber in induction of cerebellar long-term depression. *Proc. Natl. Acad. Sci. USA* 87:3383–85

108. Salter M, Knowles RG, Moncada S. 1991. Widespread tissue distribution species distribution and changes in activity of Ca^{2+}-dependent and Ca^{2+}-independent nitric oxide synthases. *FEBS Lett.* 291:145–49

109. Salvemini D, Misko TP, Masferrer JL, Seibert K, Currie MG, Needleman P. 1993. Nitric oxide activates cyclooxygenase enzymes. *Proc. Natl. Acad. Sci. USA* 90:7240–44

110. Saxon DW, Beitz AJ. 1994. Cerebellar injury induces NOS in Purkinje cells and cerebellar afferent neurons. *NeuroReport* 5:809–12

111. Schaad NC, Vanecek J, Schulz PE. 1994. Photoneural regulation of rat pineal nitric oxide synthase. *J. Neurochem.* 62:2496–99

112. Schuman EM, Madison DV. 1991. A requirement for the intercellular messenger nitric oxide in long-term potentiation. *Science* 254:1503–6

113. Schuman EM, Madison DV. 1994. Locally distributed synaptic potentiation in the hippocampus. *Science* 263:532–36

114. Shapoval LN, Sagach VF, Pobegailo LS. 1991. Nitric oxide influences ventrolateral medullary mechanisms of vasomotor control in the cat. *Neurosci. Lett.* 132:47–50

115. Shibuki K, Okada D. 1991. Endogenous nitric oxide release required for long-term synaptic depression in the cerebellum. *Nature* 349:326–28

116. Shiells R, Falk G. 1992. Retinal on-bipolar cells contain a nitric oxide–sensitive guanylate cyclase. *NeuroReport* 3:845–48

117. Shiells RA, Falk G. 1990. Glutamate receptors of rod bipolar cells are linked to a cyclic GMP cascade via a G-protein. *Proc. R. Soc. London Ser. B* 242:91–94

118. Simmons ML, Murphy S. 1992. Induction of nitric oxide synthase in glial cells. *J. Neurochem.* 59:897–905

119. Smith WL, Marnett LJ, DeWitt DL. 1991. Prostaglandin and thromboxane biosynthesis. *Pharmacol. Ther.* 49:153–79

120. Solodkin A, Traub RJ, Gebhart GF. 1992. Unilateral hindpaw inflammation produces a bilateral increase in NADPH-diaphorase histochemical staining in the rat lumbar spinal cord. *Neurosci. Lett.* 51:495–99

121. Sonnenburg WK, Mullaney PJ, Beavo JA. 1991. Molecular cloning of cyclic GMP-stimulated cyclic nucleotide phosphodiesterase cDNA. *J. Biol. Chem.* 266:17655–61

122. Sorkin LS. 1993. NMDA evokes an L-NAME-sensitive spinal release of glutamate and citrulline. *NeuroReport* 4:479–82

123. Southam E, East SJ, Garthwaite J. 1991. Excitatory amino acid receptors coupled to the nitric oxide:cyclic GMP pathway in rat cerebellum during development. *J. Neurochem.* 56:2072–81

124. Southam E, Garthwaite J. 1991. Climbing fibres as a source of nitric oxide in the cerebellum. *Eur. J. Neurosci.* 3:379–82

125. Southam E, Garthwaite J. 1993. The nitric oxide-cyclic GMP signalling pathway in rat brain. *Neuropharmacology* 32:1267–77

126. Steel JH, Terenghi G, Chung JM, Na HS, Carlton SM, Polak JM. 1994. Increased nitric oxide synthase immunoreactivity in rat dorsal root ganglia in a neuropathic pain model. *Neurosci. Lett.* 169:81–84

127. Summy-Long JY, Bui V, Mantz S, Koehler E, Weisz J, Kadekaro M. 1993. Central inhibition of nitric oxide synthase preferentially augments release of oxytocin during dehydration. *Neurosci. Lett.* 152:190–93

128. Togashi H, Sakuma I, Yoshioka M, Kobayashi T, Yasuda H, et al. 1992. A central nervous system action of nitric oxide in blood pressure regulation. *J. Pharmacol. Exp. Ther.* 262:343–47

129. Travagli RA, Gillis RA. 1994. Nitric oxide-mediated excitatory effect on neurons of dorsal motor nucleus of vagus. *Am. Physiol. Soc.* 266:G154–60

130. Traylor TG, Sharma VS. 1992. Why NO? *Biochemistry* 31:2847–49

131. Tsou K, Snyder GL, Greengard P. 1993. Nitric oxide/cGMP pathway stimulates phosphorylation of DARPP-32, a dopamine- and cAMP-regulated phosphoprotein in the substantia nigra. *Proc. Natl. Acad. Sci. USA* 90:3462–65

132. Uhler MD. 1993. Cloning and expression of a novel cyclic GMP-dependent protein kinase from mouse brain. *J. Biol. Chem.* 268:13586–91

133. Verge VMK, Xu Z, Xu X-J, Wiesenfeld-Hallin Z, Hokfelt T. 1992. Marked increase in nitric oxide synthase mRNA in rat dorsal root ganglia after peripheral axotomy: in situ hybridization and functional studies. *Proc. Natl. Acad. Sci. USA* 89:11617–21

134. Vincent SR. 1994. Nitric oxide: a radical neurotransmitter in the central nervous system. *Prog. Neurobiol.* 42:129–60

135. Vizzard MA, Erdman SL, de Groat WC. 1993. The effect of rhizotomy on NADPH diaphorase staining in the lumbar spinal cord of the rat. *Brain Res.* 607:349–53

136. Wallace MN, Bisland SK. 1994. NADPH-diaphorase activity in activated astrocytes represents inducible nitric oxide synthase. *Neurosci. Lett.* 59:905–19

137. Wang Z-Z, Stensaas LJ, Bredt DS, Dinger B, Fidone SJ. 1994. Localization and actions of nitric oxide in the cat carotid body. *Neuroscience* 60:275–86

138. Wendland B, Schweizer FE, Ryan TA, Nakane M, Murad F, et al. 1994. Existence of nitric oxide synthase in rat hippocampal pyramidal cells. *Proc. Natl. Acad. Sci. USA* 91:2151–55

139. Williams JH, Li Y-G, Nayak A, Errington ML, Murphy KPSJ, Bliss TVP. 1993. The suppression of long-term potentiation in rat hippocampus by inhibitors of nitric oxide synthase is temperature and age dependent. *Neuron* 11:877–84

139a. Wood J, Garthwaite J. 1994. Models of diffusional spread of nitric oxide: implications for neural nitric oxide signalling and its pharmacological properties. *Neuropharmacology.* 33:1235–44

140. Wu W. 1993. Expression of nitric-oxide synthase (NOS) in injured CNS neurons as shown by NADPH diaphorase histochemistry. *Exp. Neurol.* 120:153–59

141. Wu W, Scott DE. 1993. Increased expression of nitric oxide synthase in hypothalamic neuronal regulation. *Exp. Neurol.* 121:279–83

142. Xu Z-Q, Pieribone VA, Zhang X, Grillner S, Hokfelt T. 1994. A functional role for nitric oxide in locus coeruleus: immunohistochemical and electrophysiological studies. *Exp. Brain Res.* 98:75–83

143. Yamagata K, Andreasson KI, Kaufmann WE, Barnes CA, Worley PF. 1993. Expression of a mitogen-inducible cyclooxygenase in brain neurons: regulation by synaptic activity and glucocorticoids. *Neuron* 11:371–86

143a. Yau K-W. 1994. Cyclic nucleotide-gated channels: an expanding new family of ion channels. *Proc. Natl. Acad. Sci. USA* 41:3481–83

144. Yu W-HA. 1994. Nitric oxide synthase in motor neurons after axotomy. *J. Histochem. Cytochem.* 42:451–57

145. Zhuo M, Hu Y, Schultz C, Kandel ER, Hawkins RD. 1994. Role of guanylyl cyclase and cGMP-dependent protein kinase in long-term potentiation. *Nature* 368:635–39

146. Zhuo M, Kandel ER, Hawkins RD. 1994. Nitric oxide and cGMP can produce either synaptic depression or potentiation depending on the frequency of presynaptic stimulation in the hippocampus. *NeuroReport* 5:1033–36

147. Zhuo M, Small SA, Kandel ER, Hawkins RD. 1993. Nitric oxide and carbon monoxide produce activity-dependent long-term synaptic enhancement in the hippocampus. *Science* 260:1946–50

Annu. Rev. Physiol. 1995. 57:707–36
Copyright © 1995 by Annual Reviews Inc. All rights reserved

NITRIC OXIDE SYNTHASES:
Properties and Catalytic Mechanism

Owen W. Griffith[1] and Dennis J. Stuehr[2]

[1]Department of Biochemistry, Medical College of Wisconsin, Milwaukee,
Wisconsin 53226; [2]Department of Immunology, The Cleveland Clinic and
Department of Physiology and Biophysics, Case Western Reserve University School
of Medicine, Cleveland, Ohio 44195

KEY WORDS: heme cofactor, NOS isoforms, tetrahydrobiopterin, NOS inhibitors,
reductase and oxygenase domains

INTRODUCTION

Historical Perspective

Although nitric oxide $(NO)^3$ was known since the late 1970s to be among the ligands that activate soluble guanylyl cyclase and cause vascular smooth muscle relaxation (4, 21, 44), it was not appreciated until more recently that NO is also an endogenous vasorelaxant. In 1986, Furchgott (33) and Ignarro (56) noted that NO and endothelium-derived relaxing factor (EDRF) (32, 34) comparably relax vascular smooth muscle and are similarly quenched by hemoglobin and superoxide. They proposed that EDRF is NO (33, 56) or a labile compound releasing NO (56). A variety of biological and pharmacological

---

[3]Abbreviations used: NO, nitric oxide; EDRF, endothelium-derived relaxing factor; EPR, electron paramagnetic resonance; NMDA, N-methyl-D-aspartate; NOS, nitric oxide synthase; eNOS, ecNOS, NOS-III, endothelial constitutive isoform of NOS⁻; nNOS, ncNOS, bNOS, NOS-I, neuronal (brain) constitutive isoform of NOS; iNOS, mNOS, macNOS, NOS-II, Ca2+ elevation-independent, inducible isoform of NOS; THB, tetrahydrobiopterin; NOH-ARG, N^{ω}-hydroxy-L-arginine; L- SMTC, S-methyl-L-thiocitrulline; L-NMA, N^{ω}-methyl-L-arginine; L-NNA, N^{ω}-nitro-L-arginine; CaM, calmodulin; LPS, lipopolysaccharide; NANC, non-adrenergic, non-cholinergic; ROS, reac- tive oxygen species; D-NMA, N^{ω}-methyl-D-arginine; D-NNA, N^{ω}-nitro-D-arginine; L-NAME, N^{ω}-nitro-L-arginine methyl ester; L-NAA, N^{ω}-amino-L-arginine; L-NIO, N^{δ}-iminoethyl- L-ornithine.

0066–4278/95/0315–0707$05.00

studies confirmed this conclusion with respect to NO (55, 108, 109; reviews 54, 93). The quantitative contribution of labile NO donors such as S-nitroso-thiols to EDRF activity is not yet established, but it is clear that such compounds are formed in vivo and have biological activity (38, 125).

Because NO is spontaneously and rapidly oxidized to nitrite (NO_2^-) and nitrate (NO_3^-) in oxygenated physiological solutions (136, and references therein), unambiguous chemical characterization of EDRF as NO was not easily accomplished. Early studies examining O_3-dependent chemiluminescence did not distinguish NO and NO_2^- (108, 109); however, Menon et al (91) recently showed that NO can be detected, albeit poorly, in bovine pulmonary artery effluent by chemiluminescence. Direct trapping of EDRF using endogenous targets (e.g. hemoglobin) or synthetic spin traps followed by EPR measurements have also chemically confirmed the in vivo formation of NO (47, 124). Nevertheless, measurement of biologically formed NO remains challenging (3). In addition to NO/EDRF-mediated relaxation of vascular strips, chemiluminescence, and EPR measurements, NO has been detected or quantitated by colorimetric determination of nitrite and nitrate (the Griess reaction) (41), by oxidation of oxyhemoglobin to methemoglobin monitored spectrophotometrically (24, 55), by cGMP formation in reporter cells (57), by mass spectrometry of nitrosylated species (58, 81), and by using an NO-selective electrode (84). Although none of the methods is entirely satisfactory with respect to selectivity, sensitivity, and convenience, the in vivo formation of NO is now beyond dispute.

Contemporaneously with studies identifying NO as a vasodilatory messenger, Hibbs and co-workers found that tumor cell killing by activated rodent macrophages was L-arginine-dependent (52); the cytotoxic species was shown by several investigators to be NO (51, 86, 128, 131a). Those studies elucidated the earlier finding that activated macrophages synthesize nitrite and nitrate (131) and demonstrated that NO can be cytostatic or cytocidal when formed at high rates.

Neuronal signaling in response to NMDA-receptor activation represents another area in which a physiological role for NO was independently discovered. Garthwaite and co-workers, aware that cGMP levels increase in response to glutamate binding to the NMDA receptor, found that cerebellar cells release a guanylyl cyclase-activating factor with biological activity and stability characteristics similar to NO/EDRF (36). Bredt & Snyder later isolated a NADPH- and L-arginine-dependent nitric oxide synthase (NOS) from rat cerebellar homogenates (9).

More recently it has been established that mammalian NO synthesis is mediated by at least three (and probably no more than three) NOS isoforms (27, 102, 120). Sequence data show that distinct, constitutive Ca^{2+}/calmodulin-dependent NOS isoforms are associated with EDRF formation (eNOS, ecNOS, or NOS-III)[4] (59, 78, 103, 121) and with signal transduction in central and peripheral neurons (nNOS, ncNOS, bNOS, or NOS-I) (7, 97). nNOS has a tissue distribution well beyond neurons (see below). The third NOS isoform, originally isolated (50, 126) and sequenced (83, 143) from murine macrophages, contains calmodulin (16) but is fully active at normal intracellular Ca^{2+} levels; its activity is thus independent of elevations of intracellular Ca^{2+}. Expression of this NOS isoform occurs in response to various inflammatory cytokines [e.g. IL-1, IL-2, tumor necrosis factor α (TNF-α) or lipopolysaccharide (LPS)]; in most cases interferon-γ acts synergistically (see 102, 120 for reviews of NOS induction). The Ca^{2+} elevation-independent, inducible isoform of NOS (iNOS, mNOS, macNOS, NOS-II) can be expressed in most or all nucleated cells and serves a role in killing or suppressing intracellular pathogens including viruses (61, 100–102). The observation that iNOS is apparently present in some tissues of normal animals [e.g. fetal and adult lung (74) and perhaps other tissues (102)], raises the paradox of iNOS being constitutive; additional studies are necessary to determine if such an enzyme is truly constitutive or is better characterized as chronically induced by inflammatory mediators present in normal tissues.

Early Studies of Catalytic Mechanism

Following purification of rat brain nNOS and mouse macrophage iNOS, it was established that both isoforms catalyze the NADPH- and O_2-dependent five electron oxidation of L-arginine to NO and citrulline. Two molecules of water are presumptive coproducts. Both isoforms contain one equivalent each of FAD, FMN, THB, and heme (iron protoporphyrin IX) per monomer when fully active (127). In 1990, we, in collaboration with several co-workers, established (a) that N^{ω}-hydroxy-L-arginine (NOH-ARG) is a tightly bound intermediate in the NOS reaction (130), (b) that the hydroxylated nitrogen of NOH-ARG is processed to NO (130), (c) that formation of citrulline and NO from L-arginine or NOH-ARG requires 1.5 or 0.5 equivalents of NADPH,

---

[4]There is little consensus regarding the most appropriate abbreviations to use for NOS isoforms. Tissue distribution is clearly broader than that reflected in our use of eNOS and nNOS to represent the isoforms originally isolated from vascular endothelial cells and brain (neurons), respectively. Nevertheless, these choices seem preferable to an endless expansion of new tissue-specific names for what is thought, and often known, to be the same protein. The NOS-I, NOS-II and NOS-III system (27, 111) avoids tissue references but loses any sense of origin or function for the non-cognizanti. As pointed out by Nathan & Xie (102), iNOS is most rigorously understood as indicating "independent of elevations of intracellular Ca^{2+} levels" rather than "inducible".

respectively (130), and (*d*) that the ureido oxygen of citrulline derives from O_2 rather than H_2O (76). These results are summarized in Equation 1.

$$1.$$

L-Arginine   NOH-ARG   L-Citrulline

It was subsequently shown that the hydroxyl oxygen of NOH-ARG is retained in NO (81), and the intermediacy of NOH-ARG was confirmed (73, 81, 115).

The reaction sequence shown in Equation 1 represents two successive mono-oxygenase reactions (not a dioxygenase reaction); both steps are mixed function oxidations in which the four electrons necessary to reduce each O_2 are derived from both NADPH and the amino acid substrate. In step 1, two electrons are contributed by NADPH, and a guanidino nitrogen of arginine undergoes a two electron oxidation (equivalent to contributing two electrons). In step 2, one electron is contributed by NADPH, and NOH-ARG undergoes a three electron oxidation to form citrulline and NO (127). Although step 1 represents conventional hydroxylation, step 2 is without obvious biological precedent. In 1992 we proposed three model pathways plausibly accounting for the unusual three electron oxidation of NOH-ARG (Figure 1) (127). Subsequent studies suggested that pathway A (Figure 1) best accounts for NOS-mediated synthesis of NO. The alternative pathways (B and C, Figure 1) are also consistent with available data but require more complex electron transfer schemes; we favor pathway A on the basis of simplicity and closer accord with established cytochrome P450 mechanisms (see below). The present review summarizes our most recent results (127) as they relate to the properties and catalytic mechanism of mammalian NOS. Other recent reviews also address mechanistic aspects of NOS catalysis (10, 26, 84a, 85, 87, 100).

NITRIC OXIDE SYNTHASE ISOFORMS

Genetic Studies

In 1991, Bredt et al reported the cDNA sequence coding rat cerebellar nNOS, a 160,458 kDa protein (37). Notably, the C-terminal portion of nNOS and all subsequently studied NOS isoforms show moderate homology (30–40% amino

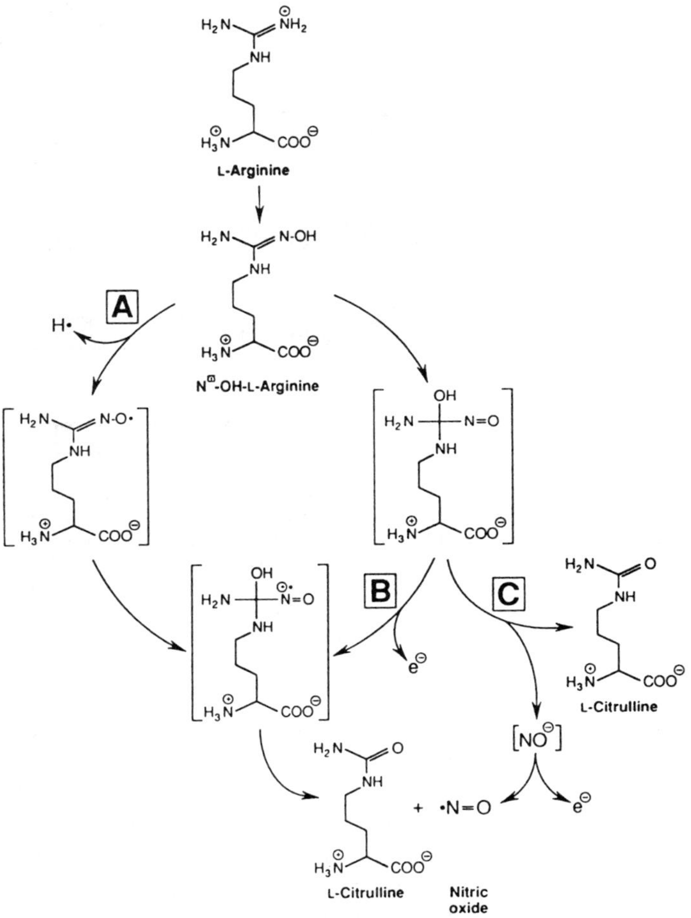

Figure 1 Early proposal for the mechanism of NOS. Three hypothetical pathways for the three electron oxidation of NOH-ARG (N^{ω}-OH-L-arginine) are shown (from 127, with permission).

acid identity; ~60% homology) to NADPH cytochrome P450 reductase (7, 120, 143), the only other mammalian enzyme known to contain both FAD and FMN. Consensus sequences for NADPH, FAD, and FMN binding sites were identified within NOS (Figure 2) (7, 120, 143).

Using isoform-specific antibodies or nucleotide probes based on the rat nNOS sequence, investigators have reported cDNA and predicted amino acid sequences for nNOS from human cerebellum (97), eNOS from human (59)

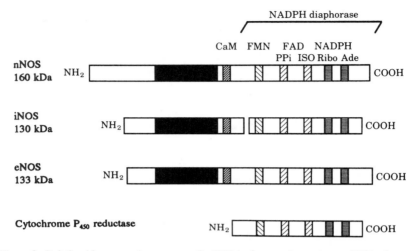

Figure 2 Relationship among the sequences for NOS isoforms and cytochrome P450 reductase. Consensus sequences for the binding of the cofactors NADPH (adenine and ribose), FAD (isoalloxazine and pyrophosphate), FMN, and for calmodulin (CaM) are labeled. The darkened N-terminal region shows 65–71% sequence identity between the three types of NOS. This region contains the putative L-arginine-binding region and probably the binding site for tetrahydrobiopterin and heme. The gap in the iNOS sequence represents a 40 amino acid deletion; all structures are single polypeptide chains (modified from 27, with permission).

and bovine (78, 103, 121) aortic endothelial cells, and iNOS from mouse macrophages (82, 83, 143), rat hepatocytes (142), rat vascular smooth muscle cells (104), human hepatocytes (39), and human chondrocytes (15), and a human adenocarcinoma cell line (122). Sequences are highly conserved across species lines for each isoform (80–94% identity), but overall sequence identity between any two isoforms is modest (50–60%) (120). Regions of high homology, however, are associated with cofactor binding sites. Following discovery of the heme cofactor (72, 90, 129, 135), its putative binding site was localized to the N-terminal region; the fifth (axial) heme iron ligand is tentatively identified as CyS 415 (rat nNOS), CyS 186 (bovine eNOS), and CyS 194 (mouse iNOS) (90, 115a). The identity of the NOS cofactors and their locations within the amino acid sequence indicates that NOS is functionally similar to a cytochrome P450 reductase–cytochrome P450 fused hybrid (see below).

Cell and Tissue Distribution

Neuronal NOS and iNOS sequences are devoid of membrane-associating elements and, as expected, the enzymes are found mainly in the soluble portion of cell or tissue homogenates (27, 102, 120, 127). On the other hand, eNOS is largely associated with endothelial cell membranes (111). Cloning studies show eNOS contains an N-terminal myristoylation site, providing a probable basis for such association (78, 103, 121). Mutagenesis of glycine to alanine at position 2 eliminated the myristoylation site and allowed expression of soluble enzyme (12). Busconi & Michel (12) recently reported that eNOS is also palmitoylated, a modification that correlates strongly with membrane association. It was suggested that myristoylation is necessary but not sufficient for membrane association and that reversible palmitoylation may control association (T Michel, personal communication). At present, the functional consequences of eNOS association with plasma membrane are poorly understood. Because eNOS can be activated by the shear stress of blood flow (11, 62), it is possible that association with the luminal plasma membrane facilitates activation, but a molecular mechanism for such acute activation is not yet apparent. Because shear stress also increases eNOS mRNA levels (103), complex control mechanisms are clearly operative.

The tissue distribution of the NOS isoforms under normal and pathophysiological conditions has received considerable attention. Originally identified in a subset of central neurons (8), nNOS has now been identified by immunological staining in a variety of cells including peripheral NANC neurons, skeletal muscle, pancreatic islet cells, kidney macula densa cells, and certain epithelial cells (10, 27, 100). Endothelial NOS expression appears to be restricted almost exclusively to the vascular endothelium (27). Although eNOS activity is found in most organs and tissues, such activity is generally attributable to the vascular endothelium contained in those tissues. Recently, eNOS was identified immunohistochemically in kidney tubular epithelial cells (133) and CA1 neurons (105). In the latter tissue, eNOS apparently plays a role in long-term potentiation, a memory related phenomenom; its role in kidney epithelium is unknown.

Following exposure to inflammatory cytokines (100–102) or LPS, iNOS has been identified in macrophages (rodent; 50, 126, 144), liver (39), vascular endothelial (63) and smooth muscle cells (42), chondrocytes (15), myocardium (119), and other tissue and cell types (reviewed, 10, 100–102, 120). It is now thought that any nucleated cell type is able to express iNOS if the proper cytokine or LPS stimulus is delivered. Although it is difficult to reproducibly obtain iNOS expression in human macrophages or monocytes, human lung macrophages have been shown to express iNOS in vivo (74).

Purification of NOS

Neuronal NOS has been purified to homogeneity directly from animal tissues (9, 88, 117); rat (7, 14, 90, 129) and human (97) nNOS can also be obtained from appropriately transfected cell lines. Endothelial NOS has been purified from vascular endothelial cells grown in culture (111, 141) and from human placenta (37). Expression systems for eNOS have been reported (78, 103, 121), but none appears to offer yields of enzyme significantly greater than the relatively low amounts present constitutively in cultured endothelial cells. Rodent macrophage (50, 126, 144) and vascular smooth muscle (42) iNOS are also readily obtained from cytokine or LPS-stimulated cells grown in culture.

Convenient purification protocols for nNOS (90, 129), eNOS (141), and iNOS (50, 126) have been reported. Most rely on protease inhibitors and some rely on other protectants (glycerol, bovine serum albumin, thiols) to limit degradation. The best purification is achieved by affinity chromatography on 2′,5′-ADP-sepharose or 2′,5′-ADP-agarose and, for nNOS and eNOS, on cal-modulin-affinity resins. A variable portion of THB is lost during purification and must be added back to achieve full activity (127).

There is considerable variation in the specific activity reported for NOS isoforms purified to homogeneity. The differences are likely to reflect the inherent instability of the enzymes, variable loss of THB and perhaps other cofactors, and differences in the protein and activity assays used. It is notable, however, that the highest specific activities reported for nNOS (9), eNOS (141), and iNOS (50, 126) are all in the range of 900–1600 nmol/min per mg protein. Such similarity suggests an identity of chemical mechanism among the isoforms, each operating with comparable catalytic efficiency. Kinetic constants and physical properties are summarized in Table 1.

PROTEIN STRUCTURE

Domain Organization and Prosthetic Group Binding

The finding of sequence homology between the C-terminal half of NOS and cytochrome P450 reductase (143) and the presumptive requirement for a heme binding site in the N-terminal portion of NOS suggest that NOS is composed of distinct reductase (C-terminal) and oxygenase (N-terminal) domains. Al-though without precedent among mammalian cytochrome P450s, bacterial cytochrome $P450_{BM3}$ is similarly composed of a cytochrome P450-like N-ter-minal domain fused to a C-terminal reductase domain that contains NADPH, FAD, and FMN binding sites arranged as in NOS (96). Limited trypsin pro-teolysis splits cytochrome $P450_{BM3}$ into two domains, generating a N-terminal fragment that contains heme and binds substrate, and a C-terminal fragment that contains FAD and FMN and binds NADPH (96).

Recently, Sheta et al reported that nNOS also contains a trypsin-sensitive region near the N-terminal end of its calmodulin-binding domain (123). Tryp-sin lysis at this position generated an N-terminal heme-containing fragment that binds L-arginine, and a C-terminal FAD- and FMN-containing fragment

Table 1 Physical properties and kinetic constants for NOS isoforms

Physical property or kinetic constant	nNOS	eNOS	iNOS
Subunit M_r	160,458 (rat) [7] [a] 161,037 (human) [97]	133,286 (cow) [78,103,121] 133,000 (human) [59]	130,556 (mouse) [82,83,143] ~131,000 (rat) [104,142] 131,000 (human) [39]
Quaternary structure	Monomer/dimer equilibrium [87]; dimer in vivo? [117]	Unknown	Dimer [50,126]
$EC_{50}^{Calmodulin}$	10 nM (rat) [9] 70 nM (pig) [88]	3.5 nM (cow) [111] 8 nM (human) [37]	N/A [b]
$EC_{50}^{Ca^{2+}}$	200 nM (rat) [9] 400 nM (pig) [88]	300 nM (cow) [111] 100 nM (human) [37]	N/A (see, however, 39)
V_{max} (highest reported)	960 nmol/min/mg (rat) [9]	900 nmol/min/mg (cow) [141]	1313 nmol/min/mg (mouse) [126] 1623 nmol/min/mg (mouse) [50]
K_m^{NADPH}		≤1 μM (human) [37]	0.3 μM (mouse) [126]
$K_m^{Arginine}$	1.5 μM (rat) [9] 3.3 μM (rat) [118] 1.2 μM (cow) [35]	5 μM (cow) [141] 3 μM (cow) [111] 1 μM (human) [37]	19 μM (rat) [29] 10 μM (mouse) [35] 2.3 μM (mouse) [130]
$K_m^{NOH-ARG}$	~25 μM (pig) [73]	—	6.6 μ (mouse) [130] 25 μM (mouse) [115]
K_m^{NMA} (as substrate)			3.1 μ (mouse) [107]
K_i^{NMA} (initial rate)	1.4 μM (rat) [9] 0.2 μM (rat) [29]	0.9 μM (cow) [111] 0.4 μM (human) [37]	6 μM (rat) [29] 13 μM (mouse) [107]
K_d^{NNA}	15 nM (cow) [8] 170 nM (pig) [71]	39 nM (human) [37]	K_i 4.4 μM (mouse) [35]

[a] Numbers in parentheses are references.
[b] Not applicable.

that catalyzed the NADPH-dependent reduction of cytochrome c. The authors concluded that nNOS is a bi-domain enzyme in which the reductase and oxygenase domains can fold, exist, and function independently of one another. A similar study carried out by Ghosh & Stuehr with the dimeric macrophage iNOS established that a bi-domain structure also exists in this isoform (D Ghosh & DJ Stuehr, submitted). In addition, these authors determined that THB binding occurs within the N-terminal domain of iNOS.

Calmodulin and Interdomain Electron Transfer

The consensus sequence for calmodulin binding is near the center of NOS, separating the reductase and oxygenase domains. On the basis of electron flow studies (see below), Abu-Soud & Stuehr (1) concluded that the calmodulin-binding region acts as a hinge between the C-terminal reductase and N-terminal oxygenase domains. When Ca^{2+}/calmodulin is not bound, the domains are not aligned, and the reductase domain can not supply electrons to heme. When Ca^{2+}/calmodulin is bound, the domains align and the enzyme is active (Figure 3). This model, which represents a novel mechanism for enzyme activation by Ca^{2+}/calmodulin, accounts for nNOS and eNOS activation by increased intracellular Ca^{2+} levels. The model also accounts for the insensitivity of iNOS to changes in Ca^{2+} levels because calmodulin is tightly bound to that isoform and does not dissociate. In iNOS, the domains are always aligned, and the enzyme is always active.

Quanternary Structure

Macrophage iNOS as isolated is a homodimeric enzyme comprised of two identical 130-kDa subunits (50, 126). Studies by Baek et al have shown that subunit dimerization is required to generate active iNOS (6). Thus macrophage

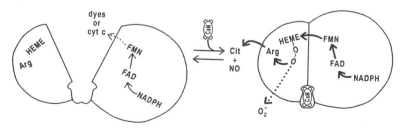

Figure 3   Role of calmodulin (CaM) in aligning the oxygenase (N-terminal) (*left*) and reductase (C-terminal) (*right*) domains of nNOS. Solid arrows indicate electron flow. Calmodulin with four associated Ca^{2+} atoms binds to a "hinge" region aligning the domains and allowing electron transfer from FMN to heme. In the absence of Ca^{2+}/calmodulin, electrons flow more slowly to other acceptors such as cytochrome c (cyt c). In the absence of arginine, activated oxygen (O-O) can dissociate from heme as superoxide (O_2^-) (*dashed arrow*).

iNOS subunits isolated by gel filtration bind only FAD, FMN, and calmodulin and do not contain heme or THB. The isolated subunits do not generate NO, but catalyze electron transfer from NADPH to acceptors such as ferricyanide or cytochrome c. Interestingly, subunit dimerization does not occur spontaneously, but requires the coincident presence of THB, L-arginine, and stoichiometric amounts of heme (6). Following dimerization, THB and heme, but not L-arginine, remain bound. Recent work suggests that intracellular levels of heme and L-arginine influence assembly of active dimeric NOS in vivo (K Baek et al, unpublished). Subunit assembly and cofactor binding thus appear to be a significant posttranslational modification leading to active macrophage iNOS.

Whereas active iNOS is clearly dimeric, nNOS may be either homodimeric or monomeric following purification (9, 88, 117). Recent analytical ultracentrifugation studies by Masters and co-workers suggest that nNOS may exist as a monomer-dimer equilibrium (87), and it is currently unclear how catalytic activity, prosthetic group binding, and subunit dimerization are related. Additional studies comparing NOS isoforms with respect to their quaternary structure, prosthetic group binding, and dependence of activity on quarternary structure are awaited with interest.

NOS COFACTORS AND ELECTRON TRANSFER

Coupled NOS Reaction

NADPH is an obligate two–electron donor, whereas heme-mediated monooxygenations typically require that electrons be delivered one at a time. Although few studies have directly probed electron transfer in NOS, structural and functional homology between cytochrome P450 reductase and the C-terminal reductase domain of NOS strongly support the scheme shown in Figure 4. As outlined at the top of the figure, the NOS flavins are thought to serve an electron storage pool and transfer function, accepting electrons two at a time from NADPH and delivering them one at a time to heme. Flavins are admirably suited to this purpose because each can accept one or two electrons, giving first a radical intermediate and then a fully reduced dihydroisoalloxazine ring. Thus the FAD and FMN cofactors of each NOS monomer can together accept up to four electrons. Studies by Stuehr and co-workers indicate that NOS as isolated contains a flavin radical (129); on the basis of redox potentials, it is likely that the native enzyme contains FAD and FMNH$^\bullet$. The lower portion of Figure 4 shows a hypothetical scheme in which two successive cycles of NOS catalysis oxidize three molecules of NADPH and two molecules of L-arginine, producing two molecules of citrulline and NO. Note that the flavin pool serves to store the extra NADPH electron delivered during the first

$$\text{NADPH} \xrightarrow{2e^-} [\text{FAD} \to \text{FMN}] \xrightarrow{1e^-} \text{HEME}$$

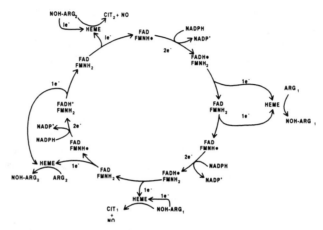

Figure 4   Role of FAD and FMN in NOS. (*Top*) The NOS flavin pool accepts electrons two at a time from NADPH and delivers electrons one at a time to heme. (*Bottom*) The role and redox state of FAD and FMN as they might operate to receive electrons from NADPH and deliver them to heme during the catalytic oxidation of two molecules of L-arginine (ARG₁ and ARG₂). Each NOH-ARG also contributes an electron to heme.

catalytic cycle so that it is available during the second cycle. As NOS catalytically oxidizes L-arginine, it alternately consumes two and then one molecule of NADPH, thus accounting for the overall stoichiometry of 1.5 NADPH oxidized per NO formed (127, 130).

There has been some debate regarding the precise stoichiometry of NADPH oxidation by NOS. Following our report that oxidation of L-arginine and NOH-ARG require 1.5 and 0.5 equivalents of NADPH, respectively (130), Marletta and co-workers pointed out that their experimentally observed stoichiometry with L-arginine is ≥ 2.0 (49, 85). Although they ultimately agreed with our net value, they suggested that the experimental basis for our (and their) correction for uncoupled NADPH oxidation (49, 85) was inadequate. In our view, mechanistic elucidation of NOS is now sufficiently advanced to settle this issue unambiguously. Mixed function oxidation of L-arginine or NOH-ARG to citrulline and NO requires three electrons or one electron (equivalent to 1.5 or 0.5 NADPH) from a cosubstrate, respectively. For fully coupled enzyme, the stoichiometry can be higher only if the product is nitroxyl (NO^-) rather than NO; if NOS is literally NO synthase and NADPH is the cosubstrate, then the stoichiometry must be as we indicate.

Hobbs et al (53) have suggested that NOS may form NO^- rather than NO. Pathway C (Figure 1) shows a possible mechanism (127). Although it is clear that NO^-, if formed, would be rapidly oxidized to NO in biological media (30, 95), we think it is unlikely that NOS would variably catalyze NO^- and NO formation. At present, we believe that the published data in support of NO formation are more compelling.

It is also unlikely that electron donors other than NADPH (e.g. thiols or THB) participate in NOS-mediated mixed function oxidation of L-arginine. Net electron contribution by such species would either reduce the stoichiometry of NADPH oxidation below 1.5, in marked disagreement with experimental findings, or would require participation of additional molecules of O_2. The stoichiometry of O_2 consumption has, in fact, been determined. For both iNOS and nNOS there are, as expected, two O_2 consumed per citrulline formed from L-arginine, and one O_2 used per citrulline formed from NOH-ARG (KJ Baek & DJ Stuehr, unpublished).

Uncoupled NOS Reaction

Uncoupled electron transfer occurs in most oxygenase enzymes and refers to a diversion or loss of electrons that otherwise would be used to generate product from substrate; oxygen is the usual acceptor of the stray electrons, giving rise to superoxide. In NOS, uncoupled electron transfer can be quantitated by monitoring the relative rates of NADPH oxidation and NO synthesis, given that 1.5 NADPH are consumed per NO formed from L-arginine under fully coupled conditions (73, 130).

As noted in Figure 3, NOS is believed to transfer electrons in a linear sequence, with calmodulin controlling the electron transfer from flavin to heme iron, the final electron-accepting cofactor. When incubated under V_{max} conditions (i.e. NADPH, L-arginine, O_2, and THB in excess), NOS shows tightly coupled electron transfer to the heme iron and also shows heme iron reduction tightly coupled to activation of O_2 and oxidation of L-arginine to NO and citrulline. However, under many conditions, electron transfer through NOS becomes uncoupled with respect to NO synthesis. These conditions provide a means to study the mechanism of NOS partial reactions. These reactions may also be physiologically relevant because uncoupled electron transfer sometimes leads to generation of a mixture of superoxide and NO, species that can then react to form peroxynitrite.

NOS electron transfer can be uncoupled by using electron acceptors such as ferricyanide and cytochrome c that are easily reduced by NOS cofactors (69, 118). Figure 3 shows where ferricyanide, cytochrome c, and O_2 are thought to accept electrons in the NOS electron transfer sequence. Based on studies with macrophage iNOS subunits (6), which do not contain heme or THB, it is clear that ferricyanide and cytochrome c can accept electrons from the NOS flavin domain. The fact that NOS binds to cytochrome c sepharose (69) is consistent with the view that NOS may directly transfer electrons to cytochrome c. Based on studies showing that cytochrome P450 reductase (77) and neuronal NOS (DJ Stuehr, unpublished) reduce ferricyanide even when depleted of FMN, it is also likely that electrons are transferred directly from FAD.

Reduction of cytochrome c is potentially complicated in that it can be reduced directly by NOS flavins or indirectly by superoxide if that species is formed. The relative contribution of superoxide to NOS cytochrome c reduction is controversial, with some groups reporting a diminution of the Ca^{2+}/calmodulin-stimulated rate in the presence of superoxide dismutase (SOD) (suggesting superoxide mediation) (29, 87) and other groups reporting complete SOD independence (69).

Both nNOS (113) and iNOS (1) catalyze the NADPH-dependent reduction of O_2 in the absence of L-arginine. Thermodynamically, O_2 is poised to accept electrons at any point in the NOS electron transfer sequence. However, mechanistic considerations (see below) suggest that reduced (ferrous) heme is the kinetically favored site of O_2 reduction. Indeed, experiments with macrophage iNOS subunits (containing flavins but not heme) and calmodulin-free nNOS (no heme reduction possible) indicate that transfer of electrons from flavins to O_2 is relatively slow (1, 6).

For nNOS, the rate of substrate-independent O_2 reduction, measured as increased NADPH consumption, increases by >100-fold upon calmodulin binding (1). The increased O_2 reduction induced by calmodulin can be blocked by heme iron-binding agents such as imidazole (138), by L-arginine (46), or by arginine analogues that may inhibit heme iron reduction or O_2 binding to heme iron [e.g. thiocitrulline (29; H Abu-Soud & D Stuehr, submitted) and nitroarginine (46)]. Because calmodulin binding to nNOS triggers electron flow onto heme iron (Figure 3), the results with the inhibitors suggest that heme mediates calmodulin-induced O_2 reduction. Marked enhancement of O_2 reduction by calmodulin dramatically illustrates the rapidity of heme iron-mediated O_2 reduction vs flavin-mediated reduction.

Calmodulin binding to nNOS also increases cytochrome c reduction 10–20-fold (29, 69, 123). Two mechanisms may be operative. On one hand, H Abu-Soud & D Stuehr (manuscript submitted) recently found that calmodulin binding increases the rate of electron loading into the NOS flavins by 20-fold. Thus increased cytochrome c reduction may simply reflect increased electron flux into the flavin centers of NOS. On the other hand, Masters and co-workers (123) and Griffith and co-workers (29) found that SOD substantially, but not completely, inhibits cytochrome c reduction by nNOS in the presence of Ca^{2+}/calmodulin. Thus calmodulin-stimulated superoxide production by the NOS heme iron may also contribute to the increase in cytochrome c reduction.

L-Arginine and its analogues exclusively affect NOS electron transfer at the heme iron. Among NOS substrates, only L-arginine and NOH-ARG support completely coupled oxygen reduction and NO synthesis. Metabolism of the arginine analogues NMA or homoarginine to NO proceeds in a partially uncoupled manner (107; H Abu-Soud & D Stuehr, submitted). Mayer et al have reported that at L-arginine concentrations below 100 μM, NADPH oxidation also becomes somewhat uncoupled from NO synthesis (46). Under such circumstances in which there is a partial uncoupling, NOS concurrently generates superoxide and NO, species that rapidly combine to form peroxynitrite. Two L-arginine analogues, L-thiocitrulline and L-nitroarginine, significantly decrease uncoupled NADPH oxidation in iNOS and nNOS by occupying the substrate binding site and inhibiting heme iron reduction (H Abu-Soud & D Stuehr, submitted) and/or O_2 binding to heme iron (29).

A role for THB in facilitating coupled electron transfer was suggested by Mayer, who showed that THB-deficient NOS concurrently generated superoxide, H_2O_2, and NO in the presence of L-arginine; adding exogenous THB caused NOS to become fully coupled (46). The mechanism by which this occurs is under investigation.

Calmodulin Binding, Superoxide Formation, and Evolutionary Divergence Among the NOS Isoforms

As noted, Ca^{2+}/calmodulin binding to nNOS in the absence of arginine dramatically increases the rate of NADPH oxidation and superoxide production (1, 46, 113). On the other hand, macrophage iNOS always contains tightly-bound calmodulin, but its maximal rate of uncoupled NADPH oxidation in the absence of arginine is just one-sixth that of nNOS with Ca^{2+}/calmodulin bound (1). Given that Ca^{2+}/calmodulin also enables heme iron reduction in iNOS (H Abu-Soud & D Stuehr, submitted) and that purified iNOS and nNOS have comparable specific activities for coupled NO synthesis, why is Ca^{2+}/calmodulin-induced, uncoupled NADPH oxidation slower in iNOS than in nNOS?

Although a definitive biochemical explanation is not available, one may speculate why evolution favored this outcome. Under physiological conditions, neurons probably maintain sufficient L-arginine levels for nNOS to catalyze tightly coupled NO synthesis in response to transient increases in intracellular Ca^{2+}. Only during episodes of prolonged Ca^{2+} influx that occur in pathologic conditions (e.g. stroke) could nNOS possibly deplete cellular L-arginine and generate significant superoxide. Because such conditions are rare, there was little pressure for nNOS to evolve a means of curtailing uncoupled heme reduction with attendant superoxide generation in the absence of L-arginine. In contrast, iNOS appears capable of continuous heme iron reduction by virtue of its bound calmodulin and has evolved to have much slower uncoupled electron transfer to oxygen in the absence of L-arginine. Because activated macrophages migrate to sites where L-arginine becomes limiting (e.g. wounds; 2), it is not surprising that iNOS has evolved so as to limit superoxide generation in such circumstances.

OVERALL MECHANISM

Heme Cofactor and Analogy to Cytochrome P450

The discovery that nNOS (72, 90, 129, 135) and iNOS (129) contain a heme cofactor that reacts with CO in the presence of NADPH to give an absorbance peak at 444–448 nm represented a seminal achievement in the mechanistic understanding of NOS catalysis. On the basis of that finding, it became possible to confidently apply much of our understanding of cytochrome P450 biochemistry to NOS. The reaction pathway shown in Figure 5 invokes the same intermediates proposed in 1992 (see Figure 1, pathway A) and provides additional mechanistic details based on recent studies with NOS and on the similarity of those reactions to reactions catalyzed by cytochrome P450s. We (25, 26) and others (75, 85, 114) have proposed essentially similar schemes previously. Electrons shown as originating from NADPH should be understood as deriving via the flavin-mediated transfers shown in Figure 4 (*bottom*).

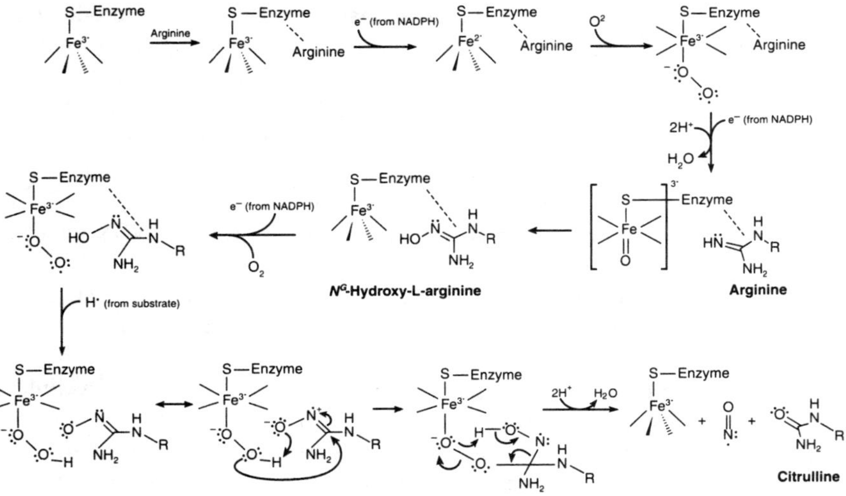

Figure 5 Chemical mechanism of NOS (modified from 26, with permission).

A few aspects of the mechanism shown in Figure 5 warrant specific comment. The hydroxylation shown at the fifth step is well-precedented in cytochrome P450 chemistry and is likely to occur by a similar mechanism in which the ferryl heme intermediate $(Fe-O)^{3+}$ first abstracts a hydrogen atom from arginine nitrogen to give $(Fe-OH)^{3+}$ and a guanidinium nitrogen radical on the substrate [e.g. ~NH-(C=N•H)+-NH_2]. The transient-iron hydroxyl and nitrogen radicals then recombine (oxygen rebound) to yield NOH-ARG and ferric heme [see Figure 1 (112) for a more complete description of this chemistry as it relates to cytochrome P450]. Marletta and co-workers have provided strong evidence for radical-mediated hydroxylation by showing formation of products consistent with radical rearrangement with some N^ω-substituted L-arginine analogues (see below) (106, 107).

To be consistent with isotope tracer results (76, 81, 115, 130) and data on NADPH stoichiometry (130), heme-mediated oxidation of NOH-ARG to citrulline and NO minimally requires (*a*) that NOH-ARG donates one electron to heme and (*b*) that an oxy-heme species provides the ureido oxygen of citrulline. The specific pathway and intermediates shown in Figure 5 are speculative but are based on the following additional considerations. In forming the peroxy-heme species, we show NOH-ARG contributing the second rather than the first electron. This ordering of steps is based on the observation that NOH-ARG does not reduce ferric heme to ferrous heme as judged by spectral studies of CO-binding (ferrous but not ferric heme binds CO to give a characteristic absorbance at ~450 nm). We regard the alternative possibility that NOH-ARG donates the first electron but then sterically hinders CO binding as less likely on the basis that L-arginine does not prevent NADPH-dependent heme reduction and CO binding. In addition, recent studies show that NOH-ARG gives a type I substrate perturbation difference spectrum (90a) consistent with the view that NOH-ARG does not interact directly with heme iron.

In principle, the one electron oxidation of NOH-ARG can occur by either loss of e^- or H•. In the absence of data addressing this issue, we (25) and others (85) have invoked e^- transfer to yield a radical cation. Recently, Korth et al (75) provided arguments and redox potential measurements supporting transfer of H• to yield the radical intermediate shown in Figure 5.

Autoinactivation

Most investigators working with purified NOS find that the enzyme is moderately unstable during catalytic turnover. As noted, turnover in the absence of L-arginine yields reactive oxygen species (ROS) such as O_2^- and H_2O_2. Because either or both ROS may damage essential cofactors or sensitive amino acid residues, instability is not unexpected. In the presence of L-arginine, ROS formation is minimized but NO is formed. Nitric oxide reacts very rapidly with any O_2^- that may be present to yield peroxynitrite $(OONO^-)$, a species with reactivity similar to the highly damaging hydroxyl radical (OH$^\bullet$). Interestingly, NO may itself inactivate NOS by binding as a sixth (axial) ligand to the iron of the heme cofactor (41a, 72, 116). In fact, because NO has high affinity for heme iron (e.g. such affinity is the basis of NO-mediated activation of guanylyl cyclase) (4, 21, 44), it is not clear how NOS avoids rapid self-inactivation. While the answer to this question is not known, a few suggestions may be offered. First, as shown in Figure 5, the reaction that forms citrulline and NO also forms hydroxy-heme rather than free heme. If loss of water from heme is slow relative to the diffusion of NO out of the active site, NO-mediated inactivation will be minimized. Second, in oxidizing NOH-ARG, peroxy-heme reacts with the guanidinium carbon of a NOH-ARG radical. Depending on the conformation of NOH-ARG in the active site, product citrulline may initially shield the heme from nascent NO; slow citrulline dissociation would then also protect heme as NO diffused away. Third, spectral studies of isolated nNOS show a fraction of the heme iron to be in a low spin state consistent with perturbation of the heme iron d-orbitals by a sixth ligand (90a). If that ligand is an active site amino acid residue, one might imagine that the active site has closed over the heme, thereby protecting it until opened for the next catalytic cycle.

Role of THB

In principle, either of the monooxygenations catalyzed by NOS could be mediated by THB rather than heme. Hydroxylations catalyzed by the aromatic amino acid hydroxylases are, for example, mediated by THB (22), and 4α-peroxy-THB can be envisioned as replacing peroxy-heme in the oxidation of NOH-ARG to citrulline and NO (127). Prior to the discovery of a heme cofactor, such roles for THB seemed highly plausible. Although the sequence and functional analogy between NOS and the cytochrome P450 system suggests THB does not participate directly as an oxidative cofactor in NOS, such considerations provide no clue to functions that THB might have.

However, available data do suggest several possible functions for THB. As pointed out by Giovanelli et al, THB does not readily dissociate from NOS and is thus unlikely to be catalytically recycled by exogenous dihydropteridine reductase in the manner characteristic of the aromatic amino acid hydroxylases (40). They concluded that the THB cofactor of NOS was more likely to have an allosteric than a catalytic role. Consistent with this view, Klatt et al report that THB increases the affinity of nNOS for the L-arginine analogue, L-NNA and that L-arginine increases binding affinity for THB (70). Stuehr and co-workers have shown that reassembly of mouse macrophage iNOS monomers into dimers requires THB in addition to heme and L-arginine (6). That finding is also consistent with an allosteric role for THB, but it is unclear if such a dependency always occurs in vivo. Gross and co-workers, working with rat aortic smooth muscle iNOS, find that iNOS expression by cells treated with THB synthesis inhibitors yields THB-deficient, inactive iNOS dimers, not monomers (SS Gross, personal communication). It may be that the steps for monomer assembly into dimers differs for monomers in cells vs monomers assembled in vitro.

A variety of THB analogues have been used to probe THB function. Although THB is the most active cofactor, several analogues show significant activity. Klatt et al report, for example, that the 6S-isomer of THB increases nNOS activity to the same extent as the natural 6R-isomer (i.e. fourfold) but that it must be added at 60-fold higher concentrations to achieve that effect (70). In general only redox active THB analogues stimulate NOS activity; the 6-(RS)-methyl-5-deaza analogue, for example, inhibits rather than activates (48). Overall, these ongoing studies indicate that THB is more than a simple allosteric activator and suggest that it contributes in some way to NOS catalysis.

Recent studies by Ignarro et al (116) suggest a novel catalytic role for THB. While examining the NO-mediated inactivation of NOS, these investigators found that THB was uniquely highly effective in restoring NOS activity. Although a variety of thiols reduced inactivation by NO, only THB effectively restored activity once inactivation had occurred. The mechanism of this repair, if it occurs, remains to be elucidated.

NOS INHIBITORS—MECHANISTIC ASPECTS

Applications

In 1987, Hibbs and co-workers reported that several arginine analogues attenuated L-arginine-dependent, activated macrophage-mediated cell killing (52). From that initial observation, the design, synthesis, and mechanistic elucidation of NOS inhibitors has grown into a substantial enterprise. Heavy reliance on NOS inhibitors is not unexpected. NOS activity is difficult to measure in vivo or in complex biological systems (e.g. perfused organs) because its products do not accumulate. Citrulline is recycled to arginine (45), and NO is rapidly degraded to nitrite and nitrate, species that are present at significant levels endogenously. Although NO formation can be followed in vivo using stable isotopes (e.g. with L-[^{15}N-guanidino]arginine) (80), such studies are technically difficult; there are no radioisotopes of nitrogen with useful half-lives (^{13}N has $t_{1/2} = 10$ min). In the face of these difficulties, investigators have relied heavily on NOS inhibitors. Biological phenomena are assumed to be NO-mediated and/or NOS-dependent if they are attenuated by NOS-selective inhibitors, typically L-NMA, L-NNA or L-NNA methyl ester (L-NAME). Controls, if carried out at all, are generally limited to a demonstration that the biological phenomena are not perturbed by the D-enantiomer of the inhibitor (D-NMA and D-NNA do not inhibit NOS) and a showing that inhibition by the L-enantiomers (L-NMA, L-NNA, etc) is reversed by excess L-arginine.

Although heavy reliance on inhibitors to document and study NOS-dependent processes might lead to serious misinterpretations in complex systems, few problems have come to light. To date, the caveats are these: (*a*) The extent of NOS inhibition is difficult to establish in complex systems. Thus if a response is attenuated by L-NMA, for example, it is probably NOS-dependent. However, if some small response persists in the presence of L-NMA, the remaining response may truly be NOS-independent or, more likely, NOS may simply not be fully inhibited by L-NMA. With respect to the last possibility, it should be remembered that NOS inhibitors may not access all NOS-containing compartments equally and that NOS isoforms differ in their sensitivity to both arginine antagonists (35, 43, 79) and other NOS inhibitors (20, 92, 141). (*b*) None of the NOS inhibitors is likely to be completely NOS specific or resistant to metabolism to other biologically active products. Thus L-NMA is metabolized by NOS to citrulline (25, 107), a product recycled to L-arginine (45); L-arginine supports NO synthesis and decreases NOS inhibition by L-NMA. L-NAME and other L-arginine esters are reportedly muscarinic receptor antagonists (13). N^{ω}-amino-L-arginine (L-NAA), a potent NOS inhibitor (8, 31, 43), causes seizures in dogs that appear to be unrelated to NOS inhibition (18, 66). Aminoguanidine, which is structurally related to L-NAA, inhibits monoamine oxidase and aldose reductase in addition to NOS (132). Aromatic N-heterocycles identified as NOS inhibitors by Wolff et al (137–140) (see below) alter membrane fluidity, inhibit cytochrome P450, and have antifungal and other activities unrelated to NOS inhibition. These caveats notwithstanding, NOS inhibitors have contributed greatly to the elucidation of NO biology.

In view of the multiple physiological roles attributed to NO, it is not surprising that pathological consequences attend the under- or overproduction of NO in vivo. Underproduction of NO can be addressed by up-regulating the appropriate NOS isoform or by administration of NO donors; these topics are discussed elsewhere (102, 125). Overproduction of NO can be limited by down-regulating iNOS expression (19, 102) or by administering NOS inhibitors (64). The latter approach finds particular utility in cytokine-induced and septic shock, conditions characterized by the inappropriate expression of iNOS in vascular endothelial and smooth muscle cells (64). The resulting overproduction of vasoactive NO causes markedly decreased systemic vascular resistance and consequent hypotension (cardiovascular shock). In both animal models (65–67) and patient trials (64, 110), vascular resistance and blood pressure are restored to normal or near normal by giving NOS inhibitors. iNOS-mediated overproduction of NO also occurs in a number of inflammatory

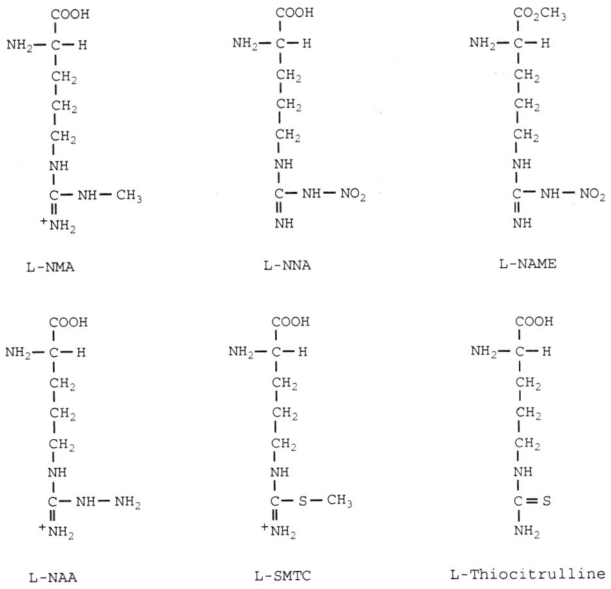

```
      COOH                    COOH                    CO₂CH₃
       |                       |                       |
NH₂— C— H               NH₂— C— H               NH₂— C— H
       |                       |                       |
      CH₂                     CH₂                     CH₂
       |                       |                       |
      CH₂                     CH₂                     CH₂
       |                       |                       |
      CH₂                     CH₂                     CH₂
       |                       |                       |
      NH                      NH                      NH
       |                       |                       |
      C— NH— CH₃              C— NH— NO₂              C— NH— NO₂
      ‖                       ‖                       ‖
      ⁺NH₂                    NH                      NH

     L-NMA                   L-NNA                   L-NAME


      COOH                    COOH                    COOH
       |                       |                       |
NH₂— C— H               NH₂— C— H               NH₂— C— H
       |                       |                       |
      CH₂                     CH₂                     CH₂
       |                       |                       |
      CH₂                     CH₂                     CH₂
       |                       |                       |
      CH₂                     CH₂                     CH₂
       |                       |                       |
      NH                      NH                      NH
       |                       |                       |
      C— NH— NH₂              C— S— CH₃               C = S
      ‖                       ‖                       |
      ⁺NH₂                    ⁺NH₂                    NH₂

     L-NAA                   L-SMTC              L-Thiocitrulline
```

Figure 6 Structures of NOS inhibitors.

disorders including arthritis; the attendant tissue destruction is prevented or reduced by NOS inhibitors (19, 89, 132, 134). It has been suggested that the Ca^{2+} influx occurring during the tissue ischemia of stroke activates nNOS to a level that causes overproduction of NO when tissue perfusion is restored; damage is reduced by NOS inhibitors (10).

Arginine Analogues

N^ω-monosubstituted L-arginine analogues represent a large and useful class of NOS inhibitors (Figure 6). In addition to L-NMA, L-NNA and L-NAA, this group includes higher N^ω-alkyl homologues of L-NMA (e.g. N^ω-ethyl-L-arginine, etc), and N^δ-iminoethyl-L-ornithine (L-NIO). Some inhibitors show modest selectivity among NOS isoforms (8, 43, 79). Initial inhibition by all arginine antagonists is competitive with L-arginine, which indicates that they occupy the arginine/citrulline binding site of the enzymes. Extent of inhibition is diminished by L-arginine and, at least initially, inhibition can be reversed by L-arginine.

For some of the arginine analogues, NOS inhibition becomes irreversible or poorly reversible with time. Recent studies with L-NMA show that it is metabolized in an arginine-like fashion by NOS to N^ω-hydroxy-N^ω-methyl-L-arginine (NOH-NMA) and, eventually, to citrulline, NO, and other products

(25, 107). Although it is clear that L-NMA is a mechanism-based inactivator of NOS, it is not clear which, if any, of the metabolites of L-NMA and NOH-NMA causes irreversible inactivation (25, 107). Other irreversible inhibitors of NOS include L-NAA and L-NIO, but their mechanism of action is also unknown. However, Clement et al (17) have shown that aminoguanidine can be N-hydroxylated by cytochrome P450, suggesting that NAA may be processed similarly to L-arginine and L-NMA. In contrast, L-NNA is not a mechanism-based inhibitor but is rather a tight-binding, slow-dissociating ligand of the arginine-binding site (35, 71).

Recently Narayanan & Griffith (98) reported that S-methyl-L-thiocitrulline (L-SMTC) (Figure 6) is an extremely potent inhibitor of isolated nNOS and iNOS and of eNOS-dependent phenomena, such as aortic ring relaxation in response to methacholine. It is a strong pressor in rats (99). For nNOS and iNOS, K_i values for L-SMTC are substantially lower than for other arginine analogues reported to date (99).

Heme-Interacting Amino Acid Inhibitors

It is apparent from the mechanism shown in Figure 5 that the guanidino nitrogen and the guanidino carbon of substrate arginine must be in close proximity to heme iron. That consideration led Narayanan & Griffith to design and synthesize arginine/citrulline analogues having side chains with functionalities expected to act as heme-binding ligands (29, 98). L-Thiocitrulline (N^δ-thioureido-L-norvaline) (Figure 6) is one of a series of compounds developed. Kinetic studies show L-thiocitrulline binding is competitive with L-arginine [K_i = 0.06 μM (nNOS) and 3.6 μM (iNOS)]; spectral studies show L-thiocitrulline binding causes a type II-like difference spectrum, consistent with interaction of the thioureido sulfur with heme iron (29). P Feldman et al have obtained similar results (manuscript submitted).

Low Molecular Weight, Non-Amino Acid Inhibitors

In addition to arginine and citrulline analogues, NOS is inhibited by a variety of low molecular weight compounds. Inhibition by NO was discussed above; see (127) for reviews on inhibition by flavin and calmodulin antagonists. We discuss here more recent developments. Because several disorders are attributable to iNOS-mediated overproduction of NO, reports that aminoguanidine is an iNOS-specific inhibitor (20, 92) have received considerable attention. At present, the mechanistic basis for selectivity has not been reported, but it seems likely that subtle differences among isoforms in their arginine and/or heme binding sites allows aminoguanidine to inhibit iNOS at much lower concentrations than are needed to inhibit the constitutive NOS isoforms. Interestingly, lower molecular weight alkyl guanidines also inhibit, albeit poorly (44a). K Narayanan & Griffith (unpublished) and others (E Furfine, personal communication) find that low molecular weight S-substituted thioureas are potent inhibitors of all NOS isoforms; these last compounds are chemically related to L-SMTC.

Wolff et al have reported that several N-heterocycles, including imidazole, phenylimidazoles, and certain antifungal agents (e.g. miconazole, clotrimazole and ketoconazole), inhibit nNOS (137, 138), eNOS (141), and iNOS (140). All bind as a sixth (axial) ligand to the heme cofactor; the antifungal agents also act as calmodulin antagonists of nNOS (137). Preliminary studies suggest that it may be possible to achieve significant isoform selectivity; e.g for 1-phenylimidazole the K_i values for nNOS, eNOS and iNOS are 38, 50, and 0.7 μM, respectively (141). In contrast, 7-nitroindazole is reported to be a relatively selective nNOS inhibitor in vivo (5) and is found to bind to nNOS, eNOS and iNOS with K_i values of 0.16, 0.8, and 1.6 μM, respectively (139, 141). Interestingly, for some isoforms, binding of N-heterocycles is at least partially competitive with arginine and/or THB, which suggests that the binding sites for heme, THB, and arginine are closely grouped (140, 141). Competitive binding also suggests that the degree and selectivity of isoform inhibition by N-hetrocycles in vivo will depend on intracellular L-arginine and THB concentrations as well as on the K_i values determined in vitro (141).

PERSPECTIVE AND FUTURE DIRECTIONS

Considering that NOS catalyzes one of the most complex single-enzyme reactions known, great progress has been made in elucidating its mechanism. Early studies demonstrating the intermediacy of NOH-ARG (130), defining the source of the citrulline (76) and NO (81) oxygens, and accurately determining the stoichiometry with respect to NADPH (130) established that NOS was a double monooxygenase able to make a single radical product by storing an "extra" NADPH electron. Discovery of the heme cofactor (72, 90, 129, 135) allowed us (26) and others (85) to propose a detailed chemical mechanism based on established cytochrome P450-catalyzed reactions. Such proposals now guide further investigations of mechanism and the development of increasingly potent inhibitors.

Several questions of mechanism remain. What is the true role(s) of THB? Is THB redox active and, if so, how is it recycled? How does this heme-dependent enzyme avoid rapid autoinactivation by NO? Do the active sites of nNOS, eNOS, and iNOS differ sufficiently to allow pharmacologically meaningful selective inhibition? If so, what level of selectivity is needed in vivo, and how is it to be achieved? In the context of the overall NOS mechanism, exactly how do known NOS inhibitors inhibit? Beyond these mechanistic issues, several aspects of regulation and intracellular localization remain unanswered. It is anticipated that the answers to these and related questions will be apparent in the next few years.

Literature Cited

1. Abu-Soud HM, Stuehr DJ. 1993. Nitric oxide synthases reveal a role for calmodulin in controlling electron transfer. *Proc. Natl. Acad. Sci. USA* 90:10769–72
2. Albina JE, Mills CD, Henry WL Jr, Caldwell MD. 1990. Temporal expression of different pathways of L-arginine metabolism in healing wounds. *J. Immunol.* 144:3877–80
3. Archer S. 1993. Measurement of nitric oxide in biological models. *FASEB J.* 7:349–60
4. Arnold WP, Mittal CK, Katsuki S, Murad F. 1977. Nitric oxide activates guanylate cyclase and increases guanosine 3′:5′-cyclic monophosphate levels in various tissue preparations. *Proc. Natl. Acad. Sci. USA* 74:3203–7
5. Babbedge RC, Bland-Ward PA, Hart SL, Moore PK. 1993. Inhibition of rat cerebellar nitric oxide synthase by 7-nitro indazole and related substituted indazoles. *Br. J. Pharmacol.* 110:225–28
6. Baek KJ, Thiel BA, Lucas S, Stuehr DJ. 1993. Macrophage nitric oxide synthase subunits. *J. Biol. Chem.* 268:21120–29
7. Bredt DS, Hwang PM, Glatt CE, Lowenstein C, Reed RR, et al. 1991. Cloned and expressed nitric oxide synthase structurally resembles cytochrome P-450 reductase. *Nature* 351:714–18
8. Bredt DS, Hwang PM, Snyder SH. 1990. Localization of nitric oxide synthase indicating a neuronal role for nitric oxide. *Nature* 347:768–70
9. Bredt DS, Snyder SH. 1990. Isolation of nitric oxide synthetase, a calmodulin-requiring enzyme. *Proc. Natl. Acad. Sci. USA* 87:682–85
10. Bredt DS, Snyder SH. 1994. Nitric oxide: a physiologic messenger molecule. *Annu. Rev. Biochem.* 63:175–95
11. Buga GM, Gold ME, Fukuto JM, Ignarro LJ. 1991. Shear stress-induced release of nitric oxide from endothelial cells grown on beads. *Hypertension* 17:187–93
12. Busconi L, Michel T. 1993. Endothelial nitric oxide synthase. N-terminal myristoylation determines subcellular localization. *J. Biol. Chem.* 268:8410–13
13. Buxton ILO, Cheek DJ, Eckman D, Westfall DP, Sanders KM, et al. 1993. N^G-nitro L-arginine methyl ester and other alkyl esters of arginine are muscarinic receptor antagonists. *Circ. Res.* 72:387–95
14. Charles IG, Chubb A, Gill R, Clare J, Lowe PN, et al. 1993. Cloning and expression of a rat neuronal nitric oxide synthase coding sequence in a baculovirus/insect cell system. *Biochem. Biophys. Res. Commun.* 196:1481–89
15. Charles IG, Palmer RMJ, Hickery MS, Bayliss MT, Chubb AP, et al. 1993. Cloning, characterization and expression of a cDNA encoding an inducible nitric oxide synthase from the human chondrocyte. *Proc. Natl. Acad. Sci. USA* 90:11419–23
16. Cho JH, Xie QW, Calaycay J, Mumford RA, Swiderek KM, et al. 1992. Calmodulin is a subunit of nitric oxide synthase from macrophages. *J. Exp. Med.* 176:599–604
17. Clement B, Schultze-Mosgau MH, Richter PH, Besch A. 1994. Cytochrome P450-dependent N-hydroxylation of an amino guanidine (amidinohydrazone) and microsomal retroreduction of the N-hydroxylated product. *Xenobiotica* 24:671–88
18. Cobb JP, Natanson C, Hoffmann WD, Lodato RF, Banks S, et al. 1992. N^ω-amino-L-arginine, an inhibitor of nitric oxide synthase, raises vascular resistance but increases mortality rates in awake canines challenged with endotoxin. *J. Exp. Med.* 176:1175–82
19. Cochran FR. 1994. Inhibition of nitric oxide synthesis as a therapeutic target for arthritis: recent reports. *Exp. Opin. Invest. Drugs* 34:529–31
20. Corbett JA, Tilton RG, Chang K, Hasan KS, Ido Y, et al. 1992. Aminoguanidine, a novel inhibitor of nitric oxide forma-

tion, prevents diabetic vascular dysfunction. *Diabetes* 41:552–56

21. Craven PA, Derubertis FR. 1978. Restoration of the responsiveness of purified guanylate cyclase to nitrosoguanidine, nitric oxide, and related activators by heme and heme proteins: Evidence for the involvement of the paramagnetic nitrosyl-heme complex in enzyme activation. *J. Biol. Chem.* 253:8433–43

22. Dix TA, Kuhn DM, Benkovic SJ. 1987. Mechanism of oxygen activation by tyrosine hydroxylase. *Biochemistry* 26:3354–61

23. Deleted in proof

24. Feelisch M, Noack EA. 1987. Correlation between nitric oxide formation during degradation of organic nitrates and activation of guanylate cyclase. *Eur. J. Pharmacol.* 139:19–30

25. Feldman PL, Griffith OW, Hong H, Stuehr DJ. 1993. Irreversible inactivation of macrophage and brain nitric oxide synthase by L-N^G-methylarginine requires NADPH-dependent hydroxylation. *J. Med. Chem.* 36:491–96

26. Feldman PL, Griffith OW, Stuehr DJ. 1993. The surprising life of nitric oxide. *Chem. Eng. News* 71(51):26–38

27. Förstermann U, Nakane M, Tracey WR, Pollock JS. 1993. Isoforms of nitric oxide synthase: functions in the cardiovascular system. *Eur. Heart J. 14(Suppl. 1)*:10–15

28. Förstermann U, Pollack JS, Schmidt HHW, Heller M, Murad F. 1991. Calmodulin-dependent endothelium derived relaxing factor/nitric oxide synthase activity is present in the particulate and cytosolic fractions of bovine aortic endothelial cells. *Proc. Natl. Acad. Sci. USA* 88:1788–92

29. Frey C, Narayanan K, McMillan K, Spack L, Gross S, et al. 1994. L-thiocitrulline: a stereospecific, heme-binding inhibitor of nitric oxide synthase. *J. Biol. Chem.* 269: In press

30. Fukuto JM, Hobbs AJ, Ignarro LJ. 1993. Coversion of nitroxyl (HNO) to nitric oxide (NO) in biological systems: the role of physiological oxidants and relevance to the biological activity of HNO. *Biochem. Biophys. Res. Commun.* 196:707–13

31. Fukuto JM, Wood KS, Byrns RE, Ignarro LJ. 1990. N^G-amino-L-arginine: a new potent antagonist of L-arginine-mediated endothelium-dependent relaxation. *Biochem. Biophys. Res. Commun.* 168:458–65

32. Furchgott RF. 1984. The role of endothelium in the responses of vascular smooth muscle to drugs. *Annu. Rev. Pharmacol. Toxicol.* 24:175–97

33. Furchgott RF. 1988. Studies on relaxation of rabbit aorta by sodium nitrite: the basis for the proposal that the acid-activatable inhibitory factor from bovine retractor penis is inorganic nitrite and the endothelium-derived relaxing factor is nitric oxide. In *Vasodilatation: Vascular Smooth Muscle, Peptides, Autonomic Nerves, and Endothelium*, ed. PM Vanhoutte, pp. 401–14. New York: Raven

34. Furchgott RF, Zawadzki JV. 1980. The obligatory role of endothelial cells in the relaxation of arterial smooth muscle by acetylcholine. *Nature* 288:373–76

35. Furfine ES, Harmon MF, Paith JE, Garvey EP. 1993. Selective inhibition of constitutive nitric oxide synthase by L-N^G-nitroarginine. *Biochemistry* 32:8512–17

36. Garthwaite J, Charles SL, Chess-Williams R. 1988. Endothelium-derived relaxing factor release on activation of NMDA receptors suggests role as intercellular messenger in the brain. *Nature* 336:385–88

37. Garvey EP, Tuttle JV, Covington K, Merrill BM, Wood ER, et al. 1994. Purification and characterization of the constitutive nitric oxide synthase from human placenta. *Arch. Biochem. Biophys.* 311:235–41

38. Gaston B, Reilly J, Drazen JM, Fackler J, Ramdev P, et al. 1993. Endogenous nitrogen oxides and bronchodilator S-nitrosothiols in human airways. *Proc. Natl. Acad. Sci. USA* 90:10957–61

39. Geller DA, Lowenstein CJ, Shapiro RA, Nussler AK, Di Silvio M, et al. 1993. Molecular cloning and expression of inducible nitric oxide synthase from human heptatocytes. *Proc. Natl. Acad. Sci. USA* 90:3491–95

40. Giovanelli J, Campos KL, Kaufman S. 1991. Tetrahydrobiopterin, a cofactor for rat cerebellar nitric oxide synthase does not function as a reactant in the oxygenation of arginine. *Proc. Natl. Acad. Sci. USA* 88:7091–95

41. Green LC, Wagner DA, Glogowski J, Skipper PL, Wishnok JS, et al. 1982. Analysis of nitrate, nitrite and [^{15}N]nitrate in biological fluids. *Anal. Biochem.* 126:131–38

41a. Griscavage JM, Rogers NE, Sherman MP, Ignarro LJ. 1993. Inducible nitric oxide synthase from a rat alveolar macrophage cell line is inhibited by nitric oxide. *J. Immunol.* 151:6329:37

42. Gross SS, Levi R. 1992. Tetrahydrobiopterin synthesis. An absolute re-

quirement for cytokine-induced nitric oxide generation by vascular smooth muscle. *J. Biol. Chem.* 267:25722–29

43. Gross SS, Stuehr DJ, Aisaka K, Jaffe EA, Levi R, et al. 1990. Macrophage and endothelial cell nitric synthesis: cell-type selective inhibition by N^G-amino-arginine, N^G-nitroarginine and N^G-methylarginine. *Biochem. Biophys. Res. Commun.* 170:96–103

44. Gruetter CA, Barry BK, McNamara DB, Gruetter DY, Kadowitz PJ, et al. 1979. Relaxation of bovine coronary artery and activation of coronary arterial guanylate cyclase by nitric oxide, nitroprusside and a carcinogenic nitrosamine. *J. Cyclic Nucleotide Res.* 5:211–24

44a. Hasan K, Heesen BJ, Corbett JA, McDaniel ML, Chang K, et al. 1993. Inhibition of nitric oxide formation by guanidines. *Eur. J. Pharmacol.* 249:101–6

45. Hecker M, Sessa WC, Harris HJ, Ånggård EE, Vane JR. 1990. The metabolism of L-arginine and its significance for the biosynthesis of endothelium-derived relaxing factor: cultured endothelial cells recycle L-citrulline to L-arginine. *Proc. Natl. Acad. Sci. USA* 87:8612–16

46. Heinzel B, John M, Klatt P, Böhme E, Mayer B. 1992. Ca^{2+}/calmodulin-dependent formation of hydrogen peroxide by brain nitric oxide synthase. *Biochem. J.* 281:627–30

47. Henry Y, Lepoivre M, Drapier JC, Ducrocq C, Boucher JL, et al. 1993. EPR characterization of molecular targets for NO in mammalian cells and organelles. *FASEB J.* 7:1124–34

48. Hevel JM, Marletta MA. 1992. Macrophage nitric oxide synthase: relationship between enzyme-bound tetrahydrobiopterin and synthase activity. *Biochemistry* 31:7160–65

49. Hevel JM, Marletta MA. 1993. Macrophage nitric oxide synthase: tetrahydrobiopterin decreases the NADPH stoichiometry. *Adv. Exp. Med. Biol.* 338:285–88

50. Hevel JM, White KA, Marletta MA. 1991. Purification of the inducible murine macrophage nitric oxide synthase. Identification as a flavoprotein. *J. Biol. Chem.* 266:22789–91

51. Hibbs JB Jr, Taintor RR, Vavrin Z, Rachlin EM. 1988. Nitric oxide: a cytotoxic activated macrophage effector molecule. *Biochem. Biophys. Res. Comm.* 157:87–94

52. Hibbs JB Jr, Vavrin Z, Taintor RR. 1987. L-arginine is required for expression of

the activated macrophage effector mechanism causing selective metabolic inhibition in target cells. *J. Immunol.* 138:550–65

53. Hobbs AJ, Fukuto JM, Ignarro LJ. 1994. Formation of free nitric oxide from L-arginine by nitric oxide synthase: direct enhancement of generation by superoxide dismutase. *Proc. Natl. Acad. Sci. USA.* 91:10992–96

54. Ignarro LJ. 1990. Biosynthesis and metabolism of endothelium-derived nitric oxide. *Annu. Rev. Pharmacol. Toxicol.* 30:535–60

55. Ignarro LJ, Buga GM, Wood KS, Byrns RE, Chaudhuri G. 1987. Endothelium-derived relaxing factor produced and released from artery and vein is nitric oxide. *Proc. Natl. Acad. Sci. USA* 84:9265–69

56. Ignarro LJ, Byrns RE, Woods KS. 1988. Biochemical and pharmacological properties of endothelium-derived relaxing factor and its similarity to nitric oxide radical. See Ref. 33, pp. 427–35

57. Ishii K, Sheng H, Warner TD, Förstermann U, Murad F. 1991. A simple and sensitive bioassay method for detection of EDRF with RFL-6 rat lung fibroblasts. *Am. J. Physiol.* 261:H598–603

58. Iyengar R, Stuehr DJ, Marletta MA. 1987. Macrophage synthesis of nitrite, nitrate, and N-nitrosamines: precursors and role of the respiratory burst. *Proc. Natl. Acad. Sci. USA* 84:6369–73

59. Janssens SP, Shimouchi A, Quertermous T, Bloch DB, Bloch KD. 1992. Cloning and expression of a cDNA encoding human endothelium-derived relaxing factor/nitric oxide synthase. *J. Biol. Chem.* 267:14519–22

60. Deleted in proof

61. Karupiah G, Xie QW, Buller ML, Nathan C, Duarte C, et al. 1993. Inhibition of viral replication by interferon-γ-induced nitric oxide synthase. *Science* 261:31445–48

62. Kelm M, Feelisch M, Deussen A, Strauer BE, Schrader J. 1991. Release of endothelium derived nitric oxide in relation to pressure and flow. *Cardiovasc. Res.* 25:831–36

63. Kilbourn RG, Belloni P. 1990. Endothelial cell production of nitrogen oxides in response to interferon γ in combination with tumor necrosis factor, interleukin-1 or endotoxin. *J. Natl. Canc. Inst.* 82:772–76

64. Kilbourn RG, Griffith OW. 1992. Overproduction of nitric oxide in cytokine-mediated and septic shock. *J. Natl. Canc. Inst.* 84:827–31

65. Kilbourn RG, Gross SS, Jubran A, Adams J, Griffith OW, et al. 1990. N^G-methyl-L-arginine inhibits tumor necrosis factor-induced hypotension: implications for the involvement of nitric oxide. *Proc. Natl. Acad. Sci. USA* 87: 3629–32

66. Kilbourn RG, Gross SS, Lodato RF, Adams J, Levi R, et al. 1992. Inhibition of interleukin-1-α-induced nitric oxide synthase in vascular smooth muscle and full reversal of interleukin-1-α-induced hypotension by N$^\omega$-amino-L-arginine. *J. Natl. Canc. Inst.* 84:1008–16

67. Kilbourn RG, Jubran A, Gross SS, Griffith OW, Levi R, et al. 1990. Reversal of endotoxin-mediated shock by N^G-methyl-L-arginine, an inhibitor of nitric oxide synthesis. *Biochem. Biophys. Res. Commun.* 172:1132–38

68. Kilbourn RG, Owen-Schaub L, Cromeens D, Flaherty M, Gross SS, et al. 1994. N^G-methyl-L-arginine, an inhibitor of nitric oxide formation, reverses IL-2-mediated hypotension in dogs. *J. Appl. Physiol.* 76:1130–37

69. Klatt P, Heinzel B, John M, Kasters M, Böhme E, et al. 1992. Ca^{2+}/calmodulin-dependent cytochrome c reductase activity of brain nitric oxide synthase. *J. Biol. Chem.* 267:11374–78

70. Klatt P, Schmid M, Leopold E, Schmidt K, Werner ER. 1994. The pteridine binding site of brain nitric oxide synthase. *J. Biol. Chem.* 269:13861–66

71. Klatt P, Schmidt K, Brunner F, Mayer B. 1994. Inhibitors of brain nitric oxide synthase. *J. Biol. Chem.* 269:1674–80

72. Klatt P, Schmidt K, Mayer B. 1992. Brain nitric oxide synthase is a haemoprotein. *Biochem. J.* 288:15–17

73. Klatt P, Schmidt K, Uray G, Mayer B. 1993. Multiple catalytic functions of brain nitric oxide synthase. *J. Biol. Chem.* 268:14781–87

74. Kobzik L, Bredt DS, Lowenstein CJ, Drazen J, Gaston B, et al. 1993. Nitric oxide synthase in human and rat lung: Immunocytochemical and histochemical localization. *Am. J. Resp. Cell Mol. Biol.* 9:371–77

75. Korth HG, Sustmann R, Thater C, Butler AR, Ingold KU. 1994. On the mechanism of the nitric oxide synthase-catalyzed conversion of N$^\omega$-hydroxy-L-arginine to citrulline and nitric oxide. *J. Biol. Chem.* 269:17776–79

76. Kwon NS, Nathan CF, Gilker C, Griffith OW, Matthews DE, et al. 1990. L-citrulline production from L-arginine by macrophage nitric oxide synthase. The ureido oxygen derives from dioxygen. *J. Biol. Chem.* 265:13442–45

77. Kurzban GP, Strobel HW. 1986. Preparation and characterization of FAD-dependent NADPH cytochrome P-450 reductase. *J. Biol. Chem.* 261:7824–30

78. Lamas S, Marsden PA, Li GK, Gordon K, Tempst P, et al. 1992. Endothelial nitric oxide synthase: molecular cloning and characterization of a distinct constitutive enzyme isoform. *Proc. Natl. Acad. Sci. USA* 89:6348–52

79. Lambert LE, Whitten JP, Baron BM, Cheng HC, Doherty NS, et al. 1991. Nitric oxide synthesis in the CNS, endothelium and macrophages differs in its sensitivity to inhibition by arginine analogues. *Life Sci.* 48:69–75

80. Leaf CD, Wishnok JS, Tannenbaum SR. 1989. L-arginine is a precursor for nitrate biosynthesis in humans. *Biochem. Biophys. Res. Commun.* 163:1032–37

81. Leone AM, Palmer RMJ, Knowles RG, Francis PL, Ashton DS, et al. 1991. Constitutive and inducible nitric oxide synthases incorporate molecular oxygen into both nitric oxide and citrulline. *J. Biol. Chem.* 266:23790–95

82. Lowenstein CJ, Glatt CS, Bredt DS, Snyder SH. 1992. Cloned and expressed nitric oxide synthase contrasts with the brain enzyme. *Proc. Natl. Acad. Sci. USA* 89:6711–15

83. Lyons CR, Orloff GJ, Cunningham JM. 1992. Molecular cloning and functional expression of an inducible nitric oxide synthase from a murine macrophage cell line. *J. Biol. Chem.* 267:6370–74

84. Malinski T, Taha Z. 1992. Nitric oxide release from a single cell measured in situ by a porphyrinic-based microsensor. *Nature* 358:676–78

85. Marletta MA. 1993. Nitric oxide synthase structure and mechanism. *J. Biol. Chem.* 268:12231–34

86. Marletta MA, Yoon PS, Iyengar R, Leaf CD, Wishnok JD. 1988. Macrophage oxidation of L-arginine to nitrite and nitrate: nitric oxide is an intermediate. *Biochemistry* 27:8706–11

87. Masters BSS. 1994. Nitric oxide synthases: why so complex? *Annu. Rev. Nutr.* 14:131–45

88. Mayer B, John M, Böhme E. 1990. Purification of a Ca^{2+}/calmodulin-dependent nitric oxide synthase from porcine cerebellum: cofactor role of tetrahydrobiopterin. *FEBS Lett.* 277: 215–19

89. McCartney-Francis N, Allen JB, Mizel DE, Albina JE, Xie Q, et al. 1993. Suppression of arthritis by an inhibitor of nitric oxide synthase. *J. Exp. Med.* 178:749–54

90. McMillan K, Bredt DS, Hirsch DJ, Sny-

der SH, Clark JE, et al. 1992. Cloned, expressed rat cerebellar nitric oxide synthase contains stoichiometric amounts of heme, which binds carbon monoxide. *Proc. Natl. Acad. Sci. USA* 89:11141–4590a.
McMillan K, Masters BSS. 1993. Optical difference spectrophotometry as a probe of rat brain nitric oxide synthase heme-substrate interaction. *Biochemistry* 32:9875–80

91. Menon NK, Pataricza J, Binder T, Bing RJ. 1991. Reduction of biological effluents in purge and trap micro reaction vessels and detection of endothelium-derived nitric oxide (edno) by chemiluminescence. *J. Mol. Cell Cardiol.* 23: 389–93

92. Misko TP, Moore WM, Kasten TP, Nickols GA, Corbett JA, et al. 1993. Selective inhibition of the inducible nitric oxide synthase by aminoguanidine. *Eur. J. Pharmacol.* 233:119–25

93. Moncada S, Palmer RMJ, Higgs EA. 1988. The discovery of nitric oxide as the endogenous nitrovasodilator. *Hypertension* 12:365–72

94. Deleted in proof

95. Murphy ME, Sies H. 1991. Reversible conversion of nitroxyl anion to nitric oxide by superoxide dismutase. *Proc. Natl. Acad. Sci. USA* 88:10860–64

96. Nakane M, Schmidt HHW, Pollock JS, Förstermann U, Murad F. 1993. Cloned human brain nitric oxide synthase is highly expressed in skeletal muscle. *FEBS Lett.* 316:175–80

97. Narayanan K, Griffith OW. 1994. Synthesis of L-thiocitrulline, L-homothiocitrulline and S-methyl-L-thiocitrulline: a new class of potent nitric oxide synthase inhibitors. *J. Med. Chem.* 37:885–87

98. Narayanan K, Spack L, Hayward M, Griffith OW. 1994. S-methyl-L-thiocitrulline: a potent inhibitor of nitric oxide synthase with strong pressor activity in vivo. *FASEB J.* 8:A360

99. Narhi LO, Fulco AJ. 1987. Identification and characterization of two functional domains in cytochrome P450$_{BM-3}$, a catalytically self-sufficient monooxygenase induced by barbiturates in *Bacillus megaterium. J. Biol. Chem.* 262:6683–90

100. Nathan C. 1992. Nitric oxide as a secretory product of mammalian cells. *FASEB J.* 6:3051–64

101. Nathan CF, Hibbs JB Jr. 1991. Role of nitric oxide synthesis in macrophage antimicrobial activity. *Curr. Opin. Immunol.* 3:65–70

102. Nathan CF, Xie QW. 1994. Regulation of biosynthesis of nitric oxide. *J. Biol. Chem.* 269:13725–28

103. Nishida K, Harrison DG, Navas JP, Fisher AA, Dockery SP, et al. 1992. Molecular cloning and characterization of the constitutive bovine aortic endothelial cell nitric oxide synthase. *J. Clin. Invest.* 90:2092–96

104. Nunokawa Y, Ishida N, Tanaka S. 1993. Cloning of inducible nitric oxide synthase in rat vascular smooth muscle. *Biochem. Biophys. Res. Commun.* 191: 89–94

105. O'Dell TJ, Huang PL, Dwason TM, Dinerman JL, Snyder SH, et al. 1994. Endothelial NOS and the blockade of LTP by NOS inhibitors in mice lacking neuronal NOS. *Science* 265:542–46

106. Olken NM, Marletta MA. 1992. N^G-allyl- and N^G-cyclopropyl-L-arginine: two novel inhibitors of macrophage nitric oxide synthase. *J. Med. Chem.* 35: 1137–44

107. Olken NM, Marletta MA. 1993. N^G-methyl-L-arginine functions as an alternate substrate and mechanism-based inhibitor of nitric oxide synthase. *Biochemistry* 32:9677–85

108. Palmer RMJ, Ashton DS, Moncada S. 1988. Vascular endothelial cells synthesize nitric oxide from L-arginine. *Nature* 333:664–66

109. Palmer RMJ, Ferrige AG, Moncada S. 1987. Nitric oxide release accounts for the biological activity of endothelium-derived relaxing factor. *Nature* 327:524–26

110. Petros A, Lamb G, Leone A, Moncada S, Bennett D, et al. 1994. Effects of a nitric oxide synthase inhibitor in humans with septic shock. *Cardiovasc. Res.* 28: 34–39

111. Pollock, JS, Förstermann U, Mitchell JA, Warner TD, Schmidt, et al. 1991. Purification and characterization of particulate endothelium-derived relaxing factor synthase from cultured and native bovine aortic endothelial cells. *Proc. Natl. Acad. Sci. USA* 88:10480–84

112. Porter TD, Coon MJ. 1991. Cytochrome P450. *J. Biol. Chem.* 266:13469–72

113. Pou S, Pou WS, Bredt DS, Snyder SS, Rosen GM. 1992. Generation of superoxide by purified brain nitric oxide synthase. *J. Biol. Chem.* 267:24173–76

114. Pufahl RA, Marletta MA. 1993. Oxidation of N^G-hydroxy-L-arginine by nitric oxide synthase: evidence for the involvement of the heme in catalysis. *Biochem. Biophys. Res. Commun.* 193:963–70

115. Pufahl RA, Nanjappan PG, Woodard RW, Marletta MA. 1992. Mechanistic probes of N-hydroxylation of L-arginine

by the inducible nitric oxide synthase from murine macrophages. *Biochemistry* 31:6822–28

115a. Renaud JP, Boucher JL, Vadon S, Delaforge M, Mansuy D. 1993. Particular ability of liver P450s3A to catalyze the oxidation of N$^\omega$hydroxyarginine to citrulline and nitrogenoxides and occurrence in NO synthases of a sequence very similar to the heme-binding sequence in P450s. *Biochem. Biophys. Res. Commun.* 192:53–60

116. Rogers NE, Ignarro LJ. 1992. Constitutive nitric oxide synthase from cerebellum is reversibly inhibited by nitric oxide formed from L-arginine. *Biochem. Biophys. Res. Commun.* 189:242–49

117. Schmidt HHW, Pollock JS, Nakane M, Gorsky LD, Förstermann U, et al. 1991. Purification of a soluble isoform of guanylyl cyclase-activating-factor synthase. *Proc. Natl. Acad. Sci. USA* 88: 365–69

118. Schmidt HHW, Smith RM, Nakane M, Murad F. 1992. Ca^{2+}/calmodulin-dependent NO synthase type I: a biopteroflavioprotein with Ca^{2+}/calmodulin-independent diaphorase and reductase activities. *Biochemistry* 31:3423–49

119. Schulz R, Nava E, Moncada S. 1992. Induction and potential biological relevance of a Ca^{2+}-independent nitric oxide synthase in the myocardium. *Br. J. Pharmacol.* 105:575–80

120. Sessa WC. 1994. The nitric oxide synthase family of proteins. *J. Vasc. Res.* 31:131–43

121. Sessa WC, Harrison JK, Barber CM, Zeng D, Durieux ME, et al. 1992. Molecular cloning and expression of a cDNA encoding endothelial cell nitric oxide synthase. *J. Biol. Chem.* 267: 15274–76

122. Sherman PA, Laubach VE, Reep BR, Wood ER. 1993. Purification and cDNA sequence of an inducible nitric oxide synthase from a human tumor cell line. *Biochemistry* 32:11600–5

123. Sheta EA, McMillan K, Masters BSS. 1994. Evidence for a biodomain structure of constitutive cerebellar nitric oxide synthase. *J. Biol. Chem.* 269: 15147–53

124. Stadler J, Bergonia HA, Di Silvio M, Sweetland MA, Billiar TR, et al. 1993. Nonheme iron-nitrosyl complex formation in rat hepatocytes: detection by electron paramagnetic resonance spectroscopy. *Arch. Biochem. Biophys.* 302: 4–11

125. Stamler JS. 1994. S-nitrosothiols and the bioregulatory actions of nitrogen oxides through reactions with thiol groups. *Curr. Top. Immunol. Microbiol.* In press

126. Stuehr DJ, Cho HJ, Kwon NS, Weise M, Nathan CF. 1991. Purification and characterization of the cytokine-induced macrophage nitric oxide synthase: a FAD- and FMN-containing flavoprotein. *Proc. Natl. Acad. Sci. USA* 88:7773–77

127. Stuehr DJ, Griffith OW. 1992. Mammalian nitric oxide synthase. *Adv. Enzymol. Rel. Areas Mol. Biol.* 65:287–346

128. Stuehr DJ, Gross SS, Sakuma I, Levi R, Nathan CF. 1989. Activated murine macrophages secrete a metabolite of arginine with the bioactivity of endothelium-derived relaxing factor and the chemical reactivity of nitric oxide. *J. Exp. Med.* 169:1011–20

129. Stuehr DJ, Ikeda-Saito M. 1992. Spectral characterization of brain and macrophage nitric oxide synthase. Cytochrome P-450-like heme proteins that contain a flavin semiquinone radical. *J. Biol. Chem.* 267:20547–50

130. Stuehr DJ, Kwon NS, Nathan CF, Griffth OW, Feldman PL, et al. 1991. N$^\omega$-hydroxy-L-arginine is an intermediate in the biosynthesis of nitric oxide from L-arginine. *J. Biol. Chem.* 266: 6259–63

131. Stuehr DJ, Marletta MA. 1985. Mammalian nitrate biosynthesis: mouse macrophages produce nitrate and nitrite in response to *Escherichia coli* lipopolysaccharide. *Proc. Natl. Acad. Sci. USA* 82:7738–42

131a. Stuehr DJ, Nathan CF. 1989. Nitric oxide. A macrophage product responsible for the cytostasis and respiratory inhibition in tumor target cells. *J. Exp. Med.* 169:1543–55

132. Szabo C, Thiemermann C. 1993. Potential therapeutic use of nitric oxide synthase inhibitors. *Curr. Opin. Invest. Drugs* 2:1165:74

133. Tracey WR, Pollock JS, Murad F, Nakane M, Förstermann U. 1994. Identification of an endothelial-like type III NO synthase in LLC-PK1 kidney epithelial cells. *Am. J. Physiol.* 266:C22–28

134. Weinberg JB, Granger DL, Pisetsky DS, Seldin MF, Misukonis MA, et al. 1994. The role of nitric oxide in the pathogenesis of spontaneous murine autoimmune disease: increased nitric oxide production and nitric oxide synthase expression in MRL-1pr mice, and reduction of spontaneous glomerulonephritis and arthritis by orally administered N^G-monomethyl-L-arginine. *J. Exp. Med.* 179:651–60

135. White KA, Marletta MA. 1992. Nitric

oxide synthase is a cytochrome P-450 type hemoprotein. *Biochemistry* 31: 6627–31

136. Wink DA, Darbyshire JF, Nims RW, Saavedra JE, Ford PC. 1993. Reactions of the bioregulatory agent nitric oxide in oxygenated aqueous media: determination of the kinetics for oxidation and nitrosation by intermediates generated in the NO/O2 reaction. *Chem. Res. Toxicol.* 6:23–27

137. Wolff DJ, Datto GA, Samatovicz RA. 1993. The dual mode of inhibition of calmodulin-dependent nitric oxide synthase by antifungal imidazole agents. *J. Biol. Chem.* 268:9430–36

138. Wolff DJ, Datto GA, Samatovicz RA, Tempsick RA. 1993. Calmodulin-dependent nitric oxide synthase. *J. Biol. Chem.* 268:9425–29

139. Wolff DJ, Gribin BJ. 1994. The inhibition of the constitutive and inducible nitric oxide synthase isoforms by indazole agents. *Arch. Biochem. Biophys.* 311:300–6

140. Wolff DJ, Gribin BJ. 1994. Interferon-γ-inducible murine macrophage nitric oxide synthase: studies on the mechanism of inhibition by imidazole agents. *Arch. Biochem. Biophys.* 311:293–99

141. Wolff DJ, Lubeski A, Umansky SC. 1994. The inhibition of the constitutive bovine endothelial nitric oxide synthase by imidazole and indazole agents. *Arch. Biochem. Biophys.* 314:360–66

142. Wood ER, Berger H Jr, Sherman PA, Lapetina EG. 1993. Hepatocytes and macrophages express an identical cytokine inducible nitric oxide synthase gene. *Biochem. Biophys. Res. Commun.* 191:767–74

143. Xie QW, Cho HJ, Calycay J, Mumford RA, Swiderek KM, et al. 1992. Cloning and characterization of inducible nitric oxide synthase from mouse macrophages. *Science* 256:225–28

144. Yui Y, Hattori R, Kosuga K, Eizawa H, Hiki K, et al. 1991. Purification of nitric oxide synthase from rat macrophages. *J. Biol. Chem.* 266:12544–47

Annu. Rev. Physiol. 1995. 57:737–69

NITRIC OXIDE:
Pathophysiological Mechanisms

Steven S. Gross

Department of Pharmacology, Cornell University Medical College, New York, NY 10021

Michael S. Wolin

Department of Physiology, New York Medical College, Valhalla, New York 10595

KEY WORDS: nitric oxide synthase, free radicals, nitrogen oxides, nitrosothiols, peroxynitrite, cytostasis, cytotoxicity

INTRODUCTION

Nitric oxide is a double-edged sword. Produced by mammalian cells at an appropriate magnitude and tempo, it serves as a key signaling molecule in physiological processes as diverse as host-defense, neuronal communication, and vascular regulation (for reviews, see 131, 132, 172). On the other hand, excessive and unregulated NO synthesis has been implicated as causal or contributing to pathophysiological conditions including many lethal and debilitating diseases of humans: vascular shock, stroke, diabetes, neurodegeneration, arthritis, and chronic inflammation. Contrary to conventional biosignaling molecules that act by binding to specific receptor molecules, NO manifests its biological actions via a wide range of chemical reactions. NO is a small, relatively stable, free-radical gas that readily diffuses into cells and cell membranes where it reacts with molecular targets. The precise reactions, which are realized in any biological setting, depend on the concentration of NO achieved and often on subtle variations in the composition of the intra- and extracellular milieu. This review summarizes the present knowledge of cellular events that lead to NO overproduction in mammalian systems and discusses reactions of NO that may contribute to cell damage or death. Our primary aim is to interpret rather than exhaustively summarize the large body of accumulated NO litera-

737

0066–4278/95/0315–0737$05.00

ture, thus the reader is referred to many recent review articles noted herein for further information.

MOLECULAR MECHANISMS OF NO OVERPRODUCTION

NOS Isoforms and NO Synthesis

Mammalian cells are endowed with at least three genes encoding distinct isoforms of NO synthase (NOS); cDNAs have been molecularly cloned, sequenced, and found to share 50–60% homology with one another at nucleotide and amino acid levels (131). Southern blot analysis suggests that there may only be three NOS genes. Two NOS gene products are constitutively expressed: one (eNOS) in endothelial cells, and a second (nNOS) in neuronal and certain other cell types including kidney macula densa cells (189), β-pancreatic cells (162), skeletal muscle (129), and epithelial cells of the lung (94), stomach, and uterus (161). The third species of NOS is inducible by immunological stimuli in virtually all nucleated mammalian cells examined (iNOS). Although all NOS isoforms require bound calmodulin for activity, only iNOS has sufficiently high avidity for calmodulin such that it remains bound at the low basal levels of calcium found in resting cells, thereby conferring iNOS with full catalytic activity (22). Thus it is thought that eNOS and nNOS produce small, physiological "puffs" of NO in response to transient elevations in intracellular calcium, whereas iNOS produces a large and continuous flux of NO until substrates become limiting. Consequently, iNOS, rather than constitutive eNOS or nNOS, is thought to be the isoform that produces the large quantities of NO that can result in tissue damage or death. Nonetheless, in some circumstances, e.g. following tissue ischemia/reperfusion (114, 141) or stroke (135), a sufficiently sustained elevation in intracellular calcium may cause the constitutive NOS isoforms to produce cytotoxic quantities of NO.

All three NOS isoforms catalyze a five-electron oxidation of one of two equivalent guanidino nitrogens in L-arginine to yield nitric oxide at the cost of 1.5 mols of NADPH and 2 mols of dioxygen (for review, see 172). This process involves two successive monooxygenation reactions, with the initial reaction yielding N^{ω}-hydroxy-L-arginine as an isolatable intermediate (174) and the final reaction giving NO and citrulline (172). NOSs contains four prosthetic groups: flavin adenine dinucleotide (FAD), flavin adenine mononucleotide (FMN), iron protoporphyrin IX (heme), and tetrahydrobiopterin (BH4). Like the highly homologous cytochrome P450 reductase–monooxygenase system (13), the flavins are used to deliver electrons singly to heme from the two-electron donor NADPH for the activation of dioxygen. Although a redox function of heme in NOS catalysis has been clearly documented (92,

116, 173), the function of BH4, a well-established redox-active cofactor for aromatic amino acid hydroxylases (81), remains obscure. In any event, BH4 appears to be necessary for each of the two successive monooxygenation steps performed by NOS (172).

Calmodulin binding to NOS causes a rapid opening of the gate to electron flux through the active site of NOS; electrons to traverse from the reduced flavins to heme, thereby initiating NO synthesis (1). Thus the continuous occupancy by calmodulin of iNOS explains the steady-state catalysis and high-output NO by this isoform. In the presence of calmodulin, when either L-arginine or BH4 is limiting, NOS utilizes dioxygen as a terminal electron acceptor (67, 147) and consumes NADPH at a rate that is uncoupled from NO synthesis. The result is the formation of a superoxide anion, which in turn can react with NO to yield higher nitrogen oxides (6, 159) that are extremely reactive and potentially cytotoxic (see below).

Regulation of iNOS Activity

Because the potential high-output source of NO in mammalian cells is iNOS, factors involved in the induction and expression of iNOS activity are key determinants of NO-mediated toxicity. To date, transcriptional activation of iNOS by cytokines and bacterial products has been considered the major means for regulating iNOS activity. However, the need for sufficient quantities of iNOS-derived NO for host-defense and perhaps other physiological processes (94, 177), concomitant with an ever-present danger of NO excess, indicate that posttranscriptional mechanisms may also be an important key for regulating iNOS.

TRANSCRIPTION OF THE iNOS GENE   Induction of iNOS has been demonstrated in many cell types including those of human origin (132). Stimuli for iNOS induction include, but are not limited to, products of gram-negative and gram-positive bacteria, interferon-γ, interleukin-1, and tumor necrosis factors. Synergism in induction of iNOS activity has been observed with the combination of interferon-γ and any other of these agents. Cloning and sequencing of the 5'-region upstream of exon 1 from the iNOS gene of mouse (112, 196) and human (20) has revealed the presence of numerous prototypical consensus sequences for genes that are transcriptionally activated by cytokines. The 1749 basepair (bp) upstream flanking region of murine iNOS contains more than 20 identifiable putative sequences for distinct transcriptional activating factors, including two sites for nuclear factor κB (NF-κB) that mediate the induction of numerous genes by bacterial lipopolysaccharide (LPS) (163), ten sites for interferon-γ response element, three interferon-γ-activated sites, two sites for interferon-α-stimulated response element, two sites for tumor necrosis factor response element, and binding sites for nuclear factor interleukin-6, and activating protein-1 (112, 196). The mRNA initiation start site of murine iNOS was found 30 bp downstream from a TATA box (196). A minimal iNOS promoter–reporter gene construct, which conferred inducibility by LPS, contained a single NF-κB site, beginning 55 bp upstream of the TATA box (196). Synergistic induction by interferon-γ required inclusion of the distal half of the 1749-bp promoter (112, 196). Curiously, although only a single NF-κB site was necessary for activation by LPS of iNOS promoter constructs when transfected into macrophages in vitro (195, 196), the capacity for induction of iNOS by LPS was lost or diminished in mice harboring knockouts of genes encoding interferon-γ (28), a subunit of the interferon-γ receptor (71), or interferon-regulatory factor-1 (79). Thus the interferon-γ signaling pathway appears to be key for induction of iNOS activity in vivo. It is noteworthy that interferon-γ may elevate levels of LPS-induced iNOS mRNA accumulation via mRNA stabilization (179) in addition to enhancing transcription of the iNOS promoter (196).

Other stimuli that induce iNOS activity, and are assumed but not proven to act at the level of transcription, include cAMP-elevating agents (55, 74, 95) UV-B irradiation (183), and respired ozone (142). Because these agents share with LPS the capacity to elicit nuclear translocation of NF-κB, directly, or via the generation of reactive oxygen radical intermediates, it is tempting to speculate that NF-κB is their common mediator. It is also of interest that NO itself can elicit nuclear translocation of NF-κB (100), which suggests that NO can potentiate its own synthesis via a feed-forward action on iNOS gene transcription.

EXPRESSION OF THE iNOS ACTIVITY   There are AUUUA consensus sequences within the 3′-untranslated region of iNOS mRNA from rodents and humans that are responsible for the instability of mRNAs encoding inflammatory mediators including interferons, tumor necrosis factors, interleukin-1, GM-CSF, cyclooxygenase II, and tissue-type plasminogen activator (2, 17). The destabilization of mRNAs conferred by this sequence is thought to be initiated by the binding of a labile protein because expression of these mRNAs is typically enhanced by inhibitors of protein synthesis. Accordingly, cycloheximide increases iNOS mRNA in rat vascular smooth muscle cells (but not macrophages) via a mechanism that is associated with an increase in iNOS mRNA half-life from 2 to >7 h (Y Hattori & S Gross, unpublished data). Immunostimulants elicit the expression of each of two partially characterized mRNA-binding proteins with specificity for AUUUA sequence motifs (10), which raises the possibility that mRNA stability is a site for regulation of iNOS expression by cytokines. TGF-β has been shown to reduce interferon-γ-induced iNOS mRNA levels in part by mRNA destabilization (179). Whether this effect of TGF-β is mediated by AUUUA binding proteins is untested.

Once expressed, the activity of NOS protein may be regulated by covalent modification. Interestingly, NO reacts with NOS or its cofactors in vitro to inhibit activity (54); whether this putative feedback inhibition occurs in vivo awaits testing. Each of the three NOS isoforms contains consensus sequences for phosphorylation by serine or threonine protein kinases (including A-, C- and calcium/calmodulin-dependent kinases; 132), and immunoprecipitation studies reveal that constitutive NOS isoforms are phosphorylated in cells in vitro (29, 118). Nonetheless, in vitro studies of the effects of phosphorylation by specific kinases on activity of NOS isoforms have not given a clear and consistent picture (132). One possible function of phosphorylation, suggested from studies with eNOS (118), could be in targeting NOS to an appropriate intracellular site. However, the role of phosphorylation in regulating the activity of NOS isoforms in vivo and hence in NO-mediated toxicities has not been determined. Moreover, there are no reports of phosphorylation of iNOS in vitro or in vivo.

Substrate and cofactor availability are likely to be important sites for regulation of iNOS activity. Induction by immunostimulants of NO synthesis in fibroblasts (187), endothelial cells (56), and vascular smooth muscle cells (57) depend on the co-induction of intracellular BH4 synthesis. At least in the latter two cell types, BH4 is undetectable in control cells but appears after LPS and interferon-γ exposure with a time course that parallels that of iNOS activity (65). BH4 synthesis is associated with the induction of mRNA encoding GTP cyclohydrolase I (GTPCH; 65), the first and rate-limiting enzyme of the de novo BH4 synthetic pathway. Importantly, iNOS and GTPCH mRNAs appear in LPS-treated cells with virtually identical time courses (65). Although not proven, the presence of apparent NF-κB and interferon-γ response element consensus sequences in the 5'-flanking region of the GTPCH gene (S Gross & J Smith, unpublished data) may explain co-induction of NOS and GTPCH mRNAs. The fact that some cells induced for iNOS activity produce substantially more NO after addition of BH4 or a BH4 precursor (56, 57, 187) indicates that intracellular levels of BH4 can be rate-limiting to NO synthesis. Induction by immunostimulants of BH4 synthesis in human endothelial cells was also shown to stimulate eNOS activity in the face of falling levels of eNOS protein (156). Thus modulation of intracellular BH4 content is likely to be an important means for regulation of NO production in vivo by many cell types. The much higher affinity of BH4 binding to iNOS (30–40 nM; S Gross, unpublished data) vs other BH4-dependent enzymes (10–100 μM) could enable low circulating levels of biopterin to selectively activate iNOS in cells that possess a more limited capacity to synthesize BH4 de novo. The concept of transcellular BH4 mobilization is unexplored.

In view of plasma levels of L-arginine in the range of 150 to 200 μM and a K_m^{ARG} of 5 to 10 μM for NOS isoforms (172), it is surprising that L-arginine availability can ever limit NO synthesis. Nonetheless, an increase in NO-mediated vasodilation has been reported upon L-arginine administration in some in vivo settings (27, 37, 117). The basis for this phenomenon is poorly understood, but in the case of macrophages, it may be related to secretion of arginase (180). Also unexplained is the fact that tissues (e.g. vascular rings) can express NO for extended periods when incubated in physiological buffers that are devoid of arginine and other amino acids. This observation has been extended to an in vivo setting, where lowering plasma arginine levels to >3 μM with arginase did not dampen basal NO production, as manifest by a lack of increase in blood pressure (53). These findings question the origin of L-arginine, which is used by cells for NO synthesis. With the exception of kidney and liver cells, arginine is not typically produced in mammalian cells, but enters from the circulation via the system y^+ transporter. Notably, activity of the y^+ transporter may be up-regulated with increased NO production (9). Perhaps the fact that endothelial cells can regenerate L-arginine from L-citrulline is of major importance to endothelial-derived NO (66). Recently, it was demonstrated that argininosuccinate synthetase (AS), an enzyme normally associated with the urea cycle, is co-induced with iNOS by LPS in macrophages (136) and vascular smooth muscle cells (64); induction was found to be synergistic with interferon-γ. In combination with argininosuccinate lyase, another urea cycle enzyme that is constitutively expressed in many cells, AS confers cells with the capacity to produce NO at maximal rates from citrulline, in the absence of any exogenous L-arginine (64). The LPS-induced rise and subsequent fall in mRNA and protein activity for AS occur in synchrony with those for iNOS, suggesting a functional coupling (64). Thus L-arginine availability to iNOS may be regulated at various levels and is an important control point for NO generation by cells.

BIOLOGICAL CHEMISTRY OF NO

The biological actions of NO are dictated by the reactions it undergoes with target molecules in cells, membranes, and the extracellular milieu. Although chemical reactions and properties of nitrogen oxides have been extensively described (see 77), our understanding of those reactions relevant to biological systems is still immature. Central to the chemistry of $NO^\bullet$, the relatively stable, free-radical gas, is its propensity to undergo electron transfer reactions or addition reactions with particular molecules, especially those having an unpaired electron (i.e. a free radical). Thus in biological systems, the dominant reactions of NO will be with another free radical such as superoxide anion (O_2^-), a transition metal (e.g. heme iron), or O_2. These NO adducts, their secondary reaction products, and products of NO oxidation and reduction are capable of reaction with metals, thiols, and additional targets to give further products, often with biological activity and relevance (169). Thus the biological chemistry of NO is complex because the reactions of NO itself, those of secondary NO–containing species (generated from NO), and the chemical environment in which NO is being produced (169) must be considered.

Chemical Properties of NO in Solution

Nitric oxide is an uncharged relatively hydrophobic gas, which is well known for its reaction in gas phase with O_2 to give nitrogen dioxide (NO_2). In aqueous media, NO dissolves to a limited extent, forming an ~2 mM saturated solution at standard temperature and pressure. The hydrophobicity of NO results in a high-diffusion capacity in biological systems; NO readily permeates cell membranes and in vivo can be detected in the gas phase of the lung (143). Studies of NO actions in bioassay systems that utilize physiological salt solutions have suggested that NO is highly unstable, with an apparent half-life of 6 to 60 s, owing to reactions with O_2 and superoxide anion (O_2^-) (44). The reaction with O_2 to form NO_2 involves two molecules of NO (see below), and thus the reaction rate falls exponentially as NO concentration is decreased linearly. At physiologically relevant levels of NO (i.e. 1–50 nM), it is unlikely that this reaction proceeds at a significant rate compared to other processes. Indeed, in an aqueous solution, NO reacts much more more slowly with O_2 than predicted from the lifetime of in vitro bioactivity (83). Thus reaction with O_2 in biological systems may be much less relevant than previously thought; reactions with O_2^- and redox metals (which typically contaminate bioassay buffers), and diffusion into the gas phase appear to be the principal means for NO inactivation in vitro. However, studies on the control of microcirculatory blood flow by NO in vivo suggest that NO-mediated vasorelaxation is not altered by the scavenging of O_2^- with added superoxide dismutase (SOD) (191) and that endothelium-derived NO-related mediators have a very limited capacity for diffusion into the vascular wall (155). These findings warrant further investigation. In any event, factors that limit NO lifetime in bioassay systems may differ from those in vivo.

The addition of NO to an aqueous saline environment under physiological conditions of temperature, oxygen tension, and pH results in accumulation of nitrite (NO_2^- and lesser amounts of nitrate (NO_3^-). To account for the formation of nitrite as a primary metabolite of NO along with smaller amounts of NO_3^- (44), the following reactions have been proposed:

$$2\ NO + O_2 \rightarrow 2\ NO_2$$

$$2\ NO_2 \leftrightarrow N_2O_4$$

$$N_2O_4 + 2\ OH^- \rightarrow NO_2^- + NO_3^- + H_2O$$

$$NO_2 + NO \rightarrow N_2O_3$$

$$N_2O_3 + 2\ OH^- \rightarrow 2\ NO_2^- + H_2O.$$

Although these reactions occur with supraphysiological concentrations of NO, reactions responsible for nitrite formation from NO in biological systems have not been rigorously established. It should be noted that the interaction of NO with O_2 has the potential to generate additional higher oxides of nitrogen, including NO_2, N_2O_3, and N_2O_4, which, if produced in biological systems, would express activities and toxicities independently of NO. As stated above, due to the multiple-order reactions involved in the synthesis of nitrogen dioxide and derived species, these products will be generated in vivo only under pathological conditions in which high concentrations of NO can be generated locally. The mechanism of nitrite generation in biological systems is still unresolved.

In many in vitro preparations, the actions of exogenously or endogenously formed NO are enhanced by SOD, despite the absence of an apparent significant source for O_2^- generation. Although it is possible that the interconversion of NO with nitroxyl (NO^-) by SOD is important for stabilization of NO (see below), it should also be considered that NO itself can be a source of O_2^- via its reaction with redox-active metal ions.

NO Considered as a Redox Array of Species

The various redox forms of nitrogen oxides and their chemical properties have recently been reviewed (169). This section focuses on the metabolic formation of NO species and their chemical properties that may contribute to pathophysiological processes in vivo. The endogenous route to all of these species is NOS, which produces NO (127). However, it is not yet resolved if this enzyme is able to release a precursor to NO such as the one-electron reduced form, NO^-, or if it can form an adduct of NO with a cosubstrate such as a thiol (RSH) to yield a nitrosothiol (RSNO). NO^- is readily interconverted with NO by SOD; moreover, certain oxidizing agents, including Fe^{3+}, can convert NO^- to NO (43, 128). RSNO compounds spontaneously decompose or are metabolized to NO (97, 127). The presence of oxygen, which is needed for NOS activity, and impurities in biological buffers, such as catalytically active metal ions, make the identification of NO species directly formed by this enzyme difficult to discern. For example, Fe^{3+} in a hemoprotein might accept electrons from NO (oxidize) or NO^- that would result in the formation of species including $Fe^{2+}NO^+$ and $Fe^{2+}NO$, respectively. The $Fe^{2+}NO^+$ complex possesses a bound nitrosonium ion (NO^+) that is competent for nitrosation reactions including nitrosothiol formation (181). The $Fe^{2+}NO$ complex predictably would be in equilibrium with Fe^{2+} and NO, and many Fe^{2+} complexes autooxidize to generate O_2^-, an oxygen species that rapidly reacts with NO to form peroxynitrite ($ONOO^-$) (see below). Oxidized species of NO, but not NO itself, readily react with thiols at physiological pH to form nitrosothiols (111), therefore the chemical formation of nitrosothiols from NO is likely to occur when NOS is assayed in the presence of metal. Thus metal or metalloprotein complexes may further interconvert NO species by catalyzing nitrosation or additional redox reactions.

The NO species normally present in physiological systems are likely to be tightly controlled by cellular redox systems that influence the production of reactive oxygen species and the redox status of thiols, metals, and metalloproteins. Based on current understanding of NO interactions, it is likely that in the absence of appreciable levels of O_2^-, nitrogen oxide species will mediate signal transduction mainly via reaction with iron-containing proteins. It has been suggested that the actions of SOD on NO allow NO^- to function as an intracellular storage form of NO and possibly as a transcellular mediator, which could be reconverted to NO at its target tissue by SOD or other oxidants (128). Because the formation of NO^- by SOD is thermodynamically unfavorable at the low levels of NO produced in tissues (128), NO^- would have to be produced via an alternate pathway and be more stable than NO in the intra- or extracellular milieu for it to function effectively as a NO surrogate. However, if NO^- were formed, it could readily be reconverted to NO, consistent with biological actions demonstrated for NO^- (43). Similar to speculations regarding NO^-, low molecular weight complexes of iron and NO could also function as an intra- or extracellular storage form of NO and perhaps serve as a transcellular mediator (126).

The biological generation of large concentrations of NO is likely to promote the formation of highly reactive and potentially toxic oxidation products of NO. It should be noted that increased production of O_2^- is often associated with NO overproduction. The species formed will include $ONOO^-$ (see below), NO_2, and higher oxides of nitrogen from the reactions shown above (N_2O_4 and N_2O_3; 44). The metabolic fate of NO-derived species under pathophysiological conditions is likely to be controlled by their local concentration and the status of the systems with which they interact. Pathological processes that originate from increased NO production probably change the redox status of these systems with time, resulting in a changing pattern of NO reactions with targets and bioactivity. Thus the chemical interactions of NO with O_2^- and the different redox forms of iron, hemoproteins, and perhaps other redox-active functional groups markedly influence the NO species that are present and the biological actions of these species.

Species Arising from the Reaction of NO with Superoxide Anion

Nitric oxide reacts with O_2^-, resulting initially in the formation of $ONOO^-$ via the reaction shown below:

$$NO + O_2^- \rightarrow ONOO^-.$$

This reaction probably occurs to a significant extent at nanomolar concentrations of NO and O_2^- as a consequence of its near-diffusion-limited rate constant ($\sim 4 \times 10^9$ M^{-1}/s^{-1}; 159). Thus the formation of $ONOO^-$ will predominate in any setting where NO and O_2^- are simultaneously produced, e.g. in an inflammatory lesion. $ONOO^-$ is a highly reactive species with a half-life of less than 1 s under biological conditions, owing to its equilibration with peroxynitrous acid (ONOOH) (6, 149). At physiological pH, the protonated form of $ONOO^-$ needs to be considered in interactions (pKa = 6.8; 149). ONOOH spontaneously decomposes to NO_2 and forms an extremely reactive species with hydroxyl radical-like properties (6, 159). Cellular generation and reactivity of $ONOO^-$ and its derived chemical species suggest that this pathway is an important process in pathophysiological actions of NO. Peroxynitrite has been demonstrated to cause lipid peroxidation, thiol oxidation, and nitrosation or nitration of several functional groups of amino acids including tyrosine (75, 149, 150). The NO_2 that is potentially derived from $ONOO^-$ would be in equilibrium with N_2O_4 and readily converted to N_2O_3 via mechanisms previously discussed; some of these species appear to have toxic effects similar to $ONOO^-$. In addition, SOD and certain metal ions appear to interact with $ONOO^-$ in a manner that permits nitration of proteins and other substances such as the amino acid tyrosine, via transfer of NO_2^+ (75). The reaction of $ONOO^-$ with tissue thiols could be an important defense mechanism against these reactive NO-derived species (see below).

Reactions of NO Species with Heme and Nonheme Iron

The multiple redox forms of NO species and oxidation states of iron suggest an enormous number of possible interactions. We focus here on some of the interactions that occur in physiological or pathophysiological processes. NO reacts rapidly with oxygen-bound Fe^{2+}-hemoglobin (or myoglobin) to form the corresponding met-hemoprotein (Fe^{3+}-Hb) and nitrate (34). The reversible binding of NO to the iron of reduced (Fe^{2+}) hemoproteins is a well-established interaction that results in the formation of NO-heme. Many of these NO-hemoprotein complexes have been subjected to detailed spectroscopic study to better understand heme function and ligand binding. However, these species are generally quite unstable in the presence of oxygen, and only minimal work has been done to characterize mechanisms involved in their decomposition.

NO-heme complexes, derived from unidentified hemoproteins other than hemoglobin, have been detected in tumor tissue (3). In addition, nitrogen oxide species have the potential to modulate the oxidative, lipid peroxidation–associated effects of hemoproteins, in both a stimulatory and an inhibitory manner, via processes that are likely to depend on the redox state of the hemoproteins and nitrogen oxide species present (30, 80). This process may be important in cells with high levels of hemoproteins such as erythrocytes, and skeletal and cardiac muscle during pathological conditions associated with hemolysis or disturbed hemoprotein redox control.

Evidence is also emerging that NO can participate in the release of iron from its tissue-bound storage forms (68). NO is known to inhibit key cellular enzymes with iron-sulfur complexes and cause the release of detectable low molecular weight iron-NO-sulfur species (68). These complexes were observed over 25 years ago in liver tissue exposed to carcinogens or nitrates (193) and they appear to possess $Fe(RS)_2(NO)_2$-type structures (3). The formation and release of $Fe(RS)_2(NO)_2$ complexes may be a sensitive indication of NO generation and contribute to physiological regulatory processes because they are released by membrane receptor–mediated stimulation of endothelium (126). Although many other interactions between NO-related species and redox-active metals are possible, these interactions are potentially controlled by the local concentrations of each NO species and by the status of redox mechanisms that influence the oxidation state of metals.

Reactions of NO Species with Thiols

Although it is often assumed that NO readily reacts with thiols (RSH) to form nitrosothiols (RSNO), a recent study demonstrates that this process is unlikely to occur under physiological conditions (111). In contrast, the study shows that the formation of nitrosothiols is a process associated with the oxidative metabolism of NO. Indeed, large concentrations of the thiol-containing protein bovine-serum albumin were required before removal of NO could be detected in gas headspace under an argon atmosphere (5). Although it is possible that nitrosothiols form directly from interactions between NO and thiols in an environment where the reactivity of these species has been enhanced via processes such as coordination to metal ions or protein functional groups, or by extremes in pH, additional studies are needed to determine if these are biologically important interactions.

Protein nitrosothiols readily form in tissues and blood and may serve as either surrogate forms of NO or as NO reservoirs (46, 169). One protein, glyceraldehyde-3-phosphate dehydrogenase, has been shown to form a nitrosothiol that reacts with NAD, the cofactor for this enzyme, in a manner that covalently links it to the protein through either the ADP-ribose group (32, 33) or via a covalent linkage with the entire NAD molecule (115). Interestingly, exposure of the thiol glutathione (GSH) to ONOO⁻ results in the formation of a nitrosothiol-like species (194). In non-aqueous systems, exposure of thiols to NO_2, a reactive metabolite of NO and ONOO⁻, causes thiol nitrosation (148); this reaction also takes place in physiological buffers (C Davidson et al, unpublished observations). Nitrosothiols show varying degrees of stability under physiological conditions (45) and may spontaneously decompose to form NO and thiol radicals (RS•) (137). Nitrosothiols perhaps more readily transfer their NO group to other reactive thiols, e.g. cysteine, which is either free or protein-incorporated (46, 140). Recent evidence suggests that ONOO⁻-mediated thiol-nitrosation, together with NO transfer between protein thiols, functions as an efficient mechanism of protein nitrosothiol formation (121). Nitrosothiols also readily produce disulfides (137), and protein thiol nitrosation and/or disulfide formation may function in biological regulation (169). In most instances, exogenous nitrosothiols affect tissues through their formation of NO in a manner that is not associated with their spontaneous decomposition rates; therefore, transnitrosation reactions and mechanisms for metabolizing nitrosothiols to release NO may be significant (45, 97). Cell surface electron transport chains have been demonstrated (25) that could cause a one-electron reduction of a nitrosothiol to release NO and regenerate the parent thiol.

Reactions of NO Species with Amines

Several of the oxidation products of NO have the potential to react with amines to yield products of pathophysiological significance. A wealth of information in the cancer literature (predating the discovery of NO as an endogenous product of mammalian cell metabolism) shows that products of NO metabolism can cause nitrosation of various species including amines (76, 103). Indeed, it has been demonstrated in vivo that arginine-derived NO causes nitrosamine formation (104), which is of concern because nitrosamines are chemical modifiers of nucleic acids and well-established cancer-causing agents. Exposure of purine bases, deoxynucleosides, deoxynucleotides, isolated DNA, or DNA in intact cells to high levels of NO has been demonstrated to cause oxygen-dependent mutagenic deamination reactions (133, 190). Although the levels of NO employed in these deamination reactions appear to be quite high, it is noteworthy that endogenously formed NO has been shown to cause DNA strand breaks in cell culture systems (175a, 198).

Stable Products of NO Metabolism

Urinary nitrate is the primary excretion product of NO in humans (185). The observation that humans with inflammatory disease excrete elevated levels of nitrate was first reported in 1818 (146). In 1916 it was shown that humans were net producers of nitrate (120). It was not until 1981 that experimental evidence showed that nitrifying bacteria were not the major source of the nitrate produced in animals (52). In contrast to the in vivo setting, cultured cells metabolize NO predominantly to nitrite, along with a smaller amount (20–25%) of nitrate (38). Interactions of NO and its metabolites with hemoglobin (and myoglobin) appear to be responsible for nitrate formation in vivo. In oxygenated blood, NO is converted by erythrocytes to nitrate; only small increases in intracellular Fe^{3+}-Hb accumulate from this reaction due to the efficiency of methemoglobin reductase (185, 186). In contrast, addition of NO to venous blood results in the formation of NO-hemoglobin and less nitrate than that formed in oxygenated blood. Erythrocytes also convert micromolar concentrations of nitrite to nitrate over a period of minutes, via the oxidation of Fe^{2+}-hemoglobin (185). In vivo, the inactivation of NO as nitrate (in the absence of excess superoxide generation) relies on efficient diffusion of NO into hemoglobin- and myoglobin-rich cells. The nitrate formed is cleared by the kidney at a rate of ~20 mL/min (185). Additional products of NO metabolism in vivo are circulating S-nitrosated proteins (mainly albumin), which may be of physiological importance because of their relatively long lifetimes and surrogate NO actions arising from NO release or nitroso-transfer (46). Although nitrosated plasma proteins form in vivo and in vitro in the presence of NO, they presumably arise from a reaction with an oxidation product of NO, rather than NO itself (as discussed above).

CELLULAR TARGETS OF NO

Signal Transduction Processes

HEMOPROTEINS   At low concentrations, NO reacts with Fe^{2+}-hemoproteins to elicit many of its biological actions. For guanylyl cyclase and cyclooxygenase, interaction with NO translates into enzyme activation. On the other hand, NO has been observed to inhibit a host of other hemoproteins involved in the synthesis of bioactive mediators or redox cell–signaling events; these include: cytochromes P450 (84), lipoxygenases (130), thromboxane synthetase, catalase, and peroxidase. Hemoglobin in red cells and myoglobin in skeletal and cardiac muscle appear to be biological sinks that serve to disarm NO.

Guanylyl cyclase   The heme group of the soluble form of guanylyl cyclase is clearly one of the most sensitive and important sites of action of NO, based on the well-established role of cGMP in many NO-mediated responses. Prior to the discovery of NO as a product of mammalian metabolism, it was thought that NO-releasing agents stimulated soluble guanylyl cyclase by a mechanism requiring heme (26). It was subsequently realized that the soluble form of guanylyl cyclase is a hemoprotein that could form an NO-heme complex (48, 72). The finding that soluble guanylate cyclase could be similarly activated by

NO-heme and the iron-free precursor of heme, protoporphyrin IX, led to the hypothesis that NO binding to heme eliminates the coordination between heme-iron and the protein chain of guanylate cyclase, thus mimicking a protoporphyrin IX-like binding interaction (73, 192). This view was recently confirmed by spectral studies (170, 197). The stimulation of soluble guanylate cyclase by NO mechanisms can be attenuated by extracellular and intracellular superoxide anion (21, 44, 139). Indeed, the cytosolic form of Cu,Zn-SOD appears necessary to preserve the cell's capacity to release nondegraded NO-like species (125, 139) and hence stimulate soluble guanylyl cyclase (21, 139). Although it is known that superoxide anion inactivates NO with regard to stimulation of guanylyl cyclase (44), whether this oxygen species can also interact directly with guanylate cyclase in a manner that prevents stimulation by NO has not been tested.

Arachidonate-metabolizing enzymes   NO may have a regulatory role in modulating the production of biologically active metabolites of arachidonic acid. Induced expression of iNOS by inflammatory mediators occurs concurrently with that of cyclooxygenase-2 (COX-2) in several systems that have been investigated (158). Endogenous NO production appears to up-regulate prostaglandin release by direct stimulation of COX-1 and COX-2, reportedly via nitrosation of heme in a manner analogous to that known for guanylate cyclase (158). Nonetheless, this mechanism is difficult to reconcile with the apparent role of heme in activation of molecular oxygen for COX catalysis. Many studies have investigated the role of prostaglandins in the actions of nitrovasodilator drugs, with inconclusive results (18). Additional hemoprotein-mediated pathways of arachidonic acid metabolism, including 12-lipoxygenase in platelets (130) and cytochromes P450 in liver and other cells (84, 168), are inhibited by endogenously generated NO or by nitrovasodilator drugs. Thus NO has the potential to modulate arachidonic acid metabolism and inhibit multiple processes mediated by cytochrome P450, including the metabolism of hormones and xenobiotics. Although not proven, the actions of NO are likely to originate from direct reaction of NO with Fe^{2+}-heme in enzyme active sites.

THIOL-CONTAINING PROTEINS   The detection of S-nitrosated proteins in vivo and evidence that such chemical modification can alter protein activity have led to the view that nitrosation of protein thiols may be a fundamental signal transduction process (46, 169). Indeed, any essential protein that contains a thiol that is critical to function should be considered as a target for NO and could contribute to NO-mediated cytotoxicity. Candidate molecules for regulation by thiol-nitrosation include proteins that are themselves involved in signal transduction processes, receptors (12, 106), G proteins (101), protein kinases (49, 142), protein phosphatases (100), transcription-activating factors

(59, 100, 142, 144), and proteases (31). Early reports had suggested that NO could also modulate protein function via ADP-ribosylation of specific proteins (see 15 for review), most notably glyceraldehyde-phosphate dehydrogenase (33). Although this may be true in essence, we now know that ADP-ribosylation is non-enzymatic, can result in incorporation of nicotinamide as well as ribose moeities into protein, and is preceded by a critical thiol-nitrosation step (115). As the reaction of NO with thiol is alone sufficient to suppress GAPDH activity, it is unclear to what extent ADP-ribosylation per se contributes to NO-mediated inhibition of GAPDH.

Receptors   One of the best candidates for regulation of a receptor protein by nitrosothiol formation is the N-methyl-D-aspartate (NMDA) receptor (106). Excess stimulation of this receptor by NMDA results in neurotoxicity, triggered by concurrent production of NO and O_2^-, which form reactive $ONOO^-$ species (106, 110) and associated $OH\cdot$ (61). Although NO participates directly in NMDA-mediated neurotoxicity, nitrosation of a critical receptor thiol on the NMDA receptor, by a competent NO-derived species, leads to receptor desensitization and neuroprotection by a mechnism that seems to involve the subsequent generation of a protein disulfide bond (106, 110).

Signal amplification systems   NO has been reported to directly activate G proteins $Gi_{\alpha 1}$ and p21^{ras} in association with an increase in GTPase activity (101). Interestingly, the src family protein tyrosine kinase P56^{lck} is activated by NO donors in human peripheral blood mononuclear cells, whereas tyrosine phosphatase activity is inhibited (100). C-kinase may also be subject to inhibition by NO (49). These observations suggest that NO can influence activity of multiple proteins via alterations in phosphorylation status. The relative importance of other posttranslational modifications of proteins, which arise from direct reaction with NO species (i.e. cysteine nitrosation and tyrosine nitration), are yet to be realized. NO and NO donors also interfere with ion currents through calcium-activated potassium channels (12, 154) and voltage-gated calcium channels (8) in vascular smooth muscle. Moreover, NO donors can block NADPH oxidase and the resulting superoxide burst in neutrophils (23), which suggests a mechanism by which NO can simultaneously derail signal pathways that are initiated by reactive oxygen species and reduce the potential for toxic levels of $ONOO^-$ synthesis. At the cellular level, NO has been shown to increase cytoplasmic motility (42), a finding that could be related to the ability of NO to modulate cell secretion rates (14, 123, 162).

Transcription   NO has been considered to affect biological systems by reactions with proteins that result in altered enzymatic activity. Nonetheless, the dependence of numerous transcription factors on key thiols for DNA-binding (e.g. zinc-finger proteins) raises the possibility that NO can also modulate gene activity directly as well as through increasing cGMP. In *Escherichia coli,*, NO interacts with an Fe-S complex in the SoxR protein to trigger a cascade of gene expression that enables the bacterium to survive in an oxidative environment (70). A mammalian counterpart to this bacterial system remains to be shown. NO has been reported to elicit nuclear translocation of NF-κB (100), induce expression of the AP-1 subunits *c-fos*, and *junB* (59), and activate CREB (144).

Energy Metabolism

Early studies on macrophage-induced injury to neoplastic cells (50, 51, 68) led to the realization that endogenously produced NO is a potent inhibitor of mitochondrial respiration and energy metabolism (68, 175). It is now known that NO has an inhibitory effect on mitochondrial aconitase, a key enzyme of the Krebs cycle, and on NADH ubiquinone oxidoreductase (Complex I) and succinate-ubiquinone oxidoreductase (Complex II) in the mitochondrial electron transport chain (68, 175); of these enzymes, aconitase seems to be the most sensitive site of inhibition (167). The inhibition of aconitase and mitochondrial complexes by NO is associated with the release of iron from iron-sulfur centers (4Fe/4S) in these proteins, and it is notable that function can be restored by iron salts (68). Because $ONOO^-$ has an inhibitory effect on mitochondrial function that is similar to NO (151), the species of NO that is the actual inhibitor remains to be elucidated. However, generation of NO from nitrite + ascorbate, in the absence of oxygen needed for $ONOO^-$ formation, has similarly been reported to elicit the appearance of iron-nitroso-sulfur complexes that are associated with inhibition of mitochondrial function (68). The levels of NO produced during the induction of NOS activity in vascular smooth muscle cells, for instance, also appears to be sufficient to inhibit mitochondrial respiration and to enhance anaerobic glycolysis (47, 57). Inhibition of mitochondrial respiration was one of the initial processes investigated to explain the mechanism of action of nitrovasodilator drugs (11). Inhibition of mitochondrial respiration by NO is readily reversible (167) and may function in physiological regulatory processes that control tissue oxygen utilization (91, 165).

Glyceraldehyde-3-phosphate dehydrogenase is also a target of NO and is inhibited in rat liver as an increasing function of NO production (121, 122). This important glycolytic enzyme is directly inhibited by S-nitrosation and appears to be a target for the suppressant effect of NO on ATP generation by cells. Based on observations of enhanced anaerobic glycolysis under conditions where NO inhibits mitochondrial respiration (47, 57), it is likely that the inhibition of this dehydrogenase requires either greater levels of NO than needed to inhibit respiration, or the simultaneous presence of oxidants of NO to promote thiol-nitrosation. It should be noted that the combined inhibition of glycolysis and aerobic mitochondrial respiration would fully incapacitate intracellular ATP synthesis and result in cell death. Another mode by which NO can rob cells of energy stores and thereby kill them involves activation of nuclear poly-ADP ribosyl transferase (198). Poly-ADP ribosyl transferase is normally activated by DNA strand breaks, where it adds long chains of NAD at the expense of NADH; this NADH would otherwise be used by cells to generate ATP via oxidative phosphorylation. Perhaps secondarily to the initiation of DNA scission (175a), activation of poly-ADP ribosyl transferase by NO has been demonstrated to contribute to neurotoxicity in vitro (198). The chemistry that underlies this facet of NO-mediated toxicity awaits clarification but would likely involve $ONOO^-$ and its reactive degradation products rather than NO per se.

DNA Synthesis

Because NO inhibits mitochondrial respiration, and hence ATP synthesis (see above), this could explain the ability of NO to inhibit cell proliferation (68, 175). However, the anti-proliferative effect of NO occurs prior to inhibition of ATP synthesis; therefore, respiratory inhibition cannot be regarded as the only, or even the primary, mechanism for NO-mediated cytostasis (68). It is noteworthy that the synthesis of ribonucleotides from deoxyribonucleotides is rate-limiting for DNA synthesis and cell division in prokaryotic and eukaryotic cells (39, 41). Deoxyribonucleotide synthesis is catalyzed by ribonucleotide reductase (RR), a highly regulated enzyme comprised of two subunits, each containing active-site species that have potential for reaction with NO (39, 41, 99, 107).

DNA synthesis is inhibited in association with the induction of NO synthesis by immunostimulants in murine adenocarcinoma cells (107). Similarly, DNA synthesis is inhibited in L1210 murine lymphoma cells when co-cultured with immunostimulant-activated macrophages (99). The intermediacy of NO in both cases was indicated by findings that inhibition of DNA synthesis occurs concomitantly with NO synthesis and can be prevented by selective inhibitors of NOS. That RR itself is the target of NO-mediated inhibition of DNA synthesis is indicated by findings that an adenocarcinoma subclone that overexpresses RR by 40-fold is substantially less sensitive to NO than wild-type cells (107) and that DNA synthesis can be restored in L1210 cells by administering deoxyribonucleotides, an approach that would circumvent a block in RR (99). In vitro studies show that NO-producing agents and NO-producing cytosol from immunostimulant-activated cells also block RR activity in association with a quenching of the characteristic electron paramagnetic resonance (EPR) spectrum of RR (108). Omitting arginine from experiments with NO-producing cytosol, or including arginine-based NOS inhibitors diphenyleneiodonium (a flavoprotein inhibitor that blocks NOS) (171), or a heme-based scavenger of NO, could individually protect against the inhibition of RR (99, 107). Thus NO can react with and inactivate RR, thereby inhibiting DNA synthesis and cell proliferation.

More detailed studies have addressed the specific site on RR that reacts with NO to inhibit activity. RR is a heterodimer composed of a large subunit, R1, which binds allosteric effectors and contains essential cysteine residue(s), and a small subunit, R2, which contains a tyrosyl radical that is critical for catalytic activity, as well as binuclear iron-center that is responsible for production and stabilization of the tyrosyl radical (39, 41). Because selective overexpression of R2 subunits dampens the ability of NO to inhibit RR activity (107), R2 rather than R1 appears to be the most relevant target of NO. Using EPR spectroscopy and an R2-overexpressing cell line, it was shown that endogenously derived NO elicits the disappearance of an EPR signal attributable to the tyrosyl radical and causes the appearance of two new signals prototypical of iron-thio-nitroso complexes (109). The time course of appearance of these changes in EPR spectrum is consistent with the view that loss of the critical tyrosyl radical on R2 mediates the inhibition of DNA synthesis caused by NO (109). Scavenging of RR tyrosyl radicals by NO may arise as a direct interaction, or due to nitrosation of the Fe-Fe group of R2 and consequent destabilization of the tyrosyl radical.

Iron Release

Iron release was shown to be an important effector mechanism of tumor cell cytotoxicity by activated rodent macrophages (68) prior to discovering the role of NO in this process. Indeed, the limitation of cell growth by iron availability is ubiquitous throughout nature. As discussed above, the reaction of NO with Fe^{2+}-heme and nonheme iron is likely to predominate over other possible reactions when NO is produced at low physiological levels (1–50 nM) in an environment poor in superoxide anion. When NO is produced in excess, especially in a superoxide-rich environment, iron metabolism can become profoundly disturbed in both NO-generating cells and NO target cells, leading to substantial loss of intracellular iron (68). In a setting of excess iron, cytotoxicity is primarily attributed to the formation of highly reactive oxygen radicals by Fe^{2+}-iron via the Fenton reaction (58). In view of this toxicity, but also the necessity for biosynthesis and cell growth, complex regulatory processes have evolved for controlling iron levels in cells, and NO has multiple actions on these iron-regulatory processes.

Iron is transported in the circulation mainly as Fe^{3+}-bound transferrin, a 58-kDa glycoprotein that can bind two iron and two carbonate ions (166). The Fe^{3+} cation is otherwise practically insoluble at physiological pH ($\sim 10^{-17}$ M); thus the transferrin complex serves as a soluble nontoxic form of iron that can enter cells by endocytosis of specific membrane-bound transferrin receptors. EPR studies have provided evidence that NO can directly bind to transferrin (36), although the precise nature and consequences of this interaction are unclear. Once inside cells, iron is sequestered within ferritin, a 450-kDa storage protein, which forms a shell that can accommodate 4500 hydrated Fe^{3+} ions. Ferritin is composed of 24 subunits of two types H (20 kDa) and L (21 kDa); the H subunits have ferroxidase activity and catalyze dioxygen-dependent oxidation of Fe^{2+} to Fe^{3+} for iron sequestration. Release of iron from ferritin requires reduction from Fe^{3+} to Fe^{2+}; this process can be driven by NO or superoxide anion (152, 153) and may be a major source of the iron released by cytokine-activated macrophages. EPR has demonstrated a NO-ferritin adduct of unknown structure (36).

Expression of the key proteins involved in iron homeostasis, including ferritin H and L chains, the transferrin receptor, and 5-aminolevulinate synthetase (the rate-limiting enzyme in heme biosynthesis), is regulated by the iron-responsive element-binding protein (IRE-BP) (see 93 for review). When activated, IRE-BP has high affinity for a variable 25–35 nucleotide sequence that produces stem-loop secondary structure (iron-responsive elements, IREs) in mRNAs encoding each of these proteins (93). In the case of ferritin subunits and 5-aminolevulinate synthase mRNAs, the iron-responsive element is present in the 5'-untranslated region; binding of IRE-BP inhibits initiation of translation and hence expression of these proteins. In contrast, multiple iron-responsive elements are present in the 3'-untranslated region of transferrin receptor mRNA, which, when occupied by IRE-BP, results in reduced mRNA degradation and an increase in transferrin receptor mRNA and protein expression. The net effect of these events is that intracellular iron levels are autoregulated via an "iron sensor" in IRE-BP that balances cellular uptake of iron for biosynthesis against sequestration for protection against iron-mediated toxicity.

Nitric oxide has been found to activate the iron sensor of IRE-BP. Evidence suggests that the iron sensor is a 4Fe/4S cluster in IRE-BP that has now been identified as the cytosolic homologue of mitochondrial aconitase (82), a known target of NO, or an NO oxidation product such as $ONOO^-$. IRE-BP has aconitase activity similar to that of the mitochondrial enzyme but little affinity for iron-responsive elements when its 4Fe/4S cluster is intact (60). However, loss of the labile Fe_a iron atom from the cluster, to give the 3Fe/4S species, simultaneously abolishes aconitase activity and triggers avid binding to iron-responsive elements in mRNA (60). In a manner analogous to that for mitochondrial aconitase, NO (or a derived species) appears to trigger iron loss from the 4Fe/4S clusters of IRE-BP, leading to the 3Fe/4S IRE-binding protein form. This model serves to explain the finding that NO coordinately elevates transferrin receptor expression while it reduces ferritin levels (35, 184). NO thereby mimics the signal for low intracellular iron (activation of IRE-BP binding to cognate mRNA sequences) in the face of an actual NO-mediated release of protein-bound iron. The potential biological consequences of this scenario include cytostasis due to iron insufficency for cell growth and proliferation, and cytotoxicity due to the generation of toxic oxygen radical species arising from Fe^{2+} excess.

The predicted ability of NO to suppress levels of 5-aminolevulinate synthase mRNA and hence, heme synthesis, has not been investigated. If operative, such a process could serve to limit NO synthesis by virtue of the required heme prosthetic group for NOS activity. It is noteworthy that overproduction of NO in vivo has been associated with a suppression of of phenobarbital-induced cytochrome P450-bound heme in rats (84).

Antioxidant Defense Mechanisms and NO-Dependent Injury

As discussed above, NO and reactive oxygen species such as O_2^- have the potential to release iron from tissue storage sites that can then participate in lipid peroxidation and related cellular injury processes (119). Conversely, the loss of intracellular iron as a NO complex (e.g. iron-nitroso-sulfur complex) has also been suggested to function as a protective mechanism via reducing the ability of iron to participate in injury-producing actions of reactive oxygen species (68, 80). It is noteworthy that iron-nitroso-sulfur complexes will eventually decompose after release from cells, in the absence of conditions needed for their regeneration, and release iron that could participate in tissue injury, especially in situations such as inflammation, where reactive oxygen species are generated and where iron-binding mechanisms might be altered. Little evidence is available to discern the actual role of NO, i.e. protective or injury-potentiating, in iron-mediated oxidative tissue damage. Conceivably, both opportunities exist, with the ultimate action depending on relative levels of NO and tissue-redox status.

Exposure of human neutrophils to NO and NO-generating compounds suppresses the detection of superoxide anion in association with a depletion of intracellular glutathione levels, formation of nitrosothiols, and stimulation of the hexose monophosphate pathway (24). Based on this evidence and the known interactions of NO with thiols as discussed above, it appears that NO may be oxidized to nitrogen oxide species that react with glutathione-SH groups to form S-nitroso-glutathione, which can then release NO and generate the disulfide form of glutathione. Oxidized glutathione is reduced by glutathione reductase employing NADPH generated from the hexose monophosphate pathway. Because $ONOO^-$ readily forms when NO is generated, even in the absence of inflammatory cells (96), NO is such an effective scavenger of O_2^- that it competes with tissue SOD. Indeed, analysis of the kinetic rate constant for reaction between NO and O_2^- suggests it may be several-fold faster than that for dismutation of O_2^- by SOD (159). Evidence is emerging that NO may play a cytoprotective role by preventing the formation and actions of endogenously produced reactive oxygen species (134). This could occur if $ONOO^-$ and its derived products are less perturbing or toxic than alternative reactive species derived from O_2^-, because the formation of toxic species such as hydroxyl radical–related iron-H_2O_2 complexes, hypochlorous acid, chloroamines, etc, will be suppressed by reducing the rate of H_2O_2 formation from O_2^-. Nonetheless, processes activated by NO metabolism that result in the depletion of NADPH and glutathione-dependent antioxidant and detoxification defense mechanisms could also elicit oxidant stress in cells by impairing the normal removal of endogenously generated hydrogen peroxide, and derived reactive species, thereby contributing to the cytotoxicity of NO.

Recently Cu,Zn-SOD was found to be modified by $ONOO^-$ via nitration of critical tyrosine groups (75). Although in vitro nitration of tyrosine does not appear to inhibit the cytosolic form of SOD (Cu,Zn-SOD), nitration has inhibited mitochondrial SOD (Mn-SOD) (75). The effects of nitration on other proteins of importance for cell integrity and function are not known. Because nitrotyrosine is readily detectable at sites of inflammation where $ONOO^-$ is likely to be formed (7), this reaction is probably important in vivo and could emerge as a mechanism for posttranslational regulation of protein activity by NO/O_2^-.

To summarize, the toxicity of NO originates predominantly from its oxidized metabolites, including $ONOO^-$, NO_2, and their derived species, when the actions of these metabolites exceeds the cellular capacity to detoxify them. Glutathione is emerging as a key metabolite that interacts with reactive species derived from NO oxidation because it may function to convert these species to less toxic ones. Depletion of glutathione, inhibition of mitochondrial SOD, and perhaps the loss of other antioxidant defense mechanisms could then permit a rise in the endogenous levels of reactive oxygen species normally produced by metabolism, which is likely to enhance the toxicity of NO. By this route, reactive nitrogen and oxygen species may act in concert to inactivate key metabolic enzymes and cause lipid peroxidation and DNA strand breaks that result in irreversible cell injury and death.

NO IN DISEASE

NO overproduction has been linked as causative or contributing to diverse pathophysiological conditions associated with primary vascular, inflammatory, and neuro-degenerative disorders. In contrast, a diminished capacity for NO synthesis, or enhanced degradation, may contribute to chronic hypertensive disease. Prior to its discovery as a product of mammalian cell metabolism, NO was widely identified as an environmental pollutant that is mutagenic, carcinogenic, and toxic to the airways. Extensive prior literature and space limitations herein require that we limit our focus to NO as a mediator of circulatory shock and tissue injury arising from ischemia/reperfusion. These are diseases in which some of the best-defined roles of NO-related mechanisms are evolving.

Circulatory Shock

Overproduction of NO within the blood vessel wall has been implicated as the basis for septic- and cytokine-induced circulatory shock (86). These conditions are associated with excessive activation of guanylate cyclase and cGMP. Via this mechanism, excessive NO synthesis contributes to the profound vasodilation and hypotension caused by LPS (89, 176) and the cytokines tumor necrosis factor (TNF) (87), IL-1 (88), and IL-2 (90). In animal models of septic shock and in the human disease, low doses of the NO synthase inhibitor N^ω-methyl-L-arginine restores blood pressure and vascular tone (86). Moreover, the well-known hyporesponsivity to pressor amines, which is associated with endotoxic shock, can also be overcome with inhibitors of NOS (40).

Biochemical confirmation of NO overproduction has been obtained in immunostimulant-treated patients and animals. In humans, IL-2 induces the appearance of arginine-derived nitrate in plasma (69, 138); this implicates NO as the mediator of the hypotension experienced in patients treated with IL-2 for cancer chemotherapy. In association with the ability of LPS to induce vascular dysfunctions in rat, a widespread induction of iNOS has been observed in tissue homogenates (157). EPR studies have revealed that LPS elicits the progressive accumulation of nitroso-heme in the plasma of rats (182). Although the source of vasoregulatory NO in normal physiology appears to be exclusively of endothelial or neural origin, NO synthesis can also be further induced by LPS in endothelial cells (56, 85), and induced in other vascular cell types including smooth muscle cells (4, 16, 57). Although vascular smooth muscle is normally the target of endothelium-derived NO, after immunostimulant exposure, smooth muscle will produce copious amounts of NO. Whether smooth muscle cells are the dominant site of NO overproduction in LPS- and cytokine-induced circulatory shock will likely be revealed by future immunohistochemical localization studies of inducible NOS in the septic blood vessel. Induction of NOS by immunostimulants has also been reported to occur in cardiac myocytes and endocardium where NO can suppress myocardial contractility (178). The possibility that NO is the identity of the elusive myocardial depressant factor of septic shock awaits investigation.

Although NOS inhibitors clearly restore vascular tone in septic-, endotoxic-, and cytokine-treated animals, improved mortality has yet to be demonstrated. Indeed, NOS inhibition has been suggested to both benefit (86) and worsen (62, 63) disease outcome in animal models (86). It is possible that NO, in addition to being toxic, also has some protective function in sepsis, perhaps by mopping-up reactive oxygen species, or by providing some degree of vasodilatory tone to counterbalance sympathetically mediated vasoconstriction. Thus achieving sub-maximal inhibition of NOS inhibitors may be preferred over complete inhibition. The arginine-binding site of NOSs appear to differ for inducible and endothelial isoforms (56), thus iNOS-selective agents may be developed that will have advantages over present nonselective agents. In any event, as animal models of septic shock often poorly reflect features of the clinical condition, meaningful evaluation of the utility of present NOS inhibitors in sepsis can only be achieved by controlled trials in human patients.

Ischemia/Reperfusion Injury

Nitric oxide has been reported to function in both protective- and injury-producing processes in tissue ischemia/reperfusion. In an ischemia/reperfusion model of the rat mesenteric microcirculation associated with reduced endogenous NO production, administration of nitric oxide–generating agents caused inhibition of leukocyte adherence, emigration and venular extravasation of albumin, suppression of mast cell degranulation, and reduced platelet-leukocyte aggregation (98). Similarly, in the cat coronary circulation, endogenous NO functioned to reduce the area of necrotic injury, neutrophil accumulation, and loss of endothelium-dependent relaxation (188). In the rat brain, occlusion of the middle cerebral artery increased cerebral NO levels acutely from $<10^{-8}$ M to $\sim10^{-6}$ M; levels subsequently declined and increased again upon reoxygenation (113). In this model, NO appears to function in a protective role during ischemia to reduce infarct size (124) and preserve cerebral blood flow upon reperfusion (145). Interestingly, endothelial NO synthase levels in the rat brain increased over a 24 h period of ischemia throughout the ischemic region, in apparent association with degenerative changes in endothelial function (199).

The production of NO metabolites has also been implicated as contributing to injury associated with ischemia/reperfusion. Superoxide anion and NO appear to have a cooperative role in hypoxia/reoxygenation injury of cultured neurons (19). In hearts of anesthetized pigs, NO production was decreased by hypoxia and increased upon reoxygenation; inhibitors of NO synthesis and scavengers of reactive oxygen species could each protect against reoxygenation-elicited injury, measured as a decrease in contractility and an increase in lipid peroxidation (114). Inhibition of NO biosynthesis also appears to limit ischemia/reperfusion-elicited infarct size in the rabbit heart (141). Consistent with a potential role for NO in post-ischemic/reperfusion injury of saline perfused rabbit hearts is the detection of a nitrogen-centered radical during reperfusion (200). Hindlimb ischemia/reperfusion in the rat, a model in which neutrophil-derived reactive oxygen species contribute to increased permeability in the limb and lung, also shows a role for NO metabolism in the injury processes (164). In general, more work is needed in these models to determine if the production of reactive oxygen species by NO synthase (in the absence of adequate levels of L-arginine) is contributing to the observed pathophysiology attributed to NO. The observed protective role for NO metabolism in ischemia/reperfusion appears to originate from its inhibitory actions on leukocyte accumulation and, perhaps, other processes, whereas the role of NO-derived metabolites in injury has generally been suggested to result from the formation of reactive NO species such as $ONOO^-$. Based on the known chemistry and interactions of NO metabolites with tissues, it is likely that the levels of reactive oxygen species and NO, combined with the antioxidant protective mechanisms, e.g. glutathione and radical scavengers, have a major role in determining if NO will be defensive or injury-producing.

SUMMARY AND FUTURE PERSPECTIVES

NO differs from all other mammalian cell-signaling molecules; it was selected early in evolution for its diffusibility and reactivity, rather than its mere shape. With NO, nature walks a tightrope: How are appropriate reactions necessary for physiology favored over those that are predictably cytostatic or cytotoxic? How is the destructive potential of NO focused on foreign microbes while minimizing risk to self? What fail-safe mechanisms and chemical reactions have evolved to disarm NO when and if levels do become threatening? The answers to these and other key questions will undoubtedly come with an improved understanding of NO-based biochemistry and a fuller appreciation of the mechanisms governing NO synthesis by cells.

Literature Cited

1. Abu-Soud HM, Stuehr DJ. 1993. Nitric oxide synthases reveal a role for calmodulin in controlling electron transfer. *Proc. Natl. Acad. Sci. USA* 90:10769–72
2. Asson-Batres MA, Spurgeon SL, Diaz J, DeLoughery TG, Bagby GC Jr. 1994. Evolutionary conservation of the AU-rich 3′ untranslated region of messenger RNA. *Proc. Natl. Acad. Sci. USA* 91: 1318–22
3. Bastian NR, Yim C-Y, Hibbs JB, Samlowski WE. 1994. Induction of iron-derived EPR signals in murine cancers by nitric oxide. Evidence for multiple intracellular targets. *J. Biol. Chem.* 269: 5127–31
4. Beasley D, Schwartz JH, Brenner BM. 1991. Interleukin-1 induces prolonged L-arginine dependent cyclic guanosine monophosphate and nitrite production in rat vascular smooth muscle cells. *J. Clin. Invest.* 87:602–8
5. Beaton ED, Liu Z, McLaughlin BE, Brien JF, Nakatsu K, Marks GS. 1993.

A novel method for detection of nitric oxide binding sites by using a chemiluminescence-headspace gas technique. *J. Pharmacol. Toxicol. Meth.* 30: 217–22

6. Beckman JS, Beckman TW, Chen J, Marshall PA, Freeman BA. 1990. Apparent hydroxyl radical formation by peroxynitrite: implications for endothelial injury from nitric oxide and superoxide. *Proc. Natl. Acad. Sci. USA* 87: 1620–24

7. Beckman JS, Ye YZ, Anderson PG, Chen J, Accavitti MA, et al. 1994. Extensive nitration of protein tyrosines in human atherosclerosis detected by immunohistochemistry. *Biol. Chem. Hoppe-Seyler* 375:81–86

8. Blatter LA, Wier WG. 1994. Nitric oxide decreases $[Ca^{2+}]_i$ in vascular smooth muscle by inhibition of the calcium current. *Cell Calcium* 15:122–31

9. Bogle RG, Baydoun AR, Pearson JD, Moncada S, Mann GE. 1992. L-arginine transport is increased in macrophages generating nitric oxide. *Biochem. J.* 284: 15–18

10. Bohjanen PR, Petryniak B, June CH, Thompson CB, Lindsten T. 1992. AU RNA-binding factors differ in their binding specificities and affinities. *J. Biol. Chem.* 267:6302–9

11. Boime I, Hunter FE Jr. 1971. Effects of glyceryltrinitrate, mannitol hexanitrate and erythritol tetranitrate on electron transport and phosphorylation in liver mitochondria. *Biochem. Pharmacol.* 20: 533–45

12. Bolotina VM, Najiba S, Palacino JJ, Pagano PJ, Cohen RA. 1994. Nitric oxide directly activates calcium-dependent potassium channels in vascular smooth muscle. *Nature* 368:850–53

13. Bredt DS, Hwang PM, Glatt CE, Lowentein C, Reed RR, Snyder SH. 1991. Cloned and expressed nitric oxide synthase structurally resembles cytochrome P-450 reductase. *Nature* 351: 714–18

14. Brown JF, Hanson PJ, Whittle BJ. 1993. The nitric oxide donor, S-nitroso-N-acetyl-penicillamine, inhibits secretory activity in rat isolated parietal cells. *Biochem. Biophys. Res. Commun.* 195: 1354–59

15. Brune B, Dimmeler S, Molina y Vedina L, Lapetina EG. 1993. Nitric oxide: a signal for ADP-ribosylation of proteins. *Life Sci.* 54:61–70

16. Busse R, Mulsch A. 1990. Induction of nitric oxide synthase by cytokines in vascular smooth muscle cells. *FEBS Lett.* 275:87–90

17. Caput D, Beutler B, Hartog K, Thayer R, Brown-Shimer S, Cerami A. 1986. Identification of a common nucleotide sequence in the 3′-untranslated region of mRNA molecules specifying inflammatory mediators. *Proc. Natl. Acad. Sci. USA* 83:1670–74

18. Caterina RD, Dorso CD, Tack-Goldman, K, Weksler BB. 1985. Nitrates and endothelial prostacyclin production: studies in vitro. *Circulation* 71:176–82

19. Cazveieille C, Muller A, Meynier F, Bonne C. 1993. Superoxide and nitric oxide cooperation in hypoxia/reoxygenation-induced neuron injury. *Free Radic. Biol. Med.* 14:389–95

20. Chartrain NA, Geller DA, Koty PP, Sitrin NF, Nussler AK, et al. 1994. Molecular cloning, structure, and chromosomal localization of the human inducible nitric oxide synthase gene. *J. Biol. Chem.* 269:6765–72

21. Cherry PD, Omar HA, Farrell KA, Stuart JS, Wolin MS. 1990. Superoxide anion inhibits cGMP-associated bovine pulmonary arterial relaxation. *Am. J. Physiol.* 259:H1056–62

22. Cho HJ, Xie QW, Calaycay J, Mumford RA, Swiderek KM, et al. 1992. Calmodulin as a tightly bound subunit of calcium-, calmodulin-independent nitric oxide synthase. *J. Exp. Med.* 176:599–604

23. Clancy RM, Leszczynska-Piziak J, Abramson SB. 1992. Nitric oxide, an endothelial cell relaxation factor, inhibits neutrophil superoxide anion production via a direct action on the NADPH oxidase. *J. Clin. Invest.* 90:1116–21

24. Clancy RM, Levartovsky D, Leszczynska-Piziak J, Yegudin J, Abramson SB. 1994. Nitric oxide reacts with intracellular glutathione and activates the hexose monophosphate shunt in human neutrophils: evidence for S-nitrosoglutathione as a bioactive intermediary. *Proc. Natl. Acad. Sci. USA* 91:3680–84

25. Crane FL, Sun IL, Clark MG, Grebing C, Low H. 1985. Transplasma-membrane redox systems in growth and development. *Biochem. Biophys. Acta* 811: 233–64

26. Craven PA, DeRubertis FR. 1978. Restoration of the responsiveness of purified guanylate cyclase to nitrosoguanidine, nitric oxide, and related activators by heme and hemoproteins. *J. Biol. Chem.* 253:8433–43

27. Creager MA, Gallagher SJ, Girerd XJ, Coleman SM, Dzau VJ, Cooke JP. 1992. L-arginine improves endothelium-dependent vasodilation in hypercholester-

olemic humans. *J. Clin. Invest.* 90:1248–53

28. Dalton DK, Pitts-Meek S, Keshav S, Figari IS, Bradley A, Stewart TA. 1993. Multiple defects of immune cell function in mice with disrupted interferon-gamma genes. *Science* 259:1739–42

29. Dawson TM, Steiner JP, Dawson VL, Dinerman JL, Uhl GR, Snyder S. 1993. Immunosuppressant FK506 enhances phosphorylation of nitric oxide synthase and protects against glutamate neurotoxicity. *Proc. Natl. Acad. Sci. USA* 90:9808–12

30. Dee G, Rice-Evans C, Obeyesekera S, Meraji S, Jacobs M, Buckdorfer KR. 1991. The modulation of ferryl myoglobin formation and its oxidative effects on low density lipoproteins by nitric oxide. *FEBS Lett.* 294:38–42

31. Devi L, Petanceska S, Liu R, Arbabha B, Bansinath M, Garg U. 1994. Regulation of neuropeptide-processing enzymes by nitric oxide in cultured astrocytes. *J. Neurochem.* 62:2387–93

32. Dimmeler S, Brune B. 1992. Characterization of a nitric-oxide-catalyzed ADP-ribosylation of glyceraldehyde-3-phosphate dehydrogenase. *Eur. J. Biochem.* 210:305–10

33. Dimmeler S, Lottspeich F, Brune B. 1992. Nitric oxide causes ADP-ribosylation and inhibition of glyceraldehyde-3-phosphate dehydrogenase. *J. Biol. Chem.* 267:16771–74

34. Doyle MP, Hockstra JW. 1981. Oxidation of nitrogen oxides by bound dioxygen in hemoproteins. *J. Inorg. Biochem.* 14:351–58

35. Drapier J-C, Hirling H, Wietzerberg J, Kaldy P, Kuhn LC, 1993. Biosynthesis of nitric oxide activates iron regulatory factor in macrophages. *EMBO J.* 12:3643–49

36. Drapier J-C, Pellat C, Henry Y. 1991. Generation of EPR-detectable nitrosyl-iron complexes in tumor target cells cocultured with activated macrophages. *J. Biol. Chem.* 266:10162–67

37. Drexler H, Fischell TA, Pinto FJ, Chenzbraun A, Botas J, et al. 1994. Effect of L-arginine on coronary endothelial function in cardiac transplant recipients: relation to vessel wall morphology. *Circulation* 89:1615–23

38. Durante W, Schini VB, Catovsky S, Kroll MH, Vanhoutte PM, Schafer AI. 1993. Plasmin potentiates induction of nitric oxide synthase by interleukin-1β in vascular smooth muscle cells. *Am. J. Physiol.* 264:H617–24

39. Elledge SJ, Zhou SJ, Allen JB. 1992. Ribonucleotide reductase: regulation, regulation. *Trends Biochem. Sci.* 17:119–23

40. Fleming I, Julou-Schaeffer G, Gray GA, Parratt JR, Stoclet JC. 1991. Evidence that an L-arginine/nitric oxide dependent elevation of tissue cyclic GMP content is involved in depression of vascular reactivity by endotoxin. *Br. J. Pharmacol.* 103:1047–52

41. Fontecave M, Nordlund EH, Reichard P. 1992. The redox centers of ribonucleotide reductase of *E. coli. Adv. Enzymol.* 65:147–83

42. Fukushima T, Sekizawa K, Jin Y, Sasaki H. 1994. Interferon-gamma increases cytoplasmic motility of alveolar macrophages via nitric oxide-dependent signaling pathways. *Am. J. Respir. Cell Mol. Biol.* 10:65–71

43. Fukuto JM, Hobbs AJ, Ignarro LJ. 1993. Conversion of nitroxyl (HNO) to nitric oxide (NO) in biological systems: the role of physiological oxidants and relevance to the biological activity of HNO. *Biochem. Biophys. Res. Commun.* 196:707–13

44. Furchgott RF, Khan MT, Jothianandan KD. 1990. Comparison of properties of nitric oxide and endothelium-derived relaxing factor: some cautionary findings. In *Endothelium-Derived Relaxing Factors*, ed. GM Rubanyi, PM Vanhoutte, pp. 8–21. Basal: Karger

45. Gaston B, Drazen JM, Jansen A, Sugarbaker DA, Loscalzo J, et al. 1994. Relaxation of human bronchial smooth muscle by S-nitrosothiols in vitro. *J. Pharmacol. Exp. Ther.* 268:978–84

46. Gaston B, Drazen JM, Loscalzo J, Stamler JS. 1994. The biology of nitrogen oxides in airways. *Am. J. Respir. Crit. Care Med.* 149:538–51

47. Geng Y-J, Hansson GK, Holme E. 1992. Interferon-γ and tumor necrosis factor synergize to induce nitric oxide production and inhibit mitochondrial respiration in vascular smooth muscle cells. *Circ. Res.* 71:1268–76

48. Gerzer R, Bohme E, Hofmann F, Schultz G. 1981. Soluble guanylate cyclase purified from bovine lung contains heme and copper. *FEBS Lett.* 123:71–74

49. Gopalakrishna R, Chen ZH, Gundimeda U. 1993. Nitric oxide and nitric oxide-generating agents induce a reversible inactivation of protein kinase C activity and phorbol ester binding. *J. Biol. Chem.* 268:27180–85

50. Granger DL, Lehninger AL. 1982. Sites of inhibition of mitochondrial electron transport in macrophage-injured neoplastic cells. *J. Cell Biol.* 95:527–35

51. Granger DL, Taintor JJ, Cook JL, Hibbs

JB Jr. 1980. Injury of neoplastic cells by murine macrophages leads to inhibition of mitochondrial function. *J. Clin. Invest.* 65:357–70

52. Green LC, Tannenbaum SR, Goldman P. 1981. Nitrate synthesis in the germfree and conventional rat. *Science* 212: 56–58

53. Griffith OW, Park K, Levi R, Gross SS. 1992. The role of plasma arginine in nitric oxide synthesis: studies with arginase-treated rats. In *Biology of Nitric Oxide*, ed. S Moncada, M Marletta, JB Hibbs, pp. 6–10. London: Portland

54. Griscavage JM, Rogers NE, Sherman MP, Ignarro LJ. 1993. Inducible nitric oxide synthase from rat alveolar macrophage cell line is inhibited by nitric oxide. *J. Immunol.* 151:6329–37

55. Gross SS, Hattori Y, Vane JR. 1994. cAMP stimulates induction of NOS by immunostimulants in vascular smooth muscle In *Biology of Nitric Oxide,* ed. M Feelisch, R Busse, S Moncada. London: Portland. In press

56. Gross SS, Jaffe EA, Levi R, Kilbourn RG. 1991. Cytokine-activated endothelial cells express an isotype of nitric oxide synthase which is tetrahydrobiopterin-dependent, calmodulin-independent and inhibited by arginine analogs with a rank-order of potency characteristic of activated macrophages. *Biochem. Biophys. Res. Commun.* 178: 823–29

57. Gross SS, Levi R. 1992. Tetrahydrobiopterin synthesis: an absolute requirement for cytokine-induced nitric oxide generation by vascular smooth muscle. *J. Biol. Chem.* 257:25722–29

58. Gutteridge JMC. 1989. Iron and oxygen: a biologically damaging mixture. *Acta Paediatr. Scand. Suppl.* 361:78–85

59. Haby C, Lisovoski F, Aunis D, Zwiller J. 1994. Stimulation of the cyclic GMP pathway by NO induces expression of the early genes *c-fos* and *jun-B* in PC-12 cells. *J. Neurochem.* 62:496–501

60. Haile DJ, Rouault TA, Tang CK, Chin J, Hartford JB, Klausner RD. 1992. Reciprocal control of RNA-binding and aconitase activity in the regulation of the iron-responsive element binding protein: role of the iron-sulfur cluster. *Proc. Natl. Acad. Sci. USA* 89:7536–40

61. Hammer B, Parker WD Jr, Bennett JP Jr. 1993. NMDA receptors increase hydroxyl radicals in vivo by using nitric oxide synthase and protein kinase. *NeuroReport* 5:72–74

62. Harbrecht BG, Billiar TR, Stadler J, Demetris AJ, Ochoa JB, et al. 1992. Nitric oxide synthesis serves to reduce hepatic damage during acute murine endotoxemia. *Crit. Care Med.* 20:1568–74

63. Harbrecht BG, Billiar TR, Stadler J, Demetris AJ, Ochoa J, et al. 1992. Inhibition of nitric oxide synthesis during endotoxemia promotes intrahepatic thrombosis and an oxygen radical–mediated hepatic injury. *J. Leukocyte Biol.* 52:390–94

64. Hattori Y, Campbell EB, Gross SS. 1994. Argininosuccinate synthetase mRNA and activity are induced by immunostimulants in vascular smooth muscle. Role in the regeneration of arginine for nitric oxide synthesis. *J. Biol. Chem.* 269:9405–8

65. Hattori Y, Gross SS. 1993. GTP cyclohydrolase I mRNA is induced by LPS in vascular smooth muscle: characterization, sequence and relationship to nitric oxide synthase. *Biochem. Biophys. Res. Commun.* 195:435–41

66. Hecker M, Sessa WC, Harris HJ, Anggard EE, Vane JR. 1990. The metabolism of L-arginine and its significance for the biosynthesis of endothelium-derived relaxing factor: cultured endothelial cells recycle L-citrulline to L-arginine. *Proc. Natl. Acad. Sci. USA* 87: 8612–16

67. Heinzel B, John M, Klatt P, Bohme E, Mayer B. 1992. Ca^{2+}/calmodulin-dependent formation of hydrogen peroxide by brain nitric oxide synthase. *Biochem. J.* 281:627–30

68. Hibbs JB, Taintor RR, Vavrin Z, Granger DL, Drapier J-C, et al. 1990. Synthesis of nitric oxide from a terminal guanidino nitrogen atom of L-arginine: a molecular mechanism regulating cellular proliferation that targets intracellular iron. In *Nitric Oxide from L-arginine: A Cellular Bioregulatory System*, ed. S Moncada, JB Hibbs, pp. 189–223. Amsterdam: Elsevier Sci.

69. Hibbs JB, Westenfelder C, Taintor R, Vavrin Z, Kablitz C, et al. 1992. Evidence for cytokine-inducible nitric oxide synthesis from L-arginine in patients receiving interleukin-2 therapy. *J. Clin. Invest.* 89:867–77

70. Hidalgo E, Demple B. 1994. An iron-sulfur center essential for transcriptional activation by the redox-sensing SoxR protein. *EMBO J.* 13:138–46

71. Huang S, Hendriks W, Althage A, Hemmi S, Bluethmann H, et al. 1993. Immune response in mice that lack the interferon-gamma receptor. *Science* 259:1742–45

72. Ignarro LJ, Degnan JN, Baricos WH, Kadowitz PJ, Wolin MS. 1982. Activation of purified guanylate cyclase by

nitric oxide requires heme: comparison of the heme-deficient, heme-reconstituted and heme-containing forms of soluble enzyme from bovine lung. *Biochem. Biophys. Acta* 718:49–59

73. Ignarro LJ, Wood KS, Wolin MS. 1984. Regulation of purified soluble guanylate cyclase by porphyrins and metalloporphyrins: a unifying concept. *Adv. Cycl. Nucleotide Res.* 17:267–74

74. Imai T, Hirata Y, Kanno K, Marumo F. 1994. Induction of nitric oxide synthase by cyclic AMP in rat vascular smooth muscle cells. *J. Clin. Invest.* 93:543–49

75. Ischiropoulos H, Zhu L, Chen J, Tsai M, Martin JC, et al. 1992. Peroxynitrite-mediated tyrosine nitration catalyzed by superoxide dismutase. *Arch. Biochem. Biophys.* 298:431–37

76. Iyengar R, Stuehr DJ, Marletta MA. 1987. Macrophage synthesis of nitrite, nitrate and N-nitrosamines: precursors and role of the respiratory burst. *Proc. Natl. Acad. Sci. USA* 84:6369–73

77. Jones K. 1973. *The Chemistry of Nitrogen.* Oxford: Pergamon

78. Deleted in proof

79. Kamijo R, Harada H, Matsuyama T, Bosland M, Gerecitano J, et al. 1994. Requirement for transcription factor IRF-1 in NO synthase induction in macrophages. *Science* 263:1612–15

80. Kanner J, Harel S, Granit R. 1991. Nitric oxide as an antioxidant. *Arch. Biochem. Biophys.* 289:130–36

81. Kaufman S. 1993. The phenylalanine hydroxylating system. *Adv. Enzymol. Relat. Areas Mol. Biol.* 67:77–264

82. Kennedy MC, Mende-Mueller L, Blondin GA, Beinert H. 1992. Purification and characterization of cytosolic aconitase from beef liver and its relationship to the iron-responsive element binding protein (IRE-BP). *Proc. Natl. Acad. Sci. USA* 89:11730–34

83. Kharitonov VG, Sundquist AR, Sharma VS. 1994. Kinetics of nitric oxide autooxidation in aqueous solution. *J. Biol. Chem.* 269:5881–83

84. Khatsenko O, Gross SS, Rifkind A, Vane JR. 1993. Nitric oxide mediates the decrease in cytochrome P-450-dependent metabolism caused by immunostimulants. *Proc. Natl. Acad. Sci. USA* 90:11147–51

85. Kilbourn RG, Belloni P. 1990. Endothelial cell production of nitrogen oxides in response to interferon in combination with tumor necrosis-factor, interleukin-1, or endotoxin. *J. Natl. Cancer Inst.* 82:772–76

86. Kilbourn RG, Griffith OW. 1992. Over-production of nitric oxide in cytokine-mediated and septic shock. *J. Natl. Cancer Inst.* 84:1671–72

87. Kilbourn RG, Gross SS, Jubran A, Adams J, Griffith OW, et al. 1990. N^G-methyl-L-arginine inhibits tumor necrosis factor-induced hypotension: implications for the involvement of nitric oxide. *Proc. Natl. Acad. Sci. USA* 87:3629–32

88. Kilbourn RG, Gross SS, Lodato RF, Adams J, Levi R, et al. 1992. N$^\omega$-aminoarginine inhibits interleukin-1-induced nitric oxide synthesis in vascular smooth muscle and fully reverses interleukin-1-induced hypotension. *J. Natl. Cancer Inst.* 84:1008–16

89. Kilbourn RG, Jubran A, Gross SS, Griffith OW, Levi R, et al. 1990. Reversal of endotoxin-mediated shock by N^G-methyl-L-arginine, an inhibitor of nitric oxide synthesis. *Biochem. Biophys. Res. Commun.* 172:1132–38

90. Kilbourn RG, Owen-Schaub L, Gross SS, Griffith OW, Logothetis C. 1992. Interleukin-2-mediated hypotension in the awake dog is reversed by inhibitors of nitric oxide formation. In *Biology of Nitric Oxide,* ed. S Moncada, M Marletta, JB Hibbs, pp. 236–42. London: Portland

91. King CE, Melinyshyn MJ, Mewburn JD, Curtis SE, Winn MJ, et al. 1994. Canine hindlimb blood flow and O$_2$ uptake after inhibition of EDRF/NO synthesis. *J. Appl. Physiol.* 76:1166–71

92. Klatt P, Schmidt K, Mayer B. 1992. Brain nitric oxide synthase is a haemoprotein. *Biochem. J.* 288:15–17

93. Klausner RD, Roualt TA, Harford JB. 1993. Regulating the fate of mRNA: the control of cellular iron metabolism. *Cell* 72:19–28

94. Kobzik L, Bredt DS, Lowenstein CJ, Drazen J, Gaston B, et al. 1993. Nitric oxide synthase in human and rat lung: immunocytochemical and immunohistochemical localization. *Am. J. Respir. Cell Mol. Biol.* 9:371–77

95. Koide M, Kawahara Y, Nakayama I, Tsuda T, Yokoyama M. 1993. Cyclic AMP-elevating agents induce an inducible type of nitric oxide synthase in cultured vascular smooth muscle cells. Synergism with the induction elicited by inflammatory cytokines. *J. Biol. Chem.* 268:24959–66

96. Kooy NW, Royall JA. 1994. Agonist-induced peroxynitrite production from endothelial cells. *Arch. Biochem. Biophys.* 310:352–59

97. Kowaluk EA, Fung H-L. 1990. Spontaneous liberation of nitric oxide cannot

account for in vitro vascular relaxation S-nitrosothiols. *J. Pharmacol. Exp. Ther.* 255:1256–64

98. Kurose I, Wolf R, Grisham MB, Granger DN. 1994. Modulation of ischemia/reperfusion-induced microvascular dysfunction by nitric oxide. *Circ. Res.* 74:376–82

99. Kwon NS, Stuehr DJ, Nathan CF. 1991. Inhibition of tumor cell ribonucleotide reductase by macrophage-derived nitric oxide. *J. Exp. Med.* 174:761–67

100. Lander HM, Sehajpal P, Levine DM, Novogrodsky A. 1993. Activation of human peripheral blood mononuclear cells by nitric oxide-generating compounds. *J. Immunol.* 150:1509–16

101. Lander HM, Sehajpal PK, Novogrodsky A. 1993. Nitric oxide signaling: a possible role for G proteins. *J. Immunol.* 151:7182–87

102. Deleted in proof

103. Leaf CD, Wishok JS, Tannenbaum SR. 1990. Nitric oxide: the dark side. In *Nitric Oxide From L-arginine: A Cellular Bioregulatory System,* ed. S Moncada, EA Higgs, pp. 291–99. Amsterdam: Elsevier Sci.

104. Leaf CD, Wishok JS, Tannenbaum SR. 1991. Endogenous incorporation of nitric oxide from L-arginine into N-nitrosomorpoline stimulated by *Escherichia coli* lipopolysaccharide in the rat. *Carcinogenesis* 12:537–39

105. Lee JH, Wilcox GL, Beitz AJ. 1992. Nitric oxide mediates *Fos* expression in the spinal cord induced by mechanical noxious stimulation. *NeuroReport* 3:841–44

106. Lei S, Pan Z-H, Aggarwal SK, Chen H-SV, Hartman J, et al. 1992. Effect of nitric oxide production on the redox modulatory site of the NMDA receptor-channel complex. *Neuron* 8:1992

107. Lepoivre M, Chenais B, Yapo A, Lemaire G, Thelander L, Tenu J-P. 1990. Alterations of ribonucleotide reductase activity following induction of the nitrite-generating pathway in adenocarcinoma cells. *J. Biol. Chem.* 265:14143–49

108. Lepoivre M, Fieschi F, Coves J, Thelander L, Fontecave M. 1991. Inactivation of ribonucleotide reductase by nitric oxide. *Biochem. Biophys. Res. Commun.* 179:442–48

109. Lepoivre M, Flaman J-M, Henry Y. 1992. Early loss of the tyrosyl radical in ribonucleotide reductase of adenocarcinoma cells producing nitric oxide. *J. Biol. Chem.* 267:22994–3000

110. Lipton SA, Choi Y-B, Pan Z-H, Lei SZ, Chen H-SV, et al. 1993. A redox-based mechanism for the neuroprotective and neurodestructive effects of nitric oxide and nitroso-compounds. *Nature* 364:626–32

111. Liu X, Gillespie JS, Martin W. 1994. Non-adrenergic, non-cholinergic relaxation of the bovine retractor penis muscle: role of S-nitrosothiols. *Br. J. Pharmacol.* 111:1287–95

112. Lowenstein CJ, Alley EW, Raval P, Snowman AM, Snyder SH, et al. 1993. Macrophage nitric oxide synthase gene: two upstream regions mediate induction by interferon-gamma and lipopolysaccharide. *Proc. Natl. Acad. Sci. USA* 90:9730-34

113. Malinski T, Bailey F, Zhang ZG, Chopp M. 1993. Nitric oxide measured by a porphyrinic microsensor in rat brain after transient middle cerebral artery occlusion. *J. Cereb. Blood Flow Metab.* 13:355–58

114. Matheis G, Sherman MP, Buckberg GD, Haybron DM, Young HH, Ignarro LJ. 1992. Role of L-arginine-nitric oxide pathway in myocardial reoxygenation injury. *Am. J. Physiol.* 262:H616–20

115. McDonald LJ, Moss J. 1993. Stimulation by nitric oxide of an NAD linkage to glyceraldehyde-3-phosphate dehydrogenase. *Proc. Natl. Acad. Sci. USA* 90:6238–41

116. McMillan K, Bredt DS, Hirsch DJ, Snyder SH, Clark JE, et al. 1992. Cloned, expressed rat cerebellar nitric oxide synthase contains stoichiometric amounts of heme, which binds carbon monoxide. *Proc. Natl. Acad. Sci. USA* 89:11141–45

117. McQueston JA, Cornfield DN, McMurtry IF, Abman SH. 1993. Effects of oxygen and exogenous L-arginine on EDRF activity in fetal pulmonary circulation. *Am. J. Physiol.* 264:H865–71

118. Michel T, Li GK, Busconi L. 1993. Phosphorylation and subcellular translocation of endothelial nitric oxide. *Proc. Natl. Acad. Sci. USA* 90:6252–56

119. Minotti G. 1992. The role of an endogenous non-heme iron in microsomal redox reactions. *Arch. Biochem. Biophys.* 297:189–96

120. Mitchell HH, Shonle HA, Grindley HS. 1916. The origin of nitrates in urine. *J. Biol. Chem.* 24:461–90

121. Mohr S, Stamler JS, Brune B. 1994. Mechanism of covalent modification of glyceraldehyde-3-phosphate dehydrogenase at its active site thiol by nitric oxide, peroxynitrite and related nitrosylating agents. *FEBS Lett.* 348:223–27

122. Molina y Vedia L, McDonald B, Reep B, Brune B, DiSilvo M, et al. 1992. Nitric oxide-induced S-nitrosylation of

glyceraldehyde-3-phosphate dehydrogenase inhibits enzymatic activity and increases endogenous ADP ribosylation. *J. Biol. Chem.* 267:24929–32

123. Moretto M, Lopez FJ, Negro-Vilar A. 1993. Nitric oxide regulates luteinizing hormone-releasing hormone secretion. *Endocrinology* 133:2399–402

124. Morikawa E, Haung Z, Moskowitz MA. 1992. L-arginine decreases infarct size caused by middle cerebral arterial occlusion in SHR. *Am. J. Physiol.* 263: H1632–35

125. Mugge A, Elwell JH, Peterson TE, Harrison DG. 1991. Release of intact endothelium-derived relaxing factor depends on endothelial superoxide dismutase activity. *Am. J. Physiol.* 260: C219–25

126. Mulsch A, Mordvinteev PI, Vanin AF, Busse R. 1993. Formation and release of dinitrosyl iron complexes by endothelial cells. *Biochem. Biophys. Res. Commun.* 196:1303–8

127. Mulsch A, Vanin A, Mordvinteev PI, Hauschildt S, Busse R. 1992. NO accounts completely for the oxygenated nitrogen species generated by enzymatic L-arginine oxygenation. *Biochem. J.* 288:597–603

128. Murphy ME, Sies H. 1991. Reversible conversion of nitroxyl anion to nitric oxide by superoxide dismutase. *Proc. Natl. Acad. Sci. USA* 88:10860–64

129. Nakane M, Schmidt HH, Pollack JS, Förstermann U, Murad F. 1993. Cloned human brain nitric oxide synthase is highly expressed in skeletal muscle. *FEBS Lett.* 316:175–80

130. Nakatsuka M, Osawa Y. 1994. Selective inhibition of the 12-lipoxygenase pathway of arachidonic acid metabolism by L-arginine or sodium nitroprusside in intact human platelets. *Biochem. Biophys. Res. Commun.* 200:1630–34

131. Nathan C. 1992. Nitric oxide as a secretory product of mammalian cells. *FASEB J.* 6:3051–64

132. Nathan C, Xie QW. 1994. Regulation of the biosynthesis of nitric oxide. *J. Biol. Chem.* 269:13725–28

133. Nguyen T, Brunson D, Crespi CL, Penman BW, Wishnok JS, Tannenbaum SR. 1992. DNA damage and mutation in human cells exposed to nitric oxide in vitro. *Proc. Natl. Acad. Sci. USA* 89: 3030–34

134. Niu X-F, Smith CW, Kubes P. 1994. Intracellular oxidative stress induced by nitric oxide synthesis inhibition increases endothelial cell adhesion to neutrophils. *Circ. Res.* 74:1133–40

135. Nowicki JP, Duval D, Poignet H, Scatton B. 1991. Nitric oxide mediates neuronal death after focal cerebral ischemia. *Eur. J. Pharmacol.* 204:339–40

136. Nussler AK, Billiar TR, Liu ZZ, Morris SM Jr. 1994. Coinduction of nitric oxide synthase and argininosuccinate synthetase in a murine macrophage cell line. Implications for regulation of nitric oxide production. *J. Biol. Chem.* 269: 1257–61

137. Oae S, Shinhama K. 1983. Organic thionitrites and related substances. A review. *Org. Prep. Proced. Int.* 15:165–98

138. Ochoa JB, Curti B, Peitzman AB, Simmons RL, Billiar TR, et al. 1992. Increased circulating nitrogen oxides after human tumor immunotherapy correlate with toxic hemodynamic changes. *J. Natl. Cancer Inst.* 84:864–67

139. Omar HA, Cherry PD, Mortelliti MP, Burke-Wolin T, Wolin MS. 1991. Inhibition of coronary artery superoxide dismutase attenuates endothelium-dependent and independent nitrovasodilator relaxation. *Circ. Res.* 69:601–8

140. Park J-W, Billman GE, Means GE. 1993. Transnitrosylation as a predominant mechanism in the hypotensive effect of S-nitrosoglutathione. *Biochem. Mol. Biol. Int.* 30:885–91

141. Patel VC, Yellon DM, Singh KJ, Neild GH, Woolfson RG. 1993. Inhibition of nitric oxide limits infarct size in the in situ rabbit heart. *Biochem. Biophys. Res. Commun.* 194:234–38

142. Pendino KJ, Laskin JD, Shuler RL, Punjabi CJ, Laskin DL. 1993. Enhanced production of nitric oxide by rat alveolar macrophages after inhalation of a pulmonary irritant is associated with increased expression of nitric oxide synthase. *J. Immunol.* 151:7196–205

143. Persson MG, Agvald P, Gustafsson LE. 1994. Detection of nitric oxide in exhaled air during administration of nitroglycerin in vivo. *Br. J. Pharmacol.* 111: 825–28

144. Peunova N, Enikolopov G. 1993. Amplification of calcium-induced gene transcription by nitric oxide in neuronal cells. *Nature* 364:450–53

145. Prado R, Watson BD, Wester P. 1993. Effects of nitric oxide synthase inhibition on cerebral blood flow following bilateral carotid artery occlusion and recirculation in the rat. *J. Cereb. Blood Flow Metab.* 13:720–23

146. Prout W. 1818. Further observations on the proximate principles of the urine. *Med.-Chir. Trans.* 9:472–84

147. Pou S, Pou WS, Bredt DS, Snyder SH, Rosen GM. 1992. Generation of super-

oxide by purified brain nitric oxide synthase. *J. Biol. Chem.* 267:24137–41

148. Pryor WA, Church DF, Govindan CK, Crank G. 1982. Oxidation of thiols by nitric oxide and nitrogen dioxide: synthetic utility and toxicological implications. *J. Org. Chem.* 47:156–59

149. Radi R, Beckman JS, Bush KM, Freeman BA. 1991. Peroxynitrite oxidation of sulfhydryls. The cytotoxic potential for superoxide and nitric oxide. *J. Biol. Chem.* 266:4244–50

150. Radi R, Beckman JS, Bush KM, Freeman BA. 1991. Peroxynitrite-induced membrane lipid peroxidation: the cytotoxic potential of superoxide and nitric oxide. *Arch. Biochem. Biophys.* 288:481–87

151. Radi R, Rodriguez M, Castro L, Telleri R. 1994. Inhibition of mitochondrial electron transport by peroxynitrite. *Arch. Biochem. Biophys.* 308:89–95

152. Reif DW. 1993. Ferritin as a source of iron for oxidative damage. *Free Radic. Med. Biol.* 12:417–27

153. Reif DW, Simmons RD. 1990. Nitric oxide mediates iron release from ferritin. *Arch. Biochem. Biophys.* 283:537–41

154. Robertson BE, Schubert R, Hescheler J, Nelson MT. 1993. cGMP-dependent protein kinase activates Ca-activated K channels in cerebral artery smooth muscle cells. *Am. J. Physiol.* 265:C299–C303

155. Rosenblum WI, Nelson GH, Povlishock JT. 1987. Laser-induced endothelial damage inhibits endothelium-dependent relaxation in the cerebral microcirculation of the mouse. *Circ. Res.* 60:169–76

156. Rosencranz-Weiss P, Sessa WC, Milstein S, Kaufman S, Watson CA, Pober J. 1994. Regulation of nitric oxide synthesis by proinflammatory cytokines in human umbilical vein endothelial cells. *J. Clin. Invest.* 93:2235–43

157. Salter M, Knowles RG, Moncada S. 1991. Widespread tissue distribution, species distribution and changes in activity of Ca^{2+}-dependent and Ca^{2+}-independent nitric oxide synthases. *FEBS Lett.* 291:145–49

158. Salvemini D, Misko TP, Masferrer JL, Seibert K, Currie MG, Needleman P. 1993. Nitric oxide activates cyclooxygenase enzymes. *Proc. Natl. Acad. Sci. USA* 90:7240–44

159. Saran M, Michel C, Bors W. 1990. Reaction of NO with O_2^-. Implications for the action of endothelium-derived relaxing factor (EDRF). *Free Radic. Res. Commun.* 10:221–26

160. Deleted in proof

161. Schmidt HH, Gagne GD, Nakane M, Pollock JS, Miler MF, Murad F. 1992. Mapping of neural nitric oxide synthase in the rat suggests frequent co-localization with NADPH diaphorase but not with soluble guanylyl cyclase, and novel paraneural functions for nitrinergic signal transduction. *J. Histochem. Cytochem.* 40:1439–56

162. Schmidt HH, Warner TD, Ishii K, Scheng H, Murad F. 1992. Insulin secretion from β-pancreatic cells caused by L-arginine-derived nitrogen oxides. *Science* 258:1376–78

163. Schreck R, Albermann K, Baeuerle PA. 1992. Nuclear factor kappa B: an oxidative stress-responsive transcription factor of eukaryotic cells. *Free Radic. Res. Commun.* 17:221–37

164. Seekamp A, Mulligan MS, Till GO, Ward PA. 1993. Requirements for neutrophil products and L-arginine in ischemia-reperfusion injury. *Am. J. Pathol.* 142:1217–26

165. Shen W, Xu X-B, Ochoa M, Zhao G, Wolin MS, Hintze TH. 1994. Nitric oxide in the regulation of oxygen consumption in the conscious dog. *Circ. Res.* 75:1086–95

166. Shongwe MS, Smith CA, Ainscough EW, Baker HM, Brodie AM, Baker EN. 1992. Anion binding by human lactoferrin: results from crystallographic and physicochemical studies. *Biochemistry* 31:4451–58

167. Stadler J, Billiar TR, Curran RD, Stuehr DJ, Ochoa JB, Simmons RL. 1991. Effect of endogenous and exogenous nitric oxide on mitochondrial respiration of rat hepatocytes. *Am. J. Physiol.* 260:C910–16

168. Stadler J, Trockfeld J, Schmalix WA, Brill T, Stewert JR, et al. 1994. Inhibition of cytochromes P4501A by nitric oxide. *Proc. Natl. Acad. Sci. USA* 91:3559–63

169. Stamler JS, Singel DJ, Loscalzo J. 1992. Biochemistry of nitric oxide and its redox-active forms. *Science* 258:1898–902

170. Stone JR, Marletta MA. 1994. Soluble guanylate cyclase from bovine lung: activation with nitric oxide and carbon monoxide and spectral characterization of the ferrous and ferric states. *Biochemistry* 33:5636–40

171. Stuehr DJ, Fasehun OA, Kwon NS, Gross SS, Gonzales JA, et al. 1991. Inhibition of macrophage and endothelial cell nitric oxide synthase by diphenyleneiodonium. *FASEB J.* 5:98–103

172. Stuehr DJ, Griffith OW. 1992. Mammalian nitric oxide synthases. *Adv. Enzymol.* 65:287–346

173. Stuehr DJ, Ikeda-Saito M. 1992. Spectral characterization of brain and macrophage nitric oxide synthases. Cytochrome P-450-like hemeproteins that contain a flavin semiquinone radical. *J. Biol. Chem.* 267:20547–50

174. Stuehr DJ, Kwon NS, Nathan CF, Griffith OW, Feldman PL, Wiseman J. 1991. N$^\omega$-hydroxy-L-arginine is an intermediate in the biosynthesis of nitric oxide from L-arginine. *J. Biol. Chem.* 266:6259–63

175. Stuehr DJ, Nathan CF. 1989. Nitric oxide. A macrophage product responsible for cytostasis and respiratory inhibition in tumor cells. *J. Exp. Med.* 169:1543–55

175a. Surez-Pinzon WL, Strynadka K, Schultz R, Rabinovitch A. 1994. Mechanism of cytokine-induced destruction of rat insulinoma cells: the role of nitric oxide. *Endocrinology* 134:1006–10

176. Thiemmerman C, Vane J. 1990. Inhibition of nitric oxide synthesis reduces the hypotension induced by bacterial lipopolysaccharides in the rat in vivo. *Eur. J. Pharmacol.* 182:591–95

177. Tojo A, Gross SS, Zhang L, Tisher CC, Schmidt HHHW, et al. 1994. Immunocytochemical localization of distinct isoforms of nitric oxide synthase in the juxtaglomerular apparatus of normal rat kidney. *J. Am. Nephrol. Soc.* 4:1438–47

178. Ungureanu D, Kelly RA, Kobnitz L, Pimental D, Michel T, Smith TW. 1993. Abnormal contractile function due to nitric oxide synthesis in rat cardiac myocytes follows exposure to activated macrophage-conditioned medium. *J. Clin. Invest.* 91:2314–19

179. Vodovitz Y, Bogdan C, Paik J, Xie QW, Nathan C. 1993. Mechanisms of suppression of macrophage nitric oxide release by transforming growth factor beta. *J. Exp. Med.* 178:605–14

180. Vodovitz Y, Kwon NS, Prospichil M, Manning J, Paik J, Nathan C. 1994. Inactivation of nitric oxide synthase after prolonged incubation of mouse macrophages with IFN-gamma and bacterial lipopolysaccharide. *J. Immunol.* 152:4110–18

181. Wade R, Castro C. 1990. Redox activity of iron(III) porphyrins and heme proteins with nitric oxide. Nitrosyl transfer to carbon, oxygen, nitrogen, and sulfur. *Chem. Res. Toxicol.* 3:89–291

182. Wang QZ, Jacobs J, DeLeo J, Kruszyna R, Smith R, Wilcox D. 1991. Nitric oxide hemoglobin in mice and rats in endotoxic shock. *Life Sci.* 49:P155–60

183. Warren JB. 1994. Nitric oxide and human skin blood flow responses to acetylcholine and ultraviolet light. *FASEB J.* 8:9247–251

184. Weiss G, Goosen B, Doppler W, Fuchs D, Pantopoulos K, et al. 1993. Transitional regulation via iron-responsive elements by the nitric oxide/NO-synthase pathway. *EMBO J.* 12:3651–57

185. Wennmalm A, Benthin G, Edlund A, Jungersten L, Kieler-Jensen N, et al. 1993. Metabolism and excretion of nitric oxide in humans. An experimental and clinical study. *Circ. Res.* 73:1121–27

186. Wennmalm A, Benthin G, Petersson A-S. 1992. Dependence of the metabolism of nitric oxide (NO) in healthy human whole blood on the oxygenation of its red cell hemoglobin. *Br. J. Pharmacol.* 106:507–8

187. Werner-Felmayer G, Werner ER, Fuchs D, Hausen A, Reibnegger G, Wachter H. 1990. Tetrahydrobiopterin-dependent formation of nitrite and nitrate in murine fibroblasts. *J. Exp. Med.* 172:1599–607

188. Weyrich AS, Ma X-L, Leffer AM. 1992. The role of L-arginine in ameliorating reperfusion injury after myocardial ischemia in the cat. *Circulation* 86:279–88

189. Wilcox CS, Welch WJ, Murad F, Gross SS, Taylor G, et al. 1992. Nitric oxide synthase in macula densa regulates glomerular capillary pressure. *Proc. Natl. Acad. Sci. USA* 89:11993–97

190. Wink DA, Kasprzak KS, Maragos CM, Elespuru RK, Misra M, et al. 1991. DNA deaminating ability and genotoxicity of nitric oxide and its progenitors. *Science* 254:1001–3

191. Wolin MS, Cherry PD, Rodenburg JM, Messina EJ, Kaley G. 1990. Methylene blue inhibits vasodilation of skeletal muscle arterioles to acetylcholine and nitric oxide via the extracellular generation of superoxide anion. *J. Pharmacol. Exp. Ther.* 254:872–76

192. Wolin MS, Wood KS, Ignarro LJ. 1982. Guanylate cyclase from bovine lung: a kinetic analysis of the regulation of the purified soluble enzyme by protoporphyrin IX, heme and nitrosyl-heme. *J. Biol. Chem.* 257:13312–20

193. Woolum JC, Commoner B. 1970. Isolation and identification of a paramagnetic complex from livers of carcinogen-treated rats. *Biochim. Biophys. Acta* 201:131–40

194. Wu M, Pritchard KA, Kaminski PM, Fayngersh RP, Hintze TH, Wolin MS. 1994. Involvement of nitric oxide and nitrosothiols in relaxation of pulmonary arteries to peroxynitrite. *Am. J. Physiol.* 266:H2108–13

195. Xie QW, Kashiwabara Y, Nathan C. 1994. Role of transcription factor NF-

kappa B/Rel in induction of nitric oxide synthase. *J. Biol. Chem.* 269:4705–8

196. Xie QW, Whisant R, Nathan C. 1993. Promoter of the mouse gene encoding calcium-independent nitric oxide synthase confers inducibility by interferon-gamma and bacterial lipopolysaccharide. *J. Exp. Med.* 177:1779–84

197. Yu AE, Hu S, Spiro TG, Burstyn JN. 1994. Raman resonance spectroscopy of soluble guanyl cyclase reveals displacement of distal and proximal heme ligands by NO. *J. Am. Chem. Soc.* 116: 4117–18

198. Zhang J, Dawson VL, Dawson TM, Snyder SH. 1994. Nitric oxide activation of poly(ADP-ribose) synthase in neurotoxicity. *Science* 263:687–89

199. Zhang ZG, Chopp M, Zaloga C, Pollock JS, Förstermann U. 1993. Cerebral endothelial nitric oxide synthase expression after focal cerebral ischemia in rats. *Stroke* 24:2016–22

200. Zweier JL, Flaherty JT, Weisfeldt ML. 1987. Direct measurement of free radical generation following reperfusion of ischemic myocardium. *Proc. Natl. Acad. Sci. USA* 84:1401–7

Annu. Rev. Physiol. 1995. 57:771–90

NITRIC OXIDE IN THE REGULATION OF BLOOD FLOW AND ARTERIAL PRESSURE

Jason G. Umans

Department of Medicine and Committee on Clinical Pharmacology, University of Chicago, Chicago, Illinois 60637

Roberto Levi

Department of Pharmacology, Cornell University Medical College, New York, NY 10021

KEY WORDS: arginine, hypertension, vascular pharmacology, arteries, blood pressure

INTRODUCTION

Nitric oxide (NO), the active moiety of the endothelium-derived relaxing factor (EDRF) that was discovered by Furchgott & Zawadzki (30), serves as an important intercellular mediator in the vasculature, kidney, endocrine system, and central nervous system. Accordingly, NO contributes to the complex regulation of local and systemic vascular resistance, distribution of blood flow and oxygen delivery, sodium balance, and arterial pressure. Excessive NO synthesis may result in systemic hypotension, as in septic shock; conversely, impaired NO synthesis may lead to pathologic vasoconstriction, to tissue ischemia with organ dysfunction, and to the genesis or perpetuation of hypertension. Although appreciation of the role of NO in integrative cardiovascular physiology is quite recent, a rapidly expanding literature describes its effects in humans and animals. This review focuses on the systemic vascular pharmacology of NO, rather than on its important roles in the pulmonary and uteroplacental circulations, citing selected investigations that bear on its role in several aspects of hemodynamic regulation.

0066–4278/95/0315–0771$05.00

VASCULAR PHARMACOLOGY OF NITRIC OXIDE

The vascular pharmacology of endogenously synthesized NO is largely predicted by the known effects of nitrovasodilator drugs. These exogenous agents act as NO donors, activating the cytosolic form of vascular smooth muscle guanylyl cyclase, thus leading to accumulation of cyclic GMP (cGMP). cGMP, acting via specific protein kinases, relaxes preconstricted vascular preparations, with or without endothelium, and diminishes tissue sensitivity to a variety of vasoconstrictor agonists. Indeed, while some effects of NO in cells may not depend on cGMP (10, 35, 114), vascular relaxation by nitrovasodilators depends directly on the quantity of NO liberated and is proportional and temporally related to cGMP accumulation (28, 43). cGMP-mediated relaxation in the vascular myocyte likely occurs via impairment of vasoconstrictor-induced calcium mobilization (or by enhanced calcium resequestration) as well as by diminished calcium sensitivity of the contractile apparatus (88, 118).

ENDOTHELIAL NITRIC OXIDE SYNTHESIS AND NO SYNTHASE INHIBITORS

Of the three NO synthases (NOSs) now well-characterized in terms of their genetic sequence and localization, cellular distribution, and physiological regulation, the endothelial subtype (eNOS) normally accounts for basal (76) and stimulated NO synthesis in endothelial cells throughout the vasculature. It is a complex, multicomponent oxidase that forms NO from one of the two equivalent terminal guanidino nitrogens of its substrate, arginine, in a five-electron oxidation using molecular oxygen, along with NADPH as cosubstrate, and FAD, FMN, heme, calmodulin, and tetrahydrobiopterin as cofactors. This endothelial enzyme binds calmodulin in a calcium-dependent manner, thus accounting for the low basal rate of NO synthesis that is observed at resting concentrations of cytosolic free calcium in endothelial cells, and accounting for the maximal NO synthesis observed at the concentrations of cytosolic free calcium that are achieved following stimulation by vasodilator agonists (69). Although some controversy remains over the manner in which endothelial cells transduce the shear stress that results from intraluminal flow into an increase in cytosolic free calcium (26, 27, 39), it is likely that shear stress serves as the major physiologic stimulus for vascular NO synthesis in vivo (15).

Many studies reveal that basal NO synthesis serves to buffer the action of endogenous or exogenous vasoconstrictors. These studies demonstrate that the potency and efficacy of vasoconstrictor agonists are augmented by endothelial denudation of isolated vascular rings, isolated beds, or vessels studied in situ, as well as by pharmacological maneuvers that interfere with the generation, transit, or effect of endothelium-derived NO. Accordingly, assessing the magnitude of the enhanced vasoconstriction following NO inhibition serves as the basis for the design of most experiments, either in vivo or in vitro, to determine contributions of basal NO release. The pharmacologic probes most often reported in such studies may be classified as: (a) agents such as the guanidino-substituted analogues of L-arginine, which compete with arginine as substrate for the enzyme; (b) compounds such as diphenyleneiodonium (DPI), which interfere with the enzyme or its obligate cofactors (110); (c) substances such as hemoglobin and pyocyanin (78), which scavenge NO during its brief extracellular transit; or (d) agents such as methylene blue, which generate superoxide anion (78, 83) to not only inactivate NO, but also to irreversibly oxidize smooth muscle guanylyl cyclase to interfere with NO's ultimate vasodilator effect. In contrast, the effects of basal or stimulated NO synthesis may be enhanced by those compounds that stabilize NO by depleting superoxide anion or that stabilize cGMP by inhibiting its phosphodiesterases, or in some cases, by supplemental L-arginine, which increases availability of substrate for NO synthesis.

The best-studied of the NO synthesis inhibitors are the guanidino-substituted analogues of L-arginine, including N^{ω}-methyl-arginine (NMA), N^{ω}-nitro-arginine (and its more soluble precursor N^{ω}-nitro-arginine methyl ester (L-NAME), and others. These analogues (but not their D-isomers) all compete with arginine as substrate for NOS, thus appearing more efficacious in the setting of limited arginine availability. Although all these inhibitors are initially reversible on addition of excess substrate and follow competitive kinetics, prolonged treatment with NMA irreversibly alkylates NOSs, and the NOS inhibition due to sustained nitro-arginine exposure is only poorly reversed by subsequent addition of arginine (89). More recently, Vallance and co-workers (121) discovered that asymmetric dimethylarginine, an inhibitor of NOS with potency similar to NMA (111), is synthesized endogenously in humans and accumulates in patients with renal failure. Although a causal link of this endogenous NOS inhibitor with hypertension in these patients or with any other disorder remains to be demonstrated, the endogenous synthesis of such inhibitors suggests added complexity in the regulation of NO synthesis in vivo.

Inhibition of NO synthesis or effect does not appear to contract most vascular tissues from normotensive animals in vitro in the absence of other vasoconstrictor stimuli. The extent to which NO inhibitors augment vascular contraction varies among different vasoconstrictor agents and appears greatest at submaximal levels of vasoconstrictor tone. In support of this is a report suggesting the "compensatory release" of NO by the perfused mesentery exposed to increasing vasoconstrictor tone, as evidenced by increased production of nitrite, a stable NO degradation product, together with augmented vasoconstriction following NOS inhibition (42). This notion of compensatory NO release, due likely to increased shear stress in constricted vessels under constant flow conditions, provides an appealing mechanism of vascular adaptation to increments in blood pressure.

Nitric Oxide in the Microvasculature

The hemodynamic effects of systemic NOS inhibition (see below), taken together with the vascular pharmacology of NO as deduced from studies of conduit-size arteries, suggests a similar role for endothelium-derived NO in the microcirculation. Indeed, a wealth of data now confirm that basal and stimulated release of NO from microvascular endothelium serves as an important regulator of small artery and arteriolar tone in skeletal, splanchnic, renal, cerebral, and coronary circulations (50, 53, 58, 60, 119, 123). Because locally regulated microvascular dilation permits the efficient distribution of blood flow within tissues so as to better match oxygen and substrate delivery with metabolic demand, endothelial NO may contribute to this aspect of microvascular control. Indeed, inhibition of NO synthesis impairs parenchymal oxygenation in the deep renal medulla, a tissue that functions at the brink of hypoxia due to countercurrent exchange (12). Local NO inhibition also decreases perfusion, oxygen utilization, and muscle pO_2 in the rabbit hindlimb (96). Such results suggest that the physiologic supply-independence of tissue oxygen utilization, which is disrupted in experimental endotoxemia (87), might depend on endothelial NO synthesis; however, studies in the dog fail to support such a contribution (107). Finally, recent experiments using isolated small arteries from the rat mesentery and other tissues reveal acetylcholine-stimulated, endothelium-dependent relaxation, which is mediated, in large part, by endogenous hyperpolarizing vasodilators rather than by NO (50, 119). Collectively, these investigations, using microvascular or whole-animal preparations, underscore the complexity and regional heterogeneity of NO's role in various aspects of microvascular control.

NITRIC OXIDE AS A MEDIATOR OF HYPOXIC CORONARY VASODILATION

In isolated guinea pig hearts, hypoxic coronary vasodilation (HCVD) is associated with an early and rapid increase in cGMP spillover and a secondary increase in adenosine overflow into the coronary effluent (92). NOS inhibition with NMA antagonizes the early phase of HCVD as well as the associated increase in cGMP spillover, whereas adenosine-receptor blockade antagonizes only the later phase of HCVD. It is plausible that endothelial cells sense local oxygen tension and that this signal is then transduced into a rise in intracellular Ca^{2+}, NOS activation, and NO-mediated vasodilation. Adenosine, released from endothelial cells and cardiac myocytes as a hypoxic metabolite, is likely to sustain the vasodilation initiated by NO (92), by a mechanism possibly dependent on adrenergic receptor activation (29). PGE_2 and prostacyclin may also contribute to this second phase of HCVD (92). Because inhibition of NOS, adenosine, and cyclooxygenase fails to completely block HCVD (13, 92), further mechanisms have been proposed, including an increase in the open probability of ATP-sensitive K^+ channels in coronary smooth muscle (122). However, such a mechanism is not supported by results using the rabbit heart (56). Furthermore, NO itself appears to activate K_{ATP} channels in porcine coronary artery smooth muscle cells, producing hyperpolarization and relaxation (81), and a major portion of K_{ATP}-channel activation may actually result from the action of adenosine A_1 receptors (86). Thus mechanisms previously regarded as NO-independent may not be so.

Although NO acts as a primary mediator of HCVD, its role in reactive hyperemia is still at issue. Whether NO contributes to reactive hyperemia after brief ischemic periods (62) or simply sustains the vasodilation initiated by other agents (38) is presently unclear.

HYPOTENSIVE EFFECTS OF NITRIC OXIDE IN VIVO

Consistent with predictions based on their actions in vitro, the nitrovasodilators exert direct hypotensive effects in vivo, owing principally to decreases in systemic vascular resistance that are associated with increases in circulating levels of cGMP. In this respect, phosphodiesterase inhibitors potentiate this hypotensive effect, presumably by inhibiting intracellular cGMP hydrolysis (77, 94). Similarly, the vasodilating and hypotensive effects of muscarinic cholinergic agonists are associated with dose-dependent increases in circulating cGMP (49), which are in large part NO mediated.

The above observation, as well as the hypotensive effects of other agents shown to be endothelium-dependent vasodilators in vitro, suggests that not only basal but also pharmacologically stimulated endothelial NO synthesis may lower arterial blood pressure. Regional variations in the response to NO-mediated vasodilators can be attributed to differences in the distribution of endothelial cell surface receptors among various vascular beds (116). Finally, inhibition of NO synthesis interferes with the hypotensive effect of acetylcholine (ACh), principally by shortening the duration of ACh-induced hypotension, with little effect on the maximal fall in blood pressure (1). Because dietary or enzymatic arginine depletion may augment the apparent efficacy of the guanidino-substituted arginine analogues, there appears to be some role for circulating arginine in maintaining the acute hypotensive effect of EDRF-releasing vasodilators.

HYPERTENSIVE EFFECTS OF ACUTE AND CHRONIC INHIBITION OF NITRIC OXIDE SYNTHESIS

The discovery that NOS inhibitors augment vasoconstrictor activity in vitro led researchers to hypothesize that such inhibition might lead to hypertension in vivo. Indeed, acute administration of NOS inhibitors to anesthetized or awake animals results in significant, dose-dependent, and long-lasting pressor effects in all mammals studied (2, 98, 120). Likewise, lower, subpressor doses of NOS inhibitors potentiate the pressor responses to exogenously infused vasoconstrictors in conscious rats (21). The direct pressor effects of NOS inhibition were selectively blunted or reversed by excess L-arginine and were associated with a reflex bradycardia. Many workers found it surprising that inhibition of a single, widely distributed, but locally acting vasodilator system, with effects in both the arterial and venous (40) circulations, could result in profound elevations of arterial pressure and were puzzled as to why the pressure increments were not rapidly corrected by homeostatic mechanisms. Thus while the acute hypertensive effect of NO inhibition surely depended upon a vascular effect involving withdrawal of a generalized basal vasodilator mechanism, additional actions at sites other than the resistance vasculature were postulated.

The acute hypertensive effect of NOS inhibition led to investigation of cardiovascular adaptations to chronic inhibition of the enzyme, resulting in the development of a new, mechanistically based animal model of persistent hypertension leading to end-organ dysfunction. Oral administration of L-NAME to Munich-Wistar rats for 4–6 weeks produced progressive severe hypertension, renal vasoconstriction, and impaired renal function. After 1 week of inhibition, the hypertension could be partially reversed by large doses of supplemental L-arginine. Significantly, following 2 months of enzyme inhibition, a 2-week drug-free period only partially reversed the hypertension, which suggests persistent changes in vascular structure, vascular reactivity, or renal function. Although plasma renin activity was elevated at the end of the study, the hypertension was only partly attenuated by the angiotensin II (AII) receptor antagonist losartan, and renal histology was notable both for segmental glomerular sclerosis and for microvascular changes consistent with malignant hypertension (99). Renal micropuncture studies using a similar model of oral L-NAME-induced chronic hypertension revealed increased glomerular pressure, decreased glomerular capillary ultrafiltration coefficient, and single nephron glomerular filtration rate (GFR), likewise associated with glomerular sclerosis and proteinuria (7). Other investigators have confirmed the persistence of hypertension with chronic administration of NOS inhibitors to rats, although some suggest a greater role for endogenous AII in the genesis of hypertension (59, 97) and others suggest more prompt and complete reversal of the hypertension with either L-arginine administration (51) or discontinuation of the inhibitor (34). Manning and co-workers administered L-NAME continuously to dogs, which resulted in hypertension that persisted over 11 days (74). Initially, L-NAME infusion augmented the pressor response to phenylephrine, an effect that did not persist; retention of salt and water was only transient. While some details may differ among these studies—especially those relating to the occurrence of renal microvascular lesions, alterations in pressor responsiveness or in salt and water balance, and reversibility of the hypertension with drugs, withdrawal of inhibitors, or with excess L-arginine— it remains striking that genetically normal animals may be rendered chronically, and even malignantly, hypertensive without surgical or dietary interventions by a mechanistically well-defined intervention. Further study of these models and their interactions with other forms of experimental hypertension may provide important insights into hypertensive disorders in humans.

CENTRAL NERVOUS SYSTEM CONTRIBUTIONS TO THE PRESSOR EFFECT OF NO SYNTHASE INHIBITION

The identification of NO as a messenger within the central nervous system, the stimulation of NO synthesis by activation of N-methyl-D-aspartate (NMDA) receptors (36), and the known role of neural influences in the long-term control of arterial pressure and autonomic outflow suggest that central alterations in NO effect contribute to the integrated responses that follow systemic NOS inhibition. Activation of baroreflex mechanisms by cardiopulmonary afferent projections to the nucleus tractus solitarius (NTS) in rats depends upon activation of soluble guanylyl cyclase, suggesting that NO may act as a transmitter in NTS (65). Further, unilateral injection of a NO donor into this nucleus leads to systemic hypotension and bradycardia (72). Conversely, microinjection of NMA into NTS of rabbits increased arterial pressure, sympathetic outflow, and, in sinoaortic deafferented and vagotomized animals, led to tachycardia as well (45). Exogenous NO also altered blood pressure and autonomic tone when administered to the ventrolateral medulla of cats (108): Increased NO in the rostral ventrolateral medulla decreased blood pressure and renal sympathetic outflow, whereas increased NO in the caudal ventrolateral medulla blocked these effects. These actions were apparently mediated by guanylyl cyclase, and opposing effects were obtained following local injection of NMA. Collectively, these results suggest that NO serves as an important central mediator of baroreflex function, especially when stimulated by cardiopulmonary afferents.

Sakuma and colleagues noted that systemic administration of NMA to anesthetized rats following sinoaortic deafferentation increased renal sympathetic nerve activity in spite of markedly increased blood pressure (101), a finding yet to be reproduced in humans (44). To further dissect central contributions to these autonomic and blood pressure effects, these workers performed high-cervical cord transections, which blunted the pressor effect of NMA and blocked the increase in renal nerve activity. Further, low doses of intracisternal NMA markedly augmented renal nerve activity and increased arterial pressure, albeit minimally; both actions could be blocked by cervical transection or by arginine administration (117). Collectively, these results underscore important contributions of central nervous system NO, as well as vascular NO, to the control of blood pressure and modulation of sympathetic tone.

NITRIC OXIDE IN THE RENAL MICROCIRCULATION AND IN THE REGULATION OF RENIN RELEASE

The ability of chronic inhibition of NO synthesis to produce sustained hypertension associated with structural renal lesions suggests altered renal responses to increased perfusion pressure and to volume excess; such changes may involve the glomerular microcirculation, blood flow to the renal medulla, or regulation of renin secretion. Although it is not surprising that eNOS is expressed in renal vasculature, recent studies have also identified the neuronal isoform of the enzyme within the kidney, including the macula densa (84, 125); moreover, renal tubular cells exhibit constitutive NOS activity as well as an inducible, calcium-insensitive NOS following cytokine exposure (54, 75).

Following acute inhibition of NO synthesis with NMA, micropuncture studies demonstrated graduated effects on glomerular hemodynamics as a function of dose (23). A low intrarenal dose of NMA resulted in a small increment in afferent arteriolar resistance with only a minor fall in single nephron GFR and no change in efferent resistance, glomerular capillary hydraulic pressure, or ultrafiltration coefficient (K_f). Increasing the dose produced similar effects on pressure and resistance, but also decreased K_f, whereas systemic administration of pressor doses of NMA led to glomerular hypertension and efferent arteriolar vasoconstriction. The effect on K_f is consistent with work demonstrating mesangial cell responses to exogenous NO (105). There is also evidence for a selective effect of NO in the afferent arteriole; microperfusion studies (55) demonstrated selective afferent arteriolar NO synthesis during AII-induced vasoconstriction, thus accounting for the well-known increased sensitivity of the efferent arteriole to this vasoconstrictor.

Renin secretion, the rate-limiting step in systemic AII production, is principally controlled by three mechanisms: tubular salt delivery to the macula densa, renal sympathetic nerve activity, and a local baroreceptor mechanism sensitive to afferent arteriolar stretch. It now appears that NO plays an important role, in concert with a number of other paracrine factors, in mediating cell-cell communication within the juxtaglomerular apparatus (JGA) and in transducing the tubular signal to the granular (secretory) cell. NO is synthesized in the macula densa as well as in JGA arteriolar endothelial cells and may act on either granular cells or the extraglomerular mesangial cells, which are physically interposed between the macula densa and the granular cells. Whole-animal experiments suggest tonic inhibition of renin secretion by endogenous NO, with stimulation of renin release by NOS inhibitors (109). Likewise, in vitro studies using cultured juxtaglomerular cells or renal cortical slices (8, 41) demonstrate augmented basal renin release following NMA and inhibition of pharmacologically stimulated renin release by either nitrovasodilators or supplemental L-arginine. By contrast, L-NAME inhibited renin release in the isolated perfused kidney (33). Recent studies in the isolated perfused JGA and in primary cultures of mouse juxtaglomerular cells demonstrate distinct, opposing effects of NO on renin secretion, depending on different cellular mechanisms (104) and on which juxtaglomerular cells are most directly exposed to exogenous L-arginine or NOS inhibitors (46). In summary, although there is evidence that NO participates in the regulation of renal renin secretion, its role in vivo remains unclear.

RENAL CONTRIBUTIONS TO THE PRESSOR EFFECT OF NO SYNTHASE INHIBITION

The natriuresis that follows acute increases in renal perfusion pressure is accompanied by augmented renal synthesis of NO as revealed by increases in urinary excretion of nitrate and nitrite (112). Further, inhibition of this pressure natriuresis by local, intrarenal infusion of NOS inhibitors (73, 103) implies a key role for intrarenal NO synthesis in mediating this effect. Indeed, a profound antidiuretic and antinatriuretic effect of renal NOS inhibition is revealed by prolonged NOS inhibition, use of subpressor doses of inhibitors, or maneuvers that clamp renal perfusion pressure during the systemic hypertensive response to NOS inhibition (57, 63). Likewise, renal NO synthesis is augmented by volume expansion that results from dietary salt-loading (106), and renal NOS inhibition blocks the homeostatic natriuresis that follows extracellular volume expansion either acutely (3) or after chronic ingestion of a high-salt diet. Also, rats placed on a high-salt diet for 2 weeks increase their urinary excretion of the NO degradation products nitrate and nitrite in proportion to their excretion of sodium (106). Furthermore, increasing dietary sodium intake potentiates the systemic pressor effect of L-NAME in dogs, along with a further increase in positive salt balance due to NOS inhibition (102). Collectively, such data suggest reciprocal interactions between dietary sodium, volume expansion, blood pressure, and renal NO synthesis, which may bear importantly on the pathogenesis of salt-sensitive forms of hypertension.

Dilation of medullary vessels by endogenous NO so as to facilitate transmission of increased perfusion pressure to the renal interstitium may underlie the diminished tubular salt and water resorption that is the hallmark of pressure natriuresis. Indeed, doses of L-NAME that impair sodium excretion also decrease renal interstitial hydrostatic pressure (85), and nitro-arginine is likewise antinatriuretic when infused directly into the renal medullary interstitium (79). Furthermore, pressure natriuresis is known to be impaired in experimental hypertension, and two recent studies implicate altered NO synthesis in this defect (52, 93). Exogenous L-arginine restores blunted pressure-natriuresis in hypertensive Dahl salt–sensitive rats ingesting a high-salt diet (93). Moreover, L-arginine was found to normalize the blunted pressure-natriuresis that is observed in renally denervated and hormonally clamped spontaneously hypertensive rats (SHRs) (52). By contrast, L-arginine was without effect in the Wistar-Kyoto rat; pressure natriuresis was blunted by NMA in this normotensive control, but not in the SHR. This suggests that pressure natriuresis normally depends on NO synthesis, which is not limited by substrate availability. In the hypertensive SHR, however, limited NO synthesis, due in part to limited substrate availability, results in the observed defect in sodium excretion. In summary, defects in renal NO synthesis contribute to impaired salt excretion and thus to the maintenance of hypertension in two genetic animal models of this disorder.

PATHOPHYSIOLOGIC ENDOTHELIAL DYSFUNCTION

Many have reasoned that endothelial dysfunction may act in a manner similar to NOS inhibition to augment pressor responses and cause hypertension by impairing the vasodilator effector limb of an important homeostatic pathway. Also, high pressures, per se, might impair endothelial NO synthesis, contributing to the perpetuation of established hypertension, whatever its initial cause. To this end, many studies have assessed the effect of hypertension—and its subsequent pharmacological control—on endothelium-dependent relaxation induced by vasodilator agonists in vivo, in situ, or in vitro. Observations in a number of models of hypertensive rats—including the New Zealand and Dahl strains and animals made hypertensive by the 1-kidney–1-clip method, by aortic coarctation, or by administration of DOCA with high salt—all demonstrate marked impairment of endothelium-dependent aortic relaxation, some decreased sensitivity to nitrovasodilators, and restoration of relaxation following normalization of blood pressure (68, 71, 126). Similarly, the vasodilator response to ACh injected into the brachial artery was blunted in hypertensive humans (91). Although the effect of ACh was largely NO-independent in this preparation, abnormalities of local NO synthesis were also observed (16).

Diederich and colleagues (24) noted impairment of ACh-induced endothelium-dependent relaxation of norepinephrine-preconstricted, isolated, mesenteric resistance arteries from stroke-prone SHRs, despite well-preserved responses to nitrovasodilators, due apparently to the opposing action of an endothelium-derived prostanoid vasoconstrictor. Interestingly, similar contributions of such prostanoid vasoconstrictors have been deduced from clinical experiments (113). Subsequently, Li & Bukoski (66) noted that synthesis of this interfering vasoconstrictor in rat vessels could only be demonstrated when norepinephrine was used as the preconstrictor agent for these in vitro protocols. Not only was ACh-induced relaxation impaired in some SHR microvascular preparations, but L-NAME's ability to augment norepinephrine-induced vasoconstriction was diminished as well, thus suggesting an additional defect in basal NO synthesis (67). By contrast, Angus and colleagues (5) failed to observe any decrease in ACh-induced relaxation in small mesenteric arteries from SHRs, or to identify a similar defect in subcutaneous resistance vessels from humans with essential hypertension. Collectively, these and other studies suggest alterations in endothelial function in vessels from some hypertensive animals, with some difficulties in the mechanistic interpretation of results from complex in vitro protocols. Indeed, although many studies purport to assess "the activity of the NO system" by measuring ACh or vasodilator-stimulated endothelium-dependent relaxation, it is unclear whether such responses actually predict any changes in the basal elaboration of NO, which may be much more relevant to modulation of blood pressure in vivo.

Cyclosporin, used commonly in transplant immunosuppression, leads to both systemic hypertension and to renal vasoconstriction so severe as to decrease GFR. Because cyclosporin is toxic to endothelial cells in culture, it has been suggested that endothelial dysfunction may contribute to the vasoconstriction and hypertension that often attend its use. Indeed, chronic cyclosporin administration impaired endothelium-dependent relaxation of rat renal arteries (25). Such an impairment is manifest in vivo as inhibition of acetylcholine-induced vasodilation, natriuresis, diuresis, and cGMP excretion in rats treated with cyclosporin (32). In humans, however, the effects of cyclosporin on basal NO synthesis remain unclear; the hypotensive effect of infused L-arginine is preserved in renal allograft recipients receiving cyclosporin, whereas the arginine-induced renal vasodilation is not (37).

The physiologic vasodilation that is a hallmark of normal pregnancy is associated with augmented synthesis of NO and evidence of cGMP-mediated vasodilation (20, 82). Preeclampsia, a hypertensive disorder unique to human pregnancy, is accompanied by pathognomonic lesions of glomerular endothelial cells (31) and may be principally an endothelial cell disorder (100). NO production is impaired in umbilical vessels from preeclamptic pregnancies (95). McCarthy and co-workers (80) demonstrated impaired endothelium-dependent relaxation of subcutaneous resistance arteries from women with preeclampsia that, however, was not due to altered NO synthesis. Most recently,

Baylis & Engels (6) reported that chronic NOS inhibition in pregnant rats leads to a syndrome of hypertension, proteinuria, and poor fetal outcome reminiscent of human preeclampsia.

Local generation of NO within the epicardial coronary arteries serves to inhibit platelet adhesion and aggregation, to oppose vasospasm in response to locally released vasoconstrictors, and to inhibit smooth muscle proliferation. Defective endothelial NO synthesis may therefore aggravate the local effects of atherosclerotic lesions that might result in coronary or other arterial occlusions. Accordingly, ACh-induced relaxation is impaired even in anatomically normal coronary segments in patients with coronary atherosclerosis (70), endothelial NO synthesis is directly inhibited by oxidized low-density lipoprotein (4, 127), and NO generation is impaired in humans and animals with hyperlipidemias (11, 22). Hyperlipidemia also impairs microvascular NO synthesis, as demonstrated by impaired HCVD (see above) in the genetically hypercholesterolemic Watanabe rabbit (64). Of note, supplemental L-arginine appears to ameliorate the defective NO synthesis observed in some hyperlipidemias (22).

Finally, while basal NO synthesis may be augmented in some tissues, vasodilator-stimulated endothelial NO synthesis is impaired in diabetes mellitus (17) by mechanisms that may involve a direct effect of hyperglycemia via protein kinase C (115, 124) or via advanced glycosylation end-products (14). Collectively, the major disease processes that contribute to cardiovascular risk appear to share in the ability to impair endothelial function and the regulated synthesis of NO, which suggests that dysfunctional NO generation either serves as a marker for fundamental defects in endothelial function or, indeed, is an important pathogenetic factor in the progression of vascular disease.

COMPENSATORY NITRIC OXIDE SYNTHESIS IN HYPERTENSION

Mesenteric arterial rings, obtained from a DOCA-salt rat model of volume-dependent hypertension and studied ex vivo, exhibit normal vasoconstriction and vasodilation when compared with rings from normotensive controls (9). Yet, endothelial denudation or NO synthesis inhibition selectively unmasks enhanced vasoconstrictor responses in rings from such hypertensive animals, which suggests that basal endothelial NO synthesis is augmented. The increased NO synthesis is apparently compensatory for a while, preventing increases in vascular contractility and peripheral resistance during the development of DOCA-salt hypertension. Similarly, in vivo protocols that assess basal NO synthesis by measuring the magnitude of the acute pressor response to infused NMA suggest that NO synthesis is augmented in hypertensive uninephrectomized DOCA salt–loaded rats. By contrast, no such increase was found in rats made equally hypertensive with infused AII, in hypertensive SHRs, or in normotensive uninephrectomized controls (61). This latter study suggests a selective augmentation of NO synthesis to blunt vascular resistance in volume-dependent as compared with vasoconstrictor-induced hypertension. This important observation has been extended by studies in Dahl-Rapp salt-sensitive (SS/Jr) and salt-resistant (SR/Jr) rats fed a high-salt diet; the latter strain manifests an augmented pressor response to NMA, whereas the former strain exhibits normalization of blood pressure (or prevention of hypertension) following dietary supplementation with L-arginine, despite continued ingestion of a high-salt diet (18). No similar hypotensive effect of L-arginine supplementation was observed in the SHR. Importantly, urinary cGMP was augmented in normotensive SR/Jr rats ingesting a high-salt diet, and similar cGMP excretion rates were only observed in the SS/Jr rats when they received supplemental arginine. Such data support a role of augmented NO synthesis in the normal adaptation to volume loading and suggest that pathophysiologic substrate limitation interferes with this homeostatic augmentation of NO synthesis in this hypertensive animal model. More recently, the same workers reported that dexamethasone, administered in doses sufficient to inhibit the induction of NOS activity by endotoxin, not only augmented the development of salt-sensitive hypertension in SS/Jr rats but also blocked the protective effect of L-arginine supplementation in these animals (19). This latter finding supports a role for inducible NOS in the vascular adaptation to salt loading in the Dahl rat.

SUBSTRATE LIMITATION OF NITRIC OXIDE SYNTHESIS IN VIVO

Intravenous L-arginine has long been used as a provocative agent in endocrine assessment. However, its hemodynamic effects have only been assessed quite recently. Infusion of 30 g L-arginine to normotensive subjects lowered mean arterial pressure and total peripheral resistance, increased heart rate and cardiac output, and resulted in concomitant elevations of plasma citrulline and cGMP as well as of urinary nitrate plus nitrite (48). The latter three markers suggest that arginine infusion augments NO synthesis. The same authors (47) noted similar hypotensive and vasodilator responses following L-arginine infusion in patients with essential and secondary hypertension. These systemic hemodynamic responses following arginine infusion to hypertensive subjects stand in apparent contrast with those obtained by Panza and coworkers (90) in studies of the local forearm circulation. Although it is still unclear whether intravenous arginine may exert hemodynamic effects indirectly, rather than by providing additional substrate for NOS, these early results support substrate limitation of basal and stimulated NO synthesis in at least some human vascular beds. This suggests an important species difference because, as already noted, NO synthesis in normotensive rats does not appear to be limited by substrate availability.

CONCLUSIONS

In the short time since Furchgott first suggested the existence of an EDRF, and then with others, its identity as NO, a rapidly evolving literature has provided compelling evidence for this key mediator's role in vascular control. NO not only serves as an important locally acting vasodilator but also acts as a central factor in the short- and long-term regulation of multiple determinants of arterial pressure. NO synthesis is abnormal in a variety of animal models of hypertension and in other disorders that increase cardiac risk in humans. While impaired NO synthesis or endothelial dysfunction may, in some cases, be a result of hypertension, in others it may contribute to the initiation or perpetuation of this disorder. Finally, pharmacologic inhibition of NO synthesis provides a new experimental model of hypertension in which blood pressure is elevated by direct effects on resistance vessels, diminished venous capacitance, altered sympathetic outflow, enhanced salt-sensitivity, and defective pressure-natriuresis. By contrast, recent investigations have shown that many other physiologic roles of the endothelium once thought to depend on NO are due to other mediators or may be due to effects of NO that do not depend on guanylyl cyclase, thus suggesting caution on the part of investigators as they explore the role of this key factor in more integrated physiologic systems.

Literature Cited

1. Aisaka K, Gross SS, Griffith OW, Levi R. 1989. L-arginine availability determines the duration of acetylcholine-induced systemic vasodilation in vivo. *Biochem. Biophys. Res. Commun.* 163: 710–17
2. Aisaka K, Gross SS, Griffith OW, Levi R. 1989. N^G-methylarginine, an inhibitor of endothelium-derived nitric oxide synthesis, is a potent pressor agent in the guinea pig: does nitric oxide regulate blood pressure in vivo? *Biochem. Biophys. Res. Commun.* 160:881–86
3. Alberola A, Pinilla JM, Quesada T, Romero JC, Salom MG, Salazar FJ. 1992. Role of nitric oxide in mediating renal response to volume expansion. *Hypertension* 19:780–84
4. Andrews H, Bruckdorfer K, Dunn R, Jacobs M. 1987. Low-density lipoproteins inhibit endothelium-dependent relaxation in rabbit aorta. *Nature* 327: 237–39
5. Angus JA, Dyke AC, Jennings GL, Korner PI, Sudhir K, et al. 1992. Release of endothelium-derived relaxing factor

from resistance arteries in hypertension. *Kidney Int. Suppl.* 37:S73–78

6. Baylis C, Engels K. 1993. Adverse interactions between pregnancy and a new model of systemic hypertension produced by chronic blockade of endothelial derived relaxing factor (EDRF) in the rat. *Clin. Exp. Hypertens. B* 11:117–29

7. Baylis C, Mitruka B, Deng A. 1992. Chronic blockade of nitric oxide synthesis in the rat produces systemic hypertension and glomerular damage. *J. Clin. Invest.* 90:278–81

8. Beierwaltes WH, Carretero OA. 1992. Nonprostanoid endothelium–derived factors inhibit renin release. *Hypertension* 19:68–73

9. Bockman CS, Jeffries WB, Pettinger WA, Abel PW. 1992. Enhanced release of endothelium-derived relaxing factor in mineralocorticoid hypertension. *Hypertension* 20:304–13

10. Bolotina VM, Najibi S, Palacino JJ, Pagano PJ, Cohen RA. 1994. Nitric oxide directly activates calcium-dependent potassium channels in vascular smooth muscle. *Nature* 368:850–53

11. Bossaller C, Habib GB, Yamamoto H, Williams C, Wells S, Henry PD. 1987. Impaired muscarinic endothelium-dependent cyclic guanosine 5'-monophosphate formation in atherosclerotic human coronary artery and rabbit aorta. *J. Clin. Invest.* 79:170–74

12. Brezis M, Heyman SN, Dinour D, Epstein FH, Rosen S. 1991. Role of nitric oxide in renal medullary oxygenation. Studies in isolated and intact rat kidneys. *J. Clin. Invest.* 88:390–95

13. Brown IP, Thompson CI, Belloni FL. 1993. Role of nitric oxide in hypoxic coronary vasodilation in isolated perfused guinea pig heart. *Am. J. Physiol.* 264:H821–29

14. Bucala R, Tracey KJ, Cerami A. 1991. Advanced glycosylation products quench nitric oxide and mediate defective endothelium-dependent vasodilatation in experimental diabetes. *J. Clin. Invest.* 87:432–38

15. Buga BM, Gold ME, Fukuto JM, Ignarro LJ. 1991. Shear stress–induced release of nitric oxide from endothelial cells grown on beads. *Hypertension* 17:187–93

16. Calver A, Collier J, Moncada S, Vallance P. 1992. Effect of local intra-arterial N^G-monomethyl-L-arginine in patients with hypertension: the nitric oxide dilator mechanism appears abnormal. *J. Hypertens.* 10:1025–31

17. Calver A, Collier J, Vallance P. 1992. Inhibition and stimulation of nitric oxide synthesis in the human forearm arterial bed of patients with insulin-dependent diabetes. *J. Clin. Invest.* 90:2548–54

18. Chen PY, Sanders PW. 1991. L-arginine abrogates salt-sensitive hypertension in Dahl/Rapp rats. *J. Clin. Invest.* 88:1559–67

19. Chen PY, Sanders PW. 1993. Role of nitric oxide synthesis in salt-sensitive hypertension in Dahl/Rapp rats. *Hypertension* 22:812–18

20. Conrad KP, Joffe GM, Kruszyna H, Kruszyna R, Rochelle LG, et al. 1993. Identification of increased nitric oxide biosynthesis during pregnancy in rats. *FASEB J.* 7:566–71

21. Conrad KP, Whittemore SL. 1992. N^G-monomethyl-L-arginine and nitroarginine potentiate pressor responsiveness of vasoconstrictors in conscious rats. *Am. J. Physiol.* 262:R1137–44

22. Creager MA, Gallagher SH, Girerd XJ, Coleman SM, Dzau VJ, Cooke JP. 1992. L-arginine improves endothelium-dependent vasodilatation in hypercholesterolemic humans. *J. Clin. Invest.* 90:1248–53

23. Deng A, Baylis C. 1993. Locally produced EDRF controls preglomerular resistance and ultrafiltration coefficient. *Am. J. Physiol.* 264:F212–15

24. Diederich D, Yang ZH, Buhler FR, Luscher TF. 1990. Impaired endothelium-dependent relaxations in hypertensive resistance arteries involve cyclooxygenase pathway. *Am. J. Physiol.* 258:H445–51

25. Diederich D, Yang ZH, Luscher TF. 1992. Chronic cyclosporine therapy impairs endothelium-dependent relaxation in the renal artery of the rat. *J. Am. Soc. Nephrol.* 2:1291–97

26. Dull RO, Davies PF. 1991. Flow modulation of agonist (ATP)-response (Ca+) coupling in vascular endothelial cells. *Am. J. Physiol.* 261:H149–54

27. Falcone JC, Kup L, Meininger GA. 1993. Endothelial cell calcium increases during flow induced dilation in isolated arterioles. *Am. J. Physiol.* 264:H653–59

28. Feelisch M, Noack EA. 1987. Correlation between nitric oxide formation during degradation of organic nitrates and activation of guanylate cyclase. *Eur. J. Pharmacol.* 139:19–30

29. Feigl EO. 1993. Adenosine coronary vasodilation during hypoxia depends on adrenergic receptor activation. *Adv. Exp. Med. Biol.* 346:199–205

30. Furchgott RF, Zawadzki JV. 1980. The obligatory role of endothelial cells in

the relaxation of arterial smooth muscle by acetylcholine. *Nature* 288:373–76

31. Gaber LW, Spargo BH, Lindheimer MD. 1994. Renal pathology in preeclampsia. *Clin. Obstet. Gynaecol.* 8: 443–68

32. Gallego MJ, Farre AL, Riesco A, Monton M, Grandes SM, et al. 1993. Blockade of endothelium-dependent responses in conscious rats by cyclosporin A: effect of L-arginine. *Am. J. Physiol.* 264:H708–14

33. Gardes J, Poux JM, Gonzalez MF, Alhenc-Gelas F, Menard J. 1992. Decreased renin release and constant kallikrein secretion after injection of L-NAME in isolated perfused rat kidney. *Life Sci.* 50:987–93

34. Gardiner SM, Kemp PA, Bennett T, Palmer RM, Moncada S. 1992. Nitric oxide synthase inhibitors cause sustained, but reversible, hypertension and hindquarters vasoconstriction in Brattleboro rats. *Eur. J. Pharmacol.* 213: 449–51

35. Garg UC, Hassid A. 1990. Nitric oxide–generating vasodilators inhibit mitogenesis and proliferation of BALB/C 3T3 fibroblasts by a cyclic GMP–independent mechanism. *Biochem. Biophys. Res. Commun.* 171:474–79

36. Garthwaite J, Charles SL, Chess-Williams R. 1988. Endothelium-derived relaxing factor release on activation of NMDA receptors suggests role as intercellular messenger in the brain. *Nature* 336:385–88

37. Gaston RS, Schlessinger SD, Sanders PW, Barker CV, Curtis JJ, Warnock DG. 1993. Cyclosporin (CsA) inhibits the renal vasodilatory response to L-arginine in human renal allograft recipients. *J. Am. Soc. Nephrol.* 4:550 (Abstr.)

38. Gattullo D, Pagliaro P, Dalla Valle R. 1994. The effect of the inhibition of the endothelial release of nitric oxide on coronary reactive hyperaemia in the anaesthetized dog. *Life Sci.* 54: 791–98

39. Geiger RV, Berk BC, Alexander RW, Rerem RM. 1992. Flow-induced calcium transients in single endothelial cells: spatial and temporal analysis. *Am. J. Physiol.* 262:C1411–17

40. Glick MR, Gehman JD, Gascho JA. 1993. Endothelium-derived nitric oxide reduces baseline venous tone in awake instrumented rats. *Am. J. Physiol.* 265: H47–H51

41. Greenberg SG, He XR, Briggs JP, Schnermann JB. 1992. Nitroprusside directly inhibits renin release from isoproterenol-stimulated juxtaglomeru-

lar granular cells. *J. Am. Soc. Nephrol.* 3:544

42. Gross SS, Aisaka K, Levi R. 1992. Vasoconstrictors release nitric oxide from the isolated perfused guinea pig mesenteric vasculature in a concentration-dependent manner. *Br. J. Pharmacol.* 107:P282

43. Gruetter CA, Gruetter DY, Lyon JE, Kadowitz PJ, Ignarro LJ. 1981. Relationship between cyclic guanosine 3':5'-monophosphate formation and relaxation of coronary arterial smooth muscle by glyceryl trinitrate, nitroprusside, nitrite and nitric oxide: effects of methylene blue and methemoglobin. *J. Pharmacol. Exp. Ther.* 219:181–86

44. Hansen J, Jacobsen TN, Victor RG. 1994. Is nitric oxide involved in the tonic inhibition of central sympathetic outflow in humans? *Hypertension.* In press

45. Harada S, Tokunaga S, Momohara M, Masaki H, Tagawa T, et al. 1993. Inhibition of nitric oxide formation in the nucleus tractus solitarius increases renal sympathetic nerve activity in rabbits. *Circ. Res.* 72:511–16

46. He XR, Greenberg SG, Schnermann JB, Briggs JP. 1993. Role of nitric oxide in regulation of macula densa mediated renin secretion. *FASEB J.* 7:A221 (Abstr.)

47. Hishikawa K, Nakaki T, Suzuki H, Kato R, Saruta T. 1993. Role of L-arginine-nitric oxide pathway in hypertension. *J. Hypertens.* 11:639–45

48. Hishikawa K, Nakaki T, Tsuda M, Esumi H, Ohshima H, et al. 1992. Effect of systemic L-arginine administration on hemodynamics and nitric oxide release in man. *Jpn. Heart J.* 33:41–48

49. Honma M, Ui M. 1978. Plasma cyclic GMP: response to cholinergic agents. *Eur. J. Pharmacol.* 47:1–10

50. Hwa JJ, Ghibaudi L, Williams P, Chatterjee M. 1994. Comparison of acetylcholine-dependent relaxation in large and small arteries of rat mesenteric vascular bed. *Am. J. Physiol.* H952–58

51. Ikeda K, Gutierrez OG Jr, Yamori Y. 1992. Dietary N^G-nitro-L-arginine induces sustained hypertension in normotensive Wistar-Kyoto rats. *Clin. Exp. Pharmacol. Physiol.* 19:583–86

52. Ikenaga H, Suzuki H, Ishii N, Itoh H, Saruta T. 1993. Role of NO on pressure-natriuresis in Wistar-Kyoto and spontaneously hypertensive rats. *Kidney Int.* 43:205–11

53. Imig JD, Gebremedhin D, Harder DR, Roman RJ. 1993. Modulation of vascular tone in renal microcirculation by

erythrocytes: role of EDRF. *Am. J. Physiol.* 264:H190–95

54. Ishii K, Chang B, Kerwin JF Jr, Wagenaar FL, Huang ZJ, Murad F. 1991. Formation of endothelium-derived relaxing factor in porcine kidney epithelial LLC-PK1 cells: an intra- and intercellular messenger for activation of soluble guanylate cyclase. *J. Pharmacol. Exp. Ther.* 256:38–43

55. Ito S, Arima S, Ren YL, Juncos LA, Carretero OA. 1993. Endothelium-derived relaxing factor/nitric oxide modulates angiotensin II action in the isolated microperfused rabbit afferent but not efferent arteriole. *J. Clin. Invest.* 91:2012–19

56. Jiang C, Collins P. 1994. Inhibition of hypoxia-induced relaxation of rabbit isolated coronary arteries by N^G-monomethyl-L-arginine but not glibenclamide. *Br. J. Pharmacol.* 111:711–16

57. Johnson RA, Freeman RH. 1992. Pressure natriuresis in rats during blockade of the L-arginine/nitric oxide pathway. *Hypertension* 19:333–38

58. Jones CJ, DeFily DV, Patterson JL, Chilian WM. 1993. Endothelium-dependent relaxation competes with alpha-1- and alpha-2-adrenergic constriction in the canine epicardial coronary microcirculation. *Circulation* 87:1264–74

59. Jover B, Herizi A, Ventre F, Dupont M, Mimran A. 1993. Sodium and angiotensin in hypertension induced by long-term nitric oxide blockade. *Hypertension* 21:944–48

60. Kaley G, Koller A, Rodenburg JM, Messina EJ, Wolin MS. 1992. Regulation of arteriolar tone and responses via L-arginine pathway in skeletal muscle. *Am. J. Physiol.* 262:H987–92

61. King AJ, Mercer P, Troy JL, Brenner BM. 1991. Endothelium-derived relaxing factor and the vascular reply to systemic hypertension. *J. Am. Soc. Nephrol.* 2:1072–77

62. Kirkeboen KA, Naess PA, Offstad J, Ilebekk A. 1994. Effects of regional inhibition of nitric oxide synthesis in intact porcine hearts. *Am. J. Physiol.* 266:H1516–27

63. Lahera V, Salom MG, Miranda-Guardiola F, Moncada S, Romero JC. 1991. Effects of N^G-nitro-L-arginine methyl ester on renal function and blood pressure. *Am. J. Physiol.* 261:F1033–37

64. Levi R, Park KH, Ru X, Roberts J, Parker TS. 1993. Decreased NO production and impaired hypoxic coronary-vasodilatation in the genetic hypercholesterolemic rabbit. *FASEB J.* 7: A244

65. Lewis SJ, Machado BH, Ohta H, Talman WT. 1991. Processing of cardiopulmonary afferent input within the nucleus tractus solitarii involves activation of soluble guanylate cyclase. *Eur. J. Pharmacol.* 203:327–28

66. Li J, Bukoski RD. 1993. Endothelium-dependent relaxation of hypertensive resistance arteries is not impaired under all conditions. *Circ. Res.* 72:290–96

67. Li F, Joshua IG. 1993. Decreased arteriolar endothelium–derived relaxing factor production during the development of genetic hypertension. *Clin. Exp. Hypertens. A* 15:511–26

68. Lockette W, Otsuka Y, Carretero O. 1986. The loss of endothelium-dependent vascular relaxation in hypertension. *Hypertension* 8:II61–II66

69. Loeb AL, Izzo NJ Jr, Johnson RM, Garrison JC, Peach MJ. 1988. Endothelium-derived relaxing factor release associated with increased endothelial cell inositol trisphosphate and intracellular calcium. *Am. J. Cardiol.* 62:G36–G40

70. Ludmer PL, Selwyn AP, Shook TL, Wayne RR, Mudge GR, et al. 1986. Paradoxical acetylcholine–induced coronary artery constriction in patients with coronary artery disease. *N. Engl. J. Med.* 315:1046–51

71. Lüscher TF, Vanhoutte PM, Raij L. 1987. Antihypertensive treatment normalizes decreased endothelium-dependent relaxations in rats with salt-induced hypertension. *Hypertension* 9:III193–97

72. Machado BH, Bonagamba LG. 1992. Microinjection of S-nitrosocyteine into the nucleus tractus solitarii of conscious rats decreases arterial pressure but L-glutamate does not. *Eur. J. Pharmacol.* 221:179–82

73. Majid DS, Williams A, Navar LG. 1993. Inhibition of nitric oxide synthesis attenuates pressure-induced natriuretic responses in anesthetized dogs. *Am. J. Physiol.* 264:F79–F87

74. Manning RD Jr, Hu L, Mizelle HL, Montani J-P, Norton MW. 1993. Cardiovascular responses to long-term blockade of nitric oxide synthesis. *Hypertension* 22:40–48

75. Markewitz BA, Michael JR, Kohan DE. 1993. Cytokine-induced expression of a nitric oxide synthase in rat renal tubule cells. *J. Clin. Invest.* 91:2138–43

76. Martin W, Furchgott RF, Villani GM, Jothianandan D. 1986. Depression of contractile responses in rat aorta by spontaneously released endothelium-derived relaxing factor. *J. Pharmacol. Exp. Ther.* 237:529–38

77. Martin W, Furchgott RF, Villani GM,

Jothianandan D. 1986. Phosphodiesterase inhibitors induce endothelium-dependent relaxation of rat and rabbit aorta by potentiating the effects of spontaneously released endothelium-derived relaxing factor. *J. Pharmacol. Exp. Ther.* 237:539–47

78. Martin W, Villani GM, Jothianandan D, Furchgott RF. 1985. Selective blockade of endothelium-dependent and glyceryl trinitrate–induced relaxation by hemoglobin and by methylene blue in the rabbit aorta. *J. Pharmacol. Exp. Ther.* 232:708–16

79. Mattson DL, Roman RJ, Cowley AW Jr. 1992. Role of nitric oxide in renal papillary blood flow and sodium excretion. *Hypertension* 19:766–69

80. McCarthy AL, Woolfson RG, Raju SK, Poston L. 1993. Abnormal endothelial cell function of resistance arteries from women with preeclampsia. *Am. J. Obstet. Gynecol.* 168:1323–30

81. Miyoshi H, Nakaya Y, Moritoki H. 1994. Nonendothelial-derived nitric oxide activates the ATP-sensitive K+ channel of vascular smooth muscle cells. *FEBS Lett.* 345:47–49

82. Molnar M, Hertelendy F. 1992. N-omega-nitro-L-arginine, an inhibitor of nitric oxide synthesis, increases blood pressure in rats and reverses the pregnancy-induced refractoriness to vasopressor agents. *Am. J. Obstet. Gynecol.* 166:1560–67

83. Moncada S, Palmer RM, Gryglewski RJ. 1986. Mechanism of action of some inhibitors of endothelium-derived relaxing factor. *Proc. Natl. Acad. Sci. USA* 83:9164–68

84. Mundel P, Bachmann S, Bader M, Fischer A, Kummer W, et al. 1992. Expression of nitric oxide synthase in kidney macula densa cells. *Kidney Int.* 42:1017–19

85. Nakamura T, Alberola AM, Granger JP. 1993. Role of renal interstitial pressure as a mediator of sodium retention during systemic blockade of nitric oxide. *Hypertension* 21:956–60

86. Nakhostine N, Lamontagne D. 1993. Adenosine contributes to hypoxia-induced vasodilation through ATP-sensitive K+ channel activation. *Am. J. Physiol.* 265:H1289–93

87. Nelson DP, Samsel RW, Wood LDH, Schumacker PT. 1988. Pathological supply dependence of systemic and intestinal oxygen uptake during endotoxemia. *J. Appl. Physiol.* 64:2410–19

88. Nishimura J, van Breemen C. 1989. Direct regulation of smooth muscle contractile elements by second messengers. *Biochem. Biophys. Res. Commun.* 163:929–35

89. Olken NM, Marletta MA. 1993. NG-methyl-L-arginine functions as an alternate substrate and mechanism-based inhibitor of nitric oxide synthase. *Biochemistry* 32:9677–85

90. Panza JA, Casino PR, Badar DM, Quyyumi AA. 1993. Effect of increased availability of endothelium-derived nitric oxide precursor on endothelium-dependent vascular relaxation in normal subjects and in patients with essential hypertension. *Circulation* 87:1475–81

91. Panza JA, Casino PR, Kilcoyne CM, Quyyumi AA. 1993. Role of endothelium-derived nitric oxide in the abnormal endothelium-dependent vascular relaxation of patients with essential hypertension. *Circulation* 87:1468–74

92. Park KH, Rubin LE, Gross SS, Levi R. 1992. Nitric oxide is a mediator of hypoxic coronary vasodilatation: relationship to adenosine and cyclooxygenase-derived metabolites. *Circ. Res.* 71:992–1001

93. Patel A, Layne S, Watts D, Kirchner KA. 1993. L-arginine administration normalizes pressure natriuresis in hypertensive Dahl rats. *Hypertension* 22:863–69

94. Pearl RG, Rosenthal MH, Murad F, Ashton JP. 1984. Aminophylline potentiates sodium nitroprusside–induced hypotension in the dog. *Anesthesiology* 61:712–15

95. Pinto A, Sorrentino R, Sorrentino P, Guerritore T, Miranda L, et al. 1991. Endothelial-derived relaxing factor released by endothelial cells of human umbilical vessels and its impairment in pregnancy-induced hypertension. *Am. J. Obstet. Gynecol.* 164:507–13

96. Pohl U, Lamontagne D. 1991. Impaired tissue perfusion after inhibition of endothelium derived nitric oxide. *Basic Res. Cardiol.* 86(Suppl. 2):97–105

97. Pollock DM, Polakowski JS, Divish BJ, Opgenorth TJ. 1993. Angiotensin blockade reverses hypertension during long-term nitric oxide synthase inhibition. *Hypertension* 21:660–66

98. Rees DD, Palmer RM, Moncada S. 1989. Role of endothelium-derived nitric oxide in the regulation of blood pressure. *Proc. Natl. Acad. Sci. USA* 86:3375–78

99. Ribeiro MO, Antunes E, de Nucci G, Lovisolo SM, Zatz R. 1992. Chronic inhibition of nitric oxide synthesis. A new model of arterial hypertension. *Hypertension* 20:298–303

100. Roberts JM, Taylor RN, Musci TJ, Rodgers GM, Hubel CA, McLaughlin MK.

1989. Preeclampsia: an endothelial cell disorder. *Am. J. Obstet. Gynecol.* 161: 1200–4

101. Sakuma I, Togashi H, Yoshioka M, Saito H, Yanagida M, et al. 1992. N^G-methyl-L-arginine, an inhibitor of L-arginine-derived nitric oxide synthesis, stimulates renal sympathetic nerve activity in vivo. A role for nitric oxide in the central regulation of sympathetic tone? *Circ. Res.* 70:607–11

102. Salazar FJ, Alberola A, Pinilla JM, Romero JC, Quesada T. 1993. Salt-induced increase in arterial pressure during nitric oxide synthesis inhibition. *Hypertension* 22:49–55

103. Salom MG, Lahera V, Miranda-Guardiola F, Romero JC. 1992. Blockade of pressure natriuresis induced by inhibition of renal synthesis of nitric oxide in dogs. *Am. J. Physiol.* 262:F718–22

104. Schricker K, Kurtz A. 1993. Liberators of NO exert a dual effect on renin secretion from isolated mouse renal juxtaglomerular cells. *Am. J. Physiol.* 265:F180–86

105. Schultz PJ, Tayeh MA, Marletta MA, Raij L. 1991. Synthesis and action of nitric oxide in rat glomerular mesangial cells. *Am. J. Physiol.* 261:F600–6

106. Schultz PJ, Tolins JP. 1993. Adaptation to increased dietary salt intake in the rat: role of endogenous nitric oxide. *J. Clin. Invest.* 91:642–50

107. Schumacker PT, Kazaglis J, Connolly HV, Samsel RW, O'Connor MF, Umans JG. 1994. Systemic and gut oxygen extraction during endotoxemia: role of nitric oxide synthesis. *Am. J. Respir. Crit. Care Med.* In press

108. Shapoval LN, Sagach VF, Pobegailo LS. 1991. Nitric oxide influences ventrolateral medullary mechanisms of vasomotor control in the cat. *Neurosci. Lett.* 132:47–50

109. Sigmon DH, Carretero OA, Beierwaltes WH. 1992. Endothelium-derived relaxing factor regulates renin release in vivo. *Am. J. Physiol.* 263:F256–61

110. Stuehr DJ, Fasehun OA, Kwon NS, Gross SS, Gonzalez JA, et al. 1991. Inhibition of macrophage and endothelial cell nitric oxide synthase by diphenyleneiodonium and its analogs. *FASEB J.* 5:98–103

111. Stuehr DJ, Gross SS, Sakuma I, Levi R, Nathan CF. 1989. Activated murine macrophages secrete a metabolite of arginine with the bioactivity of endothelium-derived relaxing factor and the chemical reactivity of nitric oxide. *J. Exp. Med.* 169:1011–20

112. Suzuki H, Ikenaga H, Hishakawa K, Nakaki T, Kato R, Saruta T. 1992. Increases in NO$_2^-$/NO$_3^-$ excretion in the urine as an indicator of the release of endothelium-derived relaxing factor during elevation of blood pressure. *Clin. Sci.* 82:631–34

113. Taddei S, Virdis A, Mattei P, Salvetti A. 1993. Vasodilation to acetylcholine in primary and secondary forms of human hypertension. *Hypertension* 21: 929–33

114. Tare M, Parkington HC, Coleman HA, Neild TO, Dusting GJ. 1990. Hyperpolarization and relaxation of arterial smooth muscle caused by nitric oxide derived from endothelium. *Nature* 346: 69–71

115. Tesfamariam B, Brown ML, Cohen RA. 1991. Elevated glucose impairs endothelium-dependent relaxation by activating protein kinase C. *J. Clin. Invest.* 87:1643–48

116. Thomas GR, Thiemermann C, Walder C, Vane JR. 1988. The effects of endothelium-dependent vasodilators on cardiac output and their distribution in the anaesthetized rat: a comparison with sodium nitroprusside. *Br. J. Pharmacol.* 95:986–92

117. Togashi H, Sakuma I, Yoshioka M, Kobayashi T, Yasuda H, et al. 1992. A central nervous system action of nitric oxide in blood pressure regulation. *J. Pharmacol. Exp. Ther.* 262: 343–47

118. Twort CH, van Breemen C. 1988. Cyclic guanosine monophosphate–enhanced sequestration of Ca^{2+} by sarcoplasmic reticulum in vascular smooth muscle. *Circ. Res.* 62:961–64

119. Umans JG. 1993. Endothelium-dependent relaxation of rat mesentery: mediation by nitric oxide and charybdotoxin-sensitive K-channels. *J. Am. Soc. Nephrol.* 4:571

120. Umans JG, Lindheimer MD, Barron WM. 1990. Pressor effect of endothelium-derived relaxing factor inhibition in conscious virgin and gravid rats. *Am. J. Physiol.* 259:F293–96

121. Vallance P, Leone A, Calver A, Collier J, Moncada S. 1992. Accumulation of an endogenous inhibitor of nitric oxide synthesis in chronic renal failure. *Lancet* 339:572–75

122. von Beckerath N, Cyrys S, Dischner A, Daut J. 1991. Hypoxic vasodilatation in isolated, perfused guinea-pig heart: an analysis of the underlying mechanisms. *J. Physiol.* 442:297–319

123. Wei EP, Kukreja R, Kontos HA. 1992. Effects in cats of inhibition of nitric

oxide synthesis on cerebral vasodilation and endothelium derived relaxing factor from acetylcholine. *Stroke* 23:1623–28

124. Weisbrod RM, Brown ML, Cohen RA. 1993. Effect of elevated glucose on cyclic GMP and eicosanoids produced by porcine aortic endothelium. *Arterioscler. Thromb.* 13:915–23

125. Wilcox CS, Welch WJ, Murad F, Gross SS, Taylor G, et al. 1992. Nitric oxide synthase in macula densa regulates glomerular capillary pressure. *Proc. Natl. Acad. Sci. USA* 89:11993–97

126. Winquist RJ, Bunting PB, Baskin EP, Wallace AA. 1984. Decreased endothelium-dependent relaxation in New Zealand genetic hypertensive rats. *J. Hypertens.* 2:541–45

127. Yang X, Cai B, Sciacca RR, Cannon PJ. 1994. Inhibition of inducible nitric oxide synthase in macrophages by oxidized low density lipoproteins. *Circ. Res.* 74:318–28

Annu. Rev. Physiol. 1995. 57:791–804

CELL BIOLOGY OF ATHEROSCLEROSIS

Russell Ross

Department of Pathology, SM30, University of Washington, Seattle, Washington 98195

KEY WORDS: endothelium, smooth muscle, macrophage, T cell, response to injury, artery

INTRODUCTION

The lesions of atherosclerosis are responsible for changes in the heart that can lead to myocardial infarction, in the brain to cerebral infarction or stroke, and in the peripheral vasculature to gangrene and loss of function. Lesions of atherosclerosis represent the principal cause of death in the United States, Europe, and part of Asia (58). The advanced lesions of atherosclerosis, the sources of these potentially disastrous clinical events, consist of an extensive inflammatory, fibroproliferative response that intrudes into the lumen of the affected artery, compromises the flow of blood and, thus, oxygen to the affected part, and leads to clinical sequelae. The lesions represent a culmination of interactions between two types of leukocytes, circulating blood monocytes and T lymphocytes, that interact with the lining endothelium, enter into the artery wall, and have the potential to release various bioactive molecules. Ultimately, these interactions result in the migration and proliferation of smooth muscle cells, which elaborate connective tissue within the intima of the affected artery and produce the advanced lesions of atherosclerosis. Platelet mural thrombi and, later, occlusive thrombi can markedly affect the progress of the disease and lead to sudden death. Thus three cellular components in the circulation—monocytes, T lymphocytes, and platelets—together with two cells of the artery wall—endothelium and smooth muscle—interact in multiple ways to generate the lesions of atherosclerosis. The nature of the cells, their interactions, and the molecules they form represent the subject of this review.

791

0066–4278/95/0315–0791$05.00

THE LESIONS OF ATHEROSCLEROSIS

The lesions of atherosclerosis can be arbitrarily divided into three categories for ease of discussion: the fatty streak, the intermediate or fibrofatty lesion, and the fibrous plaque or advanced complicated lesion of atherosclerosis.

The Fatty Streak

The fatty streak consists of an intimal collection of lipid-filled, monocyte-derived macrophages, with a varying number of T lymphocytes (CD4+ and CD8+ T cells) (13, 54). The accumulation of lipid-filled macrophages, or foam cells, represents the bulk of the lesion and occupies two to five or six layers of the intima of the artery; these macrophages give the lesion a yellow discoloration when viewed en face, thus the derivation of the term fatty streak. Fatty streaks are distributed randomly throughout the arterial tree, but early lesions are commonly found at sites where changes in blood flow such as decrease of flow, back currents, or eddy currents occur at branches, bifurcations, and curves in the system (6, 57).

The Intermediate or Fibrofatty Lesion

The fibrofatty lesion consists of layers of lipid-filled macrophages and T cells that alternate with layers of varying numbers of smooth muscle cells surrounded by a relatively poorly developed connective tissue matrix of fine collagen fibrils, elastic fibers, and proteoglycans. Some of the smooth muscle cells may contain lipid droplets. When the intermediate lesion has a layered appearance, this suggests that leukocytes entered into the artery and were followed by the migration and possible replication of smooth muscle cells. As the lesions progress, the cells undergo a rearrangement that may lead to the advanced lesion or fibrous plaque.

The Fibrous Plaque

The advanced lesion of atherosclerosis, the fibrous plaque, is characteristically covered by a dense cap of fibrous connective tissue that contains numerous smooth muscle cells surrounded by dense layers of connective tissue matrix, made up principally of collagen with some elastic fibers. The smooth muscle cells in the fibrous cap look unusual; they appear to occupy slit-like or lacunar-like spaces that are surrounded by dense, multiple layers of basement membrane collagen when examined by electron microscopy (46). The fibrous cap, which varies in density, may also contain monocyte-derived macrophages and some T lymphocytes (12). When the fibrous cap is uniformally thick and dense, it apparently provides stability to the lesion, whereas when it is nonuniform and the "shoulders" are thin and macrophage-rich, the lesion may be unstable (15). The fibrous cap covers a deeper layer containing some smooth muscle cells and numerous macrophages that are often associated with a core of lipid and necrotic material. The macrophages are frequently observed close to numerous T lymphocytes. Beneath the core, there may be additional layers of smooth muscle cells and connective tissue matrix. When the lesion becomes thick, small microvascular channels, vasa vasora, may be present, presumably to provide appropriate nutrients and oxygen to the cells of the thickened lesion. When the shoulders of the lesion are thin and poorly formed, rheological forces may affect them and lead to rupture or ulceration with secondary hemorrhage, which may occur either from the lumen of the vessel or from the vasa vasora within the lesion. If this form of thrombus is sufficiently great, it may lead to occlusion of the artery with disastrous clinical consequences (8, 15).

Thus the lesions of atherosclerosis represent a continuum from fatty streak to fibrofatty lesion to fibrous plaque. It is questionable whether each type of lesion acts as a precursor for the other. However, a "geographic" pathology study of atherosclerosis demonstrated that fatty streaks occur at anatomic sites where fibrous plaques are later found or where no lesions are later found. These observations suggest that with growth and time some fatty streaks may progress to fibrous plaques, whereas others may either remain stable or regress and disappear (31).

THE CELLS OF THE LESIONS

The Endothelium

The endothelial cells act not only as a liner for the blood vessels, but they play numerous functional roles that, when disturbed, may participate in atherogenesis (17). These functions include

1. provision of a nonadherent surface for leukocytes and platelets;
2. a permeability barrier that controls the exchange of nutrients and fluid between the plasma and the artery wall;
3. maintenance of vascular tone by release of small vasodilatory molecules such as nitric oxide (NO) and prostacyclin (PGI_2), and vasoconstrictive molecules such as endothelin (ET) and angiotensin-II (A-II);
4. formation and secretion of a series of growth-regulatory molecules and cytokines;
5. formation and maintenance of connective tissue matrix, including the basement membrane upon which it lies, collagen, and elastic fibers and proteoglycans;
6. the capacity to modify substances from the plasma such as lipoproteins that endothelial cells can oxidize or otherwise modify as they are transported into the artery wall;

7. provision of a nonthrombogenic surface by the formation of molecules such as an ectoADPase, PGI_2, and heparin sulfate; and
8. provision of anticoagulant and procoagulant activities.

Alterations in one or more of these functions of the endothelium are important during the early phases of atherogenesis. Data demonstrate that one of the earliest changes in the endothelium associated with atherogenesis results in the attachment and subsequent adherence of leukocytes from the formation of a series of cell-surface, adhesive glycoproteins; these include intercellular adhesion molecule-1 (ICAM-1) and vascular cell adhesion molecule-1 (VCAM-1), which can adhere in a ligand-receptor fashion to receptors on appropriately activated monocytes or T lymphocytes (7, 35, 53). Other molecules such as platelet-endothelial cell-adhesion molecule (PECAM) can lead to platelet adhesion if the endothelium is appropriately activated in this process (1).

One of the earliest changes in the endothelium, however, is seen in its permeability, wherein increased amounts of lipoprotein (in hypercholesterolemic individuals) are transported by the endothelium and localize in the subendothelial space of the intima (50). During transcytosis, many of these lipoprotein particles may be modified by oxidation or glycation by the endothelium (55). The formation of oxidized LDL (oxLDL) may in turn have repercussions on the endothelium because oxLDL may induce expression of genes that can cause the endothelial cells to form chemotactic molecules, additional cell adhesion, and possibly growth-regulatory molecules or cytokines.

Nagel et al (33) demonstrated that the endothelial cells have shear response elements that can induce changes in gene expression in the endothelium at sites of alterations in blood flow, particularly where there is altered (decreased) shear and back currents and eddy currents, such as occur at branches and bifurcations in the arterial tree. The capacity of the endothelium to maintain normal arterial tone represents an important contribution of these cells via several molecules, including NO (14) and eicosanoids such as PGI_2 and PGE_2 (2). Ironically, the capacity of endothelium to form NO may also play a role in its capacity to further oxidize LDL to form oxLDL, which may also result from endothelial lipoxygenases (5). NO is not only vasodilatory but can play a role in the prevention of platelet adherence and aggregation, as well as in leukocyte adhesion; yet NO appears important in maintaining the normal lumen diameter of the artery (30). In contrast with NO, the endothelial cells can also form ET and A-II, both of which can induce vasoconstriction. Thus the balance between these forces is essential in determining the dimensions of the lumen and the effects of the lesions of atherosclerosis on vascular flow to critical regions of heart muscle or segments of the brain (11, 49).

The endothelial cells, like the epithelia, represent a unique monolayer of cells that have strict growth requirements; they attach to one another and to the underlying matrix by a series of cell-surface integrin molecules that bind to collagen or other matrix molecules. One aspect of endothelial cells that may be critical in atherogenesis is their inability, when wounded or injured, to crawl over one another to regenerate the wound site, as do fibroblasts or smooth muscle cells. If the endothelium is constantly injured at particular branch sites where the rheologic properties of the blood impinge upon it, there may be sufficient turnover of the endothelium to replace the injured cells over many years that the endothelial cells exhaust their capacity to replicate. Although endothelial cells that are several cell layers away from these sites may be capable of replicating and filling the site, they have no way to reach those regions. Consequently, with time, there may be loss of endothelial cells at local sites, concomitant with the loss of normal physiologic properties provided by the endothelium. If this occurs, these sites might become thrombogenic or more adhesive for leukocytes, which would result in an increase in lesion formation, particularly if risk factors such as hyperlipidemia, hypertension, cigarette smoking, diabetes, or others were present within the environment of the artery wall.

The capacity of the endothelium to prevent platelet adhesion, thrombosis, and coagulant activity is critical because it can form both anticoagulant and procoagulant substances. The endothelium may prevent fibrinolysis by forming plasminogen activator and urokinase, together with plasminogen activator inhibitor (PAI-1). Its ability to form heparin sulfate, NO, PGI_2, and an ectoADPase on the cell surface provides the endothelium with important antithrombotic properties. Any shift in the balance among these properties could alter the thrombotic or coagulant states of the endothelium and could be important in the initiation and progression of atherogenesis (19, 29).

When properly stimulated, the endothelium is the source of a number of growth-regulatory molecules and cytokines, including platelet-derived growth factor (PDGF), fibroblast growth factor (FGF), transforming growth factor β (TGFβ), insulin-like growth factor-I (IGF-I), and interleukin-1 (IL-1). Thus the endothelial cells can serve as a source of paracrine stimulation for neighboring smooth muscle and monocyte-derived macrophages. Finally, the endothelium is truly a connective tissue synthetic cell that maintains the basement membrane upon which it rests. Under appropriate stimulation, it synthesizes and secretes various forms of collagen, elastic fiber proteins, and proteoglycans.

Smooth Muscle

Smooth muscle cells located in the media constitute the bulk of the normal artery wall. By maintaining their attachments to neighbor cells and surrounding connective tissue matrix, smooth muscle cells provide the tonus of the artery that normally dampens the differences between diastole and systole. With increasing age, there is a gradual thickening of the intima of the artery, which at birth in humans is a virtual space that exists between the basement membrane underlying the endothelium and the internal elastic lamina of the artery. With time, individual smooth muscle cells normally appear within the intima. In adults, small intimal masses of cells or a concentric, uniform thickening of the intima will occur. It is in these regions that the lesions of atherosclerosis develop through further accumulation of smooth muscle cells, the connective tissue matrix that they elaborate, and lipid, together with monocyte-derived macrophages and T lymphocytes. Various stimuli can induce smooth muscle cells to migrate from the media into the intima and to proliferate there. These stimuli include chemotactic factors and mitogens possibly released from neighboring endothelium, from activated macrophages within the lesions, and from nearby smooth muscle cells.

Smooth muscle cells can be the source of a series of growth factors, including PDGF, FGF, IGF-I, monocyte-colony stimulating factor (M-CSF), TGFβ, and heparin-binding epidermal growth factor-like growth factor (HB-EGF). When the genes for these molecules, as well as the cytokines, i.e. IL-1 and tumor necrosis factor α (TNFα), are induced by various agents, the cells can stimulate their neighbors in a paracrine fashion and themselves in an autocrine fashion (28, 51). The susceptibility of the cells to activation will depend in part on their phenotype. At least two phenotypic states have been described for smooth muscle: contractile, in which cells have more contractile myofilaments in their cytosol, and synthetic, in which cells have relatively few contractile elements but do have a well-developed, rough endoplasmic reticulum and Golgi complex. These changes in phenotypic state may also relate to cell-surface adhesive molecules such as specific integrins that form on the surface of the smooth muscle cells (3, 56).

Embryonic human smooth muscle has been shown to contain α2β1 integrins that bind to collagen, as well as integrins that can bind to fibronectin, e.g. α3β1 and α5β1. In the mature adult, the cells of the media convert from α2β1 to α1β1, whereas in the lesions of atherosclerosis, most of the cells have converted back to α2β1, the phenotype found during embryogenesis. These differences in integrin phenotype may provide differences in the responsiveness of the cells to chemotactic and mitogenic agents, as well as provide information about their capacity to migrate directionally under appropriate stimulation (52). Skinner et al have observed that smooth muscle cells with only α1β1 integrins are unable to migrate, whereas cells containing α2β1 can migrate chemotactically to PDGF in a Boyden chamber assay (52).

When smooth muscle cells are in a contractile state, they can respond to agents such as ET, catecholamines, A-II, PGE$_2$, PGI$_2$, neuropeptides, NO, and leukotrienes that induce vasoconstriction or vasodilation. When the cells are in the synthetic state, they may express genes for the growth-regulatory molecules and cytokines discussed above and may be responsive to many of these factors as well. The form of connective tissue matrix elaborated by the smooth muscle cells is decided in part by the local environment and by the stimuli to which they are exposed. It is becoming clear that the matrix that surrounds the smooth muscle cells has a striking effect upon their responsiveness to these various molecules and to their state of activity.

Monocyte-Derived Macrophage

It has become widely appreciated that all forms of the lesions of atherosclerosis contain the elements of specialized, chronic inflammation, with large numbers of monocyte-derived macrophages, as well as varying numbers of T lymphocytes (21, 23). Normally, the macrophage is not only a scavenger cell but can also be an antigen-presenting cell. Macrophages are a rich source of growth-regulatory molecules and cytokines, and as such may be the principal mediator of cell migration and proliferation within the lesions of atherosclerosis (41).

Macrophages are also the principal source of foam cells in the lesions because they take up lipid and oxLDL through scavenger receptors or bulk phase endocytosis and a putative oxLDL receptor (18). Macrophages can oxidize LDL through various activities, including the formation of lipoxygenase and NO (34). When they do so, the fatty acids undergo peroxidation, become covalently cross-linked to the apoprotein B moiety of the LDL particle, and are taken up via the scavenger receptor to localize in the macrophage, thus resulting in foam cell formation (36).

The uptake of oxLDL and other substances within the lesions of atherosclerosis may serve as a stimulus to induce gene expression for several growth-regulatory molecules and cytokines, which can be chemotactic agents, growth agonists, or antagonists. The macrophage can make agents that induce monocyte proliferation (M-CSF, GM-CSF), smooth muscle proliferation [PDGF-AA, PDGF-BB, HB-EGF, basic FGF (bFGF), TGFβ], and endothelial proliferation [vascular endothelial growth factor (VEGF), FGF, and transforming growth factor α (TGFα)] (25, 27, 45). The macrophage can also make growth inhibitors [interferon γ (IFNγ), IL-1, TGFβ]. Activated macrophages can also produce a series of chemotactic molecules for other monocytes [M-CSF, GM-CSF, monocyte chemotactic protein-1 (MCP-1), oxLDL], for endothelial cells (VEGF, bFGF), and for smooth muscle cells (TGFβ, PDGF, FGF) (41).

Studies have shown that macrophages as well as smooth muscle cells replicate within forming lesions of atherosclerosis (20, 38). Macrophage proliferation was demonstrated in hyperlipidemic rabbits by incorporation of tritiated thymidine into immunocytochemically demonstrable macrophages (38) and by an antibody to proliferating cell nuclear antigen (PCNA), which is present in cells that are actively traversing the cell cycle (20). Thus replicating macrophages may be particularly important in progression of lesions. The relative numbers of macrophages, their localization within the lesions, and the genes that they express will have an impact on whether lesion progression occurs. For example, if macrophages secrete growth-regulatory molecules and/or cytokines that stimulate other macrophages, smooth muscle cells, or endothelium to migrate and replicate, the lesions will expand. At the same time, the macrophages, due to their capacity to oxidize LDL, can be important because oxLDL is thought to be the principal mode by which LDL induces atherogenesis. The use of antioxidants in nonhuman primates (48) and rabbits has been shown to reduce atherosclerotic lesion formation and the relative numbers of smooth muscle cells and macrophages within the lesion. Probucol has been used for its antiatherogenetic effect (4, 24) with some success, and vitamin E has been used in several clinical trials.

The presentation of antigen by macrophages may play a role, particularly in immune-induced atherosclerosis, and possibly in common atherosclerosis. The role of immunity in this disease is poorly understood. Because macrophages are derived from circulating blood monocytes, are specific populations of monocytes attracted to the lesions? Do some monocytes have stem cell–like qualities that permit replication of large numbers of macrophages within the lesions? Our knowledge of monocyte entrance into and macrophage exit from the lesions is rudimentary at best. Understanding macrophage turnover in the atherosclerotic lesion could lead to better control of their accumulation within the lesions. Because macrophages play a critical role in the inflammatory response, control of this component is essential in modifying the process of atherogenesis.

The T Lymphocyte

T lymphocytes have been observed within the lesions of atherosclerosis, suggesting that there may be a component of immunity that participates in the process of atherogenesis (22). Both CD4+ and CD8+ T cells are present in the lesions; however, no specific antigen(s) has been associated with the process (26).

Clearly, a specialized, immune form of atherogenesis occurs in the process of cardiac transplant rejection, during which time a concentric lesion of atherosclerosis forms in the coronary arteries of the rejected heart. These concentric lesions contain all of the cellular elements previously described in the lesions of common atherosclerosis. However, they are even more richly endowed in macrophages and T lymphocytes than in lesions of common atherosclerosis (47).

Although no specific antigens are responsible for common atherosclerosis, antibodies have been described for oxLDL (37). Clonal expansion of lymphocytes does not appear to take place in the lesions. High levels of HLA-DR are present in endothelium of vessels in transplanted hearts with advanced atherosclerosis, which may account for the induction of the T cell response in atherogenesis during transplant rejection. However, this finding does not explain the large numbers of T cells in common atherosclerosis that are found in lesions associated with risk factors, including hyperlipidemia, diabetes, and hypertension. Lesion expansion may occur during atherogenesis by formation of interleukin-2 (IL-2) by the monocyte-derived macrophages, which stimulate lymphocyte proliferation. In turn, the activated lymphocytes could release IFNγ, GM-CSF, or TNFα, all of which can activate and chemotactically attract macrophages (41).

Platelets

Since the time of Duguid (10), platelets have been implicated in the pathogenesis of the lesions of atherosclerosis. In studies of atherogenesis in hyperlipidemic nonhuman primates, rabbits, and swine, platelet mural thrombi have been associated with lesion formation at branches and bifurcations during all of the phases of the disease (9, 12). Massive thrombi can be found over advanced lesions of atherosclerosis if endothelial denudation, ulceration, or fracture of the lesions occurs. Mural thrombi contain adherent and aggregated platelets and are a source for the release of platelet contents that include such growth-regulatory molecules as PDGF, TGFα, TGFβ, and IGF-I. The vasoconstrictive agent thromboxane A2 (TXA2) also plays a role in reducing the vascular lumen, which imposes a greater strain on the tissue supplied by the artery at a time when it can least afford to face such a dilemma. Platelets appear to play a role postinfarction in continuing the process of lesion progression (16). Thus it appears that platelets play a ubiquitous role in atherogenesis that is still being elucidated.

CELLULAR INTERACTIONS IN ATHEROGENESIS

All the cells discussed above are able to interact during the various phases of atherogenesis. For example, during the earliest phases of fatty streak formation, the first two cells to appear within the intima of the artery are monocytes, which become converted to macrophages, and T lymphocytes. Although no specific antigen presentation has yet been described, interactions among these two cells could lead to macrophage activation and replication, as well as to lymphocyte replication. Further interactions between the cells could result in growth factor and cytokine gene expression by the macrophages. Similarly, interactions between the overlying endothelium and the monocyte-derived macrophages could lead to chemoattraction of monocytes, as well as to macrophage replication. Once smooth muscle cells are attracted into the lesion by chemotactic factors generated by activated macrophages and/or endothelial cells, the interactions between macrophages and smooth muscle, endothelium and smooth muscle, and between smooth muscle cells themselves could play critical roles in generating intermediate and ultimately advanced lesions of atherosclerosis (41).

An extensive and complex network of interacting cells represents a critical part of the process of atherogenesis. Based on the local microenvironment, specific genes can be expressed in each of these cell types that result in the formation and release of numerous factors including small molecules such as NO and eicosanoids, growth-regulatory molecules (both stimulatory and inhibitory), and chemotactic agents. The net result of these interactions will determine whether the lesions progress, regress, or remain stable (41).

RESPONSE-TO-INJURY HYPOTHESIS

In 1973, a hypothesis was formulated to explain the accumulated experimental and clinical observations concerning the process of atherogenesis (43). This hypothesis has been tested, modified, retested, and remodified over the past twenty years (39–44). The most recent version is represented in Figure 1. Stated simply, the hypothesis suggests that the various sources or risk factors associated with increased atherogenesis may induce some form of endothelial dysfunction that has been referred to as endothelial injury. Dysfunctional changes in the endothelium may result in alterations in permeability, adhesive characteristics, growth-stimulatory characteristics, or others. These changes may ultimately lead to monocyte-endothelial attachment, adherence, and transmigration so that the monocytes enter the subendothelium, become activated as macrophages, and are joined by T lymphocytes, which apparently enter the artery in a similar fashion. Together, these two cells constitute the first ubiquitous lesion of atherosclerosis, the fatty streak. Activation of these cells can result in their formation of molecules that may attract smooth muscle cells to migrate and replicate within the lesions. Through a process of costimulation, remodeling, and formation of all of the elements of connective tissue by smooth muscle and by the endothelial cells, fibrous plaques ultimately form with a fibrous cap that covers a core of lipid and necrotic material, particularly in hyperlipidemic individuals.

This inflammatory, fibroproliferative response associated with the various injurious agents that are linked with atherogenesis begins as a protective mechanism (32). However, as in many other disease entities, if the source of the injury continues unabated, what begins as an optimal inflammatory response may become excessive, destroy tissue, stimulate an excessive, fibroproliferative response, and ultimately result in a hyperplastic lesion. This lesion contains accumulations of cells and connective tissue that impinge on the lumen of the artery, decrease the blood flow through the artery, and result in

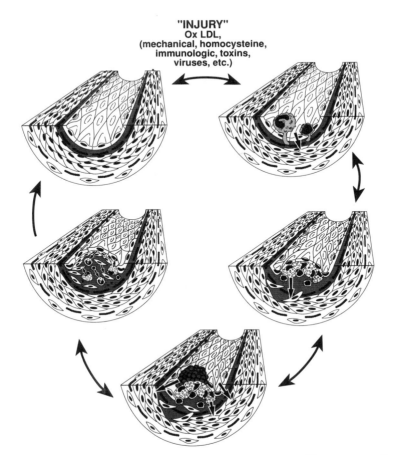

Figure 1 The response-to-injury hypothesis of atherosclerosis. Several different sources of injury to the endothelium can lead to endothelial cell dysfunction. One of the parameters associated with endothelial cell dysfunction that results from exposure to agents, such as oxLDL, is increased adherence of monocytes/macrophages and T lymphocytes. These cells migrate between the endothelium and localize subendothelially. The macrophages become large foam cells through lipid accumulation and, with the T cells and smooth muscle, form a fatty streak. The fatty streak can then progress to an intermediate, fibrofatty lesion and ultimately to a fibrous plaque. As the lesions accumulate increasing numbers of cells, and the macrophages scavenge the lipid, some of the lipid-laden macrophages may emigrate back into the blood stream by pushing apart the endothelial cells. Upon doing so, sites at such branches and bifurcations (where blood flow is irregular with eddy currents and back currents) may become thrombogenic, and platelet mural thrombi may form. Such thrombi can release many potent growth-regulatory molecules from the platelets that join with those released by the activated macrophages and possibly by lesion smooth muscle cells into the artery wall. Platelet thrombi can also form at sites where endothelial dysjunction has occurred. Ultimately, the formation and release of numerous growth-regulatory molecules and cytokines develop into a network of activated macrophages, smooth muscle, T cells, and endothelium and lead to progression of the atherosclerotic lesion to a fibrous plaque or advanced, complicated lesion. Each of the stages of lesion formation is potentially reversible. Thus lesion regression can occur if the injurious agents are removed, or when protective factors intervene to reverse the inflammatory and fibroproliferative processes.

damage to the tissue that is served by the artery (41). Thus what starts out as a protective response, in its excess becomes the disease entity atherosclerosis.

SUMMARY

The process of atherosclerosis is a life-threatening disease that affects critical organs including the heart and brain. It results from the influence of noxious agents associated with hyperlipidemia, hypertension, diabetes, cigarette smoking, homocysteinemia, and other agents that may, in altering the homeostatic condition of the artery wall, injure the endothelium and smooth muscle. The result is a protective, inflammatory, fibroproliferative response that becomes excessive and in its excess results in the disease process we call atherosclerosis.

ACKNOWLEDGMENTS

This work is supported in part by the National Heart, Lung, and Blood Institute, grant HL18645, and by an unrestricted grant for cardiovascular research from Bristol-Myers Squibb Company.

Literature Cited

1. Bogen S, Pak J, Garifallou M, Deng X, Muller WA. 1994. Monoclonal antibody to murine PECAM-1 (CD31) blocks acute inflammation in vivo. *J. Exp. Med.* 179:1059–64

2. Botting R, Vane JR. 1989. Vasoactive mediators derived from the endothelium. *Arch. Mal. Coeur* 82:11–14

3. Campbell GR, Campbell JH, Manderson JA, Horrigan S, Rennick RE. 1988. Arterial smooth muscle. A multifunctional mesenchymal cell. *Arch. Pathol. Lab. Med.* 112:977–86

4. Carew TE, Schwenke DC, Steinberg D. 1987. Antiatherogenic effect of probucol unrelated to its hypocholesterolemic effect: Evidence that antioxidants in vivo can selectively inhibit low density lipoprotein degradation in macrophage-rich fatty streaks slowing the progression of atherosclerosis in the WHHL rabbit. *Proc. Natl. Acad. Sci. USA* 84:7725–29

5. Chester AH, O'Neil GS, Moncada S,

Tadjkarimi S, Yacoub MH. 1990. Low basal and stimulated release of nitric oxide in atherosclerotic epicardial coronary arteries. *Lancet* 336:897–900

6. Cornhill JF, Barrett WA, Herderick EE, Mahley RW, Fry DL. 1985. Topographic study of sudanophilic lesions in cholesterol-fed minipigs by image analysis. *Arteriosclerosis* 5:415–26

7. Cybulsky MI, Gimbrone MA Jr. 1991. Endothelial expression of a mononuclear leukocyte adhesion molecule during atherogenesis. *Science* 251:788–91

8. Davies MJ, Thomas A. 1984. Thrombosis and acute coronary-artery lesions in sudden cardiac ischemic death. *N. Engl. J. Med.* 310:1137–40

9. Davies MJ, Woolf N, Rowles PM, Pepper J. 1988. Morphology of the endothelium over atherosclerotic plaques in human coronary arteries. *Br. Heart J.* 60:459–64

10. Duguid JB. 1946. Thrombosis as a factor in the pathogenesis of coronary athero-

sclerosis. *J. Pathol. Bacteriol.* 58:207–12

11. Dzau VJ. 1990. Atherosclerosis and hypertension: mechanisms and interrelationships. *J. Cardiovasc. Pharmacol.* 15 (Suppl. 5):S59–64

12. Faggiotto A, Ross R. 1984. Studies of hypercholesterolemia in the nonhuman primate. II. Fatty streak conversion to fibrous plaque. *Arteriosclerosis* 4:341–56

13. Faggiotto A, Ross R, Harker L. 1984. Studies of hypercholesterolemia in the nonhuman primate. I. Changes that lead to fatty streak formation. *Arteriosclerosis* 4:323–40

14. Furchgott RF. 1983. Role of endothelium in responses of vascular smooth muscle. *Circ. Res.* 53:557–73

15. Fuster V, Badimon L, Badimon JJ, Chesebro JH. 1992. The pathogenesis of coronary artery disease and the acute coronary syndromes. *N. Engl. J. Med.* 326:242–50

16. Fuster V, Stein B, Ambrose JA, Badimon L, Badimon JJ, Chesebro JH. 1990. Atherosclerotic plaque rupture and thrombosi: evolving concepts. *Circulation* 82(Suppl. II):II47–59

17. Gimbrone MA Jr. 1976. Culture of vascular endothelium. *Prog. Hemost. Thromb.* 3:1–28

18. Goldstein JL, Ho YK, Basu SK, Brown MS. 1979. Binding site of macrophages that mediates uptake and degradation of actylated low density lipoprotein, producing massive cholesterol deposition. *Proc. Natl. Acad. Sci. USA* 76:333–37

19. Gordon D, Augustine AJ, Smith KM, Schwartz SM, Wilcox JN. 1989. Localization of cells expressing tPA, PAI1, and urokinase by in situ hybridization in human atherosclerotic plaques and in the normal rhesus monkey. *Thromb. Haemostasis* 62:131

20. Gordon D, Reidy MA, Benditt EP, Schwartz SM. 1990. Cell proliferation of human coronary arteries. *Proc. Natl. Acad. Sci. USA* 87:4600–04

21. Gown AM, Tsukada T, Ross R. 1986. Human atherosclerosis: II. Immunocytochemical analysis of the cellular composition of human atherosclerotic lesions. *Am. J. Pathol.* 125:191–207

22. Hansson GK, Jonasson L, Seifert PS, Stemme S. 1989. Immune mechanisms in atherosclerosis. *Arteriosclerosis* 9:567–78

23. Jonasson L, Holm J, Skalli O, Bondjers G, Hansson GK. 1986. Regional accumulations of T cells, macrophages, and smooth muscle cells in the human ath-erosclerotic plaque. *Arteriosclerosis* 6:131–38

24. Kita T, Nagano Y, Yokode M, Ishii K, Kume N, et al. 1987. Probucol prevents the progression of atherosclerosis in Watanabe heritable hyperlipidemic rabbit, an animal model for familial hypercholesterolemia. *Proc. Natl. Acad. Sci. USA* 84:5928–31

25. Libby P, Friedman GB, Salomon RN. 1989. Cytokines as modulators of cell proliferation in fibrotic diseases. *Am. Rev. Respir. Dis.* 140:1114–17

26. Libby P, Hansson GK. 1991. Involvement of the immune system in human atherogenesis: current knowledge and unanswered questions. *Lab. Invest.* 64:5–15

27. Libby P, Ordovas JM, Auger KR, Robbins AH, Birinyi LK, Dinarello CA. 1986. Endotoxin and tumor necrosis factor induce interleukin-1 gene expression in adult human vascular endothelial cells. *Am. J. Pathol.* 124:179–85

28. Libby P, Warner SJC, Salomon RN, Birinyi LK. 1988. Production of platelet-derived growth factor–like mitogen by smooth muscle cells from human atheroma. *N. Engl. J. Med.* 318:1493–98

29. Loskutoff DJ, Curriden SA. 1990. The fibrinolytic system of the vessel wall and its role in the control of thrombosis. *Ann. NY Acad. Sci.* 598:238–47

30. Lüscher TF. 1990. Imbalance of endothelium-derived relaxing and contracting factors. A new concept in hypertension? *Am. J. Hypertens.* 3:317–30

31. McGill HC Jr. 1984. Persistent problems in the pathogenesis of atherosclerosis. *Arteriosclerosis* 4:443–51

32. Munro JM, Cotran RS. 1988. The pathogenesis of atherosclerosis: atherogenesis and inflammation. *Lab. Invest.* 58:249–61

33. Nagel T, Resnick N, Atkinson WJ, Dewey CF Jr, Gimbrone MA Jr. 1994. Shear stress selectively upregulates intercellular adhesion molecule-1 expression in cultured human vascular endothelial cells. *J. Clin. Invest.* 94:885–91

34. Parthasarathy S, Printz DJ, Boyd D, Joy L, Steinberg D. 1986. Macrophage oxidation of low density lipoprotein generates a modified form recognized by the scavenger receptor. *Arteriosclerosis* 6:505–10

35. Poston RN, Haskard DO, Coucher JR, Gall NP, Johnson-Tidey RR. 1992. Expression of intercellular adhesion molecule-1 in atherosclerotic plaques. *Am. J. Pathol.* 140:665–73

36. Rosenfeld ME, Khoo JC, Miller E, Parthasarathy S, Palinski W, Witztum

JL. 1990. Macrophage-derived foam cells freshly isolated from rabbit atherosclerotic lesions degrade modified lipoproteins, promote oxidation of LDL, and contain oxidation specific lipid-protein adducts. *J. Clin. Invest.* 87:90–99

37. Rosenfeld ME, Palinski W, Ylä-Herttuala S, Butler S, Witztum JL. 1990. Distribution of oxidation specific lipid-protein adducts and apolipoprotein B in atherosclerotic lesions of varying severity from WHHL rabbits. *Arteriosclerosis* 10:336–49

38. Rosenfeld ME, Ross R. 1990. Macrophage and smooth muscle cell proliferation in atherosclerotic lesions of WHHL and comparably hypercholesterolemic fat-fed rabbits. *Arteriosclerosis* 10:680–87

39. Ross R. 1981. George Lyman Duff Memorial Lecture: Atherosclerosis—a problem of the biology of arterial wall cells and their interactions with blood components. *Arteriosclerosis* 1:293–311

40. Ross R. 1986. The pathogenesis of atherosclerosis—an update. *N. Engl. J. Med.* 314:488–500

41. Ross R. 1993. The pathogenesis of atherosclerosis: a perspective for the 1990s. *Nature* 362:801–9

42. Ross R. 1993. The 1992 Rous-Whipple Lecture. Atherosclerosis: a defense mechanism gone awry. *Am. J. Pathol.* 413:985–1002

43. Ross R, Glomset JA. 1973. Atherosclerosis and the arterial smooth muscle cell. *Science* 180:1332–39

44. Ross R, Glomset JA. 1976. The pathogenesis of atherosclerosis. *N. Engl. J. Med.* 295:369–77; 420–25

45. Ross R, Masuda J, Raines EW, Gown AM, Katsuda S, et al. 1990. Localization of PDGF-B protein in macrophages in all phases of atherogenesis. *Science* 248:1009–12

46. Ross R, Wight TN, Strandness E, Thiele B. 1984. Human atherosclerosis. I. Cell constitution and characteristics of advanced lesions of the superficial femoral artery. *Am. J. Pathol.* 114:79–93

47. Salomon RN, Hughes CC, Schoen FJ, Payne DD, Pober JS, Libby P. 1991. Human coronary transplantation-associated arteriosclerosis. Evidence for a chronic immune reaction to activated graft endothelial cells. *Am. J. Pathol.* 138:791–98

48. Sasahara M, Raines EW, Chait A, Carew TE, Steinberg D, et al. 1994. Inhibition of hypercholesterolemia-induced atherosclerosis in the nonhuman primate by probucol. I. Is the extent of atherosclerosis related to resistance of LDL to oxidation? *J. Clin. Invest.* 94:155–64

49. Shimokawa H, Vanhoutte PM. 1989. Impaired endothelium-dependent relaxation to aggregating platelets and related vasoactive substances in porcine atherosclerosis. *Circ. Res.* 64:900–14

50. Simionescu N, Vasile E, Lupu F, Popescu G, Simionescu M. 1986. Prelesional events in atherogenesis. Accumulation of extracellular cholesterol–rich liposomes in the arterial intima and cardiac valves of the hyperlipidemic rabbit. *Am. J. Pathol.* 123:109–25

51. Sjölund M, Hedin U, Sejersen T, Heldin C-H, Thyberg JJ. 1988. Arterial smooth muscle cells express platelet-derived growth factor (PDGF) A chain mRNA, secrete a PDGF-like mitogen, and bind exogenous PDGF in a phenotype- and growth state-dependent manner. *Cell Biol.* 106:403–13

52. Skinner MP, Raines EW, Ross R. 1994. Dynamic expression of $\alpha1\beta1$ and $\alpha2\beta1$ integrin receptors by human vascular smooth muscle cells: $\alpha2\beta1$ integrin is required for chemotaxis across type I collagen-coated membranes. *Am. J. Pathol.* 145:1070–81

53. Springer TA. 1990. Adhesion receptors of the immune system. *Nature* 346:425–34

54. Stary HC. 1989. Evolution and progression of atherosclerotic lesions in coronary arteries of children and young adults. *Arteriosclerosis* 9(Suppl. I):I19–32

55. Steinberg D. 1991. Antioxidants and atherosclerosis. *Circulation* 84:1420–25

56. Thyberg J, Hedin U, Sjölund M, Palmberg L, Bottger BA. 1990. Regulation of differentiated properties and proliferation of arterial smooth muscle cells. *Arteriosclerosis* 10:966–90

57. Wissler RW, Vesselinovitch D. 1983. Atherosclerosis—relationship to coronary blood flow. *Am. J. Cardiol.* 52(2):2A

58. World Health Organization. 1985. Classification of atherosclerotic lesions. *WHO Tech. Rep. Serv.* 143:1–20

Annu. Rev. Physiol. 1995. 57:805–26

ANGIOTENSIN-CONVERTING ENZYME INHIBITION AND VENTRICULAR REMODELING AFTER MYOCARDIAL INFARCTION

Janice M. Pfeffer, Thomas A. Fischer, and Marc A. Pfeffer

Department of Medicine, Harvard Medical School, and Brigham and Women's Hospital, Boston, Massachusetts 02115

KEY WORDS: ventricular dilatation, myocyte hypertrophy, myocardial fibrosis, bradykinin, clinical trials

INTRODUCTION

Despite the trend for a decrease in fatality rates due to coronary heart disease, hospitalizations for acute myocardial infarction and its long-term sequelae have remained high. In the United States, approximately 675,000 people were hospitalized in 1990 with a first-listed diagnosis of acute myocardial infarction. In-hospital mortality rates were 5% in patients less than 65 years of age and 17.6% in those greater than 65 years of age (26). Acute infarct mortality in the elderly has become particularly worrisome as evidenced by the 1990 Medicare mortality statistics showing death rates of 23% during the first 30 days postinfarct and 36% at the end of one year (61). In addition to the acute morbidity and mortality of sustaining a myocardial infarction, patients surviving the in-hospital phase are in jeopardy of developing heart failure later on. A clinical history of a prior myocardial infarction increases the age-adjusted risk of developing heart failure 7- and 18-fold for men and women, respectively (44). An update of the Framingham Heart Study found that coronary artery disease was increasingly prevalent as the cause of heart failure and accounted for 59% of new cases in men and 48% in women (Figure 1) (35, 36). Once the diagnosis of heart failure was made, the five-year survival rate was only

805

0066–4278/95/0315–0805$05.00

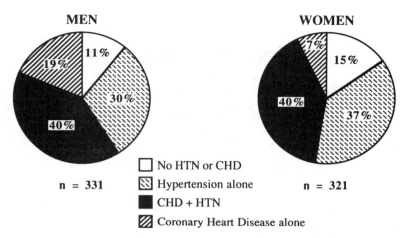

Figure 1 Prevalence of coronary heart disease (CHD) and hypertension (HTN) alone and in combination among Framingham Heart Study subjects with congestive heart failure, by gender. (Reprinted with permission from *J. Am. Coll. Cardiol.* 1993. 22(Suppl. A):6a–13.)

25% in men and 38% in women. The risk for developing cardiovascular morbidity and mortality following myocardial infarction is not uniform; the two most important prognostic indices are age and a measure of residual ventricular function. Although left ventricular ejection fraction is widely available and generally used to assess cardiac function, a quantitative determination of left ventricular volumes at end-systole or diastole has yielded more discriminative prognostic information (110). Even relatively small increases in ventricular volume were associated with a major independent increase in the risk of death in patients with coronary artery disease or in recent survivors of myocardial infarction (32, 110).

The power failure following the loss of contractile tissue as a result of myocardial infarction evokes a constellation of responses that act to maintain systemic perfusion. These compensatory mechanisms include an augmentation of the sympathetic nervous system, changes in regional vascular resistance, sodium retention, and activation of the renin-angiotensin-aldosterone system. The heart adapts to the augmented load placed on the residual myocardium by an increase in contractility (systolic reserve) and/or cavitary volume (diastolic reserve, or Frank-Starling mechanism). If the overload is sufficient in magnitude and duration, the use of these compensatory mechanisms eventuates in concurrent or disparate changes in ventricular mass, cavitary volume, and stiffness, which may become mechanically disadvantageous, compromising ventricular performance. The rat model of myocardial infarction produced by

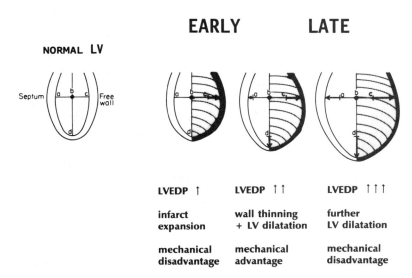

EARLY   **LATE**

NORMAL LV

LVEDP ↑   LVEDP ↑↑   LVEDP ↑↑↑

infarct   wall thinning   further
expansion   + LV dilatation   LV dilatation

mechanical   mechanical   mechanical
disadvantage   advantage   disadvantage

Figure 2   Schema of volume changes occurring in the left ventricle (LV) during the early and late post-infarction phases. In the normal left ventricle, the lengths ba and bc represent the distance (minor radius) from the midpoint of the left ventricle to the septum and free wall, respectively; the length bd represents the distance (major radius) from the midpoint to the apex. These distances are presented in the infarcted left ventricles as a frame of reference. The directional arrows attached to the normal radii illustrate the extent of and the regions involved in volume changes during the various post-infarction phases, but are not drawn to scale. The shaded area represents an infarction comprising 50% of the surface area of the left ventricle. (Adapted from Pfeffer JM. 1991. *Am. J. Cardiol.* 68:17d–25. With permission from *Am. J. Cardiol.*)

coronary artery ligation has been used extensively to study this remodeling process (Figure 2) (62, 65).

Structural Ventricular Remodeling in the Rat after Myocardial Infarction

ACUTE PHASE   In the very early period of necrosis, edema, and vascular congestion after a large transmural myocardial infarction, the left ventricle may dilate as the result of infarct expansion (i.e. a thinning and dilatation of the necrotic region), which provides no mechanical advantage to the impaired ventricle (38). The alteration in the infarcted wall is the result of myocyte slippage, or a decrease in the number of cells across the wall (109). As necrotic tissue is resorbed and a thin scar is formed, collagen fibers form a strong, structural network that acts to limit further infarct expansion (23, 104). Hypertrophy of the residual viable myocytes takes place, increasing contractile mass to near normal levels in small to moderate infarcts, but not in large infarcts (3, 4, 77). During the formation of a discrete scar, increases in cavitary volume occur that restore stroke volume (69).

CHRONIC PHASE   After the healing process is complete and a discrete scar is formed, changes in ventricular mass and volume may continue; in small infarcts, the ratio of cavitary volume-to-mass is normal, suggesting a normalization of wall stress, whereas in moderate to large infarcts, volume is further increased out of proportion to mass as filling pressures rise, which suggests that the stimulus to volume enlargement is still present (65). Ventricular dilatation that remains unchallenged by a concomitant increase in mass may become mechanically disadvantageous in that an augmented shortening load may be sustained throughout ejection because chamber volume is reduced relatively little while ventricular pressure is rising (108).

ANGIOTENSIN-CONVERTING ENZYME INHIBITION AND REMODELING OF THE IN-FARCTED LEFT VENTRICLE   The process of ventricular remodeling after myocardial infarction can be modified by the long-term administration of an angiotensin-converting enzyme (ACE) inhibitor (64). Following coronary artery ligation in the rat, 3 months of therapy with captopril reduced ventricular volume [whether initiated before (2 days) or after (21 days) scar formation was complete]. This resulted from both a downward displacement on the pressure-volume relation (a reduction in filling pressure, or less ventricular distension) and an attenuation of the rightward shift of that relation (less structural ventricular dilatation) that occurs with time in untreated rats with infarcts (Figure 3). Long-term therapy with ACE inhibitors of large infarcts reduced cardiac mass proportional to the attenuation in ventricular dilation. In contrast, therapy of moderate infarcts led to a reduction in mass that was less than the attenuation in volume. Hence cavitary volume-to-mass ratio remained unchanged in large infarcts but was reduced in moderate infarcts (63). These alterations in cardiac mass and cavitary volume were associated with a more favorable ventricular performance and a prolongation in survival (70).

RENIN-ANGIOTENSIN SYSTEM

The effectiveness of ACE inhibition in reducing cardiac mass and volumes while maintaining cardiac output in hypertension and myocardial infarction has sparked considerable interest in the role of the renin-angiotensin system (RAS) in cardiac remodeling. Angiotensin II has multiple effects on the heart and periphery, acting directly or indirectly in the regulation of growth, vascular resistance, and contractility (6, 16, 56). The effects of angiotensin II are mediated through its receptors, which are located on ventricular and smooth muscle cells and are linked to guanine nucleotide–binding proteins that control the generation of various downstream second messenger pathways (81, 96). These receptors can be divided into two distinct types: the AT1 receptor, which mediates most of the

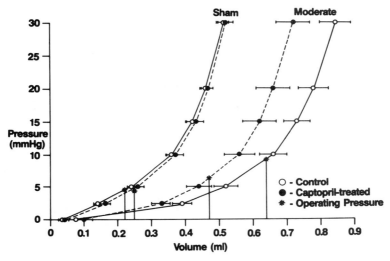

Figure 3 Graph showing left ventricular pressure-volume relation from rats 3 months after either sham operation or left anterior, descending coronary artery ligation. Animals treated in the long term with captopril are shown as solid circles. Infarcted animals treated with captopril had a shift in pressure-volume relation to the left with respect to comparably sized infarcts in rats not receiving long-term therapy. Left ventricular end-diastolic pressure was also reduced in the active therapy group, which resulted in lower operating pressure on the basis of structural change as well as on reduced left ventricular end-diastolic pressure. (From Pfeffer MA, Braunwald E. 1990. Ventricular remodeling after myo- cardial infarction. *Circulation* 81:1161–72. Reproduced with permission from the Am. Heart Assoc.)

known physiologic and pathophysiologic effects of angiotensin II, and the AT2 receptor, which is present in fetal development, but the role of which in cardiovascular homeostasis is not well characterized. Two subtypes of the AT1 receptor have been identified, although their functional significance has not been characterized (40, 41, 82). In the rat heart, angiotensin II receptor expression is increased during the embryonic period and decreased with maturation (28, 87, 93). The expression of the AT1 receptor is sustained during embryonic develop- ment, whereas the expression of the AT2 receptor falls to extremely low levels after birth (51). Cardiac fibroblasts in the neonatal rat also express substantially more of the AT1 receptor than the AT2 receptor subtype (84). Adult ventricular myocytes almost exclusively exhibit the AT1 receptor subtype (53).

Cardiac Renin–Angiotensin System

The presence of a tissue RAS in the heart has been documented by the identification of messenger RNA for its various components such as an- giotensinogen, ACE, and prorenin (6, 17). The mRNA for angiotensinogen

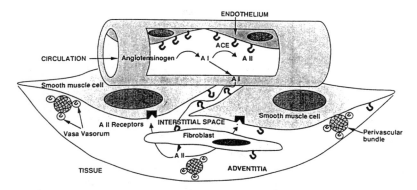

Figure 4   Schematic representation shows the localization of ACE and the formation of angiotensin II (AII) in the plasma and interstitial compartments. A I indicates angiotensin I. (From Johnston CI. 1994. Tissue angiotensin-converting enzyme in cardiac and vascular hypertrophy, repair, and remodeling. *Hypertension* 23:258–68. Reproduced with permission from the Am. Heart Assoc.)

has been detected in adult rat and mouse hearts and has been shown to be upregulated by thyroid hormone, corticosteroids, and an increase in wall tension such as that purported in aortic banding and the residual myocardium after myocardial infarction (7, 18, 46, 48, 49, 83). ACE, the peptidase responsible for converting angiotensin I to II and for degrading bradykinin, is found predominantly attached to endothelial cells (Figure 4) (42). Cardiac ACE has been detected primarily around the cardiac valves and the adventitial and endothelial layers of major arteries (71, 111). The presence of ACE activity in adult and neonatal rat cardiomyocytes, as well as in fibroblasts, indicates that ACE is present to varying extents in most cardiac cell types (17, 43). The expression of ACE mRNA has also been demonstrated in the human myocardium using quantitative polymerase chain reaction (PCR) techniques (91). The upregulation of ACE mRNA has been shown in experimentally induced pressure overload and post-infarction heart failure (21, 37, 85). Nevertheless, the amount of ACE mRNA in human ventricular myocardium is quite low and detectable only by PCR techniques. Questionable as well is whether the renin activity in the heart is of cardiac origin (19, 103). Recent physiologic studies have failed to demonstrate a local generation of renin in either the myocardium or in the small arteriolar vessels of the microcirculation in the cremaster muscle of spontaneously hypertensive rats (15, 101). However, the use of cocultures of isolated endothelial cells and myocytes indicates that the majority of angiotensin II in the adult rat heart may be produced by microvascular endothelial cells and to only a small extent by the myocytes, which suggests that there may be an autocrine/paracrine pathway for angiotensin II generation in the heart (97). An alternative pathway for angiotensin II generation in the human heart has recently been described (99). An enzyme, a chymotrypsin-like proteinase (chymase), that is not affected by ACE inhibition has been cloned and characterized (45, 100). However, no difference has been found between normal and failing human hearts in chymase-like activity or expression of chymase mRNA (92, 98). There are no specific inhibitors of human heart chymase currently available; thus its functional significance for the generation of angiotensin II in normal and diseased hearts (cells) remains to be determined.

CARDIAC RAS IN LEFT VENTRICULAR OVERLOAD   An increase in the gene transcripts for angiotensinogen and ACE in the ventricular myocardium has been demonstrated in animal models of pressure overload and myocardial infarction (7, 22, 34, 49, 85). Despite the evidence that the expression of angiotensinogen and ACE mRNA in the heart is at least 20-fold lower than in the liver and lung, generation of angiotensin II occurs in response to a functional overload of the heart, which suggests a potentially important linkage between the cardiac RAS and workload (18, 47, 85, 86). In the animal model of myocardial infarction, however, an increase in angiotensinogen formation is only transient (49). An increase in cardiac ACE induced by a functional overload has been demonstrated by several groups. An elevation of ACE activity has been observed in hypertrophied left ventricles of rats with aortic banding, in the residual viable myocardium after myocardial infarction, and in hearts following isoproterenol infusion (7, 34, 58). ACE activity is increased within the first few days of a myocardial infarction and remains elevated during the following weeks (72). Despite the evidence for an increase in cardiac ACE activity in response to a functional overload, the expression of ACE mRNA is a delayed response and might be secondary to the preceding formation of another, not yet identified, trophic signal. However, caution should be used in interpretation because the data derived from animal studies on the expression of ACE are primarily derived from crude heart extracts and not from separate cell populations. Which cell types within the heart are responsible for the generation of ACE are therefore not well known, but there is increasing evidence that the coronary vascular endothelium may be the major source of cardiac ACE (42, 97). A number of excellent reviews of the molecular basis of the cardiac RAS are available (6, 19, 29, 47).

ACE INHIBITION POST-INFARCTION

The structural remodeling of the left ventricle after myocardial infarction is a time-dependent process involving both the region of necrosis and the residual myocardium. The processes of scar formation, ventricular dilatation, and myocyte hypertrophy are interdependent contributors to this reconstruction; each is dominant at a different phase post-infarction. The initial observations of the hemodynamic benefits of ACE inhibition post-infarction have expanded considerably to include its effects on the kallikrein-kinin system, the role of the cardiac RAS in myocyte hypertrophy, and collagen metabolism. These multiple effects unique to the ACE inhibitor act in concert to more favorably remodel the infarcted left ventricle.

Contributors to Remodeling by ACE Inhibition

HEMODYNAMICS   ACE inhibitors are effective as afterload and preload reducing agents. They lower left ventricular filling and systemic arterial pressures and decrease systemic vascular resistance, yet maintain or increase cardiac output without changing heart rate when administered acutely or chronically in heart failure. ACE inhibitors are arterial vasodilators, but their ability to lower filling pressure post-infarction has been attributed to the additive production of venodilatation (74). ACE inhibitors may also lower left ventricular end-diastolic pressure by their effect on diastolic function. Following an intracoronary injection of an ACE inhibitor, the hypertrophied left ventricles of hypertensive patients demonstrated an improvement of active relaxation, accompanied by a decrease in left ventricular end-diastolic pressure and volume, which suggests that the cardiac RAS plays an important role in diastolic function (31).

Bradykinin   In addition to inhibiting the formation of angiotensin II, a potent vasoconstrictor, the ACE inhibitors potentiate bradykinin, a local vasodilator. The various effects of ACE inhibition that are mediated by bradykinin via the B_2 receptor have been reviewed by Gavras (24). The vasopressor response to chronic infusions of angiotensin II is increased when bradykinin B_2 receptors are blocked, which suggests a blood pressure modulating effect of endogenous kinins (50). When bradykinin receptors are blocked by an antagonist, the antihypertensive effect of ACE inhibitors in renovascular hypertension is attenuated by ~30% (8, 9). In another study, the antihypertensive and antihypertrophic effects of low and high dose ACE inhibition were examined in rats with abdominal aortic constriction concurrently given a bradykinin B_2 receptor antagonist (76). Only the high dose of the ACE inhibitor prevented the development of hypertension and left ventricular hypertrophy, effects that were not, however, blocked by the B_2 receptor antagonist. In another animal model of hypertension, the stroke-prone spontaneously hypertensive rat, both low and high doses of an ACE inhibitor were initiated prenatally, and a B_2 receptor antagonist was added at 6 weeks of age; both agents were continued until 20 weeks of age (27). Once again, the high, but not low, dose of ACE inhibitor prevented the development of hypertension and cardiac hypertrophy, whereas blockade of the bradykinin receptor did not blunt these responses. On the other hand, both low and high doses of the ACE inhibitor improved cardiac function, an effect that was abolished by B_2 receptor blockade. When circulating and tissue (heart) levels of angiotensin and bradykinin peptides were measured in rats after 1 week of ACE inhibitors of sufficient dose to lower plasma angiotensin II levels, plasma and tissue levels of angiotensin I were increased by 25-fold and bradykinin levels by 8-fold (13). Another bradykinin-mediated effect of ACE inhibition is the inhibition (via the B_2 receptor) of endothelin secretion (55). An independent kallikrein-kinin system, which may participate in the regulation of cardiac function, has recently been demonstrated in the heart (60).

MYOCYTE HYPERTROPHY   A sustained increase of workload results in a hypertrophic response of the myocardium that has been associated with a cascade of alterations in gene expression. Recent studies have indicated that exogenous or locally generated angiotensin II has a role in this altered gene expression. The induction of immediate, early response genes involved in growth and differentiation by angiotensin II has been shown in neonatal and adult rat cardiomyocytes (59, 79, 80). This induction appears to be mediated via activation by angiotensin II of phospholipid-derived second messenger systems, such as phospholipase C and protein kinase C, through the AT1 subtype receptor (80). Within 6 h in isolated neonatal cardiomyocytes, angiotensin II also induced the late genes, skeletal alpha-actin and atrial natriuretic peptide, and resulted in the upregulation of the genes for angiotensinogen and transforming growth factor-beta (TGF-β), which suggests a positive feedback mechanism for the regulation of cardiac hypertrophy (79). An increased expression of *c-myc* and *c-jun* has also been demonstrated in surviving myocytes of right and left ventricles of rats 2 to 3 days following myocardial infarction, a time by which an increase in myocyte volume has been documented (75). There were greater than six- and twofold increases in angiotensin II receptor mRNA in myocytes from the left and right ventricles, respectively, as well as a 44% increase in angiotensin II receptor density in left ventricular myocytes. Mediation of cardiac hypertrophy by the AT1 receptor and upregulation of its gene and that of TGF-β1 have also been shown in rats with coarctation of the abdominal aorta (20). In other models of cardiac hypertrophy, the spontaneously hypertensive and two-kidney renal hypertensive rats, ventricular angiotensin II (type 1A) mRNA levels and angiotensin II receptor densities were increased three- and twofold, respectively (93). Exogenous angiotensin II has been shown to increase protein synthesis in embryonic and neonatal cells and in denervated transplanted rat hearts that had atrophied (5, 25). In rat hearts hypertrophied by banding of the ascending aorta, an increase in cardiac ACE activity and in mRNA and protein levels has been shown, as well a decrease in intracardiac conversion of angiotensin I to II by ACE inhibition (85, 86).

COLLAGEN   Although the cardiomyocytes occupy 70 to 85% of the volume of the myocardium, 65% of the cells of the heart are fibroblasts, coronary vascular endothelial cells, and smooth muscle cells (105, 107). The fibroblasts synthesize and degrade fibrillar collagen, types I and III, the major structural proteins of the heart. Weber & Brilla show that in pathologic hypertrophy the relative proportions of myocardial cells change, with collagen concentration rising disproportionately (106). They suggest that this increase in interstitial fibrosis and loss of tissue homogeneity is the culprit factor in the development of heart failure. The RAS has been shown to be involved in pathologic myocardial fibrosis. Angiotensin II increased collagen synthesis and inhibited collagenase activity in cultured adult cardiac fibroblasts (11). The AT1 subtype receptor for angiotensin II and its mRNA are expressed by both neonatal and adult cultured cardiac fibroblasts, but the message is more highly expressed by the adult cell (12, 102). When angiotensin II infusion (3 days) was used to produce hypertension in the rat, there was an increase in aortic fibronectin mRNA expression that was blocked by the AT1 receptor blocker losartan, and not by the equipotent antihypertensive agents prazosin,

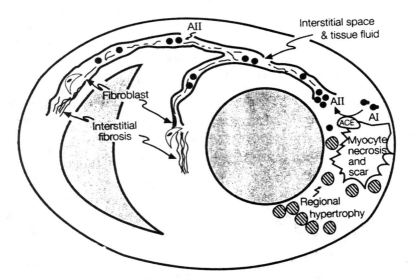

Figure 5   Diagrammatic cross-sectional illustration of the heart to show how circulating factors or locally released substances influence pathological remodeling at sites distant from an infarction. These substances travel through tissue fluid of the interstitial space, which is a milieu common to both ventricles. (From Weber et al. 1993. *Blood Pressure.* 2:6–21, with permission.)

hydralazine, or L-arginine (33). ACE inhibition reduced fibronectin mRNA whether or not blood pressure was lowered. The angiotensin II infusion resulted in similar increases in mRNA for collagen types I and IV (14). Twelve week administration of ACE inhibitors to spontaneously hypertensive rats, a genetic model of hypertension, lowered blood pressure, reduced left ventricular hypertrophy, and caused regression of interstitial fibrosis (10). When weanling spontaneously hypertensive rats were treated for 4 months with a low and a high dose of an ACE inhibitor, aortic ACE activity was inhibited and collagen content was reduced, whereas plasma ACE activity was reduced only by the high dose (1). In the rat model of myocardial infarction produced by coronary artery ligation, the collagen concentration appears to double in the residual viable free wall of the left ventricle and to increase by 27% in the noninfarcted septum (52). The increase in interstitial fibrosis in the remote septum following infarction of the free wall may be the result of circulating or locally released substances that travel through the interstitium (Figure 5) or to the local generation of angiotensin II, as suggested by the increase in tissue ACE activity in the noninfarcted region (83, 107). Long-term (6 to 8 weeks) therapy with an ACE inhibitor reduced this abnormal accumulation of myocardial collagen (54, 83).

CLINICAL STUDIES

Remodeling

The rationale for the use of ACE inhibition to prevent the development of congestive heart failure following myocardial infarction is a laudatory example of how the results of animal experiments can initiate a program of clinical research that leads to solid advances in patient management. The initial clinical studies of the prophylactic use of ACE inhibitors post-infarction began in the mid-1980s and were based on the finding that the chronic administration of an ACE inhibitor attenuated ventricular enlargement and improved function as well as survival in animals (64, 70). The clinical end points as well as the target population of these early studies were direct extrapolations from the animal work. The two original studies included patients with recent Q wave infarction and reduced left ventricular ejection fraction (≤40%) and excluded the more severely affected patients who already manifested overt congestive heart failure (68, 88). The primary end point of these studies was quantitative left ventricular volume based on echocardiography or biplane-contrast left ventriculography. Gleaned from the animal studies as well was the concept that a sufficient length of time was required to detect relatively small increases in ventricular volume.

In both studies, the control or conventional therapy groups demonstrated progressive ventricular enlargement (68, 88). In the catheterization-based study, it was also determined that ventricular dilation was due to true structural change and not just to acute distention because the filling pressures in the placebo-treated patients that showed ventricular enlargement had not changed (68). In contrast, those patients randomized to the ACE inhibitor did not show ventricular enlargement beyond the baseline value at acute infarction. One of the findings from these detailed mechanistic studies was the reduction in left ventricular filling and pulmonary arterial systolic pressures in the asymptomatic patients given ACE inhibition therapy (Figure 6). Indeed, in rats, post-infarction therapy with an ACE inhibitor regressed right ventricular hypertrophy as a consequence of reducing left ventricular end-diastolic pressure and pulmonary arterial systolic pressure (64). This preservation of right ventricular function may be an important feature of a favorable outcome. In many respects, it was the interest generated by the consistency of the results from both clinical and animal studies that led to several major international trials of the use of ACE inhibition in acute myocardial infarction (66).

Clinical Outcome Studies

Although the above findings and other mechanistic studies have confirmed the hypothesis that ACE inhibition can favorably alter progressive ventricular enlargement in highly selected patients, the clinical relevance of these apparently minor structural changes had not been determined and thus became the focus of international clinical investigations (57, 73). These large studies were designed with a sample size sufficient to address clinical end points, such as

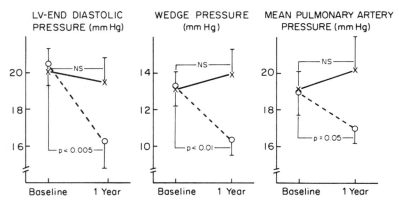

Figure 6 Change in left ventricular end-diastolic pressure, pulmonary capillary wedge pressure, and mean pulmonary-artery pressure between baseline and one-year evaluation in the placebo (*crosses*) and captopril (*circles*) groups. Values are means ± SEM. There was no significant difference (NS) between the baseline and one-year values in the placebo group. (Reprinted by permission of the *N. Engl. J. Med.* 1988. 319:80.)

Table 1   Clinical trials of ACE inhibition following myocardial infarction

Trial	n	ACE inhibitor	Selection criteria	Initiation	Follow-up duration (months)	Lives saved/ 1000 treated
SAVE	2231	Captopril	EF ≤ .40	3–16 day	42	42
AIRE	2006	Ramipril	CHF	3–10 day	15	57
SMILE	1556	Zofenopril	Ant	<24 h	12	41
TRACE	1749	Trandolapril	↓ WMI	3–7 day	36	76
CONSENSUS-II	6090	Enalapril	All	<24 h	4	—
ISIS-4	54,824	Captopril	All	<24 h	1.3	4
GISSI-3	18,895	Lisinopril	All	<24 h	1.5	8
Chinese	11,345	Captopril	All	<36 h	1.3	*

Ant indicates anterior infarct; CHF, congestive heart failure; EF, ejection fraction; ↓ WMI, decreased wall motion index as determined by echocardiography; * not available.

mortality and the development of cardiovascular morbidity. Although all these patients had sustained an acute myocardial infarction, the inclusion and exclusion criteria differed as did the duration of follow-up. In light of the diversity of these trials and the cumulative enrollment of almost 100,000 patients, a broad base of information was generated regarding the clinical importance of ACE inhibition in patients following an acute myocardial infarction (Table 1).

The Survival and Ventricular Enlargement (SAVE) study selected patients who had survived the acute phase of a myocardial infarction with objective evidence of left ventricular dysfunction [evidence of failure (EF) ≤40%], yet did not have heart failure that required therapy with an ACE inhibitor (67). Patients were randomized to receive an ACE inhibitor or placebo in addition to optimal conventional therapy. The average length of follow-up was 3.5 years, with the last patient followed for a minimum of 2 years. Deaths from all causes were reduced by 19% in those randomized to the ACE inhibitor, and mortality attributed to a cardiovascular etiology was reduced by 21%. This improvement in survival was supported by a consistent reduction in nonfatal cardiovascular end points, such as the development of overt congestive heart failure or the experiencing of a myocardial infarction following randomization. An echocardiographic substudy of SAVE confirmed that ACE inhibition attenuated the time-dependent ventricular enlargement (89). More importantly, because of the larger population and prolonged observation period, this study provided new evidence linking progressive enlargement with a heightened risk for experiencing an adverse cardiovascular event. Patients who developed heart failure or late cardiovascular death had more ventricular enlargement 1 year after the original infarct (89).

The Acute Infarction Ramipril Efficacy (AIRE) study randomized patients selected for clinical characteristics consistent with transient signs and symptoms of heart failure during acute myocardial infarction (95). This study demonstrated that ACE inhibitor therapy was associated with a 27% reduction in all cause mortality. The patient populations of the SAVE and AIRE studies differed to some extent: The majority (60%) of the SAVE group, selected by an ejection fraction criterion, did not develop rales and would not have been eligible for the AIRE study, whereas a substantial portion of the AIRE population would have an ejection fraction >40%, thus excluding them from the SAVE study. Together, these studies make a strong statement that either the clinical recognition of transient heart failure complicating myocardial infarction or a quantitative determination of a depressed ejection fraction in an asymptomatic patient is an indication for the initiation of ACE inhibitor therapy in the early convalescent period of an acute myocardial infarction.

The categorization of acute myocardial infarction by electrocardiography has long been used to differentiate risk groups (90). The Survival of Myocardial Infarction Long-term Evaluation (SMILE) study selected a high-risk group based on the anterior location of the infarct (determined electrocardiographically) and the absence of thrombolytic therapy (2). In this high-risk group, with only 6 weeks of follow-up post-infarction, a strong trend for a reduction in mortality and a significant reduction in the combined end point of mortality or development of severe heart failure was observed in those patients treated with an ACE inhibitor. Preliminary results indicated an even greater survival benefit with longer follow-up.

Other investigators have taken a different approach and tested the potential benefits of therapy in a broader group of patients post-infarction (except hypotensive individuals) in whom ACE inhibition was initiated within 24 h of the onset of symptoms. With less stringent selection criteria in these trials, the broader use of ACE inhibitor in the acute myocardial infarct population can be better determined.

The Second Cooperative North Scandinavian Enalapril Survival study (CONSENSUS-II) sought to initiate ACE inhibitor therapy promptly (the first day of an acute myocardial infarction) to a broad population (94). In this 6000-patient study, intravenous therapy with an ACE inhibitor was followed by oral dose to produce a prompt and sustained inhibition of the RAS. CONSENSUS-II was terminated by the safety committee at a time when no apparent benefit or harm was documented. Nonetheless, larger studies have now demonstrated that the initiation of an oral ACE inhibitor on the first day following myocardial infarction is safe and does have some survival efficacy.

The Fourth International Study of Infarct Survival (ISIS-4) examined the use of an ACE inhibitor post-infarction in more than 58,000 patients (39). After only 28 days of therapy, the preliminary results showed a small, but significant, reduction in the 35-day mortality rates: 7.3% (conventional therapy) vs 6.9% (conventional therapy plus ACE inhibitor). Although the percent and absolute (approximately 5 lives per 1000 patients treated) benefit of ACE inhibition was relatively small, it was well-tolerated in the broad population of acute myocardial infarction.

Similar results were presented by the Gruppo Italiano per lo Studio della Sopravvivenza nell'Infarto Miocardico (GISSI-3) that also studied the effects of early and sustained oral administration of an ACE inhibitor for the first 7 weeks of an acute myocardial infarction in a broad patient population (30). Once again, the ACE inhibitor was associated with a small, but definite, reduction in mortality: 7.1% (conventional therapy plus placebo) and 6.3% (conventional therapy plus ACE inhibition). In this trial of almost 19,000 patients, approximately 8 lives were saved per 1000 patients treated with this short-term therapy.

The studies in which therapy is initiated early and the follow-up is short term demonstrate that ACE inhibitors can be administered safely during the acute phase of myocardial infarction and that this early use can result in further improvement in survival. In considering the overall trial experience, the clinician can expect even greater benefits when patients are selected for signs and symptoms of congestion, objective measures of left ventricular dysfunction in asymptomatic patients, or other indicators of high risk. In these cases, the benefits are increased with long-term therapy as observed in the original animal studies.

Coronary Heart Disease Events

Clinical studies have, however, provided another (nonremodeling) mechanism of benefit of ACE inhibitor therapy that was not delineated from the pilot work in animals. The Studies of Left Ventricular Dysfunction (SOLVD) was a program of two parallel studies of the long-term use of an ACE inhibitor in patients with left ventricular dysfunction (EF ≤35%) who were either symptomatic (treatment arm) or asymptomatic (prevention arm). Combined, these studies randomized over 9000 patients to therapy with an ACE inhibitor or placebo and had the key ingredient of long-term follow-up. In addition to the anticipated reduction in the development of heart failure and its related mortality, the SOLVD trial demonstrated that patients with chronic ACE inhibitor therapy were less likely to experience a myocardial infarction, a reduction in risk that was only evident with prolonged follow-up (112). Comparable findings were observed in the SAVE trial. Again, it was only with long-term therapy that this important reduction in the incidence of recurrent myocardial infarction was observed (67). In both studies, this reduction in myocardial infarction by two different ACE inhibitors had a prominent role in the overall improvement in cardiovascular outcome.

This new and somewhat unexpected observation from these clinical trials has stimulated a great deal of clinical as well as basic investigation. The mechanistic link between ACE inhibition and the observed reduction in coronary events is unclear but appears to go beyond systemic hemodynamic actions (112). Local vascular effects, including smooth muscle proliferation, enhanced endothelial cell function, and antiatherosclerotic, antithrombolytic, and profibrinolytic actions, are all being evaluated as potential mechanisms for the favorable actions of ACE inhibitors. A component of these actions may be an ACE inhibitor–mediated increase in local bradykinin, which raises the question of whether the newly developed and more specific angiotensin-receptor antagonists will share these properties.

Another key observation from both trials was that left ventricular ejection fraction, a major determinant of survival and the risk of heart failure, was not a particularly important prognostic factor for experiencing a myocardial infarction following randomization (78). It also appeared that the efficacy of the ACE inhibitor in reducing the risk of a myocardial infarction was not strongly influenced by baseline ejection fraction. These two observations are particularly intriguing because they indicate that the benefits of ACE inhibitor therapy in reducing recurrent myocardial infarctions and their sequelae may not be restricted to patients with a depressed left ventricular ejection fraction.

Future Directions

Well-designed investigations answer a focused question and in so doing pose additional ones for further research. The observation that recurrent myocardial infarctions are reduced with long-term ACE inhibition in patients with left ventricular dysfunction has raised the speculation of whether this therapy would be helpful in reducing coronary heart disease, morbidity, and mortality in an even broader population.

Two studies, the Canadian-based Heart Outcomes Prevention Evaluation (HOPE) and the National, Heart, Lung and Blood Institute sponsored Prevention of Events with ACE inhibitor therapy (PEACE), are designed to address the specific issue of whether the addition of an ACE inhibitor to conventional therapy would reduce mortality and the manifestations of coronary heart disease in a broader patient population. The HOPE study is selecting patients that have documented coronary disease, are at high risk for coronary disease on the basis of a history of peripheral or cerebral vascular disease, or are diabetics with other known risk factors. In the PEACE study, coronary disease will be documented by a history of prior myocardial infarction or by angiographic studies. Patients that are already known to benefit from ACE inhibitor therapy for symptomatic congestive heart failure or a left ventricular ejection fraction of 40% or less will be excluded. These two studies will greatly supplement current information on ACE inhibitor therapy after myocardial infarction and will test the concept of ACE inhibition as preventive therapy for those at risk of experiencing a myocardial infarction.

With the development of angiotensin II receptor blockers, the basic investigative and clinical communities now have a more specific tool with which to dissect further the renin-angiotensin-bradykinin system. These angiotensin II receptor blockers are devoid of the augmentation of bradykinin-mediated actions produced by ACE inhibition. However, it is important to acknowledge that since the clinical benefits described above were obtained with ACE inhibition, it cannot be assumed that these benefits will be achieved with an angiotensin II blocker.

Summation

ACE inhibitors, which were originally developed and used in severe refractory heart failure, are now shown to have definite benefits in treating patients with acute myocardial infarction. Basic animal studies formed the foundation for the line of investigation that has led to these clinical benefits. In turn, these clinical observations have provided the stimulus for a whole new area of basic studies providing an excellent example of the cross-fertilization and interdependence of basic and clinical investigation.

Literature Cited

1. Albaladejo P, Bouaziz H, Duriez M, Gohlke P, Levy BI, et al. 1994. Angiotensin converting enzyme inhibition prevents the increase in aortic collagen in rats. *Hypertension* 23:74–82
2. Ambrosioni E, Borghi C, Magnani B, on behalf of SMILE pilot study. 1991. Early treatment of acute myocardial infarction with ACE inhibition: safety considerations. *Am. J. Cardiol.* 68: 101D–10
3. Anversa P, Beghi C, Kikkawa Y, Olivetti G. 1985. Myocardial response to infarction in the rat: morphometric measurement of infarct size and myocyte cellular hypertrophy. *Am. J. Pathol.* 118: 484–92
4. Anversa P, Beghi C, Kikkawa Y, Olivetti G. 1986. Myocardial infarction in rats. Infarct size, myocyte hypertrophy, and capillary growth. *Circ. Res.* 58:26–37
5. Baker KM, Aceto JF. 1990. Angiotensin II stimulation of protein synthesis and cell growth in chick heart cells. *Am. J. Physiol.* 259:H610–18
6. Baker KM, Booz GW, Dostal DE. 1992. Cardiac actions of angiotensin II: role of an intracardiac renin-angiotensin system. *Annu. Rev. Physiol.* 54:227–41
7. Baker KM, Chernin MI, Wixson SK, Aceto JF. 1990. Renin-angiotensin system involvement in pressure-overload cardiac hypertrophy in rats. *Am. J. Physiol.* 259:H324–32
8. Bao G, Gohlke P, Qadri F, Unger T. 1992. Chronic kinin receptor blockade attenuates the antihypertensive effect of ramipril. *Hypertension* 20:74–79
9. Benetos A, Gavras H, Stewart JM, Vavrek RJ, Hatinoglou S, Gavras I. 1986. Vasodepressor role of endogenous bradykinin assessed by a bradykinin antagonist. *Hypertension* 8:971–74
10. Brilla CG, Janicki JS, Weber KT. 1991. Cardioreparative effects of lisinopril in rats with genetic hypertension and left ventricular hypertrophy. *Circulation* 83: 1771–79
11. Brilla CG, Reams GP, Maisch B, Weber KT. 1993. Renin-angiotensin system and myocardial fibrosis in hypertension: reg-

ulation of the myocardial collagen matrix. *Eur. Heart J.* 14:57–61 (Suppl.)

12. Burgess ML, Carver WE, Terracio L, Wilson SP, Wilson MA, Borg TK. 1994. Integrin-mediated collagen gel contraction by cardiac fibroblasts. Effects of angiotensin II. *Circ. Res.* 74:291–98

13. Campbell DJ, Kladis A, Duncan AM. 1994. Effects of converting enzyme inhibitors on angiotensin and bradykinin peptides. *Hypertension* 23:439–49

14. Crawford DC, Chobanian AV, Brecher P. 1994. Angiotensin II induces fibronectin expression associated with cardiac fibrosis in the rat. *Circ. Res.* 74:727–39

15. Danser AHJ, van Kats JP, Admiraal PJJ, Derkx FHM, Lamers JMJ, et al. 1994. Cardiac renin and angiotensins. Uptake from plasma versus in situ synthesis. *Hypertension* 24:37–48

16. Dostal DE, Booz GW, Baker KM. 1994. The cardiac renin-angiotensin system: an overview. In *The Cardiac Renin-Angiotensin System,* ed. K Lindpaintner, D Ganten, pp.1–20 Armonk, NY: Futura

17. Dostal DE, Rothblum KN, Conrad KM, Cooper GR, Baker KM. 1992. Detection of angiotensin I and II in cultured rat cardiac myocytes and fibroblasts. *Am. J. Physiol.* 263:C851–63

18. Dzau VJ, Ellison KE, Brody T, Ingelfinger J, Pratt RE. 1987. A comparative study of the distributions of renin and angiotensinogen messenger ribonucleic acids in rat and mouse tissues. *Endocrinology* 120:2334–38

19. Dzau VJ, Re R. 1994. Tissue angiotensin system in cardiovascular medicine. A paradigm shift? (editorial). *Circulation* 89:493–98

20. Everett AD, Tufro-McReddie A, Fisher A, Gomez RA. 1994. Angiotensin receptor regulates cardiac hypertrophy and transforming growth factor-beta 1 expression. *Hypertension* 23:587–92

21. Fabris B, Jackson B, Kohzuki M, Perich R, Johnston CI. 1990. Increased cardiac angiotensin-converting enzyme in rats with chronic heart failure. *Clin. Exp. Pharmacol. Physiol.* 17:309–14

22. Finckh M, Hellmann W, Ganten D, Furtwangler A, Allgeier J, et al. 1991. Enhanced cardiac angiotensinogen gene expression and angiotensin-converting enzyme activity in tachypacing-induced heart failure in rats. *Basic Res. Cardiol.* 86:303–16

23. Fishbein MC, MacLean D, Maroko PR. 1978. Experimental myocardial infarction in the rat: qualitative and quantitative changes during pathologic evolution. *Am. J. Pathol.* 90:57–70

24. Gavras H. 1994. Corcoran Lecture. Angiotensin-converting enzyme inhibition and the heart. *Hypertension* 23:813–18

25. Geenen DL, Malhotra A, Scheuer J. 1993. Angiotensin II increases cardiac protein synthesis in adult rat heart. *Am. J. Physiol.* 265(HCP 34):H238–43

26. Gillum RF. 1994. Trends in acute myocardial infarction and coronary heart disease death in the United States. *J. Am. Coll. Cardiol.* 23:1273–77

27. Gohlke P, Linz W, Scholkens BA, Kuwer I, Bartenbach S, et al. 1994. Angiotensin-converting enzyme inhibition improves cardiac function. Role of bradykinin. *Hypertension* 23:411–18

28. Grady EF, Sechi LA, Griffin CA, Schambelan M, Kalinyak JE. 1991. Expression of AT2 receptors in the developing rat fetus. *J. Clin. Invest.* 88:921–33

29. Griendling KK, Murphy TJ, Alexander RW. 1993. Molecular biology of the renin-angiotensin system. *Circulation* 87:1816–28

30. Gruppo Italiano per lo Studio della Sopravvivenza nell'Infarto Miocardico. 1994. GISSI-3: effects of lisinopril and transdermal glyceryl trinitrate singly and together on 6-week mortality and ventricular function after acute myocardial infarction. *Lancet* 343:1115–22

31. Haber HL, Powers ER, Gimple LW, Wu CC, Subbiah K, et al. 1994. Intracoronary angiotensin–converting enzyme inhibition improves diastolic function in patients with hypertensive left ventricular hypertrophy. *Circulation* 89:2616–25

32. Hammermeister KE, DeRouen TA, Dodge HT. 1979. Variables predictive of survival in patients with coronary disease: selection by univariate and multivariate analyses from the clinical, electrocardiographic, exercise, arteriographic, and quantitative angiographic evaluations. *Circulation* 59:421–30

33. Himeno H, Crawford DC, Hosoi M, Chobanian AV, Brecher P. 1994. Angiotensin II alters aortic fibronectin independently of hypertension. *Hypertension* 23:823–26

34. Hirsch AT, Talsness CE, Schunkert H, Paul M, Dzau VJ. 1991. Tissue-specific activation of cardiac angiotensin-converting enzyme in experimental heart failure. *Circ. Res.* 69:475–82

35. Ho KK, Anderson KM, Kannel WB, Grossman W, Levy D. 1993. Survival after the onset of congestive heart failure in Framingham Heart Study subjects. *Circulation* 88:107–15

36. Ho KK, Pinsky JL, Kannel WB, Levy

D. 1993. The epidemiology of heart failure: the Framingham Study. *J. Am. Coll. Cardiol.* 22:6A-13

37. Holtz J, Studer R, Reinecke H, Just H, Drexler H. 1992. Modulation of myocardial sarcoplasmic reticulum Ca($^{2+}$)-ATPase in cardiac hypertrophy by angiotensin-converting enzyme? *Basic Res. Cardiol.* 87 Suppl. 2:191–204

38. Hutchins GM, Bulkley BH. 1978. Infarct expansion versus extension: two different complications of acute myocardial infarction. *Am. J. Cardiol.* 41:1127–32

39. ISIS-4. 1993. Present. 66th Sci. Sess. Am. Heart Assoc.

40. Iwai N, Inagami T, Ohmichi N, Nakamura Y, Saeki Y, Kinoshita M. 1992. Differential regulation of rat AT1a and AT1b receptor mRNA. *Biochem. Biophys. Res. Commun.* 188:298–303

41. Iwai N, Yamano Y, Chaki S, Konishi F, Bardhan S, et al. 1991. Rat angiotensin II receptor: cDNA sequence and regulation of the gene expression. *Biochem. Biophys. Res. Commun.* 177:299–304

42. Johnston CI. 1994. Tissue angiotensin-converting enzyme in cardiac and vascular hypertrophy, repair, and remodeling. *Hypertension* 23:258–68

43. Johnston CI, Mooser V, Sun Y, Fabris B. 1991. Changes in cardiac angiotensin-converting enzyme after myocardial infarction and hypertrophy in rats. *Clin. Exp. Pharmacol. Physiol.* 18:107–10

44. Kannel WB, Savage D, Castelli WP. 1982. Cardiac failure in the Framingham Study: Twenty-year follow-up. In *Congestive Heart Failure: Current Research and Clinical Applications,* ed. EB Braunwald, MB Mock, JT Watson pp.15–30. New York: Grune & Stratton

45. Kinoshita A, Urata H, Bumpus FM, Husain A. 1991. Multiple determinants for the high substrate specificity of an angiotensin II-forming chymase from the human heart. *J. Biol. Chem.* 266:19192–97

46. Kunapuli SP, Kumar A. 1987. Molecular cloning of human angiotensinogen cDNA and evidence for the presence of its mRNA in rat heart. *Circ. Res.* 60:786–90

47. Lindpaintner K, Ganten D. 1991. The cardiac renin-angiotensin system. An appraisal of present experimental and clinical evidence. *Circ. Res.* 68:905–21

48. Lindpaintner K, Jin MW, Niedermaier N, Wilhelm MJ, Ganten D. 1990. Cardiac angiotensinogen and its local activation in the isolated perfused beating heart. *Circ. Res.* 67:564–73

49. Lindpaintner K, Lu W, Neidermaier N,

Schieffer B, Just H, et al. 1993. Selective activation of cardiac angiotensinogen gene expression in post-infarction ventricular remodeling in the rat. *J. Mol. Cell Cardiol.* 25:133–46

50. Madeddu P, Parpaglia PP, Demontis MP, Varoni MV, Fattaccio MC, Glorioso N. 1994. Chronic inhibition of bradykinin B2-receptors enhances the slow vasopressor response to angiotensin II. *Hypertension* 23:646–52

51. Matsubara H, Kanasaki M, Murasawa S, Tsukaguchi Y, Nio Y, Inada M. 1994. Differential gene expression and regulation of angiotensin II receptor subtypes in rat cardiac fibroblasts and cardiomyocytes in culture. *J. Clin. Invest.* 93:1592–601

52. McCormick RJ, Musch TI, Bergman BC, Thomas DP. 1994. Regional differences in LV collagen accumulation and mature cross-linking after myocardial infarction in rats. *Am. J. Physiol.* 266:H354–59

53. Meggs LG, Coupet J, Huang H, Cheng W, Li P, et al. 1993. Regulation of angiotensin II receptors on ventricular myocytes after myocardial infarction in rats. *Circ. Res.* 72:1149–62

54. Michel JB, Lattion AL, Salzmann JL, Cerol ML, Philippe M, et al. 1988. Hormonal and cardiac effects of converting enzyme inhibition in rat myocardial infarction. *Circ. Res.* 62:641–50

55. Momose N, Fukuo K, Morimoto S, Ogihara T. 1993. Captopril inhibits endothelin-1 secretion from endothelial cells through bradykinin. *Hypertension* 21:921–24

56. Morgan HE, Baker KM. 1991. Cardiac hypertrophy; mechanical, neural, and endocrine dependence. *Circulation* 83(1):13–25

57. Nabel EG, Topol EJ, Galeana A, Ellis SG, Bates ER, et al. 1991. A randomized placebo-controlled trial of combined early intravenous captopril and recombinant tissue-type plasminogen activator therapy in acute myocardial infarction. *J. Am. Coll. Cardiol.* 17(2):467–73

58. Nagano M, Higaki J, Nakamura F, Higashimori K, Nagano N, et al. 1992. Role of cardiac angiotensin II in isoproterenol-induced left ventricular hypertrophy. *Hypertension* 19:708–12

59. Neyses L, Nouskas J, Luyken J, Fronhoffs S, Oberdorf S, et al. 1993. Induction of immediate-early genes by angiotensin II and endothelin-1 in adult rat cardiomyocytes. *J. Hypertens.* 11:927–34

60. Nolly H, Carbini LA, Scicli G, Carretero OA, Scicli AG. 1994. A local kallikrein-

kin system is present in rat hearts. *Hypertension* 23:919–23

61. Pashos CL, Newhouse JP, McNeil BJ. 1993. Temporal changes in the care and outcomes of elderly patients with acute myocardial infarction, 1987 through 1990. *J. Am. Med. Assoc.* 270:1832–36

62. Pfeffer JM. 1991. Progressive ventricular dilation in experimental myocardial infarction and its attenuation by angiotensin-converting enzyme inhibition. *Am. J. Cardiol.* 68:17D-25

63. Pfeffer JM, Pfeffer MA. 1988. Angiotensin converting enzyme inhibition and ventricular remodeling in heart failure. *Am. J. Med.* 84:37–44 (Suppl. 3a)

64. Pfeffer JM, Pfeffer MA, Braunwald E. 1985. Influence of chronic captopril therapy on the infarcted left ventricle of the rat. *Circ. Res.* 57:84–95

65. Pfeffer JM, Pfeffer MA, Fletcher PJ, Braunwald E. 1991. Progressive ventricular remodeling in rat with myocardial infarction. *Am. J. Physiol.* 29:H1406–14

66. Pfeffer MA. 1994. Angiotensin converting enzyme inhibition use in acute myocardial infarction. *Am. J. Cardiol.* 74:1A-5

67. Pfeffer MA, Braunwald E, Moye LA, Basta L, Brown EJ Jr, et al. 1992. Effect of captopril on mortality and morbidity in patients with left ventricular dysfunction after myocardial infarction. Results of the Survival and Ventricular Enlargement Trial. *N. Engl. J. Med.* 327:669–77

68. Pfeffer MA, Lamas GA, Vaughan DE, Parisi AF, Braunwald E. 1988. Effect of captopril on progressive ventricular dilatation after anterior myocardial infarction. *N. Engl. J. Med.* 319:80–86

69. Pfeffer MA, Pfeffer JM, Fishbein MC, Fletcher PJ, Spadaro J, et al. 1979. Myocardial infarct size and ventricular function in rats. *Circ. Res.* 44:503–12

70. Pfeffer MA, Pfeffer JM, Steinberg C, Finn P. 1985. Survival after an experimental myocardial infarction: beneficial effects of long-term therapy with captopril. *Circulation* 72:406–12

71. Pinto JE, Viglione P, Saavedra JM. 1991. Autoradiographic localization and quantification of rat heart angiotensin-converting enzyme. *Am. J. Hypertens.* 4:321–26

72. Pinto YM, de Smet BG, van Gilst WH, Scholtens E, Monnink S, et al. 1993. Selective and time related activation of the cardiac renin-angiotensin system after experimental heart failure: relation to ventricular function and morphology. *Cardiovasc. Res.* 27:1933–38

73. Ray SG, Pye M, Oldroyd KG, Christie J, Connelly DT, et al. 1993. Early treatment with captopril after acute myocardial infarction. *Br. Heart J.* 69:215–22

74. Raya TE, Gay RG, Aguirre M, Goldman S. 1989. Importance of venodilatation in prevention of left ventricular dilatation after chronic large myocardial infarction in rats: a comparison of captopril and hydralazine. *Circ. Res.* 64:330–37

75. Reiss K, Capasso JM, Huang HE, Meggs LG, Li P, Anversa P. 1993. ANG II receptors, c-myc, and c-jun in myocytes after myocardial infarction and ventricular failure. *Am. J. Physiol.* 264:H760–69

76. Rhaleb NE, Yang XP, Scicli AG, Carretero OA. 1994. Role of kinins and nitric oxide in the antihypertrophic effect of ramipril. *Hypertension* 23:865–68

77. Rubin SA, Fishbein MC, Swan HJ. 1983. Compensatory hypertrophy in the heart after myocardial infarction in the rat. *J. Am. Coll. Cardiol.* 1(Suppl 6):1435–41

78. Rutherford JD, Pfeffer MA, Moye LA, Davis BR, Flaker GC, et al. 1994. Effects of captopril on ischemic events after myocardial infarction. Results of the Survival and Ventricular Enlargement Trial. *Circulation* 90:1731–38

79. Sadoshima J, Izumo S. 1993. Molecular characterization of angiotensin II—induced hypertrophy of cardiac myocytes and hyperplasia of cardiac fibroblasts. Critical role of the AT1 receptor subtype. *Circ. Res.* 73:413–23

80. Sadoshima J, Izumo S. 1993. Signal transduction pathways of angiotensin II—induced *c-fos* gene expression in cardiac myocytes in vitro. Roles of phospholipid-derived second messengers. *Circ. Res.* 73:424–38

81. Sadoshima J, Xu Y, Slayter HS, Izumo S. 1993. Autocrine release of angiotensin II mediates stretch-induced hypertrophy of cardiac myocytes in vitro. *Cell* 75:977–84

82. Sasamura H, Hein L, Krieger JE, Pratt RE, Kobilka BK, Dzau VJ. 1992. Cloning, characterization, and expression of two angiotensin receptor (AT-1) isoforms from the mouse genome. *Biochem. Biophys. Res. Commun.* 185:253–59

83. Schieffer B, Wirger A, Meybrunn M, Seitz S, Holtz J, et al. 1994. Comparative effects of chronic angiotensin-converting enzyme inhibition and angiotensin II type 1 receptor blockade on cardiac remodeling after myocardial infarction in the rat. *Circulation* 89:2273–82

84. Schorb W, Booz GW, Dostal DE, Con-

rad KM, Chang KC, Baker KM. 1993. Angiotensin II is mitogenic in neonatal rat cardiac fibroblasts. *Circ. Res.* 72: 1245–54

85. Schunkert H, Dzau VJ, Tang SS, Hirsch AT, Apstein CS, Lorell BH. 1990. Increased rat cardiac angiotensin-converting enzyme activity and mRNA expression in pressure overload left ventricular hypertrophy. Effects on coronary resistance, contractility, and relaxation. *J. Clin. Invest.* 86:1913–20

86. Schunkert H, Jackson B, Tang SS, Schoen FJ, Smits JF, et al. 1993. Distribution and functional significance of cardiac angiotensin-converting enzyme in hypertrophied rat hearts. *Circulation* 87:1328–39

87. Sechi LA, Griffin CA, Grady EF, Kalinyak JE, Schambelan M. 1992. Characterization of angiotensin II receptor subtypes in rat heart. *Circ. Res.* 71: 1482–89

88. Sharpe N, Smith H, Murphy J, Hannan S. 1988. Treatment of patients with symptomless left ventricular dysfunction after myocardial infarction. *Lancet* 1: 255–59

89. St. John Sutton M, Pfeffer MA, Plappert T, Rouleau JL, Moye LA, et al. 1994. Quantitative two-dimensional echocardiographic measurements are major predictors of adverse cardiovascular events after acute myocardial infarction: the protective effects of captopril. *Circulation* 89:68–75

90. Stone PH, Raabe DS, Jaffe AS, Gustafson N, Muller JE, et al. 1988. Prognostic significance of location and type of myocardial infarction: independent adverse outcome associated with anterior location. *J. Am. Coll. Cardiol.* 11:453–63

91. Studer R, Muller B, Reinecke H, Just H, Holtz J, Drexler H. 1992. Quantified RNA-polymerase chain reaction demonstrates augmented gene expression of angiotensin-converting enzyme in ventricles of patients with heart failure. *Circulation* 86:I-119 [Abstr.]

92. Studer R, Reinecke H, Muller B, Holtz J, Just H, Drexler H. 1994. Increased angiotensin-I converting enzyme gene expression in the failing human heart: quantification by competitive RNA polymerase chain reaction. *J. Clin. Invest.* 94:301–10

93. Suzuki J, Matsubara H, Urakami M, Inada M. 1993. Rat angiotensin II (type 1A) receptor mRNA regulation and subtype expression in myocardial growth and hypertrophy. *Circ. Res.* 73:439–47

94. Swedberg K, Held P, Kjekshus J, Rasmussen K, Ryden L, Wedel H, on Be-

half of the Consensus II Study Group. 1992. Effects of the early administration of enalapril on mortality in patients with acute myocardial infarction. Results of the Cooperative New Scandinavian Enalapril Survival Study II (CONSENSUS II). *N. Engl. J. Med.* 327:678–84

95. The Acute Infarction Ramipril Efficacy (AIRE) Study Investigators. 1993. Effect of ramipril on mortality and morbidity of survivors of acute myocardial infarction with clinical evidence of heart failure. *Lancet* 342:821–28

96. Timmermans PBMWM, Wong PC, Chiu AT, Herblin WF, Benfield P, et al. 1993. Angiotensin II receptors and angiotensin II receptor antagonists. *Pharmacol. Rev.* 45:205–51

97. Ungureanu D, de Zegontita J, De Uguarte D, Ellingsen O, Nishida M, et al. 1993. De novo synthesis of angiotensin II by cardiac microvascular endothelial cells in vitro. *Circulation* 88:I-191 [Abstr.]

98. Urata H, Boehm KD, Philip A, Kinoshita A, Gabrovsek J, et al. 1993. Cellular localization and regional distribution of an angiotensin II-forming chymase in the heart. *J. Clin. Invest.* 91:1269–81

99. Urata H, Kinoshita A, Misono KS, Bumpus FM, Husain A. 1990. Identification of a highly specific chymase as the major angiotensin II-forming enzyme in the human heart [published erratum appears in *J. Biol. Chem.* 25; 266(18):12114]. *J. Biol. Chem.* 265: 22348–57

100. Urata H, Kinoshita A, Perez DM, Misono KS, Bumpus FM, et al. 1991. Cloning of the gene and cDNA for human heart chymase. *J. Biol. Chem.* 266:17173–79

101. Vicaut E, Hou X. 1994. Local renin-angiotensin system in the microcirculation of spontaneously hypertensive rats. *Hypertension* 24:70–76

102. Villarreal FJ, Kim NN, Ungab GD, Printz MP, Dillmann WH. 1993. Identification of functional angiotensin II receptors on rat cardiac fibroblasts. *Circulation* 88:2849–61

103. von Lutterotti N, Catanzaro DF, Sealey JE, Laragh JH. 1994. Renin is not synthesized by cardiac and extrarenal vascular tissues. A review of experimental evidence. *Circulation* 89:458–70

104. Vracko R, Thorning D, Frederickson RG. 1989. Connective tissue cells in healing rat myocardium. *Am. J. Pathol.* 134:993–1006

105. Weber KT, Brilla CG. 1991. Pathological hypertrophy and cardiac interstit-

ium. Fibrosis and renin-angiotensin-aldosterone system. *Circulation* 83:1849–65

106. Weber KT, Brilla CG. 1993. Structural basis for pathologic left ventricular hypertrophy. *Clin. Cardiol.* 16: II10–14

107. Weber KT, Brilla CG, Cleland JG, Cohn JN, Hansson L, et al. 1993. Cardioreparation and the concept of modulating cardiovascular structure and function. *Blood Press.* 2:6–21

108. Weber KT, Janicki JS. 1979. The heart as a muscle-pump system and the concept of heart failure. *Am. Heart J.* 98: 371–84

109. Weisman H, Bush D, Mannisi J, Weisfeldt M, Healy B. 1988. Cellular mechanisms of myocardial infarct expansion. *Circulation* 78:186–201

110. White HD, Norris RM, Brown MA, Brandt PWT, Whitlock RML, Wild CJ. 1987. Left ventricular end-systolic volume as the major determinant of survival after recovery from myocardial infarction. *Circulation* 76:44–51

111. Yamada H, Fabris B, Allen AM, Jackson B, Johnston CI, Mendelsohn AO. 1991. Localization of angiotensin-converting enzyme in rat heart. *Circ. Res.* 68:141–49

112. Yusuf S, Pepine CJ, Garces C, Pouleur H, Salem D, et al. 1992. Effect of enalapril on myocardial infarction and unstable angina in patients with low ejection fractions. *Lancet* 340:1173–78

Annu. Rev. Physiol. 1995. 57:827–72

TRAFFIC SIGNALS ON ENDOTHELIUM FOR LYMPHOCYTE RECIRCULATION AND LEUKOCYTE EMIGRATION

Timothy A. Springer

The Center for Blood Research, Harvard Medical School, 200 Longwood Avenue, Boston, Massachusetts 02115

KEY WORDS: selectin, integrin, adhesion, homing, inflammation

INTRODUCTION

The circulatory and migratory properties of white blood cells have evolved to allow efficient surveillance of tissues for infectious pathogens and rapid accumulation at sites of injury and infection. Lymphocytes continually patrol the body for foreign antigen by recirculating from blood, through tissue, into lymph, and back to blood. Lymphocytes acquire a predilection, based on the environment in which they first encounter foreign antigen, to home to or recirculate through that same environment (39, 40). Granulocytes and monocytes cannot recirculate, but emigrate from the bloodstream in response to molecular changes on the surface of blood vessels that signal injury or infection. Lymphocytes can similarly accumulate in response to inflammatory stimuli. The nature of the inflammatory stimulus determines whether lymphocytes, monocytes, neutrophils, or eosinophils predominate, and thus exercises specificity in the molecular signals or "area codes" that are displayed on endothelium and control traffic of particular leukocyte classes.

Recent findings show that the "traffic signals" for lymphocyte recirculation and for neutrophil and monocyte localization in inflammation are strikingly similar at the molecular level. These traffic signal or area code molecules are

827

0066–4278/95/0315–0827$05.00

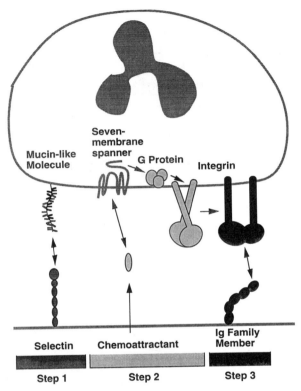

Figure 1 Three sequential steps provide the traffic signals that regulate leukocyte localization in the vasculature. Selectin molecules that bind carbohydrate ligands, often displayed on mucin-like molecules, are responsible for the initial tethering of a flowing leukocyte to the vessel wall and labile, rolling adhesions (*Step 1*). Tethering brings leukocytes into proximity with chemoattractants that are displayed on or released from the endothelial lining of the vessel wall. Chemoattractants bind to receptors that span the membrane seven times on the surface of leukocytes. These couple to G proteins, which transduce signals that activate integrin adhesiveness (*Step 2*). The integrins can then bind to immunoglobulin superfamily (IgSF) members on the endothelium, increasing adhesiveness and resulting in arrest of the rolling leukocyte (*Step 3*). Following directional cues from chemoattractants and using integrins for traction, leukocytes then cross the endothelial lining of the blood vessel and enter the tissue.

displayed together on endothelium but act on leukocytes in a sequence that was first defined for neutrophils and appears to hold true with slight modification for lymphocyte homing as well (Figure 1). The selectin (Step 1) allows cells to tether and roll, the chemoattractant (Step 2) tells cells to activate integrin adhesiveness and put on the brakes, and the Ig family member (Step 3) binds integrins and causes cells to come to a full stop. These three steps, with multiple molecular choices at each step, provide great combinatorial diversity in signals. Accordingly, the selective responses of different leukocyte classes to inflammatory agents, as well as the preferential recirculation patterns of distinct lymphocyte subpopulations, can be explained by their distinct receptivity to combinations of molecular signals. Following an overview of leukocytes and endothelium, and of the molecules important in their interactions, I review the traffic signals that enable selective emigratory behavior of monocytes and neutrophils, and then elaborate how a paradigm of three or four sequential signals can be extended to lymphocyte recirculation. This review updates and extends about twofold a previous one (240). For recent reviews see 12, 25, 26, 36, 42, 73, 90, 97, 143, 159, 160, 167, 172, 196, 206, 223, 280.

THE FUNCTION OF LEUKOCYTE CLASSES CORRELATES WITH CIRCULATORY BEHAVIOR

Neutrophilic granulocytes are among the most abundant leukocytes in the bloodstream and the first to appear at sites of bacterial infection or injury. Neutrophils are produced at the prodigious rate of 10^9 cells/kg body wt/day in the bone marrow and have a half-life in the circulation of 7 h. Their lifespan after extravasation is hours or less (54). Their primary function is to phagocytose and eliminate foreign microorganisms and damaged tissue.

Monocytes are far less numerous in the blood than neutrophils, where their half-life is about 24 h (113). Like neutrophils, they are phagocytic and accumulate in response to traumatic injury or bacterial infection. However, monocytes differ from neutrophils, in that they accumulate at sites where T lymphocytes have recognized antigen, as in delayed type hypersensitivity reactions and graft rejection. Monocytes are important effector cells in antigen-specific T cell immunity, are activated by T cell products such as γ-interferon, and can organize around parasites into protective structures called granulomas. After extravasation, monocytes may also differentiate into longer-lived tissue macrophages or mononuclear phagocytes such as the Kupffer cells of the liver, which have a half-life of weeks to months.

In contrast to the neutrophil and monocyte, a lymphocyte may emigrate and recirculate many thousands of times during its life history. Recirculation of lymphocytes correlates with their role as antigen receptor–bearing surveillance cells. Lymphocytes function as the reservoir of immunological memory, and recirculate through tissues to provide systemic memory. Few of the body's lymphocytes are present at any one time in the bloodstream, where their half-life is 2 h. Distinct subsets of lymphocytes extravasate through the microvasculature in tissues such as skin and gut, and through specialized high endothelial venules (HEV) in lymphoid organs (39, 159, 196). After migrating through tissue, lymphocytes find their way into the lymphatics. They percolate through draining lymph nodes in the lymphatic system and finally enter the thoracic duct, through which they return to the bloodstream. This journey is completed roughly every 1 to 2 days.

ENDOTHELIUM

By displaying specific signals, the endothelium is the most active player in controlling leukocyte traffic. Vascular endothelium is diversified at a number of levels. Large vessels differ from small vessels and capillaries, venular endothelium differs from arterial endothelium, and endothelial phenotype varies between tissues. The preferential migration of leukocytes from postcapillary venules may be related to factors such as shear stress, which is lower there and hence more favorable for leukocyte attachment than in capillaries or arterioles, or to events that occur when leukocytes pass through capillaries. However, when flow is controlled so that shear stress is equivalent in arterioles and venules (152), or when the direction of blood flow is reversed (182), attachment and emigration is far greater from venules, suggesting molecular differences in their endothelial surfaces. In agreement with this, P-selectin is much more abundant on postcapillary venules than on large vessels, arterioles, or capillaries (168), and induction of E-selectin and vascular cell adhesion molecule-1 (VCAM-1) expression in inflammation is most prominent on postcapillary venules (25). The mucin-like cluster of differentiation 34 (CD34) molecule is well expressed on capillaries and is absent from most large vessels (82), and CD36 is expressed on microvascular but not large vessel endothelium (251). The extracellular matrix may exert an influence on endothelial differentiation, as exemplified by modulation of adhesiveness (279). The high endothelium in lymphoid tissue, which expresses addressins for lymphocyte recirculation, is one of the most dramatic examples of endothelial specialization (196).

Inflammatory cytokines dramatically and selectively modulate the transcription and expression of adhesion molecules and chemoattractants in endothelial cells (203). Tumor necrosis factor (TNF) and interleukin-1 (IL-1) increase adhesiveness of endothelium for neutrophils and lymphocytes and induce intercellular adhesion molecule-1 (ICAM-1), E-selectin, and VCAM-1. IL-4, synergistically with other cytokines, increases adhesion of lymphocytes and induces VCAM-1 (164, 259). It is likely that the precise mixture of chemoattractants and cytokines produced at inflammatory sites in vivo determines which types of leukocytes emigrate. Thus injection into skin of IL-1α induces emigration of neutrophils and monocytes; as do lipopolysaccharide (LPS) and TNF-α, but with more prolonged emigration of the monocytes. IFN-γ induces emigration of monocytes but not neutrophils (113). IFN-γ and TNF-α, but not

IL-1α or LPS, recruit lymphocytes, and IL-4 is ineffective by itself but synergizes with TNF (33, 60, 118).

Acting more quickly than cytokines, vasoactive substances such as histamine and thrombin modulate endothelial function in seconds or minutes. They induce secretion of the storage granules of endothelial cells and platelets. Furthermore, they dilate arterioles and increase plasma leakage, which raises the hematocrit within microvessels, and thereby alters the rheology of blood so as to increase the collision of leukocytes with the vessel wall (218). Furthermore, arteriolar dilation and the ensuing increased blood flow in inflammatory sites are responsible for two of the cardinal signs of inflammation, rubor (redness) and calor (heat), and greatly enhance the discharge and, thus, accelerate the accumulation of leukocytes.

Area Code Molecules

SELECTINS   Multiple protein families, each with a distinct function, provide the traffic signals for leukocytes. The selectin family of adhesion molecules (Figure 2) has an N-terminal domain homologous to Ca^{2+}-dependent lectins (25, 144, 167, 206, 238). The name selectin capitalizes on the derivation of lectin and select from the same Latin root, meaning to separate by picking out. Selectins are limited in expression to cells of the vasculature (Figure 2). L-selectin is expressed on all circulating leukocytes, except for a subpopulation of lymphocytes (85, 126, 151). P-selectin is stored preformed in the Weibel-Palade bodies of endothelial cells and the α granules of platelets. In response to mediators of acute inflammation such as thrombin or histamine, P-selectin is rapidly mobilized to the plasma membrane to bind neutrophils and monocytes (86, 140, 168). E-selectin is induced on vascular endothelial cells by cytokines such as IL-1, LPS, or TNF and requires de novo mRNA and protein synthesis (27).

CARBOHYDRATES AND MUCIN-LIKE MOLECULES   All selectins appear to recognize a sialylated carbohydrate determinant on their counter-receptors (26, 143, 206). E-selectin and P-selectin recognize carbohydrate structures that are distinct, but are both closely related to the tetrasaccharide sialyl Lewis x and its isomer sialyl Lewis a (Figure 2). The actual ligand structures for E- and P-selectin are more complex than sialyl Lewis a or x, as shown by display of the ligand for E-selectin, but not P-selectin, on fucosyl transferase-transfected cells that express sialyl Lewis x (141). The affinity of E-selectin for soluble sialyl Lewis x or a is quite low, with K_d = 0.2–0.8 mM (183), which suggests that a higher affinity ligand may yet be identified. P-selectin is specific for carbohydrate displayed on the P-selectin glycoprotein ligand (PSGL-1), suggesting either that PSGL-1 expresses a specific carbohydrate structure or that

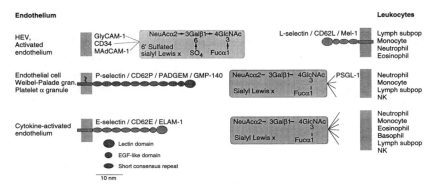

Figure 2 Selectins and their ligands. The selectins are shown to scale, based on electron micrographs of P-selectin (260), the X-ray structure of E-selectin lectin and EGF domains (91), and estimates of the sizes of the short consensus repeats (SCR) (238). P-selectin is shown palmitylated on a transmembrane cysteine (84). The carbohydrates are not to scale. Sialyl Lewis a and x contain Galβ1–3(Fucα1–4)GlcNAc and Galβ1–4(Fucα1–3)GlcNAc linkages, respectively.

PSGL-1 protein forms part of the ligand binding site (173). The affinity of P-selectin for PSGL-1 is high with a $K_d = 70$ nM(260). Structure-function studies suggest that the Ca^{2+}-binding site and a cluster of basic residues on E-selectin coordinate with the fucosyl and sialic acid carboxylate moieties, respectively, of sialyl Lewis x (78, 91).

The carbohydrate ligands for L- and P-selectin are O-linked to specific mucin-like molecules. Mucins are serine- and threonine-rich proteins that are heavily O-glycosylated and have an extended structure. L-selectin recognizes at least two mucins in HEV (Figure 3): glycosylation-dependent cell adhesion molecule-1 (GlyCAM-1), which is secreted (144), and CD34, which is on the cell surface (17). The carbohydrate ligand for L-selectin is related to sialyl Lewis a and x (19, 83), contains sialic acid and sulfate, and is O-linked to mucin-like structures of HEV (206). Structural studies on the carbohydrates of GlyCAM-I show that 6′ sulfated sialyl Lewis x (Figure 2) is a major oligosaccharide capping group and is a candidate for the ligand structure (101).

The mucin-like P-selectin glycoprotein ligand (PSGL-1) is a disulfide-linked dimer of 120-kDa subunits (173) that is sensitive to O-glycoprotease, which selectively cleaves mucin-like domains (186, 245). PSGL-1 (Figure 3) was isolated by screening for cDNA that expressed ligand activity (212). COS cells must be transfected both with the PSGL-1 cDNA and α-3/4 fucosyl transferase cDNA to express P-selectin ligand activity. By contrast, COS cells cotransfected with cDNA for α-3/4 fucosyl transferase and another mucin-like molecule that is expressed by neutrophils, CD43, lack P-selectin ligand activity.

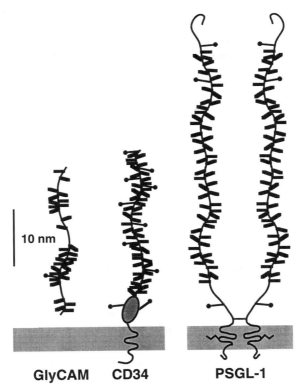

GlyCAM   CD34   PSGL-1

Figure 3 Mucin-like carriers of selectin ligands. The GlyCAM (144) and CD34 (17, 227) molecules synthesized by peripheral lymph node HEV and MAdCAM-1 molecule synthesized by mucosal HEV (see Figure 5) bear O-linked carbohydrates that bind to L-selectin. CD34 has a globular domain that may be Ig-like (13) and is resistant to O-glycoprotease (250). The PSGL-1 molecule on neutrophils bears O-linked carbohydrates that bind to P-selectin (186, 212). A cysteine in the transmembrane region is predicted to be palmitylated. O-linked sites and N-linked sites are shown as bars and lollipops, respectively. The length of the mucin-like domains, and the percent of serines and threonines that are O-glycosylated, are proportioned to measurements for CD43 (45 nm per 224 amino acids and 75–90% of O-glycosylation) (65).

FUNCTION OF SELECTINS AND THEIR LIGANDS   Selectins mediate functions unique to the vasculature, the tethering of flowing leukocytes to the vessel wall, and the formation of labile adhesions with the wall that permit leukocytes subsequently to roll in the direction of flow. One study demonstrated this with purified P-selectin incorporated into supported planar lipid bilayers on one wall of a flow chamber (147). At wall shear stresses within the range of those found in postcapillary venules, neutrophils formed labile attachments to the

P-selectin in the bilayer and rolled in response to fluid drag forces. In other studies, intravascular infusion of a soluble L-selectin/IgG chimera inhibited neutrophil rolling attachments in vivo (153), as did infusion of anti-L-selectin monoclonal antibodies (266). More recent studies have shown that neutrophils roll on E-selectin in purified form (148) or on the endothelial cell surface both in vitro (1) and in vivo (188), that monoclonal antibody (mAb) to P-selectin decreases neutrophil rolling in vivo (28), and that neutrophil rolling in the microvasculature of mice genetically deficient in P-selectin is almost completely absent (165).

P- and L-selectin may cooperate with one another because inhibition of either almost completely inhibits neutrophil rolling in vivo (153, 165, 266, 267). E- and L-selectin also appear to cooperate (135, 148, 200, 265). A class of ligand that is closely associated with L-selectin on the neutrophil surface is required for the initial tethering during flow to E-selectin bilayers, after which another class of ligands that mediates rolling takes over (145).

Selectins can mediate tethering of a flowing cell in the span of a millisecond. Other adhesion receptors require minutes to develop similar adhesive strength and do not mediate rolling (51, 147). It has been hypothesized that selectins differ from other adhesion molecules not in affinity (K_{eq}), but in having much more rapid association (K_{on}) and dissociation (K_{off}) rate constants (147), as has recently been confirmed (Table 1). Rolling is intermittent and appears mediated by random association and dissociation of selectin-ligand bonds, a small number of which tether a leukocyte to the vessel wall at any one time. A rapid association rate facilitates the initial tethering in flow. A rapid dissociation rate ensures that even with multiple selectin-ligand bonds, it will not take long before the bond that is most upstream randomly dissociates, allowing the cell

Table 1   Fast on and off rates of a selectin and affinity modulation of an integrin

	K_{on} $(M^{-1}s^{-1})$	K_{off} (s^{-1})	K_d (μM)
P-selectin	1.4×10^{7a}	1^b	0.07^c
LFA-1 low affinity[d]	3×10^2	0.03	100
LFA-1 high affinity[e]	ND^f	ND	0.6

[a] Calculated from $K_{on} = K_{off}/K_d$

[b] At very low P-selectin densities in lipid bilayers, neutrophils, attach transiently, i.e. they subsequently detach rather than roll. Measurements of the cellular dissociation rate suggest that the $t_{1/2}$ for dissociation of a single selectin-ligand bond is about 0.7 s (R Alon & T Springer, unpublished data).

[c] For binding of monomeric, truncated P-selectin to neutrophils (260).

[d] k_{on}, k_{off}, and K_d were measured by competitive inhibition by monomeric, truncated ICAM-1 of binding of Fab to LFA-1 on resting lymphocytes (157).

[e] Same as d but for phorbol ester-stimulated lymphocytes. Approximately 20% of the cell surface LFA-1 was in the high affinity state (157).

[f] ND = not determined.

to roll forward a small distance until it is held by the next most upstream bond (96, 147).

The elongated molecular structure of selectins and mucins and their segmental flexibility (65, 260) are predicted to enhance their accessibility for binding to counter-structures on closely opposed cells (147). P-selectin and PSGL-1 are currently the most elongated adhesion molecules known (Figure 3 and 4) and can bridge together two cells with plasma membranes about 0.1 μm apart. Expression on cytoplasmic protrusions further enhances accessibility. L-selectin is clustered on microvilli of neutrophils (79, 200), which project about 0.3 μm above the surface of a cell with a diameter of 7 μm, and contain 90% of the L-selectin (D Bainton et al, unpublished data). In keeping with this topographic distribution, rolling in vivo requires the integrity of the L-selectin cytoplasmic domain and is inhibited by cytochalasin B (125). Lymphocytes bind through microvilli to HEV (7, 261). Conversely, the mucin-like CD34 molecule (227) is concentrated on filopodia of nonspecialized endothelial cells found in the microvasculature of most tissues (82). These filopodia are concentrated near junctions between endothelial cells, and electron micrographs of granulocytes binding to the microvasculature in inflammatory sites suggest that the earliest binding event is to these filopodia (62).

CHEMOATTRACTANTS   Chemoattractants are important in activation of integrin adhesiveness and in directing the migration of leukocytes. In chemotaxis, cells move in the direction of increasing concentration of a chemoattractant, which typically is a soluble molecule that can diffuse away from the site of its production, where its concentration is highest (70, 274). Leukocytes, which can sense a concentration difference of 1% across their diameter, move steadily in the direction of the chemoattractant. There is much interplay between adhesion molecules and chemoattractants because adhesion to a surface is required to provide the traction necessary for migration directed by chemoattractants, and chemoattractants can activate adhesiveness.

The alternative mechanism to chemotaxis is haptotaxis. In haptotaxis, cells migrate to the region of highest adhesiveness (45). Thus on a gradient of an adhesive ligand affixed to the surface of other cells or to the extracellular matrix, and in the absence of a chemotactic gradient, motile cells will tend to accumulate in the region of highest ligand density. Both chemotaxis and haptotaxis can contribute to cell localization, but haptotaxis has yet to be demonstrated in vivo.

Classical leukocyte chemoattractants act broadly on neutrophils, eosinophils, basophils, and monocytes (Table 2). A recently described family of chemoattractive cytokines, termed chemokines, are 70–80 residue polypeptides and have specificity for leukocyte subsets (12, 172). Two subfamilies of chemokines have been defined by sequence homology and by the sequence

Table 2 Leukocyte chemoattractants

Chemoattractant	Origin	Responding cells
Classical chemoattractants[a]		
N-formyl peptides	Bacterial protein processing	Monocyte, neutrophil, eosinophil, basophil
C5a	Complement activation	Monocyte, neutrophil, eosinophil, basophil
Leukotriene B4	Arachidonate metabolism	Monocyte, neutrophil
Platelet-activating factor (PAF)	Phosphatidylcholine metabolism	Monocyte, neutrophil, eosinophil
CXC chemokines[b]		
IL-8/NAP-1	T lymphocyte, monocyte, endothelial cell, fibroblast, keratinocyte, chondrocyte, mesothelial cell	Neutrophil, basophil
CTAP-III/β-thromboglobulin/NAP-2	Successive N-terminal cleavage of platelet basic protein released from α-granules	Neutrophil, basophil, fibroblast
gro/MGSA	Fibroblast, melanoma, endothelial cell, monocyte	Neutrophil, melanomas, fibroblast
ENA-78	Epithelium	Neutrophil
CC chemokines[c]		
MCP-1	T lymphocyte, monocyte, fibroblast, endothelial cell, smooth muscle	Monocyte, T lymphocyte subpopulation, basophil
MIP-1α	Monocyte, B and T lymphocyte	Monocyte, T lymphocyte subpopulation, basophil, eosinophil
RANTES	T lymphocyte, platelet	Monocyte, T lymphocyte subpopulation, eosinophil
I-309	T lymphocyte, mast cell	Monocyte

References:
[a] (70, 232), [b] (12, 29, 43, 137, 172), [c] (2, 12, 43, 124, 172, 208, 214–216, 253, 255).

around two cysteine residues (Table 2). The CXC or α chemokines tend to act on neutrophils and nonhematopoietic cells involved in wound healing, whereas the CC or β chemokines tend to act on monocytes and in some cases on eosinophils and lymphocyte subpopulations.

It has long been debated whether chemoattractants can act in the circulation, where they would be rapidly diluted and swept downstream by blood flow. Tethering and rolling of leukocytes through selectins would enhance exposure to chemoattractants by prolonging contact with the vessel wall. However, retention of chemoattractants at their site of production by noncovalent interactions with molecules on the vessel wall and within the inflammatory site may also be important. Heparin-binding sites on chemokines provide a mechanism for retention in the extracellular matrix (109) to enhance concentration gradients and perhaps to present chemokines on the endothelium to circulating leukocytes (207, 253).

CHEMOATTRACTANT RECEPTORS   Leukocyte chemoattractant receptors have multiple functions. They not only direct migration, but also activate integrin adhesiveness, and stimulate degranulation, shape change, actin polymerization, and the respiratory burst (232). Chemoattractant receptors are G protein-coupled receptors that span the membrane seven times. Ligand binding to the seven membrane-spanner is coupled to exchange of GTP for GDP bound to the associated G protein heterotrimer and results in activation by the G protein α and $\beta\gamma$ subunits of signaling effectors such as phospholipase C-β_2 (277). This results in release of diacylglycerol and inositol phosphates, and mobilization of Ca^{2+}. Neutrophils and lymphocytes express $G\alpha_{i2}$ and $G\alpha_{i3}$ subunits (18, 232). The $G\alpha$ subunits of the α_i class are ADP-ribosylated and irreversibly inactivated by pertussis toxin. All the biological effects of leukocyte chemoattractants are inhibited by pertussis toxin. Coupling through $G\alpha_i$ subunits has been confirmed by reconstitution in transfected cells (277). The lipid mediators LTB4 and PAF are as active as formylated bacterial peptides C5a and IL-8 in stimulating chemotaxis, but less active in stimulating the respiratory burst and other functions of neutrophils (232); this correlates with their ability to couple to distinct $G\alpha$ subunits in transfected cells (6).

Cloning of the receptors for formylated bacterial peptides C5a and PAF has shown that they are expressed on both neutrophils and monocytes, whereas the receptor for IL-8 is expressed only on neutrophils (181). The receptor for MCP-1 is expressed on monocytic cells but not on neutrophils (52). Thus the specificity of chemoattractants is regulated by the cellular distribution of their receptors.

INTEGRINS   Integrins are perhaps the most versatile of the adhesion molecules. Integrin adhesiveness can be rapidly regulated by the cells on which they are expressed. Each integrin contains a noncovalently associated α and β subunit, with characteristic structural motifs (Figure 4). Five integrins are important in the interaction of leukocytes with endothelial cells. Their cellular distribution, ligand specificity, and structure are summarized in Table 3 and Figure 4.

ACTIVATION OF INTEGRINS   The adhesiveness of LFA-1 and VLA-4 on T lymphocytes is activated by cross-linking of the antigen receptor and other surface molecules (73, 223, 238). Increased adhesiveness occurs within a few minutes, is not accompanied by any change in quantity of surface expression, and appears to result from both conformational changes that increase affinity for ligand, and altered interaction with the cytoskeleton (73, 81, 88). However,

Table 3 Integrins in leukocyte-endothelial interactions

Subunits	Names	Distribution	Ligands
Leukocyte integrins[a]			
$\alpha^L\beta_2$	LFA-1, CD11a/CD18	B and T lymphocyte, monocyte, neutrophil	ICAM-1, ICAM-2, ICAM-3
$\alpha^M\beta_2$	Mac-1, CR3, CD11b/CD18	Monocyte, neutrophil	ICAM-1, iC3b, fibrinogen, factor X
$\alpha^x\beta_2$	p150,95, CR4, CD11c/CD18	Monocyte, neutrophil, eosinophil	iC3b, fibrinogen
α^4 Integrins[b]			
$\alpha^4\beta_1$	VLA-4, CD49d/CD29	B and T lymphocyte, monocyte, neural crest-derived cells, fibroblast, muscle	VCAM-1, fibronectin
$\alpha^4\beta_7$	LPAM-1, CD49d/CD-	B and T lymphocyte subpopulations	MAdCAM-1, VCAM-1, fibronectin

References
[a](133, 238) [b](24, 31, 50, 100, 105, 107, 108, 110, 211, 238).

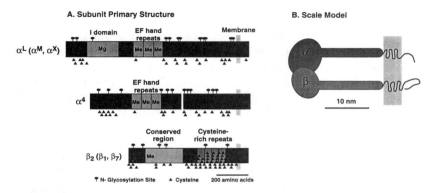

Figure 4   Integrins that bind endothelial ligands. (*A*) Schematics of representative integrin α and β subunits. The structures of α^L (142) and β_2 (134) integrin subunits are shown as representative of α^M and α^X or β_1 and β_7, respectively; cysteines are identical, and glycosylation sites vary but are sparse in the I domain and EF hand repeats. The EF hand repeats are divalent metal-binding motifs that may bind Ca^{2+} or Mg^{2+} (labeled Me). A binding site for Mg^{2+} and Mn^2 but not Ca^{2+} has been identified in the I domain (171). The α^4 integrin subunit has a posttranslational proteolytic cleavage site (252). A putative divalent cation binding site has been defined in the conserved domain of the integrin β_3 subunit and is shown for β_2 (156). (*B*) Scale model of an integrin based on electron micrographs of the integrins gpIIbIIIa (44) and VLA-5 ($\alpha^5\beta_1$) (184).

it is unlikely that recognition by T cell receptors of antigen on endothelial cells (204) is a step in lymphocyte trafficking because traffic of lymphocytes that can and cannot recognize specific antigen is increased in antigen-induced inflammation. Although evidence has been presented that binding of neutrophils to selectins can activate adhesiveness of integrins (155), other evidence has failed to confirm this (148, 158; T Diacovo & T Springer, unpublished data).

Thus far the best candidates for activation of integrin adhesiveness within the vasculature are chemoattractants. Adhesiveness of Mac-1 and LFA-1 on neutrophils and monocytes is activated by N-formylated peptide and IL-8 (38, 74, 154, 154, 229, 276). In contrast to LFA-1 on lymphocytes and neutrophils, Mac-1 on neutrophils is increased about tenfold on the surface by chemoattractant-stimulated fusion of secretory granules with the plasma membrane (221); however, this is neither sufficient nor necessary for increased adhesiveness (195, 262). The transient nature of the activation of integrin adhesiveness (76, 154) provides a mechanism for de-adhesion and, perhaps, for retraction of the trailing edge of a leukocyte from the substrate during cell migration.

Conformational changes in LFA-1 and Mac-1 that are associated with increased adhesiveness are suggested by the reaction of mAb and antigen-binding fragments (Fab), i.e. they react only with these molecules after cellular activation (72, 127, 138, 201). After chemoattractant activation of neutrophils, saturation binding shows that 10% of the surface Mac-1 molecules express an activation epitope, yet mAb to this epitope completely blocks binding to ligands such as ICAM-1 and fibrinogen, which suggests that ligand binding is mediated by a subpopulation of activated Mac-1 molecules (72). The I domain of leukocyte integrins is important in ligand binding (71, 171) and expresses activation epitopes (72, 138). Recent measurements of the affinity of cell surface LFA-1 for soluble, monomeric ICAM-1 (Table 1) have directly demonstrated that cellular activation increases the affinity of a subpopulation of LFA-1 molecules by approximately 200-fold (157).

Surprisingly, the integrin VLA-4, by contrast to LFA-1 and Mac-1, appears to be capable of supporting rolling. Lymphocytes can tether in flow and subsequently roll on VCAM-1. If activated while rolling by phorbol ester or TS2/16 mAb to the β_1 subunit, the lymphocytes arrest and develop firm adhesion. Activated lymphocytes tether as efficiently as resting lymphocytes but do not roll. Fibronectin can support development of firm adhesion in static conditions but not in tethering or rolling in flow. VCAM-1 is less efficient than selectins in mediating tethering and rolling (R Alon et al, submitted).

IgSF MEMBERS ON ENDOTHELIUM AS INTEGRIN LIGANDS   In a paradigm first established with ICAM-1 binding to LFA-1, several immunoglobulin superfamily (IgSF) members, expressed on endothelium, bind to integrins expressed on leukocytes (Figure 5). ICAM-1, ICAM-2, and ICAM-3 are products of distinct and homologous genes and were all initially identified by their ability to interact with LFA-1 (68, 210, 243). ICAM-1 has also been found to bind to Mac-1 through a distinct site in its third Ig domain (74, 75, 230) (Figure 5). Induction of ICAM-1 on endothelium and other cells by inflammatory cytokines may increase cell-cell interactions and leukocyte extravasation at inflammatory sites, whereas constitutive expression of ICAM-2 may be important for leukocyte trafficking in uninflamed tissues, as in lymphocyte recirculation. ICAM-3 is restricted to leukocytes. All three ICAMs contribute to antigen-specific interactions, thus inhibition with mAb to all three is required to completely block LFA-1-dependent antigen-specific T cell responses (67).

VCAM-1 is inducible by cytokines on endothelial cells, and on a more restricted subset of nonvascular cells than ICAM-1 (25). A single VCAM-1 gene gives rise through alternative splicing to a seven domain isoform and to a second isoform that contains either six domains or three domains and a glycosyl phosphatidylinositol membrane anchor (130, 176, 259) (Figure 5). VCAM-1 is a ligand for the integrin $\alpha^4\beta_1$ (VLA-4) and binds weakly to $\alpha^4\beta_7$ (50, 77, 211). In contrast to the shorter isoforms, the seven domain isoform of VCAM-I has two binding sites for VLA-4 in highly homologous domains 1 and 4 (191, 192, 268, 269).

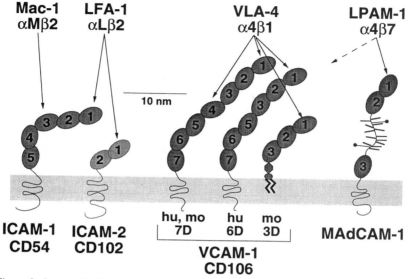

Figure 5 Ig superfamily adhesion receptors on endothelium, and their integrin-binding sites. Members of the Ig superfamily share the immunoglobulin domain, composed of 90 to 100 amino acids arranged in a sandwich of two sheets of anti-parallel β-strands, which is stabilized by one or (in the N-terminal domain of the molecules shown) two disulfide bonds. The immunoglobulins and T cell receptors are the only known members of this family that undergo somatic diversification. The function of the IgSF in adhesion evolutionarily predates specialization for antigen recognition. The shape and size of the ICAM-1 molecule, with its unpaired Ig domains and bend, was determined by electron microscopy (131, 242), as was that of VCAM-1 (192). Immunoglobulin domains are ellipsoids with a length of 4 nm parallel to the β-strands and 2.5 nm in the other dimensions. The mucin-like region of MAdCAM-1 is modeled as described in the legend to Figure 3. N-linked glycosylation sites in the Ig domains of this and the other molecules are not shown. References for structures (in parentheses) and for localization of the domains to which integrins bind (in brackets) follow: ICAM-1 (226, 244) [75, 242]; ICAM-2 (243); VCAM-1 (176, 190, 205) [191, 192, 268, 269]; MAdCAM-1 (34).

An addressin for lymphocyte recirculation to mucosa is expressed on Peyer's patch HEV and on other venules (248). Now termed mucosal addressin cell adhesion molecule (MAdCAM-1), it contains three Ig-like domains and a mucin-like region interposed between domains 2 and 3 (34) (Figure 5). MAdCAM-1 binds the integrin $\alpha^4\beta_7$ but not $\alpha^4\beta_1$ (24, 108). Furthermore, carbohydrates attached to the mucin-like domain of MAdCAM-1 bind L-selectin and mediate lymphocyte rolling (20). Thus MAdCAM-1 has a dual function as an integrin and selectin ligand.

OTHER MOLECULES   CD31 is an IgSF member expressed on leukocytes, platelets, and at cell-cell junctions on endothelium (3, 4, 177, 185, 228, 247, 254).

CD31 can bind homophilically to itself and also heterophilically to an uncharacterized counter-receptor. mAb cross-linking of CD31, similarily to many but not all other lymphocyte surface molecules, can trigger integrin adhesiveness (254). Interaction between CD31 on endothelial junctions and CD31 on leukocytes appears to be required for transmigration but not for integrin-mediated binding of leukocytes to endothelium (178). CD31-CD31 interaction may represent a fourth step in transendothelial migration that overlaps the integrin-mediated step and may contribute to the maintenance of the permeability barrier function of endothelia during transmigration.

CD44 is a widely distributed molecule in the body that is homologous with cartilage-link protein, is extensively alternatively spliced, and can bear heparin sulfate or chondroitin sulfate side chains (98). The best understood function of CD44 is as a major surface receptor for hyaluronate (11, 64). Alternatively spliced forms of CD44 are important in tumor metastasis (92) and in localization of antibody-secreting cells (9). CD44 (H-CAM, Hermes) was at one time mistakenly thought to be the human equivalent of murine mel-14 (L-selectin). It participates in vitro in lymphocyte interaction with HEV and activated endothelium (119, 189). However, lack of cell surface CD44 has no effect on lymphocyte recirculation in vivo (41).

Toward a Multi-Step Model of Neutrophil Emigration in Inflammation

INTEGRINS AND SELECTINS   Patients who are genetically deficient in the leukocyte integrins, owing to mutations in the common β_2 integrin CD18 subunit, provided early evidence that adhesion molecules are required for leukocyte extravasation in vivo (8, 133). Leukocyte adhesion deficiency-I (LAD-I) patients have life-threatening bacterial infections, and neutrophils in these patients fail to cross the endothelium and accumulate at inflammatory sites, despite higher than normal levels of neutrophils in the circulation. In vitro, LAD-I neutrophils or normal neutrophils treated with mAb to the leukocyte integrins are deficient in binding to and migrating across resting or activated endothelial monolayers (35, 231). Even though capable of binding to activated endothelium through selectins, LAD-I neutrophils fail to transmigrate (231). mAb to the leukocyte integrin β_2 subunit, and in some cases the integrin α^M subunit, have been found to have profound effects in vivo (97). These mAb prevent the neutrophil-mediated injury that occurs when ischemic tissue is reperfused, and thus can prevent death from shock after blood loss, limb necrosis after frostbite or after amputation and replantation, and tissue necrosis from myocardial ischemia and reperfusion. mAb to leukocyte integrins and to ICAM-1 can also inhibit lymphocyte and monocyte-mediated antigen-specific responses in vivo, including delayed-type hypersensitivity, granuloma formation, and allograft rejection (97).

Whereas mAb to the leukocyte integrin β_2 subunit blocked accumulation of leukocytes in tissue in response to chemoattractants, and prevented stable adhesion of leukocytes in the local vasculature, it had no effect on the number of rolling leukocytes on the vessel wall (10). Furthermore, leukocyte integrins were found to mediate binding of neutrophils to endothelial monolayers in a parallel wall flow chamber at subphysiologic, but not at physiologic, shear stresses found in postcapillary venules (146, 231).

Parallel studies showed that selectins were required for leukocyte accumulation in vivo and acted at an early step. Antagonists of L-selectin and E-selectin inhibit neutrophil and monocyte influx into skin, peritoneal cavity, and lung in response to inflammatory agents (122, 123, 151, 180, 272). mAb to L-selectin was shown to inhibit neutrophil accumulation on cytokine-stimulated endothelium at physiologic shear stress (229). Stimulation of neutrophils with chemoattractants results in shedding into the medium within minutes of L-selectin, with kinetics similar to upregulation of surface expression of the integrin Mac-1. Based on this, and the evidence reviewed above, it was hypothesized that selectins might act at a step prior to integrins (132).

Further studies showed that selectins mediate rolling, and function prior to development of firm adhesion through integrins. At sites of inflammation, leukocytes first attach to the vessel wall in a rolling interaction, then become arrested or firmly adherent at a single location on the vessel wall before diapedesis (56). This process was fully reconstituted with purified components of the endothelial surface (147). At physiologic shear stresses, neutrophils attach to and form labile rolling adhesions on phospholipid bilayers containing purified P-selectin, but not on bilayers containing ICAM-1. Chemoattractants stimulate strong, integrin-mediated adhesion to bilayers containing ICAM-1 under static conditions but not in shear flow. At physiologic shear stresses, if both P-selectin and ICAM-1 are present in the phospholipid bilayer, resting neutrophils attach and roll identically as on bilayers containing P-selectin alone. However, when chemoattractant is added to the buffer flowing through the chamber, the rolling neutrophils arrest, spread, and firmly adhere through the integrin-ICAM-1 interaction. Chemoattractant does not enhance interaction of neutrophils with bilayers containing P-selectin alone, but rather inhibits it. These findings show that purified adhesion molecules and chemoattractants representing the endothelial signals can reproduce the key events in leukocyte localization in vivo, and prove that the selectin-mediated step is a prerequisite for the chemoattractant and integrin-mediated steps (147). Complementary in vivo studies showed that mAb to L-selectin, or L-selectin/IgG chimeras, decreased the number of rolling leukocytes (153, 266) and the number of leukocytes that subsequently became firmly adherent, whereas mAb to the β_2 integrin subunit only decreased firm adherence of leukocytes. This suggests that L-selectin acts at a step prior to leukocyte integrins (266). In static assays, a factor derived from cytokine-stimulated endothelium induced shedding of L-selectin, and if transmigration was blocked with CD18 mAb, induced release of neutrophils from inverted endothelial monolayers, also suggesting that L-selectin acted prior to leukocyte integrin-mediated emigration (229). In elegant confirmation of a three-step model in a static assay of neutrophil adhesion to histamine-stimulated endothelium, juxtacrine cooperation between P-selectin and platelet-activating factor (PAF) was found (158). P-selectin tethered neutrophils to endothelium and thereby augmented stimulation by PAF of CD18-dependent neutrophil adhesion. Stimulation of adhesiveness was by PAF and not by P-selectin, as shown with PAF receptor antagonists.

The requirement for the carbohydrate ligands of selectins for leukocyte emigration in vivo has received strong support from studies of two patients with a genetic defect in biosynthesis of fucose and who therefore lack the ligands for E-selectin and P-selectin (80, 264). The defect, designated LAD-II, has many clinical similarities to LAD-I including strikingly depressed neutrophil emigration into inflammatory sites.

CHEMOATTRACTANTS   Chemoattractants are required for transendothelial migration in vitro and in vivo and can induce all steps required for transmigration in vivo. Injection of chemoattractants into skin or muscle leads to robust emigration of neutrophils from the vasculature and accumulation at the injection site (58). Injection of lipopolysaccharide or cytokines that induce IL-8 synthesis also elicits neutrophil emigration. Moreover, mAb to IL-8 markedly inhibits neutrophil emigration into lung and skin in several models of inflammation (179, 220).

The effects of pertussis toxin provide further evidence for the importance of $G\alpha_i$ protein-coupled receptors in leukocyte emigration in vivo. Pretreatment of neutrophils with pertussis toxin inhibits emigration into inflammatory sites (187, 234).

Chemoattractants impart directionality to leukocyte migration. By contrast to intradermal injection, intravascular injection of IL-8 does not lead to emigration (99). Cytokine-stimulated endothelial monolayers grown on filters secrete IL-8 into the underlying collagen layer. Neutrophils added to the apical compartment emigrate into the basilar compartment, but not when the IL-8 gradient is disrupted by addition of IL-8 to the apical compartment (109). Although IL-8 acts as an adhesion inhibitor in some assays (87), the results are partially attributable to disruption of a gradient of IL-8 on activated endothelial monolayers when exogenous IL-8 is added on the same side as the neutrophils.

Chemoattractants act on the local tissue, as well as on leukocytes. Neutrophil chemoattractants injected into the same skin site hours apart will stimulate neutrophil accumulation the first but not the second time, whereas a second injection into a distant site will stimulate accumulation. Desensitization occurs for homologous chemoattractants only (57, 59). Thus chemoattractants must act on and homologously desensitize a cell type that is localized in tissue. In some cases this localized cell may be the mast cell. Some chemoattractants stimulate the mast cell (which localizes in tissue adjacent to the vasculature), or its better studied relative the basophil, to release histamine (29, 137) and TNF (270). Histamine induces P-selectin and TNF induces E-selectin on endothelium. Thus chemoattractants may indirectly increase selectin expression on endothelium, as well as directly activate integrin adhesiveness on leukocytes.

A Three-Step Area Code for Signaling Neutrophil and Monocyte Traffic

The above evidence indicates that emigration from the vasculature of neutrophils and monocytes is regulated by at least three distinct molecular signals (Figure 1, Figure 6A). A key feature is that selectin-carbohydrate, chemoattractant-receptor, and integrin-Ig family interactions act in sequence, not in parallel. This concept has been confirmed by the observation that inhibition of any one of these steps gives essentially complete, rather than partial, inhibition of neutrophil and monocyte emigration. An important consequence of a sequence of steps, at any one of which there are choices of multiple receptors or ligands that have distinct distributions on leukocyte subpopulations or endothelium, is that it provides great combinatorial diversity for regulating the selectivity of leukocyte localization in vivo, as has been emphasized in several reviews (36, 143, 223, 240, 280).

The term area code for models for cell localization in the body (106, 239) is particularly apt because it is now known that at least three sequential steps are involved. The concepts of area codes and traffic signals can be combined by thinking of how telephone traffic is routed by digital signals. Each type of leukocyte responds to a particular set of area code signals. Inflammation alters the expression and location of the signals on vascular endothelium. It is as if leukocytes carry "cellular phones." An example of how this model works is shown for the two cell types for which the signals are best understood, neutrophils and monocytes (Figure 6B). Chemoattractants provide the greatest number of molecular choices (or "digits") and the greatest cellular specificity.

Refinements to the three-step model are in order. First, selectins actually mediate two steps, initial tethering to the vessel wall and rolling (Figure 6A), which can be distinguished for E-selectin by dependence on different classes of neutrophil ligands (145). Thus selectins can cooperate, and some selectin-ligand combinations may be more important in tethering and others in rolling. Second, the steps are overlapping, rather than strictly sequential (Figure 6A). Although L-selectin is shed from neutrophils soon after activation (132), the

A   Neutrophils

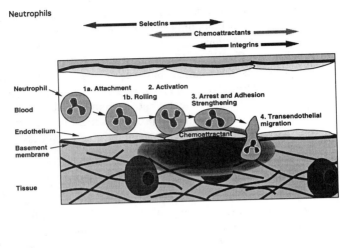

Lymphocytes

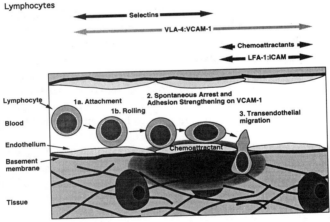

Figure 6 The three-step area code model. (*A*) Selectins, chemoattractants, and integrins act in sequence with some overlap. The sequence in which these signals act on neutrophils and lymphocytes may differ. (*B*) Combinatorial use of different molecules at each step can generate a large number of different area codes, and specificity for distinct leukocyte subpopulations. All of the known selectin and integrin interactions are shown in the hundreds and ones place, respectively; however, only a subset of the chemoattractants is shown in the tens place (see Table 1) due to space limitations. The area codes symbolize how specificity for monocytes, neutrophils, or both can be generated at inflammatory sites.

kinetics of shedding by neutrophils in whole blood (min) are much slower than the transition from rolling to integrin-mediated attachment (ms-s) (266). L-selectin is shed more slowly from lymphocytes than from neutrophils (121, 235). Furthermore, ligands for P-selectin (173) and E-selectin (145) remain on

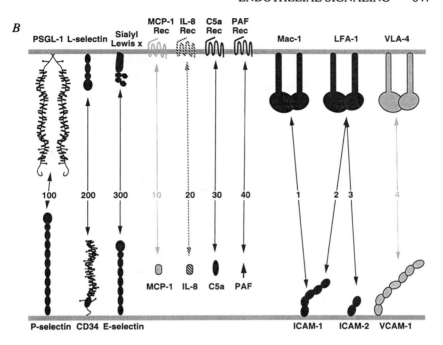

B

PSGL-1 L-selectin Sialyl Lewis x

MCP-1 Rec   IL-8 Rec   C5a Rec   PAF Rec

Mac-1   LFA-1   VLA-4

100   200   300   10   20   30   40   1   2   3   4

MCP-1 IL-8 C5a PAF

P-selectin CD34 E-selectin

ICAM-1   ICAM-2   VCAM-1

Monocyte Area Codes	111, 211, 311, 112, 212, 312, 113, 213, 313, 114, 214, 314, 134, 234, 334, 144, 244, 344
Neutrophil Area Codes	121, 221, 321, 122, 222, 322, 123, 223, 323
Monocyte and Neutrophil Area Codes	131, 231, 331, 132, 232, 332, 133, 233, 333, 141, 241, 341, 142, 242, 342, 143, 243, 343
Null Area Codes	124, 224, 324

the neutrophil surface after activation. Thus interactions with selectins will continue after activation of integrins, probably persisting until transendothelial migration is completed. Chemoattractants are required not only for activation of integrin adhesiveness, but also for directional cues during the subsequent step of transendothelial migration. Finally, β_1 integrins that bind to extracellular matrix components are undoubtedly required during migration through the subendothelial basement membrane.

Lymphocyte Recirculation: Distinct Traffic Patterns for Naive and Memory Lymphocytes

Patrolling the body in search of foreign antigen, lymphocytes follow circuits through nonlymphoid and lymphoid tissues (Figure 7). The peripheral lymph nodes draining skin and muscle, and the gut-associated lymphoid tissues such

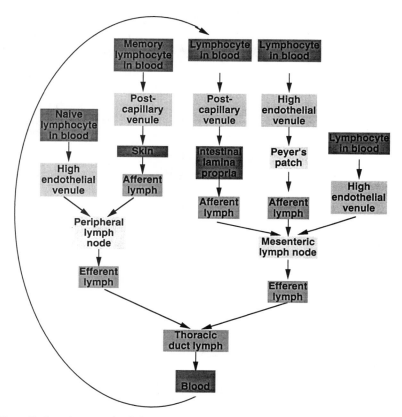

Figure 7 Lymphocyte recirculation routes.

as Peyer's patch, differ in the types of antigens to which lymphocytes are exposed. When collected from lymph draining gut or skin, lymphocytes from adult animals, but not newborns, show a twofold or higher preference to recirculate to the type of organ from which they came and to reappear in the draining lymph (39, 40, 117, 159). This suggests that priming by specific antigen in a particular environment may induce expression of surface receptors that enable preferential recirculation to the type of secondary organ where specific antigen was first encountered. Evidence exists for separate streams of lymphocytes that recirculate through the skin, gut, and lung and that drain into their associated lymphoid tissues (159, 196).

Our understanding of the mechanisms of this selectivity has been advanced by the discovery that "naive" and "memory" lymphocytes prefer different recirculation pathways (162). When naive lymphocytes encounter antigen, those lymphocytes with receptors specific for the antigen are stimulated to clonally expand and are converted to memory lymphocytes that have altered expression of adhesion receptors and circulatory patterns. Lymphocytes that emigrate in the hind leg of a sheep through flat endothelium in the skin and drain through the afferent lymphatics to the popliteal lymph node are all of the memory phenotype. By contrast, lymphocytes in the efferent lymph from the popliteal lymph node, derived mostly from traffic through HEV, are predominantly of the naive phenotype. Thus, at least for peripheral tissues and lymph nodes, memory lymphocytes emigrate preferentially through tissue endothelium, whereas naive lymphocytes enter the lymph node through HEV (Figure 7). Memory lymphocytes are more sensitive to specific antigen than naive lymphocytes and thus better able to respond to antigen in peripheral tissues, which have fewer antigen-presenting cells than do lymph nodes (160).

Traffic through HEV

The high or cuboidal-shaped endothelial cells found in HEV are specialized for emigration of lymphocytes into peripheral lymph nodes that drain skin and the lymphoid tissues of the mucosa: Peyer's patches, tonsils, and appendix. Emigration into the spleen, by contrast, involves sinusoidal endothelia and molecular mechanisms that are distinct and not yet characterized. About 25% of lymphocytes that circulate through an HEV will bind and emigrate, a much higher percent than through nonspecialized flat venules (30, 275). HEV phenotype is developmentally regulated. The carbohydrate ligands for L-selectin are absent from peripheral lymph node HEV at birth but are displayed at adult levels by 6 weeks (196). If peripheral lymph nodes are deprived of afferent lymph, the HEV convert from a high to a flat-walled endothelial morphology, lose expression of L-selectin ligands, and lose the ability to support lymphocyte traffic (169, 170). Introduction of antigen into the node leads to a full restoration of HEV phenotype and function. Furthermore, intense antigenic stimulation can induce formation of HEV in diverse non-lymphoid tissues (161, 196).

Molecular Mechanisms Defined by the HEV-Binding Assay

When lymphocyte suspensions are overlayed on thin sections cut from frozen lymph nodes, the lymphocytes specifically bind to the morphologically distinct HEV (241). Specific differences have been demonstrated between binding to peripheral lymph node and Peyer's patch HEV (37, 275). T lymphocytes bind one and one-half-fold better than B lymphocytes to peripheral lymph node HEV in vitro, and show a similar preference to recirculate to this site in vivo. B lymphocytes bind two- to threefold better to Peyer's patch than to peripheral lymph node HEV and show similar preference in recirculation in vivo. These preferences are reflected in the preponderance of T cells in peripheral lymph nodes, and the preponderance of B lymphocytes in Peyer's patch, where they are important in secretion of IgA and IgM into the mucosa (246). Certain lymphoma cells possess marked preference for binding to Peyer's patch or peripheral lymph node HEV in vitro (37) and for metastasis in vivo to mucosal or peripheral lymphoid tissue, respectively (16). Assay of lymphoma cell binding to HEV in the Stamper-Woodruff assay has led to the identification of two important adhesion pathways.

MOLECULES INVOLVED IN BINDING TO PERIPHERAL NODE HEV   The L-selectin molecule was initially defined in the mouse with the Mel-14 mAb as a molecule on lymphocytes required for binding to peripheral lymph node, but not Peyer's patch, HEV (85). Conversely, the MECA-79 carbohydrate antigen was defined with mAb that bound specifically to peripheral lymph node HEV and blocked lymphocyte binding. The isolated MECA-79 antigen, termed the peripheral node addressin (249), binds to L-selectin on lymphocytes (22). An L-selectin/IgG chimera was also found to specifically bind to HEV in peripheral lymph node and to block lymphocyte binding (273). The L-selectin/IgG chimera was used to isolate two distinct mucin-like ligands, GlyCAM-1, which is secreted by HEV (144), and CD34, a surface molecule on HEV (17). MECA-79 mAb recognizes a carbohydrate determinant that is expressed on multiple protein species in HEV, including GlyCAM-I and CD34 and, compared to L-selectin, recognizes an overlapping but distinct set of glycoproteins (22, 144). Sialylation and sulfation of the O-linked side chains of the GlyCAM-1 and CD34 molecules are required for activity in binding to L-selectin (22, 111, 206). HEV differ from other tissues in carbohydrate processing; GlyCAM-1 and CD34 expressed in transfectants, and CD34 expressed in other vascular endothelia, do not bind L-selectin chimera under conditions in which binding to HEV is detectable (144). However, an L-selectin ligand with a presumably lower affinity is certainly present on most endothelia, as shown by L-selectin-dependent rolling in vivo and binding in vitro (125, 153, 229, 236, 237, 265, 266).

MOLECULES INVOLVED IN BINDING TO PEYER'S PATCH HEV   Elegant screens for mAb with specificity for Peyer's patch HEV, and ability to block lympho-cyte binding to HEV, yielded mAb MECA-367 to the mucosal addressin now termed MAdCAM-1 (248). MAdCAM-1 is expressed on endothelia in mucosal tissues, not only on HEV in Peyer's patch, but also on venules in intestinal lamina propria and in the lactating mammary gland (213, 248). MAdCAM-1 has both IgSF domains and a mucin-like domain (34) (Figure 5).

Similar elegant screens for mAbs with specificity for lymphoma cells that bound to Peyer's patch HEV and with the ability to block binding to HEV in the Stamper-Woodruff assay yielded mAbs to the α^4 subunit of the Peyer's patch homing receptor (104). The α^4 subunit was found to be associated with a novel β subunit, β_p (105), which is identical to β_7 (108). The integrin $\alpha^4\beta_7$, but not $\alpha^4\beta_1$ binds to Peyer's patch HEV (108), and $\alpha^4\beta_7$ binds directly to MAdCAM-1 (24).

An Area Code Model for Lymphocyte Migration Through HEV

PERIPHERAL LYMPH NODE HEV   Although the L-selectin:mucin and $\alpha^4\beta_7$: MAdCAM-1 interactions were identified in parallel assays, recent studies suggest that multiple steps are involved in lymphocyte interaction with HEV and raise the possibility that these interactions function in distinct, rather than parallel, steps in this process. Soon after its discovery as a peripheral lymph node homing receptor, L-selectin also was found to be present on neutrophils and eosinophils and to be important in emigration of, at least, neutrophils (151). As expected from their strong expression of L-selectin, neutrophils and other leukocytes can bind avidly to HEV in the Stamper-Woodruff assay, yet do not normally home to peripheral lymph nodes in vivo. Injection of *Escherichia coli* supernatant induces acute emigration of neutrophils through HEV of the draining lymph node. Thus signals other than those mediated by L-selectin can regulate the class of leukocyte that home into a lymph node (151). Although peripheral node HEV is far richer than any other site in the body in expression of the carbohydrate receptor for L-selectin (112), this is insufficient to explain the specificity of lymphocyte homing to this organ. The findings suggest that L-selectin is required for lymphocyte emigration through peripheral lymph node HEV and may help regulate recirculation of the L-selectin-positive subset of lymphocytes; however, L-selectin is insufficient to determine the specificity of the cell types that emigrate, and other currently undefined molecules are required to achieve specificity.

In vivo studies strongly suggest that lymphocyte emigration through HEV is a multi-step process that utilizes area code models similar to those of other leukocytes. mAb to L-selectin almost completely blocks emigration of lymphocytes from blood into peripheral lymph nodes (85, 94). However, mAb to the integrin LFA-1 also markedly reduces or almost completely abolishes lymphocyte migration into peripheral lymph nodes (41, 95). Thus molecules of step 1 and 3 (see Figure 1) are required for homing to peripheral lymph nodes in vivo. LFA-1 on blood lymphocytes requires activation for binding to its counter-structures ICAM-1 and ICAM-2 (238), which are expressed on HEV (69, 76). Binding of L-selectin does not trigger activation of LFA-1 because lymphocytes attach and roll in flow on purified peripheral node addressin identically whether or not purified ICAM-1 is present on the substrate; an additional stimulus is required before lymphocytes will arrest and strengthen adhesion through LFA-1 (M Lawrence et al, in preparation).

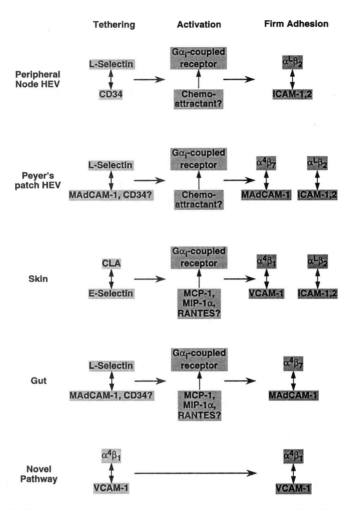

Figure 8 The three- or four-step area code paradigm for lymphocytes. For skin and gut, the pathways shown may mediate recirculation and increased accumulation in inflammation. The novel pathway shown at the bottom may be important when VCAM-1 expression on endothelium is induced by cytokines and may cooperate with the other illustrated pathways. For each organ, the interacting molecules are shown on the top for lymphocytes and on the bottom for endothelia. See text for support for the molecular assignments at each step, based primarily on in vivo data.

G protein–coupled receptors are required for lymphocyte recirculation and likely provide the signals required to activate the adhesiveness of LFA-1. Pertussis toxin causes lymphocytosis and profoundly depresses lymphocyte recirculation (271). Murine lymphocytes treated with pertussis toxin in vitro and reinfused fail to emigrate into either peripheral lymph nodes or Peyer's patches (175). This suggests that G protein–coupled receptors of the α_i class are required for lymphocyte emigration through HEV. Results with mice with a transgene for the ADP-ribosylating subunit of pertussis toxin selectively expressed in the T lineage suggest that $G\alpha_i$ proteins are not only required for emigration from the bloodstream, but also for emigration from the thymus (48, 49). Despite lack of emigration, pertussis toxin–treated lymphocytes bind normally to lymph node HEV in vitro. These findings provided the basis for an early proposal for a two-step model, in which G protein–coupled receptors function subsequent to binding of lymphocytes to HEV (233).

Thus emigration of lymphocytes through peripheral node HEV requires three sequential area code signals that are analogous to those involved in neutrophil emigration from the bloodstream (Figure 8). Identification of a putative lymphocyte chemoattractant secreted by peripheral lymph node HEV, and a chemoattractant receptor that is predicted to be selectively expressed on the naive subset of lymphocytes that recirculate through peripheral node HEV, will be a subject of intense research interest in coming years.

PEYER'S PATCH   mAb to L-selectin block 50% of lymphocyte emigration from blood to Peyer's patch and to the remainder of the intestine (93, 94). This is consistent with the lower level of L-selectin ligand in Peyer's patch HEV than in peripheral lymph node HEV (15, 163, 273). mAb to certain epitopes on the integrin α^4 and β_7 subunits inhibit recirculation by approximately 50% of lymphocytes to Peyer's patch and intestine, but have no effect on recirculation to peripheral lymph node; furthermore, mAb specific for the $\alpha^4\beta_7$ complex are equally as effective as mAb to α^4 (93). Moreover, recirculation is inhibited by mAb to MAdCAM-1 (248), implicating $\alpha^4\beta_7$ binding to MAdCAM-1 in recirculation to mucosal tissue. mAb to LFA-1 block recirculation to Peyer's patch by 50 to 80%, but have no effect on recirculation to the remainder of the intestine (41, 95). Thus both LFA-1 and $\alpha^4\beta_7$ contribute to emigration into mucosal lymphoid tissue.

G protein–coupled receptors act subsequent to a rolling interaction in Peyer's patch HEV. In contrast with peripheral lymph nodes, Peyer's patches may be visualized by intravital microscopy (30). Normally, lymphocytes roll along Peyer's patch HEV for only a few seconds, then arrest and emigrate. However, prior treatment of lymphocytes with pertussis toxin completely blocks arrest and emigration, and prolongs the rolling indefinitely, so that the lymphocytes pass out of the Peyer's patch rather than emigrate (14). It remains to be established, but seems likely, that a chemoattractant presented or secreted by Peyer's patch binds to a $G\alpha_i$-coupled receptor on lymphocytes and activates LFA-1 and $\alpha^4\beta_7$ to mediate arrest and emigration (Figure 8). Lymphoma cells or lymph node lymphocytes can bind to Peyer's patch HEV or purified MAdCAM-1 without any apparent need for activation; however, activation increases the strength of binding to MAdCAM-1 (24, 108). The pertussis toxin studies suggest that activation of blood lymphocytes is required for the last step of arrest and emigration (14, 233). Truncation of the cytoplasmic domain of β_7 greatly decreases binding to HEV. Thus interactions with the cytoplasmic domain can regulate the avidity of $\alpha^4\beta_7$ for MAdCAM-1 (63), similar to regulation of the avidity of LFA-1 for ICAM-1 (102, 103) by the β_2 integrin subunit cytoplasmic domain.

Recirculation of Memory Lymphocytes

DISTINCT PATHWAYS THROUGH SKIN AND GUT   Memory lymphocytes are imprinted so that they are more likely to return to the type of tissue, such as skin or mucosa, where they first encountered antigen (39, 40, 159). The surface phenotypes of gut and skin-homing memory cells are distinct (163). Furthermore, staining of lymphocytes in sections of skin and gut with mAb shows distinctive expression of adhesion molecules that may contribute to selective extravasation in these tissues, or to subsequent localization within these tissues in specific anatomic compartments (Table 4).

Table 4   Naive and memory lymphocyte subsets[a]

Molecule	Naive lymphocytes	Memory lymphocytes
CD45RO	Negative	Positive
CD45RA	High	Low
CD2	Low	High
LFA-3	Negative	Positive
L-selectin	Positive	Positive and negative subsets
α^4	Low	High

	Memory lymphocytes subsets	
	Gut associated	Skin associated
CLA	Negative	Positive
$\alpha^E\beta7$ (HML-1)	Positive	Negative
$\alpha^4\beta_7$[b]	High	Low
$\alpha^4\beta_1$	Low	High
α^6	Low	High

[a] References: (107, 163, 219), [b] but see (129).

SKIN HOMING LYMPHOCYTES   Lymphocytes that extravasate in the skin and appear in afferent lymph have a distinct pattern of expression of adhesion molecules (163) (Table 4). Furthermore, as shown by staining of tissue sections, T lymphocytes localized in the skin, but not in the gut, express a carbohydrate termed cutaneous lymphocyte–associated antigen (CLA) (198). CLA is closely related to sialyl Lewis a and x (21) and is a ligand for E-selectin (23). Binding of a subpopulation of memory lymphocytes that bears CLA to E-selectin may contribute to the tropism of this subset to the skin (89, 197, 224). E-selectin is induced on dermal endothelial cells in delayed type hypersensitivity (61) and in chronically inflamed skin (197). Cloned T cells derived from challenged skin express high levels of CLA and bind to E-selectin, whereas T cell clones derived from blood lymphocytes do not (5). Both types of clones bind to P-selectin.

GUT HOMING LYMPHOCYTES   The most organized lymphoid structures in the wall of the gut are the Peyer's patches. They underlie follicle-associated epithelia that contain M cells, which are specialized for uptake of antigen from the gut lumen. Other lymphocytes localize more diffusely in the lamina propria underlying the digestive epithelium and in the epithelial layer. Studies on gut afferent lymph reveal the presence of memory and naive lymphocytes (163); whether there is differential migration of naive and memory lymphocytes through Peyer's patch HEV and lamina propria postcapillary venules, both of which contribute to gut afferent lymph (Figure 7), remains unclear. Gut-homing memory lymphocytes display a surface phenotype distinct from skin-homing lymphocytes (Table 4). When injected into the bloodstream, memory lymphocytes from gut afferent lymph display a strong preference to return to gut afferent lymph, whereas naive lymphocytes redistribute randomly (163). Gut afferent memory lymphocytes display an α^4 high, β_1 integrin low phenotype, suggesting they are $\alpha^4\beta_7^+$ (163) in common with a subpopulation of memory lymphocytes in blood (219). Expression of MAdCAM-1 on Peyer's patch HEV and postcapillary venules in lamina propria (248), and 50% inhibition by mAb to α^4 and β_7 of migration into Peyer's patches and intestine (93), suggest a role for $\alpha^4\beta_7$ interaction with MAdCAM-1 in both sites.

A subpopulation of gut lymphocytes distinct from those in lamina propria localize within the epithelium on the external surface of the basement membrane and express the human mucosal lymphocyte (HML-1) integrin $\alpha^E\beta_7$ (47, 128, 193). The α^E integrin subunit contains an I domain and a novel proteolytic cleavage site preceded by a stretch of acidic residues, just N-terminal to the I domain (222). Binding of intraepithelial lymphocytes (IEL) to epithelial cell monolayers in vitro is inhibited by mAb to α^E, which suggests that $\alpha^E\beta_7$ may help mediate localization of IEL in epithelia in vivo (46). Intraepithelial T lymphocytes may undergo thymus-independent differentiation in situ, and their recirculation pattern is undefined. HML-1 is expressed on a subpopulation (2–6%) of blood T cells, which are in the memory subset and are CLA⁻ and L-selectin⁻ (199). Transforming growth factor β (TGF-β) together with mitogen induces expression of HML-1 on peripheral T cells and increases expression on IEL (128, 193). TGF-β also induces switching of B lymphocytes to production of the IgA class of immunoglobulin (55), the predominant class secreted in the mucosa. These dual effects on differentiation of mucosa] lymphocytes suggest the possibility that TGF-β may be an environment-specific cytokine that imprints lymphocytes, when first exposed to antigen, to recirculate selectively to the gut.

Alteration of Lymphocyte Trafficking in Inflammation

Antigen injected into the tissue of sensitized individuals induces localized accumulation of lymphocytes. These lymphocytes, and those accumulating in tissues in autoimmune disease, are almost all memory cells (120, 202). The phenotype of these cells is quite similar to that of lymphocytes trafficking through these sites under basal conditions. This suggests that the signals for lymphocytes trafficking may be qualitatively the same in the basal and inflammatory states and that they are upregulated in inflammation. Accumulation of lymphocytes induced by specific antigen, or by injection of IFN-γ or TNF-α, is significantly inhibited by mAb to either the LFA-1α or the integrin α^4 subunit (53, 114, 115, 217, 278). A combination of mAb to LFA-1 and α^4 gives almost complete inhibition of lymphocyte emigration and the resulting induration and plasma leakage (116). mAb to E-selectin and VCAM-1 also inhibit lymphocyte accumulation in delayed type hypersensitivity in skin (225). Multiple signals are thus required for augmented trafficking of lymphocytes into skin in inflammation (Figure 8). Both antigen responsive and nonresponsive lymphocytes traffic into sites of antigenic stimulation (166). Antigen-specific lymphocytes may accumulate in the site because stimulation through their antigen receptors increases adhesiveness of integrins and causes them to be retained, whereas nonresponsive lymphocytes more rapidly enter the lymphatics and leave the site.

The interaction between VCAM-I and VLA-4 mediates rolling and firm adhesion (R Alon et al, *J. Cell. Biol.,* in press), thus it does not fit neatly into the three-step paradigm established for neutrophils. mAb to LFA-1 or VLA-4 alone do not completely inhibit lymphocyte accumulation in inflammation, and patients with LAD-I show delayed-type hypersensitivity reactions. This suggests that the functions of VLA-4 and LFA-1 are partially overlapping in the step of firm adhesion, but they may also act in series, as in VLA-4-mediated rolling followed by LFA-1-mediated firm adhesion. VLA-4 may act together with selectins to augment T lymphocyte tethering and rolling in the vasculature. All or most memory T lymphocytes lack L-selectin (32, 126, 163, 257). The CLA$^+$ subset can bind E-selectin, and T lymphocytes can also bind P-selectin (66, 174). Peripheral blood T lymphocytes are substantially less efficient than neutrophils in tethering in hydrodynamic flow to E-selectin and P-selectin (T Diacovo et al, unpublished data); therefore, cooperation of VCAM-I with E-selectin or P-selectin, or among all three molecules, may be important in enhancing lymphocyte accumulation in inflammation.

Inflammation also affects traffic through HEV. Antigen injected into tissue drains to the regional lymph node and greatly increases blood flow to the node and traffic of naive lymphocytes through HEV (161). Furthermore, memory lymphocytes now appear to enter the node directly; this is associated with induction of VCAM-I on non-HEV vascular endothelia within the node (161). Entry is inhibited by mAb to α^4, which suggests a role for interaction of VCAM-I with $\alpha^4\beta_1$ (114, 161).

Lymphocyte chemoattractants are interesting candidates for the step 2 signal (see Figure 1) for lymphocyte accumulation at inflammatory sites. Pertussis toxin treatment inhibits lymphocyte emigration in response to antigen in delayed-type hypersensitivity (234). Identification of lymphocyte chemoattractants has been hampered by the low motility of lymphocytes compared to monocytes or neutrophils (194), and by the low signal-to-background ratio, typically less than 2, in most chemotaxis assays. Recent interest has focused on chemokines (Table 2). A number of chemokines, all of which were isolated based on chemoattractive activity for neutrophils or monocytes, or by cloning genes of unknown function, have subsequently been tested and found to be chemoattractive for lymphocyte subpopulations (12, 172). These include IL-8 (139) (but see 136, 150), RANTES (216), MIP-1β (253), MIP-1α and β (215, 255), and IP-10 (256). There are differences among reports in the subsets found to be chemoattracted, and some reports use lymphocytes preactivated by T cell receptor cross-linking, which may be relevant to migration within inflammatory sites, but not to emigration from blood. Of interest, MIP-1β can induce binding of the naive, CD8$^+$ subset to VCAM-1, either in solution or when immobilized on a substrate, mimicking presentation by an endothelial cell surface (253; S Shaw, personal communication); the specific effect is modest, equal to background binding. The RANTES cytokine, by contrast to MIP-1 β, selectively attracts the memory T lymphocyte subset (216).

Vascular endothelium may present chemoattractant to lymphocytes in a functionally relevant way, as well as provide a permeability barrier that stabilizes the chemoattractant gradient. A transendothelial chemotaxis assay more accurately simulates lymphocyte emigration from the bloodstream than filter chemotaxis assays and yields signals >10 times background (43). Since lymphocytes, responding to specific antigen in tissue, signal emigration of further lymphocytes into the site, a chemoattractant was sought in material secreted by mitogen-stimulated mononuclear cells. Purification to homogeneity guided by the transendothelial lymphocyte chemotaxis assay revealed that MCP-1, previously thought to be solely a monocyte chemoattractant, is a major lymphocyte chemoattractant (43). Subsequent studies using the transendothelial chemotaxis assay have confirmed that lymphocytes respond to RANTES and MIP-1α (CC chemokines), but do not respond to IL-8 or IP-10 (CXC chemokines) (209). MCP-1, RANTES, and MIP-1α selectively attract the memory T lymphocyte subset and the CD4 and CD8 subsets. All also attract monocytes, but not neutrophils, with MCP-1 being more potent than RANTES or MIP-1α as a monocyte chemoattractant. The physiologically relevant transendothelial assay suggests that CC chemokines tend to attract both monocytes and lymphocytes, in agreement with the long-standing clinical observation that lymphocyte emigration into inflammatory sites is always accompanied by emigration of monocytes. The converse is not true. Monocytes sometimes emigrate in the absence of lymphocytes, correlating with activity of chemoattractants such as C5a and PAF on monocytes, but not on lymphocytes. Teleologically, it is important that monocytes accompany lymphocytes into inflammatory sites in order to present antigen and to carry out effector functions in which monocytes are activated by T lymphocytes. MCP-1 is abundantly expressed at sites of antigen challenge and autoimmune disease (149, 172, 263), and together with MIP-1 α and RANTES, is an excellent candidate to provide the step 2 signal required to activate integrin adhesiveness and emigration of both monocytes and lymphocytes in vivo (Figure 8).

The finding that resting T lymphocytes that tether and roll on VCAM-I can spontaneously arrest and develop firm adhesion on VCAM-1 (R Alon et al, *J. Cell Biol.,* in press) has provocative implications for the multi-step model. It suggests that the VLA-4:VCAM-I interaction not only can mediate the steps of rolling and firm adhesion, but may also short-circuit the step of stimulation by chemoattractants of firm adhesion through integrins. This is intriguing; although a twofold stimulation of adhesiveness of VLA-4 to VCAM-1 has been demonstrated by MIP-1β in one system (253), with the chemoattractant that is most effective in eliciting transendothelial chemotaxis of T lymphocytes, MCP-1, it is difficult to detect stimulation of integrin adhesiveness on lymphocytes (M Carr & T Springer, unpublished data). Therefore, an alternative pathway may exist in which VCAM-1 can mediate both tethering and arrest of lymphocytes, perhaps in cooperation with other endothelial molecules, prior to stimulation by chemoattractants. After arrest, chemoattractants would guide transendothelial migration, and perhaps stimulate further increases in the adhesiveness of the integrins VLA-4 and LFA-1, which are important in migration across the endothelium and basement membrane.

CONCLUDING REMARKS

A three-step or area code model of leukocyte emigration from the bloodstream, established and validated in vitro and in vivo with neutrophils (Figure 1 and 6B), appears extendible with only slight modification to all subclasses of leukocytes including lymphocytes (Figure 8). Multiple adhesion and chemoattractant receptors are used combinatorially in a series of steps that enable leukocytes to progress from initial tethering in flow to firm adhesion and emigration. The distinct distribution of receptors on leukocyte subsets for signals that are displayed on endothelium regulates selection of the subclasses of leukocytes that emigrate at inflammatory sites and the distinctive recirculation behavior of lymphocyte subsets.

Many important developments await. Strong evidence suggests that G protein–coupled receptors are required for lymphocyte recirculation, but many of the putative lymphocyte chemoattractants specific to HEV, mucosa, and skin, and the receptors for these chemoattractants on lymphocytes, remain to be identified. Specific mucin-like molecules that present carbohydrate ligands to selectins have recently been identified. Are there similar mucin-like molecules on lymphocytes that present carbohydrates to P-selectin or E-selectin, and do these differ from the PSGL-1 molecule on neutrophils? It is likely that endothelial cells express molecules that retain chemoattractants on the luminal surface, preventing them from being washed away by blood flow, as already suggested for MIP-1β and IL-8. Are these molecules specifically regulated? The mucin-like ligands of selectins have many features such as extended structure, sulfation, and negative charge in common with proteoglycans, and thus might have a second function of binding chemokines through their heparin-binding sites and presenting them to leukocytes. Presenting molecules might be required not only to prevent chemoattractants from being washed away by blood flow, but also to generate maximal chemoattractant activity, analogous to proteoglycans that must bind fibroblast growth factor to enable signaling through a second receptor molecule. It will be interesting to determine whether chemoattractant receptors on leukocytes couple to distinct G proteins and signaling effectors, allowing for selectivity in which integrins are upregulated in avidity. For example, do chemoattractants differ in ability to upregulate adhesiveness of two integrins such as LFA-1 and VLA-4 expressed on the same cell? Finally, after the area code is dialed and cells emigrate across the endothelium, much remains to be learned about the "7 digit code" that regulates leukocyte migration and localization within specific anatomic compartments.

ACKNOWLEDGMENTS

I thank the National Institutes of Health for supporting most of the cited work and Uli von Andrian for comments on the manuscript.

Literature Cited

1. Abbassi O, Kishimoto TK, McIntire LV, Anderson DC, Smith CW. 1993. E-selectin supports neutrophil rolling in vitro under conditions of flow. *J. Clin. Invest.* 92:2719–30

2. Alam R, Forsythe PA, Stafford S, Lett-Brown MA, Grant JA. 1992. Macrophage inflammatory protein-1α activates basophils and mast cells. *J. Exp. Med.* 176:781–86

3. Albelda SM, Muller WA, Buck CA, Newman PJ. 1991. Molecular and cellular properties of PECAM-1 (endoCAM/CD31): a novel vascular cell-cell adhesion molecule. *J. Cell Biol.* 114:1059–68

4. Albelda SM, Oliver PD, Romer LH, Buck CA. 1990. EndoCAM: a novel endothelial cell-cell adhesion molecule. *J. Cell Biol.* 110:1227–37

5. Alon R, Rossiter H, Springer TA, Kupper TS. 1994. Distinct cell surface ligands mediate T lymphocyte attachment and rolling on P- and E-selectin under physiological flow. *J. Cell Biol.* In press

6. Amatruda TT, Gerard NP, Gerard C, Simon MI. 1993. Specific interactions of chemoattractant factor receptors with G-proteins. *J. Biol. Chem.* 268:10139–44

7. Anderson AO, Anderson ND. 1976. Lymphocyte emigration from high endothelial venules in rat lymph nodes. *Immunology* 31:731–48

8. Anderson DC, Springer TA. 1987. Leukocyte adhesion deficiency: An inherited defect in the Mac-1, LFA-1, and p150,95 glycoproteins. *Annu. Rev. Med.* 38:175–94

9. Arch R, Wirth K, Hofmann M, Ponta H, Matzku S, et al. 1992. Participation in normal immune responses of a metastasis-inducing splice variant of CD44. *Science* 257:682–85

10. Arfors KE, Lundberg C, Lindbom L, Lundberg K, Beatty PG, Harlan JM. 1987. A monoclonal antibody to the membrane glycoprotein complex CD18 inhibits polymorphonuclear leukocyte accumulation and plasma leakage in vivo. *Blood* 69:338–40

11. Aruffo A, Stamenkovic I, Melnick M, Underhill CB, Seed B. 1990. CD44 is the principal cell surface receptor for hyaluronate. *Cell* 61:1303–13

12. Baggiolini M, Dewald B, Moser B. 1994. Interleukin-8 and related chemotactic cytokines-CXC and CC chemokines. *Adv. Immunol.* 55:97–179

13. Barclay AN, Birkeland ML, Brown MH, Beyers AD, Davis SJ, et al. 1993. *The Leucocyte Antigen Facts Book.* London: Academic

14. Bargatze RF, Butcher EC. 1993. Rapid G protein-regulated activation event involved in lymphocyte binding to high endothelial venules. *J. Exp. Med.* 178: 367–72

15. Bargatze RF, Streeter PR, Butcher EC. 1990. Expression of low levels of peripheral lymph node-associated vascular addressin in mucosal lymphoid tissues: possible relevance to the dissemination of passaged akr lymphomas. *J. Cell. Biochem.* 42:219–27

16. Bargatze RF, Wu NW, Weissman IL, Butcher EC. 1987. High endothelial venule binding as a predictor of the dissemination of passaged murine lymphomas. *J. Exp. Med.* 166:1125–31

17. Baumhueter S, Singer MS, Henzel W, Hemmerich S, Renz M, et al, 1993. Binding of L-selectin to the vascular sialomucin, CD34. *Science* 262:436–38

18. Beals CR, Wilson CB, Perlmutter RM.

1987. A small multigene family encodes G_i signal-transduction proteins. *Proc. Natl. Acad. Sci. USA* 84:7886–90

19. Berg EL, Magnani J, Warnock RA, Robinson MK, Butcher EC. 1992. Comparison of L-selectin and E-selectin ligand specificities: The L-selectin can bind the E-selectin ligands sialyl Le^x and sialyl Le^a. *Biochem. Biophys. Res. Commun.* 184:1048–55

20. Berg EL, McEvoy LM, Berlin C, Bargatze RF, Butcher EC. 1993. L-selectin-mediated lymphocyte rolling on MAdCAM-1. *Nature* 366:695–98

21. Berg EL, Robinson MK, Mansson O, Butcher EC, Magnani JL. 1991. A carbohydrate domain common to both sialyl Le^a and sialyl Le^x is recognized by the endothelial cell leukocyte adhesion modecule ELAM-1. *J. Biol. Chem.* 266:14869–72

22. Berg EL, Robinson MK, Warnock RA, Butcher EC. 1991. The human peripheral lymph node vascular addressin is a ligand for LECAM-1, the peripheral lymph node homing receptor. *J. Cell Biol.* 114:343–49

23. Berg EL, Yoshino T, Rott LS, Robinson MK, Warnock RA, et al. 1991. The cutaneous lymphocyte antigen is a skin lymphocyte homing receptor for the vascular lectin endothelial cell-leukocyte adhesion molecule 1. *J. Exp. Med.* 174:1461–66

24. Berlin C, Berg EL, Briskin MJ, Andrew DP, Kilshaw PJ, et al. 1993. $\alpha 4\beta 7$ integrin mediates lymphocyte binding to the mucosal vascular addressin MAdCAM-1. *Cell* 74:185–95

25. Bevilacqua MP. 1993. Endothelial-leukocyte adhesion molecules. *Annu. Rev. Immunol.* 11:767–804

26. Bevilacqua MP, Nelson RM. 1993. Selectins. *J. Clin. Invest.* 91:379–87

27. Bevilacqua MP, Pober JS, Mendrick DL, Cotran RS, Gimbrone MA. 1987. Identification of an inducible endothelial-leukocyte adhesion molecule, ELAM-1. *Proc. Natl. Acad. Sci. USA* 84:9238–42

28. Bienvenu K, Granger DN. 1993. Molecular determinants of shear rate–dependent leukocyte adhesion in postcapillary venules. *Am. J. Physiol.* 264:H1504–8

29. Bischoff SC, Krieger M, Brunner T, Rot A, Tscharner VV, et al. 1993. RANTES and related chemokines activate human basophil granulocytes through different G protein-coupled receptors. *Eur. J. Immunol.* 23:761–67

30. Bjerknes M, Cheng H, Ottaway CA. 1986. Dynamics of lymphocyte-endo-thelial interactions in vivo. *Science* 231:402–5

31. Bochner BS, Luscinskas FW, Gimbrone MA Jr, Newman W, Sterbinsky SA, et al. 1991. Adhesion of human basophils, eosinophils, and neutrophils to interleukin 1-activated human vascular endothelial cells: contributions of endothelial cell adhesion molecules. *J. Exp. Med.* 173:1553–56

32. Bradley LM, Atkins GG, Swain SL. 1992. Long-term CD4+ memory T cells from the spleen lack MEL-14, the lymph node homing receptor. *J. Immunol.* 148:324–31

33. Briscoe DM, Cotran RS, Pober JS. 1992. Effects of tumor necrosis factor, lipopolysaccharide, and IL-4 on the expression of vascular cell adhesion molecule-1 in vivo. *J. Immunol.* 149:2954–60

34. Briskin MJ, McEvoy LM, Butcher EC. 1993. MAdCAM-1 has homology to immunoglobulin and mucin-like adhesion receptors and to IgA1. *Nature* 363:461–64

35. Buchanan MR, Crowley CA, Rosin RE, Gimbrone MA, Babior BM. 1982. Studies on the interaction between GP-180-deficient neutrophils and vascular endothelium. *Blood* 60:160–65

36. Butcher EC. 1991. Leukocyte-endothelial cell recognition: Three (or more) steps to specificity and diversity. *Cell* 67:1033–36

37. Butcher EC, Scollay RG, Weissman IL. 1980. Organ specificity of lymphocyte migration: Mediation by highly selective lymphocyte interaction with organ-specific determinants on high endothelial venules. *Eur. J. Immunol.* 10:556–61

38. Buyon JP, Abramson SB, Philips MR, Slade SG, Ross GD, et al. 1988. Dissociation between increased surface expression of Gp165/95 and homotypic neutrophil aggregation. *J. Immunol.* 140:3156–60

39. Cahill RNP, Poskitt DC, Frost H, Trnka Z. 1977. Two distinct pools of recirculating T lymphocytes: Migratory characteristics of nodal and intestinal T lymphocytes. *J. Exp. Med.* 145:420–28

40. Cahill RNP, Poskitt DC, Hay JB, Heron I, Trnka Z. 1979. The migration of lymphocytes in the fetal lamb. *Eur. J. Immunol.* 9:251–53

41. Camp RL, Scheynius A, Johansson C, Puré E. 1993. CD44 is necessary for optimal contact allergic responses but is not required for normal leukocyte extravasation. *J. Exp. Med.* 178:497–507

42. Carlos TM, Harlan JM. 1994. Leukocyte-endothelial adhesion molecules. *Blood.* 84:2068–2101

43. Carr MW, Roth SJ, Luther E, Rose SS, Springer TA. 1994. Monocyte chemoattractant protein-1 is a major T lymphocyte chemoattractant. *Proc. Natl. Acad. Sci. USA* 91:3652–56

44. Carrell NA, Fitzgerald LA, Steiner B, Erickson HP, Phillips DR. 1985. Structure of human platelet membrane glycoproteins IIb and IIIa as determined by electron microscopy. *J. Biol. Chem.* 260: 1743–49

45. Carter SB. 1967. Haptotaxis and the mechanism of cell motility. *Nature* 213: 256–60

46. Cepek KL, Parker CM, Madara JL, Brenner MB. 1993. Integrin $\alpha^E\beta7$ mediates adhesion of T lymphocytes to epithelial cells. *J. Immunol.* 150:3459–70

47. Cerf-Bensussan N, Jarry A, Brousse N, Lisowska-Grospierre B, Guy-Grand D, Griscelli C. 1987. A monoclonal antibody (HML-1) defining a novel membrane molecule present on human intestinal lymphocytes. *Eur. J. Immunol.* 17:1279–85

48. Chaffin KE, Beals CR, Wilkie TM, Forbush KA, Simon MI, Perlmutter RM. 1990. Dissection of thymocyte signaling pathways by in vivo expression of pertussis toxin ADP-ribosyltransferase. *EMBO J.* 9:3821–29

49. Chain KE, Perlmutter RM. 1991. A pertussis toxin–sensitive process controls thymocyte emigration. *Eur. J. Immunol.* 21:2565–73

50. Chan BMC, Elices MJ, Murphy E, Hemler ME. 1992. Adhesion to vascular cell adhesion molecule 1 and fibronectin: comparison of $\alpha^4\beta1$ (VLA-4) and $\alpha^4\beta7$ on the human B cell line JY. *J. Biol. Chem.* 267:8366–70

51. Chan P-Y, Lawrence MB, Dustin ML, Ferguson LM, Golan DE, Springer TA. 1991. Influence of receptor lateral mobility on adhesion strengthening between membranes containing LFA-3 and CD2. *J. Cell Biol.* 115:245–55

52. Charo IF, Myers SJ, Herman A, Franci C, Connolly AJ, Coughlin SR. 1994. Molecular cloning and functional expression of two monocyte chemoattractant protein 1 receptors reveals alternative splicing of the carboxyl-terminal tails. *Proc. Natl. Acad. Sci. USA* 91: 2752–56

53. Chisholm PL, Williams CA, Lobb RR. 1993. Monoclonal antibodies to the integrin α-4 subunit inhibit the murine contact hypersensitivity response. *Eur. J. Immunol.* 23:682–88

54. Cline MJ. 1975. *The White Cell.* Cambridge: Harvard Univ. Press

55. Coffman RL, Lehman DA, Shrader IR. 1999. Transforming growth factor β specifically enhances IgA production by lipopolysaccharide-stimulated murine B lymphocytes. *J. Exp. Med.* 170:1039–44

56. Cohnheim J. 1889. *Lectures on General Pathology: A Handbook for Practitioners and Students.* London: The New Sydenham Soc.

57. Colditz IG. 1991. Desensitisation mechanisms regulating plasma leakage and neutrophil emigration. In *Vascular Endothelium: Interactions with Circulating Cells,* ed. JL Gordon, pp. 175–87. New York: Elsevier

58. Colditz IG. 1992. Sites of antigenic stimulation: Role of cytokines and chemotactic agonists in acute inflammation. In *Animal Health and Production in the 21st Century,* ed. KJ Beh. Melbourne: CSIRO

59. Colditz IG, Movat HZ. 1984. Desensitization of acute inflammatory lesions to chemotaxins and endotoxin. *J. Immunol.* 133:2163–68

60. Colditz IG, Watson DL. 1992. The effect of cytokines and chemotactic agonists on the migration of T lymphocytes into skin. *Immunology* 76:272–78

61. Cotran RS, Gimbrone MA Jr, Bevilacqua MP, Mendrick DL, Pober JS. 1986. Induction and detection of a human endothelial activation antigen in vivo. *J. Exp. Med.* 164:661–66

62. Cross AH, Raine CS. 1992. Central nervous system endothelial cell-polymorphonuclear cell interactions during autoimmune demyelination. *Am. J. Pathol.* 139:1401–9

63. Crowe DT, Chiu H, Fong S, Weissman IL. 1994. Regulation of the avidity of integrin $\alpha4\beta7$ by the $\beta7$ cytoplasmic domain. *J. Cell Biol.* 269:14411–18

64. Culty M, Miyake K, Kincade PW, Sikorski E, Butcher EC, Underhill C. 1990. The hyaluronate receptor is a member of the CD44 (H-CAM) family of cell surface glycoproteins. *J. Cell Biol.* 111:2765–74

65. Cyster JG, Shotton DM, Williams AF. 1991. The dimensions of the T lymphocyte glycoprotein leukosialin and identification of linear protein epitopes that can be modified by glycosylation. *EMBO J.* 10:893–902

66. Damle NK, Klussman K, Dietsch MT, Mohagheghpour N, Aruffo A. 1992. GMP-140 (P-selectin/CD62) binds to chronically stimulated but not resting CD4+ T lymphocytes and regulates their production of proinflammatory cytokines. *Eur. J. Immunol.* 22:1789–93

67. deFougerolles AR, Qin X, Springer TA.

1994. Characterization of the function of ICAM-3 and comparison to ICAM-1 and ICAM-2 in immune responses. *J. Exp. Med.* 179:619–29

68. deFougerolles AR, Springer TA. 1992. Intercellular adhesion molecule 3, a third adhesion counter-receptor for lymphocyte function-associated molecule 1 on resting lymphocytes. *J. Exp. Med.* 175:185–90

69. deFougerolles AR, Stacker SA, Schwarting R, Springer TA. 1991. Characterization of ICAM-2 and evidence for a third counter-receptor for LFA-1. *J. Exp. Med.* 174:253–67

70. Devreotes PN, Zigmond SH. 1988. Chemotaxis in eukaryotic cells: A focus on leukocytes and *Dictyostelium. Annu. Rev. Cell Biol.* 4:649–86

71. Diamond MS, Garcia-Aguilar J, Bickford JK, Corbi AL, Springer TA. 1993. The I domain is a major recognition site on the leukocyte integrin Mac-1 (CD11b/CD18) for four distinct adhesion ligands. *J. Cell Biol.* 120:1031–43

72. Diamond MS, Springer TA. 1993. A subpopulation of Mac-1 (CD11b/CD18) molecules mediates neutrophil adhesion to ICAM-1 and fibrinogen. *J. Cell Biol.* 120:545–56

73. Diamond MS, Springer TA. 1994. The dynamic regulation of integrin adhesiveness. *Curr. Biol.* 4:506–17

74. Diamond MS, Staunton DE, deFougerolles AR, Stacker SA, Garcia-Aguilar J, et al. 1990. ICAM-1 (CD54): A counter-receptor for Mac-1 (CD11b/CD18). *J. Cell Biol.* 111:3129–39

75. Diamond MS, Staunton DE, Marlin SD, Springer TA. 1991. Binding of the integrin Mac-1 (CD11b/CD18) to the third Ig-like domain of ICAM-1 (CD54) and its regulation by glycosylation. *Cell* 65:961–71

76. Dustin ML, Springer TA. 1989. T cell receptor cross-linking transiently stimulates adhesiveness through LFA-1. *Nature* 341:619–24

77. Elices MJ, Osborn L, Takada Y, Crouse C, Luhowskyj S, et al. 1990. VCAM-1 on activated endothelium interacts with the leukocyte integrin VLA-4 at a site distinct from the VLA-4/fibronectin binding site. *Cell* 60:577–84

78. Erbe DV, Wolitzky BA, Presta LG, Norton CR, Ramos RJ, et al. 1992. Identification of an E-selectin region critical for carbohydrate recognition and cell adhesion. *J. Cell. Biol.* 119:215–27

79. Erlandsen SL, Hasslen SR, Nelson RD. 1993. Detection and spatial distribution of the β2 integrin (Mac-1) and L-selectin (LECAM-1) adherence receptors on human neutrophils by high-resolution field emission SEM. *J. Histochem. Cytochem.* 41:327–33

80. Etzioni A, Frydman M, Pollack S, Avidor I, Phillips ML, et al. 1992. Recurrent severe infections caused by a novel leukocyte adhesion deficiency. *N. Engl. J. Med.* 327:1789–92

81. Faull RJ, Kovach NL, Harlan HM, Ginsberg MH. 1994. Stimulation of integrin-mediated adhesion of T lymphocytes and monocytes: Two mechanisms with divergent biological consequences. *J. Exp. Med.* 179:1307–16

82. Fina L, Molgaard HV, Robertson D, Bradley NJ, Monaghan P, et al. 1990. Expression of the CD34 gene in vascular endothelial cells. *Blood* 75:2417–26

83. Foxall C, Watson SR, Dowbenko D, Fennie C, Lasky LA, et al. 1992. The three members of the selectin receptor family recognize a common carbohydrate epitope, the sialyl Lewis ^{x} oligosaccharide. *J. Cell Biol.* 117:895–902

84. Fujimoto T, Stroud E, Whatley RE, Prescott SM, Muszbek L, et al. 1993. P-selectin is acylated with palmitic acid and stearic acid at cysteine 766 through a thioester linkage. *J. Biol. Chem.* 268:11394–400

85. Gallatin WM, Weissman IL, Butcher EC. 1983. A cell-surface molecule involved in organ-specific homing of lymphocytes. *Nature* 304:30–34

86. Geng J-G, Bevilacqua MP, Moore KL, McIntyre TM, Prescott SM, et al. 1990. Rapid neutrophil adhesion to activated endothelium mediated by GMP-140. *Nature* 343:757–60

87. Gimbrone MA, Obin MS, Brock AF, Luis EA, Hass PE, et al. 1989. Endothelial interleukin-8: A novel inhibitor of leukocyte-endothelial interactions. *Science* 246:1601–3

88. Ginsberg MH, Du X, Plow EF. 1992. Inside-out integrin signalling. *Curr. Opin. Cell Biol.* 4:766–71

89. Graber N, Gopal TV, Wilson D, Beall LD, Polte T, Newman W. 1990. T cells bind to cytokine-activated endothelial cells via a novel, inducible sialoglycoprotein and endothelial leukocyte adhesion molecule-1. *J. Immunol.* 145:819–30

90. Granger DN, Kubes P. 1994. The microcirculation and inflammation: Modulation of leukocyte-endothelial cell adhesion. *J. Leukocyte Biol.* 55:662–75

91. Graves BJ, Crowther RL, Chandran C, Rumberger JM, Li S, et al. 1994. Insight into E-selectin/ligand interaction from the crystal structure and mutagenesis of

the lec/EGF domains. *Nature* 367:532–38

92. Günthert U. 1993. CD44: a multitude of isoforms with diverse functions. *Curr. Top. Microbiol. Immunol.* 184:47–63

93. Hamann A, Andrew DP, Jablonski-Westrich D, Holzmann B, Butcher EC. 1993. The role of α4 integrins in lymphocyte homing to mucosal tissues in vivo. *J. Immunol.* 152:3282–93

94. Hamann A, Jablonski-Westrich D, Jonas P, Thiele H-G. 1991. Homing receptors reexamined: mouse LECAM-1 (MEL-14 antigen) is involved in lymphocyte migration into gut-associated lymphoid tissue. *Eur. J. Immunol.* 21:2925–29

95. Hamann A, Westrich DJ, Duijevstijn A, Butcher EC, Baisch H, et al. 1988. Evidence for an accessory role of LFA-1 in lymphocyte-high endothelium interaction during homing. *J. Immunol.* 140:693–99

96. Hammer DA, Apte SM. 1992. Simulation of cell rolling and adhesion on surfaces in shear flow: general results and analysis of selectin-mediated neutrophil adhesion. *Biophys. J.* 63:35–57

97. Harlan JM, Winn RK, Vedder NB, Doerschuk CM, Rice CL. 1992. In vivo models of leukocyte adherence to endothelium. In *Adhesion: Its Role in Inflammatory Disease,* ed. JR Harlan, D Liu, pp. 117–50. New York: Freeman

98. Haynes BF, Liao H-X, Patton KL. 1991. The transmembrane hyaluronate receptor (CD44): Multiple functions, multiple forms. *Cancer Cells* 3:347–50

99. Hechtman DH, Cybuisky MI, Fuchs HJ, Baker JB, Gimbrone MA Jr. 1991. Intravascular IL-8: Inhibitor of polymorphonuclear leukocyte accumulation at sites of acute inflammation. *J. Immunol.* 147:883–92

100. Hemler ME. 1990. VLA proteins in the integrin family: Structures, functions, and their role on leukocytes. *Annu. Rev. Immunol.* 8:365–400

101. Hemmerich S, Rosen SD. 1994. 6′-Sulfated sialyl Lewis x is a major capping group of GlyCAM-1. *Biochemistry* 33:4830–35

102. Hibbs ML, Jakes S, Stacker SA, Wallace RW, Springer TA. 1991. The cytoplasmic domain of the integrin lymphocyte function-associated antigen 1 subunit: sites required for binding to intercellular adhesion molecule 1 and the phorbol ester-stimulated phosphorylation site. *J. Exp. Med.* 174:1227–38

103. Hibbs ML, Xu H, Stacker SA, Springer TA. 1991. Regulation of adhesion to ICAM-1 by the cytoplasmic domain of

104. Holzmann B, McIntyre BW, Weissman IL. 1989. Identification of a murine Peyer's patch–specific lymphocyte homing receptor as an integrin molecule with an alpha chain homologous to human VLA-4 alpha. *Cell* 56:37–46

105. Holzmann B, Weissman IL. 1989. Peyer's patch–specific lymphocyte homing receptors consist of a VLA-4-like α chain associated with either of two integrin β chains, one of which is novel. *EMBO J.* 8:1735–41

106. Hood L, Huang HV, Dreyer WJ. 1987. The area-code hypothesis: The immune system provides clues to understanding the genetic and molecular basis of cell recognition during development. *J. Supramol. Struc.* 7:531–59

107. Horgan KJ, Luce GEG, Tanaka Y, Schweighoffer T, Shimizu Y, et al. 1992. Differential expression of VLA-α4 and VLA-β1 discriminates multiple subsets of CD4+CD45R0+ "memory" T cells. *J. Immunol.* 149:4082–87

108. Hu MC-T, Crowe DT, Weissman IL, Holzmann B. 1992. Cloning and expression of mouse integrin βp(β7): A functional role in Peyer's patch–specific lymphocyte homing. *Proc. Natl. Acad. Sci. USA* 89:8254–58

109. Huber AR, Kunkel SL, Todd RF III, Weiss SJ. 1991. Regulation of transendothelial neutrophil migration by endogenous interleukin-8. *Science* 254:99–102

110. Hynes RO. 1992. Integrins: Versatility, modulation, and signaling in cell adhesion. *Cell* 69:11–25

111. Imai Y, Lasky LA, Rosen SD. 1993. Sulphation requirement for GlyCAM-1, an endothelial ligand for L-selectin. *Nature* 361:555–57

112. Imai Y, Singer MS, Fennie C, Lasky LA, Rosen SD. 1991. Identification of a carbohydrate based endothelial ligand for a lymphocyte homing receptor. *J. Cell Biol.* 113:1213–21

113. Issekutz AC, Issekutz TB. 1993. Quantitation and kinetics of blood monocyte migration to acute inflammatory reactions, and IL-1α, TNF-α, and IFN-γ. *J. Immunol.* 151:2105–15

114. Issekutz TB. 1991. Inhibition of in vivo lymphocyte migration to inflammation and homing to lymphoid tissues by the TA-2 monoclonal antibody: A likely role for VLA-4 in vivo. *J. Immunol.* 147:4178–84

115. Issekutz TB. 1992. Inhibition of lymphocyte endothelial adhesion and in vivo lymphocyte migration to cutaneous in-

flammation by TA-3, a new monoclonal antibody to rat LFA-1. *J. Immunol.* 149: 3394–402

116. Issekutz TB. 1993. Dual inhibition of VLA-4 and LFA-1 maximally inhibits cutaneous delayed type hypersensitivity-induced inflammation. *Am. J. Pathol.* 143:1286–93

117. Issekutz TB, Chin W, Hay JB. 1982. The characterization of lymphocytes migrating through chronically inflamed tissues. *Immunology* 46:59–66

118. Issekutz TB, Stoltz JM, Meide PVD. 1988. Lymphocyte recruitment in delayed-type hypersensitivity: The role of IFN-γ. *J. Immunol.* 140:2989–93

119. Jalkanen S, Bargatze RF, de los Toyos J, Butcher EC. 1987. Lymphocyte recognition of high endothelium: antibodies to distinct epitopes of an 85–95 kD glycoprotein antigen differentially inhibit lymphocyte binding to lymph node, mucosal and synovial endothelial cells. *J. Cell Biol.* 105:983–93

120. Janossy G, Bofill M, Rowe D, Muir J, Beverley PC. 1989. The tissue distribution of T lymphocytes expressing different CD45 polypeptides. *Immunology* 66:517–25

121. Jung TM, Gallatin WM, Weissman IL, Dailey MO. 1988. Down-regulation of homing receptors after T cell activation. *J. Immunol.* 141:4110–17

122. Jutila MA, Lewinsohn D, Berg EL, Butcher E. 1988. Homing receptors in lymphocyte, neutrophil, and monocyte interaction with endothelial cells. In *Leukocyte Adhesion Molecules,* ed. TA Springer, DC Anderson, AS Rosenthal, R Rothlein, pp. 227–35. New York: Springer-Verlag

123. Jutila MA, Rott L, Berg EL, Butcher EC. 1989. Function and regulation of the neutrophil MEL-14 antigen in vivo: Comparison with LFA-1 and MAC-1. *J. Immunol.* 143:3318–24

124. Kameyoshi Y, Dörschner A, Mallet AI, Christophers E, Schröder JM. 1992. Cytokine RANTES released by thrombin-stimulated platelets is a potent attractant for human eosinophils. *J. Exp. Med.* 176:587–92

125. Kansas GS, Ley K, Munro JM, Tedder TF. 1993. Regulation of leukocyte rolling and adhesion to high endothelial venules through the cytoplasmic domain of L-selectin. *J. Exp. Med.* 177:833–38

126. Kansas GS, Wood GS, Fishwild DM, Engleman EG. 1985. Functional characterization of human T lymphocyte subsets distinguished by monoclonal anti-leu-8. *J. Immunol.* 134:2995–3002

127. Keizer GD, Visser W, Vliem M, Figdor

CG. 1988. A monoclonal antibody (NKI-L16) directed against a unique epitope on the alpha-chain of human leukocyte function-associated antigen I induces homotypic cell-cell interactions. *J. Immunol.* 140:1393–400

128. Kilshaw PJ, Murant SJ. 1990. A new surface antigen on intraepithelial lymphocytes in the intestine. *Eur. J. Immunol.* 20:2201–7

129. Kilshaw PJ, Murant SJ. 1991. Expression and regulation of $\beta_7(\beta p)$ integrins on mouse lymphocytes: Relevance to the mucosal immune system. *Eur. J. Immunol.* 21:2591–97

130. Kinashi T, St. Pierre Y, Huang C-H, Springer TA. 1993. Expression of glycophosphatidylinositol (GPI)-anchored and non GPI-anchored isoforms of vascular cell adhesion molecule I (VCAM-1) in stromal and endothelial cells. *J. Leukocyte Biol.* In press

131. Kirchhausen T, Staunton DE, Springer TA. 1993. Location of the domains of ICAM-1 by immunolabeling and single-molecule electron microscopy. *J. Leukocyte Biol.* 53:342–46

132. Kishimoto TK, Jutila MA, Berg EL, Butcher EC. 1989. Neutrophil Mac-1 and MEL-14 adhesion proteins inversely regulated by chemotactic factors. *Science* 245:1238–41

133. Kishimoto TK, Larson RS, Corbi AL, Dustin ML, Staunton DE, Springer TA. 1989. The leukocyte integrins: LFA-1, Mac-1, and p 150,95. *Adv. Immunol.* 46:149–82

134. Kishimoto TK, O'Connor K, Lee A, Roberts TM, Springer TA. 1987. Cloning of the beta subunit of the leukocyte adhesion proteins: Homology to an extracellular matrix receptor defines a novel supergene family. *Cell* 48:681–90

135. Kishimoto TK, Warnock RA, Jutila MA, Butcher EC, Lane C, et al. 1991. Antibodies against human neutrophil LECAM-1 (LAM-1/Leu-8/DREG-56 antigen) and endothelial cell ELAM-1 inhibit a common CD18-independent adhesion pathway in vitro. *Blood* 78: 805–11

136. Kudo C, Araki A, Matsushima K, Sendo F. 1991. Inhibition of IL-8-induced W3/25$^+$ (CD4$^+$) T lymphocyte recruitment into subcutaneous tissues of rats by selective depletion of in vivo neutrophils with a monoclonal antibody. *J. Immunol.* 174:2196–201

137. Kuna P, Reddigari SR, Schall TJ, Rucinski D, Sadick M, Kaplan AP. 1993. Characterization of the human basophil response to cytokines, growth factors, and histamine releasing factors of

the intercrine/chemokine family. *J. Immunol.* 150:1932–43

138. Landis RC, Bennett RI, Hogg N. 1993. A novel LFA-1 activation epitope maps to the I domain. *J. Cell Biol.* 120:1519–27

139. Larsen CG, Anderson AO, Appella E, Oppenheim JJ, Matsushima K. 1989. The neutrophil-activating protein (NAP-1) is also chemotactic for T lymphocytes. *Science* 241:1464–66

140. Larsen E, Celi A, Gilbert GE, Furie BC, Erban JK, et al. 1989. PADGEM protein: A receptor that mediates the interaction of activated platelets with neutrophils and monocytes. *Cell* 59:305–12

141. Larsen GR, Sako D, Ahern TJ, Shaffer M, Erban J, et al. 1992. P-selectin and E-selectin: Distinct but overlapping leukocyte ligand specificities. *J. Biol. Chem.* 267:11104–10

142. Larson RS, Corbi AL, Berman L, Springer TA. 1989. Primary structure of the LFA-1 alpha subunit: An integrin with an embedded domain defining a protein superfamily. *J. Cell Biol.* 108:703–12

143. Lasky LA. 1992. Selectins: Interpreters of cell-specific carbohydrate information during inflammation. *Science* 258:964–69

144. Lasky LA, Singer MS, Dowbenko D, Imai Y, Henzel WJ, et al. 1992. An endothelial ligand for L-selectin is a novel mucin-like molecule. *Cell* 69:927–38

145. Lawrence MB, Bainton DF, Springer TA. 1994. Neutrophil tethering to and rolling on E-selectin are separable by requirement for L-selectin. *Immunity* 1:137–45

146. Lawrence MB, Smith CW, Eskin SG, McIntire LV. 1990. Effect of venous shear stress on CD18-mediated neutrophil adhesion to cultured endothelium. *Blood* 75:227–37

147. Lawrence MB, Springer TA. 1991. Leukocytes roll on a selectin at physiologic flow rates: distinction from and prerequisite for adhesion through integrins. *Cell* 65:859–73

148. Lawrence MB, Springer TA. 1993. Neutrophils roll on E-selectin. *J. Immunol.* 151:6338–46

149. Leonard EJ, Yoshimura T. 1990. Human monocyte chemoattractant protein-1 (MCP-1). *Immunol. Today* 11:97–101

150. Leonard EJ, Yoshimura T, Tanaka S, Raffeld M. 1991. Neutrophil recruitment by intradermally injected neutrophil attractant/activation protein-1. *J. Invest. Dermatol.* 96:690–94

151. Lewinsohn DM, Bargatze RF, Butcher EC. 1987. Leukocyte-endothelial cell recognition: Evidence of a common molecular mechanism shared by neutrophils, lymphocytes, and other leukocytes. *J. Immunol.* 138:4313–21

152. Ley K, Gaehtgens P. 1991. Endothelial, not hemodynamic, differences are responsible for preferential leukocyte rolling in rat mesenteric venules. *Circ. Res.* 69:1034–41

153. Ley K, Gaehtgens P, Fennie C, Singer MS, Lasky LA, Rosen SD. 1991. Lectin-like cell adhesion molecule I mediates leukocyte rolling in mesenteric venules in vivo. *Blood* 77:2553–55

154. Lo SK, Detmers PA, Levin SM, Wright SD. 1989. Transient adhesion of neutrophils to endothelium. *J. Exp. Med.* 169:1779–93

155. Lo SK, Lee S, Ramos RA, Lobb R, Rosa M, et al. 1991. Endothelial-leukocyte adhesion molecule 1 stimulates the adhesive activity of leukocyte integrin CR3 (CD11b/CD18, Mac-1,$\alpha_m\beta_2$) on human neutrophils. *J. Exp. Med.* 173:1493–500

156. Lotus JC, O'Toole TE, Plow EF, Glass A, Frelinger AL III, Ginsberg MH. 1990. A β_3 integrin mutation abolishes ligand binding and alters divalent cation-dependent conformation. *Science* 249:915–18

157. Lollo BA, Chan KWH, Hanson EM, Moy VT, Brian AA. 1993. Direct evidence for two affinity states for lymphocyte function-associated antigen 1 on activated T cells. *J. Biol. Chem.* 268:1–8

158. Lorant DE, Patel KD, McIntyre TM, McEver RP, Prescott SM, Zimmerman GA. 1991. Coexpression of GMP-140 and PAF by endothelium stimulated by histamine or thrombin: A juxtacrine system for adhesion and activation of neutrophils. *J. Cell Biol.* 115:223–34

159. Mackay CR. 1992. Migration pathways and immunologic memory among T lymphocytes. *Semin. Immunol.* 4:51–58

160. Mackay CR. 1993. Immunological memory. *Adv. Immunol.* 53:217–65

161. Mackay CR, Marston W, Dudler L. 1992. Altered patterns of T cell migration through lymph nodes and skin following antigen challenge. *Eur. J. Immunol.* 22:2205–10

162. Mackay CR, Marston WL, Dudler L. 1990. Naive and memory T cells show distinct pathways of lymphocyte recirculation. *J. Exp. Med.* 171:801–17

163. Mackay CR, Marston WL, Dudler L, Spertini O, Tedder TF, Hein WR. 1992. Tissue-specific migration pathways by

phenotypically distinct subpopulations of memory T cells. *Eur. J. Immunol.* 22:887–95

164. Masinovsky B, Urdal D, Gallatin WM. 1990. IL-4 acts synergistically with IL-1 β to promote lymphocyte adhesion to microvascular endothelium by induction of vascular cell adhesion molecule-1. *J. Immunol.* 145:2886–95

165. Mayadas TN, Johnson RC, Rayburn H, Hynes RO, Wagner DD. 1993. Leukocyte rolling and extravasation are severely compromised in P-selectin-deficient mice. *Cell* 74:541–54

166. McCluskey RT, Benacerraf B, McClusky JW. 1963. Studies on the specificity of the cellular infiltrate in delayed type hypersensitivity reactions. *J. Immunol.* 90:466

167. McEver RP. 1991. Selectins: Novel receptors that mediate leukocyte adhesion during inflammation. *Thromb. Haemost.* 65:223–28

168. McEver RP, Beckstead JH, Moore KL, Marshall-Carlson L, Bainton DF. 1989. GMP-140, a platelet alpha-granule membrane protein, is also synthesized by vascular endothelial cells and is localized in Weibel-Palade bodies. *J. Clin. Invest.* 84:92–99

169. Mebius RE, Dowbenko D, Williams A, Fennie C, Lasky LA, Streeter SR. 1993. Expression of GlyCAM-1, an endothelial ligand for L-selectin, is affected by afferent lymphatic flow. *J. Immunol.* 151:6769–76

170. Mebius RE, Streeter PR, Breve J, Duijvestijn AM, Kraal G. 1991. The influence of afferent lymphatic vessel interruption on vascular addressin expression. *J. Cell Biol.* 115:85–95

171. Michishita M, Videm V, Arnaout MA. 1993. A novel divalent cation-binding site in the A domain of the β2 integrin CR3 (CD11b/CD18) is essential for ligand binding. *Cell* 72:857–67

172. Miller MD, Krangel MS. 1992. Biology and biochemistry of the chemokines: A family of chemotactic and inflammatory cytokines. *Crit. Rev. Immunol.* 12:17–46

173. Moore KL, Stults NL, Diaz S, Smith DF, Cummings RD, et al. 1992. Identification of a specific glycoprotein ligand for P-selectin (CD62) on myeloid cells. *J. Cell Biol.* 118:445–56

174. Moore KL, Thompson LF. 1992. P-selectin (CD62) binds to subpopulations of human memory T lymphocytes and natural killer cells. *Biochem. Biophys. Res. Commun.* 186:173–81

175. Morse SI, Barron BA. 1970. Studies on the leukocytosis and lymphocytosis induced by *Bordetella pertussi.* III. The distribution of transfused lymphocytes in pertussis-treated and normal mice. *J. Exp. Med.* 132:663–72

176. Moy P, Lobb R, Tizard R, Olson D, Hession C. 1993. Cloning of an inflammation-specific phosphatidylinositol-linked form of murine vascular cell adhesion molecule-1. *J. Biol. Chem.* 268:8835–41

177. Muller WA, Ratti CM, McDonnell SL, Cohn ZA. 1989. A human endothelial cell-restricted, externally disposed plasmalemmal protein enriched in intercellular junctions. *J. Exp. Med.* 170:399–414

178. Muller WA, Weigl SA, Deng X, Phillips DM. 1993. PECAM-1 is required for transendothelial migration of leukocytes. *J. Exp. Med.* 178:449–60

179. Mulligan MS, Jones ML, Bolanowski MA, Baganoff MP, Deppeler CL, et al. 1993. Inhibition of lung inflammatory reactions in rats by an anti-human IL-8 antibody. *J. Immunol.* 150:5585–95

180. Mulligan MS, Varani J, Dame MK, Lane CL, Smith CW, et al. 1991. Role of endothelial-leukocyte adhesion molecule 1 (ELAM-1) in neutrophil-mediated lung injury in rats. *J. Clin. Invest.* 88:1396–406

181. Murphy PM. 1994. The molecular biology of leukocyte chemoattractant receptors. *Annu. Rev. Immunol.* 12:593–633

182. Nazziola E, House SD. 1992. Effects of hydrodynamics and leukocyte-endothelium specificity on leukocyte-endothelium interactions. *Microvasc. Res.* 44:127–42

183. Nelson RM, Dolich S, Aruffo A, Cecconi O, Bevilacqua MP. 1993. Higher-affinity oligosaccharide ligands for E-selectin. *J. Clin. Invest.* 91:1157–66

184. Nermut MV, Green NM, Eason P, Yamada SS, Yamada KM. 1988. Electron microscopy and structural model of human fibronectin receptor. *EMBO J.* 7:4093–99

185. Newman PJ, Berndt MC, Gorski J, White GC, Lyman S, et al. 1990. PECAM-1 (CD31) cloning and relation to adhesion molecules of the immunoglobulin gene superfamily. *Science* 247:1219–22

186. Norgard KE, Moore KL, Diaz S, Stults NL, Ushiyama S, et al. 1993. Characterization of a specific ligand for P-selectin on myeloid cells: A minor glycoprotein with sialylated 0-linked oligosaccharides. *J. Biol. Chem.* 268:12764–74

187. Nourshargh S, Williams TJ. 1990. Evidence that a receptor-operated event on

the neutrophil mediates neutrophil accumulation in vivo. *J. Immunol.* 145: 2633–38

188. Olofsson AM, Arfors K-E, Ramezani L, Wolitzky BA, Butcher EC, von Andrian UH. 1994. E-selectin mediates leukocyte rolling in interleukin-1 treated rabbit mesentery venules. *Blood.* In press

189. Oppenheimer-Marks N, Davis LS, Lipsky PE. 1990. Human T lymphocyte adhesion to endothelial cells and transendothelial migration: alteration of receptor use relates to the activation status of both the T cell and the endothelial cell. *J. Immunol.* 145:140–48

190. Osborn L, Hession C, Tizard R, Vassallo C, Luhowskyj S, et al. 1989. Direct cloning of vascular cell adhesion molecule 1 (VCAM-1), a cytokine-induced endothelial protein that binds to lymphocytes. *Cell* 59:1203–121 1

191. Osborn L, Vassallo C, Benjamin CD. 1992. Activated endothelium binds lymphocytes through a novel binding site in the alternately spliced domain of vascular cell adhesion molecule-1. *J. Exp. Med.* 176:99–107

192. Osborn L, Vassallo C, Browning BG, Tizard R, Haskard DO, et al. 1994. Arrangement of domains, and amino acid residues required for binding of vascular cell adhesion molecule-1 to its counter-receptor VLA-4(α4β1). *J. Cell Biol.* 124(4):601–8

193. Parker CM, Cepek K, Russell GJ, Shaw SK, Posnett D, et al. 1992. A family of β7 integrins on human mucosal lymphocytes. *Proc. Natl. Acad. Sci. USA* 89: 1924–28

194. Parrott DMV, Wilkinson PC. 1981. Lymphocyte locomotion and migration. *Prog. Allergy* 28:193–284

195. Philips MR, Buyon JP, Winchester R, Weissman G, Abramson SB. 1988. Upregulation of the iC3b receptor (CR3) is neither necessary nor sufficient to promote neutrophil aggregation. *J. Clin. Invest.* 82:495–501

196. Picker LJ, Butcher EC. 1992. Physiological and molecular mechanisms of lymphocyte homing. *Annu. Rev. Immunol.* 10:561–91

197. Picker LJ, Kishimoto TK, Smith CW, Warnock RA, Butcher EC. 1991. ELAM-1 is an adhesion molecule for skin-homing T cells. *Nature* 349:796–98

198. Picker LJ, Michie SA, Rott LS, Butcher EC. 1990. A unique phenotype of skin-associated lymphocytes in humans: preferential expression of the HECA-452 epitope by benign and malignant T cells at cutaneous sites. *Am. J. Pathol.* 136: 1053–68

199. Picker LJ, Terstappen LWMM, Rott LS, Streeter PR, Stein H, Butcher EC. 1990. Differential expression of homing-associated adhesion molecules by T cell subsets in man. *J. Immunol.* 145:3247–55

200. Picker LJ, Warnock RA, Burns AR, Doerschuk CM, Berg EL, Butcher EC. 1991. The neutrophil selectin LECAM-1 presents carbohydrate ligands to the vascular selectins ELAM-1 and GMP-140. *Cell* 66:921–33

201. Pircher H, Groscurth P, Baumhutter S, Aguet M, Zinkernagel RM, Hengartner H. 1986. A monoclonal antibody against altered LFA-1 induces proliferation and lymphokine release of cloned T cells. *Eur. J. Immunol.* 16:172–81

202. Pitzalis C, Kingsley G, Haskard D, Panayi G. 1988. The preferential accumulation of helper-inducer T lymphocytes in inflammatory lesions: evidence for regulation by selective endothelial and homotypic adhesion. *Eur. J. Immunol.* 18:1397–404

203. Pober JS, Cotran RS. 1990. Cytokines and endothelial cell biology. *Physiol. Rev.* 70:427–52

204. Pober JS, Doukas J, Hughes CCW, Savage COS, Munro JM, Cotran RS. 1990. The potential roles of vascular endothelium in immune reactions. *Hum. Immunol.* 28:258–62

205. Polte T, Newman W, Gopal TV. 1990. Full length vascular cell adhesion molecule 1 (VCAM-1). *Nucleic Acids Res.* 18:5901

206. Rosen SD. 1993. Cell surface lectins in the immune system. *Semin. Immunol.* 5:237–47

207. Rot A. 1992. Endothelial cell binding of NAP-1/IL-8: role in neutrophil emigration. *Immunol. Today* 13:291–94

208. Rot A, Krieger M, Brunner T, Bischoff SC, Schall TJ, Dahinden CA. 1992. RANTES and macrophage inflammatory protein 1a induce the migration and activation of normal human eosinophil granulocytes. *J. Exp. Med.* 176: 1489–95

209. Roth SJ, Carr MW, Rose SS, Springer TA. 1994. Characterization of transendothelial chemotaxis of T lymphocytes. *Am. J. Pathol.* Submitted

210. Rothlein R, Dustin ML, Marlin SD, Springer TA. 1986. A human intercellular adhesion molecule (ICAM-1) distinct from LFA-1. *J. Immunol.* 137: 1270–74

211. Rüegg C, Postigo AA, Sikorski EE, Butcher EC, Pytela R, Erle DJ. 1992. Role of integrin α4β7/α4βP in lymphocyte adherence to fibronectin and

VCAM-1 and in homotypic cell clustering. *J. Cell Biol.* 117:179–89

212. Sako D, Chang X-J, Barone KM, Vachino G, White HM, et al. 1993. Expression cloning of a functional glycoprotein ligand for P-selectin. *Cell* 75:1179–86

213. San Gabriel-Masson C. 1992. *Adhesion of lymphocytes to the lactating mammary gland in the mouse.* PhD thesis. Penn. State Univ. 105 pp.

214. Schall TJ. 1991. Biology of the RANTES/SIS cytokine family. *Cytokine* 3:165–83

215. Schall TJ, Bacon K, Camp RDR, Kaspari JW, Goeddel DV. 1993. Human macrophage inflammatory protein α(MIP-1α) and MIP-1β chemokines attract distinct populations of lymphocytes. *J. Exp. Med.* 177:1821–25

216. Schall TJ, Bacon K, Toy KJ, Goeddel DV. 1990. Selective attraction of monocytes and T lymphocytes of the memory phenotype by cytokine RANTES. *Nature* 347:669–71

217. Scheynius A, Camp RL, Puré E. 1993. Reduced contact sensitivity reactions in mice treated with monoclonal antibodies to leukocyte function-associated molecule-1 and intercellular adhesion molecule-1. *J. Immunol.* 150:655–63

218. Schmid-Schönbein GW, Usami S, Skalak R, Chien S. 1980. The interaction of leukocytes and erythrocytes in capillary and postcapillary vessels. *Microvasc. Res.* 19:45–70

219. Schweighoffer T, Tanaka Y, Tidswell M, Erle DJ, Horgan KJ, et al. 1993. Selective expression of integrin α4β7 on a subset of human CD4+ memory T cells with hallmarks of gut-trophism. *J. Immunol.* 151:717–29

220. Sekido N, Mukaida N, Harada A, Nakanishi I, Watanabe Y, Matsushima K. 1993. Prevention of lung reperfusion injury in rabbits by a monoclonal antibody against interleukin-8. *Nature* 365:654–57

221. Sengelov H, Kjeldsen L, Diamond MS, Springer TA, Borregaard N. 1993. Subcellular localization and dynamics of Mac-1 (α_mβ2) in human neutrophils. *J. Clin. Invest.* 92:1467–76

222. Shaw SK, Cepek KL, Murphy EA, Russell GJ, Brenner MB, Parker CM. 1994. Molecular cloning of the human mucosal lymphocyte integrin αE subunit. *J. Biol. Chem.* 269:6016–25

223. Shimizu Y, Newman W, Tanaka Y, Shaw S. 1992. Lymphocyte interactions with endothelial cells. *Immunol. Today* 13:106–12

224. Shimizu Y, Shaw S, Graber N, Gopal TV, Horgan KJ, et al. 1991. Activation-independent binding of human memory T cells to adhesion molecule ELAM-1. *Nature* 349:799–802

225. Silber A, Newman W, Sasseville VG, Pauley D, Beall D, et al. 1994. Recruitment of lymphocytes during cutaneous delayed hypersensitivity in nonhuman primates is dependent on E-selectin and VCAM-1. *J. Clin. Invest.* 93:1554–63

226. Simmons D, Makgoba MW, Seed B. 1988. ICAM, an adhesion ligand of LFA-1, is homologous to the neural cell adhesion molecule NCAM. *Nature* 331:624–27

227. Simmons DL, Satterthwaite AB, Tenen DG, Seed B. 1992. Molecular cloning of a cDNA encoding CD34, a sialomucin of human hematopoietic stem cells. *J. Immunol.* 148:267–71

228. Simmons DL, Walker C, Power C, Pigott R. 1990. Molecular cloning of CD31, a putative intercellular adhesion molecule closely related to carcinoembryonic antigen. *J. Exp. Med.* 171:2147–52

229. Smith CW, Kishimoto TK, Abbass O, Hughes B, Rothlein R, et al. 1991. Chemotactic factors regulate lectin adhesion molecule 1 (LECAM-1)-dependent neutrophil adhesion to cytokine-stimulated endothelial cells in vitro. *J. Clin. Invest.* 87:609–18

230. Smith CW, Marlin SD, Rothlein R, Toman C, Anderson DC. 1989. Cooperative interactions of LFA-1 and Mac-1 with intercellular adhesion molecule-1 in facilitating adherence and trans-endothelial migration of human neutrophils in vitro. *J. Clin. Invest.* 83:2008–17

231. Smith CW, Rothlein R, Hughes BJ, Mariscalco MM, Schmalstieg FC, Anderson DC. 1988. Recognition of an endothelial determinant for CD18-dependent neutrophil adherence and trans-endothelial migration. *J. Clin. Invest.* 82:1746–56

232. Snyderman R, Uhing RJ. 1992. Chemoattractant stimulus-response coupling. In *Inflammation: Basic Principles and Clinical Correlates,* ed. JI Gallin, IM Goldstein, R Snyderman, pp. 421–39. New York: Raven

233. Spangrude GJ, Braaten BA, Daynes RA. 1984. Molecular mechanisms of lymphocyte extravasation. 1. Studies of two selective inhibitors of lymphocyte recirculation. *J. Immunol.* 132:354–62

234. Spangrude GJ, Sacchi F, Hill HR, Van Epps DE, Daynes RA. 1985. Inhibition of lymphocyte and neutrophil chemo-

taxis by pertussis toxin. *J. Immunol.* 135:4135–43

235. Spertini O, Kansas GS, Munro JM, Griffin JD, Tedder TF. 1991. Regulation of leukocyte migration by activation of the leukocyte adhesion molecule (LAM-1) selectin. *Nature* 349:691–94

236. Spertini O, Luscinskas FW, Gimbrone MA Jr, Tedder TF. 1992. Monocyte attachment to activated human vascular endothelium in vitro is mediated by leukocyte adhesion molecule-1 (L-selectin) under nonstatic conditions. *J. Exp. Med.* 175:1789–92

237. Spertini O, Luscinskas FW, Kansas GS, Munro JM, Griffin JD, et al. 1991. Leukocyte adhesion molecule-1 (LAM-1, L-selectin) interacts with an inducible endothelial cell ligand to support leukocyte adhesion. *J. Immunol.* 147: 2565–73

238. Springer TA. 1990. Adhesion receptors of the immune system. *Nature* 346:425–33

239. Springer TA. 1990. Area code molecules of lymphocytes. In *Cell to Cell Interaction: a Karger Symposium,* ed. MM Burger, B Sordat, RM Zinkernagel, pp. 16–39. Basel: Karger

240. Springer TA. 1994. Traffic signals for lymphocyte recirculation and leukocyte emigration: The multi-step paradigm. *Cell* 76:301–14

241. Stamper HB Jr, Woodruff JJ. 1976. Lymphocyte homing into lymph nodes: In vitro demonstration of the selective affinity of recirculating lymphocytes for high-endothelial venules. *J. Exp. Med.* 144:828

242. Staunton DE, Dustin ML, Erickson HP, Springer TA. 1990. The arrangement of the immunoglobulin-like domains of ICAM-1 and the binding sites for LFA-1 and rhinovirus. *Cell* 61:243–54

243. Staunton DE, Dustin ML, Springer TA. 1989. Functional cloning of ICAM-2, a cell adhesion ligand for LFA-1 homologous to ICAM-1. *Nature* 339:61–64

244. Staunton DE, Marlin SD, Stratowa C, Dustin ML, Springer TA. 1988. Primary structure of intercellular adhesion molecule 1 (ICAM-1) demonstrates interaction between members of the immunoglobulin and integrin supergene families. *Cell* 52:925–33

245. Steininger CN, Eddy CA, Leimgruber RM, Mellors A, Welply JK. 1992. The glycoprotease of *Pasteurella haemolytica* A1 eliminates binding of myeloid cells to P-selectin but not to E-selectin. *Biochem. Biophys. Res. Commun.* 188: 760–66

246. Stevens SK, Weissman IL, Butcher EC. 1982. Differences in the migration of B and T lymphocytes: Organ-selective localization in vivo and the role of lymphocyte-endothelial cell recognition. *J. Immunol.* 2:844–51

247. Stockinger H, Gadd SJ, Eher R, Majdic O, Schreiber W, et al. 1990. Molecular characterization and functional analysis of the leukocyte surface protein CD31. *J. Immunol.* 145:3889–97

248. Streeter PR, Lakey-Berg E, Rouse BTN, Bargatze RF, Butcher EC. 1988. A tissue-specific endothelial cell molecule involved in lymphocyte homing. *Nature* 331:41–46

249. Streeter PR, Rouse BTN, Butcher EC. 1988. Immunohistologic and functional characterization of a vascular addressin involved in lymphocyte homing into peripheral lymph nodes. *J. Cell Biol.* 107: 1853–62

250. Sutherland DR, Marsh JCW, Davidson J, Baker MA, Keating A, Mellors A. 1992. Differential sensitivity of CD34 epitopes to cleavage by *Pasteurella haemolytica* glycoprotease: Implications for purification of CD34-positive progenitor cells. *Exp. Hematol.* 20:590–99

251. Swerlick RA, Lee KH, Wick TM, Lawley TJ. 1992. Human dermal microvascular endothelial but not human umbilical vein endothelial cells express CD36 in vivo and in vitro. *J. Immunol.* 148:78–83

252. Takada Y, Elices MJ, Crouse C, Hemler ME. 1989. The primary structure of α-4 subunit of VLA-4: Homology to other integrins and possible cell-cell adhesion function. *EMBO J.* 8:1361–68

253. Tanaka Y, Adams DH, Hubscher S, Hirano H, Siebenlist U, Shaw S. 1993. T-cell adhesion induced by proteoglycan-immobilized cytokine MIP-1β. *Nature* 361:79–82

254. Tanaka Y, Albelda SM, Horgan KJ, Van Seventer GA, Shimizu Y, et al. 1992. CD31 expressed on distinctive T cell subsets is a preferential amplifier of βI integrin-mediated adhesion. *J. Exp. Med.* 176:245–53

255. Taub DD, Conlon K, Lloyd AR, Oppenheim JJ, Kelvin DJ. 1993. Preferential migration of activated CD4+ and CD8+ T cells in response to MIP-1α and MEP-1β. *Science* 260: 355–58

256. Taub DD, Lloyd AR, Conlon K, Wang JM, Ortaldo JR, et al. 1993. Recombinant human interferon-inducible protein 10 is a chemoattractant for human monocytes and T lymphocytes and promotes

T cell adhesion to endothelial cells. *J. Exp. Med.* 177:1809–14

257. Tedder TF, Matsuyama T, Rothstein D, Schlossman SF, Morimoto C. 1990. Human antigen-specific memory T cells express the homing receptor (LAM-1) necessary for lymphocyte recirculation. *Eur. J. Immunol.* 20:1351–55

258. Terry RW, Kwee L, Levine JF, Labow MA. 1993. Cytokine induction of an alternatively spliced murine vascular cell adhesion molecule (VCAM) mRNA encoding a glycosylphosphatidylinositol-anchored VCAM protein. *Proc. Natl. Acad Sci. USA* 90:5919–23

259. Thornhill MH, Wellicome SM, Mahiouz DL, Lanchbury JSS, Kyan-Aung U, Haskard DO. 1991. Tumor necrosis factor combines with IL-4 or IFN-gamma to selectively enhance endothelial cell adhesiveness for T cells: The contribution of vascular cell adhesion molecule-1-dependent and -independent binding mechanisms. *J. Immunol.* 146: 592–98

260. Ushiyama S, Laue TM, Moore KL, Erickson HP, McEver RP. 1993. Structural and functional characterization of monomeric soluble P-selectin and comparison with membrane P-selectin. *J. Biol. Chem.* 268:15229–37

261. Van Ewijk W, Brons NHC, Rozing J. 1975. Scanning electron microscopy of homing and recirculating lymphocyte populations. *Cell. Immunol.* 19: 245–61

262. Vedder ND, Harlan JM. 1988. Increased surface expression of CB11b/CD18 is not required for stimulated neutrophil adherence to cultured endothelium. *J. Clin. Invest.* 81:676–82

263. Villiger PM, Terkeltaub R, Lotz M. 1992. Production of monocyte chemoattractant protein-1 by inflamed synovial tissue and cultured synoviocytes. *J. Immunol.* 149:722–27

264. von Andrian UH, Berger EM, Ramezani L, Chambers JD, Ochs HD, et al. 1993. In vivo behavior of neutrophils from two patients with distinct inherited leukocyte adhesion deficiency syndromes. *J. Clin. Invest.* 91:2893–97

265. von Andrian UH, Chambers JD, Berg EL, Michie SA, Brown DA, et al. 1993. L-selectin mediates neutrophil rolling in inflamed venules through sialyl Lewis^x-dependent and -independent recognition pathways. *Blood* 82:182–91

266. von Andrian UH, Chambers JD, McEvoy LM, Bargatze RF, Arfors KE, Butcher EC. 1991. Two-step model of leukocyte-endothelial cell interaction in inflammation: Distinct roles for LECAM-1 and the leukocyte β2 integrins in vivo. *Proc. Natl. Acad. Sci. USA* 88:7538–42

267. von Andrian UH, Hansell P, Chambers JD, Berger EM, Filho IT, et al. 1992. L-selectin function is required for β2-integrin-mediated neutrophil adhesion at physiological shear rates in vivo. *Am. J. Physiol.* 263:H1034–44

268. Vonderheide RH, Springer TA. 1992. Lymphocyte adhesion through VLA-4: Evidence for a novel binding site in the alternatively spliced domain of VCAM-1 and an additional α4 integrin counter-receptor on stimulated endothelium. *J. Exp. Med.* 175:1433–42

269. Vonderheide RH, Tedder TF, Springer TA, Staunton DE. 1994. Residues within a conserved amino acid motif of domains I and 4 of VCAM-1 are required for binding to VLA-4. *J. Cell Biol.* 125:215–22

270. Walsh LJ, Lavker RM, Murphy GF. 1990. Biology of disease. Determinants of immune cell trafficking in the skin. *Lab. Invest.* 63:592–600

271. Wardlaw AC, Parton R. 1983. *Bordetella pertussis* toxins. *Pharmacol. Ther.* 19:1–53

272. Watson SR, Fennie C, Lasky LA. 1991. Neutrophil influx into an inflammatory site inhibited by a soluble homing receptor-IgG chimaera. *Nature* 349:164–67

273. Watson SR, Imai Y, Fennie C, Geoffrey JS, Rosen SD, Lasky LA. 1990. A homing receptor-IgG chimera as a probe for adhesive ligands of lymph node high endothelial venules. *J. Cell Biol.* 110: 2221–29

274. Wilkinson PC. 1982. *Chemotaxis and Inflammation.* London: Churchill Livingstone. 249 pp.

275. Woodruff JJ, Clarke LM, Chin YH. 1987. Specific cell-adhesion mechanisms determining migration pathways of recirculating lymphocytes. *Annu. Rev. Immunol.* 5:201–22

276. Wright SD, Meyer BC. 1986. Phorbol esters cause sequential activation and deactivation of complement receptors on polymorphonuclear leukocytes. *J. Immunol.* 136:1759–64

277. Wu D, LaRosa GJ, Simon MI. 1993. G protein-coupled signal transduction pathways for interleukin-8. *Science* 261: 101–3

278. Yednock TA, Cannon C, Fritz LC, Sanchez-Madrid F, Steinman L, Karin N. 1992. Prevention of experimental autoimmune encephalomyelitis by antibodies against α4β1 integrin. *Nature* 356: 63–66

279. Zhu D, Cheng C-F, Pauli BU. 1991. Mediation of lung metastasis of murine melanomas by a lung-specific endothelial cell adhesion molecule. *Proc. Natl. Acad. Sci. USA* 88:9568–72

280. Zimmerman GA, Prescott SM, McIntyre TM. 1992. Endothelial cell interactions with granulocytes: tethering and signaling molecules. *Immunol. Today* 13:93–100

SUBJECT INDEX

CUMULATIVE INDEXES

CONTRIBUTING AUTHORS, VOLUMES 53–57

CUMULATIVE TITLES

CHAPTER TITLES, VOLUMES 53–57

899

ANNUAL REVIEWS

a nonprofit scientific publisher
4139 El Camino Way
P.O. Box 10139
Palo Alto, CA 94303-0139 • USA

Annual Reviews publications may be ordered directly from our office; through stockists, booksellers and subscription agents, worldwide; and through participating professional societies. **Prices are subject to change without notice. We do not ship on approval.**

- **Individuals:** Prepayment required on new accounts. in US dollars, checks drawn on a US bank.
- **Institutional Buyers:** Include purchase order. Calif. Corp. #161041 • ARI Fed. I.D. #94-1156476
- **Students / Recent Graduates:** $10.00 discount from retail price, per volume. *Requirements:* 1. be a degree candidate at, or a graduate within the past three years from, an accredited institution; 2. present proof of status (photocopy of your student I.D. or proof of date of graduation); 3. Order direct from Annual Reviews; 4. prepay. This discount **does not** apply to standing orders, *Index on Diskette*, Special Publications, ARPR, or institutional buyers.
- **Professional Society Members:** Many Societies offer *Annual Reviews* to members at reduced rates. Check with your society or contact our office for a list of participating societies.
- **California orders** add applicable sales tax. • **Canadian orders** add 7% GST. Registration #R 121 449-029.
- **Postage paid** by Annual Reviews (4th class bookrate/surface mail). UPS ground service is available at $2.00 extra per book within the contiguous 48 states only. UPS air service or US airmail is available to any location at actual cost. UPS requires a street address. P.O. Box, APO, FPO, not acceptable.
- **Standing Orders:** Set up a standing order and the new volume in series is sent automatically each year upon publication. Each year you can save 10% by prepayment of prerelease invoices sent 90 days prior to the publication date. Cancellation may be made at any time.
- **Prepublication Orders:** Advance orders may be placed for any volume and will be charged to your account upon receipt. Volumes not yet published will be shipped during month of publication indicated.

N O T E	For copies of individual articles from any *Annual Review*, or copies of any article cited in an *Annual Review*, call **Annual Reviews Preprints and Reprints (ARPR)** toll free 1-800-347-8007 (fax toll free 1-800-347-8008) from the USA or Canada. From elsewhere call 1-415-259-5017.

ANNUAL REVIEWS SERIES *Volumes not listed are no longer in print*	**Prices, postpaid, per volume.** **USA/other countries**	Regular Order Please send Volume(s):	Standing Order Begin with Volume:
☐ *Annual Review of* **ANTHROPOLOGY**			
Vols. 1-20 (1972-91) ....$41 / $46			
Vols. 21-22 (1992-93) ....$44 / $49			
Vol. 23-24 (1994 and Oct. 1995) ....$47 / $52		Vol(s). _____	Vol. _____
☐ *Annual Review of* **ASTRONOMY AND ASTROPHYSICS**			
Vols. 1, 5-14, 16-29 (1963, 67-76, 78-91) ....$53 / $58			
Vols. 30-31 (1992-93) ....$57 / $62			
Vol. 32-33 (1994 and Sept. 1995) ....$60 / $65		Vol(s). _____	Vol. _____
☐ *Annual Review of* **BIOCHEMISTRY**			
Vols. 31-34, 36-60 (1962-65,67-91) ....$41 / $47			
Vols. 61-62 (1992-93) ....$46 / $52			
Vol. 63-64 (1994 and July 1995) ....$49 / $55		Vol(s). _____	Vol. _____
☐ *Annual Review of* **BIOPHYSICS AND BIOMOLECULAR STRUCTURE**			
Vols. 1-20 (1972-91) ....$55 / $60			
Vols. 21-22 (1992-93) ....$59 / $64			
Vol. 23-24 (1994 and June 1995) ....$62 / $67		Vol(s). _____	Vol. _____

❑ *Annual Review of* **CELL AND DEVELOPMENTAL BIOLOGY** (new title beginning
    Vols. 1-7   (1985-91) ....$41 / $46   with volume 11)
    Vols. 8-9   (1992-93) ....$46 / $51
    Vol.   10-11   (1994 and Nov. 1995) ....$49 / $54 Vol(s). _____ Vol. _____

❑ *Annual Review of* **COMPUTER SCIENCE** (Series suspended)
    Vols. 1-2   (1986-87) ....$41 / $46
    Vols. 3-4   (1988-89/90) ....$47 / $52 Vol(s). _____
Special package price for
    Vols. 1-4   (if ordered together) ....$100 / $115 ❑ Send all four volumes.

❑ *Annual Review of* **EARTH AND PLANETARY SCIENCES**
    Vols. 1-6, 8-19 (1973-78, 80-91) ....$55 / $60
    Vols. 20-21   (1992-93) ....$59 / $64
    Vol.   22-23   (1994 and May 1995) ....$62 / $67 Vol(s). _____ Vol. _____

❑ *Annual Review of* **ECOLOGY AND SYSTEMATICS**
    Vols. 2-12, 14-17, 19-22..(1971-81, 83-86, 88-91) ..$40 / $45
    Vols. 23-24   (1992-93) ....$44 / $49
    Vol.   25-26   (1994 and Nov. 1995) ....$47 / $52 Vol(s). _____ Vol. _____

❑ *Annual Review of* **ENERGY AND THE ENVIRONMENT**
    Vols. 1-16   (1976-91) ....$64 / $69
    Vols. 17-18   (1992-93) ....$68 / $73
    Vol.   19-20   (1994 and Oct. 1995) ....$71 / $76 Vol(s). _____ Vol. _____

❑ *Annual Review of* **ENTOMOLOGY**
    Vols. 10-16, 18, 20-36 (1965-71, 73, 75-91) ....$40 / $45
    Vols. 37-38   (1992-93) ....$44 / $49
    Vol.   39-40   (1994 and Jan. 1995) ....$47 / $52 Vol(s). _____ Vol. _____

❑ *Annual Review of* **FLUID MECHANICS**
    Vols. 2-4, 7   (1970-72, 75)
           9-11, 16-23 (1977-79, 84-91) ....$40 / $45
    Vols. 24-25   (1992-93) ....$44 / $49
    Vol.   26-27   (1994 and Jan. 1995).... ....$47 / $52 Vol(s). _____ Vol. _____

❑ *Annual Review of* **GENETICS**
    Vols. 1-12, 14-25 (1967-78, 80-91) ....$40 / $45
    Vols. 26-27   (1992-93) ....$44 / $49
    Vol.   28-29   (1994 and Dec. 1995) ....$47 / $52 Vol(s). _____ Vol. _____

❑ *Annual Review of* **IMMUNOLOGY**
    Vols. 1-9   (1983-91) ....$41 / $46
    Vols. 10-11   (1992-93) ....$45 / $50
    Vol.   12-13   (1994 and April 1995) ....$48 / $53 Vol(s). _____ Vol. _____

❑ *Annual Review of* **MATERIALS SCIENCE**
    Vols. 1, 3-19 (1971, 73-89) ....$68 / $73
    Vols. 20-23   (1990-93) ....$72 / $77
    Vol.   24-25   (1994 and Aug. 1995) ....$75 / $80 Vol(s). _____ Vol. _____

❑ *Annual Review of* **MEDICINE: Selected Topics in the Clinical Sciences**
    Vols. 9, 11-15, 17-42 (1958, 60-64, 66-42) ....$40 / $45
    Vols. 43-44   (1992-93) ....$44 / $49
    Vol.   45-46   (1994 and April 1995) ....$47 / $52 Vol(s). _____ Vol. _____